THIRD CANADIAN EDITION

Human Sexuality in a World of Diversity

Spencer A. Rathus
NEW YORK UNIVERSITY

Jeffrey S. Nevid
ST. JOHN'S UNIVERSITY

Lois Fichner-Rathus
THE COLLEGE OF NEW JERSEY

Edward S. Herold
UNIVERSITY OF GUELPH

Pearson Canada
Toronto

Dedicated with love to our children Taylor Lane Rathus and Michael Zev Nevid, who were born at the time the first edition of this book was written.

—S.A.R., L.F.-R., J.S.N.

Dedicated with love to my wife Yvette and our daughter Malia.

—E.S.H.

Library and Archives Canada Cataloguing in Publication

Human sexuality in a world of diversity / Spencer A. Rathus . . . [et al.]. — 3rd Canadian ed.

Includes bibliographical references and index.
ISBN 978-0-205-62277-1

1. Sex—Textbooks. 2. Sex customs—Canada—Textbooks. I. Rathus, Spencer A.

HQ21.H84 2010 306.7 C2008-908102-1

ISBN-13: 978-0-205-62277-1
ISBN-10: 0-205-62277-1

Vice President, Editorial Director: Gary Bennett
Editor-in-Chief: Ky Pruesse
Sponsoring Editor: Alexandra Dyer
Executive Marketing Manager: Judith Allen
Senior Developmental Editor: Jennifer Murray
Production Editor: Richard di Santo
Copy Editor: Susan Marshall
Proofreaders: Laurel Sparrow, Susan Broadhurst
Production Coordinator: Sarah Lukaweski
Composition: Macmillan Publishing Solutions
Permissions and Photo Research: Sandy Cooke
Art Director: Julia Hall
Cover and Interior Design: Miguel Angel Acevedo
Cover Image: Getty Images

1 2 3 4 5 13 12 11 10 09

Printed and bound in the United States of America.

Brief Contents

Contents

Preface

Living in Canadian society in the twenty-first century means navigating an increasingly complex world full of messages and issues related to human sexuality. Underlying all of this is an astounding diversity, as our sexuality is shaped by both human biology and a richness of sociocultural factors. The approach that has separated *Human Sexuality in a World of Diversity* from other human sexuality textbooks is its full embrace of this richness of human diversity.

Before writing this edition, we searched extensively for new Canadian materials from a number of sources including Canadian researchers themselves. Numerous new Canadian references have been added, including data from several national surveys such as the 2006 census. Various theories used to explain sexual attitudes and behaviours are detailed in the first chapter. These theories are then illustrated in almost every chapter, demonstrating the usefulness of theory in guiding our understanding of diverse aspects of human sexuality.

The third Canadian edition is more concise than most other human sexuality textbooks—because we are mindful of the experience of many enthusiastic users who find other textbooks too long and detailed for their courses. Yet, we have maintained a high standard of scholastic rigour as in our emphasis on theory and research throughout the textbook. We also offer many real-world applications that are useful to students.

Changes to the Third Canadian Edition

The third Canadian edition of *Human Sexuality in a World of Diversity* embodies many exciting changes—changes that reflect the rapid developments in the behavioural and social sciences, and in biology and medicine. We also highlight the major changes that the internet is bringing into our lives.

In addition to what is listed in the following sections, there are literally hundreds of new references throughout the text that reflect the newest research in the field of human sexuality. No part of the text has been left untouched by change. The following are just a few examples of the topics that have been updated in the chapters.

Chapter 1
Feminist and queer theory
Thinking critically about sexual advice on the internet
Sexuality and ethics
Sexuality and spirituality
The influence of gender and other social variables on the sexuality of Canadians
The sexual scripts of young people in Kenya
Sexual satisfaction in different countries

Chapter 2
Focus groups
Use of thermography to measure sexual arousal
The Tuskegee syphilis study: Research gone wrong
Canadian research consent forms—do they affect study findings?

Chapter 3
East Asian women and Pap tests
Sexual difficulties after hysterectomy
Canadian Cancer Society no longer recommends a monthly self–breast exam

Health Canada approves use of breast implants
Health Canada approves contraceptive that allows women to have only four periods
Circumcision and sexual sensations

Chapter 4
Pheromones
Effects of recreational drugs on sexual response
Sexual response variations by gender and sexual orientation
Factors influencing sexual arousal in women and men
Women who have persistent sexual arousal
New techniques for helping men with spinal cord injuries to ejaculate

Chapter 5
Transsexuals
Third gender/third sex
Gender and sexual advice literature
Highly sexual women
International survey on what men value most

Chapter 6
Neurobiological research on love
Attraction and evolutionary theory

Chapter 7
Virtual dating
Internet dating scams
Jealousy and the use of Facebook
Women and sex blogs
Sexual consent
Sexual compatibility

Chapter 8
Sexual dreams
Masturbation and other sexual behaviours around the world
Gay male and lesbian sexual behaviours
Sexual advice given in sex manuals and magazines

Chapter 9
Definitions of terms involved in sexual orientation
Asexuality as a sexual orientation
The structure of the brain and sexual orientation
The psychological and social adjustment of lesbians, gay males, and bisexuals
Canadian data on harassment of gay males and lesbians
Increasing resilience among LGBTQ youth
Relationship innovation in gay male relationships
Gay men's bathhouses

Chapter 10
Births by province and territory
Sexual orientation and teen pregnancy
Comparisons of maternal and infant mortality around the world

Chapter 11
Contraceptives
Emergency contraception available on pharmacy shelves
Canadian trends regarding contraceptive use
Discovery of a gene that controls ovulations

Number and rate of abortions by province
Women who have repeat abortions

Chapter 12
Childhood sexuality
Effects on children of having lesbian or gay male parents
Sex education
Meeting the needs of gay, lesbian, and bisexual youth
Statistics Canada data on rates of sexual intercourse among youth
Sexual orientation and sexual behaviour among youth
Statistics Canada data on same-sex marriages
Esther Perel's book *Mating in Captivity* challenges commonly held views of the relationship between intimacy and sex

Chapter 13
Female pain disorders
Women's sexual dysfunctions—research by Lori Brotto
Alternative approaches to enhancing women's sexuality: Mindfulness, acupuncture, and yoga—research by Lori Brotto
Sexual dysfunctions across cultures
Optimal sexuality

Chapter 14
Sexually transmitted infections (STIs)
Vaccine for HPV and cervical cancer prevention
Biological, psychological, and social factors that account for high rates of STI infections
The one-minute HIV test
"Barebacking" among men who have sex with men

Chapter 15
Paraphilias
"Normal" voyeurism
Women's submissive desires as expressed on blogs

Chapter 16
The complexity of sexual consent
"Rophies"—the date rape drug
Characteristics of male and female victims of sexual coercion
The (highly controversial!) evolutionary view of sexual assault
Brain differences between pedophiles and other men
Sexual harassment of women wearing the hijab in Egypt

Chapter 17
Prostitution as sex work
A brothel for women
Legal challenges to Canadian prostitution laws
Media stereotypes of sex workers
Internet use of sexually explicit materials
Women who visit sex shops

It should be noted that the sex education material that was in the epilogue of the second edition has been moved to Chapter 12 in this third edition. Also, discussion of sexual orientation has been expanded throughout the textbook rather than being confined to one chapter.

The Themes of *Human Sexuality in a World of Diversity*

The third Canadian edition of *Human Sexuality in a World of Diversity* builds upon the strong themes for which it has come to be known. Four themes are woven throughout the text:

1. The rich diversity found in gender roles, sexual attitudes, and sexual behaviours and customs
2. Critical thinking
3. Making responsible sexual decisions
4. Sexual health

Theme 1: Human Diversity Colleges and universities are undertaking the mission of broadening students' perspectives so that they will appreciate and tolerate human diversity. Canada is a nation of hundreds of different ethnic and religious groups, many of which endorse culturally distinctive beliefs about appropriate gender roles for men and women, and distinctive sexual practices and customs. Diversity is even greater within the global village of the world's nearly 200 nations and those nations' own subcultures. *Human Sexuality in a World of Diversity* incorporates a multicultural, multiethnic perspective that reflects the diversity of sexual experience in our society and around the world. Discussion of diversity encourages respect for people who hold diverse beliefs and attitudes.

Theme 2: Critical Thinking Colleges and universities are also encouraging students to become critical thinkers. Today's students are so inundated with information about gender and sexuality that it can be difficult to sort truth from fiction. Critical thinking requires thoughtful analysis and probing of the claims and arguments of others in light of evidence. Moreover, it requires a willingness to challenge conventional wisdom and common knowledge that many of us take for granted. Throughout this book we raise issues that call for critical thinking.

Theme 3: Responsible Sexual Decision Making We also encourage students to make responsible sexual decisions, on the basis of accurate information. Responsible sexual decision making is based not only on acquiring accurate information, but also on carefully evaluating this information in the light of one's own moral values.

Theme 4: Sexual Health *Human Sexuality in a World of Diversity* places a strong emphasis on issues relating to sexual health, including extensive coverage of such topics as HIV/AIDS and other STIs, innovations in contraception and reproductive technologies, breast cancer, menstrual distress, sex and disabilities, and diseases that affect the reproductive tract. The text encourages students to take an active—in fact, a proactive—role in health promotion.

Feature Boxes and Additional Learning Aids

The third Canadian edition of *Human Sexuality in a World of Diversity* continues to use a variety of features that stimulate student interest and enhance understanding.

Canadian Trends is a new feature that discusses the attitudes and behaviours of Canadians as reported in national surveys.

Innovative Canadian Research is a new feature that emphasizes significant new research contributions made by Canadian scholars.

A World of Diversity boxes highlight the rich variety of human sexual customs and practices in Canadian society and around the world. They also include presentation of opinions that are contrary to commonly held beliefs.

Applied Knowledge, another feature box, assists students in their personal decisions, giving information and advice.

A Closer Look boxes provide in-depth discussions of societal issues and research.

Each chapter begins with an **outline** that organizes the subject matter. **Key terms** are boldfaced in the text and a **running glossary** provides their definitions in the margins close to where they appear. Selected **Web sites** listed in the margins point students to online information about human sexuality and coping with issues of sexuality in their own lives.

At the end of each chapter, **Summing Up** organizes and reviews the subject matter according to the heads within the chapter.

Test Yourself provides multiple-choice and critical thinking questions, prepared by Sue Wicks McKenzie and Edward Herold, that are designed to help students study and to promote class discussion. The **Answer Key** is printed at the end of the book.

Student Supplements

MyPsychKit, www.mypsychkit.com A new online resource, MyPsychKit, provides a wealth of study tools for students looking to clarify and deepen their understanding of the foundations of human sexuality. Each chapter includes learning objectives, updated weblinks for additional sources of information, animations and simulations, flash-card glossary terms, and an online practice test with multiple-choice and true/false questions.

For additional information, see Allyn & Bacon's Sexuality and Gender Website **www.ablongman.com/sexandgender**.

Instructor Supplements

Instructor's Resource CD-ROM (ISBN 0-205-69230-3): This CD-ROM gathers together the following instructor supplements:

Instructor's Resource Manual: This manual includes a variety of resources, including Chapter-at-a-Glance tables (correlating chapter topics and learning objectives with the offered resources), teaching tips, activities, additional lecture material, and recommended readings, videos, and Web sites.

Test Item File: This test bank in Microsoft Word format includes approximately 2000 multiple choice, true or false, and essay questions. This test bank is also available in MyTest format (see below).

PowerPoints: Chapter-by-chapter presentations highlight the key points from the text, supported by diagrams and visuals.

Some of these instructor supplements are also available for download from a password-protected section of Pearson Education Canada's online catalogue (vig.pearsoned.ca). Navigate to your book's catalogue page to view a list of those supplements that are available. See your local sales representative for details and access.

MyTest: MyTest from Pearson Education Canada is a powerful assessment-generation program that helps instructors easily create and print quizzes, tests, exams, as well as homework or practice handouts. Questions and tests can all be authored online, allowing instructors ultimate flexibility and the ability to efficiently manage assessments at any time, from anywhere. MyTest for *Human Sexuality in A World of Diversity* includes over 2000 questions in multiple-choice, true or false, and essay format. These questions are also available in Microsoft Word format on the Instructor's Resource CD-ROM.

Video Workshop Student Learning Guide and Instructor Teaching Guide: A CD-ROM with 14 video clips (50 minutes) of course-specific video footage comes with a workbook that includes 10 questions for each video. The Student Guide with CD may be packaged with this textbook at no extra cost, and an Instructor Guide is available from your Pearson representative. To view clip samples and content, visit www.ablongman.com/html/videoworkshop/disciplines/features.html.

Pearson Advantage: For qualified adopters, Pearson Education is proud to introduce the **Pearson Advantage**. The Pearson Advantage is the first integrated Canadian service program committed to meeting the customization, training, and support needs for your course. Our commitments are made in writing and in consultation with faculty. Your local Pearson Education sales representative can provide you with more details on this service program.

Innovative Solutions Team: Pearson's Innovative Solutions Team works with faculty and campus course designers to ensure that Pearson technology products, assessment tools, and online course materials are tailored to meet your specific needs. This highly qualified team is dedicated to helping schools take full advantage of a wide range of educational technology, by assisting in the integration of a variety of instructional materials and media formats.

Acknowledgments

The authors owe a great debt of gratitude to the many researchers and scholars whose contributions to the body of knowledge of human sexuality are represented in these pages. Underscoring the interdisciplinary nature of this area of study, we have drawn upon the work of scholars in such fields as psychology, sociology, medicine, anthropology, theology, and philosophy, to name a few. We are also indebted to the many researchers who have generously allowed us to quote from their work and to reprint tabular material representing their findings.

The authors and publishers wish to thank the many professional colleagues who provided feedback on this text at various stages in its development. The following people, along with a few who wish to remain anonymous, reviewed the previous edition and/or manuscript chapters: Shaniff Esmail, University of Alberta; Michelle Everest, University of Western Ontario; Robin Milhausen, University of Guelph; David E. Reagan, Camosun College; Hilary Rose, Concordia University; Monika Stelzl, St. Thomas University.

As the Canadian author, I am deeply grateful to all of those Canadian scholars who provided me with copies of their current research as well as helpful ideas that allowed me to provide major updates to this third Canadian edition of *Human Sexuality in a World of Diversity*.

I owe considerable thanks to past and current research assistants. John Sakaluk, Leah Todd, and Ashley Ronson each made important contributions to this third edition. Their hard work, organizational strengths, and many useful ideas are much appreciated.

I am grateful to the many people at Pearson Education Canada for all their valuable assistance with this revision. Alexandra Dyer, Sponsoring Editor, helped to guide significant changes to the new edition, using faculty reviews to develop a detailed revision plan. Jennifer Murray, Senior Developmental Editor, was especially helpful and patient. I very much appreciated all of her constructive suggestions, feedback, and unwavering enthusiasm for this project. Richard di Santo was very important in coordinating production editorial activities, and Susan Marshall was extremely detailed and thorough in her copy editing.

Edward S. Herold, PhD

CHAPTER ONE

What Is Human Sexuality?

We are about to embark on the study of human sexuality. But why, you may wonder, do we need to study human sexuality? Isn't sex something to do rather than to talk about? Isn't sex a natural function? Don't we learn what we need to know from personal experience or from our parents or our friends?

Yes, we can learn how our bodies respond to sexual stimulation—what turns us on and what turns us off—through personal experience. Personal experience teaches us little, however, about the biological processes that bring about sexual response and orgasm. Nor does experience inform us about the variations in sexual behaviour that exist around the world, or in the neighbourhood.

Experience does not prepare us to recognize the signs of sexually transmitted infections (STIs) or to evaluate the risks of pregnancy. Nor does experience help us deal with most sexual problems, or dysfunctions.

Concerns about AIDS and unwanted teenage pregnancies have focused greater attention today on the importance of sex education. Many children now receive some form of sex education as early as elementary school. Many young people today do receive accurate information through sex education courses in the schools, but they are usually taught about STIs and contraception, not about sexual techniques.

You may know more about human sexuality than your parents or grandparents did at your age—perhaps more than they do today. But how much do you really know? What, for example, happens inside your body when you are sexually stimulated? What causes erection or vaginal lubrication? What do we know of the factors that determine a person's sexual orientation? What are the causes of sexual dysfunctions? How do our sexual responsiveness and interests change as we age? Can you contract a sexually transmitted disease and not know that you have it until you wind up sterile? Can you infect others without having any symptoms yourself?

These are just a few of the issues we will explore in this book.

Choices, Information, and Decision Making

Making choices is deeply intertwined with our sexual experience. Although sex is a natural function, the ways in which we express our sexuality are matters of personal choice. We choose how, where, and with whom to become sexually involved. We may face a wide array of sexual decisions: Whom should I date? When should my partner and I become sexually intimate? Should I initiate sexual relations or wait for my partner to approach me? Should my partner and I practise contraception? If so, which method? Should I use a condom to protect against sexually transmitted infections (or insist that my partner do this)? Should I be tested for HIV? Should I insist that my partner be tested for HIV before we engage in sexual relations?

In this textbook, we will present information that can help you make responsible sexual decisions. Information alone, however, is not enough to make decisions. Many issues raise moral concerns, such as premarital and extramarital sex, contraception, and abortion. No single value system defines us all. Each of us has a unique set of moral values—as a Canadian, as a member of one of Canada's hundreds of cultural groups, as an individual. Indeed, the world of diversity in which we live is a mosaic of different moral codes and cultural traditions and beliefs. Gathering information and weighing the scientific evidence will alert you to what is possible in the contemporary world, but only you can determine which of your options are compatible with your own moral values.

Making decisions involves choosing among various courses of action. The act of not making a formal decision may itself represent a tacit decision. For example, we may vacillate about whether to use a particular form of birth control but continue to engage in unprotected sex. Is this because we have not made a decision or because we have decided that whatever will be, will be?

Gathering information helps us to predict the outcomes of the decisions we make. This textbook provides you with a broad database concerning scientific developments and ways of relating to other people—including people who come from other cultures.

We also will encourage you to try to understand other people's sexual beliefs and values in light of their cultural backgrounds. Understanding is an essential milestone on the pathway to respect, and respect is vital to resolving conflicts and establishing healthy relationships.

Gender One's personal, social, and legal status as male or female.

Coitus (co-it-us or co-EET-us). Sexual intercourse.

Erotic Arousing sexual feelings or desires.

Foreplay Mutual sexual stimulation that may or may not lead to sexual intercourse.

Human sexuality The ways in which we experience and express ourselves as sexual beings.

What Is Human Sexuality?

What is human sexuality? This is not a trick question. Consider the meaning, or rather meanings, of the word *sex*. The word derives from Latin roots that mean "to cut or divide," signifying the division of organisms into male and female **genders**. One use of the term *sex*, then, refers to our gender, or state of being male or female. The word *sex* (or *sexual*) is also used to refer to those anatomic structures, called sex (or sexual) organs, that play a role in reproduction or sexual pleasure. We may also speak of sex when referring to physical activities that involve our sex organs and are engaged in for purposes of reproduction or pleasure: masturbation, hugging, kissing, **coitus**, and so on. Sex also relates to **erotic** feelings, experiences, or desires, such as sexual fantasies and thoughts, sexual urges, or feelings of sexual attraction to another person.

Sexual behaviour includes, but is not limited to, behaviour involving reproduction. Masturbation, for example, is performed for pleasure, not reproduction. Kissing, hugging, manual manipulation of the genitals, and oral–genital contact are all sexual behaviours that can provide sensual stimulation, even though they do not directly lead to reproduction. They may also be used as forms of **foreplay**, which may or may not lead to coitus.

We can now define **human sexuality** as the ways in which we experience and express ourselves as sexual beings. Our awareness of ourselves as females or males is part of our sexuality, as is the capacity we have for erotic experiences and responses. Our sexuality is an essential part of ourselves, whether or not we ever engage in sexual intercourse or sexual fantasy, and even if we lose sensation in our genitals because of injury.

Sex as Leisure

Glenn Meaney and B. J. Rye (2007), researchers at St. Jerome's University at the University of Waterloo, have conceptualized sex as a fun and healthy activity that can be defined as leisure. They state that sex is leisure when it is voluntary, is not work, and serves some personal need. Sex is not leisure when it is not voluntary, is seen as an obligation, or is viewed as work.

At its most basic level, sex provides physical pleasure. It is a fun activity that can be enjoyed alone or with others. Sexuality can also be a key component of personality development as one discovers which sexual activities are enjoyable and with whom they can be enjoyable. Sexuality is also an important part of our identity. This is most certainly true for gay, lesbian, bisexual, or transgender people. It is also true for people who engage in certain sexual variations, such as sadomasochism. Meaney and Rye (2007) argue that learning about one's sexual likes and dislikes through experimentation can lead to sexual self-actualization, a state in which a person is comfortable with his or her sexuality.

Clearly sex is a common leisure activity for many Canadians. Yet, sex is typically not listed as an option when researchers study the types of leisure activities that Canadians engage in.

Innovative Canadian Research

WHAT IS THIS THING CALLED SEX?

New Brunswick researchers Hilary Randall and Sandra Byers (2003) asked university students to indicate which behaviours they would define as "having sex" with someone if they were the ones engaging in those behaviours. The only behaviours that most students considered as sex were penile-vaginal intercourse and penile-anal intercourse. Only about one-fifth considered oral-genital contact as sex and even fewer (10%) considered touching of genitals leading to orgasm as sex. Interestingly, for each of the behaviours there was a slight increase in the percentage of students defining that behaviour as sex if it resulted in orgasm.

However, when the researchers modified the question, far more students indicated that they would define someone as their "sexual partner" if that person were engaging in those behaviours with them. For example, about two-thirds considered anyone with whom they had oral-genital contact to be a sexual partner, and about one-half considered touching of genitals as an indicator.

University of Calgary researchers Eileah Trotter and Kevin Alderson (2007) asked university students to define loss of virginity. The students' definition of loss of virginity was more narrow than that of "having sex." For example, only about half considered that anal intercourse qualified as loss of virginity. Almost all accepted penile-vaginal intercourse as the marker for virginity loss. However, a small percentage indicated that orgasm had to be experienced with penile-vaginal intercourse for it to count as loss of virginity.

The researchers also presented students with a list of behaviours and asked them to define the behaviours as sexual if they were performed by opposite-sex couples or by same-sex couples. For most of the behaviours, students were more likely to define them as sexual for opposite-sex couples than for same-sex couples. An exception was oral-genital sex. Slightly more of the students classified this behaviour as having sex if the couples were the same sex rather than the opposite sex (Trotter & Alderson, 2007).

The Study of Human Sexuality

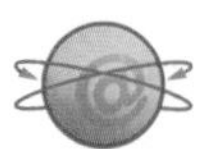

Sex Information and Education Council of Canada (SIECCAN)
www.sieccan.org

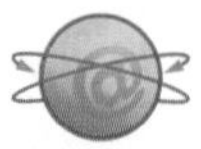

The Society for the Scientific Study of Sexuality (SSSS)
www.sexscience.org

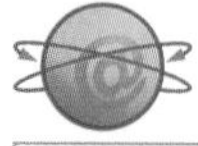

The American Association of Sex Educators, Counselors and Therapists (AASECT)
www.aasect.org

The study of human sexuality draws upon the scientific expertise of anthropologists, biologists, medical researchers, sociologists, and psychologists, to name but a few of the professionals involved in the field. These disciplines all make contributions because sexual behaviour reflects our biological capabilities, our psychological characteristics, and social and cultural influences. Biologists inform us about the physiological mechanisms of sexual arousal and response. Medical science teaches us about sexually transmitted diseases and the biological bases of sexual dysfunctions. Psychologists examine how our sexual behaviour and attitudes are shaped by perception, learning, thought, motivation and emotion, and personality. Sociologists consider the sociocultural contexts of sexual behaviour. For example, they examine relationships between sexual behaviour and religion, race, and social class. Anthropologists focus on cross-cultural similarities and differences in sexual behaviour. Scientists from many disciplines explore parallels between the sexual behaviour of humans and that of other animals.

There are a number of organizations promoting sex research and sex education. In Canada, a leading organization is the Sex Information and Education Council of Canada (SIECCAN), which publishes the *Canadian Journal of Human Sexuality*. Two major international organizations are the Society for the Scientific Study of Sexuality (SSSS), which publishes the *Journal of Sex Research*, and the American Association of Sex Educators, Counselors and Therapists (AASECT), which provides education and certification for educators, counsellors, and therapists.

Canadian Society and Sexuality

In order to understand the complexity of factors influencing sexual attitudes and behaviours in Canada, it is important to be aware of the diverse nature of Canadians. Particularly today, immigration patterns are changing the landscape of Canadian

Values The qualities in life that are deemed important or unimportant, right or wrong, desirable or undesirable.

society. Two-thirds of our population growth is now a result of immigration, with the overwhelming majority of immigrants (69%) moving to our larger cities such as Toronto, Vancouver, and Montreal. Immigrants comprise 20% of Canadian society and 50% of Toronto's population (Statistics Canada, 2007a). Of course, prior to the European discovery of North America, Canada was inhabited by First Nations people. Currently, 4% of Canada's population is made up of First Nations people (Bailey, 2008).

The first European explorers to the region of Canada were mainly French or British, and for many years these two ethnic groups have been the dominant ones in Canada. In the latter half of the twentieth century, an increasing number of immigrants came from non-European countries. In the 2006 Census, 59% of immigrants came from Asia and less than one-fifth came from Europe. As a result, Canadians of French or British ancestry today make up only about half of the population (Statistics Canada, 2008a).

The most notable change in the Canadian mosaic has been the dramatic increase in the proportion of visible minorities. In 2006, 16% of Canadians (5 million) were members of visible minorities, with South Asian Canadians surpassing Chinese Canadians as the largest group (Statistics Canada, 2008a).

The **values** of immigrants often differ from those of people born in Canada. In South Asian communities, for example, arranged marriages are still fairly common. Some immigrants from Muslim countries maintain the practice of female circumcision, a procedure usually performed on young girls that involves surgical removal of the clitoris and in some cases parts of the labia. This practice, often referred to as "genital mutilation," is contrary to Canadian values. (The Canadian and U.S. governments have declared performing female circumcisions illegal; however, within some immigrant communities, the procedure is still being done.) Parents in some groups use sex selection techniques, such as abortion, to ensure that they have a boy rather than a girl. And, since sex is a taboo subject in many cultures, parents in these cultures do not provide sex education to their children.

For the most part, the sexual attitudes and behaviours of immigrants are more conservative than the rest of Canadian society. This is particularly pronounced in relation to the age of first intercourse. Among young people born in Canada who are between the ages of 20 and 24, about three-quarters had their first sexual intercourse before the age of 20, compared with less than half of those not born in Canada (Maticka-Tyndale et al., 2001).

Children of immigrant parents often get caught in a culture clash between the traditional values of their parents and the more permissive values of Canadian society. A Manitoba study of ethno–racial minority youth found that sex was such a taboo subject within the family setting and parental sexual values were so restrictive that young people felt they could not communicate their real thoughts and questions to their parents (Migliardi, 2007). Some parents used severe punishment to control a teenager's behaviour, especially that of girls.

COMPARING CANADA WITH OTHER COUNTRIES Tremendous variation in sexual attitudes and behaviour is found among the different countries of the world. Many of these variations will be presented throughout this textbook. For example, Table 1.1 shows how countries differ with respect to sexual satisfaction among people over the age of 40. The research took place in 29 countries and 27 500 men and women were surveyed (Laumann et al., 2006). Western countries with higher gender equality, such as Canada, had the highest rates of sexual satisfaction. The lowest levels of satisfaction were in Indonesia and Japan.

In general, men reported higher levels of sexual satisfaction than did women. According to Laumann et al. (2006), in societies that have greater gender equality, sexual pleasure is considered as important for women as it is for men. However, in male-centred cultures where sex is more reproduction-focused, sexual pleasure for

Innovative Canadian Research

ETHNOCULTURAL COMMUNITIES AND SEXUALITY

There has been relatively little research on the sexuality of Canadian ethnic minority groups. Fortunately, some Canadian researchers have begun to study these under-studied groups.

Based on its concern over the spread of HIV/AIDS, Health Canada sponsored a study of a diversity of ethnic groups in Canada. The study, entitled "Ethnocultural Communities Facing AIDS," was conducted in consultation with representatives of each of the ethnic groups involved. Participants came from South Asian, Chinese, South African, Caribbean, Latin American, and Arabic communities. Most of the participants reported that a double standard exists for sexual behaviour, whereby women are expected to be virgins at marriage and monogamous after marriage, while men are allowed to be sexually permissive before and to some extent after marriage. In the South Asian community, girls are not even allowed to date. It is often taken for granted that at least some men will have sex with prostitutes and/or have sex with women from outside their ethnic group. Homosexuality is treated as if it did not exist in their communities, and as a result homosexuals are made to feel ashamed. Gender roles are rigidly prescribed, with the man considered to be the "boss" of the family. Women are not expected to have much interest in or knowledge of sex, and they lack the power to ask their husbands to use condoms.

Researchers in Vancouver and Montreal led by Lori Brotto (2005) from the University of British Columbia compared the sexuality of Asian and European Canadian university students. The Asian students had more conservative sexual attitudes and less sexual experience than the European Canadian students. In addition, the European Canadian women had higher rates of sexual desire, arousal, sexual receptivity, and sexual pleasure. The Asian men had higher rates of erectile dysfunction and less sexual satisfaction than the European Canadian men.

Importantly, Brotto et al. (2005) found that the degree of mainstream acculturation, but not the length of residence in Canada, was significantly related to sexual attitudes and experiences. In other words, Asian students who kept the strongest ties to their cultural heritage had the most conservative sexual attitudes and experiences. Similarly, in another study, Woo and Brotto (in press) found that, among Vancouver Asian Canadians, those who identified less with Canadian culture had the highest rates of sexual problems and less communication with a partner about sexual issues. They were also more likely to avoid sexual contact, and when they did engage in sexual relations, their encounters were less sensual in nature.

Eleanor Maticka-Tyndale at the University of Windsor and two visiting researchers from Iran, Khosro Refaie Shirpak and Maryam Chinichian (2007), conducted research with immigrants from Iran. As in the "Ethnocultural Communities" study, they found maintaining female virginity prior to marriage was considered essential for a girl to maintain a good reputation and the honour of her family. The Iranian adults were fearful of having their children exposed to sexuality from the broader Canadian society and especially from the media. Based on images they saw on Canadian television, the Iranian immigrants believed that most Canadian adolescents begin having sexual intercourse by the age of 13 or 14. They also perceived that Canadians do not seem to care about marital loyalty and having extramarital relationships. Accordingly, the women worried that their husbands would be tempted to engage in affairs because of the sexual freedoms in Canada. The men worried that in Canada it would be too easy for their wives to walk out of a marriage. Respondents also believed that sex education in Canadian schools emphasized the use of condoms rather than abstinence before marriage.

Maticka-Tyndale et al. (2007) also studied the sexual health needs of immigrants from Iran. Some of the women expressed concerns that their husbands might want to engage in sexual practices such as oral sex which were commonplace in Canada but were not acceptable according to traditional Muslim culture. The immigrants acknowledged that their own lack of sex education resulted in embarrassment when discussing sexual health topics with medical professionals. Women who had a male physician would avoid having a Pap smear taken because of embarrassment. Also, some women felt it was not appropriate to have a Pap smear taken before marriage because they worried this might affect their virginity status. Both males and females stated that modesty and shyness prevented them from discussing sexual problems, or asking questions about sex, when talking to a health professional. Maticka-Tyndale et al. recommended that health professionals need to be more culturally sensitive when interacting with immigrants, especially when talking about sexual health issues.

women is not considered to be important. Not surprisingly, many women in those cultures view sex as a marital duty.

There are also many cross-cultural differences regarding adolescent sexuality. Eleanor Maticka-Tyndale from the University of Windsor has conducted a groundbreaking study of adolescent sexual practices in Kenya (see A World of Diversity, p. 9). This study shows a sexual "script" for adolescent sexuality that diverges from the scripts most Canadians are familiar with.

TABLE 1.1

Positive Responses to Aspects of Subjective Sexual Well-Being by Country and by Gender Arranged by Cluster Membership: Percentage Distributions

	Emotional Satisfaction with Sexual Relationship[1]		Satisfaction with Sexual Function[2]	
Country	**Men**	**Women**	**Men**	**Women**
Gender-equal sexual regime				
1. Western European and European Linked Western Countries (high levels of sexual satisfaction). n = 14 503 (male = 7224; female = 7279)				
Australia	72.3	68.0	82.1	82.7
Austria	83.4	70.6	91.4	91.1
Belgium	72.3	67.3	86.7	78.1
Canada	73.7	62.5	87.4	87.6
France	59.9	53.2	85.2	69.6
Germany	69.0	59.9	87.7	85.9
Mexico	71.8	62.3	85.2	64.4
New Zealand	76.9	61.6	70.6	64.1
South Africa	64.7	46.7	77.7	65.5
Spain	76.0	69.1	90.2	78.4
Sweden	57.8	59.7	89.4	84.5
United Kingdom	71.3	67.5	73.9	74.6
U.S.A.	77.1	68.0	83.9	82.4
Mean	71.2	62.8	83.9	77.6

	Emotional Satisfaction with Sexual Relationship		Satisfaction with Sexual Function	
Country	**Men**	**Women**	**Men**	**Women**
Male-centred sexual regime				
2. Islamic and selected Asian and European countries (middle levels of sexual satisfaction). n = 8997 (male = 4394; female = 4603)				
Algeria	46.3	24.6	70.2	47.6
Brazil	60.8	41.3	88.2	69.6
Egypt	44.4	27.6	73.2	52.2
Israel	59.3	54.8	76.0	75.1
Italy	48.8	40.6	90.9	82.1
Korea	54.0	47.2	60.9	46.3
Malaysia	50.9	58.0	60.1	44.5
Morocco	53.7	45.0	82.2	77.3
Philippines	48.7	38.5	71.3	56.8
Singapore	50.6	39.2	65.1	55.1
Turkey	55.6	33.0	88.6	56.7
Mean	52.1	40.9	75.2	60.3

(Continued)

TABLE 1.1
(Continued)

Country	Emotional Satisfaction with Sexual Relationship		Satisfaction with Sexual Function	
	Men	Women	Men	Women
3. East Asian countries (low levels of sexual satisfaction). n = 3500 (male = 1750; female = 1750)				
China	36.0	32.8	68.7	45.5
Indonesia	18.5	19.9	73.8	61.0
Japan	23.6	15.5	60.3	39.7
Taiwan	28.7	25.4	60.0	42.3
Thailand	42.6	22.8	67.6	61.3
Mean	29.9	23.3	66.1	50.0

[1]Extremely/very satisfying as opposed to moderately/slightly/not satisfying.

[2]Very/somewhat satisfying as opposed to neither satisfied nor dissatisfied or somewhat/very dissatisfied.

Source: With kind permission from Springer Science+Business Media. Table adapted from Laumann et al., 2006. A Cross-National Study of Subjective Sexual Well-Being Among Older Women and Men: Findings from the Global Study of Sexual Attitudes and Behaviors. Archives of Sexual Behavior, *Vol. 35, No. 2, pp. 145–161.*

When it comes to sexuality, there are many cultural variations. Consider the issue of women going topless at the beach. In many European countries and Australia, it is commonplace for women to go topless at public beaches. In Canada, however, this has not been the case. In fact, until a few years ago, it was illegal for women to go topless. In 1991, University of Guelph student Gwen Jacobs caused a sensation when, on a hot summer day in downtown Guelph, she removed her shirt, exposing her breasts. She was arrested by the police and convicted of committing an indecent act in a public place. Jacobs brought her case to the Ontario Court of Appeal, arguing that because men had the right to go topless she had a constitutional right to go topless as well. In 1996 the Ontario Court of Appeal overturned the conviction, stating that her act was not degrading or dehumanizing and carried no sexual connotation.

This ruling brought out the central issue in the debate over toplessness: Is it a sexual act or not? In a study of university students in Australia, Herold, Corbesi, and Collins (1994) found that women who had gone topless at the beach believed that this was a "natural" act and not sexual when done at the beach. Conversely, women who had never gone topless argued that it was indeed sexual and a type of exhibitionism.

Despite the court ruling, few women in Canada are willing to go topless in public, even at the beach. The perception that others would view this as exhibitionist and disapprove is an obvious deterrent. How do you feel about this issue? Do you think a woman going topless on a beach is sexual or not?

COMPARING CANADA AND THE UNITED STATES Although there are many similarities between Canadians and Americans, there are also many differences. For example, a much higher proportion of the U.S. population comes from Spanish or African backgrounds. Consequently, ethnic comparisons in the United States are often based on three categories: African Americans, Latin Americans, and European Americans. In Canada, ethnic comparisons are typically between French-speaking people in Quebec and English-speaking Canadians across the country. It is important to be aware of social and demographic differences

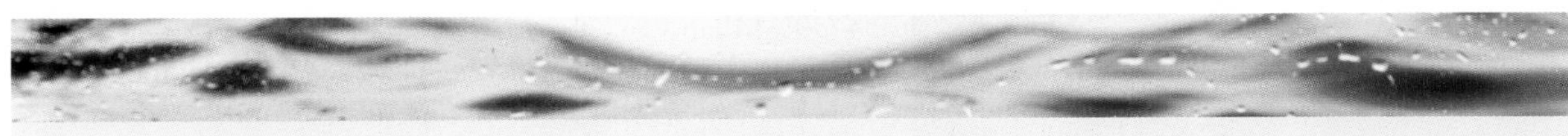

A World of Diversity

THE SEXUAL SCRIPTS OF YOUNG PEOPLE IN KENYA

While most Canadian researchers study the attitudes and behaviours of Canadians, some are conducting important research in other countries. Eleanor Maticka-Tyndale at the University of Windsor has studied sexual practices in a number of countries around the world. Most recently, she conducted several studies in African countries. Her groundbreaking research on the sexual scripts of adolescents in Kenya illustrates the powerful role of culture in influencing sexual behaviour (Maticka-Tyndale et al., 2005).

A key cultural belief in Kenya is that once puberty is reached, the male sex drive requires release and the female is ready for sex. There is also the belief that delaying the age of engaging in sex will have negative consequences. If the male waits to a later age to experience sex, it is believed that he may lose the capacity to impregnate his wife and will not be able to produce children. Females are concerned that if intercourse is delayed to a later age, their vaginas will become blocked and they will not be able to engage in sex.

Both boys and girls feel pressure from peer groups to engage in sex at a young age. Having intercourse is referred to as "playing sex." Boys assume that girls are easily available when it comes to sex. A girl may indicate an interest in a particular boy by acting in a sexually suggestive manner, such as by opening her legs when he is looking at her. However, the actual initiation of a sexual relationship begins with the male. The boy asks someone who knows the girl he is interested in to say that he is attracted to that girl. Then he gives the go-between person a material gift and/or some money to give to the chosen girl to indicate the sincerity of his interest. Along with the gift, the boy may also state that he loves the girl. However, expressions of love do not have the emotional meaning they do in Canada; rather, they refer to having sex. Both boys and girls are uncomfortable openly talking about sex, thus much of the communication is nonverbal.

If the girl accepts the gift, this signals that she is open to having a dating relationship with the boy. Dating and sex are linked together such that when a boy and girl begin dating, they will also engage in playing sex (having intercourse). There is no intermediate stage such as in Canada where adolescents gradually proceed to intercourse by first engaging in kissing, petting, etc. In Kenya, the sexual encounter consists generally of a brief episode of sexual intercourse. Sexual pleasure for the girl is not expected. Rather sex is seen as something to do and to finish quickly. The objective is to satisfy a basic need that males are seen to have. This is an exchange process whereby girls provide sex to obtain material goods.

The girl may delay accepting the boy's initiatives if she feels that the initial material gift was not large enough. Indeed, girls discuss strategies with their peers for obtaining more money or more expensive gifts from the boy. Many girls prefer to obtain gifts from adult men because adults can provide more material goods than can younger boys.

Typically, a girl initially refuses to engage in sex. This strategy helps to preserve her reputation as a "good" girl as well as to encourage the boy to provide more gifts. However, if the girl continues to give a "no" message to having sex, it is common practice for the boy to force her to have sex, especially if he feels that the amount of his gift is sufficient.

between the two countries because they account for some major differences in sexual attitudes and behaviours.

The birth rate in Canada is lower than that in the United States, especially for women in their twenties. According to Statistics Canada (2006), this is because Canadian women marry later than do American women. As well, the teenage pregnancy rate is much higher in the United States than in Canada. Population growth in Canada is more dependent on immigration from other countries than in the United States.

The American population (about 10 times as large as Canada's) is widely spread throughout the various regions of the United States, whereas the majority of people in Canada live in large metropolitan areas near the U.S. border. And since most new immigrants choose to live in these areas, they also have the highest rates of population growth. Canada's population is especially concentrated in the areas of Southern Ontario, Montreal, the Vancouver region, and the Calgary–Edmonton corridor (Statistics Canada, 2002a). Almost two-thirds of Canada's 30 million people live in the two largest provinces, Ontario and Quebec.

More Americans (39%) than Canadians (33%) attend university shortly after high school. However, in the United States, income plays a larger role in determining if someone attends university, with 63% of Americans from the top income quartile attending university compared with only 15% of those whose family income is in the bottom quartile. In Canada, this income gap is lower, with 45% of those from the top income quartile attending university compared with 24% of those from the bottom income quartile (Statistics Canada, 2005a).

Americans go to church more often than do Canadians. University of Lethbridge sociologist Reginald Bibby (2006) found that only a third of Canadians go to church once a week or more. In a 2006 survey by Ipsos Reid, two-thirds of Americans said that religion plays a role in their daily lives compared with only about one-third of Canadians (MacQueen, 2006).

Michael Adams, founder of the Canadian polling firm Environics Research, has conducted numerous large-scale surveys in Canada and the United States. In his 2003 book, *Fire and Ice*, he concludes that the Canadian identity is distinct from that of Americans and that the cultural gap between the two countries is increasing. Adams's surveys indicate that Canadians are more liberal and tolerant than Americans. For example, more Canadians (78%) than Americans (64%) believe that immigration is good for the country (Bibby, 2006).

Since 1971 Canada has adopted multiculturalism as an official policy. According to this policy, Canadian society is openly accepting of differing cultural attitudes and traditions as espoused by diverse immigrant groups. The United States, on the other hand, has adhered to the "melting pot" theory, which encourages immigrants to adapt to American ways of thinking and acting.

Recently in Canada there has been a questioning of how far Canadian society should go in accommodating the values of immigrant groups that conflict with basic Canadian values. In 2007 the Quebec government established a commission to examine the issue of "reasonable accommodation." People expressed a wide range of opinions to the commission. The most heated reactions were to the wearing of the hijab, or head scarf, among some Muslim women (Patriquin, 2007). A 2007 national survey conducted by the Institute for Research on Public Policy found that the majority of Canadians wanted limits to the "reasonable accommodation" of immigrants. Quebecers by far had the strongest feelings on this issue as they believed that the culture of Quebec was threatened by various immigrant and minority groups (Patriquin, 2007).

When it comes to sexuality issues, Canadians are somewhat more liberal than are Americans. For example, more Canadians (80%) are accepting of premarital sex than are Americans (64%) (Bibby, 2006). In other chapters of this textbook, we will present more comparisons of American and Canadian attitudes and behaviours.

POLITICS AND SEX IN CANADA AND THE U.S. In the United States, Christian fundamentalists, otherwise known as the "religious right," have a greater presence than in Canada. Consequently, in the U.S. they have had a much stronger voice in persuading governments to take a conservative stance on the regulation of sexual values. For example, the religious right has persuaded the U.S. Congress to spend hundreds of millions of dollars on educational programs that teach abstinence from sex and that do not allow for the teaching of contraceptive methods to adolescents. In contrast, the Canadian approach includes discussion of birth control as well as abstinence. For example, to promote the teaching of more comprehensive sex education in Canadian schools, Health Canada sponsored the development of the Canadian Guidelines for Sexual Health Education. This is discussed in more detail in Chapter 12.

When George W. Bush won his second presidential term in office in 2004, he received overwhelming support from Christian fundamentalists. In return, he vowed to have the American government be guided by conservative Christian values.

Two major concerns of Christian fundamentalists have been the banning of same-sex marriage and the restriction of abortion rights. Many political analysts believe that Bush's opposition to same-sex marriage played an important role in his re-election.

In general, Canadian politicians have largely maintained a separation between religion and the state. The Canadian Charter of Rights and Freedoms has helped to maintain this separation, as the Charter views individual rights as taking precedence over religious values. This has been shown in judicial decisions regarding same-sex marriage. Despite protests from various religious groups, the Canadian courts have consistently decided that not allowing same-sex marriage was a violation of the individual rights of gays and lesbians. Former Canadian prime minister Paul Martin adopted a similar position. Although he is a practising Roman Catholic and received intense pressure from Catholic Church officials to oppose same-sex marriage, Martin stated that his own religious values should not override personal freedoms.

In 2005 Canada became the fourth country in the world to allow legal same-sex marriage. The main political opposition to this legislation came from the federal Conservative party and the Alberta Conservative party. In fact, the leader of the federal Conservatives, Stephen Harper, indicated that if his party were to form the government he would have another vote in the House of Commons to overturn the law. Here Harper was going against public opinion, as a survey conducted by the Strategic Council after the same-sex legislation was passed found that 55% of Canadians wanted the next government to leave the legislation in place and only 39% wanted the law repealed. Shortly after the Conservative party formed a minority government in 2006, it did introduce legislation to overturn the same-sex law. However, it did not succeed, because the other parties which formed the majority of Parliament defeated the motion.

Despite the fears of some Canadian religious groups that they would be forced to sanctify same-sex marriages, Bill C-68 governing same-sex marriage specifically states that the legislation is only binding on city halls and not on religious organizations.

The federal Conservative party, after it united with the more socially conservative Alliance party of Canada, hinted at introducing restrictive legislation in other areas of sexuality. In 2008, the Harper Conservatives were able to pass legislation that raised the legal age of consent to 16 from 14. Previously, the federal Conservatives had followed a middle-of-the-road approach. In fact, it was the Conservative government of Brian Mulroney that in 1987 lowered the age of sexual consent from 18 to 14.

Issues around sexuality have generally had a higher profile in U.S. politics than in Canada. However, in the 2005 British Columbia election, lawyer John Ince formed the Sex Party, which ran three candidates. The party did not expect to win any seats but wanted to make Canadians aware of the role politicians play in deciding what kinds of sexual activities are acceptable or not. The Sex Party called for a sex-positive approach in Canadian schools and other institutions and for the repeal of sex-negative laws so that prostitution would be fully legal. Much of the platform of the Sex Party is based on John Ince's book, *The Politics of Lust* (2003), in which he argues that powerful antisexual forces in Canada and the U.S. are causing anxiety, fear, and negativity about sexual pleasure.

It should be noted that with the election of Barack Obama as president of the United States, there may be a change in policies regarding sexual issues in the U.S.

Sexuality and Values

Our society is pluralistic. It embraces a wide range of sexual attitudes and values. Some readers may be liberal in their sexual views and behaviour. Others may be conservative or traditional. Some will be staunchly pro-choice on abortion, others adamantly pro-life. Some will approve of sex for couples who are dating casually. Others will hold the line at emotional commitment. Still others will believe that people should wait until marriage.

What Role Do Our Values Play in Making Responsible Sexual Decisions?
In making decisions about sexual behaviour, people consider not only their knowledge of biology and sexuality but also their values. There are a variety of value systems, some of which are based on religion and some of which are not. This South-Central Asian couple are following ancient Hindu traditions in their marriage ceremony.

People's sexual attitudes, experiences, and behaviours are shaped to a large extent by their cultural traditions and beliefs. Because our world consists of diverse peoples and cultures, the study of human sexuality is really the study of human sexualities. In this book we highlight the many ways in which people experience their sexuality.

Sexuality and Ethics

Some sexual choices can have negative consequences for individuals and society. Thus all societies have restrictions on certain kinds of sexual behaviours, such as rape. Sexual ethics govern what societies consider to be unacceptable sexual behaviours. Glenn Meaney and B. J. Rye (2007) at St. Jerome's University at the University of Waterloo have analyzed three distinct ethical frameworks: the ethics of divinity, community, and autonomy.

The ethics of divinity (which generally have religious roots) are based on a fundamental belief in a natural law of right and wrong. Those who break the law are viewed as sinners. The belief that sex should only occur in marriage is an example of the ethics of divinity, as all major religions consider this belief to be a fundamental value that should not be questioned.

The ethics of community are based on what is perceived as the "greater good" for the community. Here, there is a wide variation among societies regarding what is acceptable sexual behaviour. Nevertheless, there is an intolerance for behaviours that are not considered ethical. Laws against rape are based on the ethics of community values that one should not force someone to engage in sex against his or her will.

The ethics of autonomy value the rights and freedoms of individuals. People are allowed to satisfy their own sexual needs as long as they do not impede the rights of others. The belief that same-sex relationships are acceptable as they do not cause harm to others is an example of the ethics of autonomy.

The framework presented by Meaney and Rye (2007) helps us to understand the relationship between various ethical positions and sexual decision making. It should be noted, however, that there are many other approaches to understanding this topic. For example, in their national survey of Americans, Laumann et al. (1994) categorized their respondents' moral values into the three categories of traditional, relational, and recreational. These categories overlap with those of Meaney and Rye.

Ethics and Sexual Rights

Based on the ethics of autonomy, there have been recent movements promoting the sexual rights and freedoms of people around the world. The World Association for Sexual Health (WASH) has been at the forefront in promoting sexual rights. At the 2005 World Congress of Sexology meeting in Montreal, participants recommended that governments and international agencies should recognize, promote, ensure, and protect sexual rights for all.

To achieve this goal of sexual rights for all, WASH assumed the following principles:

- Gender equality must be advanced.
- Sexual violence and abuse should be eliminated.
- Universal access to comprehensive sexuality education must be provided.
- Reproductive health programs must be broadened to include broader sexual issues.
- HIV/AIDS and other sexually transmitted diseases should be halted and their effects reversed.
- Sexual concerns and dysfunctions must be identified and treated.
- Sexual pleasure needs to be recognized as a component of well-being.

The principles listed above may seem obvious to many Canadians. However, they are seen as problems by societies with different ethical principles, particularly the ethics of divinity. For example, Muslim societies are opposed to allowing sexual relations among same-sex couples or among those who are not married. Eleanor Maticka-Tyndale and Lisa Smylie (in press) of the sociology department at the University of Windsor have analyzed the problematic aspects of these principles. They note that many developing countries are offended by the underlying assumption of the sexual rights proposals, namely, that Western countries consider their sexual values to be superior to those of other countries. Similar concerns have also been expressed by some social theorists from Western countries. Maticka-Tyndale and Smylie argue that sexual rights proposals are more likely to be accepted if they are tied to more mainstream international human rights commitments. They also make the case that consensus-building efforts need to be made and are more likely to be successful than attempting to pressure conservative societies to adopt policies contrary to their fundamental values.

Sexuality and Spirituality

While researchers have paid considerable attention to the role of religion as a predictor of sexual attitudes and behaviours, research into the spiritual aspect of sexuality has been limited. Peggy Kleinplatz, a researcher and therapist at the University of Ottawa, and Stanley Krippner, a researcher in Israel, believe that sexual relations can be more fulfilling when they extend beyond the purely physical aspects, that is, the techniques of sex which are emphasized in many sex manuals (Kleinplatz & Krippner, 2007). They argue that many people want to transform their sex routine into a spiritual experience that makes "them feel utterly alive. . . . Sharing such moments with one's partner feels like a sacred destiny fulfilled (p. 306)." For example, tantric sex, which is based on tantric yoga stemming from religious practices in India, emphasizes prolonged sexual union as a way to achieve heightened consciousness and enlightenment.

To meet the desire of couples who wish to have a spiritually based sexual relationship, workshops on tantric sex are given in many Canadian cities. Kleinplatz and Krippner (2007) are critical of tantric teachers who focus on the sexual techniques but neglect the spiritual foundations of this approach to sexual relationships.

Thinking Critically About Human Sexuality

We are flooded with so much information about sex that it is difficult to separate truth from fiction. Newspapers, TV shows, books, magazines, and the internet contain one feature after another about sex. Many of these presentations contradict one another, contain half-truths, or draw misleading or unsubstantiated conclusions. A scientific approach to human sexuality encourages people to think critically about claims and findings that are presented as truths.

We tend to assume that authority figures such as doctors and government officials provide us with factual information and are qualified to make decisions that affect our lives. When two doctors disagree on the need for a hysterectomy, however, or two officials disagree about whether condoms should be distributed in public schools, we wonder how both can be correct. Critical thinkers never say, "This is true because so-and-so says it is true."

To help students evaluate claims, arguments, and widely held beliefs, most universities and colleges encourage critical thinking. The core of critical thinking is skepticism—not taking things for granted. It means being skeptical of things that are presented in print, uttered by authority figures or celebrities, or passed along by friends. Another aspect of critical thinking is the thoughtful analysis and probing of claims and arguments. Critical thinking requires willingness to challenge the conventional wisdom and common knowledge that many of us take for granted. It means scrutinizing definitions of terms and evaluating the premises of arguments and their logic. It also means finding reasons to support your beliefs, rather than relying on feelings. When people think critically, they maintain open minds. They suspend their beliefs until they have obtained and evaluated the evidence.

Principles of Critical Thinking

Here are some suggestions for critical thinking:

1. Be skeptical. Politicians, religious leaders, and other authority figures attempt to convince you of their points of view. Even researchers and authors may hold certain biases. Accept no opinion as fact—until you have personally weighed the evidence.
2. Examine definitions of terms. Some statements are true when a term is defined in one way but are not true when it is defined in another. Consider the statement "Love is blind." If love is defined as head-over-heels infatuation, there may be substance to the statement. Infatuated people tend to idealize loved ones and overlook their faults. If, however, love is defined as deep caring and commitment involving a more realistic (if still somewhat slanted) appraisal of the loved one, then love is not so much blind as a bit nearsighted.
3. Examine the assumptions or premises of arguments. Consider the statement "Abortion is murder." *Webster's New World Dictionary* defines murder as "the unlawful and malicious or premeditated killing of one human being by another." The statement can be true, according to this dictionary, only if the victim is held to be a human being (and if the act is unlawful and either malicious or premeditated). Most pro-life advocates argue that embryos and fetuses are human beings. Most pro-choice advocates claim that they are not. Hence the argument that abortion is murder would rest in part on the assumption that the embryo or fetus is a human being.
4. Be cautious in drawing conclusions from evidence. Recent research found that teenagers who listen to rap, hip-hop, pop, and rock music with sexually explicit lyrics or lyrics that refer to women as sex objects are more likely to initiate sexual activity at early ages (Martino et al., 2006). The popular media

seem obsessed with the idea that "dirty" songs instigate sex, and lots of it. However, teens who choose to dwell on these songs may differ in their values from those who do not, so that they not only spend hours with their iPods blasting sexual lyrics into their ears but they also choose to have sex at an early age. The evidence of a connection between listening to this music and having sex is open to various interpretations, which brings us to our next principle of critical thinking.

5. Consider alternative interpretations of research evidence. For example, teens who dwell on sexual song lyrics may also be more open to sexual activity because they are less traditional than teens who (literally) turn off these songs. This example shows that correlations between events do not necessarily reveal cause and effect.
6. Consider the kinds of evidence upon which conclusions are based. Some conclusions, even seemingly "scientific" conclusions, are based on anecdotes and personal endorsements. They are not founded on sound research.
7. Do not oversimplify. Consider the statement "Homosexuality is inborn." There is some evidence that sexual orientation may involve inborn predispositions, such as genetic influences. However, biology is not destiny in human sexuality. Gay male, lesbian, and heterosexual sexual orientations appear to develop as the result of a complex interaction of biological and environmental factors.
8. Do not overgeneralize. Consider the belief that gay males are effeminate and lesbians are masculine. Yes, some gay males and lesbians fit these stereotypes; however, many do not. Overgeneralizing makes us vulnerable to accepting stereotypes.

Throughout this text, we will give you plenty of opportunities to apply these principles, but it is up to you to practise them.

Canadian Trends

CANADIANS ON THE INTERNET

A Statistics Canada 2007 survey found that about three-fourths of Canadians surf the internet for personal reasons (Statistics Canada, 2008). Among people who used the internet at home, two-thirds went online every day during a typical month. Younger people were more likely to use the internet. For example, 96% of those between the ages of 16 and 24 used the internet, compared with only 29% of those 65 years of age and over. Higher rates of internet use were also found among those with university education, those with higher incomes, and those living in urban areas. Rates of internet use were highest among those in three provinces: British Columbia, Alberta, and Ontario.

With regard to personal use, the most common online activities were for email (92%) and for general browsing or fun or leisure (76%); 59% of Canadians searched for medical or health-related information (Statistics Canada, 2008).

Many Canadians are being exposed to all kinds of sexual issues and behaviours on the internet that they might not otherwise know about. While much has been written about online pornography, many other aspects of the internet have been less explored. Many sexual health organizations have educational websites, several of which are noted in this text. As well, numerous discussion groups may be found online for all kinds of sexuality issues, such as those relating to gays and lesbians. An increasing number of Canadians find dating and marriage partners on the internet. Many fetish communities have websites on the internet for people interested in bondage and discipline activities. Finally, the growth in internet social networking has been phenomenal. In 2007 about half of Canadian internet users had Facebook accounts, with the majority being between the ages of 18 and 34 (Boesveld, 2008).

Applied Knowledge

THINKING CRITICALLY ABOUT SEXUAL ADVICE ON THE INTERNET

Every day, many people surf the internet in the hope of finding websites that will answer questions they have about sex. How can they evaluate the merits of these websites? How can they separate the helpful wheat from the useless and sometimes harmful chaff?

Unfortunately, there are no easy answers. Many of us believe the things we see posted. Anecdotes about how Tyrone increased the size of his penis by 30% and how Maria learned to reach orgasm "every time" can have a powerful allure.

Be on guard. A price we pay for freedom of speech is that nearly anything can be posted on a website or appear in print. Authors can make extravagant claims with little fear of punishment. They can lie about the effectiveness of a new sexual cure-all as easily as they can lie about sightings of Elvis Presley or UFOs.

How can you protect yourself? Try some critical thinking:

1. First, in this instance, do "judge the book by its cover." Does the website look well organized? Do the links within the web pages work? A credible website will look professional and will be well maintained.
2. Ignore websites that make extravagant claims. If it sounds too good to be true, it probably is. No method helps everyone who tries it. Very few methods work overnight. Extravagant claims are a clue to look elsewhere.
3. Check the credentials of the people who posted the information. Be suspicious if the author's title is "Dr." and is placed before the name. The degree could be a phony doctorate bought through the mail. It is better if the "doctor" has a Ph.D., Psy.D., M.D., or Ed.D. after her or his name.
4. Check authors' affiliations. Helping professionals who are affiliated with colleges, universities, clinics, and hospitals may have more to offer than those who are not.
5. Check the evidence reported on the website. Unscientific websites (and books) usually make extensive use of anecdotes. Anecdotes are unsupported stories or case studies about fantastic results with one or a few individuals. Responsible helping professionals check the effectiveness of techniques with large numbers of people. They carefully measure the outcomes.
6. Check the reference citations for the evidence. Legitimate research is reported in the journals or on the websites you will find in the References section of this book. These journals report research methods and outcomes that seem to be scientifically valid. If there are no links to reference citations on the website, or if the list of references looks suspicious, you should be suspicious too.

Are They Buying What's Being Sold?
Critical thinkers carefully consider the premises of arguments, weigh all the evidence, and arrive at their own conclusions. Critical thinking is important in matters of human sexuality and is valuable in all areas of life.

Perspectives on Human Sexuality

Human sexuality is a complex topic. No single theory or perspective can capture all its nuances. In this book we explore human sexuality from many perspectives. In this section we introduce a number of perspectives that we will draw on in subsequent chapters.

The Historical Perspective

History places our sexual behaviour in context. It informs us whether our sexual behaviour reflects trends that have been with us through the millennia or the customs of a particular culture and era.

History shows little evidence of universal sexual trends. Attitudes and behaviours vary extensively from one time and place to another. Contemporary Canadian society may be permissive when compared with the Victorian and postwar eras. Yet it looks staid when compared with the sexual excesses of some ancient societies, most notably the ruling class of ancient Rome.

PREHISTORIC SEXUALITY: FROM FEMALE IDOLS TO PHALLIC WORSHIP Information about life among our Stone Age ancestors is obtained largely from cave drawings, stone artifacts, and the customs of modern-day preliterate peoples whose existence may have changed little over the millennia.

Art produced in the Stone Age, some 20 000 years ago, suggests the worship of women's ability to bear children and perpetuate the species (Fichner-Rathus, 2004). Primitive statues and cave drawings portray women with large, pendulous breasts, rounded hips, and prominent sex organs. Most theorists regard the figurines as fertility symbols. Emphasis on the female reproductive role may also have signified ignorance of the male's contribution to reproduction.

As the ice sheets of the last ice age retreated (about 11 000 B.C.) and the climate warmed, human societies turned agrarian. Hunters and gatherers became farmers and herders. As people gained awareness of the male role in reproduction, **phallic worship** sprang into being. Knowledge of paternity is believed to have developed around 9000 B.C., which is about the time that people shifted from being hunters and gatherers to being farmers and shepherds.

In any event, the penis was glorified in art as a plough, an axe, or a sword. **Phallic symbols** figured in religious ceremonies in ancient Egypt. Ancient Greek art revered phalluses, rendering them sometimes as rings and sometimes as necklaces. Some phalluses were given wings, suggesting the power ascribed to them. In ancient Rome, a large phallus was carried like a float in a parade honouring Venus, the goddess of love.

The **incest taboo** may have been the first human taboo (Tannahill, 1980). All human societies apparently have some form of incest taboo (Harris & Johnson, 2000; Whitten, 2001). Societies have varied in terms of the strictness of the taboo, however. Brother–sister marriages were permitted among the presumably divine rulers of ancient Egypt and among the royal families of the Incas and of Hawaii, even though they were generally prohibited among commoners.

THE ANCIENT HEBREWS The ancient Hebrews viewed sex, at least sex in marriage, as a fulfilling experience intended to satisfy the divine injunction to "be fruitful and multiply." Male–male and female–female sexual behaviour was strongly condemned, because it was believed to represent a threat to the perpetuation of the family. Adultery, too, was condemned—at least for a woman. Although the Hebrew Bible (called the Old Testament in the Christian faith) permitted **polygamy**, the vast majority of the Hebrews practised **monogamy**.

The ancient Hebrews approved of sex within marriage not simply for procreation but also for mutual pleasure and fulfillment. They believed that the expression of sexual needs and desires helped strengthen marital bonds and solidify the family. (These points are noteworthy in that there are many people, both Jewish and non-Jewish, who believe that traditionally the Jewish religion had mainly negative attitudes toward sexual pleasure. David Ribner from the Bar Ilan University in Israel and Peggy Kleinplatz (2007) from the University of Ottawa provide a thorough analysis of myths regarding sexuality and Judaism.)

Phallic worship Worship of the penis as a symbol of generative power.

Phallic symbols Images of the penis.

Incest taboo The prohibition against intercourse and reproduction among close blood relatives.

Polygamy The practice of having two or more spouses at the same time.

Monogamy The practice of having one spouse.

Bisexual Sexually responsive to either gender.

Pederasty Sexual love of boys.

Courtesan A prostitute—especially the mistress of a noble or wealthy man.

Concubine A secondary wife, usually of inferior legal and social status.

Among the ancient Hebrews, a wife was considered the property of her husband. If she offended him, she could be divorced on a whim. A wife could be stoned to death for adultery. She might also have had to share her husband with his secondary wives and concubines. Men who committed adultery by consorting with the wives of other men were considered to have violated the property rights of those men. Although they were subject to harsh penalties for such violation of property rights, they were not put to death.

THE ANCIENT GREEKS The classical or golden age of ancient Greece lasted about 200 years, from about 500 B.C. to 300 B.C. Within this relatively short span lived the philosophers Socrates, Plato, and Aristotle. Like the Hebrews, the Greeks valued family life. Greek men admired the well-developed male body and enjoyed nude wrestling among men in the arena. Erotic encounters and off-colour jokes characterized the works of Aristophanes and other playwrights.

The Greeks viewed their gods—Zeus, god of gods; Apollo, who inspired art and music; Aphrodite, the goddess of carnal love whose name is the basis of the word *aphrodisiac*; and others—as voracious seekers of sexual variety. Not only were they believed to have sexual adventures among themselves, but they were also thought to have seduced mortals.

Three aspects of Greek sexuality are of particular interest to our study of sexual practices in the ancient world: male–male sexual behaviour, pederasty, and prostitution. The Greeks viewed men and women as **bisexual**. Male–male sex was considered normal.

Pederasty means "love of boys." Greek men might take on an adolescent male as a lover and pupil. Sex between men and prepubescent boys was illegal, however. Families were generally pleased if their adolescent sons attracted socially prominent mentors. Pederasty did not impede the boy's future male–female functioning, because the pederast himself was usually married, and the Greeks believed people equally capable of male–female and male–male sexual activity.

Prostitution flourished at every level of society. Prostitutes ranged from refined **courtesans** to **concubines**, who were usually slaves. They could play musical instruments, dance, engage in witty repartee, or discuss the latest political crisis.

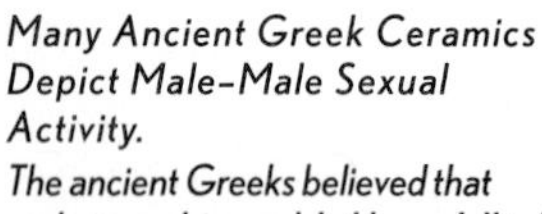

Many Ancient Greek Ceramics Depict Male–Male Sexual Activity.
The ancient Greeks believed that males were bisexual. In Homer's Iliad*, brought to the silver screen as* Troy*, Achilles is spurred to battle by the killing of his lover Patroclus. The film, however, glossed over this motive by emphasizing the family relationship between the two.*

They were also skilled in the arts of love. No social stigma was attached to visiting a courtesan. At the lower rungs of society were streetwalkers and prostitutes who lived in tawdry brothels.

Women in general held low social status. The women of Athens had no more legal or political rights than slaves. They were subject to the authority of their male next-of-kin before marriage and to that of their husbands afterward. They received no formal education and were consigned most of the time to women's quarters in their homes. They were chaperoned when they ventured out-of-doors. A husband could divorce his wife without cause and was obligated to do so if she committed adultery.

THE WORLD OF ANCIENT ROME Much is made of the sexual excesses of the Roman emperors and ruling families. Emperors such as Caligula sponsored orgies at which guests engaged in a wide variety of sexual practices. These sexual excesses were found more often among the upper classes of palace society than among average Romans. Unlike their counterparts in ancient Greece, Romans viewed male–male sexual behaviour as a threat to the integrity of the Roman family and to the position of the Roman woman.

The family was viewed as the source of strength of the Roman Empire. Although Roman women were more likely than their Greek counterparts to share their husbands' social lives, they still were considered the property of their husbands.

THE EARLY CHRISTIANS Christianity emerged within the Roman Empire during the centuries following the death of Christ. Early Christian views on sexuality were largely shaped by Saint Paul and the Church fathers in the first century and by Saint Augustine in the latter part of the fourth century.

In replacing the pagan values of Rome, the early Christians, like the Hebrews, sought to restrict sex to the marriage bed. They saw temptations of the flesh as distractions from spiritual devotion to God. Paul preached that celibacy was closer to the Christian ideal than marriage.

Christians, like Jews before them, demanded virginity of brides. Masturbation and prostitution were condemned as sinful (Allen, 2000). Early Christians taught that men should love their wives with restraint, not passion. The goal of procreation should govern sexual behaviour—the intellect should rule the flesh.

Over subsequent centuries, Christian leaders took an even more negative view of sexuality. Particularly influential were the ideas of Saint Augustine (353–430 A.D.), who associated sexual lust with the original sin of Adam and Eve in the Garden of Eden.

Nonprocreative sexual activity was deemed most sinful. Masturbation, male–male sexual behaviour, female–female sexual behaviour, oral–genital contact, anal intercourse—all were viewed as abominations in the eyes of God. Marital sex was deemed somewhat less sinful when practised for procreation and without passion.

SEXUALITY AND THE EASTERN RELIGIONS Islam, the dominant religion in the Middle East, was founded by the prophet Muhammad. Muhammad was born in Mecca, in what is now Saudi Arabia, in about 570 A.D. The Islamic tradition treasures marriage and sexual fulfillment in marriage. Premarital intercourse invites shame and social condemnation; in some fundamentalist Islamic states, it incurs the death penalty.

The family is the backbone of Islamic society. Celibacy is frowned upon (Ahmed, 1991). Muhammad decreed that marriage represents the only road to virtue (Minai, 1981). Islamic tradition permits a sexual double standard, however. Men may take up to four wives, but women are permitted only one husband. Public social interactions between men and women are severely restricted in conservative Islamic societies. Women in most traditional Islamic societies are expected to keep

An Illustration from the Kama Sutra.
The Kama Sutra, *an Indian sex manual believed to have been written sometime between the third and fifth centuries A.D., contained graphic illustrations of sexual techniques and practices.*

their heads and faces veiled in public and to avoid all contact with men other than their husbands.

In the cultures of the Far East, sexuality was akin to spirituality. To the Taoist masters of China, who influenced Chinese culture for millennia, sex was anything but sinful. Rather, they taught that sex was a sacred duty. It was a form of worship that was believed to lead toward immortality. Sex was to be performed well and often if one was to achieve harmony with nature.

The Chinese culture was the first to produce a detailed sex manual, which came into use about 200 years before the birth of Jesus. This manual helped educate men and women in the art of lovemaking. The man was expected to extend intercourse as long as possible, thereby absorbing more of his wife's natural essence, or yin. Yin would enhance his own masculine essence, or yang.

Taoists believed that it was wasteful for a man to "spill his seed." Masturbation, though acceptable for women, was ruled out for men. Sexual practices such as anal intercourse and oral–genital contact (**fellatio** and **cunnilingus**) were permissible, so long as the man did not squander yang through wasteful ejaculation. Another parallel to Western cultures was the role accorded women in traditional Chinese society. Here the "good wife," like her Western counterparts, was limited largely to the domestic roles of child rearing and homemaking.

Perhaps no culture has cultivated sexual pleasure as a spiritual ideal to a greater extent than the ancient Hindus of India. From the fifth century onward, temples show sculptures of gods, heavenly nymphs, and ordinary people in erotic poses (Gupta, 1994). Hindu sexual practices were codified in a sex manual, the *Kama Sutra*. The *Kama Sutra* illustrates sexual positions, some of which would challenge a contortionist. This manual remains the most influential sex manual ever produced.

In its graphic representations of sexual positions and practices, the *Kama Sutra* reflected the Hindu belief that sex was a religious duty, not a source of shame or guilt. In the Hindu doctrine of karma, actions in one life may determine the course of future lives: sexual fulfillment was regarded as one way to become reincarnated at a higher level of existence.

All in all, early Indian culture viewed sex as virtuous and natural. Indian society, however, grew more restrictive toward sexuality after about 1000 A.D. (Tannahill, 1980).

CHRISTIANITY IN THE MIDDLE AGES The Middle Ages, sometimes called medieval times, span the millennium of Western history from about 476 A.D. to 1450 A.D. These years are sometimes termed the Dark Ages because some historians have depicted them as an era of cultural and intellectual decay and stagnation. The Roman Catholic Church continued to grow in influence. Its attitudes toward sexuality remained largely unchanged since the time of Augustine.

Two conflicting concepts of women dominated medieval thought: one, woman as Eve, the temptress; the other, woman as Mary, virtuous and pure. Contemporary Western images of women still reflect the schism between the good girl and the bad girl—the madonna and the whore.

Fellatio A sexual activity involving oral contact with the penis.

Cunnilingus A sexual activity involving oral contact with the female genitals.

THE PROTESTANT REFORMATION During the Reformation, Martin Luther (1483–1546) and other Christian reformers such as John Calvin (1509–1564) split off from the Roman Catholic Church and formed their own sects, which led to the development of the modern Protestant denominations of Western Europe (and later, the New World). Luther disputed many Roman Catholic doctrines on sexuality. He believed that priests should be allowed to marry and rear children. To Luther, marriage was as much a part of human nature as eating or drinking (Tannahill, 1980). Calvin rejected the Roman Catholic Church's position that sex in marriage was permissible only for the purpose of procreation. He believed that sexual expression in marriage fulfilled other legitimate roles, such as strengthening the marriage bond and helping to relieve the stresses of everyday life. However, extramarital and premarital sex remained forbidden, and were sternly punished.

THE VICTORIAN ERA The middle and later parts of the nineteenth century are generally called the Victorian period after Queen Victoria of England. Victoria assumed the throne in 1837 and ruled until her death in 1901. Her name has become virtually synonymous with sexual repression. Victorian society in Europe and North America, on the surface at least, was prim and proper. Sex was not discussed in polite society. Many women viewed sex as a marital duty to be performed for procreation or to satisfy their husbands' cravings. Consider the following quotation:

> I am happy now that Charles calls on my bed chamber less frequently than of old. As it is, I now endure but two calls a week and when I hear his steps outside my door I lie down on my bed, close my eyes, open my legs and think of England.
>
> —Attributed to Alice, Lady Hillingdon, wife of the Second Baron Hillingdon

Women were assumed not to experience sexual desires or pleasures. "I would say," observed Dr. William Acton (1814–1875), an influential English physician, in 1857, "that the majority of women (happily for society) are not much troubled with sexual feeling of any kind." Women, thought Acton, were born with a sort of sexual anaesthesia.

It was widely believed among medical authorities that sex drains the man of his natural vitality. Physicians thus recommended that intercourse be practised infrequently. The Reverend Sylvester Graham (1794–1851) preached that ejaculation deprived men of the "vital fluids" they need to maintain health and vitality. Graham preached against "wasting the seed" by masturbation or frequent marital intercourse. (How frequent was frequent? In Graham's view, intercourse more than once a month could dangerously deplete the man's vital energies.) Graham recommended that young men control their sexual appetites by a diet of simple foods based on whole-grain flours. He invented the graham cracker for this purpose.

It appears, though, that the actual behaviour of Victorians was not as repressed as advertised. Despite the belief in female sexual anaesthesia, some Victorian women did experience sexual pleasure and orgasm. Consider an early sex survey conducted in 1892 by a female physician, Celia Duel Mosher. Although her sample was small and nonrandom, 35 of the 44 women who responded admitted to desiring sexual intercourse. And 34 of them reported experiencing orgasm. Women's diaries of the time also contained accounts of passionate and sexually fulfilling love affairs (Gay, 1984).

Prostitution flourished during the Victorian era. Men apparently thought that they were doing their wives a favour by looking elsewhere.

Same-sex sexual behaviour was considered indecent in Victorian society. The celebrated, gay Anglo-Irish novelist and playwright Oscar Wilde—author of *The Picture of Dorian Gray*, *An Ideal Husband*, and *The Importance of Being Earnest*—was imprisoned after being convicted of "gross indecency."

THE FOUNDATIONS OF THE SCIENTIFIC STUDY OF SEXUALITY It was against this backdrop of sexual repression that scientists and scholars first began to approach sexuality as an area of legitimate scientific study. An important

Sexologist A person who engages in the scientific study of sexual behaviour.

early contributor to the science of human sexuality was the English physician Havelock Ellis (1859–1939). Ellis compiled a veritable encyclopedia of sexuality: a series of volumes published between 1897 and 1910 entitled *Studies in the Psychology of Sex*. Ellis drew information from various sources, including case histories, anthropological findings, and medical knowledge. He challenged the prevailing view by arguing that sexual desires in women were natural and healthful. He promoted the idea that many sexual problems had psychological rather than physical causes. He also argued that a gay male or lesbian sexual orientation was a naturally occurring variation within the spectrum of normal sexuality, not an aberration. Ellis treated gay male and lesbian sexual orientations as inborn dispositions, not as vices or character flaws.

Another influential **sexologist**, the German psychiatrist Richard von Krafft-Ebing (1840–1902), described more than 200 case histories of individuals with various sexual deviations in his book *Psychopathia Sexualis*. His writings contain vivid descriptions of deviations ranging from sadomasochism (sexual gratification through inflicting or receiving pain) and bestiality (sex with animals) to yet more bizarre and frightening forms, such as necrophilia (intercourse with dead people). Krafft-Ebing viewed sexual deviations as mental diseases that could be studied and perhaps treated by medical science.

At about the same time, a Viennese physician, Sigmund Freud (1856–1939), was developing a theory of personality that has had an enormous influence on modern culture and science. Freud believed that the sex drive was our principal motivating force.

Alfred Kinsey (1894–1956), an Indiana University zoologist, conducted the first large-scale studies of sexual behaviour in the 1930s and 1940s. It was then that sex research became recognized as a field of scientific study in its own right. In 1938 Kinsey had been asked to teach a course on marriage. When researching the course, Kinsey discovered that little was known about sexual practices in American society. He soon embarked on an ambitious research project. Detailed personal interviews with nearly 12 000 people across the United States were conducted. The results of his surveys were published in two volumes, *Sexual Behavior in the Human Male* (1948) and *Sexual Behavior in the Human Female* (1953). These books represent the first scientific attempts to provide a comprehensive picture of sexual behaviour in the United States.

Kinsey's books made for rather dry reading and were filled with statistical tables rather than racy pictures or vignettes. Nevertheless, they became bestsellers. They exploded on a public that had not yet learned to discuss sex openly. Their publication—especially that of the book on female sexuality—unleashed the dogs of criticism. Kinsey's work had some methodological flaws, but much of the criticism branded it immoral and obscene. The *New York Times* refused to run advertisements for the 1948 volume on male sexuality. Many newspapers refused to report the results of his survey on female sexuality. A congressional committee in the 1950s went so far as to claim that Kinsey's work undermined the moral fibre of the nation, rendering it more vulnerable to a Communist takeover (Gebhard, 1976).

Even so, Kinsey and his colleagues made sex research a scientifically respectable field of study. They helped lay the groundwork for greater openness in discussing sexual behaviour.

THE SEXUAL REVOLUTION The period of the mid-1960s to the mid-1970s is often referred to as the sexual revolution. Dramatic changes occurred in sexual attitudes and practices during the "Swinging Sixties." Our society was on the threshold of major social upheaval, not only in sexual behaviour but also in science, politics, fashion, music, art, and cinema. The so-called Woodstock generation, disheartened by commercialism and the Vietnam War, tuned in (to rock music on the radio), turned on (to drugs), and dropped out (of mainstream society). Films became sexually explicit. Critics seriously contemplated whether the pornography classic

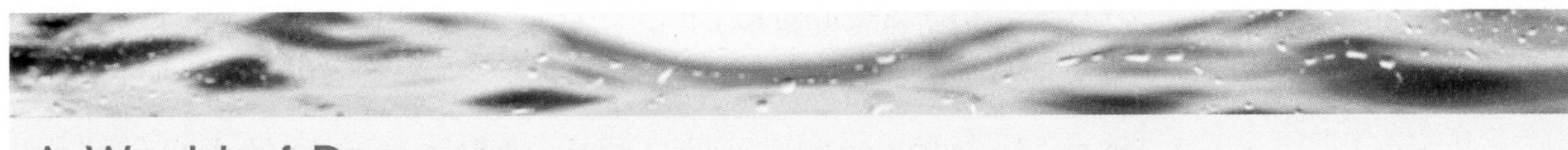

A World of Diversity

THE HISTORY OF DESIRE

Much of the historical analysis of sexual practices over various time periods has focused on the role of religion and cultural traditions. University of Toronto professor Edward Shorter, in his book *Written in the Flesh: A History of Desire* (2005), has also analyzed the role of other influences on sexual behaviour. He argues that past constraints suppressed not only the amount of sex that people had but also the variety of sexual behaviours that they experienced.

According to Shorter, features of everyday life—such as poor hygiene, inadequate diets, periods of hunger, rampant disease including plagues and sexually transmitted infections, plus lice and scabies infestation—put a damper on sexual desire and decreased the sexual attractiveness of one's partners. For most people there was also a lack of privacy, given crowded living conditions with children often sleeping in the same room as parents. Accordingly, sex was often done quickly, in the dark and under the bed covers. Finally, since death in childbirth was common, women's fear made many want to avoid having sex. With religious prohibitions against sex for pleasure added to these constraints, it is not surprising that historically, for most people, sex was not seen as a source of adventure.

Deep Throat had deep social implications. Hard rock music bellowed the message of rebellion and revolution.

No single event marked the onset of the sexual revolution. Social movements often gain momentum from a timely interplay of scientific, social, political, and economic forces. The American war (in Vietnam), the bomb (fear of the nuclear bomb), the pill (the introduction of the birth-control pill), and the tube (TV, that is) were four such forces. The pill greatly reduced the risk of unwanted pregnancy for young people. It permitted them to engage in recreational or casual sex, rather than procreative sex. Pop psychology movements, such as the Human Potential Movement of the 1960s and 1970s (the "Me Decade"), spread the message that people should get in touch with and express their genuine feelings, including their sexual feelings. "Do your own thing" became one catchphrase. "If it feels good, do it" became another. The Canadian prime minister at the time, Pierre Trudeau, declared that "the state has no place in the bedrooms of the nation." Here he was speaking in support of less restrictive laws on sexual behaviour.

The sexual revolution was tied to social permissiveness and political liberalism. In part reflecting the times, in part acting as catalyst, the media dealt openly with sex. Popular books encouraged people to explore their sexuality. Film scenes of lovemaking became so commonplace that the movie rating system was introduced to alert parents. Protests against the Vietnam War and racial discrimination spilled over into broader protests against conventional morality and hypocrisy.

Are Today's Young People More or Less Liberal in the Expression of Their Sexuality Than People in Earlier Generations?
Today the threat of HIV/AIDS hangs over every sexual encounter. While many young people today are selective in their choice of partners and take precautions to make sex safer, more teenagers are engaging in sexual activity, and at younger ages, than in previous generations. (Models for illustrative purposes only.)

GAY ACTIVISM Gay activism mushroomed during the sexual revolution. Not only did gay men and lesbians become more vocal in demanding equal rights, but they also began gay parades in major cities. Annual parades in Toronto and Montreal are among the best known of these. In the early 1980s, gay people also built social institutions to tackle the problem of AIDS, which affected gay people disproportionately to their numbers in the general population.

What, then, does history tell us about sex? Is there a universal standard for defining sexual values, or are there many standards? All societies have some form of an incest taboo. Most societies have placed a value on procreative sex within the context of an enduring relationship. Other sexual practices—masturbation, promiscuous sex, male–male sexual behaviour, female–female sexual behaviour, prostitution, polygamy, and so on—have been condemned in some societies, tolerated by others, and encouraged by others still.

The Biological Perspective

The biological perspective focuses on the roles of genes, hormones, the nervous system, and other biological factors in human sexuality. Sex, after all, serves the biological function of reproduction. We are biologically endowed with anatomic structures and physiological capabilities that make sexual behaviour possible and, for most people, pleasurable.

Study of the biology of sex acquaints us with the mechanisms of reproduction. It informs us of the physiological mechanisms of sexual arousal and response. Biology teaches us that erection occurs when the penis becomes engorged with blood. We learn that vaginal lubrication is the result of a "sweating" action of the vaginal walls. We learn that orgasm is a spinal reflex as well as a psychological event.

Knowledge of biology has furthered our understanding of sexuality and our ability to overcome sexual problems. Although the sexuality of other species is largely governed by biological processes, culture and experience play essential roles—and in some cases, the more vital roles—in human sexuality. Human sexuality involves a complex interaction of biological and psychosocial factors.

The Evolutionary Perspective

Species vary not only in their physical characteristics but also in their social behaviour, including their mating behaviour. Scientists look to the process of **evolution** to help explain such variability.

The English naturalist Charles Darwin (1809–1882), the founder of the modern theory of evolution, believed that animal and plant species were not created independently but, rather, evolved from other life forms. The mechanism by which species evolved was **natural selection**, or, in the vernacular, "survival of the fittest."

In each species, some individuals are better adapted to their environment than others. Better-adapted members are more likely to survive to reproduce. Therefore, they are also more likely to transmit their traits to succeeding generations. As the generations pass, a greater proportion of the population of the species comes to carry the traits of the fittest members. Over time, natural selection favours traits that contribute to survival and reproduction. When environmental conditions change, natural selection favours those members of a species who possess traits that help them adapt.

Some scientists suggest that there is also a genetic basis to social behaviour, including sexual behaviour, among humans and other animals (Buss, 2005). If so, we may carry traits that helped our prehistoric ancestors survive and reproduce successfully.

Does biology govern sexual behaviour? Although the sexuality of other species is largely governed by biological processes, culture and experience also play vital roles in human sexuality (Plomin & Asbury, 2005). Human sexuality involves a complex web of biological, psychological, and cultural factors.

Evolution The development of a species to its present state, a process that is believed to involve adaptations to its environment.

Natural selection The evolutionary process by which adaptive traits enable members of a species to survive to reproductive age and transmit these traits to future generations.

EVOLUTIONARY PERSPECTIVE AND EROTIC PLASTICITY

Consider the concept of "erotic plasticity" (Baumeister, 2000), the observation that in response to various social and cultural forces, people show different levels of sex drive and express their sexual desires in a variety of ways. Roy Baumeister (2000) reports evidence that women show greater erotic plasticity than men do. For example, (1) individual women show greater variation than men in sexual behaviour over time, (2) women seem to be more responsive than men to most specific cultural factors, such as cultural permissiveness or restraint, and (3) men's sexual behaviour is more consistent with their sexual attitudes than is that of women. Baumeister concludes that evolutionary, biological forces may be an important factor in the greater female erotic plasticity.

Some evolutionary psychologists argue that men are naturally more promiscuous because they are the genetic heirs of ancestors whose reproductive success was related to the number of women they could impregnate (Buss, 2005). Women, by contrast, can produce only a few offspring in their lifetimes. Thus, the theory goes, they have to be more selective with respect to their mating partners. Women's reproductive success is enhanced by mating with the fittest males, not with any Tom, Dick, or Harry who happens by. From this perspective, the male's "roving eye" and the female's selectivity are embedded in their genes.

Genes govern the biological processes of sexual maturation and the production of sex hormones. Hormones, in turn, are largely responsible for regulating the sexual behaviour of other animal species. Extending **evolutionary psychology** to human behaviour sparks considerable controversy, however. Critics contend that learning, personal choice, and sociocultural factors may be more important determinants of human behaviour than heredity (Shibley-Hyde & Durik, 2000).

The Cross-Species Perspective

The study of other animal species places human behaviour in a broader context. A surprising variety of sexual behaviours exist among animals. There are animal examples, or **analogues**, of human male–male sexual behaviour, female–female sexual behaviour, oral–genital contact, and oral–oral behaviour (that is, kissing). Foreplay is also well known in the animal world. Turtles massage their mates' heads with their claws. Male mice nibble at their partners' necks. Most mammals use only a rear-entry position for **copulation**, but some animals, such as apes, use a variety of coital positions.

Cross-species research reveals an interesting pattern. Sexual behaviour among "higher" mammals, such as primates, is less directly controlled by instinct than it is among the "lower" species, such as birds, fish, and lower mammals. Experience and learning play more important roles in sexuality as we travel up the evolutionary ladder.

Sociological and Anthropological Perspectives

Sociological and anthropological perspectives, like the historical perspective, provide insight into the ways in which cultural beliefs affect sexual behaviour and people's sense of morality. Interest in the cross-cultural perspective on sexuality was spurred by the early twentieth-century work of the anthropologists Margaret Mead (1901–1978) and Bronislaw Malinowski (1884–1942).

In *Sex and Temperament in Three Primitive Societies* (1935), Mead laid the groundwork for recent psychological and sociological research challenging gender-role stereotypes. In most cultures characterized by a gender division of labour, men typically go to business or to the hunt, and—when necessary—to war. In such cultures, men are perceived as strong, active, independent, and logical. Women are viewed as passive, dependent, nurturant, and emotional. Mead concluded that these stereotypes are not inherent in our genetic heritage. Rather, they are acquired through cultural expectations and socialization. That is, men and women learn to behave in ways that are expected of them in their particular culture.

Malinowski lived on the Trobriand island of Boyawa in the South Pacific during World War I. There he gathered data on two societies of the South Pacific, the

Evolutionary psychology The theory that dispositions toward behaviour patterns that enhance reproductive success may be genetically transmitted.

Analogue Something that is similar or comparable to something else.

Copulation Sexual intercourse.

A World of Diversity

NUDITY AND SEXUALITY DO NOT ALWAYS GO TOGETHER

In Canada nudity is associated with sexuality and public nudity is usually illegal. However, thousands of Canadians, including entire families, participate in naturism or nudism. Naturist organizations promote nudity as natural and freeing for the body and prohibit sexual touching or gazing in public. Given the naturist rather than the sexual focus of nudity, men seldom get erections in the naturist setting.

There are over 30 private naturist sites in Canada as well as a small number of public sites that allow nudity. Nudity also occurs in the summer in some secluded areas, of course, including during the practice of "skinny-dipping." Information about the Federation of Canadian Naturists can be found at www.fcn.ca.

This photo from the Canadian magazine Going Natural/Au naturel *illustrates naturism's non-sexualized nudity, as well as its acceptance of bodies of any age, shape, size, or condition.*

Trobrianders and the Amphett islanders. The Amphett islanders maintained strict sexual prohibitions, whereas the Trobrianders enjoyed greater freedom. Trobrianders, for example, encouraged their children to masturbate. Boys and girls were expected to begin to engage in intercourse when they were biologically old enough. Adolescents were expected to have multiple sex partners until they married. Malinowski found the Trobrianders less anxiety-ridden than the Amphett islanders. He attributed the difference to their sexual freedom, thus making an early plea to relax prohibitions in Western societies.

In 1951, Clellan Ford, an anthropologist, and Frank Beach, a psychologist, reviewed studies of sexual behaviour in preliterate societies around the world. They found great variety in sexual customs and beliefs among the almost 200 societies they studied. They also found some common threads.

Mangaia.
Perhaps they didn't wear coconut shells, but a generation or so ago, sex on Mangaia was free-wheeling. In other places and at other times, sex has been seen as a necessary evil to follow God's command to "be fruitful and multiply."

Kissing was quite common across the cultures they studied, though not universal. The Thonga of Africa were one society that did not practise kissing. Upon witnessing two European visitors kissing each other, members of the tribe commented that they could not understand why Europeans "ate" each other's saliva and dirt. The frequency of sexual intercourse also varies from culture to culture, but intercourse is relatively more frequent among young people everywhere. Attitudes toward public nudity also vary across cultures. Ford and Beach found that where public nudity was accepted, being nude was not considered to be sexual. However, in Canada, nudity is associated with sexuality.

Societies differ in their attitudes toward childhood masturbation as well. Some societies, such as the Hopi Native Americans of the southwest United States, ignore it. Trobrianders encourage children to stimulate themselves. Other societies condemn it.

Societies differ widely in their sexual attitudes, customs, and practices. The members of all human societies share the same anatomic structures and physiological capacities for sexual pleasure, however. The same hormones flow in their blood. Yet their sexual practices, and the pleasure they reap or fail to attain, may set them apart. Were human sexuality completely or predominantly determined by biology, we would not find such diversity.

Acquisition of Gender Roles.
According to social-learning theory, children learn gender roles that are considered appropriate in their society via the reinforcement of certain behaviour patterns and by observing the gender-role behaviours of their parents, peers, and other role models in media such as TV, films, and books.

Psychological Perspectives

Psychological perspectives focus on the many psychological influences—perception, learning, motivation, emotion, personality, and so on—that affect our sexual behaviour and our experience of ourselves as female or male. Some psychological theorists, such as Sigmund Freud, focus on the motivational role of sex in human personality. Others focus on how our experiences and mental representations of the world affect our sexual behaviour.

SIGMUND FREUD AND PSYCHOANALYTIC THEORY

Sigmund Freud, a Viennese physician, formulated a grand theory of personality termed **psychoanalysis**. Freud believed that we are all born with biologically based sex drives. These drives must be channelled through socially approved outlets if family and social life are to carry on without undue conflict. Freud proposed that the mind operates on conscious and unconscious levels. The conscious level corresponds to our state of present awareness. The **unconscious mind** consists of the darker reaches of the mind that lie outside our direct awareness. The ego shields the conscious mind from awareness of our baser sexual and aggressive urges via **defence mechanisms** such as **repression**, the motivated forgetting of traumatic experiences.

Freud introduced new and controversial ideas about people as sexual beings. For example, he originated the concept of **erogenous zones**—the idea that many parts of the body, not just the genitals, are responsive to sexual stimulation.

One of Freud's most controversial beliefs was that children normally harbour erotic interests. He believed that the suckling of the infant in the oral stage was an erotic act. So too was anal bodily experimentation, through which children learn to experience pleasure in the control of their sphincter muscles and the processes of elimination. He theorized that it was normal for children to progress through stages of development in which the erotic interest shifts from one erogenous zone to another, as, for example, from the mouth or oral cavity to the anal cavity. According to his theory of **psychosexual development**, children undergo five stages of development: oral, anal, phallic, latency, and genital, which are named according to the predominant erogenous zones of each stage. Each stage gives rise to certain kinds of conflicts. Moreover, inadequate or excessive gratification in any stage can lead to **fixation** in that stage and to the development of traits and sexual preferences characteristic of that stage.

Freud believed that it was normal for children to develop erotic feelings toward the parent of the other gender during the phallic stage. These incestuous urges lead to conflict with the parent of the same gender. In later chapters we shall see that these developments, which Freud termed the Oedipus complex, have profound implications for the assumption of **gender roles** and sexual orientation.

Psychoanalysis The theory of personality originated by Sigmund Freud, which proposes that human behaviour represents the outcome of clashing inner forces.

Unconscious mind Those parts or contents of the mind that lie outside of conscious awareness.

Defence mechanisms In psychoanalytic theory, automatic processes that protect the ego from anxiety by disguising or ejecting unacceptable ideas and urges.

Repression The automatic ejection of anxiety-evoking ideas from consciousness.

Erogenous zones Parts of the body, including but not limited to the sex organs, that are responsive to sexual stimulation.

Psychosexual development In psychoanalytic theory, the process by which sexual feelings shift from one erogenous zone to another.

Fixation In psychoanalytic theory, arrested development, which includes attachment to traits and sexual preferences that are characteristic of an earlier stage of psychosexual development.

Gender roles Complex clusters of ways in which males and females are expected to behave within a given culture.

LEARNING THEORIES To what extent does sexual behaviour reflect experience? Would you hold the same sexual attitudes and do the same things if you had been reared in another culture? We think not. Even within the same society, family and personal experiences can shape unique sexual attitudes and behaviours. Whereas psychoanalytic theory plumbs the depths of the unconscious, learning theorists focus on environmental factors that shape behaviour.

Behaviourists Learning theorists who argue that a scientific approach to understanding behaviour must refer only to observable and measurable behaviours, and who emphasize the importance of rewards and punishments in the learning process.

Modelling Acquiring knowledge and skills by observing others.

Social–cognitive theory A cognitively oriented learning theory in which observational learning, values, and expectations play key roles in determining behaviour.

Behaviourists such as John B. Watson (1878–1958) and B. F. Skinner (1904–1990) emphasized the importance of rewards and punishments in the learning process. Skinner termed events that increase the frequency or likelihood of behaviour as reinforcements. Children left to explore their bodies without parental condemnation will learn what feels good and tend to repeat it. The Trobriand child who is rewarded for masturbation and premarital coitus through parental praise and encouragement will be more likely to repeat these behaviours than the child in a more sexually restrictive culture, who is punished for the same behaviour. When sexual behaviour (such as masturbation) feels good but parents connect it with feelings of guilt and shame, the child is placed in conflict and may vacillate between masturbating and swearing off of it.

If we as young children are severely punished for sexual exploration, we may come to associate sexual stimulation in general with feelings of guilt or anxiety. Such early learning experiences can set the stage for sexual dysfunctions in adulthood.

COGNITIVE VIEWS Cognitive psychologists differ from behaviourists in that they emphasize the importance of cognitive activity (problem solving, decision making, expectations, and so on). Cognitive psychologists focus more on how individuals' choices are affected by internal thoughts, etc., rather than on how individuals may be merely responding to external rewards. They also recognize that people learn intentionally and by observing others. Observational learning, or **modelling**, refers to acquiring knowledge and skills by observing others. Observational learning involves more than direct observation of other people. It includes seeing models in films or on television, hearing about them, and reading about them. According to **social–cognitive theory**, children acquire the gender roles deemed appropriate in a society through reinforcement of gender-appropriate behaviour and through observing the gender-role behaviour of their parents, their peers, and other models on television, in films, in books, and so on.

In Chapter 5 we will more fully explore the nature of masculine and feminine gender roles, and why most males enact masculine roles and most females enact feminine roles. We will see that the acquisition of gender roles is likely to involve a complex interaction of psychological, biological, and social factors.

Sociological Perspectives

Sexual behaviour is determined not only by biological and psychological factors, but also by social factors. Social factors contribute to the shaping of our sexual attitudes, beliefs, and behaviour. Whereas anthropologists contribute to our understanding of cross-cultural variance in sexuality, sociologists focus on differences in sexuality among the subgroups of a society, as defined, for example, by differences in religion, race/ethnicity, country of origin, socioeconomic status, marital status, age, educational level, and gender.

The sociological perspective informs us of the relationship between sexuality and a particular social group within a society. Sociologists view sexual behaviour as occurring within a specific sociocultural system. They study the ways in which the values, beliefs, and norms of a group influence the sexual behaviour of its members. To a certain extent, we share attitudes and behaviour patterns with people from similar backgrounds—for example, people with the same ethnic identity. Even so, not all members of a given ethnic group act or think alike.

One of the most comprehensive surveys of relationships and sexuality in Canada was conducted in 1998 by the Compas polling organization on behalf of the Sun newspaper group. The Canadian author of this text was a consultant for that survey. The methodology for this study is described in Chapter 2. A number of sociological analyses of this study are presented in several chapters throughout this text, including in the feature box "The Influence of Gender and Other Social Variables on the Sexuality of Canadians."

Innovative Canadian Research

THE INFLUENCE OF GENDER AND OTHER SOCIAL VARIABLES ON THE SEXUALITY OF CANADIANS

Gender differences are often analyzed in studies of sexuality. However, other social variables are usually not considered.

Researchers at the University of Guelph–Dayna Fischstein, Ed Herold, and Serge Demarais (2007)–collected data from a national survey of 1479 Canadian adults over the age of 18 to determine if gender differences still exist when we take into account other social variables. The researchers examined how gender, age, marital status, education, religiosity, and geographic region affect the sexuality variables of frequency of sexual thoughts, oral sex, age at first intercourse, number of sexual partners, and intentions to engage in casual sex.

The researchers found that the men were more sexually permissive and more sexually active than were the women. It should be noted, however, that some of the gender differences were found to be small or moderate, suggesting that the gender gap may be narrowing with regard to differences in sexuality.

Other demographic variables were also significant predictors of sexual attitudes and behaviours. Generally, the younger survey participants, those with more education, and those who did not attend religious services were found to have more permissive attitudes.

The findings illustrate the value of taking into account other social variables when analyzing gender differences in sexuality.

The most substantial gender differences were seen with intentions to engage in casual sex. None of the women reported they would definitely engage in casual sex, and few reported they would probably engage in casual sex. In comparison, most men reported they would engage in casual sex if given the opportunity to do so. These findings may be explained by the sexual double standard, which allows for greater sexual freedom for men than for women. The strength of the gender effect was demonstrated by the fact that the other social factors were relatively weak predictors of intentions to engage in casual sex. Interestingly, people living in Quebec were more likely than participants from all other regions to report an interest in engaging in casual sex.

A major contribution of this study is that it provided a better understanding of the role of gender in relation to other social variables in accounting for differences in sexuality among adult Canadians. The survey findings point to the need for large-scale national surveys with heterogeneous samples rather than relying on samples of convenience, such as university populations.

Provincial Differences in Sexuality

There are many regional differences in sexual attitudes and behaviours. Studies have shown that French Canadians in Quebec have more liberal sexual attitudes and behaviours than do other Canadians (Barrett et al., 1997). For example, they are more likely to have sexual intercourse at younger ages and more likely to live in common-law relationships. They are also more likely to admit to having extramarital sex. These differences are all the more remarkable given that, until the 1960s, the dominance of the Catholic Church in Quebec meant that French people in that province were among the most conservative in Canada. However, along with the rise of the political separatism movement in the 1960s, the French in Quebec increasingly challenged Church teachings. Prior to the 1960s Quebec had the highest rate of church attendance in Canada, but today it has one of the lowest (Clark, 2003). As a result of this trend toward secularization, the Catholic Church now has far less influence over the sexual decision making of most people in Quebec. The influence of religion has also declined in English Canada, but less dramatically (Barrett et al., 2004).

Although people in Quebec generally have more liberal sexual attitudes and behaviours than other Canadians, people in Newfoundland have the highest frequency of sexual relations. Figure 1.1 shows the results of a national survey concerning the frequency of sex per month as reported by Canadians in each of the provinces (*Maclean's*/CTV Poll). The highest frequency for sexual activity was in Newfoundland, followed by Quebec and P.E.I. The lowest frequency was in Saskatchewan.

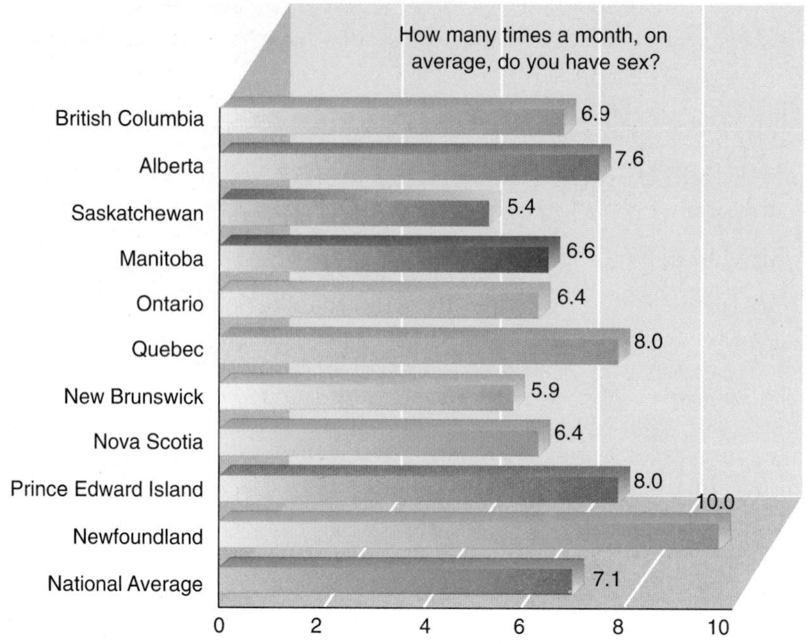

Figure 1.1 Monthly Frequency of Sex for Canadian Adults, by Province.

There are considerable differences in sexual attitudes and behaviours across Canada.

Source: Courtesy of CTV News.

For 12 of the 13 years that the poll has been conducted, Newfoundland has shown the highest frequency of sexual activity. Unfortunately, researchers have not probed deeper to determine why people in Newfoundland consistently have the highest levels of sexual activity. Can you think of possible reasons?

The Media and Sexuality

The media can play a powerful role in influencing sexual attitudes. In recent years, Canadian news and documentary programming has become far more explicit in its presentation of sexual issues. These informative programs typically discuss sexual topics in formats that are both serious and entertaining. For example, the Discovery Channel series *The Sex Files* has been bold in openly dealing with topics—such as masturbation and anal sex—that have traditionally been avoided by the mainstream media. With an audience numbering in the millions, *The Sex Files* was by far the most watched series ever produced by the Discovery Channel. The series was also shown on the Life Channel, where it was adapted as *Sexual Secrets*.

Toronto's CityTV produces *Sextv*, which uses a news-magazine format to present a diverse range of sexuality topics, including erotic art and photography. This series formed the basis for the *Sextv* digital cable channel, which is focused exclusively on sex. Numerous Canadian documentaries have been produced on such topics as domination and submission (which included scenes of people being tied up and whipped). Another sexually oriented series was *Sex, Toys and Chocolate*, with hosts Robin Milhausen and Michael Cho. This show involved guests discussing personal sexual preference in intimate detail. More recently, Robin Milhausen has appeared on the series *Three Takes* to discuss sexuality topics. There is also the series *Kink*, which showed Canadians engaging in varied bondage and sadomasochistic sexual behaviours.

Many comedy and drama series have also presented sexual themes, including the U.S. series *Sex and the City* and *The Sopranos*. These series expanded the sexual boundaries of mainstream television. And in recent years, the pay-per-view adult videos shown late at night have been moneymakers for the cable industry. Viewer ratings clearly indicate that many Canadians enjoy watching shows that present sexual topics in an open manner.

The number of gay men and lesbians presented on television has increased significantly. *Queer as Folk*, another groundbreaking series, featured the lives of five gay men and two lesbians. This show contains a lot of nudity and sexual scenes, including oral sex and group sex. Interestingly, one study found that about half the viewers were heterosexual women, many of whom admitted they were attracted by the male nudity (Bawden, 2002). *The L-Word* is situated in the lesbian community of West Hollywood, and explores relationship and sexual issues among lesbians. This show is highly popular among lesbians in Canada. There is even a Canadian cable channel (formerly Pride Vision, now OUTv) centred on gay and lesbian themes. Gay roles have also been presented on mainstream series, such as *Will and Grace*, *Ugly Betty*, *Desperate Housewives*, *The Office*, and *Cashmere Mafia*.

The media have been instrumental in bringing topics into the open that only a few years ago would have been considered too controversial. Today, attempts to push the boundaries of public acceptability include, for example, the promotion of intimate disclosure. A reporter who auditioned with about a thousand other Canadians for the American show *Blind Date* was instructed to be as detailed as possible: "We're not supposed to say, for example, we like sex. We're supposed to say we like it three times a day, especially in the morning, on the kitchen counter" (Eckler, 2000).

The Canadian Broadcast Standards Council chastised MTV in Toronto for broadcasting material that was too sexually explicit during its morning show because children could be watching at that time. The theme of the show was masturbation and it included scenes showing how to use sex toys, filmed at a sex shop. The Council did not object to the topic of masturbation itself but said that the program should have been aired after 9:00 p.m. (*Toronto Star*, 2007).

The American government has been far more restrictive than the Canadian government in censoring sex on television. For example, in the United States, the Federal Communications Commission fined CBS Television $3.6 million for an episode of *Without a Trace* that showed clothed and semi-clothed teenagers at a sex party. Interestingly, the U.S. agency is less concerned about the discussion of sexual topics as presented on *Two and a Half Men* than it is about the visual presentation of sex and nudity.

Probably the best explanation for these trends is that the media are following the old adage: "Sex sells."

Feminist Theory

Definitions of feminism and of **feminist theory** are controversial, but it is clear enough that feminist theory focuses on the subordination of women to men, analyzing the relationships between sexism, heterosexism (prejudice or discrimination against homosexuals by heterosexuals), racism, and class oppression, and exploring means of resistance—on individual and societal levels (Butler, 1993, 2003).

Feminist theory A theory that challenges acceptance of the male as the norm, traditional gender roles, and male oppression of females.

It is of interest that some feminists even challenge the very concepts of femininity and masculinity, because their existence tends to suggest that there is some sort of biological or "actual" basis to the distinction (Squier & Littlefield, 2004; Wood, 2005). They argue, instead, that femininity and masculinity might be purely social constructions that have the effect of giving women second-class citizenship—or, in many historical eras and parts of the world, no citizenship whatsoever.

In terms of topics most relevant to this book, we will find feminists asserting that men have no right to control women's bodies—for example, that abortion is the personal choice of a woman and that women have as much right as men to decide whether to engage in sexual activity, and with whom. Feminists also argue that there are few, if any, sex differences in intelligence and specific mental abilities, such as those abilities used in math and science.

Although the extent and nature of sex differences remain controversial, we can note that many traditions that subjugate women are falling by the wayside, at least

Queer theory A theory that challenges heteronormativity and heterosexism.

Homophobia Although this term derives from roots meaning "fear of homosexuals," it usually refers to hatred of homosexuals.

in developed nations. Most Canadian women, for example, are now in the workforce and many are pursuing careers in traditionally male domains, such as business, law, and medicine. Yet, in general, women's wages continue to be lower than those of men.

Queer Theory

The word *queer* was initially used as an insult to describe homosexuals. After approximately two centuries, it was gradually replaced by the word *gay* (Bhugra, 2005). However, homosexuals have reappropriated the word *queer* as a sign of pride, as shown by the title of the popular TV show *Queer Eye for the Straight Guy*. As one result of this reappropriation, a widely cited theory of the psychology and sociology of gender roles and sexual orientation is termed **queer theory** (Alexander, 2006; Valocchi, 2005).

Queer theory challenges a number of commonly held assumptions about gender and sexuality, such as the assumptions that heterosexuality is normal and superior to homosexuality (Elia et al., 2003; Gordon, 2005; Sullivan, 2003). Queer theory also challenges the assumption that people are naturally divided into heterosexuals and homosexuals (Halpern, 2003; Hird, 2004).

Queer theory argues that the concepts of heterosexuality and homosexuality are social constructs that ignore commonly experienced mismatches among people's anatomic sex, society's gender roles, and individuals' sexual desires (Schlichter, 2004). Queer theory asserts that human sexuality has always been more varied than those in power—particularly male heterosexuals—are willing to admit. They point to historical examples such as ancient Greek bisexuality and to current **homophobia** as evidence.

Multiple Perspectives on Human Sexuality

Given the complexity and range of human sexual behaviour, we need to consider multiple perspectives to understand sexuality. Each perspective has something to offer in this enterprise. Let us venture a few conclusions based on our overview of these perspectives. First, human sexuality appears to reflect a combination of biological, social, cultural, sociocultural, and psychological factors that interact in complex ways, perhaps in combinations that are unique for each individual. Second, there are few universal patterns of sexual behaviour, and views on what is right and wrong show great diversity. Third, although our own cultural values and beliefs may be deeply meaningful to us, they may not indicate what is normal, natural, or moral in terms of sexual behaviour. The complexity of human sexuality—complexity that causes it to remain somewhat baffling to scientists—adds to the wonder and richness of our sexual experience.

Summing Up

- Human sexuality concerns the ways in which we experience and express ourselves as sexual beings. The study of human sexuality draws upon the expertise of anthropologists, biologists, medical researchers, sociologists, psychologists, and other scientists.
- Along with accurate knowledge about human sexuality, our values inform our sexual decisions.
- Critical thinking is a skeptical approach to evaluating arguments, widely held beliefs, and evidence. Critical thinkers examine definitions of terms and the premises of arguments, and are cautious in drawing conclusions from evidence.
- The historical perspective suggests that there are few universal sexual trends.
- The biological perspective focuses on biological sexual processes such as genetic, hormonal, and neural factors.
- Evolutionary theory suggests that social behaviours that enhance reproductive success may be subject to natural selection.

- The cross-species perspective reveals the variety of sexual behaviours among nonhumans.
- The sociological perspective studies ways in which cultural beliefs affect sexual behaviour and attitudes.
- Psychological perspectives focus on the processes of perception, learning, motivation, emotion, and personality that affect gender and sexual behaviour. Freud formulated the theory of psychoanalysis, which proposes that biologically based sex drives come into conflict with social codes. Learning theories focus on the roles of rewards and punishments. Social–cognitive theory views people as decision makers and emphasizes the role of observational learning.
- Feminist theory challenges traditional gender roles and male oppression of females.
- Queer theory challenges heteronormativity—the view that heterosexuality is normal—and points out mismatches among anatomic sex, gender roles, and sexual desires as evidence.

Test Yourself

Multiple-Choice Questions

1. **Most Canadian university students would say that they are "having sex" when the behaviour is**
   a. oral-genital contact
   b. penile-vaginal intercourse
   c. manual stimulation of the genitals
   d. deep kissing

2. **Attention has been focused on the need for sex education today primarily because of**
   a. Canada-wide standards for sexuality education
   b. the worldwide AIDS epidemic
   c. increased interest in research
   d. increases in the incidence of sexual dysfunctions

3. **Thinking critically about human sexuality is important because it helps us to**
   a. overcome skepticism
   b. get in touch with our feelings
   c. challenge conventional wisdom
   d. accept "expert" opinions

4. **The sexual revolution resulted from**
   a. the death of Queen Victoria
   b. tabloids' sensationalizing celebrity lifestyles
   c. laws legalizing same-sex marriages
   d. many economic, social, and political factors

5. **Evolutionary psychology suggests that**
   a. behaviour patterns that favour reproduction are genetically transmitted
   b. men and women are equally promiscuous
   c. biology has nothing to do with sexuality
   d. women are more promiscuous than men

6. **Which of the following is not an ethical framework according to Meaney and Rye?**
   a. cultural tradition
   b. community
   c. autonomy
   d. divinity

7. **Punishing a child for masturbating, according to a behaviourist,**
   a. always results in sexual dysfunction
   b. results in repression
   c. may disrupt psychosexual development
   d. will not always eliminate the behaviour

8. **Ford and Beach's research on preliterate societies found**
   a. a wide variety of sexual customs and beliefs
   b. that intercourse was more common among older people
   c. that childhood masturbation was universally condemned
   d. kissing in all societies studied

9. **Margaret Mead's research laid the groundwork for more recent studies in**
   a. sociobiological research into anthropological theory
   b. research challenging gender-role stereotypes
   c. anthropological research on extramarital sex
   d. research on cross-cultural problems in infertility

10. **Historically, __________ was most likely the first sexual taboo.**
    a. incest
    b. sex before marriage
    c. male homosexuality
    d. masturbation

Answers to the Test Yourself questions in each chapter are found on page 509.

Critical Thinking Questions

1. What are your goals for this course in human sexuality? Do you think that what you learn in this course will help you later on in life? Why or why not?
2. Religions have historically been major factors influencing human sexual behaviour. Do you think this is still true in Canada today? Why or why not?
3. A friend of yours insists that something is true because she found it on the internet. As a critical thinker, do you accept your friend's argument as proof? If not, what would you do to determine the truth or falsity of your friend's claim?

Visit MyPsychKit at www.mypsychkit.com, where you can do quizzes and link to additional resources on topics discussed in this text.

CHAPTER TWO

Research Methods

Empirical Derived from or based on observation and experimentation.

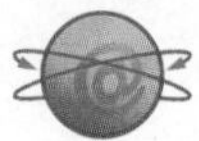

Abstracts from the *Journal of Sex Research*
Excellent reference source that includes abstracts from research published in the *Journal of Sex Research.*
www.sexuality.org/l/sex/jsexrall.html

Have you ever wondered about questions such as these: Are my sexual interests and behaviour patterns unique or shared by many others? Why do people engage in male–male or female–female sexual behaviour? You may have thought of such questions. You may even have expressed opinions on them. But scientists insist that opinions about behaviour, including sexual behaviour, be supported by evidence. Evidence, in turn, must be based on careful observations in the laboratory or in the field.

A Scientific Approach to Human Sexuality

Scientists and researchers who study human sexuality take an **empirical** approach. That is, they base their knowledge on research evidence, rather than on intuition, faith, or superstition. Scientists' and other people's intuitions or religious beliefs may suggest topics to be studied scientifically, but once the topics are selected, answers are sought on the basis of the scientific method.

Canadian Trends

THE CANADIAN RESEARCH SCENE

Relatively few Canadian researchers focus exclusively on sexological research, and few Canadian universities have more than one or two sexologists. The Canadian Sex Research Forum (CSRF), the main organization that focuses on sexuality research, holds annual meetings at which Canadian researchers discuss findings from their most recent studies. The proceedings of these meetings are published in *The Canadian Journal of Sexuality* by the Sex Information and Education Council of Canada. In Quebec, the main organization for sexologists is the *Association des sexologues du Québec* and the primary sexuality journal, published mainly in French, is *Revue Sexologique/Sexological Review.*

Canadian researchers also publish their findings in highly rated international journals such as *The Journal of Sex Research* and *Archives of Sexual Behavior.* They also discuss their studies at international conferences, such as the annual meetings held by the Society for the Scientific Study of Sexuality and the International Academy of Sex Research.

In July 2005, many Canadian researchers gave presentations at the 17th World Congress of Sexology, held in Montreal. Congress meetings are held every two years in a different country under the auspices of the World Association for Sexual Health (WAS). Researchers from every part of the globe attend these world conferences, with the official conference language being English. The Montreal conference was chaired by Montreal researcher and therapist Dr. Pierre Assalian.

At the Montreal conference, Eleanor Maticka-Tyndale and Catherine Brooke (2005) from the University of Windsor presented an analysis of Canadian sexuality research. They concluded that 85% of the research is focused on three areas—HIV/AIDS, adolescent sexuality, and sexual dysfunctions—with most research funding allocated to HIV/AIDS. Another 10% of Canadian research is on sexual violence and coercion, with the remaining 5% on either sex work or sexual relationships.

To date, only limited funding has been available for sexuality research in Canada. Two key sources of funding are the Social Sciences and Humanities Research Council and the Canadian Institutes of Health Research.

Funding for sexuality research in Canada has been based on societal concern with sexual health issues. In the 1970s, for example, concern over adolescent pregnancy led to federal funding of a number of projects. Since the 1980s the government has funded several projects on sexuality and HIV prevention, although most of the funding has been for studies dealing with the medical aspects of HIV/AIDS. Specific groups of Canadians who had been neglected in the past are now being studied, including gay males, First Nations people, drug users, and street youth. Researchers have also begun studying sexual topics that had been considered taboo, such as oral and anal sex.

Because of the huge success of drugs such as Viagra, pharmaceutical companies have been funding large-scale sexuality projects. However, the studies have been mainly focused on sexual problems, in particular, erectile dysfunction. Given the disproportionate focus on only a few content areas, it is not surprising that for many topics we have little or no Canadian data. For example, there has been little research on the topic of sexual pleasure.

Only one Canadian university research chair in sexuality has been funded. Eleanor Maticka-Tyndale holds a Canada Research Chair in Social Justice and Sexual Health at the University of Windsor.

There are also limited opportunities at the graduate level in Canadian universities for students who want to specialize in the sexuality area.

The Scientific Method

Critical thinking and the scientific approach share the hallmark of skepticism. As skeptics, scientists question prevailing assumptions and theories about sexual behaviour. They are willing to dispute the assertions of authority figures such as political and religious leaders—and even other scientists. Scientists also recognize that they cannot gain perfect knowledge. One era's "truths" may become another era's ancient myths and fallacies. Scientists are involved in the continuous quest for truth, but they do not see themselves as experiencing revelations or defining final truths.

The *scientific method* is a systematic way of gathering scientific evidence and testing assumptions through research. It has a number of elements:

1. *Formulating a research question.* Does alcohol inspire or impair sexual response? Scientists formulate research questions on the basis of their observations of, or theories about, events or behaviour. They then seek answers to such questions by conducting empirical research.
2. *Framing the research question in the form of a hypothesis.* Experiments are usually undertaken with a **hypothesis** in mind—a precise prediction about behaviour that is often derived from theory. A hypothesis is tested through research. For instance, a scientist might theorize that alcohol enhances sexual responsiveness either by directly stimulating sexual response or by reducing feelings of guilt associated with sex. He or she might then hypothesize that an intervention (called, in experimental terms, a treatment), such as drinking alcohol in a laboratory setting, will lead to heightened sexual arousal in the presence of erotic stimuli (such as sexually explicit films).
3. *Testing the hypothesis.* Scientists then test hypotheses through carefully controlled observation and experimentation. A specific hypothesis about alcohol and sexual arousal—that alcohol either increases or decreases sexual responsiveness—might be tested by administering a certain amount of alcohol to one group of people and then comparing their levels of sexual arousal following specific types of sexual stimulation (such as exposure to sexually explicit films) to the levels of sexual arousal of another group of people who were shown the films but not given any alcohol.
4. *Drawing conclusions.* Scientists then draw conclusions or inferences about the correctness of their hypotheses on the basis of their analyses of the results of their studies. If the results of well-designed research studies fail to bear out certain hypotheses, scientists can revise the theories that served as the frameworks for the hypotheses. Research findings often lead scientists to modify their theories and, in turn, generate new hypotheses that can be tested in further research.

GOALS OF THE SCIENCE OF HUMAN SEXUALITY The goals of the science of human sexuality are congruent with those of other sciences: to describe, explain, predict, and control the events (in this case, the sexual behaviours) of interest. Let us discuss some of the general goals of science and how they relate to the study of human sexuality as a science.

Description is a basic objective of science. To understand sexual behaviour, for example, we must first be able to describe it. Therefore, the description of behaviour precedes understanding. Scientists attempt to be clear, unbiased, and precise in their descriptions of events and behaviour. The scientific approach to human sexuality describes sexual behaviour through techniques as varied as the field study, the survey, the individual case study, and the laboratory experiment.

Researchers attempt to relate their observations to other factors, or **variables**, that can help explain them. For example, researchers may attempt to explain variations in the frequency of coitus by relating—or *correlating*—coitus with **demographic** variables such as age, religious or social background, and cultural expectations. The

Hypothesis A precise prediction about behaviour that is often derived from theory and is tested through research.

Variables Quantities or qualities that vary or may vary.

Demographic Concerning the vital statistics (density, race, age, etc.) of human populations.

variables that are commonly used to explain sexual behaviour include biological (age, health), psychological (anxieties, skills), and sociological (educational level, socioeconomic status, ethnicity) variables.

Theories provide frameworks within which scientists can explain what they observe and can make predictions. It is not sufficient for theories to help us make sense of events that have already occurred. Theories must also enable us to make predictions. Sex researchers study factors that may predict various types of sexual behaviour. Some researchers, for example, have examined childhood interests and behaviour patterns that may predict the development of a gay male or lesbian sexual orientation. Others have explored factors—such as the age at which dating begins and the quality of the relationships between teens and their parents—that may predict the likelihood of sexual intercourse during adolescence.

The science of human sexuality does not tell people how they *ought* to behave. It does not attempt to limit or expand the variety of their sexual activities. Rather, it furnishes information that people may use to help themselves or others make decisions about their own behaviour. For instance, the science of human sexuality provides information that increases the chances that a couple who are having difficulty becoming pregnant will be able to conceive. At the same time, it develops and evaluates means of birth control that can be used to help couples regulate their reproductive choices. The science of human sexuality also seeks to develop techniques that can help people overcome sexual dysfunctions and enhance the gratification they find in sexual relations.

Populations and Samples: Representing the World of Diversity

Researchers undertake to learn about populations. **Populations** are complete groups of people, such as the entire Canadian population. Other researchers focus on specific population groups, such as First Nations or gay males. These are termed the *populations of interest*, or *target populations.* These target populations are all sizable. It would be expensive, difficult, and all but impossible to study every individual in them.

Because of the impossibility of studying all members of a population, scientists select individuals from the population and study them. The individuals who participate in research are said to compose a **sample**. However, we cannot truly learn about the population of interest unless the sample *represents* that population. A *representative sample* is a research sample of participants who accurately represent the population of interest.

If our samples do not represent the target populations, we cannot extend, or **generalize**, the results of our research to the populations of interest. If we wished to study the sexual behaviour of Asian Canadians, our population would consist of *all* Asian Canadians. If we used only Asian Canadian college students as our sample, we could not generalize our findings to all Asian Canadians.

Including all people in Canada in a study of sexual behaviour would be impossible. We cannot even *find* all people in Canada when we conduct the census. And incorporating sex research into the census would undoubtedly cause many more people to refuse to participate. Sampling a part of a target population makes research practical and possible—if imperfect.

Population A complete group of organisms or events.

Sample Part of a population.

Generalize To go from the particular to the general.

Random sample A sample in which every member of a population has an equal chance of participating.

Stratified random sample A random sample in which known subgroups in a population are represented in proportion to their numbers in the population.

Sampling Methods

A **random sample** is one in which every member of the target population has an equal chance of participating. Researchers overcome biased sampling by drawing *random* or *stratified random* samples of populations. In a random sample, every member of a population has an equal chance of participating. In a **stratified random sample**, known subgroups of a population are represented in proportion to their numbers in the population. For instance, about 51% of the Canadian population is female. Researchers could therefore decide that 51% of their sample must be female if the sample is to represent all people in Canada. The randomness of the sample would be preserved, because the members of the subgroups would be selected randomly from their particular subgroups.

Another problem is that sexual research is almost invariably conducted with people who volunteer to participate. Volunteers may differ from people who refuse to participate. For example, volunteers tend to be more open about their sexuality than the general population.

The problem of **volunteer bias** is a thorny one for sex researchers, because the refusal of people who have been randomly selected to participate in the survey can ruin the representativeness of the sample. It would be unethical to coerce people to participate in a study on sexual behaviour (or in any other type of study), so researchers must use samples of volunteers, rather than true random samples. A low response rate to a voluntary survey is an indication that the responses do not represent the people to whom the survey was distributed.

Populations and Samples.
To what populations do you belong? College students? Returning students? What of your gender? What about your ethnic background? How do researchers obtain samples that represent populations such as these? What problems do they encounter in attempting to do so?

In some cases, samples are samples of convenience. They consist of individuals who happen to be available to the researcher and who share some characteristics with the target population—perhaps religious background or sexual orientation. Still, they may not truly represent the target group. Convenience samples often consist of European-Canadian, middle-class university students who volunteer for studies conducted at their schools.

Methods of Observation

Once scientists have chosen those whom they will study, they observe them. In this section, we consider several methods of observation: the case-study method, the survey method, naturalistic observation, ethnographic observation, participant observation, and laboratory observation.

The Case-Study Method

A **case study** is a carefully drawn, in-depth biography of an individual or a small group. The focus is on understanding one or several individuals as fully as possible by unravelling the interplay of various factors in their backgrounds. In most case studies, the researcher comes to know the individual or group through interviews or other contacts conducted over a prolonged period of time. The interviewing pattern tends to build upon itself with a good deal of freedom, in contrast to the one-shot, standardized set of questions used in survey questionnaires.

Reports of innovative treatments for sexual dysfunctions usually appear as well-described case studies. A clinician typically reports the background of the client in depth, describes the treatment, reports the apparent outcomes, and suggests factors that might have contributed to the treatment's success or failure. In writing a treatment case study, the therapist tries to provide information that may be helpful to therapists who treat clients with similar problems. Case studies or "multiple case studies" (reports concerning a few individuals) that hold promise may be subjected to controlled investigation—ideally, to experimental studies involving treatment and control groups.

Despite the richness of material that may be derived from the case-study approach, it is not as rigorous a research design as an experiment. People often have gaps in memory, especially concerning childhood events. The potential for observer bias is also a prominent concern. Clinicians and interviewers may unintentionally

Volunteer bias A slanting of research data that is caused by the characteristics of individuals who volunteer to participate, such as willingness to discuss intimate behaviour.

Case study A carefully drawn, in-depth biography of an individual or a small group of individuals that may be obtained through interviews, questionnaires, and historical records.

Survey A detailed study of a sample obtained by means such as interviews and questionnaires.

guide people into saying what they expect to hear. Then, too, researchers may inadvertently colour people's reports when they jot them down—shaping them subtly in ways that reflect their own views.

The Survey Method: Questionnaires Versus Interviews

Surveys typically gather information about behaviour through questionnaires or interviews. Researchers may interview or administer questionnaires to thousands of people from particular population groups to learn about their sexual behaviour and attitudes. Interviews such as those used by Kinsey and his colleagues (1948, 1953) have the advantages of allowing face-to-face contact and giving the interviewer the opportunity to *probe*—that is, to follow up on answers that seem to lead toward useful information. A skilled interviewer may be able to set a respondent at ease and establish a sense of trust or *rapport* that encourages self-disclosure.

University of Alberta researcher Melanie Beres (2006) interviewed seasonal workers in Jasper, Alberta, to study casual sex experiences and how the workers perceived a potential partner's willingness to engage in casual sex. The interviews were unstructured, which allowed the participants to talk about their experiences from their own perspective rather than that of the researcher. (Findings from this study are presented in Chapter 7.)

Questionnaires can be administered to many people at once, and respondents can return them unsigned. (Anonymity may encourage respondents to disclose intimate information.) Of course, questionnaires can be used only by people who can read and record their responses. Interviews can be used even with people who cannot read or write.

Most surveys have *something* to offer to our understanding of human sexuality, but some are more methodologically sound than others. None fully represents the Canadian population at large, however. Most people consider their sexuality to be among the most intimate, *private* aspects of their lives. People who willingly agree to be polled about their political preferences may resist participation in surveys concerning their sexual behaviour. As a result, it is difficult, if not impossible, for researchers to recruit a truly representative sample of the population. Bear in mind, then, that survey results provide, at best, an approximation of the sexual attitudes, beliefs, and behaviours of the Canadian population.

Increasingly, surveys are being conducted online through the internet. An Ontario survey found that research participants were more likely to fully complete an online survey than an equivalent traditional paper-and-pencil survey (Wood et al., 2006).

Let us review the sampling techniques used in some of the major studies of human sexuality in the United States and Canada. Throughout the book we shall reconsider the findings of these surveys.

Research Interview.
Interviewing is a commonly used method in surveys. Questionnaires are also used.

THE KINSEY REPORTS Alfred Kinsey and his colleagues (1948, 1953) interviewed 5300 males and 5940 females in the United States between 1938 and 1949. They asked a wide array of questions on various types of sexual experiences, including masturbation, oral sex, and coitus that occurred before, during, and outside of marriage. Kinsey adopted a *group sampling* approach. He recruited study participants from the organizations and community groups to which they belonged, such as college fraternities and sororities. He contacted representatives of groups in diverse communities and tried to persuade them to secure the cooperation of fellow group members.

Kinsey's samples did not represent the general population. People of colour, people in rural areas, older people, the poor, and Catholics and Jews were all underrepresented in his samples. Statisticians who have reviewed Kinsey's methods have concluded that there were systematic biases in his sampling methods but that it would have been impossible to obtain a true probability sample from the general population (see, for example, Cochran et al., 1953). There is thus no way of knowing whether Kinsey's results accurately mirrored the U.S. population at the time. His estimate that 37% of the male population had reached orgasm at least once through male–male sexual activity was probably too high. But the *relationships* Kinsey uncovered, such as the positive link between level of education and participation in oral sex, may be more generalizable.

To his credit, Kinsey took measures to encourage candour in the people he interviewed. For instance, study participants were assured of the confidentiality of their records. Kinsey's interviewers were also trained to conduct the interviews in an objective and matter-of-fact style. To reduce the tendency to slant responses in a socially desirable direction, participants were reassured that the interviewers were not passing judgment on them. Interviewers were trained not to show emotional reactions that the people they interviewed could interpret as signs of disapproval.

Alfred Kinsey.
Kinsey and his colleagues conducted the first large-scale scientific study of sexual behaviour in the United States.

Kinsey also checked the **reliability** of his data by evaluating the consistency of the responses given by several hundred interviewees who were re-examined after at least 18 months. Their reports of the **incidence** of sexual activities (for example, whether or not they had ever engaged in premarital or extramarital coitus) were highly reliable. That is, participants tended to give the same answers on both occasions. Kinsey recognized, however, that consistency of responses across time—or *retakes*, as he called them—did not guarantee their **validity**. That is, the retakes did not show whether the reported behaviours had some basis in fact. One indirect measure was comparison of the reports of husbands and wives—for example, with respect to the *incidence* of oral–genital sex or the *frequency* of intercourse. There was a remarkable consistency in the reports of 706 pairs of spouses; this lends support to the view that their self-reports were accurate.

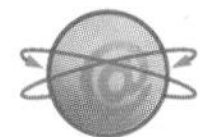

The Kinsey Institute
Home page for the Kinsey Institute, which focuses on sexual behaviour and attitudes.

www.indiana.edu/~kinsey

The 2004 Hollywood film *Kinsey* gives a realistic portrayal of the interview techniques that Kinsey and his colleagues used in their research. As portrayed in the film, many research participants experienced emotional relief by discussing, for the first time in their lives, intimate behaviours they had felt anxious and guilty about. Most important, Kinsey's interviewers' nonjudgmental response reassured participants that they were normal.

THE NHSLS STUDY The National Health and Social Life Survey of Americans was intended to provide general information about sexual behaviour in the United States and also specific information that might be used to predict and prevent the spread of AIDS. It was conducted by Edward O. Laumann of the University of Chicago and three colleagues—John H. Gagnon, Robert T. Michael, and Stuart Michaels—in the 1990s and published as *The Social Organization of Sexuality: Sexual Practices in the United States* in 1994. The NHSLS study was originally to be supported by government funds, but Republican senator Jesse Helms of North Carolina blocked federal financing on the grounds that it was inappropriate for the government to be supporting sex research (Bronner, 1998). The research team therefore obtained private funding but had to cut back the scope of the project.

The sample included 3432 people. Of this number, 3159 were drawn from English-speaking adults living in households aged 18 to 59. The other 273 were obtained by purposely oversampling African American and Latino and Latina American households, so that more information could be obtained about these ethnic groups.

The researchers identified samples of households in geographic areas—by addresses, not names. They sent a letter to each household, describing the purpose and methods of the study, and an interviewer visited each household a week later. The people targeted were assured that the purposes of the study were important

Reliability The consistency or accuracy of a measure.

Incidence A measure of the occurrence or the degree of occurrence of an event.

Validity With respect to tests, the degree to which a particular test measures the constructs or traits that it purports to measure.

The Canadian Journal of Human Sexuality

VOLUME 14 - NUMBER 1-2

PUBLISHED BY SIECCAN
THE SEX INFORMATION & EDUCATION COUNCIL OF CANADA
http://www.sieccan.org

The Canadian Journal of Human Sexuality.
Published by the Sex Information and Education Council of Canada, this is the major journal that focuses on Canadian sexuality research.

and that the identities of participants would be kept confidential. Incentives of up to $100 were offered for cooperating. A high completion rate of close to 80% was obtained in this way.

CANADIAN MEDIA-SPONSORED SURVEYS In 1984, *Maclean's* magazine began using survey organizations to ask Canadians about a diversity of social issues, including sexuality.

These were the first national surveys to ask Canadians questions about their sexual behaviours. Decima, the polling organization that conducted the interviews, was apprehensive about asking survey questions about sex over the telephone. Allen Gregg, president of Decima, feared that "people will hang up on us" (Jenish, 1994, p. 26). A key interview strategy, however, was to ask the sexual questions at the end of the interview, after the interviewer had established a rapport with the respondent. Not only did almost all of the respondents answer the questions, but many also volunteered for follow-up interviews.

The *Maclean's* surveys typically involve telephone surveys of about 1600 adult Canadians selected randomly from the 10 provinces. The sample includes a disproportionate number from the smaller provinces in order to allow for adequate statistical analysis of respondents from all provinces. The sample is considered to be a statistically accurate representation of the Canadian population as a whole within 2.8 percentage points, 19 times out of 20. The accuracy is reduced for those questions that have lower response rates (Jenish, 1994).

In 1998 the Compas survey organization, on behalf of the Sun newspaper chain, conducted one of the more comprehensive national surveys about relationships and sexuality (Compas, 1998). There were 1479 respondents in this survey. Their demographic characteristics, such as age and education, were proportionally similar to those of the Canadian population. Questions were asked regarding sexual orientation, age of first intercourse, number of intercourse partners, sexual frequency, oral sex, sexual communication, sexual problems, sex and the workplace, attitudes toward casual sex, and attitudes toward toplessness and prostitution. More than 95% of those who took part in the survey responded to the sexuality questions. The highest nonresponse was for the question on oral sex, with 15% of the females and 5% of the males not responding.

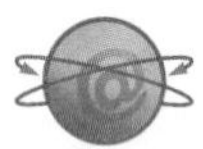

Statistics Canada
Statistics Canada offers census documents and statistics.
www.statcan.ca

MAGAZINE SURVEYS OF READERS Unlike *Maclean's* magazine, which hires a research organization to conduct national surveys of the Canadian population, most magazines simply ask their readers to complete questionnaires included in the magazine and mail them back. Major readership surveys have been conducted by popular magazines, such as *Psychology Today*, *Redbook*, *Ladies' Home Journal*, *McCall's*, *Cosmopolitan*, and even *Consumer Reports*. Although these surveys all offer some useful information and may be commended for obtaining large samples (ranging from 20 000 to 106 000!), their sampling techniques are inherently unscientific and biased. The samples may therefore represent only those readers who were willing to complete and mail in the surveys.

Canadian Trends

SURVEYING CANADIAN EXPERIENCES

Many of the Canadian studies on sexuality are based on limited samples, such as university or high school students. Statistics Canada does, however, fund some large-scale national surveys that include questions on sexuality and/or fertility, such as the National Longitudinal Study of Children and Youth and the National Population Health Survey. These studies use computer-assisted telephone interviews to collect the data.

Since 1988 the Canadian government has sponsored research on the health-related behaviours of school children between the ages of 11 and 15. The research series is titled "The Health Behaviour of School-Aged Children." The studies are being conducted by researchers at Queen's University and are part of a larger international study involving 41 countries. The last survey was conducted in 2006. (Findings related to sexual behaviour and contraceptive use among students in grade 10 are presented in Chapters 11 and 12.)

Two national Canada Youth and AIDS surveys have focused on the sexual health of adolescents. The first was conducted in 1989 (King et al., 1989). The second was conducted in 2002 by researchers at four Canadian universities: Acadia, Alberta, Laval, and Queen's (Boyce et al., 2003). The main objective was to understand the determinants of adolescent sexuality and sexual health for different age groups. The study involved students in grades 7, 9, and 11 from all provinces and territories except Nunavut. The study was coordinated by education ministers from across Canada and funded by Health Canada.

Students needed the consent of a parent/guardian to take part in the study. Fewer sexual questions were asked of the grade 7 students in order to make the survey more acceptable to parents and school boards.

The original sample size objective was 33 000 students. However, a number of school districts that were approached did not take part in the survey. Because of objections and concerns raised by several school administrators regarding some of the sexual questions, the final sample ended up being 11 074.

Reginald Bibby at the University of Lethbridge in Alberta is one of Canada's foremost experts on adolescents. He has been surveying Canadian social trends since 1975. The latest of his surveys, his seventh, was conducted in 2005 with a national sample of 1600 respondents. Bibby has also specialized in surveying trends among Canadian youth. Bibby's (2001) survey of 3500 Canadian youth aged 15 to 19 is one of the most comprehensive in that it analyzed relationship issues such as dating in addition to sexual attitudes and behaviours.

Four national surveys on contraceptive use were sponsored by the Ortho-Janssen pharmaceutical company beginning in the 1990s. The 2002 study sampled women aged 15 to 44 from across Canada (Fisher, Boroditsky, & Morris, 2004). Of 3345 questionnaires mailed out, 1582 were returned. The surveys studied the contraception awareness, attitudes, and behaviours of a representative sample of Canadian women of childbearing age. The surveys also included some questions on sexual behaviours, such as whether respondents have ever experienced sexual intercourse, have experienced sexual intercourse in the previous six months, and have experienced certain sexual difficulties in the previous year.

RELIABILITY OF THE SURVEY METHOD How do we know whether respondents are telling us the truth when they take part in sex surveys? Reliability can be determined by checking for consistency in responses. In a study of gay males in Toronto, for example, reliability was determined by giving the same interviews to the men 72 hours apart (Coates et al., 1986). The high degree of response consistency between the two interviews indicated that the data were reliable. Also in Toronto, in a study of men with AIDS or an AIDS-related condition and their male partners, Coates et al. (1988) found a high degree of agreement between the men regarding details about their sexual encounters. Reliability of responses was very high for behaviours such as anal intercourse but somewhat less so for less risky behaviours such as anal finger insertion.

McGill University researchers Eric Ochs and Yitzchak Binik (1999) obtained data from 70 heterosexual couples concerning 68 sexual behaviours to determine the degree of consistency in the responses of the partners. On individually completed questionnaires, both partners in a couple gave similar responses, suggesting high reliability. Similarly, among university students in British Columbia, only a few gave responses that were biased in a socially desirable direction (Meston, Heiman, Trapnell, and Paulhus, 1998).

It should be noted that some surveys are less reliable than others. Surveys conducted by Statistics Canada and other government agencies tend to be more reliable than those sponsored by private companies whose purpose may be to sell a product or to persuade the public to a point of view. It is important to evaluate the methodology used in a survey in assessing the accuracy of its findings.

LIMITATIONS OF THE SURVEY METHOD Many people refuse to participate in surveys. Samples are thus biased by the inclusion of large numbers of volunteers, who are in general willing to take the time to participate. In the case of sex surveys, they also tend to be more sexually permissive and liberal-minded than nonvolunteers. At an Ontario university, for example, students who volunteered for a study on human sexuality were more sexually experienced, more interested in sexual variety, and had more permissive attitudes toward sexuality than those students who did not volunteer (Bogaert, 1996).

Many of the Canadian researchers who study sexuality are based in university social science departments, and for the sake of convenience they frequently obtain samples from students in their departments. However, since relatively few males are enrolled in many social science courses it is difficult to make adequate gender comparisons. Researchers at an Ontario university found that fewer males than females volunteered to take part in a sexuality study, which of course exacerbated the gender-ratio problem (Senn & Demarais, 2001). Interestingly, more students volunteered to take part in the sexuality study than in a study on memory.

Respondents may recall their behaviour inaccurately or may purposely misrepresent it. People may not recall the age at which they first engaged in petting or masturbated to orgasm. People may have difficulty remembering or calculating the frequencies of certain behaviours, such as the weekly frequency of marital intercourse. ("Well, let's see. This week I think it was four times, but last week only two times, and I can't remember the week before that.") Kinsey and Hunt speculated that people who desire more frequent sex tend to underestimate the frequency of marital coitus, whereas people who want less frequent sex tend to overestimate it.

Even people who consent to participate in surveys of sexual behaviour may feel pressured to answer questions in the direction of **social desirability**. Some respondents, that is, try to ingratiate themselves with their interviewers by offering what they believe to be socially desirable answers.

Some people may not divulge sensitive information for fear of the interviewer's disapproval. Others may fear criminal prosecution. Even though interviewers may insist that they are nonjudgmental and that study participants will remain anonymous, respondents may fear that their identities will be uncovered someday.

Survey respondents can respond only to the questions posed by interviewers or included in questionnaires. A word or phrase may mean different things to different people, however. As a result, responses may differ among those whose behaviour may be the same. For example, the polling agency for the *Maclean's* magazine surveys did not consult with any sexuality researchers regarding the survey questions, and as a result some of the questions were poorly constructed. To respond to the question "Do you consider yourself sexually active?" the interviewees were asked to choose from among the following: "very sexually active," "somewhat sexually active," "not very sexually active," and "not sexually active at all." Of course, the problem with this wording is that "sexually active" can refer to activities other than intercourse, including masturbation. Thus, respondents may have differing interpretations of the meaning of this question. The response categories are also very subjective in that one person may define having sex once a week as "very sexually active," whereas another may define it as "not very sexually active."

Social desirability A response bias to a questionnaire or interview in which the person provides a socially acceptable response.

How questions are worded can strongly bias the responses that are obtained. This is particularly true in measuring attitudes toward such controversial topics as prostitution. When *Maclean's* asked Canadians whether paying for sex is acceptable,

Innovative Canadian Research

EXPLAINING GENDER DIFFERENCES IN REPORTING NUMBER OF PARTNERS

One of the big question marks in sex research is the discrepancy in number of sexual partners reported by men and women. Men consistently report having more partners than do women. One possible explanation for this difference is that men exaggerate the number of partners, whereas women report fewer partners than they have actually had so that they do not appear to be promiscuous. Researchers at the University of Alberta (Brown & Sinclair, 1999) have an alternative explanation; namely, that men and women use different estimation strategies. They found that men are more likely to give rough approximations when trying to estimate the number of partners, and that this tends to result in an overestimation. Women, on the other hand, try to do a precise count of their partners and in doing so may have forgotten some of them. Brown and Sinclair therefore concluded that men and women are not intentionally misrepresenting their sexual histories. What explanations would you give?

only 15% of men and 6% of women said that it was (DeMont, 1999). However, when Compas polling (1998) asked Canadians "Do you think that prostitution should be: Completely against the law, Legal and tightly regulated by health authorities, or Completely legal," most (69% of men and 67% of women) said that it should be legal and regulated. The *Maclean's* wording produced polling results that clearly suggested that Canadians were opposed to prostitution, whereas the Compas wording produced the opposite result. These findings could have significant public policy implications, in that those who seek more restrictive prostitution laws would use the first set of results to bolster their argument, whereas those who seek less restrictive laws would use the second.

The Naturalistic-Observation Method

In **naturalistic observation**, also called the *field study*, scientists directly observe the behaviour where it happens. Anthropologists, for example, have lived among preliterate societies and reported on their social and sexual customs. Other disciplines, too, have adopted methods of naturalistic observation in their research on human sexuality. For example, sociologists have observed the street life of prostitutes, and psychologists have observed patterns of nonverbal communication and body language between couples in dating situations.

The Ethnographic-Observation Method

Ethnographic observation provides data concerning sexual behaviours and customs that occur among various ethnic groups—those that vary widely across cultures and those that are limited to one or a few cultures. Anthropologists are the specialists who typically engage in ethnographic research. They have lived among societies of people in the four corners of the earth to observe and study human diversity. Margaret Mead (1935) reported on the social and sexual customs of various peoples of New Guinea. Bronislaw Malinowski (1929) studied the Trobriand islanders, among others. Even so, ethnographic observation has its limits for the study of sexual behaviour. Sexual activities are most commonly performed away from the watchful gaze of others, especially visitors from other cultures. Ethnographers may thus have to rely on methods such as interviewing. Alean Al-Krenawi from Israel and John Graham (1999) from the University of Calgary, for example, used ethnographic methods to study the coping strategies of six women in an Arab village in Israel who were married to the same man.

Naturalistic observation
A method in which organisms are observed in their natural environments.

Ethnographic observation
Data concerning sexual behaviours and customs that occur among various ethnic groups.

Katherine Frank.
Frank worked as a stripper in graduate school, both to augment her income and to learn about men who frequented strip clubs.

The Participant-Observation Method

In **participant observation**, the investigators learn about people's behaviour by directly interacting with them. Male–male sexual behaviour and mate swapping has been studied in this way. As a graduate student in anthropology, Katherine Frank worked as a stripper at several clubs in a southeastern U.S. city "both as a means of earning extra cash for graduate school and as part of a feminism theory project investigating female objectification and body image" (Steinberg, 2004). In reports of her experiences, Frank (2002, 2003) notes that many men told her they attend the clubs because they "just want to relax." She writes that male customers may encounter some stigma for visiting the clubs, but not as much as the strippers do.

Focus Groups

Focus group research involves bringing together a group of people to determine their attitudes regarding a specific topic. The researcher asks questions that are general in nature to guide the discussion with the intent of encouraging interaction and the free flow of ideas. Focus groups are especially valuable in exploratory research where there has been limited research on a particular topic. Researchers at the University of Guelph (Humphreys & Herold, 2007) used focus groups in developing scales to measure sexual consent attitudes and behaviours. (See Chapter 7.)

The Laboratory-Observation Method

In *Human Sexual Response* (1966), William Masters and Virginia Johnson were among the first to report direct laboratory observations of individuals and couples engaged in sexual acts. In all, 694 people (312 men and 382 women) participated in the research. The women ranged from 18 to 78 in age, the men from 21 to 80. There were 276 married couples, 106 single women, and 36 single men. The married couples engaged in intercourse and other forms of mutual stimulation, such as manual and oral stimulation of the genitals. The unmarried people participated in studies that did not require intercourse, such as measurement of female sexual arousal in response to the insertion of a penis-shaped probe, and male ejaculation during masturbation. Masters and Johnson performed similar laboratory observations of sexual response among gay people for their 1979 book *Homosexuality in Perspective.*

Their methods offered the first reliable set of data on what happens to the body during sexual response. Their instruments permitted them to directly measure vasocongestion (blood flow to the genitals), myotonia (muscle tension), and other physiological responses.

Using a transparent artificial penis outfitted with photographic equipment enabled them to study changes in women's internal sexual organs as the women became sexually aroused. From these studies, Masters and Johnson observed that sexual response can be divided into four stages (their "sexual response cycle," discussed in Chapter 4).

A methodological concern of the Masters and Johnson approach is that people engaged in sexual activities may alter their responses under observation. People may not respond publicly in the same way they would in private. The physiological monitoring equipment may also alter the subjects' natural responses.

Participant observation A method in which observers interact with the people they study as they collect data.

Correlation A statistical measure of the relationship between two variables.

Vasocongestion Congestion resulting from the flow of blood.

Penile strain gauge A device for measuring sexual arousal in men in terms of changes in the circumference of the penis.

Vaginal photoplethysmograph A tampon-shaped probe that is inserted in the vagina and suggests the level of vasocongestion by measuring the light reflected from the vaginal walls.

Correlation

What are the relationships between age and frequency of coitus among married couples? What is the connection between socioeconomic status and teenage pregnancy? In each case, two variables are being related to one another: age and frequency of coitus, and socioeconomic status and rate of teenage pregnancy. Correlational research describes the relationship between variables such as these.

A **correlation** is a statistical measure of the relationship between two variables. In correlational studies, two or more variables are related, or linked, to one another

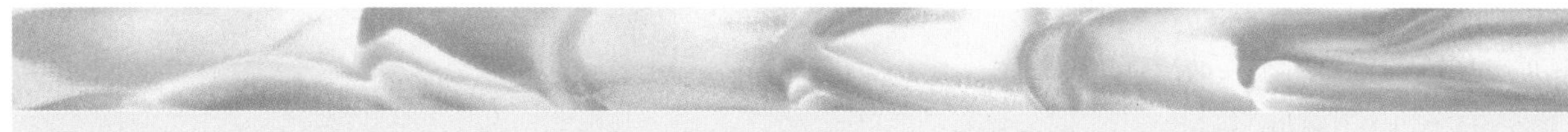

A Closer Look

PHYSIOLOGICAL MEASURES OF SEXUAL AROUSAL

Scientific studies depend on the ability to measure the phenomenon of interest. The phenomenon of sexual arousal may be measured by different means, such as self-report and physiological measures. Self-report measures of sexual arousal are considered subjective. They ask people to give their impressions of the level of their sexual arousal at a given time, such as by circling their response on a 10-point scale that ranges from zero, "not at all aroused," to 10, "extremely aroused." Physiological devices measure the degree of **vasocongestion** that builds up in the genitals during sexual arousal. (Vasocongestion—that is, congestion with blood—leads to erection in men and to vaginal lubrication in women.) In men, vasocongestion is frequently measured by a **penile strain gauge**. This device is worn under the man's clothing. It is fitted around the penis and measures his erectile response by recording changes in the circumference of the penis. The device is sensitive to small changes in circumference that may not be noticed (and thus will not be reported) by the man.

Physiological measurement of sexual arousal in women is most often accomplished by means of a **vaginal photoplethysmograph**—a tampon-shaped probe with a light and a photocell in its tip. It is inserted in the vagina and indicates the level of blood congestion by measuring the amount of light reflected from the vaginal walls. The more light that is absorbed by the vaginal walls, the less that is reflected. Less reflected light indicates greater vasocongestion.

Sex researchers sometimes measure sexual arousal in response to stimuli such as erotic films or audiotaped dramatizations of erotic scenes. What happens when physiological devices give a different impression of sexual arousal than those offered by self-report? Objectively (physiologically) measured sexual arousal does not always agree with subjective feelings of sexual arousal, as measured by self-report. For example, a person may say that he or she is relatively unaroused at a time when the physiological measures suggest otherwise. Which is the *truer* measure of arousal, the person's subjective report or the level shown on the objective instruments?

Discrepancies across measures suggest that people may be sexually aroused (as measured by physiological indicators) but psychologically unprepared to recognize it or unwilling to admit it. In the real world of human relationships, sexual arousal has psychological as well as physiological aspects. The reflexes of erection and vaginal lubrication do not necessarily translate into "Yes."

In a recent study conducted by researchers Kelly Suschinsky and Martin Lalumiere of the University of Lethbridge, and Meredith Chivers of the Centre for Addiction and Mental Health, Toronto (2007), men and women were shown sexual and nonsexual film clips. Their sexual arousal was measured with a penile strain gauge (for the men) and a vaginal photoplethysmograph (for the women). Genital responses were highest during the sexual stimuli and absent during the nonsexual stimuli. Also, only the sexual stimuli elicited subjective reports of arousal. The researchers concluded that both of the instruments were reliable measures of arousal (Suschinsky et al., 2007).

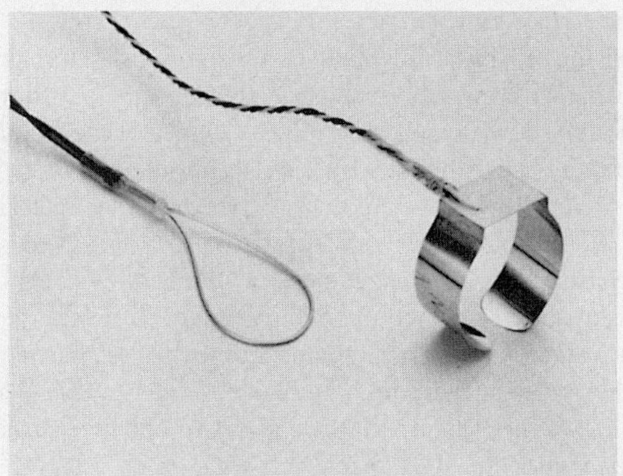

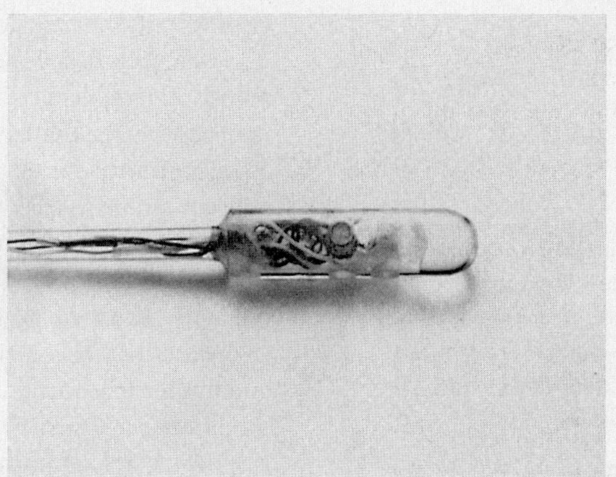

The Penile Strain Gauge and Vaginal Photoplethysmograph.
These devices measure vasocongestion in the genitals of men and women, providing an objective measure of the subjects' level of arousal. Can you think of other aspects of sexual arousal?

Innovative Canadian Research

USING A THERMOGRAPHIC CAMERA TO MEASURE SEXUAL AROUSAL

Researchers at McGill University (Kukkonen et al., 2007) have an alternative method for measuring sexual arousal. In a laboratory-controlled experiment, they first showed men and women a neutral film and then randomly assigned the participants to watch either a sexually explicit film, a humorous one, or a neutral one. The researchers used a thermographic camera to measure changes in genital and thigh temperature. The camera detected significant genital temperature changes during the showing of the erotic film but not during the showing of the other two films. There were no changes in thigh temperatures during the showing of the sex film, indicating that temperature changes during sexual arousal were specific to the genital region. There was no difference between men and women in the amount of time it took to reach the peak genital temperature. For both men and women there was a high correlation between temperature changes and subjective sexual arousal. The findings indicate that a thermographic camera is a reliable and useful instrument for measuring sexual arousal. This method is less intrusive than other measures of sexual arousal and it can be used with both men and women. Thermography makes it possible to determine whether gender differences in arousal found in previous research are true differences or are due to measurement or instrumentation error.

Figure 2.1 What Is the Relationship Between Frequency of Intercourse and Sexual Satisfaction?

Married couples who engage in more frequent sexual relations report higher levels of sexual satisfaction, but why? Because researchers have not manipulated the variables, we cannot conclude that sexual satisfaction causes high coital frequency. Nor can we say that frequent coitus causes greater sexual satisfaction. Perhaps both variables are affected by other factors, such as communication ability, general marital satisfaction, and general health.

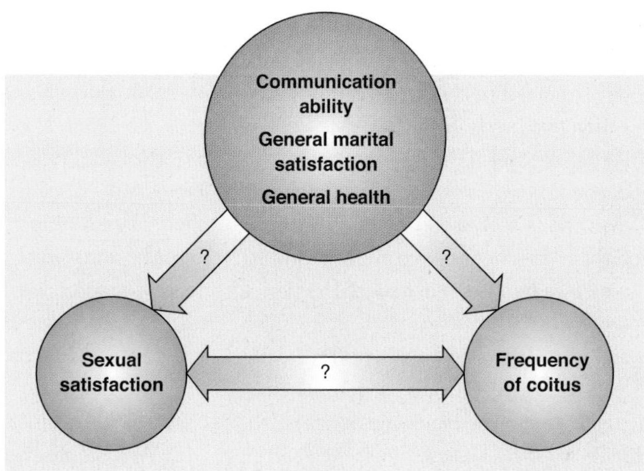

by statistical means. The strength and direction (positive or negative) of the relationship between any two variables are expressed with a statistic called a **correlation coefficient**. Correlations may be *positive* or *negative*.

Research has shown relationships (correlations) between sexual satisfaction and a host of variables: communication skills, marital satisfaction, and general health, to name a few (see Figure 2.1) Although such research may give us an idea of the factors associated with sexual satisfaction, the experimenters have not manipulated the variables of interest. For this reason we cannot say which, if any, of the factors is causally related to sexual happiness.

Research has also shown relationships between the use of sildenafil (Viagra) to enhance sexual response and risky sexual behaviour among gay and bisexual men (Kim et al., 2002). Men who use Viagra also report a greater number of sex partners and higher levels of anal sex without using a condom. There is no evidence that Viagra *causes* risky sexual behaviour. It is more likely that the effort to enhance sexual response explains both the use of Viagra and risky sexual activity.

Correlation coefficient A statistic that expresses the strength and direction (positive or negative) of the relationship between two variables.

Experiment A scientific method that seeks to confirm cause-and-effect relationships by manipulating independent variables and observing their effects on dependent variables.

The Experimental Method

The best method (though not always a feasible method) for studying *cause-and-effect* relationships is the **experiment**. Experiments permit scientists to draw conclusions about cause-and-effect relationships because the experimenter is able to control or manipulate the factors or variables of interest directly and to observe their effects.

Aspects of the Experimental Method

In an experiment on the effects of alcohol on sexual arousal, for example, a group of participants would receive an intervention, called a **treatment**, such as a dose of alcohol. (In other experiments, the intervention or treatment might involve the administration of a drug, exposure to violent sexual material, or a program of sex education.) They would then be carefully observed to learn whether that treatment made a difference in their behaviour—in this case, their sexual arousal.

In an experiment, the variables (treatments) that are hypothesized to have a causal effect are manipulated or controlled by the researcher. Consider an experiment designed to determine whether alcohol stimulates sexual arousal. The design might involve giving one group of participants a specified amount of alcohol and then measuring its effects. In such an experimental arrangement, the dose of alcohol is considered an **independent variable**, whose presence and quantity are manipulated by the researchers. The measured results are called **dependent variables**, because changes in their values are believed to depend on the independent variable or variables. In this experiment, measures of sexual arousal would be the dependent variables. Dependent variables are outcomes; they are observed and measured by the researchers, but not manipulated. Sexual arousal might be measured by means such as physiological measurement (gauging the degree of penile erection in the male, for example) or self-report (asking participants to rate their sexual arousal on a rating scale).

In a study of the effects of sex education on teenage pregnancy, sex education would be the independent variable. The incidence of teenage pregnancy would be the dependent variable. Researchers would administer the experimental treatment (sex education) and track the participants for a period of time to determine their pregnancy rates. Ideally, the incidence of pregnancy among these subjects would be compared with that among subjects who do not receive sex education but are similar to the subjects in all other respects.

EXPERIMENTAL AND CONTROL GROUPS Well-designed experiments randomly assign people or animal-study participants to experimental and control groups. Participants in **experimental groups** receive the treatment. Participants in **control groups** do not. Every effort is made to hold all other conditions constant for both groups. By using random assignment and holding other conditions constant, researchers can be reasonably confident that the independent variable (treatment), and not extraneous factors (such as the temperature of the room in which the treatment was administered or differences between the participants in the experimental and control groups), brought about the results.

Why do experimenters assign individuals at random to experimental and control groups whenever possible? Consider a study conducted to determine the effects of alcohol on sexual arousal in response to sexually explicit films. If we permitted study participants to choose whether they would drink alcohol, we might not know whether it was the alcohol itself that accounted for the results. Some other factor, called a **selection factor**, might discriminate between people who would and those who would not choose to drink alcohol. Perhaps people who chose to drink might also have more permissive attitudes toward sexually explicit material. Their permissiveness, rather than the alcohol, could affect their sexual responsiveness to these stimuli. If this were the case, experimental outcomes might reflect the effects of the selection factor rather than the alcohol.

Ottawa researchers John Bradford and Anne Pawlak conducted an experiment to determine the effectiveness of cyproterone acetate (CPA), an anti-androgen, in treating men convicted of sex crimes. The 19 men who were studied were randomly

Treatment In experiments, an intervention that is administered to participants (such as a test, a drug, or a sex education program) so that its effects can be observed.

Independent variable A condition in a scientific study that is manipulated so that its effects can be observed.

Dependent variables The measured results of an experiment, which are believed to be a function of the independent variables.

Experimental group A group of study participants who receive a treatment.

Control group A group of study participants who do not receive the experimental treatment. However, other conditions are held comparable to those of individuals in the experimental group.

Selection factor A bias that may operate in research when people are allowed to determine whether they will receive a treatment.

A World of Diversity

STUDYING THE SEXUAL BEHAVIOURS OF DIVERSE POPULATIONS

Ontario First Nations

More than 1 million Canadians identify as First Nations people. Rates of sexually transmitted infections (STIs) are much higher among First Nations people than among the general population, yet a notable lack of sex research has been conducted with this ethnic group.

Concern about the spread of AIDS, however, led to the development of the Ontario First Nations AIDS and Healthy Lifestyle Survey by researchers from the University of Toronto and representatives from the First Nations (Myers et al., 1993). Eleven reserve communities took part in the study, with participants randomly selected from the list of on-reserve members. Almost all (87%) of those selected agreed to be interviewed. Interviews were conducted face to face by trained First Nations interviewers. The questions were about sexuality and alcohol use. Each participant was given an "answer booklet," and several possible answers to each question were listed in the booklet. The interviewer would read the question from the interview schedule and the respondent would check off the answers in his or her answer book and then seal the book in an envelope. At the beginning of the sexual questions, respondents were given the choice between having the sexual acts described using slang terms or technical terms.

Of those who had sex in the previous year, 58% reported only one sexual partner, 30% reported two to four partners, and 12% had five or more partners (Calzavara et al., 1999). Almost all of those who had experienced sex in the previous 12 months had engaged in sexual intercourse, 53% had experienced oral sex, and 13% had experienced anal intercourse. Individuals who engaged in sex with partners from both within and outside of the community were more likely to experience oral and anal sex (Calzavara et al., 1999). Only 9% of those who had engaged in vaginal intercourse reported always using condoms, and only 11% of those who had engaged in anal sex always used condoms. Alcohol use was not related to whether or not a condom was used (Myers et al., 1997).

Canadian East Asians

University of British Columbia researcher Lori Brotto and her colleagues compared samples of East Asian and European Canadian female (Brotto et al., 2005) and male (Brotto et al., 2006) students. The East Asian students had more conservative sexual attitudes and fewer sexual experiences than the European Canadians.

Most cross-cultural researchers have focused only on ethnic group comparisons or length of residency as predictors of sexual attitudes and behaviours. However, Brotto et al. (2006, 2007) also considered acculturation to Western society. They found that acculturation was a much stronger predictor of sexual attitudes, experiences, and responses than was length of residence.

Gay and Bisexual Men

Until the 1980s only limited research was focused on men who have sex with men. With the advent of the AIDS epidemic, however, the Canadian government targeted millions of dollars for research into the prevention and treatment of AIDS. Because AIDS affected gay males far more than any other group in Canada, several research projects were funded to analyze sexual behaviours and condom use among gay and bisexual men. The first national survey of men who have sex with men was a joint project involving researchers from the University of Toronto, Laval University, and the University of Montreal (Myers, Orr, Locker, & Jackson, 1993). The project was designed by the researchers along with the Canadian AIDS Society and AIDS organizations from across Canada. A sample of 4803 men ranging in age from 16 to 75 was obtained from gay bars, bathhouses, and community dances in 35 Canadian cities. Data were obtained by questionnaires. The response rate was very high, with 86% of those who were approached agreeing to take part in the survey; response rates were higher in bars and at dances than in the bathhouses.

More than half (57%) attended bars at least once a week, but only 7% attended a bathhouse once a week or more.

assigned to receive either CPA or a placebo for a three-month period. The study was double blind, meaning that neither the men nor the researchers who administered the drugs knew which of the men were receiving CPA and which the placebo. (The double-blind approach controls for the placebo effect that can occur when people take any kind of medication and eliminates the possibility of the researchers' own biases distorting their findings.) As predicted by the researchers, the CPA drug was associated with a significant reduction in aspects of sex behaviour, especially deviant fantasies such as having sex with children (Bradford & Pawlak, 1993).

Respondents were asked if they had engaged in any of the following behaviours in the previous three months: deep tongue kissing, mutual masturbation, receptive and insertive oral-anal sex, receptive and insertive oral sex with and without semen in the mouth, and receptive and insertive anal intercourse with and without a condom. They were also asked whether they had been tested for HIV and whether, to their knowledge, they were HIV-positive. Twenty-three percent of the men reported at least one experience of unprotected anal intercourse in the previous three months. Two-thirds had been tested at least once for HIV, and 12% reported that they knew they were HIV-positive (Myers et al., 1996).

The second major Canadian survey of gay and bisexual men was conducted by University of Toronto researchers in 2002 with a sample of 5080 men in Ontario (Myers et al., 2004). As with the previous national survey, the researchers consulted extensively with AIDS service organizations in developing the research design.

The study recruited a more diverse sample than had the previous national survey. In particular, the researchers purposely recruited a higher proportion of men who were either under the age of 20 or over the age of 50 and those who had lower levels of education. Most importantly, the study recruited the largest number of non-Caucasian gay and bisexual men that had ever been surveyed in Canada. Compared with the previous national survey there was a notable increase in the number of gay men who were meeting partners on the internet. A key finding was an increase in the number of gay and bisexual men who reported at least one episode of unprotected anal intercourse (Myers et al., 2004).

Sex Workers

Frances Shaver from Concordia University in Montreal is one of Canada's leading experts on sex work and has conducted three major surveys on this topic. In the first study she interviewed male, female, and transgender workers in Montreal and San Francisco. In the second study Shaver compared female and male sex workers with hospital workers in Montreal and Toronto in terms of working conditions, experiences, and stresses. The third study, done in Montreal and Toronto, focused on the different types of sex work (massage, exotic dancing, escort, and domination) (Shaver, 2005).

Shaver (2005) outlined three main challenges in researching groups, such as sex workers, who are stigmatized by the general society. The first difficulty is obtaining a representative sample. Researchers have typically sampled only sex workers on the street because they are the most visible. However, those working on the streets differ in many ways from those working indoors. The second challenge arises because people whose work is illegal or stigmatized are less willing to be interviewed and may be less honest in their responses. The third challenge is the traditional stereotype that sex workers are inherently exploited victims rather than autonomous individuals who freely choose their occupation. Accompanying this stereotype is the belief that sex workers are all basically alike rather than being diverse individuals.

To overcome these challenges, Shaver relied on a number of strategies. She asked an advisory group of sex workers for advice on the types of questions to ask and how to obtain research data. It is essential to convince sex workers that the researchers are nonjudgmental and respect them and their privacy. Also, Shaver noted that researchers need to distinguish themselves from other professionals such as police officers or social workers.

One of Shaver's findings that challenges traditional wisdom is that the majority of sex workers do not work for pimps. More of her findings will be presented in the chapter on commercial sex.

Clients of Sex Workers

In Canada, the sexual behaviour of sex workers has been widely researched, but the behaviour of the male clients of female sex workers has not. Researchers find it difficult to make contact with these clients, because of the stigma attached to paying for sex. In British Columbia, researchers (Kline at al., 2007) conducted an exploratory study to determine the feasibility of being able to contact and study male clients. A total of 27 men replied to advertisements requesting the cooperation of male clients in a study aimed at improving their sexual health. However, only nine of the men agreed to take part in a focus group study. The men indicated that fears of social disgrace, identity disclosure, and personal safety made them reluctant to take part in the study.

Ethics in Sex Research

Sex researchers are required to protect the people being studied. This means that people will not be subjected to physical or psychological harm and will participate of their own free will. In colleges, universities, hospitals, and research institutions, ethics review committees help researchers weigh the potential harm of administering the independent variables and review proposed studies in light of ethical guidelines. If the committee finds fault with a proposal, it may advise the

Informed consent Agreement to participate in research after receiving adequate information about the purposes and nature of the study and about its potential risks and benefits.

researcher how to modify the research design to comply with ethical standards and may withhold approval until the proposal has been modified. Let us consider a number of ethical issues:

- *Exposing participants to harm*: Individuals may be harmed if they are exposed to pain or placed in stressful situations. For this reason, researchers do not expose children to erotic materials in order to determine the effects. Nor do researchers expose human fetuses to male or female sex hormones to learn whether they create predispositions toward tomboyishness, gay male or lesbian sexual orientations, and other variables of interest.
- *Confidentiality*: Researchers can do many things to ensure the confidentiality of participants. They can make questionnaires anonymous. Interviewers may not be given the identities of interviewees. In reports of research, enough information about participants' backgrounds can be given to make the studies useful (size of city of origin, region of country, religion, age group, race, educational level, and so on) without divulging their identities. Once the need for follow-up has passed and the results have been fully analyzed, the names and addresses of participants and their records can be destroyed.
- *Informed consent*: The principle of **informed consent** requires that people freely agree to participate after being given enough information about the procedures and purposes of the research, and its risks and benefits, to make an informed decision. Once the study has begun, participants must be free to withdraw at any time without penalty.
- *The use of deception*: Ethical conflicts may emerge when experiments require that participants not know all about their purposes and methods. For example, in experiments on the effects of violent pornography on aggression against women, participants may be misled into believing that they are administering electric shocks to women (who are actually confederates of the experimenter), even though no shocks are actually delivered. The experimenter seeks to determine participants' willingness to hurt women following exposure to aggressive erotic films. Such studies could not be carried out if participants knew that shocks would not actually be delivered.

Research is the backbone of human sexuality as a science. This textbook focuses on scientific findings that can illuminate our understanding of sexuality, help enhance sexual experience, prevent and treat sexually transmitted diseases, and build more rewarding relationships.

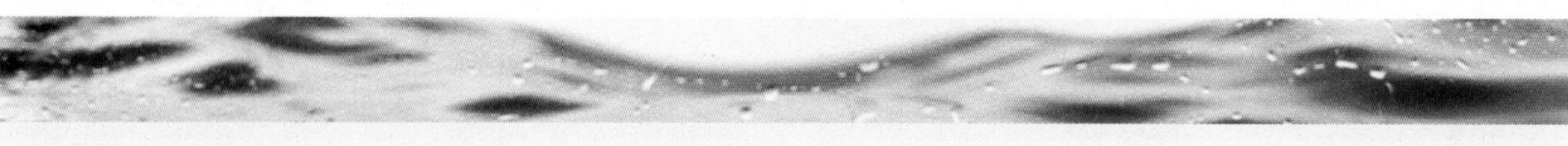

A World of Diversity

THE TUSKEGEE SYPHILIS STUDY: ETHICS TURNED UPSIDE DOWN IN RESEARCH GONE WRONG

The Tuskegee Syphilis Study, carried out in Macon County, Alabama, from 1932 to 1972, is an example of medical research gone wrong. The United States Public Health Service, in trying to learn more about syphilis and justify treatment programs for African Americans, withheld adequate treatment from a group of poor black men who had the disease, causing needless pain and suffering for the men and their loved ones.

In the wake of the Tuskegee Syphilis Study and other studies, the U.S. federal government took a closer look at research involving human subjects and made changes to prevent the moral breaches that occurred in Tuskegee from happening again.

Innovative Canadian Research

DO RESEARCH CONSENT FORMS AFFECT RESEARCH FINDINGS?

Over the years, ethics research requirements of universities and other institutions in Canada have become more stringent. Researchers at the University of Windsor and the University of Guelph (Senn & Desmarais, 2006) conducted two studies to determine if these requirements were affecting findings in sexuality research. Each participant was given one of three types of consent forms. The first described the research process only. The second also described the sexuality content of the study. The third form also included a warning about the possible negative effects of being involved in the study.

The first study involved female university students who were randomly assigned to watch one of three types of sexually explicit slides: erotica, nonviolent pornography, and violent pornography. In the second study a community sample was asked about sexual experiences, abuse, and assault.

There were no significant differences in the findings for the three different types of consent forms, except that, for the study involving sexually explicit slides, researchers discovered one major difference. The group of students who were given detailed information about the explicit slides and those who were warned about possible harm evaluated the slides significantly more negatively than those who were informed only about the research process. A surprising finding in both studies was that students who were given more detail about the content of the studies and warnings about possible harm did not feel that they were better informed than those who were told only about the research process. The results raise the question of how best to adequately inform participants about a research study, while at the same time to minimize the possibility that the type of consent form may bias the findings.

Summing Up

The scientific method is a systematic means of gathering scientific evidence and testing assumptions through empirical research. It entails formulating a research question, framing a hypothesis, testing the hypothesis, and drawing conclusions about the hypothesis.

The goals of the science of human sexuality are to describe, explain and predict sexual behaviours.

Research samples should accurately represent the population of interest. Representative samples are usually obtained through random sampling.

Case studies are carefully drawn biographies of individuals or small groups that focus on unravelling the interplay of various factors in individuals' backgrounds.

Surveys typically gather information about behaviour through interviews or questionnaires administered to large samples of people.

In naturalistic observation, scientists directly observe the behaviour of animals and humans where it happens—in the "field." The scientists remain unobtrusive.

Ethnographic research has provided us with data concerning sexual behaviours and customs that occur widely across cultures.

In participant observation, investigators learn about people's behaviour by interacting with them.

In the laboratory-observation method, people engage in the behaviour under study in the laboratory setting.

Correlational studies reveal the strength and direction of the relationships between variables. However, they do not show cause and effect.

Experiments allow scientists to draw conclusions about cause-and-effect relationships, because the scientists directly control or manipulate the variables of interest and observe their effects. Well-designed experiments randomly assign individuals to experimental and control groups.

Ethics concerns the ways in which researchers protect participants in research studies from harm.

Ethical standards require that research be conducted only when the expected benefits of the research outweigh the anticipated risks to participants and when the experimenter attempts to minimize expected risks.

Sex researchers keep the identities and responses of participants confidential to protect them from embarrassment and other potential sources of harm.

The principle of informed consent requires that people agree to participate in research only after being given enough information about the purposes, procedures, risks, and benefits to make informed decisions.

Some research cannot be conducted without deceiving people as to its purposes and procedures. In such cases, the potential harm and benefits of the proposed research are weighed carefully.

Test Yourself

Multiple-Choice Questions

1. **Researchers use a(n) ________________ often based on theory to predict behaviour.**
   a. hypothesis
   b. operational definition
   c. research question
   d. research method

2. **A representative sample**
   a. consists of at least 75 males and 75 females
   b. is a group of people who volunteer to participate in the study
   c. is a sample that accurately reflects the composition of the population
   d. is one in which each member of the population has an equal chance of participating in the study

3. **A random sample**
   a. consists of at least 75 males and 75 females
   b. is a group of people who volunteer to participate in the study
   c. is a sample that accurately reflects the composition of the population
   d. is one in which each member of the population has an equal chance of participating in the study

4. **Interviewing people about their sexual behaviour is an example of ________________ research.**
   a. survey
   b. clinical
   c. experimental
   d. experiential

5. **A problem with much of the research on human sexual behaviour is**
   a. religious bias
   b. commercial bias
   c. volunteer bias
   d. sexual bias

6. **Masters and Johnson's research on sexual response is an example of**
   a. participant observation of sexual behaviour
   b. laboratory observation of sexual behaviour
   c. correlational research on sexual behaviour
   d. experimental research on sexual behaviour

7. **Correlational studies provide information about**
   a. whether a change in one variable is causing a change in another
   b. statistical relationships between two variables
   c. the margin of error due to a variable
   d. the degree of bias in a sample

8. **If you wish to answer questions about cause-and-effect relationships, the best research method to use is a(n) ________________.**
   a. interview
   b. questionnaire
   c. laboratory observation
   d. experiment

9. **Concerns about the anonymity and confidentiality of sexual information are examples of ________________ issues.**
   a. ethical
   b. religious
   c. political
   d. commercial

10. **A basic ethical requirement for all research on human sexuality is the provision of**
    a. adequate compensation
    b. legal permission
    c. informed consent
    d. parental approval

Answers to the Test Yourself questions in each chapter are found on page 509.

Critical Thinking Questions

1. Have you ever responded to a survey on sexual behaviour (either in a magazine or on the internet)? What influenced your decision to participate or not to participate? Did you answer truthfully? Why or why not?
2. Many people question the validity of research on sexual behaviour. Do you think that research in this field contributes to our understanding of behaviour? Why or why not?
3. Is the use of deception as part of a research study ever justified? Why or why not?

Visit MyPsychKit at www.mypsychkit.com, where you can do quizzes and link to additional resources on topics discussed in this text.

CHAPTER THREE

Female and Male Anatomy and Physiology

Female Anatomy and Physiology

The French have a saying, *Vive la différence!* ("Long live the difference!"). It celebrates the differences between men and women. Given the exclusive female possession of a clitoris, some might assert that women in particular have much to celebrate. Only women possess a sex organ—the clitoris—that is solely devoted to producing pleasurable sensations

This chapter discusses the ins and outs of sexual anatomy and physiology. We will begin with discussing female structures and in the second part of the chapter will focus on males.

Some women are concerned about the appearance of their vaginal lips and worry that their shape is abnormal. To boost their sexual confidence and pleasure, some of these women are asking plastic surgeons to redesign their vaginas. Others believe that a "tighter" vagina would enhance their partner's as well as their own sexual pleasure. This is discussed in the nearby A World of Diversity box.

Girls and boys are both sometimes reared to regard their genitals with shame or disgust. Both may be reprimanded for expressing normal curiosity about them. They may be reared with a "hands-off" attitude and warned to keep their "private parts" private, even to themselves. Touching them except for hygienic purposes may be discouraged.

A World of Diversity

DESIGNER VAGINAS: THE LATEST IN SEX AND PLASTIC SURGERY

Labial reduction surgery, which promises a photogenic vagina and more confidence in the boudoir, is the hottest trend in cosmetic surgery. Critics call it genital mutilation. So what are women thinking?

While Dawn, a 42-year-old sales professional in Toronto, was having laser hair removal on her bikini area, one of the estheticians casually mentioned that her friend had recently undergone a new procedure: labial reduction, in which the edges of the labia minora–the inner folds of the labia–are surgically cut down and then stitched back together. "Are you saying my labia are big?" Dawn recalls asking the attendant. "Well, kinda," was the response. "I never thought it was an issue before, but I got it into my head," Dawn now admits. "I've hated my breasts since I had a baby, and now maybe my labia are hanging down around my knees?"

Her ex-boyfriend was shocked. "When I asked him about my labia, he said, 'OK, now you're crazy,'" she says. But her fiancé wasn't opposed to the procedure, admitting her labia were "a little bigger" than other women he'd been with.

Women like Dawn are driving the "designer vagina" trend. Dr. Robert Stubbs, a well-known certified plastic surgeon, does combined breast augmentation and labial reductions, or "tops and bottoms," on one or two women a week at his Toronto clinic. "The vulva and the vagina are the hot new areas for cosmetic surgeries," he says. These include liposuction of the mons pubis (the fleshy protuberance situated over the pubic bone), labiaplasties (the surgical reshaping of the labia or vulva), vaginal tightening (to increase friction during intercourse) and hymen repair procedures for women who want to be born-again virgins.

But as more genital nips and tucks are being done, a growing number of gynecologists, feminists and psychologists worry that women's anxieties about their physical appearance have reached a new low. They're particularly concerned about the psychological and physical damage that such procedures can inflict, with some scholars drawing parallels between labial reductions and female genital mutilation procedures, still common in some African countries but outlawed in western cultures, including Canada.

So what motivates women to go through with the surgery? According to Fiona Green, a University of Winnipeg professor of women's and gender studies, the trend reflects "a dangerous slippery slope" in the way women internalize cultural ideals as normal and start pathologizing themselves. "The irony today is that the '70s stream of feminism was about letting it all hang out, and we're so far from that now," she says.

Dr. Stubbs, arguably the "it" doctor of genital surgery in Canada, isn't too concerned about the ethics of it all. And he's happy to wade into the controversy. "A lot of my colleagues wouldn't touch this with a 10-foot pole," he admits. "But I like walking on the wild side."

Dr. Stubbs got his start doing penile enlargements. Around 20 years ago he did his first labial reductions, adding clitoral unhoodings (in which the tissue above the clitoris is trimmed, exposing more of it) to the menu about 10 years ago. He's since performed about 275 "genital enhancement" procedures on women, including about 100 combined labiaplasties, enhancements to the labia and unhoodings.

He says the vulva is by far the most popular area for surgery, and that vanity drives them to do it. "Women want their vaginas nice, neat, small and symmetrical. For women, confidence and beauty is power."

Dawn certainly bought into that thinking. After visiting Dr. Stubbs, she decided to go through with both breast augmentation and labial reduction ($6000 and $3000 respectively), agreeing to a clitoral unhooding as well. It wasn't that she was having problems with the functioning of her labia or a flagging sex life. It was that her labia seemed large. And, like 30 per cent of women, Dawn could attain orgasm only during masturbation or oral sex–not through penetration. The chance of being able to orgasm during intercourse was Dr. Stubbs' biggest selling point. "He said there'd be a possibility of that if he unhooded my clitoris."

The promise of sexual enhancement from a physical standpoint is a big draw. According to Dr. Stubbs, his patients report that unhooding the clitoris can give "three to nine times better orgasm," based on the self reports of 120 patients who have had the surgery.

But enhancing the way you look in bed is another big draw. Just ask L.A.-based Dr. David Matlock, one of the first doctors south of the border to perform labial reductions. Acknowledged by colleagues as the "pioneer in North America," he started offering the procedures after watching patients trickle into his office with torn sheets from porn magazines, wanting their labia to look like the models'.

Dr. Matlock now says he has a one-year waiting list for the procedure. He says he's confident "vaginal rejuvenation surgeries will enhance a woman's sexual gratification."

"When I woke up on the operating table, they were finishing with my breasts and then I felt a tugging on my labia and they started going at it," recalls Dawn. "I didn't feel any pain and pretty soon after that, Dr. Stubbs was holding up a piece of my labia."

Dawn claims she weighed the risks. "My main concern was if he cut a nerve, I'd have zero desire for sex and end up worse off." Post-op, Dawn was ordered to wear a genital girdle–a pelvic harness of sorts–to keep the stitches from slipping. And she was told to refrain from sex for six weeks while she healed. Her payoff has been better sex and more confidence. "The first

A World of Diversity (Continued)

time Neil and I had sex, I had my first internal orgasm. I finally love my breasts, and down there it's so clean, tidy and neat."

Dr. Stubbs admits that any surgery has multiple risks, such as anaesthesia-related complications or the potential for blood clots and blood loss. He adds that post-op, some of his unhooded patients report hypersensitivity. "We smile and say, 'It'll settle down.'"

But what happens if it doesn't settle down? "I had to restore the hood of one patient because her previous surgeon had cut too much," says Calgary-based gynecologist Bruce Allan, although he won't name names. He says 10 per cent of his cosmetic genital surgeries are now corrective: fixing another doctor's work. Dr. Allan says he started offering "laservaginal rejuvenation" surgeries three years ago after training at Dr. Matlock's clinic, where almost 20 per cent of patients also need revision surgeries after the first procedure. "There can be horrendous complications, although they're rare," Dr. Allan says. "But the laser usually gives fantastic results, like signing with a ballpoint pen versus a crayon."

Though quick fixes are an option, it's still difficult for women to know whom they can trust when it comes to choosing a doctor. Gynecologists and plastic surgeons alike say they have the best qualifications. But with more GPs getting into this niche field, it's a buyer-beware market. At the very least, consumers must make sure their doctor has outpatient surgery centre certification.

Even so, the potential for complications exists, and that has many gynecologists up in arms. "These surgeons act as if their customers are shopping for a new car," says Dr. Vyta Senikas, associate executive vice-president of the Society of Obstetricians and Gynaecologists of Canada. "But you can't trade your body in for a new model. You can't take surgery back."

Dr. Senikas says that in more than 25 years of practice, she's seen thousands of genitals and adds that she can count on one hand how many women have abnormally large genitalia needing surgery.

She is also alarmed by the latest fad for clitoral modification and wants to see scientific guidelines established to govern these procedures. "Nature gave us a hood to protect this sensitive organ," she points out, adding that 99 per cent of gynecologists wouldn't offer these surgeries as they can lead to nerve damage, infection or constant painful hyper-stimulation and scarring.

But women like Dawn are willing to go under the knife. "I did the surgeries to feel more comfortable in my own skin. I feel more connected with myself," she says. "It's nice to feel like a woman again."

(*) Names have been changed.

Source: Egan, D. (2005, October). Designer Vaginas. Chatelaine magazine. pp. 161-165. Courtesy of Danielle Egan.

Vulva The external sexual structures of the female.

Mons veneris A mound of fatty tissue that covers the joint of the pubic bones in front of the body, below the abdomen and above the clitoris. (Also known as the *mons pubis*, or simply the *mons*.)

External Sex Organs

Taken collectively, the external sexual structures of the female are termed the **vulva**. The vulva consists of the *mons veneris*, the *labia majora* and *minora* (major and minor lips), the *clitoris*, and the vaginal opening (see Figure 3.1). Figure 3.2 shows variations in the appearance of women's genitals.

The Mons Veneris

The **mons veneris** consists of fatty tissue that covers the joint of the pubic bones in front of the body, below the abdomen and above the clitoris. At puberty the mons becomes covered with pubic hair that is often thick and curly but varies from person to person in waviness, texture, and colour.

The mons cushions a woman's body during sexual intercourse, protecting her and her partner from the pressure against the pubic bone that stems from thrusting

Figure 3.1 External Female Sex Organs.

This figure shows the vulva with the labia opened to reveal the urethral and vaginal openings.

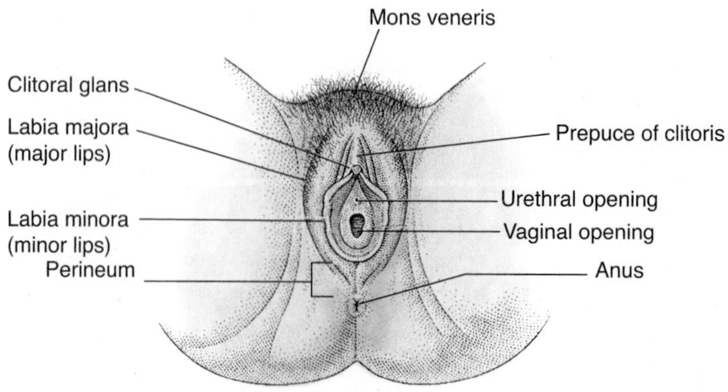

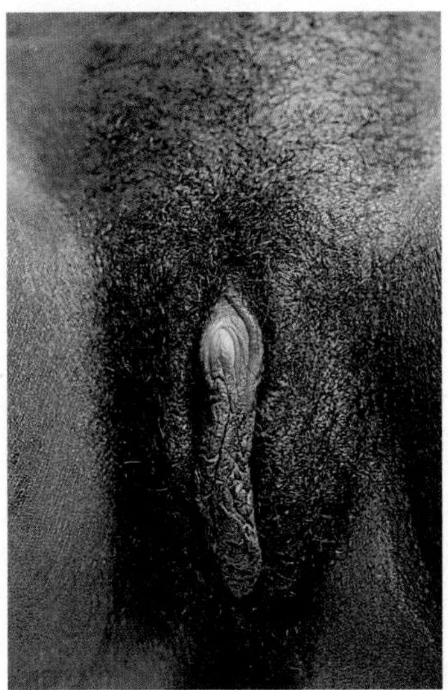

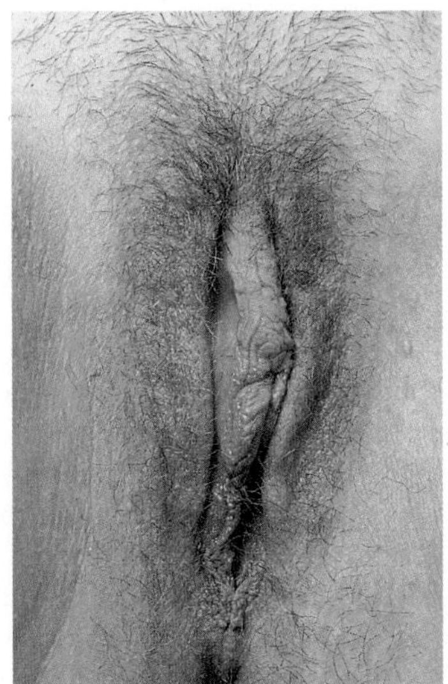

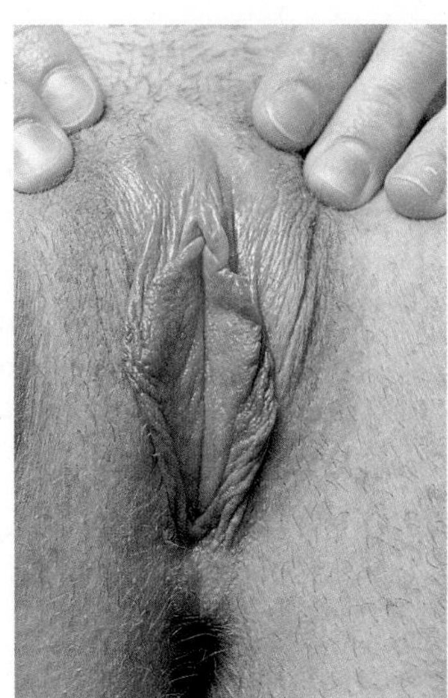

Figure 3.2 Normal Variations in the Vulva.

The features of the vulva show a great deal of variation. A woman's attitude toward her genitals is likely to reflect her general self-concept and early childhood messages rather than the appearance of her vulva per se.

motions. There is an ample supply of nerve endings in the mons, so caresses of the area can produce pleasurable sexual sensations.

The Labia Majora

The **labia majora** are large folds of skin that run downward from the mons along the sides of the vulva. The labia majora of some women are thick and bulging. In other women, they are thinner, flatter, and less noticeable. When close together, they hide the labia minora and the urethral and vaginal openings.

The outer surfaces of the labia majora, by the thighs, are covered with pubic hair and darker skin than that found on the thighs or labia minora. The inner surfaces of the labia majora are hairless and lighter in colour. They are amply supplied with nerve endings that respond to stimulation and can produce sensations of sexual pleasure. The labia majora also shield the inner portion of the female genitals.

It appears that an increasingly common practice among women in Western cultures is to remove their pubic hair. There are different methods of hair removal, such as waxing, shaving, electrolysis, and laser. At the time this book was being published, the Women's Health Institute in Vancouver was conducting research to determine the motivations for women to remove their pubic hair and to explore the perceived benefits of doing so.

The Labia Minora

The **labia minora** are two hairless, light-coloured membranes located between the major lips. They surround the urethral and vaginal openings. The outer surfaces of the labia minora merge with the major lips. At the top they join at the prepuce (hood) of the clitoris.

The labia minora differ markedly in appearance from woman to woman. The labia minora of some women form protruding flower shapes that are valued greatly in some cultures, such as that of the Hottentots of Africa. In fact, Hottentot women purposely elongate their labia minora by tugging at them.

Rich in blood vessels and nerve endings, the labia minora are highly sensitive to sexual stimulation. When stimulated they darken and swell, indicating engorgement with blood.

Labia majora Large folds of skin that run downward from the mons along the sides of the vulva.

Labia minora Hairless, light-coloured membranes, located between the labia majora.

Clitoris A female sex organ consisting of a shaft and glans located above the urethral opening. It is extremely sensitive to sexual sensations.

Corpora cavernosa Masses of spongy tissue in the clitoral shaft that become engorged with blood and stiffen in response to sexual stimulation.

Prepuce The fold of skin covering the glans of the clitoris (or penis).

Homologous Similar in structure; developing from the same embryonic tissue.

Analogous Similar in function.

Urethral opening The opening through which urine passes from the female's body.

The Clitoris

The clitoris is the only sex organ whose only known function is the experiencing of pleasure.

The **clitoris** (Figure 3.1) receives its name from the manner in which it slopes upward in the shaft and forms a mound of spongy tissue at the glans. The body of the clitoris, termed the clitoral shaft, is about 2.5 cm (1 in.) long and 0.5 cm (0.25 in.) wide. The clitoral shaft consists of erectile tissue that contains two spongy masses called **corpora cavernosa** ("cavernous bodies") that fill with blood (become engorged) and become erect in response to sexual stimulation. The stiffening of the clitoris is less apparent than the erection of the penis, because the clitoris does not swing free from the body as the penis does. The **prepuce** (meaning "before a swelling"), or hood, covers the clitoral shaft. It is a sheath of skin formed by the upper part of the labia minora. The clitoral glans is a smooth, round knob or lump of tissue. It resembles a button and is situated above the urethral opening. The clitoral glans may be covered by the clitoral hood but is readily revealed by gently separating the labia minora and retracting the hood. It is highly sensitive to touch because of its rich supply of nerve endings.

The clitoris is the female sex organ that is most sensitive to sexual sensation. The size of the clitoris varies from woman to woman, just as the size of the penis varies among men. There is no known connection between the size of the clitoris and sensitivity to sexual stimulation. The clitoral glans is highly sensitive to touch. Women thus usually prefer to be stroked or stimulated on the mons, or on the clitoral hood, rather than directly on the glans.

In a recent study, women were asked to rank the areas of their vulva which gave them the most sexual pleasure (Meyer-Bahlburg et al., 2007). The clitoris was ranked highest, followed by the area around the vaginal opening, the sides of the clitoris, below the clitoris, above the clitoris, the labia majora, and around the anus. When the women were asked to rank sources of pleasure within the vagina itself, the area deep inside the vagina was ranked highest followed by the areas just inside the opening and around the opening.

Both the clitoris and the penis develop from the same embryonic tissue, which makes them similar in structure, or **homologous**. They are not, however, fully similar in function, or **analogous**. Both organs receive and transmit sexual sensations, but the penis is directly involved in reproduction and excretion by serving as a conduit for sperm and urine, respectively.

It is ironic that many cultures—including Victorian culture—have viewed women as unresponsive to sexual stimulation. Yet women, not men, possess a sex organ that is apparently devoted solely to pleasurable sensations. The clitoris is the woman's most erotically charged organ, which is why women most often masturbate through clitoral stimulation, not vaginal insertion.

Surgical removal of the clitoral hood is common among Muslims in the Middle East and Africa. As we see in the nearby A World of Diversity feature, this "rite of passage" to womanhood leaves many scars—physical and emotional.

The Vestibule

The word *vestibule* refers to the area within the labia minora that contains the openings to the vagina and the urethra. The vestibule is richly supplied with nerve endings and is very sensitive to tactile or other sexual stimulation.

The Urethral Opening

Urine passes from the female's body through the **urethral opening** (see Figure 3.1), which is connected to the bladder by a short tube called the urethra (see Figure 3.3),

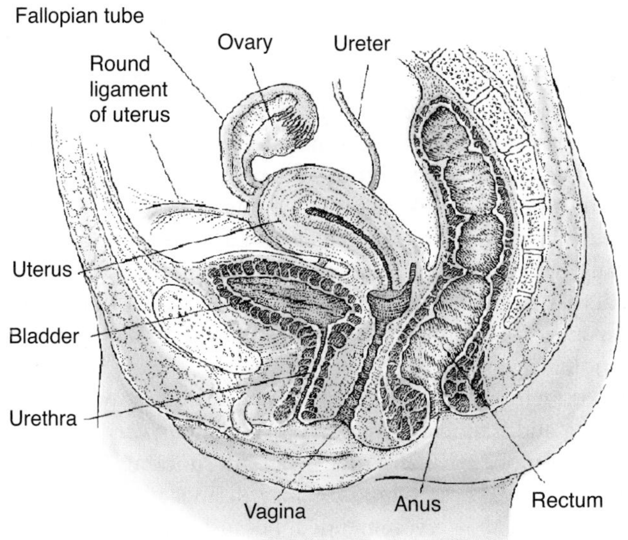

Figure 3.3 The Female Reproductive System.

This cross-section shows the location of many of the internal sex organs that compose the female reproductive system. Note that the uterus is normally tipped forward.

Clitoridectomy Surgical removal of the clitoris.

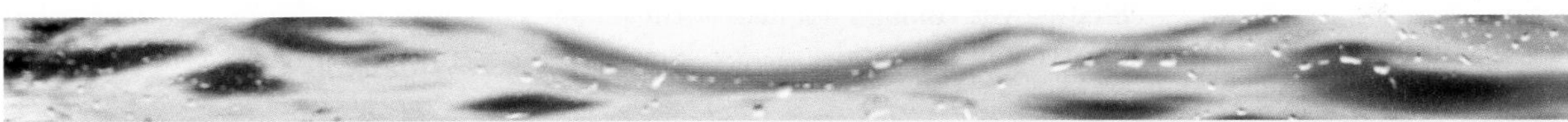

A World of Diversity

FEMALE GENITAL MUTILATION

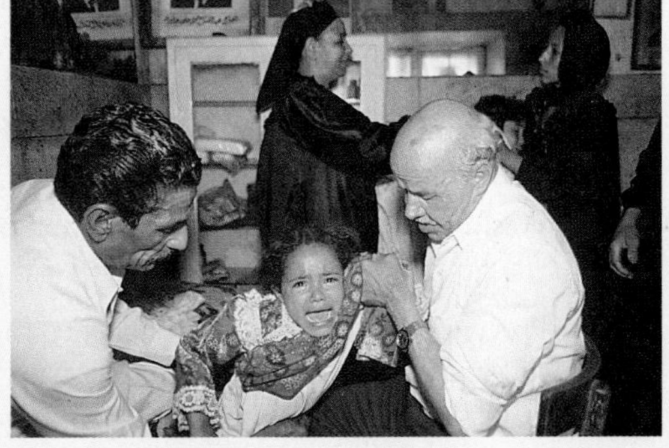

Ritual Genital Mutilation. Some predominantly Islamic cultures in Africa and the Middle East ritually mutilate or remove the clitoris as a rite of initiation into womanhood. Novelist Alice Walker drew attention to the practice in her novel Possessing the Secret of Joy. *She has called for its abolition in her book and film* Warrior Marks.

Cultures in some parts of Africa and the Middle East ritually mutilate or remove the clitoris, not just the clitoral hood. Removal of the clitoris, or **clitoridectomy**, is a rite of initiation into womanhood in many of these predominantly Islamic cultures. It is often performed as a puberty ritual in late childhood or early adolescence (not within a few days of birth, like male circumcision).

The clitoris gives rise to feelings of sexual pleasure in women. Its removal or mutilation represents an attempt to ensure the girl's chastity, because it is assumed that uncircumcised girls are consumed with sexual desires. Some groups in rural Egypt and in northern Sudan, however, perform clitoridectomies primarily because it is a social custom that has been maintained from ancient times by a sort of unspoken consensus (Missailidis & Gebre-Medhin, 2000). It is done by women to women (Nour, 2000). Some perceive it as part of their faith in Islam. However, the Koran—the Islamic Bible—does not authorize it (Crossette, 1998; Nour, 2000). The typical young woman in this culture does not see herself as a victim. She assumes that clitoridectomy is part of being female.

Clitoridectomies are performed under unsanitary conditions without benefit of anaesthesia. Medical complications are common, including infections, bleeding, tissue scarring, painful menstruation, and obstructed labour. An even more radical form of clitoridectomy, called *infibulation* or Pharaonic circumcision, is practised widely in Sudan. Pharaonic circumcision involves complete removal of the clitoris along with the labia minora and the inner layers of the labia majora. After removal of the skin tissue, the raw edges of the labia majora are sewn together. Only a tiny opening is left to allow passage of urine and menstrual discharge (Nour, 2000). Medical complications are common; they include menstrual and urinary problems and even death.

The Canadian government has outlawed ritual genital mutilation within its borders. Yet calls from Westerners to ban the practice in parts of Africa and the Middle East have sparked controversy on grounds of "cultural condescension"—that people in one culture cannot dictate the cultural traditions of another.

where urine collects. The urethral opening lies below the clitoral glans and above the vaginal opening.

The proximity of the urethral opening to the external sex organs may pose some hygienic problems for sexually active women. The urinary tract, which includes the urethra, bladder, and kidneys, may become infected from bacteria that are transmitted from the vagina or rectum. Infectious microscopic organisms may pass from the male's sex organs to the female's urethral opening during sexual intercourse. Manual stimulation of the vulva with dirty hands may also transmit bacteria through the urethral opening to the bladder. Anal intercourse followed by vaginal intercourse may transfer microscopic organisms from the rectum to the bladder and cause infection. For similar reasons, women should wipe first the vulva, then the anus, when using the bathroom.

Cystitis is a bladder inflammation that may stem from any of these sources. Its primary symptoms are burning and frequent urination (also called *urinary urgency*). Pus or a bloody discharge is common, and there may be an intermittent or persistent ache just above the pubic bone. These symptoms may disappear after several days, but consultation with a physician is recommended, because untreated cystitis can lead to serious kidney infections.

So-called honeymoon cystitis is caused by the tugging on the bladder and urethral wall that occurs during vaginal intercourse. It may occur upon beginning coital activity (though not necessarily on one's honeymoon) or upon resuming coital activity after lengthy abstinence. Figure 3.3 shows the close proximity of the urethra and vagina.

A few precautions may help women prevent serious inflammation of the bladder:

- Drinking two litres of water a day to flush the bladder.
- Drinking orange or cranberry juice to maintain an acidic environment that discourages growth of infectious organisms. Juices with added sugar should be avoided.
- Reducing the intake of alcohol and caffeine (from coffee, tea, or cola drinks), which may irritate the bladder.
- Washing hands prior to masturbation or self-examination.
- Washing one's partner's and one's own genitals before and after intercourse.
- Preventing objects that have touched the anus (fingers, penis, toilet tissue) from subsequently coming into contact with the vulva.
- Covering sex toys with condoms to prevent possible infection.
- Urinating soon after intercourse to help wash away bacteria.

The Vaginal Opening

One does not see the entire vagina, but rather the vaginal opening, or **introitus**, when one parts the labia minora, or minor lips. The introitus lies below, and is larger than, the urethral opening. Its shape resembles that of the **hymen**. The hymen is a fold of tissue across the vaginal opening that is usually present at birth and may remain at least partly intact until a woman engages in coitus. For this reason the hymen has been called the "maidenhead." Its presence has been taken as proof of virginity, and its absence as evidence of coitus. However, some women are born with incomplete hymens, and other women's hymens are torn accidentally, such as during horseback riding, strenuous exercise, or gymnastics—or even when bicycle riding. A punctured hymen is therefore poor evidence of coital experience. A flexible hymen may also withstand many coital experiences, so its presence does not guarantee virginity.

Cystitis An inflammation of the urinary bladder.

Introitus The vaginal opening.

Hymen A fold of tissue across the vaginal opening that is usually present at birth and remains at least partly intact until a woman engages in coitus.

Figure 3.4 illustrates various vaginal openings. The first three show hymen shapes that are frequently found among women who have not had coitus. The

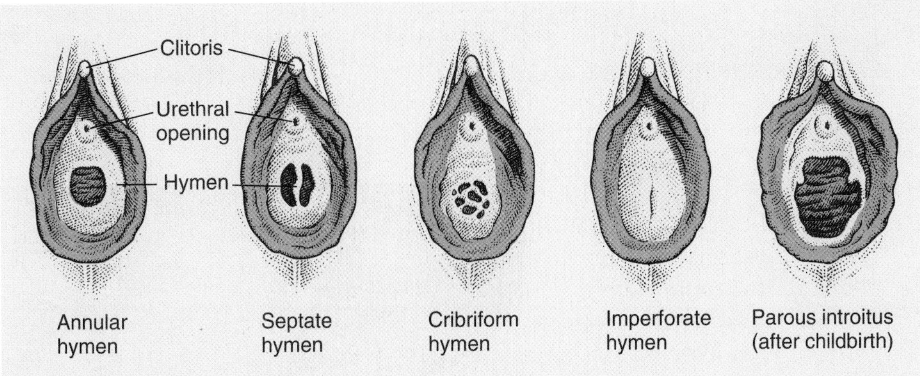

Figure 3.4 Appearance of Various Types of Hymens Before Coitus and the Introitus (at Right) As It Appears Following Delivery of a Baby.

fifth drawing shows a *parous* ("passed through") vaginal opening, typical of a woman who has delivered a baby. Now and then the hymen consists of tough fibrous tissue and is closed, or *imperforate*, as in the fourth drawing. An imperforate hymen may not be discovered until after puberty, when menstrual discharges begin to accumulate in the vagina. In these rare cases, a simple surgical incision will perforate the hymen.

The **perineum** consists of the skin and underlying tissue between the vaginal opening and the anus. The perineum is also present in males. The perineum is rich in nerve endings. Stimulation of the area may heighten sexual arousal. During labour, many physicians make a routine perineal incision, called an **episiotomy**, to facilitate childbirth. It should be noted that with this procedure it is the perineum and not the vagina that is cut.

Perineum The skin and underlying tissue that lies between the vaginal opening and the anus.

Episiotomy A surgical incision in the perineum that may be made during childbirth to protect the vagina from tearing.

Sphincters Ring-shaped muscles that surround body openings and open or close them by expanding or contracting.

Crura Anatomic structures resembling legs that attach the clitoris to the pubic bone. (Singular: crus.)

Structures That Underlie the External Sex Organs

Figure 3.5 shows what lies beneath the skin of the vulva. The vestibular bulbs and Bartholin's glands are active during sexual arousal and are found on both sides (they are shown on the right in Figure 3.5). Muscular rings (**sphincters**) that constrict bodily openings, such as the vaginal and anal openings, are also found on both sides.

The clitoral **crura** are wing-shaped, leglike structures that attach the clitoris to the pubic bone beneath. The crura contain corpora cavernosa, which engorge with blood and stiffen during sexual arousal.

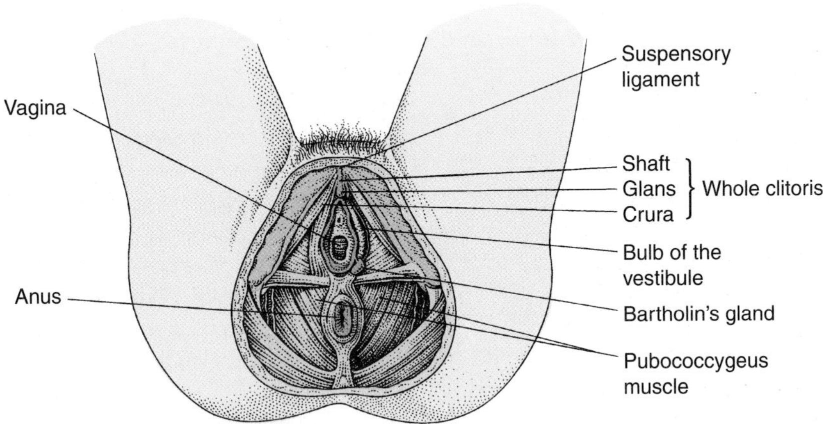

Figure 3.5 Structures That Underlie the Female External Sex Organs.

If we could see beneath the vulva, we would find muscle fibres that constrict the various body openings, plus the crura ("legs") of the clitoris, the vestibular bulbs, and Bartholin's glands.

Applied Knowledge

PERFORMING A GENITAL SELF-EXAMINATION

If you have seen the film *Fried Green Tomatoes,* you may recall the scene where a group of women are encouraged to bring mirrors to one of their meetings in order to examine their genitals.

Women readers may wish to try this while following the text and the illustrations in this chapter. You may discover some new anatomic features. You will see that your own genitals can resemble those in the illustrations and yet also be unique.

There are still many women in our society who have never examined their own genitals. This is a reflection of the negative attitudes that some women have about their genitals and also accounts for why masturbation rates are lower for women than for men.

Interestingly, in the 1970s, many feminist groups encouraged genital self-examination and some held group sessions to teach women how to do this. In a small group setting, the women would examine their own genitals and use a speculum to see their cervix.

Deborah Foster, who teaches an undergraduate sexuality course in Alberta, reports that many of her students are appalled when she suggests that they should, in the privacy of their own bedrooms, examine their own genitals in front of a mirror (Foster, in press). Foster also found that several of her female students mistakenly believe that urine comes from the same opening as does their menstrual blood.

For those women who would like to examine their own genitals, here are suggested steps for doing so.

- Choose a time when you are relaxed, such as after a bath.
- Choose a private comfortable space, such as your bedroom.
- Use a mirror and make sure there is sufficient lighting.
- Begin with looking at the larger outer lips (labia majora). These are covered with pubic hair. The colour and hair texture varies among women.
- The inner lips (labia minora) are just inside the outer lips. The size of these lips varies considerably among women. Some labia minora extend beyond the labia majora.
- The inner lips meet above the clitoris where they form the clitoral hood.
- Separate the inner lips at the top of the vulva to examine the clitoris. The size and shape of the clitoris varies from woman to woman.
- Underneath the clitoris is the urinary opening (meatus).
- Below the urinary opening is the vaginal opening.
- Just inside the vaginal opening is the vaginal ring where the pubococcygeus (P-C) muscle is located. The hymen is also located here; it may or may not be visible.
- Use your finger to explore further inside the vagina. You may notice that the inside of your vagina feels similar to the inside of your mouth—both are mucous membranes, soft and sensitive to the touch. Pressing on the front wall of the vagina and up about 5 cm (2 in.) you will feel the area where the G spot is purported to exist. (The G spot is discussed later in this chapter.)

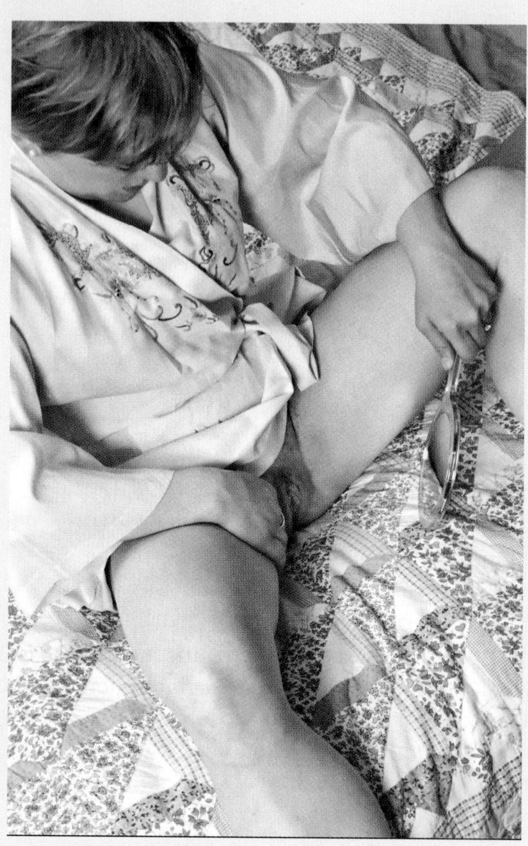

Genital Self-Examination.
For both health and pleasure reasons, women are encouraged to examine their own genitals.

Between the vagina and the anus is a smooth area of skin called the perineum. In conducting this examination it is important to appreciate the uniqueness of one's genital area with regard to shape and size, because some women may feel abnormal when the appearance of their genitals does not match that in pictures they may have seen of other women's genitals. Becoming familiar with the appearance of your genitals can make it easier to become aware of potential health issues requiring medical attention, such as rashes or warts. Also, the genital self-examination can be very useful in discovering the various pleasurable sensations that different parts of the genitals can provide.

Applied Knowledge

KEGELS

Pelvic floor muscles permit women to constrict the vaginal and anal openings. They contract automatically, or involuntarily, during orgasm, and their tone may contribute to coital sensations. Gynecologist Arnold Kegel (1952) developed exercises to build pelvic muscle tone in women who had problems controlling urination after childbirth. Kegel found that women who practised his exercises improved their urinary control along with their genital sensations during coitus. He believed that many women could enhance vaginal sensations during coitus by exercising their **pubococcygeus (P-C) muscles** through exercises that are now known as "Kegels." Kegels can benefit women of all ages.

Sex therapist Lonnie Barbach (1975) offers instructions for Kegel exercises:

1. Locate the pubococcygeus (P-C) muscle by purposely stopping the flow of urine. The muscle you squeeze to stop the urine flow is the P-C muscle. (The P-C muscle acts as a sphincter for both the urethral and vaginal openings.)
2. In order to learn to focus consciously on contracting the P-C muscle, insert a finger into the vaginal opening and contract the muscle so that it can be felt to squeeze or contain the finger.
3. Remove your finger, squeeze the P-C muscle for three seconds, and then relax. Repeat several times. This part of the exercise may be performed while seated at a classroom or business desk. No one (except the woman herself) will be the wiser. Many women practise a series of Kegel exercises consisting of 10 contractions, three times a day.
4. The P-C muscle may also be tensed and relaxed in rapid sequence. Since this exercise may be more fatiguing than the above, women may choose to practise it perhaps 10 to 25 times, once a day.

The **vestibular bulbs** are attached to the clitoris at the top and extend downward along the sides of the vaginal opening. Blood congests them during sexual arousal, swelling the vulva and lengthening the vagina. This swelling contributes to coital sensations for both partners.

Bartholin's glands lie just inside the minor lips on each side of the vaginal opening. They secrete a couple of drops of lubrication just before orgasm. This lubrication is not essential for coitus. It was once believed that Bartholin's glands were the source of the vaginal lubrication, or wetness, that women experience during sexual arousal. It is now known that engorgement of vaginal tissues during sexual excitement results in a form of "sweating" by the lining of the vaginal wall. During sexual arousal, the pressure from this engorgement causes moisture from the many small blood vessels that lie in the vaginal wall to be forced out and to pass through the vaginal lining, forming the basis of the lubrication. In less time than it takes to read this sentence (generally within 10 to 30 seconds), beads of vaginal lubrication, or "sweat," appear along the interior lining of the vagina in response to sexual stimulation, in much the same way that rising temperatures cause water to pass through the skin as perspiration.

Pubococcygeus muscle The muscle that encircles the entrance to the vagina.

Vestibular bulbs Cavernous structures that extend downward along the sides of the introitus and swell during sexual arousal.

Bartholin's glands Glands that lie just inside the minor lips and secrete fluid just before orgasm.

Vagina The tubular female sex organ that contains the penis during sexual intercourse and through which a baby is born.

Internal Sex Organs

The internal sex organs of the female include the innermost parts of the vagina, the cervix, the uterus, and two ovaries, each connected to the uterus by a fallopian tube (see Figures 3.3 and 3.6). These structures comprise the female reproductive system.

The Vagina

The **vagina** extends back and upward from the vaginal opening (see Figure 3.3). It is usually 7.5–12.5 cm (3–5 in.) long at rest. Menstrual flow and babies pass from the uterus to the outer world through the vagina. During coitus, the penis is contained within the vagina.

Figure 3.6 Female Internal Reproductive Organs.

This drawing highlights the relationship of the uterus to the fallopian tubes and ovaries. Note the layers of the uterus, the ligaments that attach the ovaries to the uterus, and the relationship of the ovaries to the fimbriae of the fallopian tubes.

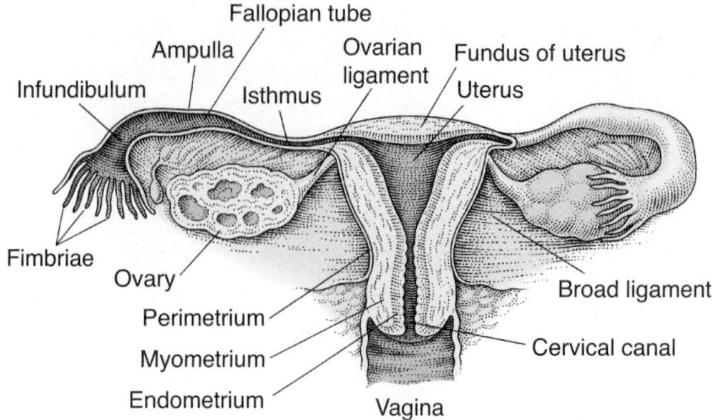

The vagina is commonly pictured as a canal or barrel, but when at rest, it is like a collapsed muscular tube. Its walls touch like the fingers of an empty glove. The vagina expands in length and width during sexual arousal. It can also expand to allow the insertion of a tampon, as well as the passage of a baby's head and shoulders during childbirth.

The vaginal walls have three layers. The inner lining, or *vaginal mucosa*, is made visible by opening the labia minora. It is a mucous membrane similar to the skin that lines the inside of the mouth. It feels fleshy, soft, and corrugated. It may vary from very dry (especially if the female is anxious about something, such as examinations) to very wet, in which case fingers slide against it readily. The middle layer of the vaginal wall is muscular. The outer or deeper layer is a fibrous covering that connects the vagina to other pelvic structures.

The vaginal walls are rich with blood vessels but poorly supplied with nerve endings. Unlike the sensitive outer third of the vaginal barrel, the inner two-thirds are insensitive to touch. The entire vaginal barrel is sensitive to pressure, however, which may be experienced as sexually pleasurable.

Douche Application of a jet of liquid to the vagina as a rinse. (From the Italian *doccia*, which means "shower bath.")

The vaginal walls secrete substances that help maintain the vagina's normal acidity (pH 4.0 to 5.0). Normally the secretions taste salty. The odour and taste of these secretions may vary during the menstrual cycle. Although the evidence is not clear, the secretions are thought to contain substances that may act as sexual attractants. Women who frequently **douche** or use feminine deodorant sprays may thus remove or mask substances that may arouse sex partners. Douching or spraying may

The Vagina Monologues.
The Vagina Monologues, *a celebrated play that presents the diversity of emotions women have about their vaginas, has been popular with audiences in Canada. A key objective of the play is to provide women with ownership and empowerment over their sexuality in general and their genitals specifically.*

also alter the natural chemical balance of the vagina, which can increase the risk of vaginal infections. Feminine deodorant sprays can also irritate the vagina and evoke allergic reactions. The normal, healthy vagina cleanses itself through regular chemical secretions that are evidenced by a mild white or yellowish discharge.

The G Spot and Female Ejaculation: Sexual Realities or Gynecological Myths?

The Grafenberg spot, or G spot, is theorized to be a part of the vagina—a bean-shaped area in the anterior (front) wall that may have special erotic significance. The G spot is believed to lie about 2.5–5 cm (1–2 in.) from the vaginal entrance and to consist of a soft mass of tissue that swells from the size of a dime to a loonie when stimulated (Figure 3.7). The name derives from the gynecologist Ernest Grafenberg, who first suggested the possible erotic import of the area. The spot can be directly stimulated by the woman's or her partner's fingers or by penile thrusting in the rear entry or the female-superior positions. It can also be stimulated with a vibrator. Some researchers suggest that stimulation of the spot produces intense erotic sensations and that, with prolonged stimulation, a distinct form of orgasm that is characterized by intense pleasure and, in some cases, a biological event formerly thought to be exclusively male: ejaculation (Perry & Whipple, 1981; Whipple & Komisaruk, 1988). These claims have been steeped in controversy. Even supporters of the existence of the G spot admit that it is difficult to locate, because it is not apparent to the eye or touch (Ladas et al., 1982). Terence Hines (2001) summarizes criticisms of the research into the G spot by noting that it is based on anecdotes and case studies with small numbers of subjects. Hines characterizes the evidence for the existence of the G spot as weak and unsupported by more rigorous anatomic and biochemical research. He dubs the G spot a "modern gynecological myth."

Research on female ejaculate is not much clearer. In a laboratory experiment, Zaviacic and his colleagues (1988a, b) found evidence of an ejaculate in 10 of 27 women studied. Some researchers believe that this fluid is urine that some women release involuntarily during orgasm. Others believe that it differs from urine (Zaviacic & Whipple, 1993). The nature of this fluid and its source remain unclear, but Zaviacic and Whipple (1993) suggest that it may represent a fluid that is released during sex by a "female prostate," a system of ducts and glands called Skene's glands, in much the same way that semen is released by the prostate gland in men. Zaviacic and Whipple suggest that "many women who felt that they may be urinating during

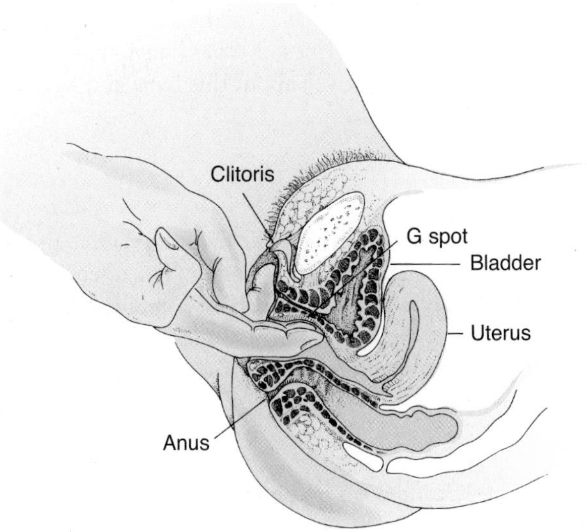

Figure 3.7 The Grafenberg Spot.

It is theorized that the G spot can be stimulated by fingers or by intercourse in the rear entry or the female-superior positions. Does stimulation of the G spot produce intense erotic sensations and a distinct form of orgasm?

Applied Knowledge

PREVENTING VAGINITIS

Vaginitis is any vaginal inflammation, whether it is caused by an infection, an allergic reaction, or chemical irritation. Vaginitis may also stem from use of birth-control pills or antibiotics that alter the natural body chemistry, or from other factors, such as lowered resistance (from fatigue or poor diet). Changes in the natural body chemistry or lowered resistance may permit microscopic organisms normally found in the vagina to multiply to infectious levels. Vaginitis may be recognized by abnormal discharge, itching, burning of the vulva, and urinary urgency. Its causes and treatments are discussed in Chapter 14.

Women with vaginitis are advised to seek medical attention, but let us note some suggestions that may help prevent vaginitis (Boston Women's Health Book Collective, 1992):

1. Wash your vulva and anus regularly with mild soap. Pat dry (taking care not to touch the vulva after dabbing the anus).
2. Wear cotton panties. Nylon underwear retains heat and moisture that cause harmful bacteria to flourish.
3. Avoid pants that are tight in the crotch.
4. Be certain that sex partners are well washed. Condoms may also reduce the spread of infections from one's sex partner.
5. Use a sterile, water-soluble jelly such as K-Y jelly if artificial lubrication is needed for intercourse. Do *not* use Vaseline. Avoid use of flavoured lubricants that contain sugar products as these can activate yeast infections. Birth-control jellies can also be used for lubrication.
6. Avoid intercourse that is painful or abrasive to the vagina.
7. Avoid diets high in sugar and refined carbohydrates because they alter the normal acidity of the vagina.

sex . . . [may be helped by] the knowledge that the fluid they expel may be different from urine and a normal phenomenon that occurs during sexual response" (p. 149). Some women, however, may expel urine during sex, perhaps because of urinary stress incontinence (Zaviacic & Whipple, 1993). Zaviacic and Whipple also suggest that stimulation of the G spot may cause some women to ejaculate but not others.

Contemporary sexologists seem to agree on a number of points concerning the G spot and "female ejaculation." One is that most or even all of the anterior wall of the vagina, not just one area, is richly supplied with nerve endings and may be sensitive to erotic stimulation (Alzate & Hoch, 1986; Levin, 2003a). However, it has not been adequately demonstrated that any particular zone of the anterior wall functions as a discrete sex organ; the area or areas that are exquisitely sensitive may vary from woman to woman (Maaita et al., 2002). Second, many females may exude a fluid through the urethra at about the time of orgasm. However, it is not clear what such fluid might be, and it is even less clear that it might correspond in some way to male ejaculation (Alzate & Hoch, 1986; Hines, 2001). Third, many sexologists wonder why other sexologists are so "sensitive" about this issue and why it has become so politicized (Alzate & Hoch, 1986).

The Cervix

The **cervix** is the lower end of the uterus. Its walls, like those of the vagina, produce secretions that contribute to the chemical balance of the vagina. The opening in the middle of the cervix, or **os**, is normally about the width of a straw, although it expands to permit passage of a baby from the uterus to the vagina during childbirth. Sperm pass from the vagina to the uterus through the cervical canal.

The Uterus

The **uterus**, or womb (see Figures 3.3 and 3.6), is the organ in which a fertilized **ovum** implants and develops until birth. The uterus usually slants forward (is *antroverted*), although about 10% of women have uteruses that tip backward (are

Vaginitis Vaginal inflammation.

Cervix The lower end of the uterus.

Os The opening in the middle of the cervix.

Uterus The hollow, muscular, pear-shaped organ in which a fertilized ovum implants and develops until birth.

Ovum Egg cell. (Plural: ova.)

Canadian Trends

CERVICAL CANCER

The incidence of cervical cancer has declined dramatically in Canada since the early 1970s, largely because most women have regular Pap tests. In 2008 there were an estimated 1350 cases of cervical cancer and 385 deaths in Canada resulting from this disease (Canadian Cancer Society, 2008). Cervical cancer is more common among women who have had many sex partners, women who became sexually active at a relatively early age, women of lower socioeconomic status, and women who smoke. All women are at risk, however.

Canadian researchers (Franco et al., 2003) have ascertained that the greatest risk factor for cervical cancer is having been infected with the sexually transmitted human papillomavirus (HPV). Indeed, the evidence strongly indicates that HPV infection is necessary for cervical cancer to occur.

A vaccine to protect women against being infected with HPV has been successfully tested and approved by the Canadian government. Some provincial governments are paying for the cost of the vaccinations for girls and young women. (This is discussed in more detail in Chapter 14.)

Most cases of cervical cancer can be successfully treated by surgery and **radiotherapy** if they are detected early. However, cervical cancer can also be prevented when precancerous changes are detected by a Pap test.

A **Pap test** involves smearing a sample of cervical cells on a slide to screen for cervical cancer and other abnormalities. The Canadian Cancer Society (2002) recommends that all women have Pap tests once they become sexually active. It also recommends that a Pap test be done once every one to three years. Most Canadian women (86%) have had a Pap test and it is estimated that half were screened for cervical cancer in 2005 (Statistics Canada, 2006b).

Women who are uncomfortable with the Pap test are less willing to be tested. In a study of older women living in Prince Edward Island, many expressed feelings of discomfort and embarrassment about the Pap test (Van Til et al., 2003). Also, Vancouver researchers Brotto et al. (in press) found that East Asian women living in Canada and Indian women living in India were less likely to have had a Pap test than were European Canadian women. There was no difference between the two Indian groups in the proportion who had ever had a Pap test.

retroverted). In most instances a retroverted uterus causes no problems, but some women with retroverted uteruses find coitus in certain positions painful. (They quickly learn more comfortable positions by trial and error.) A retroverted uterus normally tips forward during pregnancy.

Like the vagina, the uterus has three layers (also shown in Figure 3.6). The innermost layer, or **endometrium**, is richly supplied with blood vessels and glands. Its structure varies according to a woman's age and the phase of the menstrual cycle. Endometrial tissue is discharged through the cervix and vagina at menstruation. For reasons not entirely understood, in some women endometrial tissue may also grow in the abdominal cavity or elsewhere in the reproductive system. This condition is called **endometriosis**, and the most common symptom is menstrual pain. If left untreated, endometriosis may lead to infertility.

ENDOMETRIAL CANCER Cancer of the endometrial lining is called endometrial cancer. One of the symptoms of endometrial cancer is abnormal uterine staining or bleeding, especially after menopause. The most common treatment is surgery (Rose, 1996). The five-year survival rate for endometrial cancer is up to 95% if it is discovered early and limited to the endometrium (Rose, 1996). (Endometrial cancer is usually diagnosed early because women tend to report postmenopausal bleeding quickly to their doctors.)

HYSTERECTOMY A **hysterectomy** may be performed when women develop cancer of the uterus, ovaries, or cervix or have other diseases that cause pain or excessive uterine bleeding. A hysterectomy may be partial or complete. A **complete hysterectomy** involves surgical removal of the ovaries, fallopian tubes, cervix, and uterus. It is usually performed to reduce the risk of cancer spreading throughout the reproductive system. A partial hysterectomy removes the uterus but not the ovaries

Radiotherapy Treatment of a disease by X-rays or by emissions from a radioactive substance.

Pap test A test of a sample of cervical cells for cervical cancer and other abnormalities. (Named after the originator of the technique, Dr. Papanicolaou.)

Endometrium The innermost layer of the uterus.

Endometriosis A condition caused by the growth of endometrial tissue in the abdominal cavity, or elsewhere outside the uterus, and characterized by menstrual pain.

Hysterectomy Surgical removal of the uterus.

Complete hysterectomy Surgical removal of the ovaries, fallopian tubes, cervix, and uterus.

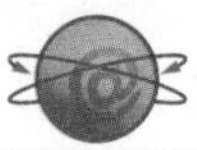

Canadian Women's Health Network
www.cwhn.ca

and fallopian tubes. Sparing the ovaries allows the woman to continue to ovulate and produce adequate quantities of female sex hormones.

The hysterectomy has become steeped in controversy. It is generally accepted that the operation can relieve symptoms associated with various gynecological disorders and improve the quality of life for many women (Kjerulff et al., 2000). However, many gynecologists believe that hysterectomy is often recommended inappropriately, before necessary diagnostic steps are taken or when less radical medical interventions might successfully treat the problem (Broder et al., 2000).

Lori Brotto and others have conducted research on the sexual difficulties women experience after a hysterectomy (Brotto et al., 2008). About half of women who had had a hysterectomy reported significant sexual difficulties and most were highly distressed about these issues. Brotto has developed a brief educational program which is effective in improving the sexual functioning and enjoyment of women who have had hysterectomies.

The Fallopian Tubes

Two uterine tubes, also called **fallopian tubes**, are about 10 cm (4 in.) in length and extend from the upper end of the uterus toward the ovaries (see Figure 3.6).

Ova pass through the fallopian tubes on their way to the uterus. The fallopian tubes are not inert passageways. They help nourish and conduct ova. The form of sterilization called tubal ligation ties off the fallopian tubes so that ova cannot pass through them or become fertilized.

In an **ectopic pregnancy**, the fertilized ovum implants outside the uterus, most often in the fallopian tube where fertilization occurred. Ectopic pregnancies can eventually burst fallopian tubes, causing hemorrhaging and death. Ectopic pregnancies are thus terminated before the tube ruptures. They are not easily recognized, however, because their symptoms—missed menstrual period, abdominal pain, and irregular bleeding—suggest many conditions. Experiencing any of these symptoms is an excellent reason for consulting a gynecologist.

The Ovaries

The two **ovaries** are almond-shaped organs each about 4 cm (1.5 in.) long. They lie on either side of the uterus, to which they are attached by ovarian ligaments. The ovaries produce ova (egg cells) and the female sex hormones **estrogen** and **progesterone**. *Estrogen* is a generic term for several hormones (such as estradiol, estriol, and estrone) that promote the changes of puberty and regulate the menstrual cycle. Progesterone too has multiple functions, including regulating the menstrual cycle and preparing the uterus for pregnancy by stimulating the development of the endometrium (uterine lining). Estrogen and progesterone levels vary with the phases of the menstrual cycle.

The human female is born with all the ova she will ever have (about 2 million), but they are immature in form. About 400 000 of these survive into puberty, each contained in the ovary within a thin capsule, or **follicle**. During a woman's reproductive years, from puberty to menopause, only 400 or so ripened ova, typically one per month, will be released by their rupturing follicles for possible fertilization.

In Canada, about 2461 cases of ovarian cancer and 1715 deaths resulting from it are reported each year (Canadian Cancer Society, 2008). Researchers have identified several risk factors that increase the chances of developing the disease: family members who have the disease, never having given birth, prolonged use of talcum powder between the anus and the vagina, infertility, a history of breast cancer, a diet rich in meat and animal fats, and cigarette smoking (Gnagy et al., 2000; Marchbanks et al., 2000).

Early detection is the key to fighting ovarian cancer. When it is detected before it spreads beyond the ovary, 90% of victims survive. Unfortunately, ovarian cancer is often "silent" in the early stages, showing no obvious signs or symptoms. The most common sign is enlargement of the abdomen, which is caused by the accumulation

Fallopian tubes Tubes that extend from the upper uterus toward the ovaries and conduct ova to the uterus. (After the Italian anatomist Gabriel Fallopio, who is credited with their discovery.)

Ectopic pregnancy A pregnancy in which the fertilized ovum implants outside the uterus, usually in the fallopian tube.

Ovaries Almond-shaped organs that produce ova and the hormones estrogen and progesterone. These are part of the endocrine system.

Estrogen A generic term for female sex hormones (including estradiol, estriol, estrone, and others) or synthetic compounds that promote the development of female sex characteristics and regulate the menstrual cycle.

Progesterone A steroid hormone secreted by the corpus luteum or prepared synthetically that stimulates proliferation of the endometrium and is involved in regulation of the menstrual cycle.

Follicle A capsule within an ovary that contains an ovum.

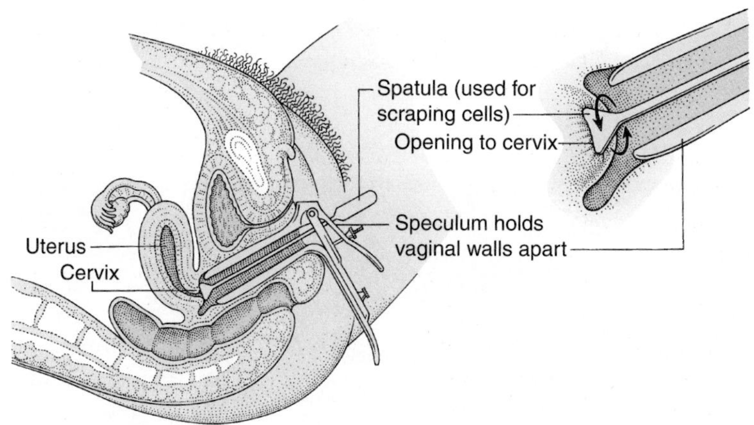

Figure 3.8 Use of the Speculum and Spatula During a Pelvic Examination.

The speculum holds the vaginal walls apart, while the spatula is used to scrape cells gently from the cervix. The Pap test screens for cervical cancer and other abnormalities.

of fluid. Periodic complete pelvic examinations are important. The Pap test, which is useful in detecting cervical cancer, does not reveal ovarian cancer.

Surgery, radiation therapy, and drug therapy are treatment options. Surgery usually includes the removal of one or both ovaries, the uterus, and the fallopian tubes.

The Pelvic Examination

With the pelvic examination, the physician first examines the woman externally for irritations, swellings, abnormal vaginal discharges, and clitoral adhesions. The physician normally inserts a speculum to help inspect the cervix and vaginal walls for discharges (which can be signs of infection), discoloration, lesions, or growths. This examination is typically followed by a Pap test to detect cervical cancer. A sample of vaginal discharge may also be taken to test for the sexually transmitted disease gonorrhea.

To take a Pap smear, the physician will hold the vaginal walls open with a plastic or (prewarmed!) metal speculum so that a sample of cells (a "smear") may be scraped from the cervix with a wooden spatula (see Figure 3.8). Women should not douche prior to Pap tests or schedule them during menstruation, because douches and blood confound analysis of the smear.

The speculum exam is normally followed by a bimanual vaginal exam in which the index and middle fingers of one hand are inserted into the vagina while the lower part of the abdomen is palpated (touched) by the other hand from the outside. The physician uses this technique to examine the location, shape, size, and movability of the internal sex organs, searching for abnormal growths and symptoms of other problems. Palpation may be somewhat uncomfortable but physical discomfort is usually mild. Severe pain is a sign that something is wrong. A woman should not try to be "brave" and hide such discomfort from the examiner.

It is normal for a woman who has not had one, or who is visiting a new doctor, to be anxious about a pelvic exam. Talking about it with the examiner often relieves psychological discomfort. If the doctor is not reassuring, the woman should feel free to consult another doctor. She should not forgo the pelvic examination itself, however. It is essential for early detection of problems.

The Breasts

> The degree of attention which breasts receive, combined with the confusion about what the breast fetishists actually want, makes women unduly anxious about them. They can never be just right; they must always be too small, too big, the wrong shape, too flabby.
>
> —as written by the feminist Germaine Greer, *The Female Eunuch*

A World of Diversity

THE STRONG BREAST REVOLUTION

In Canadian society, there is a fascination with female breasts. Among the two most viewed episodes of the Canadian Discovery Channel's *Sex Files* series were those on female breasts.

Under the direction of drama professor Kim Renders, University of Guelph female students collectively created a play, largely based on their own experiences, designed to educate and entertain. *The Strong Breast Revolution* explores breastfeeding, breast cancer, breasts and sexuality, and women's anxieties about their breasts, as well as the pleasure they give.

A mainly female audience at the university's conference on sexuality gave the play a standing ovation.

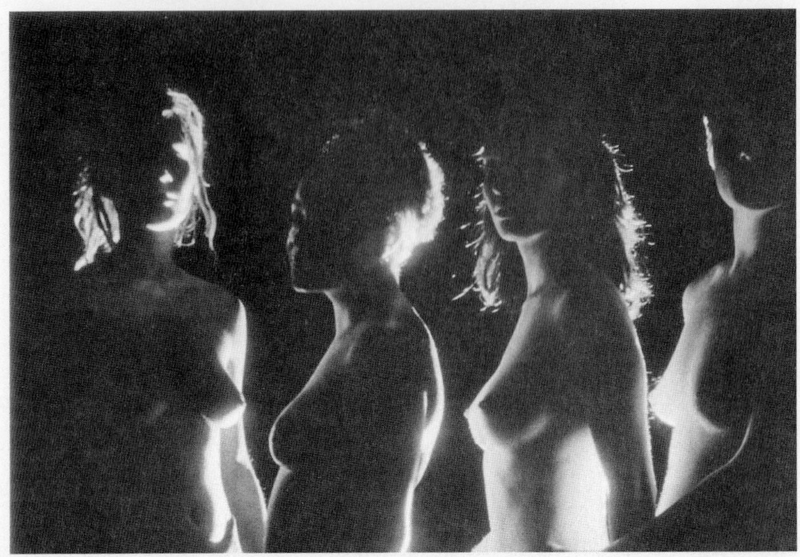

The Strong Breast Revolution.
Actors went topless to show that women should feel proud of their breasts.

Some college women recall:

> I was very excited about my breast development. It was a big competition to see who was wearing a bra in elementary school. When I began wearing one, I also liked wearing see-through blouses so everyone would know. . . .
>
> My breasts were very late in developing. This brought me a lot of grief from my male peers. I just dreaded situations like going to the beach or showering in the locker room. . . .
>
> All through junior high and high school I felt unhappy about being "overendowed." I felt just too uncomfortable in sweaters—there was so much to reveal and I was always sure that the only reason boys liked me was because of my bustline. . . .
>
> —Morrison et al., 1980, pp. 66–70

In some cultures, the breasts are viewed merely as biological instruments for feeding infants. In our culture, however, breasts have taken on such erotic significance that a woman's self-esteem may become linked to her bustline.

The breasts are **secondary sex characteristics**. That is, like the rounding of the hips, they distinguish women from men but are not directly involved in reproduction. Each breast contains 15 to 20 clusters of milk-producing **mammary glands** (see Figure 3.9). Each gland opens at the nipple through its own duct. The mammary glands are separated by soft, fatty tissue. It is the amount of this fatty tissue—not the amount of glandular tissue—that largely determines the size of the breasts. Women vary little in their amount of glandular tissue, so breast size does not determine the quantity of milk that can be produced.

Secondary sex characteristics Traits that distinguish women from men but are not directly involved in reproduction.

Mammary glands Milk-secreting glands.

Areola The dark ring on the breast that encircles the nipple.

The nipple, which lies in the centre of the **areola**, contains smooth muscle fibres that contract to make the nipple erect. The areola, or area surrounding the nipple,

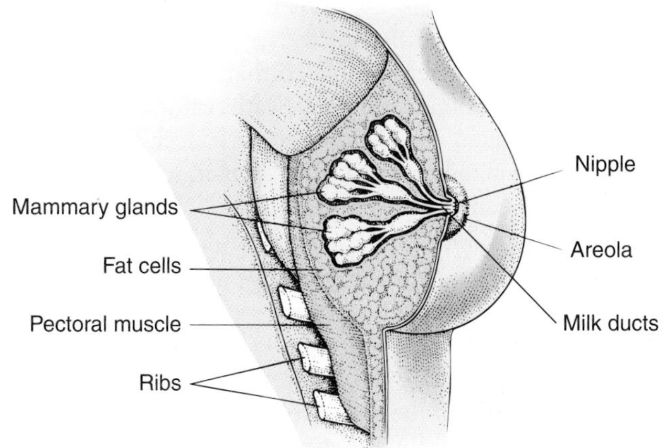

Figure 3.9 A Breast of an Adult Woman.

This drawing reveals the structures underlying the breast, including milk ducts and fat cells.

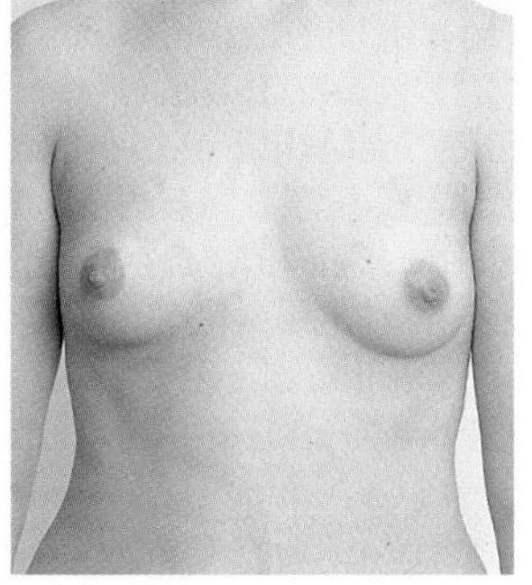
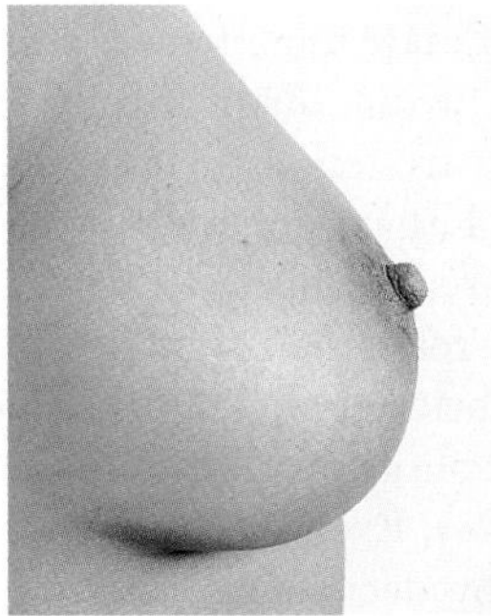
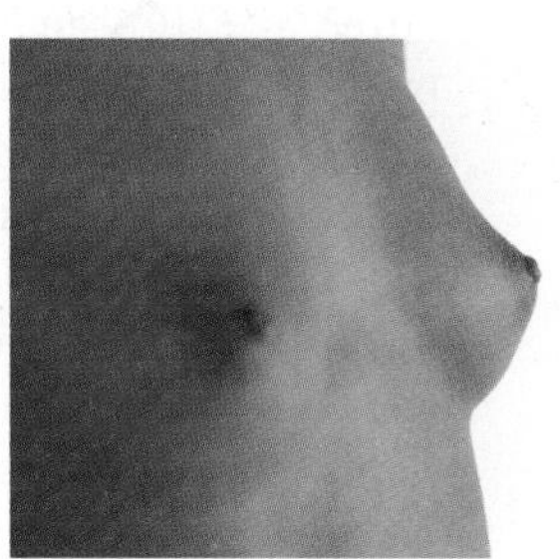

Figure 3.10 Normal Variations in the Size and Shape of the Breasts of Adult Women.

The size and shape of the breasts have little bearing on ability to produce milk or on sensitivity to sexual stimulation. Breasts have become highly eroticized in our culture.

darkens during pregnancy and remains darker after delivery. Oil-producing glands in the areola help lubricate the nipples during breastfeeding. Milk ducts conduct milk from the mammary glands through the nipples. Nipples are richly endowed with nerve endings, so stimulation of the nipples heightens sexual arousal for many women. Male nipples are similar in sensitivity. Males may also find nipple stimulation to be pleasurable. Some male heterosexuals generally do not, perhaps because they have learned to associate breast stimulation with the female sexual role.

Figure 3.10 shows normal variations in the size and shape of the breasts of adult women. The sensitivity of the breasts to sexual stimulation is unrelated to their size. Small breasts may have as many nerve endings as large breasts, but they will be more densely packed.

Women can prompt their partners to provide breast stimulation by informing them that their breasts are sensitive to stimulation. They can also guide a partner's hands in ways that provide the type of stimulation they desire. The breasts vary in sensitivity with the phases of the menstrual cycle, and some women appear less responsive to breast stimulation than others.

Breast Cancer

One in nine Canadian women is expected to develop breast cancer during her lifetime. The incidence of breast cancer increased in Canada until the early 1990s, then decreased after 1993; the five-year survival rate for women diagnosed with breast cancer is now 82% (Public Health Agency of Canada, 2003a).

During 2008, the Canadian Cancer Society estimated that there were 22 400 diagnosed cases of breast cancer among women and 5320 deaths caused by this disease. Many people are not aware that men can also get breast cancer. The Public Health Agency of Canada (2007a) estimated that in 2005, 150 men were diagnosed with breast cancer and 45 deaths were caused by this disease.

RISK FACTORS Breast cancer is rare in women under age 25. The probability rises with age. Still, the probability of a 60-year-old woman developing breast cancer before the age of 70 is only 3% (Canadian Cancer Society, 2002). Genetic factors are involved in breast cancer (Lichtenstein et al., 2000). The risk of breast cancer is higher among women with a family history of the disease (Armstrong et al., 2000).

A key risk factor in breast cancer is prolonged exposure to estrogen, which stimulates breast development in young women and also the proliferation of breast cancer cells (Brody, 1998b). The following all heighten the risk of breast cancer because they increase the woman's exposure to estrogen: early onset of menstruation (before age 14), late menopause (after age 55), delayed childbearing (after age 30), and never giving birth (Brody, 1998a). Despite the fact that birth-control pills contain estrogen, a review of 54 studies involving more than 150 000 women concluded that, generally speaking, there is no connection between using the pill and breast cancer (Gilbert, 1996). However, other research suggests that the pill may increase the risk of breast cancer in women with a family history of the disorder (Grabrick et al., 2000). Canadian researchers have also discovered that heavy use of alcohol contributes to the risk of breast cancer as well as other cancers (Aronson, 2003). Exercise, by the way, appears to reduce the risk of breast cancer, presumably by decreasing the amount of fatty tissue in the body (Dreyfuss, 1998).

DETECTION AND TREATMENT Women with breast cancer have lumps in the breast, *but most lumps in the breasts are not cancerous.* Most are either **cysts** or **benign** tumours. Breast cancer involves lumps in the breast that are **malignant**.

Early detection and treatment reduce the risk of mortality. The sooner cancer is detected, the less likely it is to have spread to critical organs. The Ontario Breast Screening Program has shown that women over the age of 50 who have a family history of breast cancer are the most likely group to benefit from regular breast cancer screening (Halapy et al., 2004).

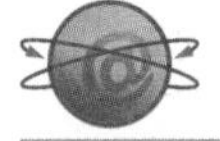

Canadian Cancer Society

www.cancer.ca

Breast cancer may be detected in various ways, including breast self-examination, physical examination, mammography, and magnetic resonance imaging (MRI). Through mammography, tiny, highly curable cancers can be detected—and treated—before they can be felt by touch (Brody, 1995a). **Mammography** and MRIs, combined together, are a kind of X-ray technique that detects cancerous lumps in the breast. In Ontario, 92% of women 50 years and older had had at least one mammogram in their lives (Pollard, 2006).

The medical community is divided on the value of mammography. Consult your doctor for the latest research information.

Cysts Saclike structures filled with fluid or diseased material.

Benign Doing little or no harm.

Malignant Lethal; causing or likely to cause death.

Mammography A special type of X-ray test that detects cancerous lumps in the breast.

The practice of breast self-examination is controversial. After reviewing the results of teaching about self-examination, in 2001 the Canadian Task Force on Preventive Health Care concluded that there was no evidence that self-examination benefited women, and that there was even a risk of some harm, such as by causing women needless worry. Based on these recommendations, Cancer Care Ontario, through its Ontario Breast Screening Program, ended its promotion of breast self-examinations (although it still provides instruction to those women who wish to be taught). In 2007 the Canadian Cancer Society no longer recommended that women conduct monthly breast self-examinations. Given the fact that the medical community is divided on this issue, women, in consultation with their doctors, will have to decide whether they wish to examine their own breasts. Only about one-third of Canadian women self-examine their breasts each month, with older women being more likely to do so (Fisher et al., 1999).

Early detection may offer another benefit. Smaller cancerous lumps can often be removed by **lumpectomy**, which spares the breast. More advanced cancers are likely to be treated by **mastectomy**.

Research is also being done on alternative ways of detecting breast cancer. The Canadian company Z-Tech has developed a quick, painless, and relatively inexpensive method (still in clinical trials) using an electrical charge instead of X-rays (Hamilton, 2002).

Many drugs are used to treat breast cancer, and others are in the research pipeline. For example, *tamoxifen* locks into the estrogen receptors of breast cancer cells, thereby blocking the effects of estrogen that would otherwise stimulate the cells to grow and proliferate.

Many women who have had mastectomies have had surgical breast implants to replace the tissue that has been removed. Other women have breast implants to augment their breast size. In 2006 Health Canada approved the use of silicone gel implants. Health Canada had previously restricted their use because of safety concerns. Approval for the implants was granted after the agency had conducted a thorough review of the research evidence and concluded that the products were safe to use. However, this issue remains quite controversial.

The Menstrual Cycle

Menstruation is the cyclical bleeding that stems from the shedding of the uterine lining (endometrium). Menstruation takes place when a reproductive cycle has not led to the fertilization of an ovum. The human menstrual cycle averages about 28 days in length.

The menstrual cycle is regulated by the hormones estrogen and progesterone and can be divided into four phases. During the first phase of the cycle, the *proliferative phase*, which follows menstruation, estrogen levels increase, causing the ripening of perhaps 10 to 20 ova (egg cells) within their follicles and the proliferation of endometrial tissue in the uterus. During the second phase of the cycle, estrogen reaches peak blood levels, and **ovulation** occurs. Normally only one ovum reaches maturity and is released by an ovary during ovulation. Then the third phase of the cycle—the *secretory*, or *luteal*, phase—begins right after ovulation and continues through the beginning of the next cycle.

The term *luteal phase* is derived from **corpus luteum**, the name given the follicle that releases an ovum. The corpus luteum functions as an **endocrine gland** and produces large amounts of progesterone and estrogen. Progesterone causes the endometrium to thicken, so that it will be able to support an embryo if fertilization occurs. If the ovum goes unfertilized, however, estrogen and progesterone levels plummet. These falloffs trigger the fourth phase, the *menstrual phase*, which leads to the beginning of a new cycle.

Ovulation may not occur in every menstrual cycle. Anovulatory ("without ovulation") cycles are most common in the years just after **menarche**. They may become frequent again in the years prior to menopause, but they may also occur irregularly among women in their twenties and thirties.

Although the menstrual cycle averages about 28 days, variations among women, and in the same woman from month to month, are quite common. Girls' cycles often are irregular for a few years after menarche but later assume reasonably regular patterns. Variations from cycle to cycle tend to occur during the proliferative phase that precedes ovulation. That is, menstruation tends to follow ovulation

Lumpectomy Surgical removal of a lump from the breast.

Mastectomy Surgical removal of the entire breast.

Menstruation The cyclical bleeding that stems from the shedding of the uterine lining (endometrium).

Ovulation The release of an ovum from an ovary.

Corpus luteum The follicle that has released an ovum and then produces copious amounts of progesterone and estrogen during the luteal phase of a woman's cycle.

Endocrine gland A ductless gland that releases its secretions directly into the bloodstream.

Menarche ("men-AR-kee") The first menstrual period.

Hypothalamus A bundle of neural cell bodies near the centre of the brain that is involved in regulating body temperature, motivation, and emotion.

Pituitary gland The gland that secretes growth hormone, prolactin, oxytocin, and others.

Hormone A substance that is secreted by an endocrine gland and regulates various body functions.

Testes The male gonads.

Testosterone The male sex hormone that fosters the development of male sex characteristics and is connected with the sex drive.

Proliferative phase The first phase of the menstrual cycle, which begins with the end of menstruation and lasts about nine or 10 days. During this phase, the endometrium proliferates.

Ovulatory phase The second stage of the menstrual cycle, during which a follicle ruptures and releases a mature ovum.

Zygote A fertilized ovum (egg cell).

reliably by about 14 days. Variations of more than two days in the postovulation period are rare.

Although hormones regulate the menstrual cycle, psychological factors can influence the secretion of hormones. Stress can delay or halt menstruation. Age of menarche is related to a number of health problems. Girls who menstruate at very young ages are at greater risk for such problems as breast and endometrial cancer. Malcolm Koo and colleagues (2002) at the University of Toronto have studied factors related to age of menarche. They found that girls who have a higher intake of dietary fibre or a lower intake of monounsaturated fat begin menstruating later.

Regulation of the Menstrual Cycle

The menstrual cycle involves finely tuned relationships between structures in the brain—the **hypothalamus** and the **pituitary gland**—and the ovaries and uterus. All these structures are parts of the endocrine system, which means that they secrete chemicals directly into the bloodstream. The ovaries and uterus are also reproductive organs. The chemicals secreted by endocrine glands are called **hormones**.

Several hormones play important roles in sexual and reproductive functions. The gonads—the **testes** (or testicles) in the male and the ovaries in the female—secrete sex hormones directly into the bloodstream. The female gonads, the ovaries, produce the sex hormones estrogen and progesterone. The male gonads, the testes, produce the male sex hormone **testosterone**. Males and females also produce sex hormones characteristic of the other gender, but in relatively small amounts.

The hypothalamus is a pea-sized structure in the front part of the brain. It is involved in regulating many states of motivation, including hunger, thirst, aggression, and sex.

The pituitary gland lies below the hypothalamus at the base of the brain. Because many pituitary secretions regulate other endocrine glands, the pituitary has also been called the *master gland*.

Phases of the Menstrual Cycle

We noted that the menstrual cycle has four stages or phases: the proliferative, ovulatory, secretory, and menstrual stages (see Figure 3.11). It might seem logical that a new cycle begins with the first day of the menstrual flow, this being the most clearly identifiable event of the cycle. Many women also count the days of the menstrual cycle beginning with the onset of menstruation. Biologically speaking, however, menstruation is really the culmination of the cycle. In fact, the cycle begins with the end of menstruation and the initiation of a series of biological events that lead to the maturation of an immature ovum in preparation for ovulation and possible fertilization.

THE PROLIFERATIVE PHASE The first phase, or the **proliferative phase**, begins with the end of menstruation and lasts about nine or 10 days in an average 28-day cycle (see Figure 3.11). During this phase the endometrium develops, or "proliferates." This phase is also known as the *preovulatory* or *follicular phase*, because certain ovarian follicles mature and the ovaries prepare for ovulation.

THE OVULATORY PHASE During ovulation, or the **ovulatory phase**, the graafian follicle ruptures and releases a mature ovum *near* a fallopian tube, not actually *into* a fallopian tube The other ripening follicles degenerate and are harmlessly reabsorbed by the body. Occasionally, two ova mature and are released during ovulation, and if both are fertilized, fraternal (nonidentical) twins develop. Identical twins develop when one fertilized ovum divides into two separate **zygotes**.

Ovulation is set into motion when estrogen production reaches a critical level. A woman's *basal body temperature*, taken by oral or rectal thermometer, dips slightly at ovulation and rises by about 0.5°C (1°F) on the day following ovulation. Many women use this information to help them conceive or avoid conceiving.

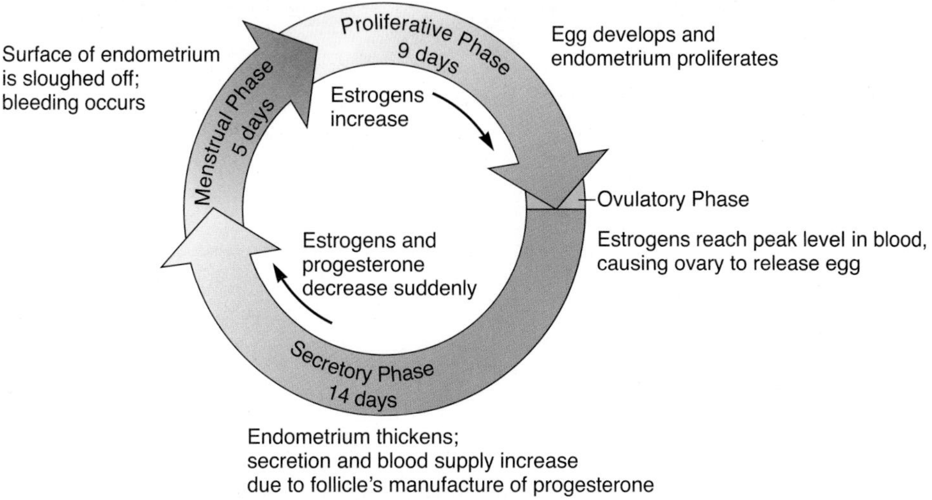

Figure 3.11 The Four Phases of the Menstrual Cycle.

The menstrual cycle consists of the proliferative, ovulatory, secretory (luteal), and menstrual phases.

THE SECRETORY PHASE The phase following ovulation is called the post-ovulatory or **secretory phase**. Some people refer to it as the *luteal phase*, which reflects the name given the ruptured (graafian) follicle—the *corpus luteum*.

Levels of progesterone and estrogen peak at around the twentieth or twenty-first day of an average cycle. These hormones cause the glands in the endometrium to secrete nutrients to sustain a fertilized ovum that becomes implanted in the uterine wall.

If implantation does not occur, the corpus luteum decomposes. After its decomposition, levels of estrogen and progesterone fall precipitously.

THE MENSTRUAL PHASE The **menstrual phase** is the sloughing off of the uterine lining (the endometrium) in the menstrual flow. Menstruation occurs when estrogen and progesterone levels decline to the point where they can no longer sustain the uterine lining. The lining then disintegrates and is discharged from the body along with the menstrual flow. Menstruation itself is the passing of the lining through the cervix and vagina.

Extremely heavy or prolonged (over a week) menstrual bleeding may reflect health problems and should be discussed with a health-care provider.

Prior to 1933, women generally used external sanitary napkins or pads to absorb the menstrual flow. In that year, however, **tampons** were introduced and altered the habits of millions of women. Women who use tampons can swim without concern while menstruating, can wear more revealing or comfortable apparel, and feel generally less burdened.

Tampons are inserted into the vagina and left in place to absorb menstrual fluid. In recent years, questions have arisen about whether or not tampons cause or exacerbate infections. For example, tampon use has been linked to toxic shock syndrome (TSS), an infection that is sometimes fatal. Signs of TSS include fever, headache, sore throat, vomiting, diarrhea, muscle aches, rash, and dizziness. Peeling skin, disorientation, and a plunge in blood pressure may follow.

Many women now use regular rather than superabsorbent tampons to reduce the chance of creating a breeding ground for staph bacteria. Some women alternate tampons with sanitary napkins during each day of menstruation. Some change their tampons three or four times a day. Other women have returned to external sanitary napkins.

Secretory phase The third phase of the menstrual cycle, which follows ovulation. Also referred to as the *luteal phase*, after the *corpus luteum*, which begins to secrete large amounts of progesterone and estrogen following ovulation.

Menstrual phase The fourth phase of the menstrual cycle, during which the endometrium is sloughed off in the menstrual flow.

Tampon A cylindrical plug of cotton that is inserted into the vagina and left in place to absorb menstrual fluid. (Comes from a French word meaning a gun barrel "plug.")

Innovative Canadian Research

MENSTRUAL SEX

Among female students at the University of Waterloo, being comfortable with one's sexuality in general was associated with being comfortable with menstruation. Women who engaged in coital sex during menstruation were more likely also to be aroused by a wide diversity of sexual activities such as group sex and spanking. This indicates that women who engage in menstrual sex are more willing to push the boundaries of what is considered to be conventional sex (Rempel & Baumgartner, 2003).

Coitus During Menstruation

Many couples continue to engage in coitus during menstruation, but others abstain. One study found that men and women are less likely to initiate sexual activity during menstruation than during any other phase of the woman's cycle (Harvey, 1987). Some people abstain because of religious prohibitions. Others express concern about the "fuss" or the "mess" of the menstrual flow. Despite traditional attitudes that associate menstruation with uncleanliness, there is no evidence that coitus during menstruation is physically harmful to either partner. Ironically, menstrual coitus may be helpful to the woman. The uterine contractions that occur during orgasm may help relieve cramping by dispelling blood congestion. Orgasm achieved through masturbation may have the same effect.

Women may be sexually aroused at any time during the menstrual cycle. The preponderance of the research evidence, however, points to a peak in sexual desire in women around the time of ovulation (Kresin, 1993).

Human coital patterns during the phases of the menstrual cycle apparently reflect personal decisions, not hormone fluctuations. Some couples may decide to increase their frequency of coitus at ovulation in order to optimize the chances of conceiving; others may abstain during menstruation because of religious beliefs or beliefs linking menses with uncleanliness. Some may also increase their coital activity preceding menstruation to compensate for anticipated abstinence during menses or increase coital activity afterward to make up for deprivation.

Menopause

Menopause, or the "change of life," is the cessation of menstruation. Menopause is a process that most commonly occurs between the ages of 46 and 50 and lasts for about two years. However, it may begin any time between the ages of 35 and 60. There is at least one case of a woman who became pregnant at age 61.

Menopause is a specific event in a long-term process known as the **climacteric** ("critical period"), the gradual decline in the reproductive capacity of the ovaries. The climacteric generally lasts for about 15 years, from ages 45 to 60 or so. After about the age of 35, the menstrual cycles of many women shorten, from an average of 28 days to 25 days at age 40 and to 23 days by the mid-forties. By the end of her forties, a woman's cycles often become erratic, with some periods close together and others missed.

Menopause The cessation of menstruation.

Climacteric A long-term process, including menopause, that involves the gradual decline in the reproductive capacity of the ovaries.

In menopause, the pituitary gland continues to pour normal levels of FSH and LH into the bloodstream, but for reasons that are not well understood, the ovaries gradually lose their capacity to respond. The ovaries no longer ripen egg cells or produce the sex hormones estrogen and progesterone.

The deficit in estrogen may lead to a number of unpleasant physical sensations, such as night sweats and hot flashes (suddenly feeling hot) and hot flushes (suddenly looking reddened) (Dennerstein et al., 2000). Hot flashes and flushes may alternate with cold sweats, in which a woman feels suddenly cold and clammy. Additional signs of estrogen deficiency include dizziness, headaches, pains in the joints, sensations of tingling in the hands or feet, burning or itchy skin, and heart palpitations. The skin usually becomes drier. There is some loss of breast tissue and decreased vaginal lubrication during sexual arousal. Women may also encounter sleep problems, such as awakening more frequently at night and having difficulty going back to sleep.

Hormone replacement therapy (HRT) Replacement of naturally occurring estrogen or estrogen and progesterone with synthetic equivalents, following menopause.

HORMONE REPLACEMENT THERAPY (HRT) Some women who experience severe physical symptoms have been helped by **hormone replacement therapy (HRT)**, which typically consists of synthetic estrogen and progesterone. These synthetic hormones are used to offset the loss of their naturally occurring counterparts. HRT may help reduce the hot flushes and other symptoms brought about by hormonal deficiencies during menopause (den Tonkelaar & Oddens, 2000).

In 2002, a major controversy over the use of HRT erupted in Canada and many other countries when researchers conducting the Women's Health Initiative study in the United States ended the project after three years instead of eight (the intended length of the study) because they found an increase in the incidence of breast cancer among women taking HRT. Because of this increased risk, the Canadian Cancer Society has advised women to avoid the use of HRT. Although this increase is statistically significant, the actual increased risk for an individual woman is still small (less than one-tenth of 1%). Similar increased risks were found for stroke, heart attack, and blood clots. On the other hand, HRT decreased risks for colorectal cancer and hip fractures (Humphries & Gill, 2003).

Because of the overall increased health risks, many women may decide not to use HRT. However, despite the risks, some women use HRT because they feel the quality of their life is better as a consequence of having fewer menopausal symptoms such as hot flashes, night sweats, dry vagina, etc. Accordingly, women are advised to explore the health benefits and risks of HRT with their doctors.

Women might also consider alternatives. Breast cancer specialist Larry Norton (cited in Duenwald, 2002) notes that progestin alone prevents or lessens hot flashes in about 70% of women. Selective serotonin reuptake inhibitors (SSRIs), such as Effexor, Paxil, and Prozac, are also of help (Stearns et al., 2003). Women using SSRIs to treat hot flashes usually take half the dose used to treat depression, which is their main usage. Vaginal dryness can be treated with estrogens that are used locally—that is, placed in the vagina rather than the bloodstream, as hormones usually are. Creams (for example, Estrace), suppositories (Vagifem), and a plastic ring (Estring) are available for that purpose.

In ending this section, we feel it is important to put the symptoms of menopause into a balanced perspective. Most women cope quite well with menopause and discover ways of minimizing unpleasant symptoms. Many are quite relieved that they no longer have to worry about the possibility of an unplanned pregnancy. Not worrying about contraception can make sexual relationships more enjoyable, and most women continue to have an active and pleasurable sex life.

Menstrual Problems

Although menstruation is a natural biological process, 50–75% of women experience some discomfort prior to or during menstruation (Sommerfeld, 2000). About 30% of Canadian women report that they usually experience extremely painful menstrual periods (Fisher et al., 1999). Taking the birth-control pill reduces the severity of menstrual periods for many women.

Dysmenorrhea

Pain or discomfort during menstruation, or **dysmenorrhea**, is the most common type of menstrual problem. Most women at some time have at least mild menstrual pain or discomfort. Pelvic cramps are the most common manifestation of dysmenorrhea. They may be accompanied by headache, backache, nausea, or bloated feelings. Women who develop severe cases usually do so within a few years of menarche. **Primary dysmenorrhea** is menstrual pain or discomfort in the absence of known organic pathology. Women with **secondary dysmenorrhea** have identified organic problems that are believed to cause their menstrual problems. Their pain or discomfort is caused by, or *secondary to,* these problems. Endometriosis, pelvic inflammatory disease, and ovarian cysts are just a few of the organic disorders that can give rise to secondary dysmenorrhea.

Menstrual cramps appear to result from uterine spasms that may be brought about by copious secretion of hormones called prostaglandins. **Prostaglandins** apparently cause muscle fibres in the uterine wall to contract, as during labour. Most contractions go unnoticed, but powerful, persistent contractions are discomfiting in themselves and may temporarily deprive the uterus of oxygen, another source of distress. Women with more intense menstrual discomfort apparently produce higher quantities of prostaglandins. Prostaglandin-inhibiting drugs, such as ibuprofen, indomethacin, and Aspirin, are thus often helpful. Menstrual pain may also be secondary to endometriosis.

Pelvic pressure and bloating may be traced to pelvic edema—the congestion of fluid in the pelvic region. Fluid retention can lead to a gain of several pounds, sensations of heaviness, and **mastalgia**—a swelling of the breasts that sometimes causes premenstrual discomfort. Orgasm (through coitus or masturbation) can help relieve menstrual discomfort by reducing the pelvic congestion that spawns bloating and pressure. Orgasm may also increase the menstrual flow and shorten this phase of the cycle.

Dysmenorrhea Pain or discomfort during menstruation.

Primary dysmenorrhea Menstrual pain or discomfort that occurs in the absence of known organic problems.

Secondary dysmenorrhea Menstrual pain or discomfort that is caused by identified organic problems.

Prostaglandins Hormones that cause muscle fibres in the uterine wall to contract, as during labour.

Mastalgia A swelling of the breasts that sometimes causes premenstrual discomfort.

Amenorrhea The absence of menstruation.

Primary amenorrhea Lack of menstruation in a woman who has never menstruated.

Secondary amenorrhea Lack of menstruation in a woman who has previously menstruated.

Premenstrual syndrome (PMS) A combination of physical and psychological symptoms (such as anxiety, depression, irritability, weight gain from fluid retention, and abdominal discomfort) that regularly afflicts many women during the four- to six-day interval that precedes their menses each month.

Amenorrhea

Amenorrhea, the absence of menstruation, is a primary sign of infertility. **Primary amenorrhea** is the absence of menstruation in a woman who has not menstruated at all by about the age of 16 or 17. **Secondary amenorrhea** is delayed or absent menstrual periods in women who have had regular periods in the past. Amenorrhea has various causes, including abnormalities in the structures of the reproductive system, hormonal abnormalities, growths such as cysts and tumours, and psychological problems, such as stress. Amenorrhea is normal during pregnancy and following menopause.

Premenstrual Syndrome (PMS)

The term **premenstrual syndrome (PMS)** describes the combination of biological and psychological symptoms that may affect women during the four- to six-day interval that precedes their menses each month. For many women, premenstrual symptoms persist during menstruation.

Fifty-eight percent of Canadian women experience premenstrual syndrome (Fisher et al., 1999). The great majority of cases involve mild to moderate levels of discomfort. PMS is not unique to our culture. Unfortunately, there has only been limited research regarding the psychological aspects of PMS.

Only a generation ago, PMS was seen as something a woman must put up with. No longer. Today there are many options to reduce the effects of PMS. These include exercise, dietary control (for example, eating several small meals a day rather than two or three large meals, limiting salt and sugar, and taking vitamin supplements), hormone treatments (usually progesterone), and medications that

Applied Knowledge

HOW TO HANDLE MENSTRUAL DISCOMFORT

Most women experience some degree of menstrual discomfort. Women with persistent menstrual distress may profit from the suggestions listed below. Researchers are exploring the effectiveness of these techniques in controlled studies. For now, you might consider running a personal experiment. Adopt the techniques that sound right for you—all of them, if you wish.

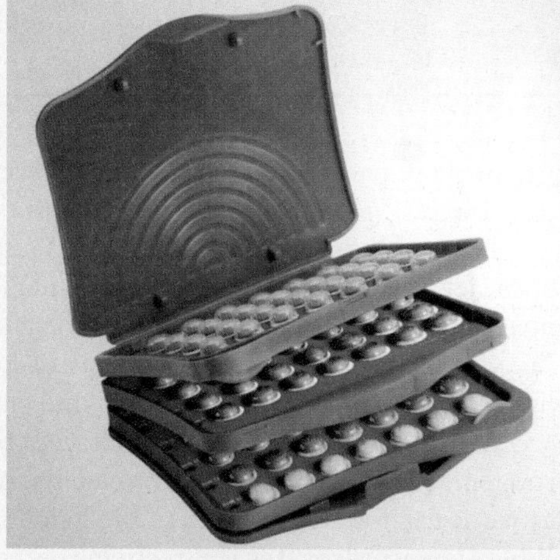

Seasonale.
Women who use Seasonale have just four periods per year.

1. Menstrual problems were once erroneously attributed to women's "hysterical" nature. This is nonsense. Menstrual problems appear, in large part, to reflect hormonal variations or chemical fluctuations in the brain during the menstrual cycle. Researchers have not yet fully identified all the causal elements and patterns, but their lack of knowledge does *not* mean that women who have menstrual problems are hysterical.
2. Keep a menstrual calendar so that you can track your menstrual symptoms systematically and identify patterns.
3. Develop strategies for dealing with days when you experience the greatest distress—strategies that will help enhance your pleasure and minimize the stress affecting you on those days. Activities that distract you from your menstrual discomfort may be helpful. Go see a movie or get into that novel you've been meaning to read.
4. Ask yourself whether you harbour any self-defeating attitudes toward menstruation that might be compounding distress. Do close relatives or friends see menstruation as an illness, a time of "pollution," a "dirty thing"? Have you adopted any of these attitudes—if not verbally, then in ways that affect your behaviour, such as by restricting your social activities during your period?
5. See a doctor about your concerns, especially if you have severe symptoms. Severe menstrual symptoms are often secondary to medical disorders such as endometriosis and pelvic inflammatory disease (PID). Check it out.
6. Develop nutritious eating habits and continue them throughout the entire cycle (that means always). Consider limiting your intake of alcohol, caffeine, fats, salt, and sweets, especially during the days preceding menstruation. Research suggests that a low-fat, vegetarian diet reduces the duration and intensity of menstrual pain and the duration of premenstrual symptoms (Barnard et al., 2000).
7. Eat several smaller meals (or nutritious snacks) throughout the day, rather than a few highly filling meals.
8. Some women find that vigorous exercise—jogging, swimming, bicycling, fast walking, dancing, skating, even jumping rope—helps relieve premenstrual and menstrual discomfort. Evidence suggests that exercise helps to relieve and possibly prevent menstrual discomfort (Choi, 1992). By the way, develop regular exercise habits. Don't become solely a premenstrual athlete.
9. Check with your doctor about vitamin and mineral supplements (such as calcium and magnesium). Vitamin B6 appears to have helped some women.
10. Ibuprofen (brand names: Medipren, Advil, Motrin, etc.) and other medicines available over the counter may be helpful for cramping. Prescription drugs such as anti-anxiety drugs (such as alprazolam) and anti-depressant drugs (serotonin-reuptake inhibitors) may also be of help (Mortola, 1998). "Anti-depressants" affect levels of neurotransmitters in a way that can be helpful for women with PMS. Their benefits do not mean that women with PMS are depressed. Ask your doctor for a recommendation.
11. Ask your gynecologist about oral contraceptives that reduce the number of menstrual periods. In 2007 Health Canada approved the use of Seasonale, an oral contraceptive that reduces the number of periods to four per year. On the horizon, waiting for approval in Canada, is the oral contraceptive Lybrel. This contraceptive, when taken every day, would end menstruation. (Menstruation would return once the user stopped taking the medication.) By providing a daily amount of hormones, Lybrel could eliminate symptoms of PMS. It should be noted that the concept of eliminating menstruation is very controversial, and many health professionals are worried about the possibility of unknown long-term health problems.

reduce anxiety or increase the amount of serotonin in the nervous system (Mortola, 1998).

Some feminists have objected to the view that PMS and menopause are problems that require medical treatment. In particular, Leonore Tiefer (2001) argues that for the sake of increasing profits, pharmaceutical companies have overmedicalized various aspects of female sexuality, such as PMS and menopause.

Male Anatomy and Physiology

In the first part of this chapter we have explored female sexual anatomy and physiology. We now turn our attention to the male.

From the earliest foundations of Western civilization, male-dominated societies elevated men and exalted male genitalia. The ancient Greeks carried oversized images of fish as **phallic symbols** in their Dionysian processions, which celebrated the wilder and more frenzied aspects of human sexuality. In the murky predawn light of Western civilization, humankind engaged in phallic worship.

Men held their own genitals in such high esteem that it was common courtroom practice for them to swear to tell the truth with their hands on their genitals—as we swear to tell the truth in the name of God or by placing our hands on the Bible. The words **testes** and **testicles** derive from the same Latin word as *testify.*

Even today, we see evidence of pride in—indeed veneration of!—the male genitalia. Men with large genitals are accorded respect from their male peers and sometimes adoration from female admirers. Slang describes men with large genitals as "well hung" or "hung like a bull" (or stallion).

Given these cultural attitudes, it is not surprising that some men belittle themselves if they feel, as many do, that they are little—that is, that their penises do not measure up to some ideal. Some men feel so insecure about the size of their penis that they have operations to lengthen it. In Toronto, plastic surgeon Ken Stubbs has performed penis enlargement operations on hundreds of men since 1993. On average, he lengthens the visible penis by 3 cm (1.25 in.) (Nichols, 1999). In examining male sexual anatomy and physiology, we attempt to sort out truth from fiction.

In our exploration of male sexual anatomy and physiology, as in our exploration of female sexual anatomy and physiology, we begin with the external genitalia and then move inward. Once inside, we focus on the route of sperm through the male reproductive system.

External Sex Organs

The external male sex organs include the penis and the scrotum (see Figure 3.12).

The Penis

> Is that a gun in your pocket, or are you just glad to see me?
>
> —Mae West

At first glance, the **penis** may seem rather simple and obvious in its structures, particularly when compared with women's organs. This apparent simplicity may have contributed to cultural stereotypes that men are straightforward and aggressive, whereas women tend to be complicated and perhaps mysterious. Yet, the apparent simplicity of the penis is misleading. Much goes on below the surface.

The penis, like the vagina, is the sex organ used in sexual intercourse. Unlike the vagina, however, the penis also serves as a conduit for urine. Both semen and urine pass out of the penis through the urethral opening. The opening is called the urethral *meatus* (pronounced me-ATE-us), which means "passage."

Phallic symbols Images of the penis that are usually suggestive of generative power.

Testes The male sex glands, suspended in the scrotum, that produce sperm cells and male sex hormones. (Singular: testis.)

Testicles Testes.

Penis The male organ of sexual intercourse.

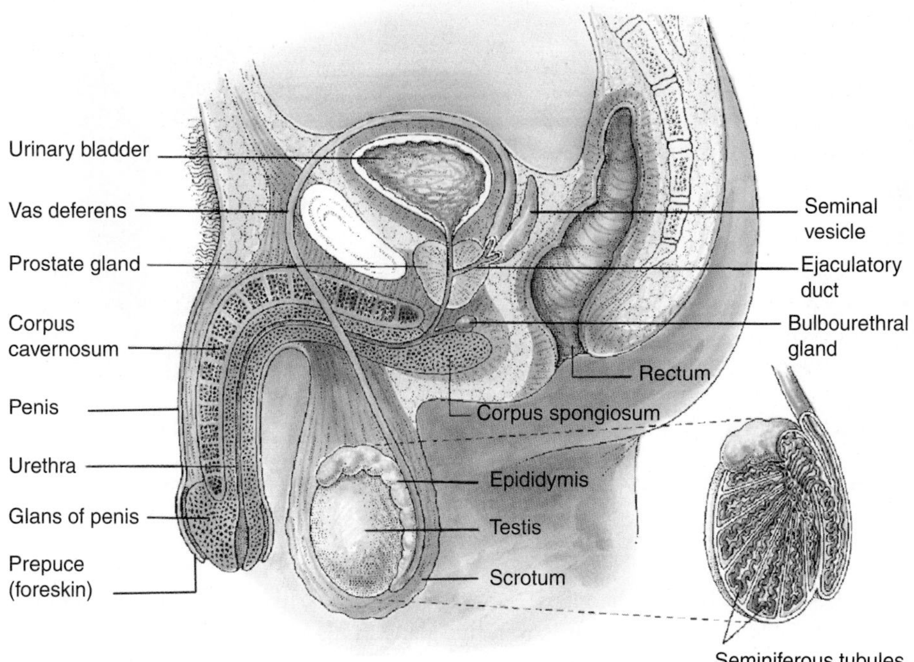

Figure 3.12 The Male Reproductive System.

The external male sex organs include the penis and the scrotum.

Many mammals, including dogs, have penile bones that stiffen the penis to facilitate copulation. Despite the slang term *boner*, the human penis contains no bones. Nor, despite another slang term, *muscle*, does the penis contain muscle tissue. However, muscles at the base of the penis, like the muscles surrounding the vaginal and urethral openings in women, are involved in controlling urination and ejaculation.

Rather than bones or muscles, the penis contains three cylinders of spongy material that run its length. The larger two of these cylinders, the **corpora cavernosa,** lie side by side and function like the cavernous bodies in the clitoris. These cylinders fill up with blood and stiffen during sexual arousal. In addition, a **corpus spongiosum** (spongy body) runs along the bottom, or ventral, surface of the penis. It contains the penile urethra that conducts urine through the penis to the urinary opening (urethral meatus) at the tip. At the tip of the penis, the spongy body enlarges to become the glans, or head, of the penis.

All three cylinders consist of spongy tissue that swells (becomes engorged) with blood during sexual arousal, resulting in erection. The urethra is connected to the bladder, which is unrelated to reproduction, and to those parts of the reproductive system that transport semen.

The glans of the penis, like the clitoral glans, is extremely sensitive to sexual stimulation. Direct, prolonged stimulation can become irritating, even painful. Men generally prefer to masturbate by stroking the shaft of the penis rather than the glans, although some prefer the latter. The **corona**, or coronal ridge, separates the glans from the body of the penis. After the glans, the parts of the penis that men tend to find most sensitive are the corona and an area on the underside of the penis called the frenulum. The **frenulum** is a thin strip of tissue that connects the underside of the glans to the shaft. Most men find the top part of the penis to be the least sensitive part.

The base of the penis, which is called the **root**, extends into the pelvis. It is attached to pelvic bones by leglike structures, called crura, that are like those that anchor the female's clitoris. The body of the penis is called the penile **shaft**. The penile shaft, unlike the clitoral shaft, is free-swinging. Thus, when sexual excitement engorges the penis with blood, the result—erection—is obvious. The skin of the penis is hairless and loose, allowing expansion during erection. It is fixed to the

Corpora cavernosa Cylinders of spongy tissue in the penis that become congested with blood and stiffen during sexual arousal.

Corpus spongiosum The spongy body that runs along the bottom of the penis, contains the penile urethra, and enlarges at the tip of the penis to form the glans.

Corona The ridge that separates the glans from the body of the penis.

Frenulum The sensitive strip of tissue that connects the underside of the penile glans to the shaft.

Root The base of the penis, which extends into the pelvis.

Shaft The body of the penis, which expands as a result of vasocongestion.

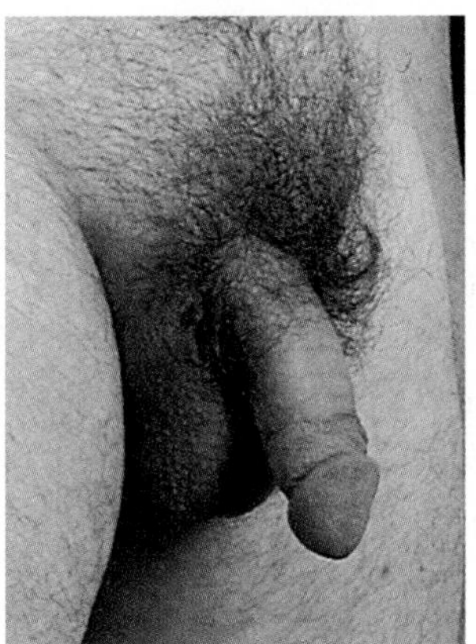
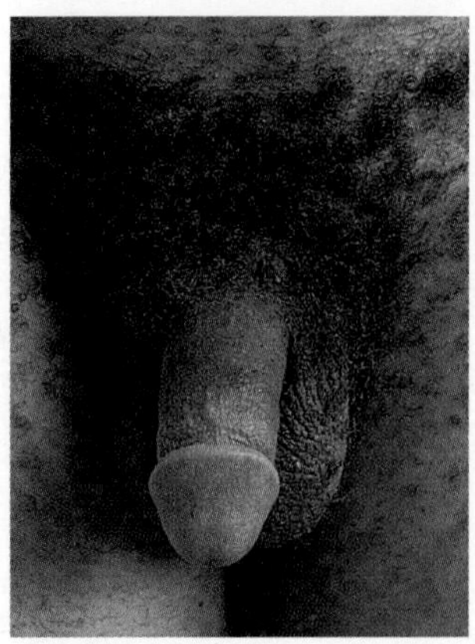
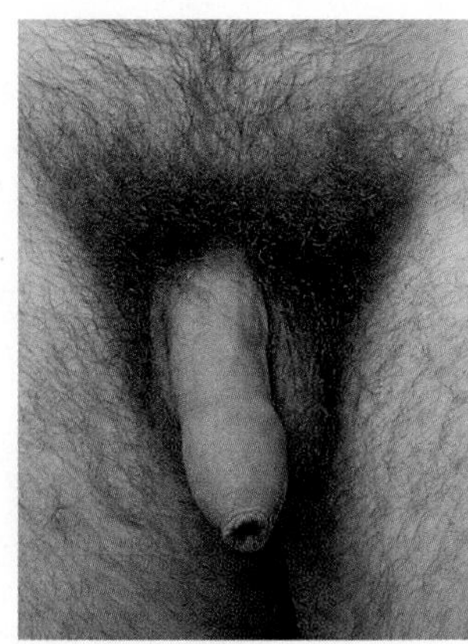

Figure 3.13 Normal Variations in the Male Genitals.

The penis and scrotum vary a good deal in appearance from one man to another. The penis in the photo to the right is uncircumcised.

Foreskin The loose skin that covers the penile glans. Also referred to as the *prepuce.*

Circumcision Surgical removal of the foreskin of the penis.

penile shaft just behind the glans. Some of it, however, like the labia minora in the female, folds over to partially cover the glans. This covering is the prepuce, or **foreskin**. It covers part or all of the penile glans just as the clitoral prepuce (hood) covers the clitoral shaft. The prepuce consists of loose skin that freely moves over the glans. However, smegma—a cheeselike, foul-smelling secretion—may accumulate below the prepuce, causing the foreskin to adhere to the glans.

CIRCUMCISION **Circumcision** is the surgical removal of the prepuce (Figure 3.13). Male circumcision has a long history both as a cultural tradition and as a religious rite. Jews traditionally carry out male circumcision shortly after a baby is born. In some societies circumcisions are performed when the male reaches puberty to signify his transition to adulthood.

Advocates of circumcision believe that it enhances hygiene because it eliminates a site where smegma might accumulate and disease organisms might flourish. Opponents of circumcision believe that it is unnecessary because regular cleaning is sufficient to reduce the risk of these problems. Some equate male circumcision with female genital mutilation and argue that the procedure is painful to the child and the child has not

A World of Diversity

ON PENIS SIZE AND SEXUAL PERFORMANCE

The belief that the size of the man's penis determines his sexual prowess is based on the assumption that men with bigger penises are better equipped to satisfy a woman sexually. The diameter of the penis may have a greater bearing on a partner's sexual sensations than its length, because thicker penises may provide more clitoral stimulation during intercourse. Even though the inner vagina is relatively insensitive to touch, some women find the *pressure* of deeper penetration sexually pleasurable. Others, however, find deeper penetration to be uncomfortable or painful, especially if thrusting is too vigorous.

There has been a notable lack of research into women's preferences regarding penis size. In a 1998 national survey of Canadian women, the Compas polling organization asked "What is the ideal penis size?" Most women preferred either an average (37%) or somewhat larger than average penis (45%). Hardly any preferred either a much larger than average one (3%) or a somewhat smaller than average one (4%), and 12% didn't express an opinion.

consented to circumcision. The number of circumcisions has been declining in Canada; today, about one-quarter of male babies are circumcised. The circumcision rate varies widely across the country—in Ontario, for example, about 50% of male babies are circumcised, compared with 20% in the Maritimes (Keung, 1999).

The Circumcision Information Resource Centre, a Montreal-based lobby group, seeks to ban male circumcision on infants and children in Canada in the same way that female circumcision has been made illegal. Some men are so upset over having been circumcised that they have made efforts to have their foreskin restored.

In a 1996 report on circumcision, the Canadian Paediatric Society concluded that the procedure is not medically necessary and recommended against circumcisions being performed as a routine practice. Still, the Society took the view that parents should have the right to decide whether to have their infants circumcised (Keung, 1999).

Some research, particularly in Africa, suggests that circumcision lessens the risk of infections from urinary tract infections (Wiswell, 2003, as cited in Liptak, 2003), HPV (Castellsague et al., 2002), HIV/AIDS (Bailey, 2000; Reynolds et al., 2004), and cancer of the penis. The protective effects of circumcision are likely to reflect a lower incidence of local inflammation and genital ulcers, both of which provide ports of entry for HIV, and the removal of cells in the foreskin—Langerhans cells—that are receptive to infection by HIV (Cohen, 2000; Szabo & Short, 2000).

Alternatively, circumcision may be less effective in developed countries. A national survey in Australia found no difference in STI rates between circumcised and uncircumcised men (Richters et al., 2006). However, there were higher rates of penile fungal infections among those men who had not been circumcised.

The perception that circumcised men experience less sexual sensation than uncircumcised men is controversial. One study by Canadian and American researchers (Payne et al., 2007) found no difference in penile sensation between these groups. However, the uncircumcised men experienced a larger increase in penile temperature with sexual arousal. In Australia, Richters et al. (2006) found that uncircumcised men were more likely to sometimes experience physical pain during intercourse.

Physicians once agreed that circumcision was the treatment of choice for **phimosis**, a condition in which it is difficult to retract the foreskin from the glans. But today, only a small minority of males with phimosis are circumcised for that reason (Rickwood et al., 2000).

PENIS SIZE In our culture the size of the penis is sometimes seen as a measure of a man's masculinity and his ability to please his sex partner. The attitudes of Canadian women toward penis size are presented in the nearby A World of Diversity feature.

Masters and Johnson (1966) reported that the penises of the 312 male subjects they studied generally ranged in length from 9 cm (3.5 in.) to a little more than 10 cm (4 in.). The average erect penis ranges from 13 cm to 18 cm (5 in. to 7 in.) in length (Reinisch, 1990). There appears to be little relationship between the size of a given penis when flaccid and when erect. Penises that are small when flaccid tend to gain more size when they become erect. Larger flaccid penises gain relatively less (Jamison & Gebhard, 1988). Nor is there a relationship between penis size and body weight, height, or build (Money et al., 1984).

Even when flaccid, the same penis can vary in size. Factors such as cold air or water and emotions of fear or anxiety can cause the penis (along with the scrotum and testicles) to draw closer to the body, reducing its size. The flaccid penis may also grow in size in warm water or when the man is relaxed.

The Scrotum

The **scrotum** is a pouch of loose skin that becomes covered lightly with hair at puberty. The scrotum consists of two compartments that hold the testes. Each testicle is held in place by a **spermatic cord**, a structure that contains the **vas deferens**, blood vessels and nerves, and the cremaster muscle. The **cremaster muscle** raises and lowers the testicle within the scrotum in response to temperature

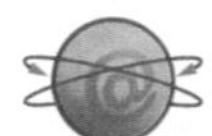

Circumcision Resource Center
Informs the general public and professionals about circumcision.
www.circumcision.org

Phimosis An abnormal condition in which the foreskin is so tight that it cannot be withdrawn from the glans.

Scrotum The pouch of loose skin that contains the testes. (From the same linguistic root as the word *shred*, which means "a long, narrow strip," probably referring to the long furrows on the scrotal sac.)

Spermatic cord The cord that suspends a testicle within the scrotum and contains a vas deferens, blood vessels, nerves, and the cremaster muscle.

Vas deferens A tube that conducts sperm from the testicle to the ejaculatory duct of the penis.

Cremaster muscle The muscle that raises and lowers the testicle in response to temperature changes and sexual stimulation.

Germ cell A cell from which a new organism develops.

Sperm The male germ cell.

Androgens Male sex hormones.

Testosterone A male steroid sex hormone.

Secondary sex characteristics Traits that distinguish the genders but are not directly involved in reproduction.

Seminiferous tubules Tiny, winding, sperm-producing tubes that are located within the lobes of the testes.

Spermatogenesis The process by which sperm cells are produced and developed.

changes and sexual stimulation. (The testes are drawn closer to the body during sexual arousal.)

Sperm production is optimal at a temperature that is slightly cooler than the 37°C (98.6°F) that is desirable for most of the body. Typical scrotal temperature is a few degrees lower than body temperature. The scrotum is loose-hanging and flexible. It permits the testes and nearby structures to escape the higher body heat, especially in warm weather. Tightening or constricting the skin surface helps retain heat and gives the scrotum a wrinkled appearance in the cold.

The scrotum is developed from the same embryonic tissue that becomes the labia majora of the female. Thus, like the labia majora, it is quite sensitive to sexual stimulation. It is somewhat more sensitive than the top side of the penis but less so than other areas of the penis.

Internal Sex Organs

The male internal sex organs consist of the testes, the organs that manufacture sperm and the male sex hormone testosterone; the system of tubes and ducts that conduct sperm through the male reproductive system; and the organs that help nourish and activate sperm and neutralize some of the acidity that sperm encounter in the vagina.

The Testes

The testes are the male gonads. In slang the testes are frequently referred to as "balls" or "nuts." These terms are considered vulgar, but they are reasonably descriptive. They also make it easier for many people to refer to the testes in informal conversation.

The testes serve two functions analogous to those of the ovaries. They secrete sex hormones and produce mature **germ cells**. In the case of the testes, the germ cells are **sperm** and the sex hormones are **androgens**. The most important androgen is testosterone.

TESTOSTERONE **Testosterone** stimulates the prenatal differentiation of male sex organs, sperm production, and the development of **secondary sex characteristics**, such as the beard, deep voice, and the growth of muscle mass.

In men, several endocrine glands—the hypothalamus, pituitary gland, and testes—keep blood testosterone levels at a more or less even level. This contrasts with the peaks and valleys in levels of female sex hormones during the phases of the menstrual cycle. Testosterone levels vary slightly with stress, time of day or month, and other factors, but a feedback loop among the endocrine glands keeps them relatively stable.

The testes usually range between 2.5 cm and 4.5 cm (1–1.75 in.) in length. The left testicle usually hangs lower, because the left spermatic cord tends to be somewhat longer.

SPERM Each testicle is divided into many lobes. The lobes are filled with winding **seminiferous tubules** (see Figure 3.12). Although packed into a tiny space, these tubules, placed end to end, would span the length of several football fields. Through a process called **spermatogenesis**, these threadlike structures produce and store hundreds of billions of sperm through the course of a man's lifetime.

Sperm cells develop through several stages. It takes about 72 days for the testes to manufacture a mature sperm cell. Each sperm cell is about 50 microns (0.0005 cm) long, one of the smallest cells in the body (Thompson, 1993).

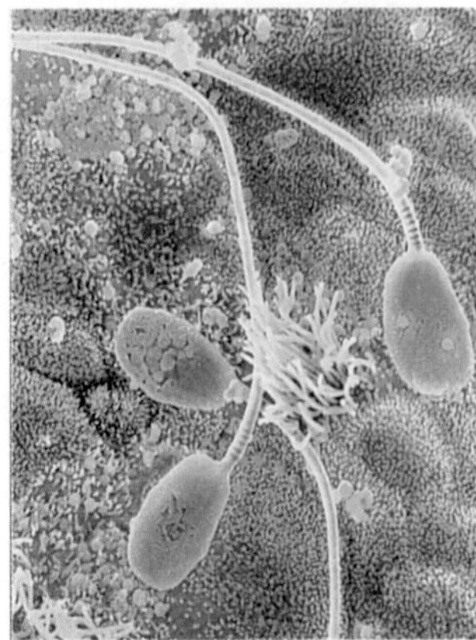

Human Sperm Cells Magnified Many Times.

During fertilization, the 23 chromosomes from the father's sperm cell combine with the 23 chromosomes from the mother's ovum, furnishing the standard ensemble of 46 chromosomes in the offspring. Among the 23 chromosomes borne by sperm cells is one sex chromosome—an X sex chromosome or a Y sex chromosome.

Ova contain X sex chromosomes only. The union of an X sex chromosome and a Y sex chromosome leads to the development of male offspring. Two X sex chromosomes combine to yield female offspring. Thus, whether the father contributes an X or a Y sex chromosome determines the baby's gender.

The testes are veritable dynamos of manufacturing power, churning out about 1000 sperm per second, or about 30 billion—yes, *billion*—per year. Mathematically speaking, 10 to 20 ejaculations hold enough sperm to populate the earth.

Sperm proceed from the seminiferous tubules through an intricate maze of ducts that converge in a single tube called the **epididymis**. The epididymis lies against the back wall of the testicle and serves as a storage facility for sperm.

The Vas Deferens

Each epididymis empties into a vas deferens. The vas is a thin, cylindrical tube about 40 cm (16 in.) long that serves as a conduit for mature sperm. In the scrotum, the vas deferens lies near the skin surface within the spermatic cord. Therefore, a **vasectomy**, an operation in which the right and left vas deferens are severed, is a convenient means of sterilization. The tube leaves the scrotum and follows a circuitous path up into the abdominal cavity. Then it loops back along the rear surface of the bladder (see Figure 3.14).

The Seminal Vesicles

The two **seminal vesicles** are small glands, each about 5 cm (2 in.) long. They lie behind the bladder and open into the **ejaculatory ducts**, where the fluids they secrete combine with sperm (see Figure 3.14).

At the base of the bladder, each vas deferens joins a seminal vesicle to form a short ejaculatory duct that runs through the middle of the prostate gland (see Figure 3.14). In the prostate, the ejaculatory duct opens into the urethra, which leads to the tip of the penis.

Is There a *Manopause*?

The scientific jury is still out on the existence of the "male menopause." Women encounter relatively sudden age-related declines in sex hormones and fertility during menopause. Men experience a gradual decline in testosterone levels as they

Epididymis A tube that lies against the back wall of each testicle and serves as a storage facility for sperm.

Vasectomy A sterilization operation in which the vas deferens are severed.

Seminal vesicles Small glands that lie behind the bladder and secrete fluids that combine with sperm in the ejaculatory ducts.

Ejaculatory duct A duct, formed by the convergence of a vas deferens with a seminal vesicle, through which sperm pass through the prostate gland and into the urethra.

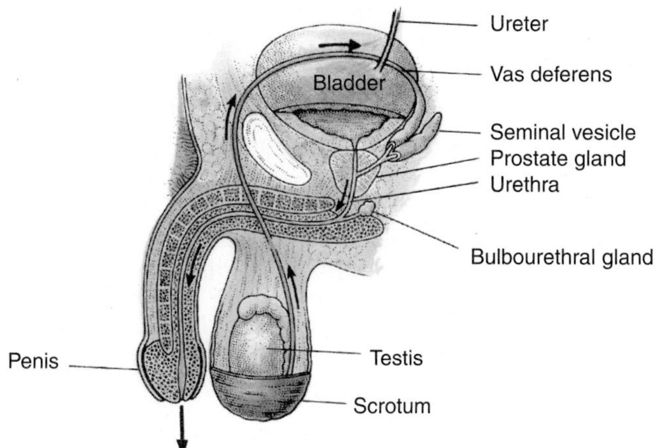

Figure 3.14 Passage of Spermatozoa.

Each testicle is divided into lobes that contain threadlike seminiferous tubules. Through spermatogenesis, the tubules produce and store hundreds of billions of sperm over the course of a man's lifetime. During ejaculation, sperm cells travel through the vas deferens, up and over the bladder, into the ejaculatory duct, and then through the urethra. Secretions from the seminal vesicles and the bulbourethral glands join with sperm to compose semen.

age, but nothing like the sharp plunge in estrogen levels that women experience during menopause (Sheehy, 1998). Testosterone levels begin to fall at about age 40 or 50 and may decline to one-third or one-half of their peak levels by age 80 (Brody, 1995c).

The drop in testosterone levels that occurs as men age may be connected to a variety of age-related symptoms, including reduced muscle mass and strength, accumulation of body fat, reduced energy levels, lowered fertility, and reduced erectile ability. However, despite a decline in testosterone levels, most men remain potent throughout their lives. Little is known about the critical levels of testosterone needed to maintain erectile ability. Certain age-related changes, such as reduced muscle mass and strength and increased body fat, may be due not to declining testosterone production but to other factors associated with aging, such as a gradual loss of *human growth hormone*, a hormone that helps maintain muscle strength and that may prevent fat buildup. Some experts believe that testosterone replacement may help avert erectile problems, bone loss, and frailty, in much the same way that estrogen replacement benefits postmenopausal women. Others worry that excessive use of the hormone may increase the risks of prostate cancer and cardiovascular disease (Tan, 2002).

The Prostate Gland

The **prostate gland** lies beneath the bladder and is approximately the shape and size of a chestnut (about 2 cm [0.75 in.] in diameter). The prostate gland contains muscle fibres and glandular tissue that secrete prostatic fluid. Prostatic fluid is milky and alkaline. It provides the texture and odour characteristic of the seminal fluid. The alkalinity neutralizes some of the acidity of the vaginal tract, prolonging the life span of sperm as seminal fluid spreads through the female reproductive system. The prostate is continually active in mature males, but sexual arousal further stimulates secretions. Secretions are conveyed into the urethra by a sievelike duct system. There the secretions combine with sperm and fluid from the seminal vesicles.

Stimulation of the prostate can heighten sexual arousal and pleasure. Some men find orgasm more intense with prostate stimulation. However, because prostate stimulation is done in the anus, there are many men as well as partners who are uncomfortable with this kind of stimulation.

A vasectomy prevents sperm from reaching the urethra but does not cut off fluids from the seminal vesicles or prostate gland. A man who has had a vasectomy thus emits an ejaculate that appears normal but contains no sperm.

Cowper's Glands

The **Cowper's glands** lie below the prostate and empty their secretions into the urethra. During sexual arousal they secrete a drop or so of clear, slippery fluid that appears at the urethral opening. The functions of this fluid are not entirely understood. It may help buffer the acidity of the male's urethra and lubricate the urethral passageway to ease the passage of seminal fluid. The fluid is not produced in sufficient amounts to play a significant role in lubricating the vagina during intercourse.

Fluid from the Cowper's glands precedes the ejaculate and often contains viable sperm. Thus, coitus may lead to pregnancy even if the penis is withdrawn prior to ejaculation. This is one reason why people who practise the "withdrawal method" of birth control are frequently called "parents."

Prostate gland The gland that lies beneath the bladder and secretes prostatic fluid, which gives semen its characteristic odour and texture.

Cowper's glands Structures that lie below the prostate and empty their secretions into the urethra during sexual arousal.

Semen The whitish fluid that constitutes the ejaculate, consisting of sperm and secretions from the seminal vesicles, prostate gland, and Cowper's glands.

Semen

Sperm and the fluids contributed by the seminal vesicles, the prostate gland, and the Cowper's glands make up **semen**, the whitish seminal fluid that is expelled through the tip of the penis during ejaculation. The seminal vesicles secrete about 70% of the fluid that constitutes the ejaculate. The remaining 30% of seminal fluid consists of sperm and fluids produced by the prostate gland and the Cowper's glands. Sperm themselves account for only about 1% of the volume of semen. This is why men with vasectomies continue to ejaculate about as much semen as before, although their ejaculates are devoid of sperm.

Semen is the medium that carries sperm through much of the male's reproductive system and the reproductive tract of the female. Semen contains water, mucus, sugar (fructose), acids, and bases. It activates and nourishes sperm, and the bases help shield sperm from vaginal acidity. The typical ejaculate contains between 200 and 400 million sperm and ranges between 3 mL and 5 mL in volume. (Five millilitres is equal to about one teaspoon.) The quantity of semen decreases with age and with frequency of ejaculation.

Diseases of the Urogenital System

Because the organs that make up the urinary and reproductive systems are near each other and share some "piping," they are referred to as the urinogenital or urogenital system. A number of diseases affect the urogenital system. The type of physician who specializes in their diagnosis and treatment is a **urologist**.

Urethritis

Men, like women, are subject to bladder and urethral inflammations, which are generally referred to as **urethritis**. The symptoms include frequent urination (urinary frequency), a strong need to urinate (urinary urgency), burning during urination, and a penile discharge. People with symptoms of urinary frequency and urinary urgency feel the pressing need to urinate repeatedly, even though they may have just done so and may have but another drop or two to expel.

Preventive measures for urethritis parallel those suggested for cystitis (bladder infection): drinking more water, drinking cranberry juice (125 mL [4 oz.], two or three times a day), and lowering intake of alcohol and caffeine. Cranberry juice is highly acidic, and acid tends to eliminate many of the bacteria that can give rise to urethritis.

Cancer of the Testes

Cancer of the testicles remains a relatively rare form of cancer. In 2004, there were 890 cases of testicular cancer resulting in 300 deaths among Canadian men (Canadian Cancer Society, 2008). It is, however, the most common form of solid-tumour cancer to strike men between the ages of 20 and 34. There is no evidence that testicular cancer results from sexual overactivity or masturbation. Men who had **cryptorchidism** as children (a condition in which one or both testicles fail to descend from the abdomen into the scrotum) stand about a 40 times greater chance of contracting testicular cancer.

Although testicular cancer was generally fatal in earlier years, the prognosis today is quite favourable, especially for cases that are detected early. Treatments include surgical removal of the diseased testis, radiation, and chemotherapy.

The surgical removal of a testicle may have profound psychological implications. Some men who have lost a testicle feel less "manly." One option is testicular replacement surgery which involves implanting a prosthetic testicle into the scrotum. Fears related to sexual performance can engender sexual dysfunctions. From a physiological standpoint, sexual functioning should remain unimpaired, because adequate quantities of testosterone are produced by the remaining testis.

Urologist A physician who specializes in the diagnosis and treatment of diseases of the urogenital system.

Urethritis An inflammation of the bladder or urethra.

Cryptorchidism A condition in which one or both testicles fail to descend from the abdomen into the scrotum.

Applied Knowledge

SELF-EXAMINATION OF THE TESTES

Self-examination (see Figure 3.15) is best performed shortly after a warm shower or bath, when the skin of the scrotum is most relaxed. The man should examine the scrotum for evidence of pea-sized lumps. Each testicle can be rolled gently between the thumb and the fingers. Lumps are generally found on the side or front of the testicle. The presence of a lump is not necessarily a sign of cancer, but it should be promptly reported to a physician for further evaluation. Men should watch for these warning signals:

1. A slight enlargement of one of the testicles.
2. A change in the consistency of a testicle.
3. A dull ache in the lower abdomen or groin. (Pain may be absent in cancer of the testes, however.)
4. Sensation of dragging and heaviness in a testicle.
5. A lump on the testicle.

Because early detection is crucial to survival, men should examine themselves monthly following puberty and have regular medical checkups.

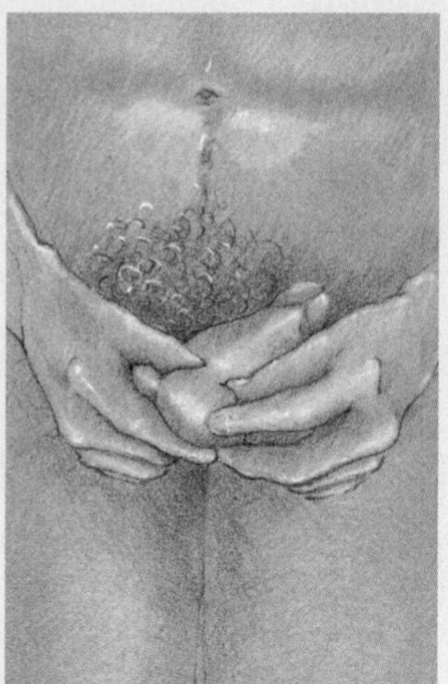

Figure 3.15 Self-Examination of the Testes.

Benign prostatic hyperplasia Enlargement of the prostate gland due to hormonal changes associated with aging and characterized by symptoms such as urinary frequency, urinary urgency, and difficulty starting the flow of urine.

Disorders of the Prostate

The prostate gland is tiny at birth and grows rapidly at puberty. It may shrink during adulthood but usually becomes enlarged past the age of 50.

BENIGN PROSTATIC HYPERPLASIA The prostate gland becomes enlarged in about half the men older than the age of 50 and in 80% of men by age 80 ("Understanding prostate," 2007). **Benign prostatic hyperplasia** (BPH) is noncancerous enlargement of the prostate gland resulting from hormonal changes associated with aging rather than other causes, such as inflammation from STIs. Because the prostate surrounds the upper part of the urethra (Figure 3.12), enlargement constricts the urethra, causing urinary frequency (including increased frequency of nocturnal urination), urinary urgency, and difficulty starting the flow of urine. Several treatments are available to relieve the pressure on the urethra and increase the flow of urine. Two types of drugs help men with BPH. The first type, 5-ARIs (5-alpha reductase inhibitors), inhibits the production of the hormone DHT (a form of testosterone), which causes enlargement of the prostate. 5-ARIs shrink the prostate, provide long-term improvement of symptoms, and reduce the risk of severe urinary retention and the need for surgery. The second type is alpha-blockers, which act by relaxing the muscles of the bladder to improve the flow of urine, providing symptom relief. Part of the prostate is also sometimes surgically removed ("Understanding prostate," 2007).

Prostate cancer involves the growth of malignant prostate tumours that can metastasize to bones and lymph nodes if not detected and treated early. Men whose diets are rich in animal fats have a substantially higher chance of developing advanced prostate cancer than do men with a low intake of animal fat. The incidence of prostate cancer also increases with age (Tarone et al., 2000). More than 80% of cases of prostate cancer are diagnosed in men aged 65 or above (National Cancer

Canadian Trends

PROSTATE CANCER

A more serious and life-threatening problem is prostate cancer, which is the most common form of cancer among Canadian men. One in seven men will develop prostate cancer during their lifetime, with most developing it after age 70. About 20 500 Canadian men were diagnosed in 2004 with prostate cancer and an estimated 4300 men died from it (Public Health Agency of Canada, 2007b).

Institute, 2000). Genetic factors are also apparently involved (Lichtenstein et al., 2000). Moreover, testosterone spurs the development of prostate cancer (D'Amico et al., 2000). A study of men in Quebec also indicated that having a vasectomy increased the risk of getting prostate cancer (Emard et al., 2001).

One of the more intriguing factors related to prostate cancer is frequency of ejaculation. Australian researchers found that men who ejaculated frequently when they were between the ages of 20 and 50 were less likely to develop prostate cancer than those men who had a low level of ejaculation frequency (Giles et al., 2003). The researchers speculate that the longer semen is left in the ducts, the greater the chance of it becoming carcinogenic. Frequent ejaculation thus acts as a "flushing" mechanism to clear the body of potentially harmful biological materials.

The early symptoms of cancer of the prostate may mimic those of benign prostate enlargement: urinary frequency and difficulty in urinating. Later symptoms include blood in the urine, pain or burning on urination, and pain in the lower back, pelvis, or upper thighs (National Cancer Institute, 2000). Most cases occur without noticeable symptoms in the early stages.

The Canadian Cancer Society (2002) recommends that men over the age of 50 discuss with their doctor the potential benefits and risks of early detection of prostate cancer. Prostate cancer is the second most common cause of death from cancer among Canadian men. Men at higher risk, especially those who have a family background of prostate cancer or are of African ancestry, should consider being tested at earlier ages. Because the medical community is divided over how often the tests should be performed, the Cancer Society has not provided more specific guidelines regarding the frequency of testing.

In testing for the possibility of prostate cancer, the physician inserts a finger into the rectum and feels for abnormalities in the prostate gland. Unfortunately, many men are reluctant to undergo a rectal examination. Avoidance of, or ignorance of the need for, regular exams is a major contributor to the death rate from prostate cancer.

When a cancerous growth is suspected on the basis of a rectal examination or a PSA blood test, further testing is usually done via additional blood tests, ultrasound, or biopsy. PSA (prostate-specific antigen) is a protein that helps transform a gel-like substance in the prostate gland into a liquid that transports sperm when it is ejaculated. In the diseased or enlarged prostate, PSA seeps into the blood at higher levels, giving higher test readings. Early detection is important because treatment is most effective before the cancer has spread. About half of Canadian men aged 40 or over have had a PSA test (Gibbons and Waters, 2003).

There is controversy over how effective screening for prostate cancer is in the general population. On the one hand, a blood test for PSA can detect evidence of prostate cancer even among men whose prostates feel normal upon physical examination (Tarone et al., 2000). However, the PSA test is only moderately reliable.

Scientists are working on other methods of prostate cancer detection. One new test uses a man's saliva to predict the probability of his developing cancer (Zheng et al., 2008). The test measures five genetic markers for predicting prostate cancer.

Prostatitis Inflammation of the prostate gland.

The most widely used treatment for prostate cancer is surgical removal of the prostate gland (Klein, E. A., 2000). However, surgical prostate removal may damage surrounding nerves, leading to problems in controlling the flow of urine or in erection or ejaculation (Stanford et al., 2000). Recently introduced surgical techniques tend to spare the surrounding nerves and to reduce, but not eliminate, the risk of complications. Other treatments include radiation, hormone treatment, and anticancer drugs (Klein, E. A., 2000). Hormone treatment in the form of androgen (testosterone) suppression therapy and anticancer drugs may shrink the tumour and relieve pain for long periods of time. One study found that the combination of radiation therapy and androgen suppressive therapy was more effective than radiation therapy alone (D'Amico et al., 2000). Men who have their prostate glands removed are more likely to experience urinary incontinence (loss of control over urination) and sexual dysfunction (trouble attaining erection) than men who use radiation (Potosky et al., 2000). In a large-scale study of men who had prostate surgery in Quebec, 75% experienced erectile dysfunction and 6.6% experienced severe problems with urination (Karakiewicz et al., 2004). Unfortunately, medical treatments such as pills like Viagra are the least likely to be successful with men whose erectile dysfunction is a result of prostate surgery (Schover et al., 2004). After prostate surgery, many men still feel uncomfortable seeking help to deal with sexual problems. Those who have the highest feelings of distress over the loss of erectile function are the most likely to seek medical assistance for this problem (Schover et al., 2004).

Because of concerns over the side effects of prostate surgery, some physicians recommend a period of watchful waiting involving regular PSA tests rather than aggressive treatment. Toronto urologist Laurence Klotz, in a trial study, found that only 25% of prostate cancer patients required radical surgery (Dalby, 2007). A large American study found that with watchful waiting, the great majority of prostate cancer patients were more likely to die from other causes than prostate cancer (Marchione, 2008).

Several prostate cancer support groups have formed across Canada for men who are either considering treatment options or undergoing treatment. These groups provide a forum where men can share their experiences, fears, and concerns.

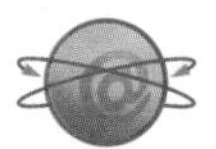

Canadian Prostate Cancer Network
Plays a key role in creating and maintaining prostate cancer support groups.

www.cpcn.org
Provides in-depth information about prostate cancer.

www.prostatecancer.ca

PROSTATITIS Many infectious agents can inflame the prostate, causing **prostatitis.** The chief symptoms are painful ejaculation and an ache or pain between the scrotum and the anal opening. In a study of men from Canada and several other countries, 19% of those with urinary tract infections reported pain on ejaculation

Innovative Canadian Research

CONCERNS ABOUT PROSTATE SURGERY

For men considering prostate surgery, a major fear is that the surgery will lead to erectile dysfunction. An interview survey in Toronto of men who experienced sexual dysfunction problems after prostate surgery concluded that the "preservation of manhood" was a central concern (Fergus et al., 2002). The researchers uncovered five major issues related to this concern:

1. choosing the type of surgery that would increase the chance of survival while minimizing the extent of sexual dysfunction
2. the belief that sexual dysfunction meant the loss of one's manhood
3. the fear that sexual dysfunction would lead to loss of status, especially among peers
4. feeling pressure to still focus on a high level of giving and receiving sexual pleasure despite loss of erectile functioning
5. working to overcome the sexual loss, typically by acknowledging the value of being alive as being more important than sexual pleasure. Also, some men refocused their sexual expression away from penile-vaginal intercourse to other kinds of sexual activities and to having a more intimate emotional relationship with their partner.

(Nickel et al., 2005). Men with more severe symptoms of urinary infection were the most likely to experience pain at ejaculation. Also, 72% of those who had painful ejaculation experienced problems with erectile dysfunction.

Prostatitis is usually treated with antibiotics. Although Aspirin and ibuprofen may relieve the pain, men with these symptoms should consult a physician. Painful ejaculation may discourage masturbation or coitus, which is ironic, because regular flushing of the prostate through ejaculation may be helpful in the treatment of prostatitis.

Researchers at Queen's University (Smith et al., 2007) studied the effect of chronic prostatitis on male patients and their partners. These couples experienced more sexual difficulties and psychological depression than did the control couples. The sexual functioning of the male significantly affected the sexual functioning of his partner. Yet the prostatitis did not seem to affect the overall intimate relationships of the couples.

Male Sexual Functions

The male sexual functions of erection and ejaculation provide the means for sperm to travel from the male's reproductive tract to the female's. There the sperm cell and ovum unite to conceive a new human being. Of course, the natural endowment of reproduction with sensations of pleasure helps ensure that it will take place with or without knowledge of these biological facts.

Erection

Erection is caused by the engorgement of the penis with blood, such that the penis grows in size and stiffens. The erect penis is an efficient conduit, or funnel, for depositing sperm deep within the vagina.

In mechanical terms, erection is a hydraulic event. The spongy, cavernous masses of the penis are equipped to hold blood. Filling them with blood causes them to enlarge, much as a sponge swells when it absorbs water. This simple description belies the fact that erection is a remarkable feat of biological engineering that involves the cooperation of the vascular (blood) system and the nervous system.

In a few moments—as quickly as 10 or 15 seconds—the penis can double in length, become firm, and shift from a funnel for passing urine to one that expels semen. Moreover, the bladder is closed off when the male becomes sexually aroused so that semen and urine will not mix.

The corpora cavernosa are surrounded by a tough, fibrous covering. Just as the rubber of a balloon resists the pressure of pumped-in air, this covering resists expansion, stiffening the penis. The corpus spongiosum, which contains the urethra, also engorges with blood during erection. It does not become hard, however, because it lacks the fibrous casing. The penile glans, which is formed by the crowning of the spongiosum at the tip of the penis, turns a dark purplish hue as it becomes engorged, but it too does not stiffen.

Erection is reversed when more blood flows out of erectile tissue than flows in, restoring the prearousal circulatory balance and shrinking the spongy masses. Loss of erection occurs when sexual stimulation ceases, or when the body returns to a (sexual) resting state after orgasm. Loss of erection can also occur in response to anxiety or perceived threats (Janssen, 2006; Janssen et al., 2006). Such loss can be abrupt, as when a man in the "throes of passion" suddenly hears a noise suggestive of an intruder. A man who fears that he will be unable to perform successfully may experience **performance anxiety**, which can prevent him from obtaining or maintaining an erection.

Men have nocturnal erections every 90 minutes or so as they sleep. They generally occur during rapid eye movement (REM) sleep. REM sleep is associated with dreaming. It is so named because the sleeper's eyes dart about rapidly under the closed eyelids during this stage.

Erection The enlargement and stiffening of the penis as a consequence of its engorgement with blood.

Performance anxiety Feelings of dread and foreboding experienced in connection with sexual activity (or any other activity that might be judged by another person).

Sacrum The thick, triangular bone located near the bottom of the spinal column.

Spinal Reflexes and Sexual Response

Men may become sexually aroused by a range of stimuli, including tactile stimulation provided by their partners, visual stimulation (as from scanning photos of nudes on the internet), or sexual fantasies. Regardless of the source of stimulation, the man's sexual responses—erection and ejaculation—occur by reflex.

Sexual reflexes are automatic, unlearned responses to sexual stimulation. Examples in women include vaginal lubrication and orgasm. We need not "try" to become aroused. We need only expose ourselves to sexual stimulation and allow reflexes to do the job for us.

Men cannot will themselves to have erections. People do not control sexual reflexes voluntarily, as they might lift an arm, but they can set the stage for them to occur by seeking sexual stimulation. Efforts to control sexual responses consciously by "force of will" can backfire and make it more difficult to become aroused (for example, to attain erection or vaginal lubrication).

The reflexes governing erection and ejaculation are controlled in the spinal cord. They are thus called spinal reflexes. Erectile responses to direct stimulation such as touching or licking involve a simple spinal reflex that does not require the direct participation of the brain (Figure 3.16). Erections can also be initiated by the brain, as when a man has sexual fantasies or catches a glimpse of an attractive person. In such cases, stimulation from the brain travels to the spinal cord, where the erectile reflex is triggered.

Tactile stimulation (touching) of the penis or nearby areas (lower abdomen, scrotum, inner thighs) causes sensory neurons to transmit nerve messages (signals) to an erection centre in the lower back, in an area of the spinal cord called the **sacrum**. The sacral erection centre controls reflexive erections, that is, erections occurring in response to direct stimulation of the penis and nearby areas. When direct penile stimulation occurs, messages in the form of nerve impulses are received by this erection centre, which in turn sends impulses to the genitalia via nerves that serve the penis. These impulses cause arteries carrying blood to the corpora cavernosa and corpus spongiosum to dilate, so that more blood flows into them, causing erection.

The sacral erection centre makes it possible for men whose spinal cords have been injured or severed above the centre to achieve erections (and ejaculate) in response to direct tactile stimulation of the penis. Erection occurs even though their injuries prevent nerve signals from reaching their brains. Because of the lack of communication between the genital organs and the brain, there are no sensations,

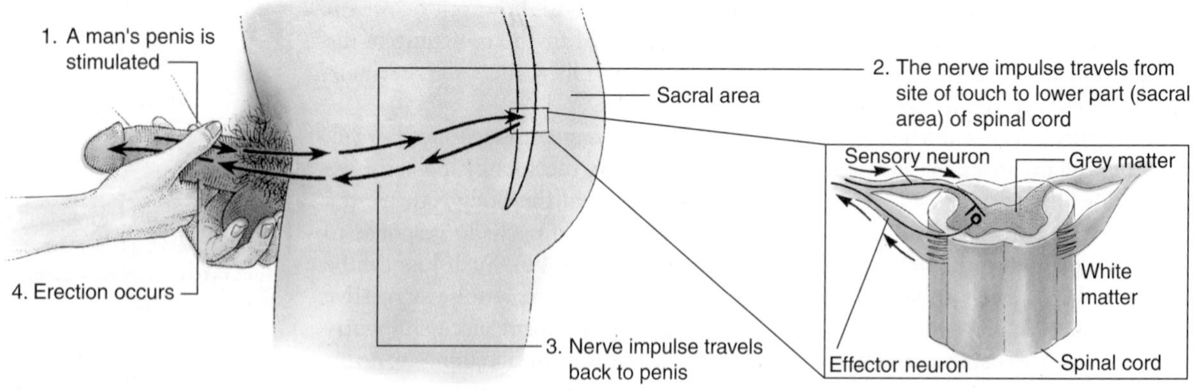

Figure 3.16 Reflexes.

Reflexes need not involve the brain, although messages to the brain may make us aware when reflexes are occurring. Reflexes are the product of "local government" in the spine.

but many spinal cord–injured men report that sex remains psychologically pleasurable, because they can observe the responses of their partners.

THE ROLE OF THE BRAIN If direct penile stimulation triggers erection at the spinal level, what is the role of the brain? Although it may seem that the penis sometimes has "a mind of its own," the brain plays an important role in regulating sexual responses.

Tactile (touch) stimulation of the penis may trigger erection through the spinal cord, but sexual sensations are then normally relayed to the brain, which generally results in pleasure and perhaps in a decision to focus on erotic stimulation. The sight of one's partner, erotic fantasies, memories, and so forth can result in messages being sent by the brain through the spinal cord to the arteries servicing the penis, maintaining or strengthening the erection.

When the brain originates messages that trigger the erectile reflex, it transmits nerve impulses to a second and higher erection centre located in the upper back in the lumbar region of the spinal cord. This higher spinal erection centre serves as a "switchboard" between the brain and the penis, allowing perceptual, cognitive, and emotional responses to make their contributions. When the nerve pathways between the brain and the upper spinal cord are blocked or severed, men cannot achieve erections in response to mental stimulation alone.

The brain can also stifle sexual response. A man who is highly anxious about his sexual abilities may be unable to achieve an erection even with intense penile stimulation. Or a man who believes that sexual pleasure is sinful or dirty may be filled with anxiety and guilt, and may be unable to achieve erection with a partner.

In some males, especially adolescents, the erectile reflex is so easily tripped that incidental rubbing of the genitals against his own undergarments, the sight of an attractive passerby, or a fleeting sexual fantasy produces erection. Spontaneous erections may occur under embarrassing circumstances, such as before classes change in middle or high school, or on a beach. In an effort to distract himself from erotic fantasies and to allow an erection to subside, many a male adolescent desperately renews his interest in his algebra or language textbook in class before the bell rings. (A well-placed towel may serve in a pinch on the beach.)

As men mature, they need more penile stimulation to achieve full erection. Partners of men in their thirties and forties should not feel that their attractiveness has waned if their lovers no longer have instant "no-hands" erections when they disrobe. It takes men longer to obtain erection as they age, and direct stimulation becomes more important.

THE ROLE OF THE AUTONOMIC NERVOUS SYSTEM Although stimulation that brings about an erection can originate in the brain, this does not mean that erection is a voluntary response, like raising your arm. Whatever the original or dominant source of stimulation—direct penile stimulation or sexual fantasy—erection remains an unlearned, automatic reflex.

Automatic responses, such as erection, involve the division of the nervous system called the **autonomic nervous system** (ANS). *Autonomic* means "automatic." The ANS controls automatic bodily processes such as heartbeat, pupil dilation, respiration, and digestion. In contrast, voluntary movement (such as raising an arm) is under the control of the *somatic* division of the nervous system.

The ANS has two branches, the **sympathetic** and the **parasympathetic**. These branches have largely opposing effects; when they are activated at the same time, their effects become balanced out to some degree. In general, the sympathetic branch is in command during processes that involve a release of bodily energy from stored reserves, such as during running, performing some other athletic task, or being gripped by fear or anxiety. The sympathetic branch also governs the general mobilization of the body, such as by increasing the heart rate and respiration rate in response to threat.

Autonomic nervous system The division of the nervous system that regulates automatic bodily processes, such as heartbeat, pupil dilation, respiration, and digestion. Abbreviated *ANS*.

Sympathetic The branch of the ANS most active during emotional responses that draw on the body's reserves of energy, such as fear and anxiety. The sympathetic ANS largely controls ejaculation.

Parasympathetic The branch of the ANS most active during processes that restore the body's reserves of energy, such as digestion. The parasympathetic ANS largely controls erection.

Premature ejaculation A sexual dysfunction in which the male persistently ejaculates too early to afford the couple adequate sexual gratification. (Yes, what is on time in one relationship may be considered premature—or late—in another.)

Peyronie's disease An abnormal condition characterized by an excessive curvature of the penis that can make erections painful.

Orgasm The climax of sexual excitement.

Paraplegic A person with sensory and motor paralysis of the lower half of the body.

The parasympathetic branch is most active during processes that restore reserves of energy, such as digestion. When we experience fear or anxiety, the sympathetic branch of the ANS quickens the heart rate. When we relax, the parasympathetic branch curbs the heart rate. The parasympathetic branch activates digestive processes, but the sympathetic branch inhibits digestive activity. Because the sympathetic branch is in command when we feel fear or anxiety, such stimuli can inhibit the activity of the parasympathetic system, thereby slowing down the digestive process and possibly causing indigestion.

The divisions of the autonomic nervous system play different roles in sexual arousal and response. The nerves that cause penile arteries to dilate during erection belong to the parasympathetic branch of the autonomic nervous system. It is thus the parasympathetic system that largely governs erection. The nerves governing ejaculation belong to the sympathetic branch, however. One implication of this division of neural responsibility is that intense fear or anxiety, which involves sympathetic nervous system activity, may inhibit erection by counteracting the activity of the parasympathetic nervous system. Because sympathetic arousal is involved in triggering the ejaculatory reflex, anxiety or fear may also accelerate ejaculation, causing **premature ejaculation**. Intense emotions such as fear and anxiety can thus lead to problems in achieving or maintaining erection, as well as causing hasty ejaculation.

Because erections seem spontaneous at times, and because they often occur when the man would rather not have them, it may seem to men that the penis has a mind of its own. Despite this common folk belief, however, the penis possesses no guiding intelligence.

ERECTILE ABNORMALITIES Some men find that their erect penises are slightly curved or bent. Some degree of curvature is perfectly normal, but men with **Peyronie's disease** have excessive curvature that can make erections painful or make it difficult to enjoy coitus. The condition is caused by a buildup of fibrous tissue in the penile shaft. Although some cases of Peyronie's disease appear to clear up on their own, most require medical attention.

Some men experience erections that persist for hours or days. This condition is called *priapism*, after Priapus of Greek myth, the son of Dionysus and Aphrodite who personified male procreative power. Priapism is often caused by leukemia, sickle-cell anemia, or diseases of the spinal cord, although in some cases the cause remains unknown. Priapism occurs when the mechanisms that drain the blood that makes the penis erect are damaged and so cannot return the blood to the circulatory system. Priapism may become a medical emergency, because erection prolonged beyond six hours can starve penile tissues of oxygen, leading to tissue deterioration. Medical intervention in the form of drugs or surgery may be required to reverse the condition and allow blood to drain from the penis.

Ejaculation

Ejaculation, like erection, is a spinal reflex. It is triggered when sexual stimulation reaches a critical point or threshold. Ejaculation generally occurs together with **orgasm**, the sudden muscle contractions that occur at the peak of sexual excitement and result in abrupt release of the sexual tension that had built up during sexual arousal. Orgasm is accompanied by subjective sensations that are generally intensely pleasurable. Ejaculation, however, is simply the expulsion of semen from the tip of the penis. Orgasm and ejaculation are *not* synonymous, nor do they always occur simultaneously. For example, **paraplegics** can ejaculate if the area of the lower spinal cord that controls ejaculation is intact. They do not experience the subjective aspects of orgasm, however, because the sensations of orgasm do not reach the brain.

Conversely, prepubertal boys may experience orgasms even though they emit no ejaculate. Orgasms without ejaculate are termed "dry orgasms." Boys do not begin to produce seminal fluid (and sperm) until puberty. Mature men, too, can experience dry orgasms. They can take the form of "little orgasms" preceding a larger orgasm, or they can follow "wet orgasms" when sexual stimulation is continued but seminal fluids have not been replenished.

Ejaculation occurs in two stages. The first stage, often called the **emission stage**, involves contractions of the prostate, the seminal vesicles, and the upper part of the vas deferens (the **ampulla**). The force of these contractions propels seminal fluid into the prostatic part of the urethral tract—a small tube called the **urethral bulb**—which balloons out as muscles close at either end, trapping the semen. It is at this point that the man perceives that orgasm is inevitable. Masters and Johnson (1966) called this feeling a sense of "ejaculatory inevitability." Men might colloquially describe the feeling as being about to "come." The man feels that a point of no return has been passed and that nothing can prevent ejaculation.

The second stage, which is often referred to as the **expulsion stage**, involves the propulsion of the seminal fluid through the urethra and out of the urethral opening at the tip of the penis. In this stage, muscles at the base of the penis and elsewhere contract rhythmically, forcefully expelling semen. The second stage is generally accompanied by the highly pleasurable sensations of orgasm.

In ejaculation, the seminal fluid is released from the urethral bulb and expelled by forceful contractions of the pelvic muscles that surround the urethral channel and the crura of the penis. During ejaculation, the bladder is closed off so that urine cannot escape. The first few contractions are most intense and occur at 0.8-second intervals. Subsequent contractions lessen in intensity, and the interval between them gradually increases. Seminal fluid is expelled in spurts during the first few contractions. The contractions are so powerful that seminal fluid may be propelled as far as 30–60 cm (12–24 in.), according to observations made by Masters and Johnson. Some men, however, report that semen travels but a few centimetres or just oozes from the penile opening. The force of the expulsion varies with the condition of the man's prostate, his general health, and his age. There is some correspondence between the force of the expulsion and the pleasure of orgasm. That is, more intense orgasms, psychologically speaking, often accompany more forceful ejaculations.

The amount of time the male is sexually aroused prior to ejaculation influences the amount of ejaculate that is produced. A longer time period of arousal usually results in a great volume of ejaculate and greater sperm concentration (Pound et al., 2002).

Although ejaculation occurs by reflex, a man can delay ejaculation by maintaining the level of sexual stimulation below the critical threshold, or "point of no return." Men who suffer from premature ejaculation have been successfully treated in programs that train them to learn to recognize their "point of no return" and maintain sexual stimulation below it.

RETROGRADE EJACULATION Some men experience **retrograde ejaculation**, in which the ejaculate empties into the bladder rather than being expelled from the body. During normal ejaculation an external sphincter opens, allowing seminal fluid to pass out of the body. Another sphincter, this one internal, closes off the opening to the bladder, preventing the seminal fluid from backing up into the bladder. In retrograde ejaculation, the actions of these sphincters are reversed. The external sphincter remains closed, preventing expulsion of the seminal fluid, while the internal sphincter opens, allowing the ejaculate to empty into the bladder. The result is a dry orgasm. No ejaculate is apparent because semen has backed up into the bladder. Retrograde ejaculation may be caused by prostate surgery (much less so now than in former years), by drugs such as tranquillizers, by certain illnesses, and by accidents. Retrograde ejaculation is usually harmless in itself, because the seminal fluid is later discharged with urine. Infertility can result, however, and there may be some changes in the sensations associated with orgasm. Persistent dry orgasms should be medically evaluated; their underlying cause may be a threat to health.

Emission stage The first phase of ejaculation, which involves contractions of the prostate gland, the seminal vesicles, and the upper part of the vas deferens.

Ampulla A sac or dilated part of a tube or canal.

Urethral bulb The small tube that makes up the prostatic part of the urethral tract and that balloons out as muscles close at either end, trapping semen prior to ejaculation.

Expulsion stage The second stage of ejaculation, during which muscles at the base of the penis and elsewhere contract rhythmically, forcefully expelling semen and generally providing pleasurable sensations.

Retrograde ejaculation Ejaculation in which the ejaculate empties into the bladder.

Summing Up

Female Anatomy and Physiology

The female external sexual structures are collectively known as the vulva. They consist of the mons veneris, the labia majora and minora, the clitoris, the vestibule, and the vaginal opening.

The structures that underlie the external female sex organs include the vestibular bulbs, Bartholin's glands, the sphincters, the clitoral crura, and the pubococcygeus (P-C) muscle.

The internal female sex organs—or female reproductive system—include the innermost parts of the vagina, the cervix, the uterus, the ovaries, and the fallopian tubes.

The G spot—an allegedly distinct area of the vagina within the anterior wall—may have special erotic significance. Some researchers suggest that prolonged stimulation of this spot produces an orgasm that is characterized by intense pleasure and, in some women, by a type of ejaculation. The nature of this ejaculate remains in doubt.

Regular pelvic examinations are essential for early detection of problems involving the reproductive tract.

In some cultures the breasts are viewed merely as biological instruments for feeding infants. In our culture, however, they have taken on erotic significance.

Breast cancer is the second leading cancer killer in women, after lung cancer. Women with breast cancer will have lumps in the breast, but most lumps in the breasts are benign.

Menstruation is the cyclical bleeding that stems from the shedding of the endometrium when a reproductive cycle has not led to the fertilization of an ovum. The menstrual cycle is regulated by estrogen and progesterone.

The menstrual cycle involves finely tuned relationships among the hypothalamus, the pituitary gland, and the ovaries and uterus.

The menstrual cycle has four stages or phases: the proliferative, ovulatory, secretory, and menstrual phases.

Couples are less likely to initiate sexual activity during menstruation than during any other phase of the woman's cycle.

Menopause, the cessation of menstruation, most commonly occurs between the ages of 46 and 50. Estrogen deficiency in menopause may give rise to night sweats, hot flashes, hot flushes, cold sweats, dry skin, loss of breast tissue, and decreased vaginal lubrication. For most women, menopausal problems are mild.

Most women experience some discomfort prior to or during menstruation. Dysmenorrhea is the most common menstrual problem, and pelvic cramps are the most common symptom.

Women with persistent menstrual problems may benefit from a number of active coping strategies for handling menstrual distress.

Male Anatomy and Physiology

The male external sex organs include the penis and the scrotum.

Semen and urine pass out of the penis through the urethral opening. The penis contains cylinders that fill with blood and stiffen during sexual arousal. Circumcision—the surgical removal of the prepuce—has been carried out for religious and hygienic reasons.

The scrotum is the pouch of loose skin that contains the testes. Each testicle is held in place by a spermatic cord, which contains the vas deferens and the cremaster muscle.

The male internal sex organs consist of the testes, a system of tubes and ducts that conduct sperm, and organs that nourish and activate sperm.

The testes secrete male sex hormones (androgens) and produce germ cells (sperm).

The hypothalamus, pituitary gland, and testes keep blood testosterone at a more or less constant level through a hormonal negative-feedback loop.

Sperm are produced by seminiferous tubules and are stored and mature in the epididymis.

Each epididymis empties into a vas deferens that conducts sperm over the bladder.

The seminal vesicles are glands that open into the ejaculatory ducts, where the fluids they secrete combine with and nourish sperm.

The prostate gland secretes fluid that accounts for the texture and odour characteristic of semen.

During sexual arousal, the Cowper's glands secrete a drop or so of clear, slippery fluid that appears at the urethral opening.

Sperm and the fluids contributed by the seminal vesicles, the prostate gland, and the Cowper's glands make up semen, the whitish fluid that is expelled through the tip of the penis during ejaculation.

Men, like women, are subject to bladder and urethral inflammations, which are generally referred to as urethritis.

Cancer of the testes is the most common form of solid-tumour cancer to strike young men between the ages of 20 and 34.

The prostate gland generally becomes enlarged in men past the age of 50. Prostate cancer involves the growth of malignant prostate tumours that can metastasize to bones and lymph nodes. The chief symptoms of prostatitis are painful ejaculation and an ache or pain between the scrotum and anal opening.

Erection is the process by which the penis becomes engorged with blood, increases in size, and stiffens.

Erection and ejaculation occur by reflex. Although erection is a reflex, penile sensations are relayed to the brain, where they generally result in pleasure. Erection and ejaculation also involve the autonomic nervous system (ANS). The parasympathetic branch of the ANS largely governs erection, whereas the sympathetic branch largely controls ejaculation.

Ejaculation, like erection, is a reflex. It is triggered when sexual stimulation reaches a critical threshold. Ejaculation usually (though not always) occurs with orgasm, but the terms are not synonymous.

In retrograde ejaculation, the ejaculate empties into the bladder rather than being expelled from the body.

Test Yourself

Multiple-Choice Questions

1. **The female external sex organs are called the**
   a. uterus
   b. ovaries
   c. vulva
   d. cervix

2. **The only organ whose sole function is to provide sexual pleasure is the ______________.**
   a. penis
   b. clitoris
   c. vagina
   d. mons

3. **Which of the following is not one of the three layers of the uterus?**
   a. the perimetrium
   b. the exometrium
   c. the endometrium
   d. the myometrium

4. **The two pituitary hormones involved in the regulation of the menstrual cycle are**
   a. GnRH and estrogen
   b. oxytocin and prolactin
   c. FSH and LH
   d. LH and testosterone

5. **During menopause, lower levels of ______________ may cause "hot flashes" and other physical symptoms.**
   a. prolactin
   b. oxytocin
   c. androgen
   d. estrogen

6. **Many Canadian men equate ______________ with masculinity.**
   a. penis size
   b. muscle mass
   c. hair length
   d. testicle size

7. **Sperm cells are carried out of the testicle through the**
   a. seminiferous tubules
   b. dartos muscle
   c. vas deferens
   d. cremasteric tube

8. **Surgical removal of the foreskin is known as**
   a. excision
   b. infibulation
   c. incision
   d. circumcision

9. **The purpose of testicular self-examination is to detect ______________ in its early stages.**
   a. AIDS
   b. infertility
   c. cancer
   d. erectile dysfunction

10. **______________ is the most common form of cancer among Canadian men.**
    a. prostate cancer
    b. testicular cancer
    c. penile cancer
    d. inguinal cancer

Answers to the Test Yourself questions in each chapter are found on page 509.

Critical Thinking Questions

1. Many people grow up with messages about what menstruating women should or should not do (such as: don't take a shower, don't go swimming, don't get a perm, don't touch babies). What negative messages did you hear as a child or adolescent? From whom did you hear these messages? Were any of them specific to your particular culture or ethnic group?
2. If you are a woman, did growing up with negative messages (if any) about menstruation affect how you feel about your body and its functions? If you are a man, do these messages affect how you might feel about a partner or potential partner's body?
3. Have you ever felt uncomfortable or embarrassed to have a partner see your body? Which parts of it do you not like? Why do you think you feel this way?
4. If you are a man, how does reading a letter to a men's magazine that starts "I may be only 8 in. long, but . . . ." make you feel about your own penis? If you are a woman, would reading such a statement make you feel differently about your partner's penis?
5. Would you have a male child circumcised? Why or why not?

Visit MyPsychKit at www.mypsychkit.com, where you can do quizzes and link to additional resources on topics discussed in this text.

CHAPTER FOUR

Sexual Arousal and Response

In this chapter we look at factors that contribute to sexual arousal and the processes related to sexual response. Because our experience of the world is initiated by our senses, we begin the chapter by focusing on the role of the senses in sexual arousal.

Making Sense of Sex: The Role of the Senses in Sexual Arousal

We come to apprehend the world around us through our senses—vision, hearing, smell, taste, and the skin senses, which include that all-important sense of touch. Each of the senses plays a role in our sexual experience, but some senses play larger roles than others.

Vision: The Better to See You With

Visual cues can be sexual turn-ons. In measuring the physiological response of males to slides of partially clothed women, researchers at Queen's University found that penile response was greater in reaction to the slides of the more attractive women (Lalumiere & Quinsey, 1998).

We may be turned on by the sight of a lover in the nude, disrobing, or dressed in evening wear. Lingerie companies hope to convince customers that they will enhance their sex appeal by wearing strategically concealing and revealing nightwear. In Toronto, a store selling erotic products has capitalized on the visual appeal of lingerie by having female models wearing lingerie stand in the store window. This visual display attracted so much attention that it caused "traffic and pedestrian chaos" (Menon, 2002, p. B5). (One cyclist was so distracted by the sight that he nearly crashed into a mailbox.) Some couples find it arousing to observe themselves making love in an overhead mirror or on videotape. Some people find sexually explicit movies arousing. Others are bored or offended by them. Though both genders can be sexually aroused by visual erotica, men are more interested in it.

Sex as a Traffic Stopper. *A lingerie model at the Miss Behav'N adult store on Queen Street West in Toronto checks out passersby—and vice versa. Scantily clad models stop traffic outside the store, which caters to female customers. Clearly, visual cues can be sexual turn-ons!*

Smell: Does the Nose Know Best?

Aphrodisiac Any drug or other agent that is sexually arousing or increases sexual desire.

Pheromones Chemical substances that are secreted externally by certain animals and that convey information to, or produce specific responses in, other members of the same species.

Although the sense of smell plays a lesser role in governing sexual arousal in humans than in lower mammals, odours can be sexual turn-ons or turn-offs. Perfume companies, for example, bottle fragrances purported to be sexually arousing. Companies have also successfully persuaded males that using a specific type of deodorant body spray would make them irresistible to women. Unilever captured much of the male market with its "Axe" body spray. Its advertisements unabashedly tell men that using the product will make them successful in attracting women sexually. Gillette has developed "Tag," a competing product.

Most Westerners prefer their lovers to be clean and fresh smelling. People in our society learn to remove or mask odours by using soaps, deodorants, and perfumes or colognes. Inclinations to find underarm or genital odours offensive may reflect cultural conditioning rather than biological predispositions. In some societies, genital secretions are considered **aphrodisiacs**.

PHEROMONES For centuries people have searched for a love potion—a magical formula that could make people fall in love or be strongly attracted to one another. Some scientists suggest that such potions may already exist in the form of chemical secretions known as **pheromones**. Pheromones are odourless chemicals that in many animals are detected through a "sixth sense"—the *vomeronasal organ (VNO)*. People possess VNOs in the mucous lining of the nose (Rodriguez et al., 2000). Infants apparently use pheromones to recognize their mothers, and adults might respond to them in seeking a mate (Martins et al., 2005). Male rodents, such as mice, are extremely sensitive to several kinds of pheromones (Leinders–Zufall et al., 2000).

Only a few years ago, most researchers did not believe that pheromones played a role in human behaviour, but today the issue has attracted new interest. In a typical study, Winnifred Cutler and her colleagues (1998) had heterosexual men wear a suspected male pheromone, and a control group wore a placebo. The men using the pheromone increased their frequency of sexual intercourse with their female partners but did not increase the frequency of masturbation. The researchers concluded that the substance increased the sexual attractiveness of the men to their partners, although they did not claim that it directly stimulated sexual behaviour.

In a double-blind experiment, 36 university women were randomly assigned to wear a perfume laced with a suspected pheromone extracted from their underarm secretions or a placebo (McCoy & Pitino, 2002). The women recorded their sexual behaviours over three menstrual cycles (12 weeks). Three-quarters (74%) of the women who used the suspected pheromone showed significant increases in their frequency of sexual intercourse, sleeping next to a partner, formal dates, and kissing, petting, and other displays of affection compared with one-quarter (23%) of the users of the placebo. Perhaps the suspected pheromone increased the women's attractiveness to men.

How Much Sexual Communication Is Occurring Below the Level of Conscious Awareness?
Research suggests that underarm secretions may make people more sexually attractive, even when others are unaware of sensing them. Are they drawn to each other's personal traits or to their pheromones?

MENSTRUAL SYNCHRONY Research by several investigators suggests that exposure to other women's sweat can modify a woman's menstrual cycle. In one study, women exposed to underarm secretions from other women, which contained steroids that may function as pheromones, showed converging shifts in their menstrual cycles (Bartoshuk & Beauchamp, 1994; Preti et al., 1986). Similar synchronization of menstrual cycles has been observed among women who share dormitory rooms. In another study, 80% of the women who dabbed their upper lips with an extract of perspiration from other women began to menstruate in sync with the

Erogenous zones Parts of the body that are especially sensitive to tactile sexual stimulation. (*Erogenous* is derived from roots that mean "giving birth to erotic sensations.")

Primary erogenous zones Erogenous zones that are particularly sensitive because they are richly endowed with nerve endings.

Secondary erogenous zones Parts of the body that become erotically sensitized through experience.

cycles of the donors after about three menstrual cycles (Cutler, 1999). A control group, whose members dabbed their lips with alcohol, showed no changes in their menstrual cycles.

ATTRACTION TO—OR DISLIKE OF—BODY ODOURS OF HETEROSEXUAL MALES AND FEMALES VERSUS GAY MALES AND LESBIANS There is reason to believe that body odours play a role in the selection of sex partners (Preti et al., 2003; Wyatt, 2003). Yolanda Martins, George Preti, Charles Wysocki, and their colleagues (2005) hypothesized that preferences for axillary (underarm) odours would be related to people's sexual orientation: heterosexual male or female, and gay male or lesbian. They collected samples of axillary odours from 24 volunteers—six exclusively male heterosexual and six exclusively female heterosexual, and six exclusively gay male and six exclusively lesbian, according to the Kinsey heterosexuality–homosexuality scale. The researchers had a number of interesting findings, as follows:

- Heterosexual males and females, and lesbians, preferred axillary odours taken from heterosexual males over those taken from gay males.
- Gay males preferred axillary odours taken from other gay males.
- Heterosexual males and females and lesbians aged 25 years and older preferred axillary odours taken from lesbians to those from gay males.
- When axillary odours of heterosexual females were compared with those of lesbians, all groups except for heterosexual males preferred the odours from heterosexual females.
- Heterosexual males preferred the odour from lesbians over the odour taken from gay male donors.

The researchers suggest that the data show that gay males and lesbians may produce axillary odours that can be distinguished from those of heterosexuals. It would also appear that gay males may perceive these typical odorants differently from the way in which heterosexual males do. We can note that, at least in the few studies that have investigated the relationships between body odour and sexual orientation, gay males are most likely to be attracted to the body odours of other gay males, and that heterosexual males are least likely to prefer the body odours of gay males.

What Does the Nose Know About Sexual Orientation? *Research by Yolanda Martins, George Preti, Charles Wysocki, and their colleagues (2005) suggests that gay males prefer the body odours of other gay males to those of heterosexuals and lesbians. Heterosexual males, however, seem least likely to prefer the body odours of gay males as compared to heterosexual males and to females, both heterosexual and lesbian.*

The Skin Senses: Sex as a Touching Experience

The sense of touch has the most direct effects on sexual arousal and response. Any region of that sensitive layer we refer to as skin can become eroticized. The touch of your lover's hand upon your cheek, or your lover's gentle massage of your shoulders or back, can be sexually stimulating.

EROGENOUS ZONES **Erogenous zones** are parts of the body that are especially sensitive to tactile sexual stimulation—to strokes and other caresses. **Primary erogenous zones** are erotically sensitive because they are richly endowed with nerve endings. **Secondary erogenous zones** are parts of the body that become erotically sensitized through experience.

Primary erogenous zones include the genitals; the inner thighs, perineum, buttocks, and anus; the breasts (especially the nipples); the ears (particularly the earlobes); the mouth, lips,

A Touching Experience.
The sense of touch is intimately connected with sexual experience. The touch of a lover's hand on the cheek, or gentle massage, can be sexually stimulating. Certain parts of the body—called erogenous zones—have special sexual significance because of their response to erotic stimulation.

and tongue; the neck; the navel; and, yes, the armpits. Preferences vary somewhat from person to person, reflecting possible biological, attitudinal, and experiential differences. Areas that are exquisitely sensitive for some people may produce virtually no reaction, or even discomfort, in others. Many women, for example, report little sensation when their breasts are stroked or kissed. Many men are uncomfortable when their nipples are caressed. On the other hand (or foot), many people find the areas between their toes sensitive to erotic stimulation and enjoy keeping a toehold on their partners during coitus.

Secondary erogenous zones become eroticized through association with sexual stimulation. For example, a woman might become sexually aroused when her lover gently caresses her shoulders, because such caresses have been incorporated as a regular feature of the couple's lovemaking.

Taste: On Savoury Sex

Some people are sexually aroused by the taste of genital secretions, such as vaginal secretions or seminal fluid. We do not know, however, whether these secretions are laced with chemicals that have biologically arousing effects or whether arousal reflects the meaning that these secretions have to the individual. That is, we may learn to become aroused by, or to seek out, flavours or odours that have been associated with sexual pleasure. (Others are turned off by the taste or odour of these secretions.)

Hearing: The Better to Hear You With

The sense of hearing also provides an important medium for sexual arousal and response. Like visual and olfactory cues, sounds can be turn-ons or turn-offs. The sounds of one's lover—be they whispers, moans of pleasure, or animated sounds that may attend orgasm—may be arousing during the heat of passion. For some people, key words or vocal intonations may become as arousing as direct stimulation of an erogenous zone. Many people are aroused when their lovers "talk dirty." Spoken vulgarities spur their sexual arousal. Others find vulgar language offensive.

Music itself can contribute to sexual arousal. Music can relax us and put us "in the mood" or evoke powerful associations ("They're playing our song!"). Many couples find background music "atmospheric"—a vital accoutrement of lovemaking.

Aphrodisiacs

An aphrodisiac is a substance that arouses or increases one's capacity for sexual pleasure or response. However, the belief that a substance has sexually stimulating effects may itself inspire sexual excitement. A person who tries a supposed aphrodisiac and feels sexually aroused may well attribute the turn-on to the effects of that substance, even if it had no direct effect on sex drive.

Foods that in some way resemble male genitals have now and then been considered aphrodisiacs. These include oysters, clams, bulls' testicles ("prairie oysters"), tomatoes, and "phallic" items such as celery stalks, bananas, and even ground-up reindeer antlers, elephant tusks, and rhinoceros horns (which is one derivation of the slang term *horny*). Sadly, myths about the sexually arousing properties of substances extracted from rhinoceroses and elephants are contributing to the rapidly diminishing numbers of these animals.

Drugs and psychoactive substances may have certain effects on sexual arousal and response. The drug arginine, an amino acid extracted from the African yohimbe tree, does stimulate blood flow to the genitals. However, its effects are limited and unreliable (Downs & Nazario, 2003).

Amyl nitrate (in the form of "snappers" or "poppers") has been used, mostly by gay men but also by some heterosexuals, in the belief that it heightens sensations of arousal and orgasm. Poppers dilate blood vessels in the brain and genitals, producing sensations of warmth in the pelvis and possibly facilitating erection and prolonging orgasm. Amyl nitrate does have some legitimate medical uses, such as helping reduce heart pain (angina) among cardiac patients. It is inhaled from ampoules that "pop" open for rapid use when heart pain occurs. However, poppers can cause dizziness, fainting, and migraine-type headaches. They should be taken only under a doctor's care for a legitimate medical need, not to intensify sexual sensations.

The drug Viagra was originally developed as a treatment for angina (heart pain) because it was thought that it would increase the blood flow to the heart. It does so, modestly. However, it is more effective at dilating blood vessels in the genital organs, thereby facilitating vasocongestion and erection in the male. Viagra and similar drugs—Levitra and Cialis—are a treatment for erectile dysfunction (also termed impotence). Is Viagra also an aphrodisiac? It is a matter of definition. Although Viagra facilitates erection, it still takes a sexual turn-on for erection to occur. If an aphrodisiac must be directly sexually arousing, Viagra is not an aphrodisiac.

But certain drugs do appear to have aphrodisiac effects, apparently because they act on the brain mechanisms controlling the sex drive. For example, drugs that affect brain receptors for the neurotransmitter dopamine, such as the antidepressant drug bupropion (trade name: Wellbutrin) and the drug L-dopa, used in the treatment of Parkinson's disease, can increase the sex drive (Modell et al., 2000).

The most potent chemical "aphrodisiac" may be a naturally occurring substance in the body—the hormone testosterone. It is the basic fuel of sexual desire in both males and females (Apperloo et al., 2003; Davis, 2000).

The safest and perhaps the most effective method for increasing the sex drive may be not a drug or substance, but exercise. Regular exercise not only enhances general health, but also boosts energy and increases the sex drive in both genders. Cindy Meston and Boris Gorzalka (1995) of the University of British Columbia conducted an experiment to see if exercise could affect sexual arousal in women. In one of the sessions, women engaged in 20 minutes of intense exercise prior to viewing an explicit film. While watching the film, the women who had exercised showed a greater increase in measures of physiological sexual arousal than women who had not exercised. However, there was no significant difference in perception of sexual arousal.

Because routine can diminish desire, perhaps the most potent aphrodisiac of all is novelty. In a study of men's physiological responses to slides of a partially nude female, researchers at Queen's University found that repeated exposure resulted in diminishing penile response (Lalumiere & Quinsey, 1998).

Partners can invent new ways of sexually discovering one another. They can make love in novel places, experiment with different techniques, wear provocative clothing, share or enact fantasies, or whatever their imaginations inspire.

Anaphrodisiacs

Some substances, such as potassium nitrate (saltpeter), have been considered inhibitors of sexual response—**anaphrodisiacs**. Saltpeter, however, does not directly dampen sexual response. As a diuretic that can increase the need to urinate, it indirectly diminishes sexual response by making the thought of sex unappealing.

Other chemicals do dampen sexual arousal and response. Tranquillizers and central nervous system depressants, such as barbiturates, can reduce sexual desire and impair sexual performance. These drugs may paradoxically enhance sexual arousal in some people, however, by lessening sexual inhibitions or fear of possible repercussions from sexual activity. Antihypertensive drugs, which are used in the treatment of high blood pressure, may produce erectile and ejaculatory difficulties in men and may reduce sexual desire in both genders. Certain antidepressant drugs, such as fluoxetine (brand name: Prozac), amitriptyline (brand name: Elavil), and imipramine (brand name: Tofranil), appear to dampen sex drive. Antidepressants may also impair erectile response and delay ejaculation in men and impair orgasmic responsiveness in women (Meston & Gorzalka, 1992). (Because they delay ejaculation, some of these drugs are used to treat premature ejaculation.)

Nicotine, the stimulant in tobacco smoke, constricts the blood vessels. Thus it can impede sexual arousal by reducing the capacity of the genitals to become engorged with blood. Chronic smoking can also reduce the blood levels of testosterone in men, which can in turn lessen sex drive or motivation.

Anti-androgen drugs may have anaphrodisiac effects. They have been used in the treatment of deviant behaviour patterns, such as sexual violence and adult sexual interest in children, with some promising results (Roesler & Witztum, 2000).

Psychoactive Drugs

Psychoactive drugs, such as alcohol and cocaine, are widely believed to have aphrodisiac effects. Yet their effects may reflect our expectations of them, or their effects on sexual inhibitions, rather than direct stimulation of sexual response.

ALCOHOL Small amounts of alcohol are stimulating, but large amounts curb sexual response. This fact should not be surprising, because alcohol is a depressant. Alcohol reduces central nervous system activity. Large amounts of alcohol can severely impair sexual performance in both men and women.

People who drink moderate amounts of alcohol may feel more sexually aroused because of their expectations about alcohol, not because of its chemical properties

Anaphrodisiacs Drugs or other agents whose effects are antagonistic to sexual arousal or sexual desire.

Anti-androgen Drug that reduces the levels of androgens in the blood system.

What Are the Effects of Alcohol on Sexual Behaviour?
Small doses of alcohol can be stimulating, can induce feelings of euphoria, and can lower inhibitions, all of which could be connected with sexual interest and facilitate social and sexual behaviour. Furthermore, alcohol reduces fear of the consequences of engaging in risky behaviour—sexual and otherwise. Alcohol also provides an excuse for engaging in otherwise unacceptable behaviour, such as sexual intercourse on the first date (or upon casual meeting). Alcohol is expected to be sexually liberating, and people often live up to social and cultural expectations. Yet, as a depressant drug, alcohol in large amounts will biochemically dampen sexual response and may make sexual response impossible.

(George et al., 2000). That is, people who expect alcohol to enhance sexual responsiveness may act the part. Moreover, men with problems achieving erection may turn to alcohol in hopes of finding a cure. The fact is that alcohol is a depressant and can reduce sexual potency rather than restore it.

Alcohol may also lower sexual inhibitions, because it allows us to ascribe our behaviour to the effects of the alcohol rather than to ourselves. Alcohol is connected with a liberated social role and thus provides an excuse for dubious behaviour. "It was the alcohol," people can say, "not me." When drinking, people may express their sexual desires and do things that they would not do when sober. For example, a person who feels guilty about sex may become sexually active when drinking because he or she can later blame the alcohol.

Alcohol can also induce feelings of euphoria. Euphoric feelings may enhance sexual arousal and also sweep away qualms about expressing sexual desires. Alcohol also appears to impair the ability to weigh information ("information processing") that might otherwise inhibit sexual impulses (MacDonald et al., 2000). When people drink, they may be less able to foresee the consequences of misconduct and less likely to ponder their standards of conduct.

HALLUCINOGENICS There is no evidence that marijuana or other hallucinogenic drugs directly stimulate sexual response. However, fairly to strongly intoxicated marijuana users claim to have more empathy with others, to be more aware of bodily sensations, and to experience time as passing more slowly. These sensations could heighten subjective feelings of sexual response. Some marijuana users report that the drug inhibits their sexual responsiveness, however (McCabe et al., 2005). The effects of the drug on sexual response may depend on the individual's prior experiences with the drug, on her or his attitudes toward the drug, and on the amount taken.

Other hallucinogenics, such as LSD and mescaline, have also been reported by some users to enhance sexual response. Again, these effects may reflect dosage level and user expectations, experiences, and attitudes toward the drugs, as well as altered perceptions.

STIMULANTS Stimulants such as amphetamines ("speed," "uppers," "bennies," "dexies") have been reputed to heighten arousal and sensations of orgasm. High doses can give rise to irritability, restlessness, hallucinations, paranoid delusions, insomnia, and loss of appetite. These drugs generally activate the central nervous system but are not known to have specific sexual effects. Nevertheless, arousing the nervous system can contribute to sexual arousal (Palace, 1995). The drugs can also elevate the mood, and perhaps sexual pleasure is heightened by general elation.

Cocaine is a natural stimulant that is extracted from the leaves of the coca plant. Cocaine is ingested in various forms, snorted as a powder, smoked in hardened rock form ("crack" cocaine) or in a freebase form, or injected directly into the bloodstream in liquid form. Cocaine produces a euphoric rush, which tends to ebb quickly. Physically, cocaine constricts blood vessels (reducing the oxygen supply to the heart), elevates the blood pressure, and accelerates the heart rate.

There is evidence that cocaine enhances sexual arousal in both males and females, in part by increasing levels of the neurotransmitter dopamine (Andersen et al., 2003; Andersen & Tufik, 2005; Festa et al., 2004). In addition, the use of crack cocaine is connected with a higher number of sex partners (Maranda et al., 2004).

More recently, crystal methamphetamine, otherwise known as "crystal meth" or "ice," is being used as an aphrodisiac that boosts sexual arousal and lowers sexual inhibitions. This drug is one of the most addictive street drugs, and the addiction is difficult to treat. Withdrawal typically results in severe pain and depression. It has several negative side effects, including irritability, insomnia, paranoia, and increased aggression. There is concern that it can also damage brain cells, causing memory loss, and can lead to heart attacks and strokes (Ah Shene, 2003). The Canadian AIDS society has warned that use of crystal meth may increase HIV infection because the lowered inhibitions encourage sexual risk-taking.

In a detailed review of research regarding the relationship between recreational drugs and sexuality, Alex Mckay (2005), research coordinator with SIECCAN in Toronto, arrived at the following conclusions: Many new users of various recreational drugs report that these drugs enhance their sexual experience; however, extensive use of these drugs usually results in diminished sexual functioning as well as numerous negative effects on the user's general health.

Sexual Response and the Brain: Cerebral Sex?

The brain may not be an erogenous zone, but it plays a central role in sexual functioning (Fisher, 2000). Direct genital stimulation may trigger spinal reflexes that produce erection in the male and vaginal lubrication in the female without the direct involvement of the brain. The same reflexes may be triggered by sexual stimulation that originates in the brain in the form of erotic memories, fantasies, visual images, and thoughts. The brain may also inhibit sexual responsiveness, as when we experience guilt or anxiety in a sexual situation or when we suddenly realize, well into a sexual encounter, that we have left the car lights turned on.

Parts of the brain—in particular the **cerebral cortex** and the **limbic system**—play key roles in sexual functioning. Cells in the cerebral cortex fire (transmit messages) when we experience sexual thoughts, images, wishes, fantasies, and the like. Cells in the cerebral cortex interpret sensory information as sexual turn-ons or turn-offs. The sight of your lover disrobing, the anticipation of a romantic kiss, a passing sexual fantasy, or the viewing of an erotic movie can trigger the firing of cortical cells. These cells, in turn, transmit messages through the

Cerebral cortex The wrinkled surface area (grey matter) of the cerebrum.

Limbic system A group of structures active in memory, motivation, and emotion; the structures that are part of this system form a fringe along the inner edge of the cerebrum.

Innovative Canadian Research

MALE AND FEMALE BRAIN RESPONSE

Researchers in Montreal (Karama et al., 2002) used magnetic resonance imaging to analyze gender differences in brain activation in response to viewing erotic films. While viewing the films, both men and women showed increased activation in similar parts of the brain. However, activation in the hypothalamus was significantly greater for the men. And only among men was the magnitude of hypothalamic activity positively related to reported levels of sexual arousal. The researchers suggested that the greater sexual arousal generally experienced by men when viewing erotica may be related to gender differences in activation of the hypothalamus.

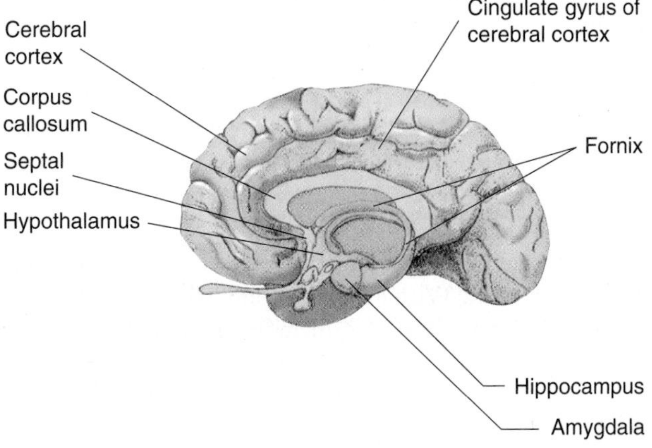

Figure 4.1 Parts of the Brain Involved in Sexual Functioning.

A view of the brain, split from top to bottom. Cells in the cerebral cortex transmit messages when we experience sexual thoughts and mental images. Cells in the cortex interpret sensory information as sexual turn-ons or turn-offs. The cerebral cortex may then transmit messages through the spinal cord that send blood coursing to the sex organs, leading to erection or vaginal lubrication. The limbic system lies along the inner edge of the cerebrum. When part of a male rat's hypothalamus is electrically stimulated, the rat engages in its courting and mounting routine. Klüver and Bucy (1939) found that destruction of areas of the limbic system triggered continuous sexual behaviour in monkeys. Electrical stimulation of the hippocampus and septal nuclei produces erections in monkeys.

spinal cord that send blood rushing to the genitals, causing erection or vaginal lubrication. The cortex also provides the conscious sense of self. The cortex judges sexual behaviour to be proper or improper, moral or immoral, relaxing or anxiety- or guilt-provoking.

Areas of the brain below the cortex, especially the limbic system (see Figure 4.1), also play roles in sexual processes (Everitt, 1990; Kimble, 1992). For example, when the rear part of a male rat's hypothalamus is stimulated by an electrical probe, the animal mechanically runs through its courting and mounting routine. It nibbles at the ears and the back of the neck of a female rat and mounts her when she responds.

Sex Hormones and Sexual Behaviour

Hormone A substance that is secreted by an endocrine gland and regulates various body functions.

Secondary sex characteristics Physical traits that differentiate males from females but are not directly involved in reproduction.

In a TV situation comedy, a male adolescent was described as "a hormone with feet." Ask parents why teenagers act the way they do, and you are likely to hear a one-word answer: hormones! **Hormones** are chemical substances that are secreted by the ductless glands of the endocrine system and discharged directly into the bloodstream.

Sex hormones released at puberty cause the flowering of **secondary sex characteristics**. In males, these include the lengthening of the vocal cords (and consequent lowering of the voice) and the growth of facial and pubic hair. In females, the breasts and hips become rounded with fatty tissue, and pubic hair grows.

Sex Hormones and Sexual Behaviour: Organizing and Activating Influences

Sex hormones have organizing and activating effects on behaviour. That is, they exert an influence on the type of behaviour that is expressed (an *organizing* effect) and on the frequency or intensity of the drive that motivates the behaviour and the ability to perform the behaviour (*activating* effects). For example, sex hormones predispose lower animals and possibly people toward stereotypical masculine or feminine mating behaviours (an organizing effect). They also facilitate sexual response and influence sexual desire (activating effects).

James Pfaus at Concordia University is an international leader in research on the sexual behaviour of rodents and other animals. He and his associates have discovered that there are many similarities in the sexual arousal and response of both animals and humans. For example, animals like humans are influenced not only by sex hormones but also by social and situational variables. Pfaus has concluded that research findings on animal sexual response can be highly predictive regarding many aspects of human sexual response (Pfaus et al., 2003).

Prenatal sex hormones are known to play a role in the sexual differentiation of the genitalia and of the brain structures, such as the hypothalamus. Their role in patterning sexual behaviour in adulthood remains unknown, however. Researchers have speculated that the brains of **transsexual** individuals may have been prenatally sexually differentiated in one direction while their genitals were being differentiated in the other (Money, 1994). It has been speculated that prenatal sexual differentiation of the brain may also be connected with sexual orientation.

What of the activating effects of sex hormones on human sex drive and behaviour? Although the countless attempts to extract or synthesize aphrodisiacs have failed to produce the real thing, men and women normally produce a genuine aphrodisiac—testosterone. Whatever the early organizing effects of sex hormones in humans, testosterone activates the sex drives of both men and women (Guzick & Hoeger, 2000).

Sex Hormones and Male Sexual Behaviour

Evidence of the role of hormones in sex drive is found among men who have declines in testosterone levels as a result of chemical or surgical castration. Surgical castration (removal of the testes) is sometimes performed as a medical treatment for cancer of the prostate or other diseases of the male reproductive tract, such as genital tuberculosis. And some convicted sex offenders have voluntarily undergone castration as a condition of release.

Regardless of the reason for castration, men who are surgically or chemically castrated usually exhibit a gradual decrease in the incidence of sexual fantasies and of sexual desire (Bradford, 1998). They also gradually tend to lose the capacities to attain erection and to ejaculate—an indication that testosterone is important in maintaining sexual functioning as well as drive, at least in males. Castrated men show great variation in their sexual interest and functioning, however. Some continue to experience sexual desires and are able to function sexually for years, even decades. Learning appears to play a large role in determining continued sexual response following castration. Males who were sexually experienced before castration show a more gradual decline in sexual activity. Those who were sexually inexperienced at the time show relatively little or no interest in sex. Male sexual motivation and functioning thus involve an interplay of hormonal influences and experience.

Further evidence of the relationship between hormonal levels and male sexuality is found in studies of men with **hypogonadism**, a condition marked by abnormally low levels of testosterone production. Hypogonadal men generally experience loss of sexual desire and a decline in sexual activity (McElduff & Beange, 2003). Here again, hormones do not tell the whole story. Hypogonadal men are capable of erection, at

Transsexual A person with a gender-identity disorder who feels that he or she is really a member of the other gender and is trapped in a body of the wrong gender.

Hypogonadism An abnormal condition marked by abnormally low levels of testosterone production.

Are Adolescents "Hormones With Feet"?
Research shows that levels of androgens are connected with sexual interest in both male and female adolescents. Hormone levels are more likely to predict sexual behaviour in adolescent males, however, perhaps because society places greater restraints on female sexuality.

least for a while, even though their sex drives may wane (Bancroft, 1984). The role of testosterone as an activator of sex drives in men is further supported by evidence of the effects of testosterone replacement in hypogonadal men. When such men obtain testosterone injections, their sex drives, fantasies, and activity are often restored to former levels (Seidman, 2003).

Though minimal levels of androgens are critical to male sexuality, there is no one-to-one correspondence between hormone levels and the sex drive or sexual performance in adults. In men who have ample supplies of testosterone, sexual interest and functioning depend more on learning, fantasies, attitudes, memories, and other psychosocial factors than on hormone levels. At puberty, however, hormonal variations may play a more direct role in stimulating sexual interest and activity in males. Udry (2001) found, for example, that testosterone levels among teenage boys predicted sexual interest, masturbation rates, and the likelihood of engaging in sexual intercourse. A positive relationship has also been found between testosterone levels in adult men and frequency of sexual intercourse (Dabbs & Morris, 1990). Moreover, drugs that reduce the levels of androgens in the blood system, called *anti-androgens*, lead to reductions in the sex drive and in sexual fantasies (Bradford, 1998).

Sex Hormones and Female Sexual Behaviour

The female sex hormones estrogen and progesterone play prominent roles in promoting the changes that occur during puberty and in regulating the menstrual cycle. Female sex hormones do not, however, appear to play a direct role in determining sexual motivation or response in human females.

In most mammals, females are sexually receptive only during *estrus* ("in heat")—a brief period of fertility corresponding to ovulation. Estrus occurs once a year in some species; in others, it occurs periodically during the year in so-called sexual or mating seasons. Estrogen peaks at time of ovulation, so there is a close relationship between fertility and sexual receptivity in most female mammals. Women's sexuality, however, is not clearly linked to hormonal fluctuations. Unlike most mammalian females, the human female is sexually responsive during all phases of the reproductive (menstrual) cycle—even during menstruation, when ovarian hormone levels are low—and after menopause.

There is some evidence, however, that sexual responsiveness in women is influenced by the presence of circulating androgens, or male sex hormones, in their bodies. The adrenal glands of women produce small amounts of androgens, just as they do in males (Guzick & Hoeger, 2000). The fact that women normally produce smaller amounts of androgens than men does not mean that they necessarily have weaker sex drives. Rather, women appear to be more sensitive to smaller amounts of androgens. For women, it seems that less is more.

Women who receive **ovariectomies**, which are sometimes carried out when a hysterectomy is performed, no longer produce female sex hormones. Nevertheless, they continue to experience sex drives and interest as before. Loss of the ovarian hormone estradiol may cause vaginal dryness and make coitus painful, but it does not reduce sexual desire. (The dryness can be alleviated by a lubricating jelly or by estrogen creams.) However, women whose adrenal glands *and* ovaries have been removed (so that they no longer produce androgens) gradually lose sexual desire. An active and enjoyable sexual history seems to ward off this loss, however, providing further evidence of the impact of cognitive and experiential factors on human sexual response.

Ovariectomy Surgical removal of the ovaries.

Research provides further evidence of the links between testosterone levels and women's sex drives (Williams, 1999). In the studies by Udry (2001), androgen levels were also found to predict sexual interest among teenage girls. In contrast to boys, however, girls' androgen levels were unrelated to the likelihood of coital experience. Androgens apparently affect sexual desire in both genders, but sexual interest may be more likely to be directly translated into sexual activity in men than in women (Peplau, 2003). This gender difference may be explained by society's imposing greater restraints on adolescent female sexuality.

Other researchers report that women's sexual activity increases at points in the menstrual cycle when levels of androgens in the bloodstream are high (Morley & Perry, 2003). Another study was conducted with women whose ovaries had been surgically removed ("surgical menopause") as a way of treating disease. The ovaries supply major quantities of estrogen. Following surgery, the women in this study were treated with estrogen-replacement therapy (ERT), with ERT *plus* androgens, or with a placebo (an inert substance made to resemble an active drug) (Sherwin et al., 1985). This was a double-blind study. Neither the women nor their physicians knew which drug the women were receiving. The results showed that the combination of androgens and ERT heightened sexual desire and sexual fantasies more than ERT alone or the placebo. The combination also helps women maintain a sense of psychological well-being (Guzick & Hoeger, 2000).

Androgens thus play a more prominent role than ovarian hormones in activating and maintaining women's sex drives. As with men, however, women's sexuality is too complex to be explained fully by hormone levels.

Factors Influencing Sexual Arousal in Women and Men

Robin Milhausen of the University of Guelph (2004) has analyzed factors that inhibit or enhance the sexual arousal of female and male university students. She found a number of factors that were common to both sexes. Both men and women agreed that the following factors could enhance their sexual arousal: a partner's positive characteristics, such as a sense of humour, self-confidence, and making the other person feel desirable; sex that was varied, such as trying different sexual activities and having sex in different settings; and anticipating a sexual encounter.

Factors that could inhibit sexual arousal in both men and women were: a partner who was self-conscious about his or her body; feeling that one is giving more sexually to the partner than receiving from the partner, such as by being the one who always initiates sex; and worries over issues such as one's reputation among peers, contracting an STI, and having to use condoms.

There were also gender differences regarding the importance given to certain factors.

Women were more inhibited than men about:

- Possible sexual violence
- Being exploited
- Being a good lover
- Taking too long to become aroused and not having an orgasm

On the other hand, women were more aroused by:

- Positive partner characteristics such as relating well to others and doing helpful chores
- Being able to trust her partner, being emotionally connected, and feeling her partner was sensitive to her needs
- Feeling the effect of hormones on her sexual behaviour

Men were more aroused than women by:

- Specific sexual stimuli such as seeing a partner's naked body, "talking dirty," seeing a partner wearing sexy outfits, and watching erotic films
- Quickly advancing to the genitals when starting to have sex

Innovative Canadian Research

GENDER, SEXUAL ORIENTATION, AND SEXUAL AROUSAL

Meredith Chivers, a researcher at the Centre for Addiction and Mental Health in Toronto, has been conducting ground-breaking research on sexual arousal. In particular she and her colleagues have studied how sexual arousal patterns vary by gender and sexual orientation (Chivers et al., 2007). The study participants were heterosexual men and women and homosexual men and women. The four groups were shown videos depicting men and women engaging in nude exercise, solitary masturbation, same-sex intercourse and male-female intercourse, and chimpanzees copulating. Genital and subjective sexual arousal were recorded.

Arousal was strongest in response to watching the sexual intercourse video and weakest for the nude exercise one. A major gender difference was that the gender of the actor was far more important for the men than for the women, whereas the level of sexual activity was more important for the women than for the men. Thus heterosexual men were almost exclusively aroused by videos of women, and homosexual men were almost exclusively aroused by videos of men. Heterosexual women responded to videos of both men and women. Women were more strongly aroused than men by the video of the chimpanzees copulating. Homosexual women were more aroused by the video of nude women exercising and masturbating than by the one of nude men engaging in those activities. Yet homosexual women were also aroused when watching heterosexual couples engaging in intercourse.

The findings clearly indicate that women have greater flexibility than men regarding which gender they are aroused by. The findings also challenge the commonly held belief that women are far less sexually responsive to sexually explicit materials than are men. Not only were the women as strongly aroused by the erotic videos as the men were, but the women became aroused as quickly as the men did.

In another study, Meredith Chivers and colleagues (Rieger, Chivers, & Bailey, 2005) compared the sexual responses of bisexual men with those of homosexual and heterosexual men when these men were watching either men or women engaging in sexual activity. As expected, the heterosexual men were more aroused by the female actors and the homosexual men were more aroused by the male actors. Most of the bisexual men experienced greater genital arousal when watching the male actors, thus responding in a similar fashion as did the homosexual males. However, the bisexual men were divided in their subjective feelings of arousal and were just as likely to say they were aroused by the female actors as by the male actors.

Chivers and colleagues (Lawrence, Latty, Chivers, & Bailey, 2005) also studied male-to-female transsexuals both prior to and after sex reassignment surgery. The transsexuals who were homosexual were more aroused by sexual images of men, while the transsexuals who were not homosexual were more aroused by images of women. The arousal responses after surgery were found to be similar to the arousal responses before the surgery.

Sexual Response

Although we may be culturally attuned to focus on gender differences rather than similarities, Masters and Johnson (1966) found that the physiological responses of men and women to sexual stimulation (whether from coitus, masturbation, or other sources) are quite alike. The sequence of changes in the body that take place as men and women become progressively more aroused is referred to as the **sexual response cycle**.

Sexual response cycle Masters and Johnson's model of sexual response, which consists of four phases.

Vasocongestion The swelling of the genital tissues with blood, which causes erection of the penis and engorgement of the area surrounding the vaginal opening.

Myotonia Muscle tension.

The Four-Phase Masters and Johnson Sexual Response Cycle

Masters and Johnson (1966) divided the cycle into four phases: *excitement*, *plateau*, *orgasm*, and *resolution*. Figure 4.2 suggests the levels of sexual arousal associated with each phase.

Both males and females experience **vasocongestion** and **myotonia** early in the response cycle. Vasocongestion is the swelling of the genital tissues with blood, which causes erection of the penis and engorgement of the area surrounding the vaginal opening. The testes, nipples, and even earlobes become engorged as blood

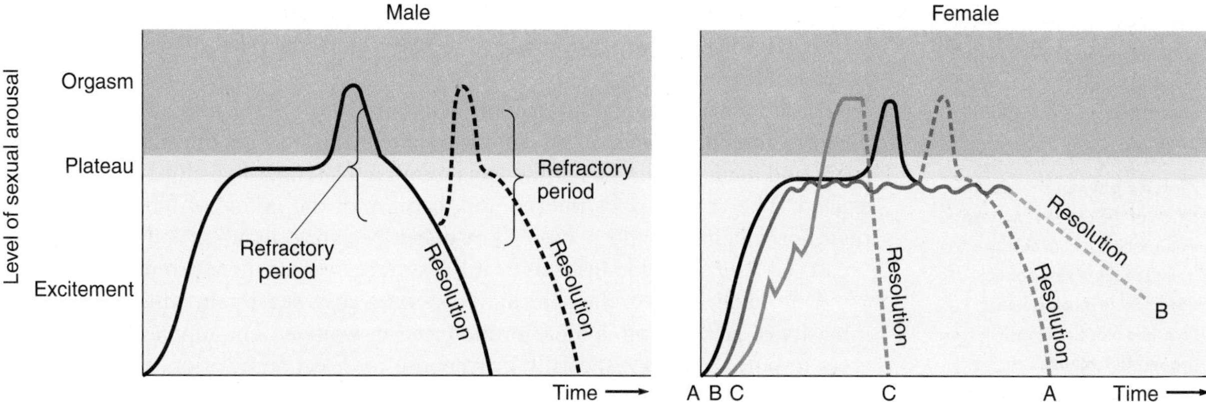

Figure 4.2 Levels of Sexual Arousal During the Phases of the Sexual Response Cycle.

Masters and Johnson divide the sexual response cycle into four phases: excitement, plateau, orgasm, and resolution. During the resolution phase, the level of sexual arousal returns to the prearoused state. For men there is a refractory period following orgasm. As shown by the broken line, however, men can become rearoused to orgasm once the refractory period is past and their levels of sexual arousal have returned to preplateau levels. Pattern A for women shows a typical response cycle; the broken line indicates multiple orgasms, should they occur. Pattern B shows the cycle of a woman who reaches the plateau phase but for whom arousal is "resolved" without her experiencing orgasm. Pattern C shows the possibility of orgasm in a highly aroused woman who passes quickly through the plateau phase.

vessels in these areas dilate. Myotonia is muscle tension. It causes voluntary and involuntary muscle contractions, which produce facial grimaces, spasms in the hands and feet, and eventually, the spasms of orgasm.

Excitement phase The first phase of the sexual response cycle, which is characterized by erection in the male, by vaginal lubrication in the female, and by muscle tension and increases in heart rate in both males and females.

EXCITEMENT PHASE In younger men, vasocongestion during the **excitement phase** produces penile erection as early as three to eight seconds after stimulation begins. Erection may occur more slowly in older men, but the responses are essentially

Innovative Canadian Research

PHYSICAL VERSUS PSYCHOLOGICAL AROUSAL

Although males and females are similar in terms of their physiological responses, they differ significantly in their subjective perception of arousal. When males are physically aroused, they are almost always subjectively aware of this. However, women vary in the degree to which they are aware of physical arousal. Researchers in British Columbia discovered that older women are more subjectively aware when they are physically aroused than are younger women (Brotto & Gorzalka, 2002). Thus, it seems that for many women it takes time and a learning process to be able to distinguish the physical signs of sexual arousal.

Vancouver therapist Rosemary Basson (2002) discusses how sexual arousal for women is a more complex process than for men. According to Basson, when a woman experiences genital vasocongestion, there can be a range of subjective responses:

1. She may not be aware of the physical arousal.
2. She may be only vaguely aware of arousal.
3. She may be aware of the physical sensations yet not define them as being sexual.
4. She may interpret the arousal as sexual but not experience the sensation as being enjoyable.

Basson analyzes a number of factors that may account for these responses, such as past negative sexual experiences, feelings of inadequacy or guilt, and distractions such as concerns over personal appearance, safety of the situation, and feelings toward one's partner.

Sex flush A reddish rash that appears on the chest or breasts late in the excitement phase of the sexual response cycle.

Plateau phase The second phase of the sexual response cycle, which is characterized by increases in vasocongestion, muscle tension, heart rate, and blood pressure in preparation for orgasm.

Orgasmic platform The thickening of the walls of the outer third of the vagina, due to vasocongestion, that occurs during the plateau phase of the sexual response cycle.

Sex skin The reddening of the labia minora that occurs during the plateau phase.

the same. Erection may subside and return as stimulation varies. The scrotal skin thickens, losing its baggy appearance. The testes increase in size. The testes and scrotum become elevated.

In the female, vaginal lubrication may start 10 to 30 seconds after stimulation begins. Vasocongestion swells the clitoris, flattens the labia majora and spreads them apart, and increases the size of the labia minora. The inner two-thirds of the vagina expand. The vaginal walls thicken and, because of the inflow of blood, turn from their normal pink to a deeper hue. The uterus becomes engorged and elevated. The breasts enlarge, and blood vessels near the surface become more prominent.

Late in this phase, the skin may take on a rosy **sex flush**, which varies with intensity of arousal and is more pronounced in women. The nipples may become erect in both genders, especially in response to direct stimulation. Both men and women show some increase in myotonia, heart rate, and blood pressure.

PLATEAU PHASE A plateau is a level region, and the level of arousal remains somewhat constant during the **plateau phase** of sexual response. Nevertheless, the plateau phase is an advanced state of arousal that precedes orgasm. Men in this phase show a slight increase in the circumference of the coronal ridge of the penis. The penile glans turns a purplish hue, a sign of vasocongestion. The testes are elevated further into position for ejaculation and may reach one and a half times their unaroused size. The Cowper's glands secrete a few droplets of fluid that are found at the tip of the penis (see Figure 4.3).

In women, vasocongestion swells the tissues of the outer third of the vagina, contracting the vaginal opening (thus preparing it to "grasp" the penis) and building the **orgasmic platform** (see Figure 4.4). The inner part of the vagina expands fully. The uterus becomes fully elevated. The clitoris withdraws beneath the clitoral hood and shortens. Thus a woman (or her partner) may feel that the clitoris has become lost. This may be mistaken as a sign that the woman's sexual arousal is waning, when it is actually increasing.

Colouration of the labia minora, referred to as the **sex skin**, appears. The labia minora become a deep wine colour in women who have borne children and bright red in women who have not. Further engorgement of the areolas of the breasts may

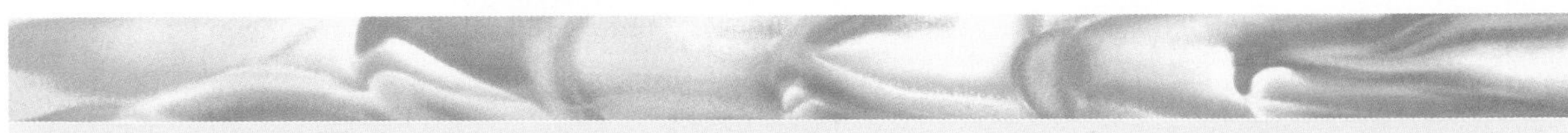

A Closer Look

WOMEN WHO EXPERIENCE PERSISTENTLY HIGH LEVELS OF SEXUAL AROUSAL

Most research on women and sexual arousal has focused on women who have low sexual arousal. Ontario researcher Meredith Chivers and New Jersey researcher Sandra Leiblum have studied women who experience persistent sexual arousal (Leiblum & Chivers, 2007). In the past these women would have been classified as "nymphomaniacs."

This research study further indicates how there can be a disconnect between physiological and psychological arousal among some women. Leiblum and Chivers (2007) believe that continuous high levels of spontaneous sexual arousal in some women can be a result of a sexual stimulus that is subconscious–but unacceptable or not noticed. In interviewing women who experience these high levels of arousal, they concluded that there are three types: (1) women who experience continuing spontaneous arousal as mildly pleasurable, (2) women who experience persistent feelings of genital arousal as mildly distracting but not bothersome, and (3) women who experience continuous, persistent, and intense genital arousal that is extremely distracting and distressing. Leiblum and Chivers believe that a variety of factors may account for these differences in women's responses to continuous sexual arousal.

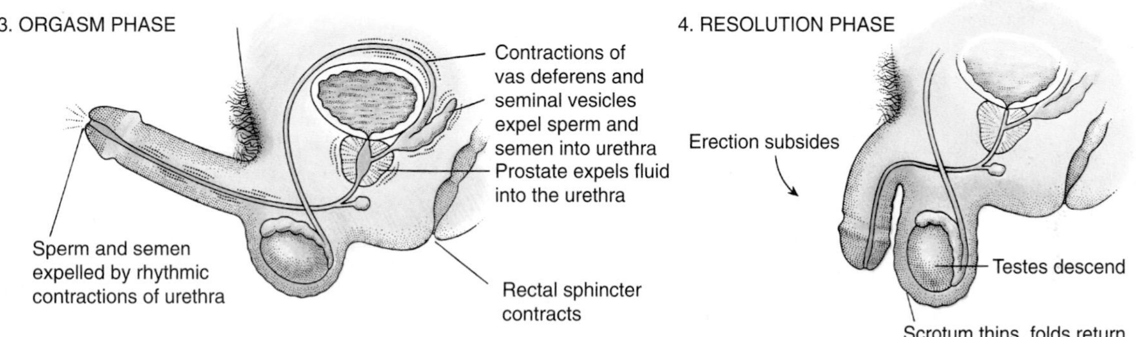

Figure 4.3 The Male Genitals During the Phases of the Sexual Response Cycle.

make it seem that the nipples have lost part of their erection (see Figure 4.5). Bartholin's glands secrete a fluid that resembles mucus.

About one man in four, and about three women in four, show a sex flush, which often does not appear until the plateau phase. Myotonia may cause facial grimaces and spasmodic contractions in the hands and feet. Breathing becomes rapid, like panting, and the heart rate may increase to 100 to 160 beats per minute. Blood pressure continues to rise. The increase in heart rate is usually less dramatic with masturbation than during coitus.

ORGASMIC PHASE The orgasmic phase in the male consists of two stages of muscular contractions. In the first stage, contractions of the vas deferens, the seminal vesicles, the ejaculatory duct, and the prostate gland cause seminal fluid to collect in the urethral bulb at the base of the penis (see Figure 4.3). The bulb expands to accommodate the fluid. The internal sphincter of the urinary bladder contracts, preventing seminal fluid from entering the bladder in a backward, retrograde ejaculation. The normal closing off of the bladder also serves to prevent urine from mixing with semen. The collection of semen in the urethral bulb produces feelings of ejaculatory inevitability—the sensation that nothing will stop the ejaculate from "coming." This sensation lasts for about two to three seconds.

In the second stage, the external sphincter of the bladder relaxes, allowing the passage of semen. Contractions of muscles surrounding the urethra and urethral bulb and the base of the penis propel the ejaculate through the urethra and out of the body. Sensations of pleasure tend to be related to the strength of the contractions and the amount of seminal fluid. The first three to four contractions are generally most intense and occur at 0.8-second intervals (five contractions every four

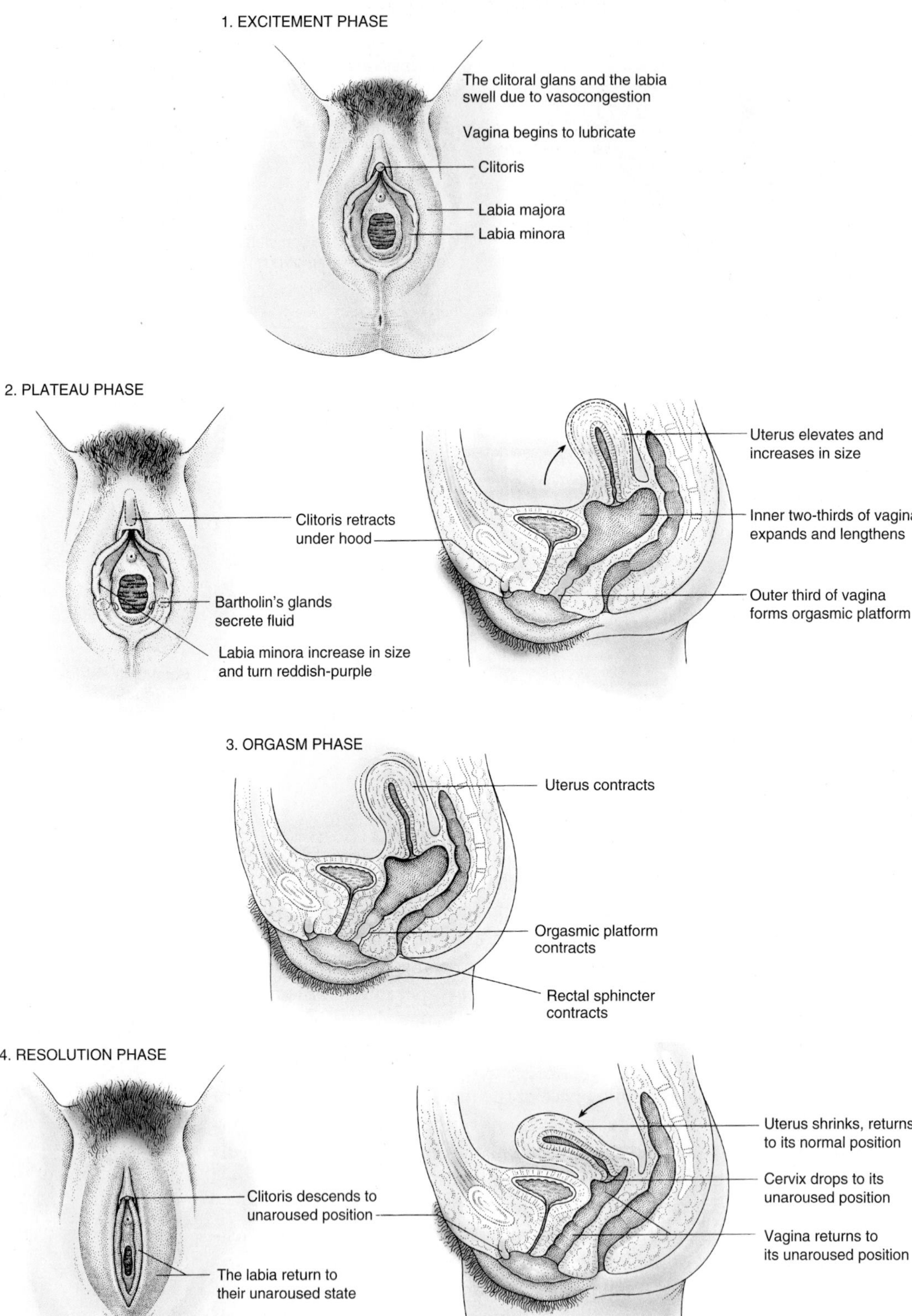

Figure 4.4 The Female Genitals During the Phases of the Sexual Response Cycle.

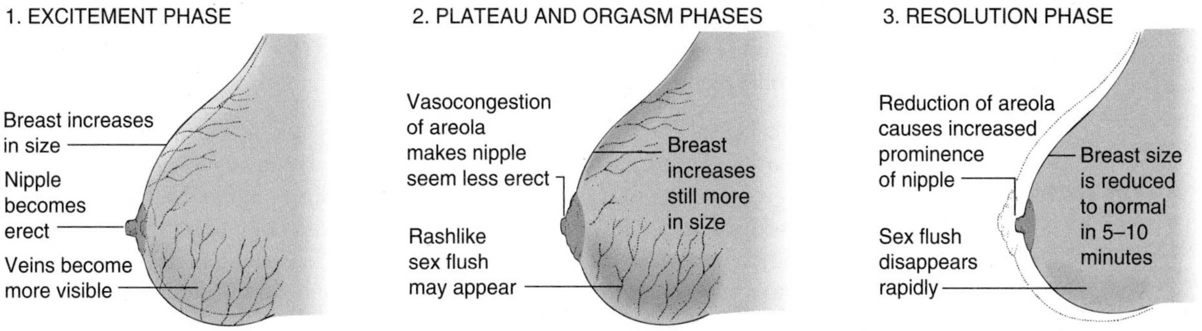

Figure 4.5 The Breasts During the Phases of the Sexual Response Cycle.

seconds). Another two to four contractions occur at a somewhat slower pace. Rates and patterns vary somewhat from man to man.

Orgasm in the female is manifested by 3 to 15 contractions of the pelvic muscles that surround the vaginal barrel. The contractions first occur at 0.8-second intervals, producing, as in the male, a release of sexual tension. Another three to six weaker and slower contractions follow. The spacing of these contractions is generally more variable in women than in men. The uterus and the anal sphincter also contract rhythmically. Uterine contractions occur in waves from the top to the

Innovative Canadian Research

SUBJECTIVE EXPERIENCE OF ORGASM

The sensations of orgasm have challenged the descriptive powers of poets. Words like *rush, warmth, explosion,* and *release* do not adequately capture them. We may assume (rightly or wrongly) that others of our gender experience pretty much what we do, but can we understand the sensations of the other gender?

Studies suggest that the orgasms of both genders may feel quite similar. In one study, Kenneth Mah from Princess Margaret Hospital in Toronto and Yitzchak Binik of McGill University (2002) developed a scale to measure the subjective experiences of orgasm among men and women. They wanted to determine what characteristics were common to human experiences of orgasm. University students were asked to rate adjectives describing their orgasm experiences occurring both in masturbation and sex with a partner. The findings supported a two-dimensional model of the psychological experience of orgasm. The first is the sensory dimension, which has the following components:

- Building sensation
- Flooding sensation
- Flushing sensation
- Shooting sensation
- Throbbing sensation
- General spasms

The second, emotional dimension of orgasm experience includes the following:

- Pleasurable satisfaction
- Relaxation
- Emotional intimacy
- Ecstasy

Mah and Binik found that, although the intimacy ratings were lower in the masturbation situation, students' ratings for orgasms obtained through masturbation were generally similar to orgasms obtained through sex with a partner. However, orgasm obtained with a partner was rated by both sexes as more satisfying than orgasm from masturbation. Orgasm ratings were similar for males and females, except that males gave a higher rating for shooting sensations, reflecting the male process of ejaculation.

In a follow-up study, Mah and Binik (2005) found that emotional intimacy affected the rating of the orgasmic experience. Orgasm was rated as more satisfying when the individuals felt emotionally connected to their partners. Also, orgasms that were seen as more psychologically intense such as involving feelings of relaxation and ecstasy were related to higher levels of orgasmic pleasure and satisfaction. Higher degrees of sexual pleasure were also reported when "throbbing" sensations and to a lesser degree "flushing" sensations were experienced.

Resolution phase The fourth phase of the sexual response cycle, during which the body gradually returns to its prearoused state.

Refractory period A period of time following a response (e.g., orgasm) during which an individual is no longer responsive to stimulation (e.g., sexual stimulation).

cervix. In both genders, muscles go into spasm throughout the body. Blood pressure and heart rate reach a peak, with the heart beating up to 180 times per minute. Respiration may increase to 40 breaths per minute.

RESOLUTION PHASE The period following orgasm, in which the body returns to its prearoused state, is called the **resolution phase**. Following ejaculation, the man loses his erection in two stages. The first occurs in about a minute. Half the volume of the erection is lost, as blood from the corpora cavernosa empties into the other parts of the body. The second stage occurs over a period of several minutes: The remaining tumescence subsides as the corpus spongiosum empties. The testes and scrotum return to normal size, and the scrotum regains its wrinkled appearance.

In women, orgasm also triggers release of blood from engorged areas. In the absence of continued stimulation, swelling of the areolas decreases, then the nipples return to normal size. The sex flush lightens rapidly. In about 5 to 10 seconds, the clitoris descends to its normal position. The clitoris, vaginal barrel, uterus, and labia gradually shrink to their prearoused sizes. The labia minora turn lighter (the "sex skin" disappears) in about 10 to 15 seconds.

Most muscle tension (myotonia) tends to dissipate within five minutes after orgasm in both men and women. Blood pressure, heart rate, and respiration may also return to their prearousal levels within a few minutes. About 30% to 40% of men and women find their palms, the soles of their feet, or their entire bodies covered with a sheen of perspiration. Both men and women may feel relaxed and satiated. However . . .

Although the processes by which the body returns to its prearousal state are similar in men and women, there is an important gender difference during the resolution phase. Unlike women, men enter a **refractory period** during which they are physiologically incapable of experiencing another orgasm or ejaculation (in much the same way as the flash attachment to a camera cannot be set off again immediately after it is used—it has to be recharged). The refractory period of adolescent males may last only minutes, whereas that of men aged 50 and above may last from several minutes (yes, it could happen) to a day. Women do not undergo a refractory period and so can become quickly rearoused to the point of repeated (multiple) orgasm if they desire and receive continued sexual stimulation (see Figure 4.2).

Myotonia and vasocongestion may take an hour or more to dissipate in people who are aroused who do not reach orgasm. Persistent pelvic vasocongestion may cause "blue balls" in males—the slang term for a throbbing ache. Some men insist that their dates should consent to coitus, on the theory that it is unfair to decline after stimulating them to the point where they have this condition. This ache can be relieved through masturbation as well as coitus, however, or can be allowed to dissipate naturally. Although it may be uncomfortable, it is not dangerous and is no excuse to pressure or coerce another person into any sexual activity. "Blue" sensations are not limited to men. Women, too, may experience unpleasant pelvic throbbing if they have become highly aroused and do not find release. And women, too, can relieve pelvic throbbing through masturbation.

Kaplan's Three Stages of Sexual Response

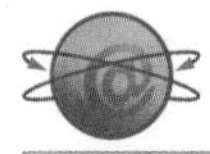

Womyns' Ware
This Vancouver-based sex shop offers sex advice.
www.womynsware.com

Helen Singer Kaplan was a prominent sex therapist and author of several professional books (1974, 1979, 1987) on sex therapy. Whereas Masters and Johnson had proposed a four-stage model of sexual response, Kaplan developed a three-stage model consisting of (1) desire, (2) excitement, and (3) orgasm. Kaplan's model is an outgrowth of her clinical experience in working with people with sexual dysfunctions. She believes that their problems can best be classified according to these three phases. Kaplan's model makes it convenient for clinicians to classify sexual dysfunctions involving desire (low or absent desire), excitement (such as problems with erection in the male or lubrication in the female), and orgasm (such as premature ejaculation in the male or orgasmic dysfunction in the female).

Kaplan's model is noteworthy for designating desire as a separate phase of sexual response. Problems in lack of sexual interest or desire are among those most commonly brought to the attention of sex therapists.

Basson's Intimacy Model of Female Sexual Response

Rosemary Basson (2001), a Vancouver therapist, has developed an intimacy-based model of female sexual response that she argues is especially relevant for women in long-term relationships. Her main criticism of previous models is that they do not take into account the factor of intimacy. According to Basson, most women in longer-term relationships are motivated to respond to sexual stimuli if they feel that becoming sexually involved will enhance intimacy with their partner.

Often a woman will begin sexual encounters with a nonsexual or neutral state of mind. Once the woman has begun to become sexually aroused for "intimacy reasons," she will continue the experience for "sexual reasons." At this point she will be responsive to sexual stimulation, such as breast or genital touching, that will increase her arousal. If the woman finds the outcome to be both physically and emotionally satisfying, it will increase her feelings of intimacy with her partner and motivate her to become sexually involved again in the future.

This model allows for the possibility that arousal may precede sexual desire and that arousal may not lead to orgasm. Basson does acknowledge the possibility that spontaneous sexual desire can occur among women outside of the intimacy model, and that this may lead to self-stimulation or casual sex.

Controversies About Orgasm

Few other topics in human sexuality have aroused more controversies over the years than orgasm. A common social expectation is that orgasm should be obtained through vaginal intercourse, yet many women cannot obtain orgasm from vaginal intercourse. Also, there are social expectations regarding the timing of intercourse. Interestingly, men who orgasm quickly during intercourse are often perceived as having a problem, whereas women who orgasm quickly are identified as being sexually healthy and desirable.

Could there be a biological reason why some women are able to experience orgasm easily while other women have difficulty obtaining an orgasm? A study of female twins in London, England, found that identical twins were more similar in their orgasm experiences than were non-identical twins, suggesting that genetics plays a role in ability to have an orgasm (Dunn, Cherkas, & Spector, 2005).

Multiple Orgasms

Kinsey's report (Kinsey et al., 1953) that 14% of his female respondents regularly had **multiple orgasms** sent shock waves through the general community and even surprised his fellow scientists. Many people were aghast that women could have more than one orgasm in succession. Masters and Johnson (1966) reported that most if not all women are capable of multiple orgasms. Though all women may have a biological capability for multiple orgasms, not all women report them. A survey of 720 female nurses showed that only 43% reported experiencing multiple orgasms (Darling et al., 1991).

It is difficult to offer a precise definition of multiple orgasms. (Note that the pattern shown by the broken line for the male in Figure 4.2 does *not* constitute a

Multiple orgasms One or more additional orgasms following the first, which occur within a short period of time and before the body has returned to a preplateau level of arousal.

multiple orgasm, even if it occurs reasonably rapidly after the first orgasm, because he *does* return to a preplateau level of sexual arousal between orgasms.) The lines of demarcation between the excitement and plateau stages of arousal are not obvious, however. Therefore, a person may experience two or more successive orgasms within a short time but not know whether these are, technically speaking, "multiple orgasms." Whether or not the orgasm fits the definition has no effect on the experience, but it does raise the question of whether both men and women are capable of multiple orgasms.

By Masters and Johnson's definition, men are not capable of achieving multiple orgasms because they enter a refractory period following ejaculation during which they are physiologically incapable of achieving another orgasm or ejaculation. Put more simply, men who want more than one orgasm during one session may have to relax for a while and allow their sexual arousal to subside. Yet women can maintain a high level of arousal between multiple orgasms and have them in rapid succession.

Women do not enter a refractory period. Women can continue to have orgasms if they continue to receive effective stimulation (and, of course, are interested in continuing). Some men thus refrain from reaching orgasm until their partners have had the desired number. This differential capacity for multiple orgasms is one of the major gender differences in sexual response.

Some men can train themselves to have two or more orgasms without ejaculation ("dry orgasms") preceding a final ejaculatory orgasm. These men may not enter a refractory period following their initial dry orgasms and may therefore be able to maintain their level of stimulation at near-peak levels. A common belief is that, for men, ejaculation defines orgasm. However, the two do not necessarily go together. For example, some men in situations of high stress may experience an "accidental" ejaculation without any pleasurable sensations of orgasm. Even in regular sexual encounters, the sensations experienced with ejaculation can range from intensely pleasurable to mildly pleasurable—at times there can even be a lack of pleasurable sensation.

Masters and Johnson found that some women experienced 20 or more orgasms by masturbating. Still, few women have multiple orgasms during most sexual encounters, and many are satisfied with just one per occasion. Some women who have read or heard about female orgasmic capacity wonder what is "wrong" with them if they are content with just one. Nothing is wrong with them, of course; a biological capacity does not create a behavioural requirement.

How Many Kinds of Orgasms Do Women Have? One, Two, or Three?

Until Masters and Johnson published their laboratory findings, many people believed that there were two types of female orgasms, as proposed by the psychoanalyst Sigmund Freud: the *clitoral orgasm* and the *vaginal orgasm.* Clitoral orgasms were achieved through direct clitoral stimulation, such as by masturbation. Clitoral orgasms were seen by psychoanalysts (mostly male psychoanalysts, naturally) as emblematic of a childhood fixation—a throwback to an erogenous pattern acquired during childhood masturbation.

The term *vaginal orgasm* referred to an orgasm achieved through deep penile thrusting during coitus and was theorized to be a sign of mature sexuality. Freud argued that women achieve sexual maturity when they forsake clitoral stimulation for vaginal stimulation. This view would be little more than an academic footnote except for the fact that some adult women who continue to require direct clitoral stimulation to reach orgasm, even during coitus, have been led to believe that they are sexually inadequate.

Despite Freudian theory, Masters and Johnson (1966) were able to find only one kind of orgasm, physiologically speaking, regardless of the source of stimulation (manual–clitoral or penile–vaginal). By monitoring physiological responses to sexual stimulation, they found that the female orgasm involves the same biological events whether it is reached through masturbation, petting, coitus, or just breast stimulation. All orgasms involve spasmodic contractions of the pelvic muscles surrounding the vaginal barrel, leading to a release of sexual tension.

In men, it also does not matter how orgasm is achieved—whether through masturbation, petting, oral sex, coitus, or fantasizing about a fellow student in chem lab—because orgasm still involves the same physiological processes: Involuntary contractions of the pelvic muscles at the base of the penis expel semen and release sexual tension. A woman or a man might prefer one source of orgasm to another (she or he might prefer achieving orgasm with a lover rather than by masturbation, or with one person rather than another), but the biological events that define orgasm remain the same.

Although orgasms attained through coitus or masturbation may be physiologically alike, there are certainly key psychological or subjective differences. (Were it not so, there would be fewer sexual relationships.) The coital experience, for example, is often accompanied by feelings of attachment, love, and connectedness to one's partner. Masturbation, by contrast, is more likely to be experienced solely as a sexual release.

The purported distinction between clitoral and vaginal orgasms also rests on an assumption that the clitoris is not stimulated during coitus. Masters and Johnson showed this to be a *false* assumption. Penile coital thrusting draws the clitoral hood back and forth against the clitoris. Vaginal pressure also heightens blood flow in the clitoris, further setting the stage for orgasm (Lavoisier et al., 1995).

One might think that Masters and Johnson's research settled the question of whether there are different types of female orgasm. Other investigators, however, have proposed that there *are* distinct forms of female orgasm, but not those suggested by psychoanalytic theory. For example, Singer and Singer (1972) suggested that there are three types of female orgasm: *vulval, uterine*, and *blended.* According to the Singers, the vulval orgasm represents the type of orgasm described by Masters and Johnson (1966) that involves *vulval* contractions, that is, contractions of the vaginal barrel. Consistent with the findings of Masters and Johnson (1966), they note that the vulval orgasm remains the same regardless of the source of stimulation, clitoral or vaginal.

According to the Singers, the uterine orgasm does not involve vulval contractions. It occurs only in response to deep penile thrusting against the cervix. This thrusting slightly displaces the uterus and stimulates the tissues that cover the abdominal organs. The uterine orgasm is accompanied by a certain pattern of breathing: Gasping or gulping of air is followed by an involuntary holding of the breath as orgasm approaches. When orgasm is reached, the breath is explosively exhaled. The uterine orgasm is accompanied by deep feelings of relaxation and sexual satisfaction.

The third type, or blended orgasm, is described as combining features of the vulval and uterine orgasms. It involves both an involuntary breath-holding response and contractions of the pelvic muscles. The Singers note that the type of orgasm a woman experiences depends on factors such as the parts of the body that are stimulated and the duration of stimulation. Each produces its own kind of satisfaction, and no one type is necessarily better than or preferable to any other.

The Singers' hypothesis of three distinct forms of female orgasm remains controversial. Researchers initially scoffed at the idea that orgasms could arise from vaginal stimulation alone. The vagina, after all, especially the inner two-thirds of the vaginal cavity, is relatively insensitive to stimulation (erotic or otherwise). Proponents of the Singers' model counter that the type of uterine orgasm described by the Singers is induced more by pressure resulting from deep pelvic thrusting than by touch.

Sex and Disability

Researchers at Trent University, in studying people with disabilities, found that the disabled are often seen as sexless and childlike (Scott & Humphreys, 2007). Such views are based on misconceptions. Some of these myths and stereotypes may be eroding, however, in part because of the success of the civil and social rights movements of the disabled.

A person may have been born with or acquire a bodily impairment or suffer a loss of function or a disfiguring change in appearance. Although the disability may require the person to make adjustments in order to perform sexually, most people with disabilities have the same sexual needs, feelings, and desires as people without disabilities. Their ability to express their sexual feelings and needs depends on the physical limitations imposed by their disabilities, their adjustment to their disabilities, and the availability of partners. The establishment of mature sexual relationships generally demands some distance from one's parents. Therefore, people with disabilities who are physically dependent on their parents may find it especially difficult to develop sexual relationships. Parents who acknowledge their children's sexual development can be helpful by facilitating dating. Far too often, parents become overprotective:

> Adolescent disabled girls have the same ideas, hopes, and dreams about sexuality as able-bodied girls. They will have learned the gender role expectations set for them by the media and others and may experience difficulty if they lack more substantive educational information about sexuality and sex function. In addition their expectations may come in conflict with the family, which may have consistently protected or overindulged the child and not permitted her to "grow up." . . . In many cases the families are intensely concerned about the sexual and emotional vulnerability of the daughter and hope that "nothing bad" will happen to her. They may, therefore, encourage her to wear youthful clothing and to stay a safe little girl. The families can mistakenly assume there may be no sexual life ahead of her and protect her from this perceived bitter reality with youthful clothing and little-girlish ways. The result can be, of course, that the young emerging woman may become societally handicapped in learning how to conduct herself as a sexual woman. She will be infantilized. (Cole, 1988, pp. 282–283)

In such families, young people with disabilities get the message that sex is not for them. As they mature, they may need counselling to help them recognize the normalcy of their sexual feelings and to help them make responsible choices for exploring their sexuality.

Unfortunately, most health-care professionals are not equipped to provide sexual counselling to the physically disabled. In a study of 226 health-care professionals in Ontario, 95% said that they had not been given adequate knowledge about sexuality and the physically disabled (Molloy & Herold, 1985). While they were highly supportive of the idea that the physically disabled should receive sexual counselling as part of their rehabilitation, relatively few had actually provided such counselling.

To what extent should caregivers assist the physically disabled to experience sexual pleasure? In Denmark, it is accepted for social workers to arrange for clients who do not have a sexual partner to engage in sex with a prostitute. In Barrie, Ontario, a group of health-care attendants sued the local association for the physically disabled over having to assist disabled clients with their sexual needs ("Workers cry foul," 1996). The attendants claimed they were fired after they refused to provide this service, which included helping clients put on condoms and get into bed to have sex as well as helping some clients to masturbate.

Physical Disabilities

According to Margaret Nosek and her colleagues (2004), sexual wellness, even among the disabled, involves five factors:

- Positive sexual self-concept; seeing oneself as valuable sexually and as a person
- Knowledge about sexuality
- Positive, productive relationships
- Coping with barriers to sexuality (social, environmental, physical, and emotional)
- Maintaining the best possible general and sexual health, given one's limitations

This model applies to all of us, of course. Let us now consider aspects of specific physical disabilities and human sexuality.

MULTIPLE SCLEROSIS Multiple sclerosis (MS) is a chronic, unpredictable disease that affects the nervous system. The tissue called myelin, which surrounds and protects nerve cells, disintegrates, leaving scar tissue in its place. MS impairs sexual functioning, and people with MS report more sexual problems than people without the disorder (Forbes et al., 2006; McCabe, 2004). However, there is a good deal of individual variation, and the progression of the disorder, and its effects, do not follow a straight line. Many people with MS in good relationships enjoy fine sex lives for many years.

Researchers at the University of Alberta (Esmail et al., 2007) interviewed couples in which the wives had MS to find out how the MS affected their sexual relationships. The wives reported that MS negatively affected their sexual functioning and enjoyment of sex, as well as their feelings of sexual desirability. They kept these feelings hidden from their husbands and instead focused on sexually pleasing their husbands. They worried that otherwise their husbands might decide to leave the relationship and find a new partner. Because the wives did not reveal their true sexual status, the husbands did not think that their spouses' sexuality had been affected by MS.

CEREBRAL PALSY **Cerebral palsy** does not generally impair sexual interest, capacity for orgasm, or fertility. Depending on the nature and degree of muscle spasticity or lack of voluntary muscle control, however, afflicted people may be limited to certain types of sexual activities and coital positions.

People with disabilities such as cerebral palsy often suffer social rejection during adolescence and perceive themselves as unfit for or unworthy of intimate sexual relationships, especially with people who are not disabled. They are often socialized into an asexual role. Sensitive counselling can help them understand and accept their sexuality, promote a more positive body image, and provide the social skills to establish intimate relationships.

SPINAL CORD INJURIES People who suffer physical disabilities as the result of traumatic injuries or physical illness must not only learn to cope with their physical limitations but also adjust to a world designed for nondisabled people. The majority of people who suffer disabling spinal cord injuries are young, active males. Automobile or pedestrian accidents account for about half of these cases. Other common causes include stabbing or bullet wounds, sports injuries, and falls. Depending on the location of the injury relative to the spinal cord, a loss of voluntary control (paralysis) can occur in either the legs (*paraplegia*) or all four limbs (*quadriplegia*). A loss of sensation may also occur in parts of the body that lie beneath the site of injury. The effect of spinal cord injuries on sexual response depends on the site and severity of the injury. Men have two erection centres in the spinal cord: a higher centre in the lumbar region

Cerebral palsy A muscular disorder that is caused by damage to the central nervous system (usually prior to or during birth) and is characterized by spastic paralysis.

Innovative Canadian Research

HELPING MEN WITH SPINAL CORD INJURIES TO EJACULATE

In an experimental study, researchers in Quebec (Courtois et al., 2007) found that some vibrators are far more successful than others in helping men with spinal cord injuries to ejaculate. Some who cannot ejaculate with a vibrator alone can ejaculate when taking the prescription oral drug Midodrine about 30 minutes prior to using the vibrator. Courtois et al. believe that with proper instruction and assistance, preferably in a hospital setting, the majority of men with spinal injuries should be able to ejaculate.

that controls psychogenic erections and a lower one in the sacral region that controls reflexive erections. When damage occurs at or above the level of the lumbar centre, men lose the capacity for psychogenic erections, the kinds of erections that occur in response to mental stimulation alone, such as when viewing erotic films or fantasizing. They may still be able to achieve reflexive erections from direct stimulation of the penis; these erections are controlled by the sacral erection centre located in a lower portion of the spinal cord. However, they cannot feel any genital sensations because the nerve connections to the brain are severed. Men with damage to the sacral erection centre lose the capacity for reflexive erections but can still achieve psychogenic erections so long as their upper spinal cord remains intact. When direct stimulation does not cause erection, the woman can insert the limp penis into the vagina and gently thrust her hips, taking care not to dislodge the penis.

Overall, researchers find that about three of four men with spinal cord injuries are able to achieve erections but that only about one in ten continues to ejaculate naturally (Spark, 1991). Others can be helped to ejaculate with the aid of a vibrator.

Although the frequency of sexual activity among men with spinal cord injuries tends to decline following the injury, about one out of three continue to engage in sexual intercourse (Komisaruk & Whipple, 2005). The men typically report increased interest in alternative sexual activities, especially those involving areas above the level of the spinal injury, such as the mouth, lips, neck, and ears.

Canadian Abilities Foundation
Provides information for the disabled on support groups in many cities across the country.
www.enablelink.org

Retention of sexual response in women also depends on the site and severity of the injury. Women may lose the ability to experience genital sensations or to lubricate normally during sexual stimulation. However, breast sensations may remain intact, making this area even more erotogenic. Most women with spinal cord injuries can engage in coitus, become impregnated, and deliver vaginally. A survey of 68 spinal cord–injured women showed that about half were able to achieve orgasm as a result of audiovisual erotic material combined with manual genital stimulation (Sipski et al., 2001).

Couples facing the challenge of spinal cord injury may expand their sexual repertoire to focus less on genital stimulation (except to attain the reflexes of erection and lubrication) and more on the parts of the body that retain sensation. Stimulation of some areas of the body, such as the ears, the neck, and the breasts (in both men and women), can yield pleasurable erotic sensations.

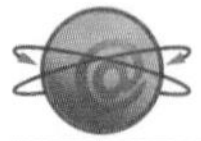

The Wellness and Disability Initiative of the BC Coalition of People With Disabilities
Collects and produces material about healthy sexuality and disability.
www.bccpd.bc.ca/programs/wdi/wdisub.htm

SENSORY DISABILITIES Sensory disabilities, such as blindness and deafness, do not directly affect genital responsiveness. Still, sexuality may be affected in many ways. A person who has been blind since birth or early childhood may have difficulty understanding a partner's anatomy. Sex education curricula have been designed specifically to enable visually impaired people to learn about sexual anatomy via models. Anatomically correct dolls may be used to simulate positions of intercourse.

Deaf people, too, often lack knowledge about sex. Their ability to comprehend the social cues involved in forming and maintaining intimate relationships may also be impaired. Sex education programs based on sign language are helping many hearing-impaired people become more socially perceptive as well as knowledgeable about the physical aspects of sex. People with visual and hearing impairments often lack self-esteem and self-confidence, problems that make it difficult for them to establish intimate relationships. Counselling may help them become more aware of their sexuality and develop social skills.

Arthritis A progressive disease characterized by inflammation or pain in the joints.

OTHER PHYSICAL DISABILITIES AND IMPAIRMENTS Specific disabilities pose particular challenges to, and limitations on, sexual functioning. **Arthritis** may make it difficult or painful for sufferers to bend their arms, knees, and hips during sexual activity. Coital positions that minimize discomfort may be helpful, as may applying moist heat to the joints before sexual relations.

A male amputee may find that he is better balanced in the lateral-entry or female-superior position than in the male-superior position. A woman with limited hand function may find it difficult or impossible to insert a diaphragm and may need to request assistance from her partner or switch to another method of contraception. Sensitivity to each other's needs is as vital to couples in which one member has a disability as it is to nondisabled couples.

Psychological Disabilities

People with psychological disabilities, such as developmental disabilities, are often stereotyped as incapable of understanding their sexual impulses. People with developmental disabilities are sometimes assumed to maintain childlike innocence through their lives or to be devoid of sexuality. On the other hand, it is widely acknowledged that individuals with limited mental capacities are vulnerable to sexual abuse and may not be able to provide consent to sexual activity with others (Plaut, 2006; Servais, 2006).

Some stereotype people with developmental disabilities in the opposite direction: as having stronger-than-normal sex drives and being incapable of controlling them. Some people with developmental disabilities do act inappropriately—by masturbating publicly, for example. The stereotypes are exaggerated, however, and even many people with developmental disabilities who act inappropriately can be trained to follow social rules.

Parents and caretakers often discourage people with developmental disabilities from learning about their sexuality or teach them to deny or suppress their sexual feelings. Although the physical changes of puberty may be delayed in people with developmental disabilities, most develop normal sexual needs. Most are capable of learning about their sexuality and can enter into rewarding and responsible intimate relationships (Gross, 2006a).

One of the greatest impediments to sexual fulfillment among people with disabilities is finding a loving and supportive partner. Some people engage in sexual relations with people with disabilities out of sympathy. By and large, however, the partners are other people with disabilities or nondisabled people who have overcome stereotypes that portray disabled people as undesirable. Many partners have had some prior positive relationship, usually during childhood, with a person who had a disability. Experience facilitates acceptance of the idea that a disabled person can be desirable. Depending on the nature of the disability, the nondisabled partner may need to be open to assuming a more active sexual role to compensate for the limitations of the partner with the disability. Two partners with disabilities need to be sensitive to each other's needs and physical limitations. People with disabilities and their partners may also need to expand their sexual repertoires to incorporate ways of pleasuring each other that are not fixated on genital stimulation.

The message is simple: Sexuality can enrich the lives of nearly all adults at virtually any age.

Applied Knowledge

A COMPREHENSIVE GUIDE TO SEX AND DISABILITY

Toronto educators Miriam Kaufman, Cory Silverberg, and Fran Odette (2007) conducted a survey among people living with disabilities regarding their beliefs, feelings, and unmet needs around sexuality. The survey responses provided the basis for their book, *The Ultimate Guide to Sex and Disability.* This sex guide is aimed at people living with disabilities, chronic pain, and illness and is inclusive of all ages and sexual identities.

The book is intended to improve readers' sexual self-esteem and sex lives, and to help them become sexually independent. Among the topics are

- where to find partners and how to talk to partners about sex and disability
- how to discuss sex with health-care providers
- instruction on masturbation, oral sex, vaginal penetration, and anal sex
- sexual positions to minimize stress and maximize pleasure
- how to deal with fatigue, pain, and spasms during sex
- adapting sex toys to make them work for you

The book also provides an extensive list of resources.

Summing Up

Each sense plays a role in sexual experience, but some play more of a role than others.

Visual information plays a major role in human sexual attraction. Visual cues can be sexual turn-ons or turn-offs.

Although the sense of smell plays a lesser role in governing sexual arousal in humans than in lower mammals, particular odours can be sexual turn-ons or turn-offs. Many organisms are sexually aroused by naturally produced chemicals called pheromones, but their role in human sexual behaviour remains unclear.

The sense of touch has the most direct effects on sexual arousal and response. Erogenous zones are especially sensitive to tactile sexual stimulation.

Taste appears to play only a minor role in sexual arousal and response.

Sounds can be turn-ons or turn-offs.

Alleged aphrodisiacs, such as foods that in some way resemble the genitals, have not been shown to contribute to sexual arousal or response.

Some drugs, such as antidepressants, dampen sexual arousal and response.

The alleged aphrodisiac effects of psychoactive drugs, such as alcohol and cocaine, may reflect our expectations of them or their effects on sexual inhibitions rather than their direct stimulation of sexual response. Alcohol is also connected with a liberated social role and thus provides an external excuse for dubious behaviour. Some people report increased sexual pleasure with an initial use of certain drugs, but frequent use can lead to sexual dysfunctions.

The brain plays a central role in sexual functioning. The cerebral cortex interprets sensory information as sexual turn-ons or turn-offs.

Sex hormones have organizing and activating effects on behaviour. Both men and women produce one genuine aphrodisiac: testosterone.

Many factors affect the sexual arousal of men and women.

Some women experience persistent sexual arousal. There are differing reactions to this.

Women show greater flexibility in sexual arousal patterns than do men.

Masters and Johnson found that the physiological responses of men and women to sexual stimulation are quite alike.

Sexual excitement is characterized by erection in the male and vaginal lubrication in the female.

The plateau phase is an advanced state of arousal that precedes orgasm.

The third phase of the sexual response cycle is characterized by orgasmic contractions of the pelvic musculature. Orgasm in the male occurs in two stages of muscular contractions. Orgasm in the female is manifested by contractions of the pelvic muscles that surround the vaginal barrel.

During the resolution phase, the body returns to its prearoused state.

Kaplan developed a three-stage model of sexual response consisting of desire, excitement, and orgasm. Kaplan's model makes it more convenient for clinicians to classify and treat sexual dysfunctions.

Basson argues that for women, intimacy plays a key role in sexual response.

Multiple orgasm is the occurrence of one or more additional orgasms following the first, within a short period of time and before the body has returned to a preplateau level of arousal.

Freud theorized the existence of two types of orgasms in women: clitoral and vaginal. Masters and Johnson found only one kind of orgasm among women. Singer and Singer suggested that there are three types of female orgasms: vulval, uterine, and blended.

People with disabilities may suffer from prejudice that depicts them as sexless or as lacking the means to express their sexual needs or feelings.

Cerebral palsy does not usually impair sexual interest, capacity for orgasm, or fertility, but afflicted people may be limited to certain types of sexual activities and coital positions. People with spinal cord injuries may be paralyzed and lose sensation below the waist. They often respond reflexively to direct genital stimulation.

Most people with developmental disabilities can learn the basics of their own sexuality and develop responsible intimate relationships.

Test Yourself

Multiple-Choice Questions

1. **There is some evidence that ______________________ have aphrodisiac effects.**
   a. antihypertensives and Prozac
   b. antidepressants and antihistamines
   c. bupropion and L-dopa
   d. amyl nitrate and alcohol

2. **Psychoactive drugs such as ______________ and ______________ are believed by many people to have aphrodisiac effects.**
   a. speed; ecstasy
   b. anti-androgens; anti-psychotics
   c. alcohol; cocaine
   d. antidepressants; antihistamines

3. **Alcohol may increase feelings of sexual arousal because**
   a. it has a stimulating effect on the nervous system
   b. it has a depressant effect on the nervous system
   c. people expect it to have an effect
   d. all of the above

4. **Frequent cocaine use can result in**
   a. urinary tract infections
   b. sexual dysfunctions
   c. phimosis
   d. damage to the foreskin

5. **Parts of the brain involved in sexual arousal and sexual response include the**
   a. cerebellum and corpus callosum
   b. cerebral cortex and limbic system
   c. thalamus and auditory bulb
   d. medulla and central sulcus

6. **Research suggests that gender differences in sexual arousal to visual stimuli may be related to different levels of activation in the**
   a. thalamus
   b. medulla
   c. olfactory bulb
   d. hypothalamus

7. **The body's basic physiological responses to sexual stimulation are vasocongestion and ______________.**
   a. orgasm
   b. resolution
   c. myotonia
   d. sex flush

8. **The three stages of Kaplan's model of sexual response are**
   a. desire, excitement, and orgasm
   b. plateau, desire, and arousal
   c. desire, resolution, and orgasm
   d. orgasm, plateau, and resolution

9. **Basson's model puts more emphasis on ______________ than either Masters and Johnson or Kaplan.**
   a. desire
   b. affection
   c. intimacy
   d. stimulation

10. **A major impediment to sexual fulfillment among people with disabilities is**
   a. the severity of the disability
   b. the absence of any sexual feelings or desires
   c. the lack of lubrication or erection
   d. the difficulty of finding a loving and supportive partner

Answers to the Test Yourself questions in each chapter are found on page 509.

Critical Thinking Questions

1. Compare and contrast Masters and Johnson's, Kaplan's, and Basson's models for sexual response.
2. You are a hearing-impaired student who uses a sign language interpreter in your human sexuality class. The interpreter seemed comfortable earlier in the semester, but now that topics are getting more personal, and the lectures are getting more graphic, the interpreter tells you that he is no longer willing to attend the lectures, and furthermore, that he really doesn't think anyone with a disability should even be thinking about sex. How might you deal with this issue?
3. If you are a woman, consider the following: Although every magazine you read has at least one article per month telling you how great it is to have multiple orgasms, you have difficulty having one, let alone several. How might this make you feel? Do you think that just because some women *can* have multiple orgasms, all women should?
4. If you are a man, consider the following: Although you know that women can have multiple orgasms, your partner sometimes has difficulty having just one. How does this make you feel? Do you think that the knowledge that women can have multiple orgasms puts pressure on males to provide them?

Visit MyPsychKit at www.mypsychkit.com, where you can do quizzes and link to additional resources on topics discussed in this text.

CHAPTER FIVE

Gender Identity and Gender Roles

Gender The psychological state of being female or being male, as influenced by cultural concepts of gender-appropriate behaviour; compare and contrast the concept of gender with *anatomic sex,* which is based on the physical differences between females and males.

Gender typing The process by which children acquire behaviour that is deemed appropriate to their sex.

Sexual differentiation The process by which males and females develop distinct reproductive anatomy.

Chromosome One of the rodlike structures found in the nucleus of every living cell that carry the genetic code in the form of genes.

Zygote A fertilized ovum (egg cell).

This chapter addresses the biological, psychological, and sociological aspects of **gender**. First we define gender as the psychological sense of being female or being male and the roles society ascribes to gender. Anatomic sex is based on, well, anatomy. But gender is a complex concept that is based partly on anatomy, partly on the psychology of the individual, and partly on culture and tradition.

Next we focus on sexual differentiation—the process by which males and females develop distinct reproductive anatomy. We then turn to gender roles—the clusters of behaviour that are deemed "masculine" or "feminine" in a particular culture. This chapter examines research findings on sex differences. We next consider **gender typing**—the processes by which boys come to behave in line with what is expected of men (most of the time) and girls with what is expected of women (most of the time). We also explore the concept of psychological androgyny, which applies to people who display characteristics associated with both gender roles in our culture.

Prenatal Sexual Differentiation

Over the years many ideas have been proposed to account for **sexual differentiation**. Aristotle believed that the anatomical difference between males and females was due to the heat of semen at the time of sexual relations. Hot semen generated males, whereas cold semen made females (National Center for Biotechnology Information, 2000).

When a sperm cell fertilizes an ovum, 23 **chromosomes** from the male parent normally combine with 23 chromosomes from the female parent. The **zygote**, the beginning of a new human being, is only 0.04 cm (1.75 in.) long. Yet, on this tiny stage, one's stamp as a unique individual has already been ensured—whether one will have black or blond hair, grow bald or develop a widow's peak, or become male or female.

The chromosomes from each parent combine to form 23 pairs. The twenty-third pair is the sex chromosomes. An ovum carries an X sex chromosome, but a sperm carries either an X or a Y sex chromosome. If a sperm with an X sex chromosome fertilizes the ovum, the newly conceived person will normally develop as a female, with an XX sex chromosomal structure. If the sperm carries a Y sex chromosome, the child will normally develop as a male (XY).

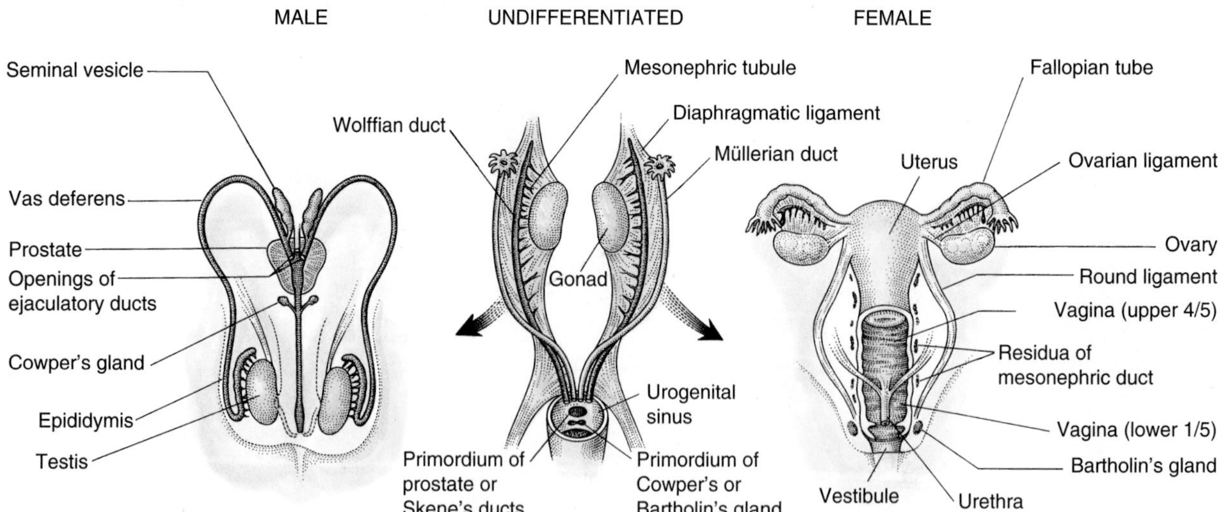

Figure 5.1 Development of the Internal Sex Organs From an Undifferentiated Stage at About Five or Six Weeks Following Conception.

After fertilization, the zygote divides repeatedly. After a few short weeks, one cell has become billions of cells. At about three weeks, a primitive heart begins to drive blood through the embryonic bloodstream. At about five to six weeks, when the **embryo** is only 0.5 cm to 1 cm (0.25 in. to 0.5 in.) long, primitive gonads, ducts, and external genitals whose gender cannot be distinguished visually have formed (see Figures 5.1 and 5.2). Each embryo possesses primitive external genitals, a pair of sexually undifferentiated gonads, and two sets of primitive duct structures, the Müllerian (female) ducts and the Wolffian (male) ducts.

Embryo The stage of prenatal development that begins with implantation of a fertilized ovum in the uterus and concludes with development of the major organ systems at about two months after conception.

During the first six weeks or so of prenatal development, embryonic structures of both genders develop along similar lines and resemble primitive female structures. At about the seventh week after conception, the genetic code (XX or XY) begins to assert itself, causing changes in the gonads, genital ducts, and external

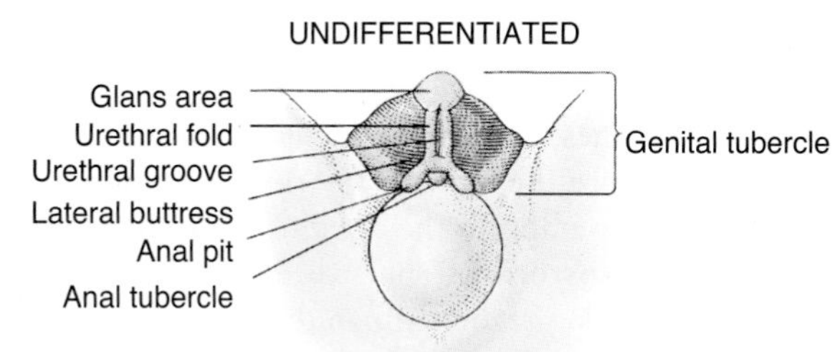

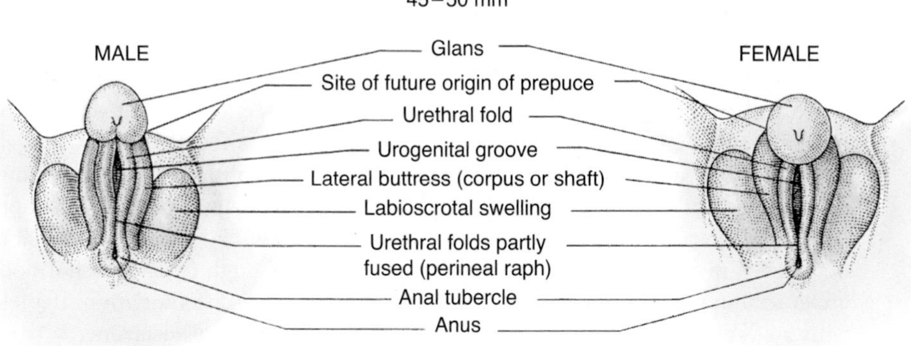

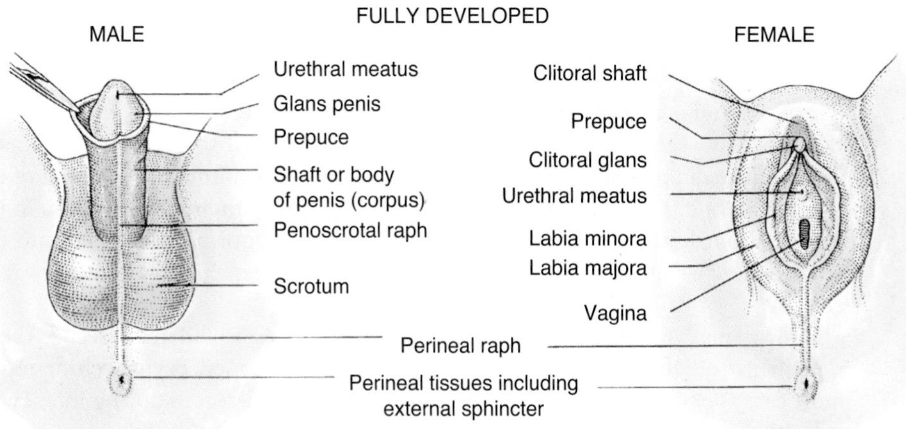

Figure 5.2 Development of the External Sex Organs From an Undifferentiated Stage at About Five or Six Weeks Following Conception.

genitals. Genetic activity on the Y sex chromosome causes the testes to begin to differentiate (National Center for Biotechnology Information, 2000). Ovaries begin to differentiate if the Y chromosome is absent. Those rare individuals who have only one X sex chromosome instead of the typical XY or XX arrangement also become females, because they too lack the Y chromosome.

Thus, the basic blueprint of the human embryo is female. The genetic instructions in the Y sex chromosome cause the embryo to deviate from the female developmental course.

By about the seventh week of prenatal development, strands of tissue begin to organize into seminiferous tubules. Female gonads begin to develop somewhat later than male gonads. The forerunners of follicles that will bear ova are not found until the fetal stage of development, about 10 weeks after conception. Ovaries begin to form at 11 or 12 weeks.

The Role of Sex Hormones in Sexual Differentiation

Without male sex hormones, or **androgens**, we would all develop into females in terms of anatomic structure (Federman, 1994). Once genes have done their work and testes develop in the embryo, they begin to produce androgens. The most important androgen, **testosterone**, spurs differentiation of the male (Wolffian) duct system (see Figure 5.1). Each Wolffian duct develops into an epididymis, vas deferens, and seminal vesicle. The external genitals, including the penis, begin to take shape at about the eighth week of development under the influence of another androgen, *dihydrotestosterone* (DHT). Yet another testicular hormone, one secreted during the fetal stage, prevents the Müllerian ducts from developing into the female duct system. It is appropriately termed the Müllerian inhibiting substance (MIS).

Small amounts of androgens are produced in female fetuses, but they are not normally sufficient to cause male sexual differentiation. In female fetuses, the relative absence of androgens causes degeneration of the Wolffian ducts and prompts development of female sexual organs. The Müllerian ducts evolve into fallopian tubes, the uterus, and the upper two-thirds of the vagina. These developments occur even in the absence of female sex hormones. Although female sex hormones are crucial in puberty, they are not involved in fetal sexual differentiation. If a fetus with an XY sex chromosomal structure failed to produce testosterone, it would develop female sexual organs.

Descent of the Testes and the Ovaries

The testes and ovaries develop from slender structures high in the abdominal cavity. By about 10 weeks after conception, they have descended so that they are almost even with the upper edge of the pelvis. The ovaries remain there for the rest of the prenatal period. Later they rotate and descend farther to their adult position in the pelvis. About four months after conception, the testes normally descend into the scrotal sac through the **inguinal canal**. After their descent, this passageway is closed.

In a small percentage of males, one or both testes fail to descend. They remain in the abdomen at birth. The condition is termed **cryptorchidism**. In most cases of cryptorchidism, the testes migrate to the scrotum during infancy. In still other cases, the testes descend by puberty. Men with undescended testes are usually treated through surgery or hormonal therapy, because they are at higher risk for cancer of the testes. Sperm production is also impaired because the undescended testes are subjected to a higher-than-optimal body temperature, causing sterility.

Androgens Male sex hormones.

Testosterone The male sex hormone that fosters the development of male sex characteristics and is connected with the sex drive.

Inguinal canal A fetal canal that connects the scrotum and the testes, allowing the latter to descend.

Cryptorchidism The condition defined by undescended testes.

Sex-Chromosomal Abnormalities

Abnormalities of the sex chromosomes can have profound effects on sexual characteristics, physical health, and psychological development. **Klinefelter syndrome**, a condition that affects about one in 500 males, is caused by an extra X sex chromosome, so the man has an XXY rather than an XY pattern. Men with this pattern fail to develop appropriate secondary sex characteristics. They have enlarged breasts and poor muscular development, and because they fail to produce sperm, they are infertile. They also tend to have mild mental retardation.

Turner syndrome occurs in about one of every 2500 females and is a consequence of having one rather than two X sex chromosomes. Females with the syndrome may not naturally undergo puberty, so hormone treatments are usually begun when pubertal changes would start to spur the growth of secondary sex characteristics.

The brain, like the genital organs, undergoes prenatal sexual differentiation. Testosterone causes cells in the hypothalamus of male fetuses to become insensitive to the female sex hormone estrogen. In the absence of testosterone, as in female fetuses, the hypothalamus does develop sensitivity to estrogen.

Sensitivity to estrogen is important in the regulation of the menstrual cycle of women after puberty. The hypothalamus detects low levels of estrogen in the blood at the end of each cycle and initiates a new cycle by stimulating the pituitary gland to secrete FSH. FSH, in turn, stimulates estrogen production by the ovaries and the ripening of an immature follicle in an ovary.

Klinefelter syndrome A sex-chromosomal disorder caused by an extra X sex chromosome.

Turner syndrome A sex-chromosomal disorder caused by loss of some X chromosome material.

Gender identity One's belief of being male or female.

Sex assignment The labelling of a newborn as a male or a female, also termed gender assignment.

Intersexual A person who possesses the gonads of one gender but external genitalia that are ambiguous or typical of the other gender. (Also termed pseudohermaphrodite.)

Gender Identity

Our **gender identity** is our psychological awareness or sense of being male or being female and one of the most obvious and important aspects of our self-concepts. **Sex assignment** (also called *gender assignment*) reflects the child's anatomic sex and usually occurs at birth. A child's sex is so important to parents that they may want to know "Is it a boy or a girl?" before they count fingers and toes.

Most children first become aware of their anatomic sex by about the age of 18 months. By 36 months, most children have acquired a firm sense of gender identity (Rathus, 2006).

Nature and Nurture in Gender Identity

What determines gender identity? Are our brains biologically programmed along masculine or feminine lines by prenatal sex hormones? Does the environment, in the form of postnatal learning experiences, shape our self-concepts as males or females? Or does gender identity reflect an intermingling of biological and environmental influences?

Gender identity is nearly always consistent with chromosomal gender. Such consistency does not, however, prove that gender identity is biologically determined. We also tend to be reared as males or females, in accordance with our anatomic genders. How, then, can we sort out the roles of nature and nurture, of biology and the environment?

Clues may be found in the experiences of rare individuals, **intersexuals**, who possess the gonads of one gender but external genitalia that are ambiguous or typical of the other gender. Intersexuals are sometimes reared as members of the gender other than their chromosomal gender. Researchers have wondered whether the gender identity of these children reflects their chromosomal and gonadal gender or the gender in accordance with which they were reared. Before going further with this, let us distinguish between hermaphrodites and intersexuals.

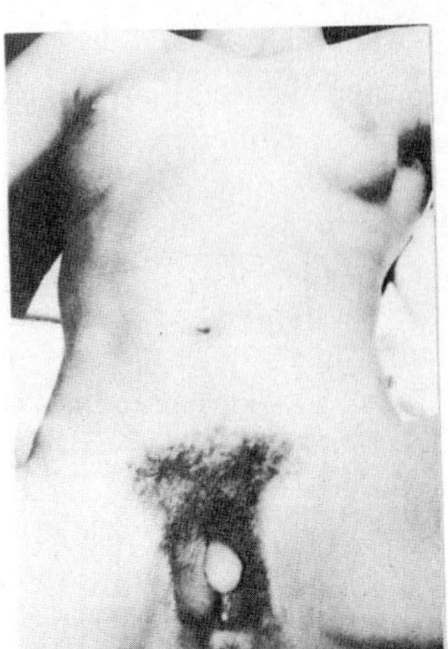

Figure 5.3 A Hermaphrodite.

This genetic (XX) female has one testicle and one ovary and the gender identity of a male.

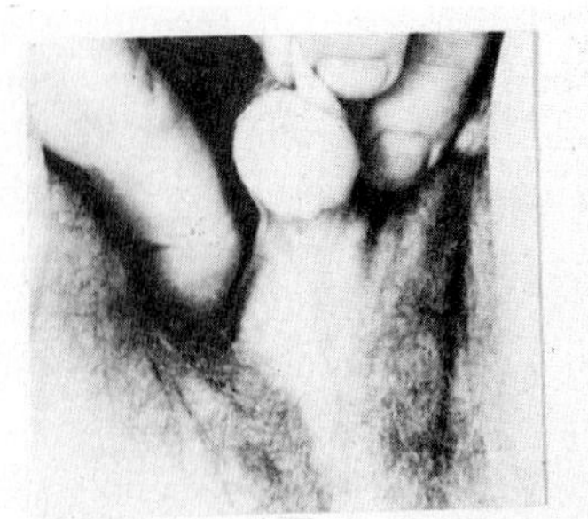

Figure 5.4 Intersexualism.

In congenital adrenal hyperplasia, a genetic (XX) female has female internal sexual structures (ovaries) but masculinized external genitals.

Hormonal errors during prenatal development produce various congenital defects. Some individuals are born with both ovarian and testicular tissue. They are called **hermaphrodites**, after the Greek myth of the son of Hermes and Aphrodite, whose body became united with that of a nymph while he was bathing. True hermaphrodites may have one gonad of each gender (a testicle and an ovary) or gonads that combine testicular and ovarian tissue.

Regardless of their genetic gender, hermaphrodites usually assume the gender identity and gender role of the gender assigned at birth. Figure 5.3 shows a genetic female (XX) with a right testicle and a left ovary. This person married and became a stepfather with a firm male identity. The roles of biology and environment remain tangled, however, because true hermaphrodites have gonadal tissue of both genders.

True hermaphroditism is extremely rare. More common is intersexualism, which occurs in perhaps one infant in 1000. Intersexuals have testes or ovaries, but not both. Unlike hermaphrodites, their gonads (testes or ovaries) match their chromosomal gender. Because of prenatal hormonal errors, however, their external genitals and sometimes their internal reproductive anatomy are ambiguous or resemble those of the other gender.

The most common form of female intersexualism is **congenital adrenal hyperplasia** (CAH), in which a genetic (XX) female has female internal sexual structures (ovaries) but masculinized external genitals (see Figure 5.4). The clitoris is so enlarged that it may resemble a small penis. The syndrome occurs as a result of excessive levels of androgens.

Another type of intersexualism, **androgen-insensitivity syndrome**, describes genetic (XY) males who, as the result of a mutated gene, have lower-than-normal prenatal sensitivity to androgens (Adachi et al., 2000; Hughes, 2000). Consequently, their genitals do not become normally masculinized. At birth their external genitals are feminized, including a small vagina, and their testes are undescended. Because of insensitivity to androgens, the male duct system (epididymis, vas deferens, seminal vesicles, and ejaculatory ducts) fails to develop. Nevertheless, the fetal testes produce Müllerian inhibiting substance, preventing the development of a uterus or fallopian tubes. Genetic males with

Hermaphrodites People who possess both ovarian and testicular tissue.

Congenital adrenal hyperplasia A form of intersexualism in which a genetic female has internal female sexual structures but masculinized external genitals.

Androgen-insensitivity syndrome A form of intersexualism in which a genetic male is prenatally insensitive to androgens. As a result, his genitals do not become normally masculinized.

Innovative Canadian Research

GENDER IDENTITY DISORDER IN BOYS AND GIRLS

One of Canada's leading researchers on gender identity is Ken Zucker, head of the Child and Adolescent Gender Identity Clinic at the Centre for Addiction and Mental Health in Toronto. This Toronto clinic maintains the world's largest database of children diagnosed with gender identity disorder. According to Zucker (2002), **intersexuality** is now the preferred term to encompass "syndromes characterized by some abnormality or anomaly in physical sex differentiation" (p. 4). This term is broader than the traditional *hermaphroditism*. Zucker's research demonstrates both biological and psychological factors. Biological influences were indicated in one of his studies, in which boys with gender identity disorder were more likely to be left-handed than a control group (Zucker et al., 2001). Social influences were indicated in another study, which found that boys were more than six times as likely as girls to be referred to a special clinic for gender identity disorder (Zucker et al., 1997). The first cross-cultural study in the field, conducted by Zucker and colleagues (Cohen-Kettenis et al., 2003) found that far more boys than girls were referred to gender identity clinics in the Netherlands as well as Canada. Zucker and his colleagues believe that society is less accepting of cross-gender in boys than in girls, so parents of cross-gender boys are more likely to see the situation as a problem in need of professional remedy. In both countries, boys were more likely to have problems with peers than were girls. This further supports the idea that cross-gender behaviour among girls is better tolerated than among boys.

androgen-insensitivity syndrome usually have no or sparse pubic and axillary (underarm) hair, because the development of hair in these locations is dependent on androgens.

Another type of intersexualism is named **Dominican Republic syndrome** because it was first documented in a group of 18 affected boys in two rural villages in that nation (Imperato-McGinley et al., 1974). Dominican Republic syndrome is a genetic enzyme disorder that prevents testosterone from masculinizing the external genitalia. The boys were born with normal testes and internal male reproductive organs, but their external genitals were malformed. Their penises were stunted and resembled clitorises. Their scrotums were incompletely formed and resembled female labia. They also had partially formed vaginas.

The boys with Dominican Republic syndrome also resembled girls at birth and were reared as females. At puberty, however, their testes swung into normal testosterone production, causing startling changes: The testes descended, their voices deepened, their musculature filled out, and their "clitorises" expanded into penises. Of the 18 boys who were reared as girls, 17 shifted to a male gender identity. Sixteen of the 18 assumed a stereotypical masculine gender role. Of the remaining two, one adopted a male gender identity but continued to maintain a feminine gender role, including wearing dresses. The other maintained a female gender identity and later sought gender-reassignment surgery to "correct" the pubertal masculinization.

Many scientists conclude that gender identity is influenced by complex interactions between biological and psychosocial factors. Some place relatively greater emphasis on psychosocial factors (Money, 1994). Others emphasize the role of biological factors (Collaer & Hines, 1995; Diamond, 1996; Legato, 2000), even though they allow that nurture plays a role in gender identity. The debate over the relative contributions of nature and nurture is likely to continue.

Intersexuality All the different types of syndromes characterized by some abnormality or anomaly in physical sex differentiation.

Dominican Republic syndrome A form of intersexualism in which a genetic enzyme disorder prevents testosterone from masculinizing the external genitalia.

Transsexualism/Transgenderism

In 1953, an ex-GI who journeyed to Denmark for a "sex-change operation" made headlines. She became known as Christine (formerly George) Jorgensen (Michel & Pédinielli, 2005). Since then, thousands of transsexuals (also called *transgendered people*) have undergone sex-reassignment surgery. (This surgery has also been

Transsexualism A condition in which people strongly desire to be of the other sex and live as a person of the other sex; referred to as *gender identity disorder* by the American Psychiatric Association.

Transgenderism (1) A synonym for transsexualism; (2) an activist movement seeking rights and pride for transgendered individuals (For many in the transgender—or "trans"—movement, the label *transgender* encompasses not only transsexual and transgender people, but also cross-dressers or transvestites, drag queens, drag kings, intersexed individuals, and anyone non-conventionally gendered [i.e., anyone identifying or behaving in a manner that runs counter to expected societal norms concerning the gender assigned them after birth].)

Gender dysphoria A sense of incongruity between one's anatomic sex and one's gender identity.

Homosexual transsexuals Extremely feminine gay men who seek sex reassignment.

Autogynephilic (aw-toe-gone-uh-FEE-lick) Descriptive of transsexuals who are sexually stimulated by fantasies that their own bodies are female; from roots meaning "self," "woman," and "love" or "desire."

referred to as *gender reassignment surgery*. In this text we use the word *sex* to refer to anatomic sex and the word *gender* to refer to the psychological state of feeling male or female. To be consistent, then, the surgery would be reassigning one's sex, not one's gender.)

In **transsexualism**, the individual wishes to possess the anatomic features of people of the other sex and to live as a person of the other sex. The term **transgenderism** is sometimes used as a synonym for transsexualism. However, transgenderism also refers to an activist movement that seeks rights and pride for various transgendered individuals, including not only transsexuals, but also intersexuals, transvestites, and anyone who is unconventionally gendered, that is, any person who identifies with or behaves in a manner that runs counter to traditional gender roles relevant to his or her assigned sex.

Many transsexuals undergo hormone treatments and surgery to create the appearance of the external genitals typical of the other sex. This can be done more precisely with male-to-female than female-to-male transsexuals. After surgery people can participate in sexual activity and even attain orgasm. One survey found that 85% of transsexual women attained orgasm during sexual activity (Lawrence, 2005). However, they cannot conceive or bear children.

What motivates transsexuals to live as people of the other sex? According to John Money (1994), transsexuals experience **gender dysphoria**. That is, they experience incongruity between their genital anatomy and their gender identity or role. Although they have the anatomic sex of one sex, they feel that they are a member of the other. The discrepancy motivates them to wish to be rid of their own primary sex characteristics (their external genitals and internal sex organs) and to live as a member of the other sex. A male-to-female transsexual perceives himself to be a female who, through some quirk of fate, was born with the wrong genital equipment. A female-to-male transsexual perceives herself as a man trapped in a woman's body.

However, some researchers contend that many men who seek to become women tend to fall into other categories: either men who are extremely feminine or men who are sexually aroused by the idea of becoming a woman. The first category includes **homosexual transsexuals**—men who are extremely feminine gays and not fully satisfied by sexual activity with other males (Blanchard, 1988, 1989). The second category refers to males who are **autogynephilic**, or sexually stimulated by fantasies of their own bodies as being female (Bailey, 2003a, 2003b; Lawrence, 2004).

Transsexuals vary in their gender sexual preferences. In a review of several studies, Lawrence (2007) concluded that there are two distinct types of male-to-female transsexuals—homosexual and nonhomosexual. In a laboratory experiment, 11 male-to-female transsexuals were shown video clips depicting sexual activity between two males, two females, and one male and one female. Five homosexual transsexual participants (attracted exclusively to males before sex reassignment) showed greater genital and subjective responses to male stimuli than to female stimuli, while six nonhomosexual transsexual participants showed the opposite pattern (Lawrence et al., 2005).

The conceptualizations of male-to-female (MTF) transsexuals presented by Blanchard, Bailey, and Lawrence have been highly controversial. In particular, transgender activists were upset by the assumption of Bailey and others that MTF transsexuals are motivated to seek sex changes by erotic interests rather than by feeling distressed over having the gender identity of one sex but the body of the other sex (Dredger, 2008).

Transgender Support Site
For individuals who are transgendered (transsexual) or are wondering whether they are transgendered.

www.heartcorps.com/journeys

Homosexual transsexuals usually show cross-gender preferences in play and dress during early childhood. Some report that they felt they belonged to the other sex for as long as they could remember (Zucker, 2005a, 2005b). Some male-to-female transsexuals recall that, as children, they preferred playing with dolls, enjoyed wearing frilly dresses, and disliked rough-and-tumble play. They were often perceived by their peers as "sissy boys." Some female-to-male transsexuals report that as children they disliked dresses and acted much like "tomboys." They preferred playing "boys' games" and doing so with boys. Female transsexuals appear to have an easier time adjusting than male transsexuals. Even during adulthood, it may be easier for a female transsexual to don men's clothes and pass as a slightly built man than it is for a brawny man to pass for a tall woman.

Phalloplasty The surgical creation of an artificial penis.

SEX REASSIGNMENT Surgery is one element of sex reassignment. Because the surgery is irreversible, health professionals conduct careful evaluations to determine that people seeking reassignment are competent to make such decisions and have thought through the consequences (Bockting & Fung, 2006). They usually require that the transsexual live openly as a member of the other sex for an extended trial period before surgery.

After the decision is reached, a lifetime of hormone treatments is begun. Male-to-female transsexuals receive estrogen, which fosters the development of female secondary sex characteristics. It causes fatty deposits to develop in the breasts and hips, softens the skin, and inhibits growth of the beard. Female-to-male transsexuals receive androgens, which promote male secondary sex characteristics. The voice deepens, hair becomes distributed according to the male pattern, muscles enlarge, and the fatty deposits in the breasts and hips are lost. The clitoris may also grow more prominent. In the case of male-to-female transsexuals, *phonosurgery* can raise the pitch of the voice (Bockting & Fung, 2006).

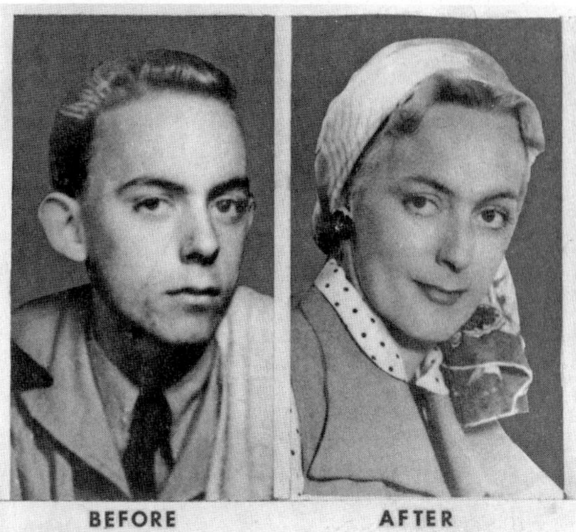

Christine Jorgensen.
The concept of sex reassignment entered our dictionaries in 1953 when Jorgensen had a sex-change operation.

Despite its complexity and intimacy, sex reassignment surgery is largely cosmetic. Medical science cannot construct internal genital organs or gonads. Male-to-female surgery is generally more successful. The penis and testicles are first removed. Tissue from the penis is placed in an artificial vagina so that sensitive nerve endings will provide sexual sensations. A penis-shaped form of plastic or balsa wood is used to keep the vagina distended during healing.

In female-to-male transsexuals, the internal sex organs (ovaries, fallopian tubes, uterus) are removed, along with the fatty tissue in the breasts. Some female-to-male transsexuals engage in a series of operations, termed **phalloplasty**, to construct an artificial penis, but the penises don't work very well and the procedures are costly. Therefore, most female-to-male transsexuals are content to have hysterectomies, mastectomies, and testosterone treatments (Bailey, 2003b).

Some transsexuals hesitate to undertake surgery because they are repulsed by the prospect of extreme medical intervention. Others forgo surgery so as not to jeopardize high-status careers or family relationships. Such people continue to think of themselves as members of the other sex, even without surgery.

OUTCOMES OF SEX REASSIGNMENT SURGERY

Most reports of the postoperative adjustment of transsexuals are positive (Smith et al., 2005). A follow-up study of 116 transsexuals at least one year after surgery found that most were content with the results and were reasonably well adjusted (Blanchard et al., 1985). Positive results for surgery were also reported in a study of 141 Dutch transsexuals (Kuiper & Cohen–Kettenis, 1988).

A study of 326 Dutch candidates for sex reassignment surgery found that about two-thirds (222 individuals) began hormone treatment, whereas 103 did not (Smith et al., 2005). Of the 222, about 15% dropped out before surgery. Generally speaking, after surgery the group was no longer gender dysphoric and most individuals functioned well sexually, psychologically, and socially. Only two male-to-female transsexuals regretted their decision. Male-to-female transsexuals outnumbered

Aaron Devor, formerly Holly Devor, is dean of graduate studies at the University of Victoria.

female-to-males, but postoperative adjustment was more favourable for female-to-males. One reason may be that society is more accepting of women who desire to become men (Smith et al., 2005). Female-to-male transsexuals tend to be better adjusted socially before surgery as well, so their superior postoperative adjustment may be nothing more than a selection factor.

Aaron Devor, formerly Holly Devor, is dean of graduate studies at the University of Victoria. Prior to 2002, he was a self-described "masculine lesbian" (Macqueen, 2003). Devor, who is one of the world's experts on transsexuals, provides a comprehensive analysis of transsexual adjustment phases in the book *FTM: Female-to-Male Transsexuals in Society* (1997). Based on interviews with 45 participants living in the U.S., Canada, and New Zealand, Devor concludes that the development of female-to-male transsexuals progresses through many stages. Table 5.1 provides a summary of these stages.

TABLE 5.1
Identity Development Stages: Female-to-Male Transsexualism

Development Stage	Some Characteristics	Some Actions Taken
Abiding Anxiety	Unfocussed gender and sex discomfort.	Preference for masculine activities and companionship.
Identity Confusion	First doubts about suitability of assigned gender and sex.	Reactive gender and sex conforming activities or preference for masculine activities and companionship.
Identity Comparison	Seeking and weighing alternative female identities.	Adoption of mannish lesbian identity. Secret identity as a man and a male.
Discovery	Learning that female-to-male transsexualism exists.	Accidental contact with information about transsexualism.
Identity Confusion	First doubts about the authenticity of own transsexualism.	Seeking more information about transsexualism.
Identity Comparison	Testing transsexual identity using transsexual reference group.	Start to disidentify as women and females. Start to identify as transsexual.
Identity Tolerance	Identify as probably transsexual.	Increasingly disidentify as women and females.
Delay	Waiting for changed circumstances. Looking for confirmation of transsexual identity.	Seeking more information about transsexualism. Reality testing in intimate relationships and against further information about transsexualism.
Identity Acceptance	Transsexual identity established.	Tell others about transsexual identity.
Delay	Transsexual identity deepens. Final disidentity as women and females. Anticipatory socialization as men.	Learning how to do gender and sex reassignments. Saving money. Organizing support system.
Transition	Changing genders, between sexes.	Gender and sex reassignments.
Identity Acceptance	Identities established as transsexual men.	Successful "passing" as men and as males.
Integration	Transsexuality mostly invisible.	Stigma management.
Identity Pride	Publicly transsexual.	Transsexual advocacy and activism.

Source: Devor, H. (1997). FTM: Female-to-Male Transsexuals in Society. *Bloomington, IN: Indiana University Press, p. 600.*

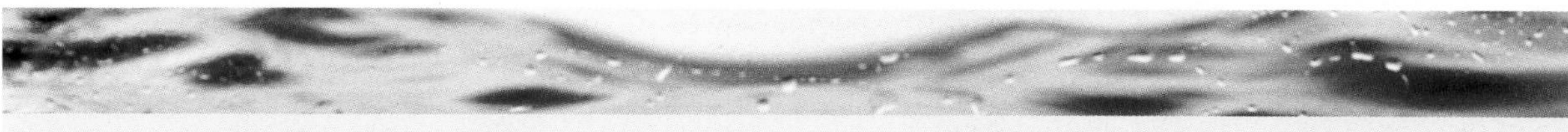

A World of Diversity

THIRD GENDER/THIRD SEX

The terms *third gender* and *third sex* describe people who are considered to be neither women nor men, along with the social category in societies that recognize three or more sexes. Being neither male nor female has ramifications not only in terms of the person's sex, but also in terms of the person's gender role, gender identity, and sexual orientation. In some cultures or to some individuals, a third sex or gender may represent an intermediate state between men and women, or it may represent a state of being both, as in the case of "the spirit of a man in the body of a woman." It may also represent the state of being neither (neuter), the ability to cross or swap sexes and gender roles, or another category that is independent of being male or being female. This last definition is favoured by those who argue for a strict interpretation of the third gender concept.

The "Ladyboys" of Thailand

The *kathoeys* (or "ladyboys") of Thailand are an example of a third gender. However, although a significant number of Thais perceive kathoeys as belonging to a third gender, including many kathoeys themselves, others see them as either a kind of man or a kind of woman.

Indigenous Cultures of North America: "Two-Spirits"

Native American cultures are also very much associated with multiple genders. They often contain social gender categories that are collectively known as *berdache* or Two-Spirit. Individual examples include the Winkte of Lakota culture, the *ninauposkitzipxpe* (manly-hearted woman) of the North Piegan (Blackfoot) community, and the Zapotec Muxe. Various scholars have debated the nature of such categories, as well as the definition of the term *third* gender. Different researchers may characterize the berdache as a gender-crosser, a mixed gender, an intermediate gender, or distinct third and fourth genders that are not dependent on male and female as primary categories. Those who have argued for the latter interpretation also argue that mixed-, intermediate-, cross- or nongender social roles should not be understood as truly representing a third gender.

Thai "Ladyboys"

Samoan "Fa'afafine"

The Fa'afafine of Samoa are feminine males who are attracted to and engage in sex with men who self-identify as heterosexual. They have been studied by Paul Vasey of the University of Lethbridge and Nancy Bartlett of Mount St. Vincent University (2007) who found that these feminine males are well accepted in Samoan society. Because of this acceptance, Fa'afafine stated that they never experienced distress about their cross-gender behaviours.

The Fa'afafine said that when they were growing up they preferred playing with girls' toys and played games that girls liked. Most disliked male activities such as rough-and-tumble play. Some recalled disliking their genitals. From a cross-cultural perspective, Vasey and Bartlett (2007) conclude that cross-gender behaviour and identification per se do not cause distress. Instead distress is caused when there is social condemnation of this behaviour.

Source: The above is adapted from the Wikipedia entry on third gender and obtains information from Agrawal (1997), Fausto-Sterling (1993), Goulet (2006), Hester (2005), Murray and Roscoe (1997), Roscoe (2000), Roughgarden (2004), Stockett (2005), Totman (2004), and Winter (2003).

Researchers have conducted relatively few studies of societal attitudes toward transsexuals. B. J. Rye (2001) from the University of Waterloo found that university students were about evenly divided in liking or disliking transsexuals. The students reported more negative attitudes toward transsexuals than toward homosexuals, however.

More recently, B. J. Rye and colleagues (2007) studied how having a transsexual person speak to a university class could change perceptions of transsexuals. In human sexuality classes, the researchers found that only 5% of the students had knowingly met a transgender person. The researchers invited a male-to-female transsexual to speak to classes of university students in a personal way about her own experience and about transgender issues in general. The students reported

A Closer Look

AN EXPERIMENT GONE WRONG

One of a pair of male twins, David Reimer, who lived in Winnipeg, lost much of his penis as a result of a circumcision accident. As this case study is related by Colapinto (2000), the parents wondered what to do. At that time, Johns Hopkins sexologist John Money believed that gender identity was sufficiently malleable that the boy could undergo sex reassignment surgery (have his testes removed and an artificial vagina constructed) and female hormone treatments, and be successfully reared as a girl.

For a number of years, the case seemed to supply evidence for the view that children may be psychosexually neutral at birth. The sex-reassigned twin, unlike his brother, seemed to develop like a "real girl," albeit with a number of "tomboyish" traits. But at the age of 14, when "she" was informed about the circumcision accident and the process of sex reassignment, David immediately decided to pursue life as a male. As an adult, he recalled that he had never felt quite comfortable as a girl—a view confirmed by the recollections of his mother. At the age of 25, he married a woman and adopted her children. He reported being sexually attracted to women only. According to researchers such as Milton Diamond (1996), this outcome would appear to support the view that gender identity may be determined to a considerable extent in the uterus, as the fetal brain is being exposed to androgens.

David Reimer

Reimer committed suicide with a sawed-off shotgun in 2004, at the age of 38. When Colapinto received the news from David's father, he wrote, "I was shocked, but I cannot say I was surprised. Anyone familiar with David's life—as a baby, after a botched circumcision, [after] an operation to change him from boy to girl—would have understood that the real mystery was how he managed to stay alive for 38 years, given the physical and mental torments he suffered in childhood and that haunted him the rest of his life" (Colapinto, 2004).

that hearing directly from a transsexual person was the best way to learn about transgender issues. They also reported that they had a better understanding of the issues and greater empathy toward transgender people after hearing the transsexual speak.

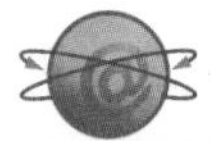

The Intersex Society of North America
For individuals with ambiguous genitals. The message is that people should feel free to be or remain what they are.
www.isna.org

Programs exist that help transsexuals come to terms with themselves and adjust to living in a society in which they rarely feel welcome. Central Toronto Youth Services has published *Families in TRANSition: A Resource Guide for Parents of Trans Youth*. It can be downloaded at **www.ctys.org**. Gay and lesbian organizations have expanded their services to include formerly excluded groups, such as transsexual and transgendered individuals. One such program is Supporting Our Youth in Toronto. This program provides cultural, recreational, and employment training opportunities as well as a mentoring and housing program (Lepischak, 2004). Such programs help create a sense of community for a group of people who feel alienated from the larger society.

BOYS WHO ARE REARED AS GIRLS Are children "psychosexually neutral" at birth? Can you surgically reassign a boy as a female, rear him as a girl, and have him feel that he is truly a girl as the years go on? Will cosmetic surgery, female sex hormone treatments, and laces and ribbons do it? Or will he be maladjusted and his male gender identity sort of "break through"? No one has sought to answer these questions by randomly selecting male babies and reassigning their genders. Evidence on the matter derives from studies of children who have lost their penises or failed to develop them through accidents or unusual medical conditions. One such case is discussed in the nearby A Closer Look box.

Gender Bending.
Some women, such as the one in the photo on the left, like the sensation of dressing up as a highly masculine male, such as shown in the photo on the right of the same woman dressed as a rugby player. According to Hamilton photographer Melanie Gillis, women who do this report feeling more powerful as a result of assuming this type of masculine persona.

Gender Roles and Stereotypes

"Why can't a woman be more like a man?" You may recall this lyric from the song that Professor Henry Higgins sings in the musical *My Fair Lady.* In the song, the professor laments that women are emotional and fickle, whereas men are logical and dependable. The "emotional woman" is a **stereotype**—a fixed, oversimplified, and sometimes distorted idea about a group of people. The "logical man" is also a stereotype, albeit a more generous one. Even emotions are stereotyped. People assume that women are more likely to experience feelings of fear, sadness, and sympathy, whereas men are more likely to experience anger and pride (Plant et al., 2000). Gender roles are stereotypes in that they evoke fixed, conventional expectations of men and women.

Our gender identities—our identification of ourselves according to our concepts of masculinity and femininity—do not determine the roles or behaviours that are deemed masculine or feminine in our culture. Cultures have broad expectations of men and women that are termed **gender roles**.

Stereotype A fixed, conventional idea about a group of people.

Gender roles Complex clusters of ways in which males and females are expected to behave.

Sexism The prejudgment that because of gender, a person will possess certain negative traits.

Sexism

We have all encountered the effects of **sexism**—the prejudgment that because of gender, a person will possess certain negative traits. These negative traits are assumed to disqualify the person for certain vocations or to prevent him or her from performing adequately in these jobs or in some social situations.

Sexism may even lead us to interpret the same behaviour in different ways, depending on whether it is performed by women or by men. We may see the man as

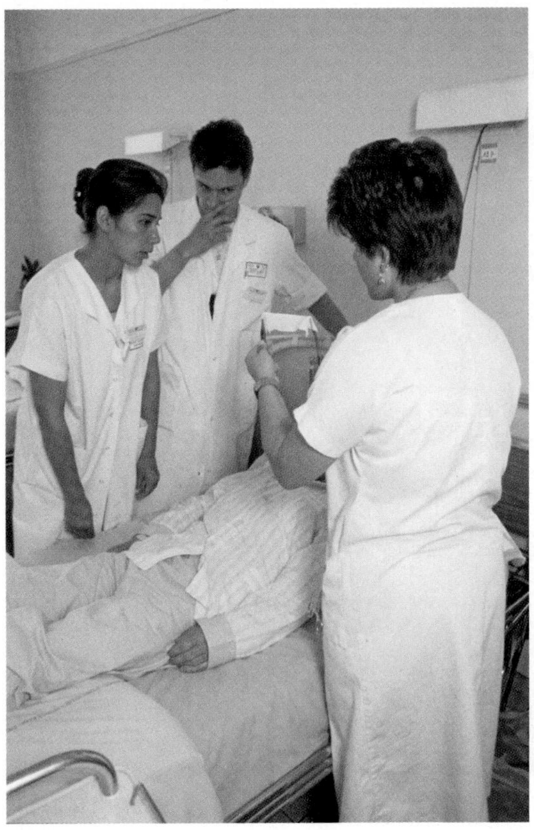

A Nurse.
If you think there is something wrong with this picture, it is because you have fallen prey to traditional gender-role stereotypes. Tradition has prevented many women from seeking jobs in "male" preserves such as construction work, the military, and various professions. Tradition has also prevented many men from obtaining work in "female" domains such as secretarial work, nursing, and teaching at the elementary school level.

"self-assertive" but the woman as "pushy." We may look upon *him* as flexible but brand *her* fickle and indecisive. *He* may be rational, whereas *she* is cold. *He* is tough when necessary, but *she* is bitchy. When the businesswoman engages in stereotypical masculine behaviours, the sexist reacts negatively by branding her abnormal or unhealthy.

The feminist movement in Canada has played a major role in reducing discrimination and helping to achieve greater equality for women. Marlene Mackie (1991) has traced the evolution of Canadian feminism in her book *Gender Relations in Canada*. She argues that feminism is not one homogeneous movement but has three major dimensions—liberal, socialist, and radical. According to Mackie, liberal feminists have worked to achieve gender equality through education and legislation. Socialist feminists have focused on structural inequalities, resulting not only from gender, but also from social class, sexual orientation, and ethnicity. Radical feminists have focused on issues such as sexual assault, harassment, and pornography, and have been instrumental in establishing sexual assault and battered women's shelters as well as in changing Canada's pornography laws.

In the 1990s, an increasing number of Canadian women became openly critical of what they viewed as extremism within the feminist movement. In *The Princess at the Window: A New Gender Morality*, Donna Laframboise (1996) critiqued feminists who appeared to espouse the stereotypes that men were inherently bad and exploitative in their relations with women and that women were morally superior to men. Indeed, because the extremist views of certain radical feminists were so widely publicized in the media, an increasing number of young women refused to identify themselves as feminists even though they upheld the most basic principles of feminism, such as the belief

Canadian Trends

GENDER AND THE WORKPLACE

Women, as well as men, now bring home the bacon. Today a majority of Canadian women work outside of the home. There has been particularly sharp growth in the employment rate of women with children. In 2006, 73% of all women with children less than age 16 living at home were part of the employed workforce, up from 39% in 1976. Among women without children, 80% of women under the age of 55 had jobs (Statistics Canada, 2006c).

Men and women have different attitudes to the workplace. A survey of 2500 Canadians found that female university graduates were more likely than male graduates to value respect, communication, and relationships in the work environment. Women were also more concerned than men about the gap between their desire for work-family balance and what their jobs allowed them to have in this respect (Perry, 2003).

Although more Canadian women today are entering a wider diversity of occupational fields, about 70% are still clustered in the traditional female occupational groups of teaching, nursing, clerical, sales, and service. Less than one-third of men are in these occupations (Drolet, 2002). Men are more likely to work in manufacturing, construction, and transportation, and in the natural sciences and engineering. The fact that there is still such a major gender segregation of occupations suggests the powerful role of gender stereotyping. This seems especially true for men who choose to enter what are considered to be female occupations. In a study of male nurses, Joan Evans at Dalhousie University found that many felt the need to justify their career choice, as they were often subject to ridicule and questioning about their sexuality (Evans, 2001).

in gender equality. Only 13% of Canadian female respondents to the national Compas survey said they definitely considered themselves to be feminists, and another 28% said they probably did (Compas, 1998).

Gender Roles and Aggression

In most psychological studies on aggression, males have been found to behave more aggressively than females. Nonetheless, females are likely to act aggressively under certain conditions. The rate of aggression among girls seems to have increased in recent years. Although bullying used to be associated with only boys, researchers, such as Wendy Craig at Queen's University and Debra Pepler of York University, are now also studying bullying among girls. As well, the Child Development Institute in Toronto offers a program called "Girls Connection" targeted specifically for aggressive girls ages 6 to 12 (Monsebraaten, 2006). The program is family centred and teaches anger management. University of Western Ontario researchers Anne Cummings and Alan Leschied (2002) have also conducted extensive research on aggression by girls and published their findings in *Research and Treatment for Aggression with Adolescent Girls.* They found that compared with boys, adolescent girls who are aggressive are more likely to experience isolation, powerlessness, and depression. Most of the girls came from broken homes and most had seen violence between their parents.

Today, bullying refers to more than physical aggression; the term has been broadened to include emotional abuse such as humiliating and degrading comments. In one study of schoolyard bullying in Toronto (Craig & Pepler, 1997), boys bullied more than girls and were more likely to bully victims of the same sex, usually by repeatedly targeting the same victim. Girls were as likely to bully boys as they were to bully other girls. There were no gender differences in the type of bullying and the use of aggression.

Two cases that occurred on opposite sides of Canada illustrate these trends. In Halifax, three teenage girls tortured another girl for two hours by repeatedly beating her unconscious, singeing her ears and tongue with cigarettes, and setting her on fire. Seeing the victim in the hospital, her father said she was so badly beaten he did not recognize her (Auld, 2007). In Vancouver, a 14-year-old girl hanged herself after suffering intense verbal abuse from a group of girls (Schmidt, 2002).

Among both genders, acting as a bully in elementary school is highly predictive of aggression in future dating relationships. An Ontario study found that bullies started dating earlier than non-bullying youth and were more likely to engage in physical and social aggression with their dating partners (Connolly, Pepler, Craig, & Taradash, 2000).

Gender and Health

Men's life expectancies are shorter, on the average, than women's. At the beginning of the twentieth century, women were expected to live 50.1 years, which was four years longer than men. By 1981 the gap increased to 7.1 years. The gender gap in life expectancy is narrowing but is still wide. Between 1979 and 2004, life expectancy among men rose 6.4 years, while among women, it increased only 3.8 years (Statistics Canada, 2006d). Life expectancy rose in 2004 for both sexes, to 80.2 years. For men, life expectancy increased to 77.8 years, while for women, it increased to 82.6 years.

The increased rate of smoking among women is a major reason why the life expectancy gap is narrowing.

Data on the health of Canadians were obtained from a longitudinal study that began in 1994. The 1998/99 survey was based on 14 619 respondents who were randomly chosen from across Canada (Catlin, 2002). The study's main conclusion was that women lead healthier lifestyles than men. Its key findings include the following:

- Women are more likely to consider health issues when selecting food.
- More men (56%) than women (38%) are overweight.
- More men (26%) than women (7%) engage in binge drinking at least once a month.
- Women are more likely than men to experience stress.
- Women are more resilient in response to illness, partly because they are more likely to have a network of friends who provide emotional support.

Another major gender difference is women's greater willingness to seek health care (Catlin, 2002). Men often let symptoms go until a problem that could have been prevented or readily treated becomes serious or life-threatening. Women, for example, are much more likely to check themselves for breast cancer than men are to check for the symptoms of prostate cancer. In 2003, the Canadian Community Health Survey with a sample of 135 000 individuals found that twice as many men as women had not looked for a regular family doctor. Slightly more men (16%) than women (14%) were considered obese. While rates of obesity have increased in Canada, they are much higher in the United States. The Canadian Community Health Survey was the first Canadian survey to ask about sexual orientation. Homosexuals and bisexuals were more likely than heterosexuals to report that they had unmet health-care needs and that they felt their lives were stressful.

On Becoming a Man or a Woman: Gender Typing

We have chronicled the biological process of sexual differentiation, and we have explored some gender differences in cognitive abilities and behaviour. In this section, we consider various explanations of **gender typing**.

Biological Perspectives

Biological views on gender typing tend to focus on the roles of genetics and prenatal influences in predisposing men and women to gender-linked behaviour patterns. Biological perspectives have also focused on the possible role of hormones in sculpting the brain during prenatal development.

THE EVOLUTIONARY PERSPECTIVE: IT'S ONLY NATURAL From the evolutionary perspective, the story of the survival of our ancient ancestors is etched in our genes. Those genes that bestow attributes that increase an organism's chances of surviving to produce viable offspring are most likely to be transmitted to future generations. We thus possess the genetic remnants of traits that helped our ancestors survive and reproduce (Buss, 2005). This heritage influences our social and sexual behaviour as well as our anatomic features.

According to the evolutionary perspective, men's traditional roles as hunters and warriors, and women's roles as caregivers and gatherers of fruits and vegetables, are bequeathed to us in our genes. Men are better suited to war and to the hunt because of physical attributes passed along since ancestral times. Upper-body strength, for example, would have enabled them to throw spears and overpower adversaries. Men also possess perceptual–cognitive advantages, such as superior visual–motor skills, which would have enabled them to aim spears or bows and arrows. Personality traits like aggressiveness also make for effective hunting.

Gender typing The process by which children acquire behaviour that is deemed appropriate to their gender.

Women, it is argued, are genetically predisposed to be empathic and nurturant because these traits enabled ancestral women to respond to children's needs and enhanced the likelihood that their children would flourish and eventually reproduce, thereby transmitting their own genetic legacy to future generations. Prehistoric women thus tended to stay close to home, care for the children, and gather edible plants, whereas men ventured from home to hunt and raid their neighbours' storehouses.

The evolutionary perspective is steeped in controversy. Although scientists do not dispute the importance of evolution in determining physical attributes, many are reluctant to attribute complex social behaviours, such as aggression and gender roles, to heredity. The evolutionary perspective implies that stereotypical gender roles—men as breadwinners and women as homemakers, for example—reflect the natural order of things. Critics contend that biology is not destiny; that our behaviour is not dictated by our genes.

PRENATAL BRAIN ORGANIZATION Researchers have sought the origins of gender-typed behaviour in the organization of the brain. Is it possible that the cornerstone of gender-typed behaviour is laid in the brain before the first breath is taken?

The hemispheres of the brain are specialized to carry out certain functions. In most people, the right hemisphere ("right brain") appears to be specialized to perform visual–spatial tasks. The "left brain" appears to be more critical to verbal functions, such as speech, in most people.

We know that sex hormones are responsible for prenatal sexual differentiation of the genitals and for the gender-related structural differences in the hypothalamus of the developing prenatal brain. Sexual differentiation of the brain may also partly explain men's (slight!) superiority at spatial-relations tasks, such as interpreting road maps and visualizing objects in space. Testosterone in the brains of male fetuses spurs greater growth of the right hemisphere and slows the rate of growth of the left hemisphere. This difference may be connected with the ability to accomplish spatial-relations tasks.

Might boys' inclinations toward aggression and rough-and-tumble play also be prenatally imprinted in the brain? Some theorists argue that prenatal sex hormones may masculinize or feminize the brain by creating predispositions that are consistent with gender-role stereotypes, such as rough-and-tumble play and aggressive behaviour in males (Cohen-Bendahen et al., 2005).

Psychological Perspectives

Children acquire awareness of gender-role stereotypes by the tender age of two to three (Rathus, 2006). Both boys and girls generally agree, when asked to describe the differences between the genders, that boys build things, play with transportation toys such as cars and fire trucks, enjoy helping their fathers, and hit other children. Both boys and girls also agree that girls enjoy playing with dolls and helping their mothers cook and clean and that they are talkative, dependent on others for help, and nonviolent. Psychologists have attempted to explain how children acquire such knowledge and adopt stereotypical behaviour patterns in terms of psychoanalytic, social–cognitive, and cognitive–developmental theories.

PSYCHOANALYTIC THEORY Sigmund Freud explained gender typing in terms of identification. Appropriate gender typing, in Freud's view, requires that boys come to identify with their fathers and girls with their mothers. Identification is completed, in Freud's view, as children resolve the **Oedipus complex** (which is sometimes called the Electra complex in girls).

According to Freud, the Oedipus complex occurs during the phallic period of psychosexual development, from the ages of three to five. During this period, the

Oedipus complex A conflict of the phallic stage in which the boy wishes to possess his mother sexually and perceives his father as a rival in love.

Socialization The process of guiding people into socially acceptable behaviour patterns by means of information, rewards, and punishments.

child develops incestuous wishes for the parent of the other gender and comes to perceive the parent of the same gender as a rival. The complex is resolved by the child's forsaking incestuous wishes for the parent of the other gender and identifying with the parent of the same gender. Through identification with the same-gender parent, the child comes to develop gender-typed behaviours that are typically associated with that gender.

SOCIAL–COGNITIVE THEORY Social–cognitive theorists explain the development of gender-typed behaviour in terms of processes such as observational learning, identification, and socialization. Children can learn what is deemed masculine or feminine by observational learning, as suggested by the results of an experiment by Perry and Bussey (1979). In this study, eight- and nine-year-old boys and girls watched adult role models indicate their preferences on each of 16 pairs of items—pairs such as toy cows versus toy horses and oranges versus apples. What the children didn't know was that the expressed preferences were made arbitrarily. The children then were asked to indicate their own preferences for the items represented in the pairs. The boys' choices agreed with the adult men's an average of 14 out of 16 times. Girls chose the pair item selected by the men an average of only 3 out of 16 times.

In social–cognitive theory, identification is viewed as a continuing and broadly based learning process in which rewards and punishments influence children to imitate adult models of the same gender—especially the parent of the same sex. Identification is more than imitation, however. In identification, the child not only imitates the behaviour of the model but also tries to become like the model in broad terms.

Socialization also plays a role in gender typing (Fagot et al., 2000). Almost from the moment a baby comes into the world, it is treated according to its gender. Parents tend to talk more to baby girls, and fathers especially engage in more roughhousing with boys. When children are old enough to speak, parents and other adults—even other children—begin to instruct children in how they are expected to behave. Parents may reward children for behaviour they consider gender-appropriate and punish (or fail to reinforce) them for behaviour they consider inappropriate for their gender. Girls are encouraged to practise caretaking behaviours, which are intended to prepare them for traditional feminine adult roles. Boys are handed Lego or doctor sets to help prepare them for traditional masculine adult roles.

Parental roles in gender typing are apparently changing. With more mothers working outside the home, daughters today are exposed to more women who represent career-minded role models than was the case in earlier generations. More parents today are encouraging their daughters to become career-minded and to engage in strenuous physical activities, such as organized sports. Many boys today are exposed to fathers who take a larger role than men used to in child care and household responsibilities.

Schools are also important socialization influences. Teachers often expect girls to perform better than boys in reading and language arts and have higher expectations of boys in math and science. Special programs in math and science held for girls after school and in the summer have helped bolster the girls' confidence and interest in these subjects.

Educators are becoming increasingly concerned about the fact that boys are failing in school at a much higher rate than girls. In Ontario, the high school dropout rate for boys is four times that of girls (Halley, 2004).

In Canada, more women than men attend university and women account for most of the growth in university enrollment. In 2001, 59% of Canadian undergraduate students were women (Statistics Canada, 2003a) and today the percentage of women at university is probably even higher.

Only recently have some educators proposed that special efforts need to be made to assist boys in catching up to the higher academic achievements of girls. The

Gender Typing Through Observational Learning.
According to social-cognitive theory, people learn about the gender roles that are available to them—and expected of them—at an early age. Gender schema theory adds that once children have learned the expected gender roles (i.e., the gender schema of their culture), they blend these roles with their self-concepts. Their self-esteem comes to be dependent on their adherence to the expected gender roles.

Durham District School Board in Whitby, Ontario, is one of the few school boards in the country to have implemented special teaching methods for improving the reading and writing skills of boys (Bauer, 2001).

COGNITIVE-DEVELOPMENTAL THEORY Psychologist Lawrence Kohlberg (1966) proposed a cognitive–developmental view of gender typing. From this perspective, gender typing is not the product of environmental influences that mechanically "stamp in" gender-appropriate behaviour. Rather, children themselves play an active role. They form concepts, or **schemas**, about gender and then exhibit behaviour that conforms to their gender concepts. These developments occur in stages and are entwined with general cognitive development.

According to Kohlberg, gender typing entails the emergence of three concepts: *gender identity*, *gender stability*, and *gender constancy*. Gender identity is usually acquired by the age of three. By the age of four or five, most children develop a concept of **gender stability**—the recognition that people retain their genders for a lifetime. Prior to this age, boys may think that they will become mommies when they grow up, and girls may think they will be daddies.

The more sophisticated concept of **gender constancy** develops in most children by the age of seven or eight. They recognize that gender does not change even when people alter their dress or behaviour. Hence gender remains constant even when appearances change. A woman who wears her hair short (or shaves it off) remains a woman. A man who dons an apron and cooks dinner remains a man.

According to cognitive–developmental theory, children are motivated to behave in gender-appropriate ways once they have established the concepts of gender stability and gender constancy. They then make an active effort to learn which behaviour patterns are considered "masculine" and which "feminine." Once they obtain this information, they imitate the "gender-appropriate" pattern.

GENDER SCHEMA THEORY: AN INFORMATION-PROCESSING APPROACH Gender schema theory proposes that children develop a **gender schema** as a means of organizing their perceptions of the world (Bem, 1993). A

Schema Concept; way of interpreting experience or processing information.

Gender stability The concept that people retain their genders for a lifetime.

Gender constancy The concept that people's genders do not change, even if they alter their dress or behaviour.

Gender schema A cluster of mental representations about male and female physical qualities, behaviours, and personality traits.

gender schema is a cluster of mental representations about male and female physical qualities, behaviours, and personality traits. Gender gains prominence as a schema for organizing experience because of society's emphasis on it. Even young children start to mentally group people of the same gender in accordance with the traits that represent that gender.

Once children acquire a gender schema, they begin to judge themselves in accordance with traits considered appropriate to their genders. In doing so, they blend their developing self-concepts with the prominent gender schema of their culture. The gender schema furnishes standards for comparison. Children with self-concepts that are consistent with the prominent gender schema of their culture are likely to develop higher self-esteem than children whose self-concepts are inconsistent.

Gender Roles and Sexual Behaviour

Gender roles have had a profound influence on dating practices and sexual behaviour. Children learn at an early age that men usually make dates and initiate sexual interactions, whereas women usually serve as the "gatekeepers" in romantic relationships (Bailey et al., 2000). In their traditional role as gatekeepers, women are expected to wait to be asked out and to screen suitors. Men are expected to make the first (sexual) move and women to determine how far advances will proceed.

Because women have the gatekeeper role, most men believe that women have the greater sexual power. When Canadians were asked "Who do you think has more control over whether a couple will have sex?" more men (65%) than women (47%) believed the woman does (Compas, 1998).

The cultural expectation that men are initiators and women are gatekeepers is embedded within the larger stereotype that men are sexually aggressive and women are sexually passive. Men are expected to have a higher number of sex partners than women do (Mikach & Bailey, 1999). Men consistently report having more sexual partners than do women. In comparing data regarding number of partners in Canada, the United States, Great Britain, and Norway, Tom Smith (1992) from the University of Chicago argues that gender differences in reporting (with men overreporting and women underreporting) seem to be the most likely explanation for the discrepancy.

Men not only initiate sexual encounters; they are also expected to dictate all the "moves" thereafter, just as they are expected to take the lead on the dance floor. The 1998 Compas survey asked Canadians "When a man and a woman decide to have sex, who do you think gets them in the mood first?" Three times as many people (60%) believed that it is the man, with only 20% believing it is the woman, and the rest saying that it is both genders equally.

According to the stereotype, women are supposed to let men determine the choice, timing, and sequence of sexual positions and techniques. Unfortunately, the stereotype favours men's sexual preferences, denying women the opportunity to give and receive their preferred kinds of stimulation.

The stereotypical masculine role also imposes constraints on men. Men are expected to take the lead in bringing their partners to orgasm, but they should not ask their partners what *they* like because men are expected to be natural experts. ("Real men" not only don't eat quiche; they also need not ask women how to make love.)

Fortunately, more flexible attitudes are emerging. Women are becoming more sexually assertive, and men are becoming more receptive to expressing tenderness and gentleness. Still, the roots of traditional gender roles run deep.

Men as Overaroused, Women as Underaroused

According to another stereotype, men become sexually aroused at puberty and remain at the ready throughout adulthood. A study conducted at an Ontario university found that 85% of the women believed that "it's easy for a woman to sexually arouse a man if she really wants to" (Clements-Schreiber & Rempel, 1995).

Women, the stereotype continues, do not share men's natural interest in sex, and a woman discovers her own sexuality only when a man ignites her sexual flame. This stereotype denies that "normal" women have spontaneous sexual desires or are readily aroused.

It was widely believed in the Victorian period (even by so-called sex experts!) that women were naturally asexual and "unbothered" by sexual desires. The contemporary residues of this stereotype hold that women do not enjoy sex as much as men and that women who openly express their sexual desires are "whores" or "sluts." In the Ontario study, however, only 25% of the women agreed that "in general, women do not really enjoy sex as much as men" (Clements-Schreiber & Rempel, 1995). But when the 1998 Compas survey asked "Who has the greater sexual needs?" far more Canadians (58%) said that men do, with only 9% saying that women do and about one-quarter believing that both women and men have equal sexual needs. There were no gender differences in the responses. Considerable gender differences were revealed, however, in the acceptability of casual sex. When single Canadians were asked if they would have sexual intercourse with an attractive person the same day they had just met, about two-thirds of the women and only one-fifth of the men said they definitely would not (Compas, 1998).

Gender and Sexual Advice Literature

Carleton University researchers Erin Connell and Alan Hunt (2006) have analyzed marital and sexual advice literature for heterosexuals from the early part of the twentieth century to the present. They found that throughout the years gender stereotypes heavily influenced the type of relational and sexual advice provided to couples. Throughout the first part of the twentieth century, this literature presented the husband as the wife's tutor and initiator of sex, while the wife was the passive student. It was the husband's responsibility to arouse his wife and to control the speed of his own orgasm. The assumption was that wives entered marriage as inexperienced virgins who lacked any knowledge of how to obtain sexual pleasure. In the period between the First and Second World Wars, marriage manuals (as they were called) increasingly emphasized the necessity of husbands providing their wives with sexual pleasure. During the sexual revolution of the 1960s, sex was no longer tied to marriage and marriage manuals were renamed sex manuals. The focus was then on the need for couples to master new sexual techniques, so as to maximize sexual pleasure. In the following years, research showed that many women did have strong sexual desires, yet the sex manuals still continued to focus on gender differences. With the onset of the HIV/AIDS epidemic in the 1980s, sexual advice books have emphasized, and continue to emphasize, the need to be sexually responsible through safer sex strategies.

THE DOUBLE STANDARD The stereotype that women are undersexed also supports the traditional double standard: It is natural for men to sow their wild oats, but women who are sexually active outside of committed relationships are sluts or *nymphomaniacs.* In a study by University of Guelph researchers of university students and patrons at a singles bar (Milhausen & Herold, 2001), the majority (79% men and 89% women) believed that women who have many sexual partners are judged more harshly than men who have many partners. In another study by the same researchers, the majority of women also believed that women are more severe in their judgments of women's sexual behaviour than men are (Milhausen & Herold, 1999).

Of the respondents in the Milhausen and Herold 2001 study, twice as many women (67%) as men (35%) believed that men have greater sexual freedom than women. The women thought it was easier for men to have many partners and to

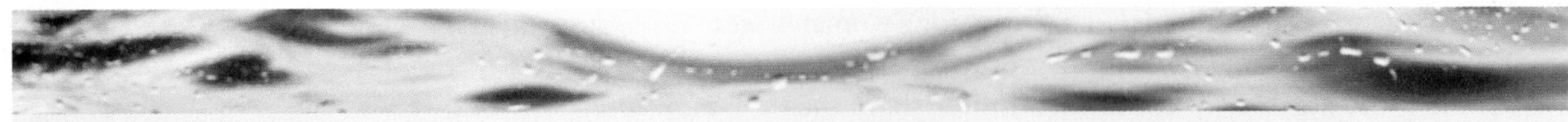

A World of Diversity

THE EYE THAT ROVES AROUND THE WORLD?

One of the more controversial sex differences is the suggestion that males are naturally polygamous, whereas females are naturally monogamous. If this were so, it would place a greater burden on societies in which men are expected to remain loyal to their mates. If the man strayed, after all, he could have the attitude, "Don't blame me. It's in my genes." Women, moreover, might wonder how realistic it is to expect that their partners will remain faithful.

Evolutionary psychologists have hypothesized a *sexual strategies theory,* which holds that men and women differ in their long-term and short-term mating strategies, with men more interested in sexual variety in the short term (Klusmann, 2002). In the long term, both males and females may seek a heavy investment in a relationship, feelings of love, companionship, and a sharing of resources. Even so, men are hypothesized to place more value on signals of fertility and reproductive value, as found in a woman's youth and physical appearance. Women are hypothesized to place relatively more value on a man's social status, maturity, and resources–cues that are relevant to his ability to provide over the long term. The qualities that men and women seek are believed to help solve adaptive problems that humans have faced over their evolutionary history.

In the short term, men are more interested in one-night stands and relatively brief affairs. According to the theory, this is because men would have a greater chance of contributing their genes to future generations by impregnating as many women as possible. Women, evolutionarily speaking, would have little to gain from such encounters. Impregnation requires a long-term commitment to child-rearing, and evolutionary forces would favour the survival of the children of women who created a long-term nurturing environment.

Because a "universal" form of behaviour is more likely to be embedded in people's genes, the evolutionary theory of different sexual strategies would find support if males and females from various cultures showed similar sex differences in short-term mating strategies. In seeking just such evidence, David Schmitt (2003) supervised a survey of 16 288 people across 10 major regions of the world, including North America, South America, Western Europe, Eastern Europe, Southern Europe, Middle East, Africa, Oceania, South/Southeast Asia, and East Asia. He indeed found that sex differences in the desire for sexual variety were culturally universal.

Do Men Around the World Have Roving Eyes?
A study of 10 different areas of the world found that in every culture surveyed, men were more likely than women to desire multiple sex partners. According to the sexual strategies theory, this sex difference reflects human adaptation to environmental forces. Does this research finding mean that it is "unnatural" to expect men to remain faithful to their partners?

Table 5.2 and Figure 5.5 reveal some of Schmitt's key findings as to the desire for variety in short-term and long-term relationships. When asked whether they would like to have more than one sex partner in the next month, men from all 10 areas of the world were significantly more likely than women to say that they would. For example, 23.1% of North American men would like more than one partner, as compared with just 2.9% of North American women (Table 5.2). When asked about the mean (average) number of sex partners they would like to have over the next 30 years, men from every area said they would like to have significantly more sex partners than the women (Figure 5.5).

The chances that any sex differences within a given region are due to chance are less than one in 1000 ($p < 0.001$).

We cannot conclude that these research findings, intriguing as they are, "prove" the validity of the evolutionary approach to understanding sex differences in "sexual strategies." For example, we could point to details such as the fact that Oceanic women reported that they wanted more sex partners in the long term than did African men (Figure 5.5). We can also accept the universality of the finding but consider rival explanations for the data. For example, in a world with common global communication, it might not be surprising that there is worldwide overlap in gender roles. This overlap might affect the ways in which parents and cultural institutions influence children around the world.

TABLE 5.2

Sex Differences in the Percentage of Men and Women Who Desire More Than One Sex Partner "in the Next Month" Across 10 World Regions

World Region	Percentage of Men Wanting More Than One Sexual Partner	Percentage of Women Wanting More Than One Sexual Partner
North America	23.1%	2.9%
South America	35.0	6.1
Western Europe	22.6	5.5
Eastern Europe	31.7	7.1
Southern Europe	31.0	6.0
Middle East	33.1	5.9
Africa	18.2	4.2
Oceania	25.3	5.8
South/Southeast Asia	32.4	6.4
East Asia	17.9	2.6

Source: Table 5. Schmitt, D. P. (2003). Universal sex differences in the desire for sexual variety: Tests from 52 nations, 6 continents, and 13 islands. Journal of Personality and Social Psychology, *85(1), 85-104.*

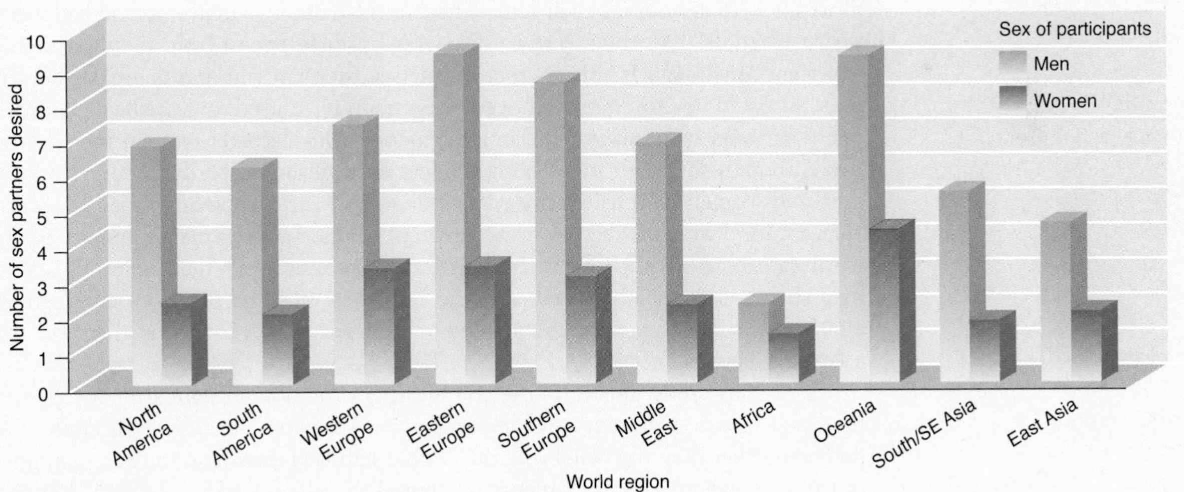

Figure 5.5 Mean Number of Sexual Partners Desired by Men and Women "in the Next 30 Years" Across 10 World Regions.

Source: Schmitt, D. P. (2003). Universal sex differences in the desire for sexual variety: Tests from 52 nations, 6 continents, and 13 islands. Journal of Personality and Social Psychology, *85(1), 85–104.*

TABLE 5.3

Word Categories Used to Describe Men and Women Having Many Sexual Partners

	Descriptions of Men		Descriptions of Women	
	Men	**Women**	**Men**	**Women**
Sexual predator	38%	37%	0%	0%
Promiscuous	40	30	75	66
Psychologically damaged	10	3	7	9
Stud	25	8	0	0
Sexually liberated	11	5	8	16

Source: Milhausen, R. R. and Herold, E. H. (2001). Reconceptualizing the sexual double standard. Journal of Psychology and Human Sexuality, *13, 63–83.*

engage in casual sex; the men, on the other hand, felt that women have greater freedom because they are the ones who decide whether or not sex will occur. The men typically felt that they were put at a disadvantage because they want sex more than women do.

Although most respondents believed a double standard exists in Canada, the majority personally endorsed a single standard for both women and men. This was determined by measuring attitudes toward such behaviours as watching sexually explicit videos and having many sexual partners. While only a minority of men held a sexual double standard, a minority of women held a reverse double standard whereby they judged the behaviour of men more negatively than that of women.

In another possible indication of a reverse double standard, both genders were more likely to discourage their female friends from dating a man who had had many sexual partners than they were to discourage a male friend from dating a highly experienced woman. It appears that people see the man who has many partners as more likely to be exploitative. Indeed, a common term used to describe a man with many partners was "player," meaning someone who deceives women into having sex. Although the majority of both genders used negative words to describe both men and women who had many partners, none of the respondents used the word "player" for a woman who has many partners. (Table 5.3 presents a summary of the word categories used.) Given the heightened awareness of such issues as sexual harassment and sexual assault, and the fact that most perpetrators are men, it appears that more negative evaluations of male sexuality exist today than was the case a few years ago.

The 2001 study illustrates the complexity of the double standard concept and the need to use a diversity of measures when studying the topic. Certainly, the divergence between the belief that the double standard exists and the fact that most of the respondents did not support it themselves calls for more research. Further research is also needed with a diversity of samples. It may be, for example, that the double standard is still practised among certain ethnic groups and in lower-income groups (Milhausen & Herold, 2001).

Highly Sexual Women

Despite the stereotype that women are undersexed, they are no less arousable than men. Nor do they wait for men to discover their sexuality. Long before they have intimate relationships, children of both genders routinely discover that touching their genitals produces pleasurable sensations.

Jocelyn Wentland (2006), as a graduate student at the University of Guelph, conducted an online survey with the objective of comparing women who were highly sexual with women who were not highly sexual. The sample of 1549 involved university students as well as a diversity of women from various communities.

More than 80% of the highly sexual women agreed that

- They want sex more than other people do;
- They think about sex more than other women do;
- They are confident about their sexual ability;
- They are comfortable initiating sex with a partner;
- They communicate their sexual desires to a partner; and
- They enjoy watching erotic videos that turn them on.

Several of the study participants said it was important for society to recognize that many women are highly interested in sex and in obtaining sexual pleasure.

Many women are attempting to change the perception of women as not being interested in sex. Sex therapist Joy Davidson (2004) in her book *Fearless Sex* encourages women to

- let go of sexual inhibitions and "bad girl" attitudes
- electrify their libidos
- liberate their most daring fantasies
- feel good about their "kinkier" sexual desires and explore them safely

In her interviews with women in Canada and the U.S., Canadian author Wendy Dennis (1992) found that some of the women specifically wanted men to be informed that women's sex drive can be just as strong as men's. This perspective is reinforced by female singers such as Nelly Furtado, whose best-selling album *Loose* contains the singles "Promiscuous" and "Maneater". Furtado states that her album is reflective of a "late blooming sexuality." "I'm admitting to all my fans that I am a woman and I love sex" (Wheeler, 2006). There are also many sex blogs put on the internet of women who openly discuss their strong sex drives. (See Chapter 15.)

In determining the strength of women's sex drive, age is an important factor to consider. Researchers surveyed women from different parts of Canada and the U.S. to determine whether there was any truth to the stereotype that women reach their sexual "peak" in their early thirties (Schmitt et al., 2002). While women in their early thirties did in fact report higher levels of sexual desire than women in any of the other age groups, they did not report having more partners. The findings were similar for both Canadian and American women. The researchers concluded that women in the 30 to 34 age group were more lustful than the average of all other women, thus supporting the idea of a sexual peak for this age group. Yet the researchers also cautioned that their findings were exploratory and that more research would be needed to confirm their conclusions.

In recent years the media have turned the spotlight on women who have sex with younger men. "Cougars" are women in their thirties and over who seek out younger men solely for sex. In her book *Cougar*, *Toronto Sun* columnist Valerie Gibson (2002) describes dating younger men as liberating, empowering, and fun. A self-proclaimed pioneer cougar, Gibson says cougars want lots of great sex with hot young men.

A trend toward casual sex is also seen among certain groups of lesbians. In Toronto, a group of lesbians rented a gay male bathhouse on a monthly basis to provide a supportive environment for women who wanted to have casual sex with other

"Cougars" are women in their thirties and over who seek out younger men solely for sex.

women. They named this bathhouse the "Pussy Palace." In her book *Good Girls Do: Sex Chronicles of a Shameless Generation*, Simona Chiose (2001) describes her visit to the Pussy Palace. She quotes one of the organizers: "We are socialized to not own our desires. The bathhouse challenges that. We're all here because we're horny" (p. 55). Chiose details the various activities that transpired at the Palace, including strip-tease dancing, masturbation, group sex, and watching lesbian sex videos. She argues that the women were able to engage in behaviours that they might not have otherwise because they were in an environment where they did not fear being judged: "I think of that night as a walk on the wild side of female sexuality, of what women are capable of and of how open they can be about their desires" (p. 56).

Yet, despite her acceptance of casual sex for others, Chiose notes that she has difficulty in accepting casual sex for herself:

> I have always been envious of friends I've had who have said in passing that they were going to meet a new man for an evening and in response to my question as to whether they thought it might become something, shrugged and said they didn't want it to be. They just wanted to get laid, to have a moment of physical and emotional union with someone they didn't know very well nor did they wish to know them. I can't do it and I'm sorry for that sometimes—for not being able to leave my thinking self behind and simply immerse myself in experience—but I am a product of the world I grew up in and it's pointless for me to try. All I would get is a nervous breakdown. (p. 53)

We end the section on gender and sex behaviour with a note of caution. Our society tends to overemphasize gender differences. In many situations these differences may actually be quite small, and there is usually greater variation within each gender than between the genders (Muehlenhard, 2000). Sometimes other variables may account for the gender difference. For example, the Compas survey of Canadians found that the respondent's age dramatically affects findings regarding gender and the reported age of first sexual intercourse. Among older Canadians, men consistently report having had intercourse at much earlier ages than women. However, among Canadians in their twenties, there is hardly any difference (Fischtein & Herold, 2002).

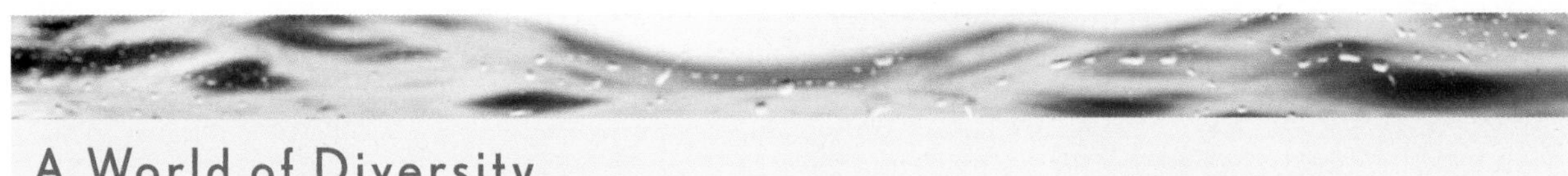

A World of Diversity

WHAT DO MEN VALUE MOST?

An international study of 27 000 men in eight countries (Germany, U.S., U.K., Spain, Brazil, Mexico, Italy, and France) analyzed characteristics of masculinity and sexual functioning (Sand et al., 2008). Contrary to the stereotype that men would value sexual performance the highest, Sand et al. found that the men valued most the characteristics of being honourable, self-reliant, and respected. These characteristics were seen by the research participants as more central to their vision of masculinity than were being seen as attractive, sexually active, or successful with women. Also, the men ranked good health, harmonious family life, and good relationships with a partner as more important to their quality of life than sexual concerns. Most importantly, across all of the societies and age ranges, the men said they valued couple relationships as more important than pure sexual pleasure (Sand et al., 2008).

Psychological Androgyny

Most people think of masculinity and femininity as opposite ends of one continuum. People tend to assume that the more masculine a person is, the less feminine he or she must be, and vice versa. Thus, a man who exhibits stereotypical feminine traits of nurturance, tenderness, and emotionality is often considered less masculine than other men. Women who compete with men in business are perceived not only as more masculine than other women but also as less feminine.

Some behavioural scientists, such as Sandra Bem (1993), argue that masculinity and femininity instead constitute separate personality dimensions. A person who is highly masculine, whether male or female, may also possess feminine traits—and vice versa. People who exhibit "masculine" assertiveness and instrumental skills (skills in the sciences and business, for example) along with "feminine" nurturance and cooperation fit both the masculine and the feminine gender-role stereotypes. They are said to show **psychological androgyny**. People who are high only in assertiveness and instrumental skills fit the masculine stereotype. People who are high only in traits such as nurturance and cooperation fit the feminine stereotype. People low in the stereotypical masculine *and* feminine patterns are considered "undifferentiated" in terms of gender-role stereotypes.

People who are psychologically androgynous may be capable of summoning up a wider range of masculine and feminine traits to meet the demands of various situations and to express their desires and talents. Researchers, for example, have found psychologically androgynous persons of both genders to show "masculine" independence under group pressures to conform and to show "feminine" nurturance in interactions with a kitten or baby (Bem, 1975; Bem et al., 1976).

People who oppose the constraints of traditional gender roles may perceive psychological androgyny as a desirable goal. Some feminist writers, however, criticize the model of psychological androgyny because it is defined in terms of, and thereby perpetuates, concepts of masculine and feminine gender roles (Lott, 1985).

Some evidence shows psychologically androgynous men and women to be more comfortable with their sexuality than are masculine men and feminine women (Walfish & Mayerson, 1980). Perhaps they can draw upon a broader repertoire of sexual behaviours. They may be comfortable with cuddling and tender holding *and* with initiating and directing sexual interactions. Researchers also find that androgynous women experience orgasm more frequently (Radlove, 1983), and express greater sexual satisfaction (Kymlicka et al., 1983), than feminine women do.

In this chapter we have explored what it means to be female, male, or another sex within a cultural setting such as ours. In the following chapter we consider how feelings of attraction and love develop in females, males, and others.

Psychological androgyny A state characterized by possession of both stereotypical masculine traits and stereotypical feminine traits.

Summing Up

During the first six weeks or so of prenatal development, embryonic structures of both genders develop along similar lines and resemble primitive female structures.

At about the seventh week after conception, the genetic code (XX or XY) begins to assert itself, causing changes in the gonads, genital ducts, and external genitals.

Testosterone spurs differentiation of the male (Wolffian) duct system. In the absence of testosterone, the Wolffian ducts degenerate, and female sex organs develop.

Abnormalities of the sex chromosomes can have profound effects on sexual characteristics, physical health, and psychological development. Examples include Klinefelter syndrome and Turner syndrome.

Gender-specific changes occur in the hypothalamus during prenatal development. Testosterone causes cells in the hypothalamus of male fetuses to become insensitive to estrogen.

One's gender identity is one's sense of being male or of being female.

Gender identity is nearly always consistent with anatomic gender.

Some individuals—hermaphrodites—are born with both ovarian and testicular tissue.

Transsexuals harbour a deep sense of discomfort about their anatomic gender. Hormone treatments and sex reassignment surgery provide transsexuals with many of the characteristics of the other gender.

Cultures have broad expectations of men and women that are termed *gender roles*. In our culture, the stereotypical female is seen as gentle, dependent, kind, helpful, patient, and submissive. The stereotypical male is tough, competitive, gentlemanly, and protective.

Sexism is the prejudgment that because of gender, a person will possess certain negative traits.

Stereotypical gender preferences for toys and play activities are in evidence at an early age. Males are more aggressive than females, but the question is *why?*

Men's life expectancies are shorter, on average, than women's. Canadian women lead healthier lifestyles than men, and are more willing to seek health care.

Biological views on gender typing focus on the roles of genetics and prenatal influences in predisposing men and women to gender-linked behaviour patterns. Psychologists have attempted to explain gender typing in terms of psychoanalytic, social–cognitive, and cognitive–developmental theories.

Gender schema theory proposes that children develop a gender schema as a means of organizing their perceptions of the world. They then begin to judge themselves in terms of traits considered appropriate to their gender.

Stereotypical gender-role expectations affect dating practices and sexual behaviour.

According to this stereotype, men are sexual initiators and women sexual gatekeepers. Men not only initiate sexual encounters; they are also expected to initiate all the "moves."

According to another stereotype, women do not share men's interest in sex. However, current research suggests that many women do have a strong interest in sexual pleasure.

Masculinity and femininity may be two independent personality dimensions. People who combine stereotypical masculine and feminine behaviour patterns are psychologically androgynous.

Test Yourself

Multiple-Choice Questions

1. The process through which males and females develop a distinct sexual anatomy is known as

a. sexualization
b. homologous development
c. sexual differentiation
d. Müllerian stage

2. The basic blueprint of the human embryo is

a. male
b. female
c. both male and female
d. neither male nor female

3. Which of the following chromosome patterns would be found in males with Klinefelter syndrome?

a. YYY
b. XXX
c. XYY
d. XXY

4. Turner syndrome results when a fertilized egg has

a. only one chromosome–an X
b. only one chromosome–a Y
c. three X chromosomes
d. three Y chromosomes

5. **Research suggests that a part of the brain known as the _______________ may be involved in the development of gender identity.**
   a. amygdala
   b. hippocampus
   c. frontal cortex
   d. hypothalamus

6. **Individuals with androgen-insensitivity syndrome, congenital adrenal hyperplasia, and Dominican Republic syndrome are considered to be**
   a. intersexuals
   b. transsexuals
   c. homosexuals
   d. asexuals

7. **Cross-cultural research by Zucker and his colleagues suggests that**
   a. more girls than boys are treated for gender identity disorder
   b. more boys than girls are treated for gender identity disorder
   c. equal proportions of boys and girls are treated for gender identity disorder
   d. gender identity disorders do not appear until early adulthood

8. **Children learn behaviours that are appropriate for their gender by the process of**
   a. gender reinforcement
   b. gender expectation
   c. gender typing
   d. gender fixation

9. **Teasing or belittling a man because he has chosen to study nursing is an example of**
   a. gender typing
   b. sexism
   c. gender reassignment
   d. homophobia

10. **In terms of gender differences in health, which of the following is *not* true?**
    a. Women are more resilient in dealing with health problems.
    b. More women than men are overweight.
    c. Women are more likely than men to experience stress.
    d. Women are more likely to consider health issues when selecting food.

Answers to the Test Yourself questions in each chapter are found on page 509.

Critical Thinking Questions

1. What is your ultimate definition of gender? Is it biological? Psychological? A bit of each?
2. When transsexuals undergo gender reassignment surgery to bring their physical appearance more in line with their gender identity, has anything really changed?
3. When you were growing up, what messages about traditional gender roles did you receive from your parents? Did you receive different messages from your friends? How have you reconciled any conflicts?
4. Have you ever experienced sexism? What were the circumstances? What effect (if any) did it have on you?
5. Do you think men have stronger sex drives than women? Why or why not?

PEARSON mypsychkit™

Visit MyPsychKit at www.mypsychkit.com, where you can do quizzes and link to additional resources on topics discussed in this text.

CHAPTER SIX

Attraction and Love

Candy and Stretch. A new technique for controlling weight gain? No, these are the names of a couple who have just met at a camera club that doubles as a meeting place for singles.

Candy and Stretch stand above the crowd—literally. She is almost six feet tall, an attractive woman in her early thirties. He is more plain looking, but "wholesome." He is in his late thirties and six feet five inches tall. Stretch has been in the group for some time. Candy is a new member. Let us follow them as they meet during a coffee break. As you will see, there are some differences between what they say and what they think.

	They Say	(They Think)
STRETCH:	Well, you're certainly a welcome addition to our group.	(Can't I ever say something clever?)
CANDY:	Thank you. It certainly is friendly and interesting.	(He's cute.)
STRETCH:	My friends call me Stretch. It's left over from my basketball days. Silly, but I'm used to it.	(It's safer than saying my name is David Stein.)
CANDY:	My name is Candy.	(At least my nickname is. He doesn't have to hear Hortense O'Brien.)
STRETCH:	What kind of camera is that?	(Why couldn't a girl named Candy be Jewish? It's only a nickname, isn't it?)
CANDY:	Just this old German one of my uncle's. I borrowed it from the office.	(He could be Irish. And that camera looks expensive.)
STRETCH:	May I? (He takes her camera, brushing her hand and then tingling with the touch.) Fine lens. You work for your uncle?	(Now I've done it. Brought up work.)
CANDY:	Ever since college.	(Okay, so what if I only went for a year?)
	It's more than being just a secretary. I get into sales, too.	(If he asks what I sell, I'll tell him anything except underwear.)
STRETCH:	Sales? That's funny. I'm in sales, too, but mainly as an executive. I run our department.	(Is there a nice way to say used cars? I'd better change the subject.)
	I started using cameras on trips. Last time I was in the Bahamas.	(Great legs! And the way her hips move—)
CANDY:	Oh! Do you go to the Bahamas, too? I love those islands.	(So I went just once, and it was for the brassiere manufacturers' convention. At least we're off the subject of jobs.)
STRETCH:		(She's probably been around. Well, at least we're off the subject of jobs.)
	I did a little underwater work there last summer. Fantastic colours. So rich in life.	(And lonelier than hell.)
CANDY:		(Look at that build. He must swim like a fish. I should learn.)
	I wish I'd had time when I was there. I love the water.	(Well, I do. At the beach, anyway, where I can wade in and not go too deep.)

So begins a relationship. Candy and Stretch have a drink and talk, talk, talk—sharing their likes and dislikes. Amazingly, they seem to agree on everything, from clothing to cars to politics. The attraction they feel is very strong, and neither of them is willing to turn the other off by disagreeing.

Attraction

Let us explore some of the factors that determine interpersonal attraction.

Physical Attractiveness: How Important Is Looking Good?

We might like to think of ourselves as so sophisticated that physical attractiveness does not move us. We might like to claim that sensitivity, warmth, and intelligence are more important. However, we may never learn about other people's personalities if they do not meet our minimum standards for physical attractiveness. Research shows that physical attractiveness is a major determinant of interpersonal and sexual attraction (Langlois et al., 2000; Sangrador & Yela, 2000; Strassberg & Holty, 2003). In fact, physical appearance is the key factor in consideration of partners for dates, sex, and long-term relationships (Wilson et al., 2005).

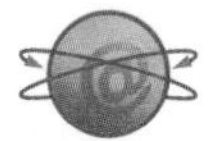

Social Psychology Network
Offers 5000 links to resources, including "romance and attraction" and "sexuality and sex research."
www.socialpsychology.org

IS BEAUTY IN THE EYE OF THE BEHOLDER? What determines physical attractiveness? In certain African tribes, long necks and round, disclike lips are signs of feminine beauty. Women thus stretch their necks and lips to make themselves more appealing. Women of the Nama tribe persistently tug at their labia majora to make them "beautiful"—that is, prominent and elongated (Ford & Beach, 1951).

In our culture, women consider taller men to be more attractive (Pawlowski & Koziel, 2002). Undergraduate women prefer their dates to be about 15 cm (6 in.) taller than they are. Undergraduate men, on the average, prefer women who are about 11 cm (4.5 in.) shorter (Gillis & Avis, 1980). Tall women are not viewed so positively.

Female plumpness is valued in many preliterate societies (Anderson et al., 1992; Frayser, 1985). Wide hips and a broad pelvis are widely recognized as sexually appealing. In our culture, however, slenderness is in style. Some young women suffer from an eating disorder called **anorexia nervosa**, by which they literally starve themselves to conform to the contemporary ideal. Both genders find slenderness (though not anorexic thinness) attractive, especially for females (Wilson et al., 2005).

Anorexia nervosa A potentially life-threatening eating disorder characterized by refusal to maintain a healthful body weight, intense fear of being overweight, a distorted body image, and, in females, lack of menstruation (amenorrhea).

Both genders find obese people unattractive (Goode, 2000), but there are gender differences in impressions of the most pleasing body shape. On average, university men think their present physiques are close to ideal and appealing to women (Fallon & Rozin, 1985). University women generally see themselves as much heavier than the figure that is most alluring to men, and heavier still than the figure they perceive as the ideal feminine form.

The hourglass figure is popular in Canada and the United States. In one study by researchers at Dalhousie University (Lalonde et al., 2004), female students rated women of average weight with a waist-to-hip ratio of 0.7 as most attractive. Small and medium waists were generally preferred, regardless of body weight. For the moderate and heavy figures, those with large hips received the lowest attractiveness ratings. With larger figures, a more tubular body shape was considered more attractive. The results indicated that in evaluating physical attractiveness, body weight, waist size, and hip size all interact to influence ratings of women's attractiveness.

Walking style or gait is also a physical feature that influences attractiveness ratings. Researchers at Queen's University (Provost et al., in press) discovered that the walking style or gait of women who were not using hormonal birth-control pills varied according to the menstrual cycle. The researchers hypothesized, on the basis of evolutionary theory, that women would be more attractive to men during the fertile period of the menstrual cycle. A sample of university men were shown images of women walking and were asked to rate the attractiveness of each woman. Contrary to prediction, the women who were shown walking during their luteal or least fertile phase were judged to be the most attractive.

Cohen and Tannenbaum (2001) conducted an internet study in which they posted various women's body shapes and asked lesbian and bisexual women to indicate which were most sexually attractive to them. The respondents, like heterosexual men and women, found women with a 0.7 waist-to-hip body ratio to be the most sexually attractive. However, they differed from the heterosexual women and men in that their first choice was for *heavy* women with a 0.7 waist-to-hip body ratio and large breasts. Their second choice was for heavy women with the same waist-to-hip body ratio but with small breasts. The authors suggest that the women in this study were rejecting what they might view as societal emphasis on excessive slenderness.

It is no secret that most men in our society are more attracted to women with ample bustlines (Hill et al., 2005). In one study, men rated a continuum of female figures that differed only in the size of the bust (Thompson & Tantleff, 1992). Men, as predicted, preferred women with larger busts, but not huge busts.

People who are attractive know it. In one study, men and women rated each other for attractiveness and also rated themselves (Marcus & Miller, 2003). By and large, the individuals' self-ratings meshed with those by others, both female and male. Women's judgments were most closely related to how men perceived them, suggesting that they were reflecting men's opinions of them more so than women's.

An experiment manipulated men's voices and asked women to rate them for attractiveness. Heterosexual women at the fertile (late follicular) phase of the menstrual cycle found men with more "masculine"— that is, deeper—voices to be more attractive (Feinberg et al., 2006). The study did not assess possible differences between heterosexual and lesbian women.

HOW NONPHYSICAL TRAITS AFFECT PERCEPTIONS OF PHYSICAL ATTRACTIVENESS Although there are physical standards for beauty in our culture, nonphysical traits also affect our perceptions of beauty. For example, the perceived beauty of a partner is likely to be enhanced by nonphysical traits such as familiarity, liking, respect, and sharing of values and goals (Kniffin & Wilson, 2004).

Females and males rate the attractiveness of faces higher when they are smiling than when they are not smiling (O'Doherty et al., 2003). So there is reason to "put on a happy face" when you meet people.

Gender-role expectations may affect perceptions of attractiveness. For example, women are more likely to be attracted to socially dominant men than men are to be attracted to socially dominant women (Buunk et al., 2002). Women who viewed videos of prospective dates found men who acted outgoing and self-expressive more appealing than men who were passive (Riggio & Woll, 1984). Another study found that highly feminine women are more likely to be attracted to dominant "macho" men than less feminine women are (Maybach & Gold, 1994). Yet men who viewed videos in the Riggio and Woll (1984) study were put off by outgoing, self-expressive behaviour in women. In yet another study, women rated videos of dominant college men (defined in this study as social control over a troublesome

Innovative Canadian Research

OPENNESS TO CASUAL SEX AMONG WOMEN AND PREFERENCE FOR MASCULINE MEN

Do women who are more accepting of casual sex differ in their preference of potential male partners than women who are less accepting of casual sex? Researchers at Queen's University and the University of Victoria (Provost et al., 2006) conducted two studies to determine the answer to this question. They predicted that women who were more sociosexual—that is, who were more open to short-term sexual relationships—would be more likely to prefer highly masculine male faces and bodies than women who were less sociosexual.

In the first study women were asked to rate the attractiveness of male faces and various masculine body types. In general, the women preferred more masculine faces and more muscular bodies. However, the women who were more sociosexual showed a much greater preference for men with muscular bodies.

In the second study (Provost et al., 2006) a different sample of women met with two equally attractive men (one highly masculinized and one less masculinized) in a "speed dating" setting. After meeting with each man, the women were asked in a questionnaire to indicate their interest in each man for a short-term or long-term relationship. A key finding was that women who were more sociosexual were more strongly attracted to the highly masculinized man for a short-term relationship. On the other hand, women who were less sociosexual preferred the less masculinized man for a long-term relationship. The researchers theorized that evolutionary theory, as discussed in the first chapter, is supported by the finding that women who are more open to having casual sex are more likely to choose more masculine-looking men for casual sex. Here Provost et al. assumed that a higher level of masculinity is associated with "healthier" genes.

interaction with an instructor) as more appealing than submissive men. Again, male viewers were put off by similarly dominant women (Sadalla et al., 1987). Men are more likely to be jealous of socially dominant men, whereas women are more likely to be jealous of physically attractive women (Dijkstra & Buunk, 2002).

WHAT DO YOU LOOK FOR IN A LONG-TERM, MEANINGFUL RELATIONSHIP? When it comes to selecting a long-term partner, women place relatively greater emphasis than men on such traits as vocational status, earning potential, expressiveness, kindness, consideration, dependability, and fondness for children. Men give relatively more consideration to youth, physical attractiveness, cooking ability (can't they switch on the microwave by themselves?), and frugality (Kniffen & Wilson, 2004).

In a recent study at the University of Guelph (Milhausen et al., 2007) women rated responsibility as more important than men did, whereas men rated physical attractiveness as more important than did women when selecting a future spouse. In contrast, when choosing a casual sex partner, women rated physical attractiveness as being more important than did men. Both men and women rated responsibility as being most important when choosing a future spouse, followed by physical attractiveness, sexual skills, and status/popularity. Importantly, this was one of the first studies to consider the importance of sexual skills in selecting a partner.

When it comes to mate selection, females in a sample of students from Germany and the Netherlands also emphasized the financial prospects and status of a potential mate, whereas males emphasized the importance of physical attractiveness (de Raad & Doddema-Winsemius, 1992). A study of more than 200 Korean college students found that in mate selection, women placed more emphasis than men on education, jobs, and family of origin (Brown, 1994). Men placed more emphasis on physical attractiveness and affection. (Yes, men were more "romantic" and women more pragmatic.)

A World of Diversity

WIDE-EYED WITH . . . BEAUTY?

Some aspects of beauty seem to be largely cross-cultural. Research suggests that European Americans, African Americans, Asian Americans, and Latino and Latina Americans tend to agree on the facial features that they find to be attractive (Cunningham et al., 1995). They all prefer female faces with large eyes, greater distance between the eyes, small noses, narrower faces with smaller chins, high, expressive eyebrows, larger lower lips, and a well-groomed, full head of hair.

Consider the methodology of a study that compared the facial preferences of people in Japan and England. Perrett (1994) created computer composites of the faces of 60 women. Figure 6.1(a) is a composite of the 15 women who were rated the most attractive. He then used computer enhancement to exaggerate the differences between the composite of the 60—that is, the average face—and the composite of the 15 most attractive women. He found that both Japanese and British men deemed women with large eyes, high cheekbones, and narrow jaws to be the most attractive (Perret, 1994). Computer enhancement resulted in the image shown in Figure 6.1(b). The enhanced composite has even larger eyes, yet higher cheekbones, and a still narrower jaw. Figure 6.1(b) was then rated as the most attractive image. Similar results were found for the image of a Japanese woman.

Susan Sprecher and her colleagues (1994) surveyed a national probability sample of 13 017 English- or Spanish-speaking people, aged 19 or above, living in households in the United States. In one section of their questionnaire, they asked respondents how willing they would be to marry someone who was older, younger, of a different religion, not likely to hold a steady job, not good-looking, and so forth. Each item was followed by a seven-point scale in which 1 meant "not at all willing" and 7 meant "very willing." As shown in Table 6.1, women were more willing than men to marry someone who was not good-looking. On the other hand, women were less willing to marry someone not likely to hold a steady job.

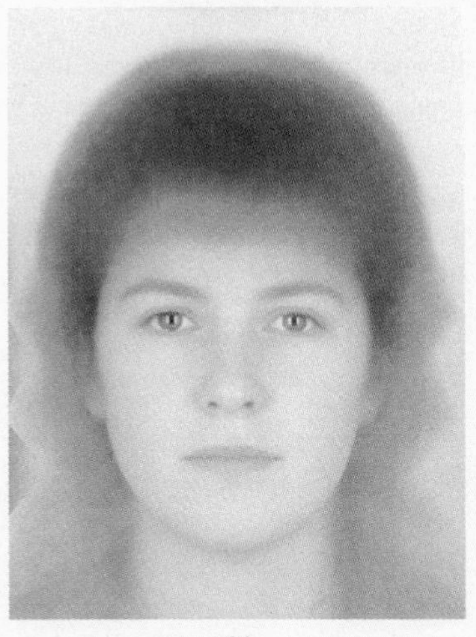

(a)

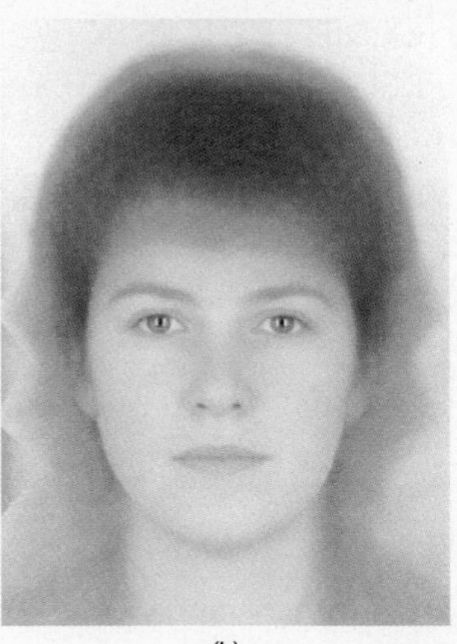

(b)

Figure 6.1 What Features Contribute to Facial Attractiveness?

In both England and Japan, features such as large eyes, high cheekbones, and narrow jaws contribute to perceptions of the attractiveness of women. (a) A computer composite of the faces of 15 women rated as the most attractive of a group of 60. (b) A computer composite that exaggerates the features of these 15 women. That is, they are developed further in the direction that separates them from the average of the full group.

TABLE 6.1
Gender Differences in Mate Preferences

How willing would you be to marry someone who ...	Men	Women
was not "good-looking"?	3.41	4.42**
was older than you by five or more years?	4.15	5.29**
was younger than you by five or more years?	4.54	2.80**
was not likely to hold a steady job?	2.73	1.62**
would earn much less than you?	4.60	3.76**
would earn much more than you?	5.19	5.93**
had more education than you?	5.22	5.82**
had less education than you?	4.67	4.08**
had been married before?	3.35	3.44
already had children?	2.84	3.11*
was of a different religion?	4.24	4.31
was of a different race?	3.08	2.84**

*Difference statistically significant at the 0.01 level of confidence.

**Difference statistically significant at the 0.001 level of confidence.

Source: Based on information in Sprecher, S., Sullivan, Q., and Hatfield, E. (1994). "Mate Selection Preferences: Gender Differences Examined in a National Sample." Journal of Personality and Social Psychology, *66(6), 1074–1080.*

A World of Diversity

SEX DIFFERENCES IN PREFERENCES IN MATES ACROSS 37 CULTURES

What do men in Nigeria, Japan, Brazil, Canada, and the United States have in common? For one thing, men in these countries report that they prefer mates who are younger than themselves. Buss (1994) reviewed survey evidence on the preferred age difference between oneself and one's mate in 37 cultures (representing 33 countries) in Europe, Africa, Asia, Australia, New Zealand, and North and South America. In every culture, men preferred younger mates (the range was from 0.38 years to 6.45 years). Women, however, preferred older mates (the range was from 1.82 years to 5.1 years). Gender differences in the preferred age of mates paralleled actual differences in age of men and women at the time of marriage.

Buss found that in all 37 cultures, men placed greater value on a prospective partner's "good looks" than did women. On the other hand, women in 36 of the 37 cultures placed greater value on "good earning capacity" in prospective mates.

The consistency of Buss's findings lends credence to the notion that there are widespread gender differences in preferences with respect to age, physical characteristics, and financial status of prospective mates. Generally speaking, men place greater value on the physical attractiveness and relative youth of prospective mates. Women place relatively greater value on the earning capacity of prospective mates. Buss interprets women's preferences for relatively older mates as additional evidence that women appraise future mates on the basis of their ability to provide for a wife and family, because age and income tend to be linked among men.

Who Is Mr. or Ms. Right?
Are your judgments of attractiveness based on universal standards or on your cultural experiences? Evolutionary psychologist David Buss found some nearly universal standards for beauty in his study of 37 cultures.

In 2005, a Compas survey asked a national sample of Canadians what they felt should be the attributes of the ideal spouse. The men valued only one characteristic more than the women did: "good-looking." Women valued such traits as "manages money well," "is financially successful," "is well educated and intelligent," and "shares your religion" more highly than did the men.

There have been relatively few studies of mate preference attributes among ethnic groups in Canada. Researchers at York University (Lalonde et al., 2004) found that, among second-generation Southeast Asian Canadians, the strength of connectedness to one's family was the strongest predictor of traditional mate attribute preference. Despite extensive exposure to Canadian values, most respondents preferred their future spouses to have traditional attributes. Men had more traditional sex-role expectations than did women.

ARE ATTRACTIVENESS PREFERENCES INHERITED? On the surface, gender differences in perceptions of attractiveness seem unbearably sexist, and perhaps they are. Yet some evolutionary psychologists believe that evolutionary forces favour the continuation of gender differences in preferences for mates because certain preferred traits offer reproductive advantages (Buss, 2005). Some physical features—such as cleanliness, good complexion, clear eyes, good teeth, good hair, firm muscle tone, and a steady gait—are universally appealing to both genders. Perhaps they are markers of reproductive potential (Buss, 2005). Youth and health may be relatively more important to a woman's appeal because these characteristics tend to be associated with her reproductive capacity: the "biological clock" limits her reproductive potential. Physical characteristics associated with a woman's youthfulness, such as smooth skin, firm muscle tone, and lustrous hair, may thus have become more closely linked to a woman's appeal (Buss, 1994). A man's reproductive value, however, may depend more on how well he can provide for his family than on his age or physical appeal. The value of men as reproducers, therefore, is more intertwined with factors that contribute to a stable environment for child-rearing, such as economic status and reliability. Evolutionary psychologists argue that these gender differences in mate preferences may have been passed down through the generations as part of our genetic heritage (Buss, 2005).

Female jealousy of younger women is another thread that spans cultures. Sexual competition, according to Margaret Mead, generally involves

> the struggle between stronger older men and weaker younger men or between more attractive younger women and more entrenched older ones. (Mead, 1967, p. 198)

The evolutionary view of gender differences in preferences for mates is largely speculative and not fully consistent with the evidence. Despite gender differences, both men and women report that they place greater weight on personal characteristics than on physical features in judging prospective mates (Buss, 1994). Many women, like men, do prefer physically appealing partners (Bixler, 1989). Women also tend to marry men similar to themselves in physical attractiveness as well as socioeconomic standing. Note also that older men are more likely than younger men to die from natural causes. From the standpoint of reproductive advantages,

Innovative Canadian Research

PARTNER PREFERENCES AND AGE, GENDER, AND ORIENTATION

Researchers at Queen's University in Ontario compared the age-based partner preferences of heterosexual men, heterosexual women, gay men, and lesbians (Silverthorne & Quinsey, 2000). Adults were shown pictures of 15 male and 15 female faces arranged into five age categories ranging from 18 to 60 years. The lesbians rated female faces aged 42 to 60 as most attractive and 19-year-olds as least attractive. Both gay and heterosexual men found younger partners to be more sexually appealing than did the women. Gay men rated younger partners as more sexually appealing than did the heterosexual men. Conversely, lesbians rated older partners as more sexually appealing than did the heterosexual women.

In another study of gay and bisexual men in three Ontario cities, Barry Adam (2000a) of the University of Windsor found that there was widespread acknowledgment of the ideal of youthfulness in the gay community. In particular, men who preferred men older than themselves noted that they often faced ridicule as a result. Nevertheless, the study showed considerable diversity in the age preferences of gay and bisexual men.

Who Is Right for You?
Research shows that people tend to pair off with others who are similar in physical characteristics and personality traits.

women would thus achieve greater success by marrying fit, younger males who are likely to survive during the child-rearing years than by marrying older, higher-status males. Moreover, similar cultural influences, rather than inherited dispositions, may explain commonalities across cultures in gender differences in mate preferences. For example, in societies in which women are economically dependent on men, a man's appeal may depend more on his financial resources than on his physical appeal.

The Attraction-Similarity Hypothesis: Who Is "Right" for You?

The **attraction–similarity hypothesis** holds that people tend to develop romantic relationships with people who are similar to themselves in physical attractiveness and other traits (Klohnen & Luo, 2003; Morry & Gaines, 2005). Researchers have found that people who are involved in committed relationships are most likely to be similar to their partners in their attitudes and cultural attributes (Amodio & Showers, 2005).

Our partners tend to be like us in race and ethnicity, age, level of education, and religion. For example, 95% of Canadians choose partners (married or common law) of the same racial background as their own (Riedmann, Lamanna, & Nelson, 2003).

Do "Opposites Attract" or Do "Birds of a Feather Flock Together"?

Attraction–similarity hypothesis The concept that people tend to develop romantic relationships with people who are similar to themselves in attractiveness.

It is not true that "opposites attract." We are actually less apt to be attracted to people who disagree with our views and tastes than to people who share them.

Why do the great majority of us have partners from our own backgrounds? One reason is propinquity, that is, relationships are made in the neighbourhood and not in heaven. Although mobility has increased in Western societies in recent decades, we tend to live among people who are reasonably similar to us in background and thus come into contact with them. Another is that we are drawn to people who are similar in their attitudes. People similar in background are more likely to be similar in their attitudes. Similarity in attitudes and tastes is a key contributor to attraction, friendships, and love relationships (Brown et al., 2003; Morry & Gaines, 2005).

Let us also note a sex difference. Evidence shows that women place greater weight on attitude similarity as a determinant of attraction to a stranger of the other sex than do men, whereas men place more value on physical attractiveness (Feingold, 1991). We also tend to assume that people we find attractive share our attitudes (Morry & Gaines, 2005). The physical attraction between Candy and Stretch motivated them to pretend that their preferences, tastes, and opinions coincided. They entered into an unspoken agreement not to discuss their religious differences. When sexual attraction is strong, perhaps we want to think that we can iron out all the kinks in the relationship. Although similarity may be important in determining initial attraction, compatibility appears to be a stronger predictor of maintaining an intimate relationship (Amodio & Showers, 2005).

Reciprocity: If You Like Me, You Must Have Excellent Judgment

When we feel admired and complimented, we tend to return these feelings and behaviours. This is called **reciprocity**. Reciprocity is a potent determinant of attraction (Levine, 2000). We tend to be much more warm, helpful, and candid when we are with strangers who we believe like us. We even tend to welcome positive comments from others when we know those remarks to be inaccurate (Levine, 2000).

Perhaps the power of reciprocity has enabled many couples to become happy with one another and reasonably well adjusted. By reciprocating positive words and actions, a person can perhaps stoke neutral or mild feelings into robust, affirmative feelings of attraction.

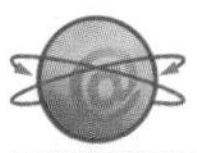

Columbia University's "Go Ask Alice"
Offers online advice about relationships in a question-and-answer format.
www.goaskalice.columbia.edu

Love

Our culture idealizes the concept of romantic love. Thus, we readily identify with the plight of the "star-crossed" lovers in *Romeo and Juliet* and *West Side Story*, who sacrificed themselves for love. We learn that "love makes the world go round" and that "love is everything." In Reginald Bibby's (2001) survey of Canadian teenagers, three-quarters viewed being loved as a very important goal. About one-half of adult Canadians report that they are very satisfied with the amount of love in their lives (*Maclean's*, 1998). Like other aspects of sexual and social behaviour among humans, the concept of love must be understood within a cultural context. Luckily (or miserably), we have such a context in Western culture.

The Greek Heritage

The concept of love can be traced back at least as far as the classical age of Greece. The Greeks distinguished four concepts related to the modern meanings of love: **storge, agape, philia**, and **eros**.

Eros is closest in meaning to our concept of passion. Eros was a character in Greek mythology (transformed in Roman mythology into Cupido, now called Cupid) who would shoot unsuspecting people with his love arrows, causing them to

Reciprocity Mutual exchange.

Storge (STORE-gay) Loving attachment and nonsexual affection; the type of emotion that binds parents to children.

Agape (AH-gah-pay) Selfless love; a kind of love that is similar to generosity and charity.

Philia (FEEL-yuh) Friendship love, which is based on liking and respect rather than sexual desire.

Eros The kind of love that is closest in meaning to the modern-day concept of passion.

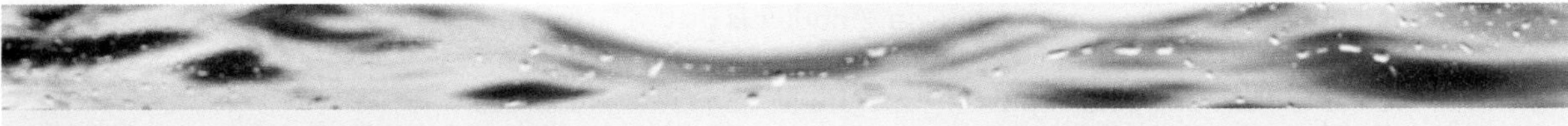

A World of Diversity

"THE (ELECTRONIC) NEARNESS OF YOU"

Physical closeness, or proximity, has always been a factor in interpersonal attraction. People have always been drawn to the boy or girl next door (or next cave?). People tend to form romantic relationships with the people they meet in the neighbourhood, in school, in their religious community, or on the job.

In the age of electronics, proximity is paradoxical. You can find yourself corresponding with, and perhaps feeling attracted to, people who are as close as the monitor in front of your nose, yet thousands of miles away in the flesh.

When you meet somebody in person, you immediately observe what they look like, you hear their voice, and—according to some researchers—perhaps you get something like a sniff of their pheromones. But when you meet somebody in a chatroom or a computer-mediated multi-user dungeon, the cues that might spark interest are different. Mantovani (2001) notes that in the case of online relationships, the use of the written (keyboarded) language becomes more important; timing and the speed of writing and responding are crucial; and punctuation and those smiley-faced emoticons can all make a difference. But frequency of contact in the virtual world, as in the real world, plays a role (Levine, 2000; Mantovani, 2001). Visiting the same chatroom repeatedly allows mutual awareness to develop and suggests similarity in interests.

"Surfing Blind?"
What "rules" of interpersonal attraction apply when people meet online? They cannot directly see or hear each other, so what cues do they rely on to determine whether there is a fit? What happens when one person wants to see, hear, or meet the other?

Deb Levine (2000) notes that people are more likely to disclose intimate information about themselves on the internet, perhaps because the actual—or unknown—distance between the parties provides a sense of security. Similarly, other people are quicker to reciprocate expressions of interest. Levine notes that flirting and erotic activity on the internet can be extremely exciting, but they can also build unrealistic expectations and disqualify participants for relationships in the physical world. (Would you want to have a real-world relationship with someone who quickly enters sexual discussions online?)

Levine and Mantovani both warn that expressions of similarity are easy to feign on the net. Levine (2000) warns against becoming overly wrapped up in people who are reluctant to exchange sound files or pictures. And she adds that it makes sense to meet in the real world within a month or so to check out the accuracy of computer-mediated impressions—preferably in a safe, public place.

fall madly in love with the person who was nearest to them at the time. Erotic love embraces sudden passionate desire: "love at first sight" and "falling head over heels in love." Younger university students are more likely to believe in love at first sight and that "love conquers all" than older (and wiser?) university students (Knox et al., 1999). Passion can be so gripping that one is convinced one's life has been changed forever. Romantic love can also be earthy and sexy. In fact, sexual arousal and desire may be the strongest component of passionate or romantic love. Romantic love begins with a powerful physical attraction or feelings of passion and is associated with strong physiological arousal.

Unlike the Greeks, we tend to use the word *love* to describe everything from feelings of affection toward another to romantic ardour to sexual intercourse ("making love"). Still, different types or styles of love are recognized in our own culture, as we shall see.

Romantic Love

Infatuation A state of intense absorption in or focus on another person, which is usually accompanied by sexual desire, elation, and general physiological arousal or excitement; passion.

The experience of *romantic love*, as opposed to loving attachment or sexual arousal per se, occurs within a cultural context in which the concept is idealized. Western culture has a long tradition of idealizing the concept of romantic love, as represented, for instance, by romantic fairy tales that have been passed down through the generations. In fact, our exposure to the concept of romantic love may begin with hearing the fairy tales of Sleeping Beauty, Cinderella, and Snow White—along with their princes charming. Later, perhaps, the concept of romantic love blossoms with exposure to romantic novels, television and film scripts, and the heady tales of friends and relatives.

During adolescence, strong sexual arousal, along with an idealized image of the object of our desires, leads us to label our feelings as love. We may learn to speak of love rather than lust, because sexual desire in the absence of a committed relationship might be viewed as primitive or animalistic. Being "in love" ennobles attraction and sexual arousal, not only to society but also to oneself. Unlike lust, love can be discussed at the dinner table. If others think we are too young to experience "the real thing"—which presumably includes knowledge of and respect for the other person's personality traits—our feelings may be called "puppy love" or a "crush."

Western society maintains much of the double standard toward sexuality. Thus, women are more often expected to justify sexual experiences as involving someone they love. Young men usually need not attribute sexual urges to love, so men are more likely to deem love a "mushy" concept. The vast majority of people in Canada nonetheless believe that romantic love is a prerequisite to marriage. Romantic love is rated by Canadian young people as the most important reason for marriage (Compas, 1998).

A national survey in 2008 found that around half of Canadians (59% of men and 51% of women) believe in love at first sight; 38% said they had actually experienced falling in love with someone at first sight (La Rose, 2008). Overall, 98% said they had been in love at least once.

When reciprocated, romantic love is usually a source of deep fulfillment and ecstasy. When love is unrequited, however, it can lead to emptiness, anxiety, or despair. Romantic love can thus teeter between states of ecstasy and misery (Hatfield, 1988). Perhaps no other feature of our lives can lift us up so high or plunge us so low as romantic love.

Infatuation or "True Love"?
Infatuation is a state of intense absorption in another person. It is characterized by sexual longing and general excitement. Infatuation is often referred to as passion or a crush. Infatuation is assumed to fade as relationships develop.

INFATUATION VERSUS "TRUE LOVE": WILL TIME TELL? Perhaps you first noticed each other when your eyes met across a crowded room. Or perhaps you met when you were both assigned to the same Bunsen burner in chemistry lab—less romantic, but closer to the flame. However it happened, the meeting triggered such an electric charge through your body that you could not get him (or her) out of your mind. Were you truly in love, however, or was it merely a passing fancy? Was it infatuation or "the real thing"—a "true," lasting, and mutual love? How do you tell them apart?

Perhaps you don't, at least not at first. **Infatuation** is a state of intense absorption in or focus on another person. It is usually accompanied by sexual desire, elation, and general physiological arousal or excitement. Some refer to infatuation as "passion." Others dub it a "crush." Both monikers suggest that it is a passing fancy. In infatuation, your heart may pound whenever the other person draws near or enters your fantasies.

For the first month or two, infatuation and the more enduring forms of romantic love are hard to differentiate. At first, both may be characterized by intense focusing or absorption. Infatuated people may become so absorbed that they cannot sleep, work, or carry out routine chores. Logic and reason are swept aside. Infatuated people hold idealized images of their love objects and overlook their faults. Caution may be cast to the winds. In some cases, couples in the throes of infatuation rush to get married, only to find, a few weeks or months later, that they are not well suited to each other.

As time goes on, signs that distinguish infatuation from a lasting romantic love begin to emerge. The partners begin to view each other more realistically and are better able to determine whether the relationship should continue. Although the tendency to idealize one's lover is strongest at the outset of a relationship, we should note that a so-called "positive illusion" tends to persist in relationships (Martz et al., 1998). That is, we maintain some tendency to differentiate our partners from the average and also to differentiate the value of our relationships from the average.

Infatuation is based on intense feelings of passion but not on the deeper feelings of attachment and caring that typify a more lasting mutual love (Hatfield & Rapson, 2002). Although infatuation may be a passing fancy, it can be supplanted by the deeper feelings of attachment and caring that characterize more lasting love relationships.

Note, too, that infatuation is not a necessary first step on the path to a lasting mutual love. Some couples develop deep feelings of love without ever experiencing the fireworks of infatuation (Barnes & Sternberg, 1997). And sometimes one partner is infatuated while the other manages to keep his or her head below the clouds.

Contemporary Models of Love: Dare Science Intrude?

Despite the importance of love, scientists have historically paid little attention to it. Some people believe that love cannot be analyzed scientifically. Love, they maintain, should be left to the poets, philosophers, and theologians. Yet researchers are now applying the scientific method to the study of love. They recognize that love is a complex concept, involving many areas of experience—behavioural, emotional, cognitive, and motivational (Berscheid, 2003). Let us consider some of the views of love that have emerged from modern theorists and researchers.

BIOLOGICAL MECHANISMS Some researchers focus on the bodily changes that occur when we experience feelings of romantic love. There are many. Some of the research focuses on the search for distinct neural pathways (road maps in the brain) that define feelings of love (Marazziti, 2005). Others involve chemistry, with a special focus on

- monoamines and neuropeptides, including dopamine and naturally produced opium look-alikes we call endorphins, that are involved in the brain's pleasure system
- the hormones oxytocin and vasopressin

There are always interesting new studies arriving on our desks. For example, we tend to have heightened levels of *nerve growth factor* (Emanuele et al., 2006), which partly explains—at least on a biological level—why new lovers are so acutely aware of everything going on around them and why everything seems so bathed in a luxurious light. (How's that for a sad attempt at poetry in a textbook?)

As we noted in the nearby "A Closer Look" feature, functional MRI research shows heightened activity in a part of the brain called the caudate nucleus. What is perhaps of interest here is that the caudate nucleus is part of the brain's "limbic system," which is intimately connected with emotional arousal.

Let us now consider several psychologically oriented views of love. They may touch indirectly on things that happen in the body, but as we will see, they do so almost apologetically.

A Closer Look

WATCHING NEW LOVE AS IT SEARS THE BRAIN

New love can look for all the world like mental illness—a blend of mania, dementia, and obsession—that cuts people off from friends and family, and prompts out-of-character behaviour: compulsive phone calling, serenades, yelling from rooftops. It could almost be mistaken for psychosis.

Now neuroscientists have produced brain scan images of this fevered activity, before it settles into the wine and roses phase of romance or the joint holiday card routines of long-term commitment. In an analysis of the images in *The Journal of Neurophysiology,* researchers argue that romantic love is a biological urge distinct from sexual arousal.

In the study, Drs. Helen Fisher of Rutgers University, Lucy Brown of Albert Einstein College of Medicine, and Arthur Aron of the State University of New York at Stony Brook led a team that analyzed about 2500 brain images from 17 college students who were in the first weeks or months of new love. The students looked at a picture of their beloved while an MRI machine imaged their brains. The researchers then compared the images with others taken while the students looked at a picture of an acquaintance.

Functional MRI technology detects increases or decreases of blood flow in the brain, which reflect changes in neural activity. In the study, a computer-generated map of particularly active areas showed hot spots deep in the brain, below conscious awareness, in areas called the caudate nucleus and the ventral tegmental area, which communicate with each other as part of a circuit. These areas are dense with cells that produce or receive a brain chemical called dopamine, which circulates actively when people desire or anticipate a reward. In studies of gamblers, cocaine users, and even people playing computer games for small amounts of money, these dopamine sites become extremely active as people score or win.

Yet falling in love is among the most irrational of human behaviours, not merely a matter of satisfying a simple pleasure or winning a reward. And the researchers found that one particular spot in the MRI Images, in the caudate nucleus, was especially active in people who scored highly on a questionnaire measuring passionate love. This passion-related region was on the opposite side of the brain from another area that registers physical attractiveness, and it appeared to be involved in longing, desire, and the unexplainable tug that people feel toward one person, among many attractive alternative partners.

This distinction, between finding someone attractive and desiring him or her, between liking and wanting, "is all happening in an area of the mammalian brain that takes care of most basic functions, like eating, drinking, eye movements, all at an unconscious level, and I don't think anyone expected this part of the brain to be so specialized," Dr. Brown said.

The intoxication of new love mellows with time, of course, and the brain imaging findings reflect some evidence of this change, as noted by Dr. Fisher. The researchers saw individual differences in their group of smitten lovers, based on how long the participants had been in the relationships. Compared with the students who were in the first weeks of a new love, those who had been paired off for a year or more showed significantly more activity in an area of the brain linked to long-term commitment.

Sources: From "Watching New Love as It Sears the Brain" by Benedict Carey. The New York Times. *May 31, 2005. Reprinted by permission.*

LOVE AS APPRAISAL OF AROUSAL Social psychologists Hatfield and Rapson (2002) define **romantic love** in terms of a state of intense physiological arousal and the cognitive appraisal of that arousal as love. The physiological arousal may be experienced as a pounding heart, sweaty palms, and butterflies in the stomach when one is in the presence of, or thinks about, one's love interest. Cognitive appraisal of the arousal means attributing it to some cause, such as fear or love. The perception that one has fallen in love is thus derived from several simultaneous events: (1) a state of intense physiological arousal that is connected with an appropriate love object (that is, a person, not an event like a rock concert), (2) a cultural setting that idealizes romantic love, and (3) the attribution of the arousal to feelings of love toward the person.

Romantic love A kind of love characterized by feelings of passion and intimacy.

STYLES OF LOVE Some psychologists speak in terms of *styles* of love. Susan and Clyde Hendrick (2002) speak of love as a positive emotion that contributes to happiness, feelings of psychological well-being, and optimism about the future. The

Hendricks (2003) developed a Love Attitude Scale that suggests the existence of six styles of love. The following is a list of these styles. Each one is exemplified by statements similar to those on the original scale. As you can see, the styles owe a debt to the Greeks:

1. *Romantic love (eros):* "My lover fits my ideal." "My lover and I were attracted to one another immediately."
2. *Game-playing love (ludus):* "I keep my lover up in the air about my commitment." "I get over love affairs pretty easily."
3. *Friendship (storge, philia):* "The best love grows out of an enduring friendship."
4. *Logical love (pragma):* "I consider a lover's potential in life before committing myself." "I consider whether my lover will be a good parent."
5. *Possessive, excited love (mania):* "I get so excited about my love that I cannot sleep." "When my lover ignores me, I get sick all over."
6. *Selfless love (agape):* "I would do anything I can to help my lover." "My lover's needs and wishes are more important than my own."

Most people who are "in love" experience a number of these styles, but the Hendricks (1986) found some interesting gender differences in styles of love. University men are significantly more likely to develop game-playing and romantic love styles. University women are more apt to develop friendly, logical, and possessive love styles.

STERNBERG'S TRIANGULAR THEORY OF LOVE Psychologist Robert Sternberg (1988) offers a "triangular theory" of love that organizes the relationships among kinds of love discussed by many theorists, including passionate love, romantic love, and companionate love (Hatfield & Rapson, 2002; Hendrick & Hendrick, 2003). The three components of love are:

1. *Intimacy:* the experience of warmth toward another person that arises from feelings of closeness, bondedness, and connectedness to the other. Intimacy also involves the desire to give and receive emotional support and to share one's innermost thoughts with the other.
2. *Passion:* an intense romantic or sexual desire for another person, which is accompanied by physiological arousal.
3. *Commitment:* a component of love that involves *dedication* to maintaining the relationship through good times and bad.

According to Sternberg's model, love can be conceptualized in terms of a triangle in which each vertex represents one of these basic elements of love (see Figure 6.2). The way the components are balanced can be represented by the shape of the triangle. For example, a love in which all three components are equally balanced—as in consummate love—would be represented by an equilateral triangle, as in Figure 6.2.

Couples are apparently well matched if they possess corresponding levels of passion, intimacy, and commitment (Drigotas et al., 1999; Sternberg, 1988). Compatibility can be represented visually in terms of the congruence of the love triangles. Figure 6.3(a) shows a perfect match, in which the triangles are congruent. Figure 6.3(b) depicts a good match; the partners are similar in the three dimensions. Figure 6.3(c) shows a mismatch; major differences exist between the partners on all three components. Relationships may run aground when partners are mismatched. A relationship may fizzle, rather than sizzle, if one partner experiences more passion than the other, or if one wants a long-term relationship when the other's idea of commitment is to stay the whole night.

According to the Sternberg model, various combinations of the three elements of love characterize different types of love relationships (Sternberg, 1986, 1988) (see Figure 6.3). For example, *infatuation* (passionate love) is typified by strong sexual

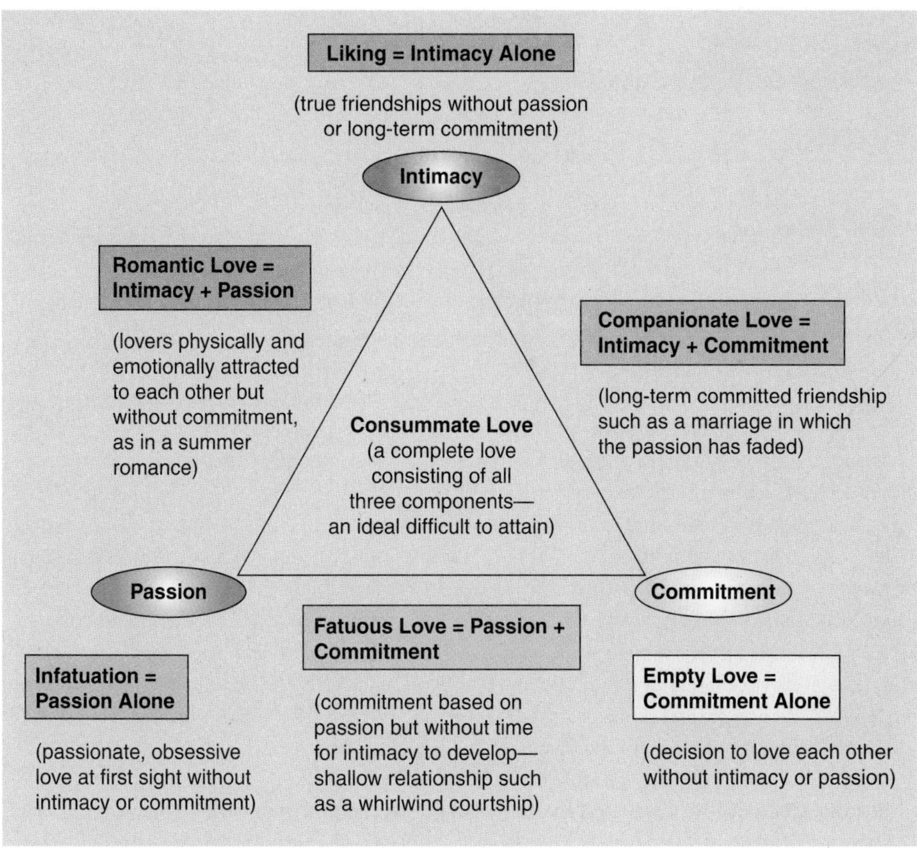

Figure 6.2 The Triangular Model of Love.

According to psychologist Robert Sternberg, love consists of three components, represented by the vertices of this triangle. Various kinds of love consist of different combinations of these components. Romantic love, for example, consists of passion and intimacy. Consummate love—the cultural ideal—consists of all three.

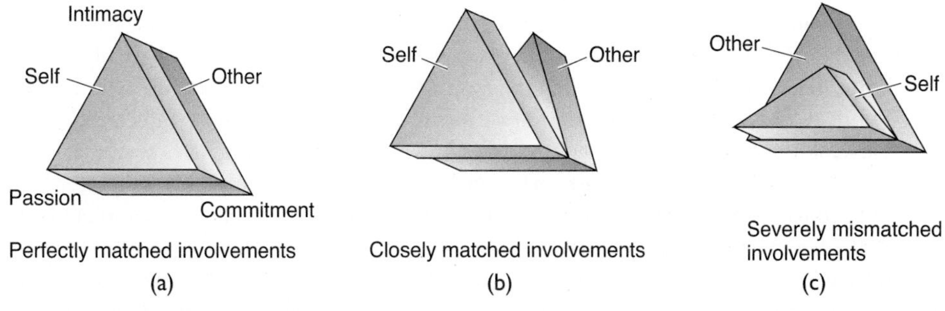

Figure 6.3 Compatibility and Incompatibility, According to the Triangular Model of Love.

Compatibility in terms of Sternberg's types of love can be represented as triangles. (a) A perfect match in which triangles are congruent. (b) A good match; the partners are similar on the three dimensions. (c) A mismatch. Major differences exist between the partners on all three components.

Applied Knowledge

UNDERSTANDING THE PHASES OF LOVE

Although romantic love may become transformed into companionate love, the process by which this transformation takes place remains vague (Shaver et al., 1988). Companionate love, however, need not be sexless or lacking in romance. Although passion may have ebbed, the giving and receiving of sexual pleasure can help strengthen bonds. Partners may feel that their sex lives have even become more deeply satisfying as they seek to please each other by practising what they have learned about each other's sexual needs and wants.

The balance among Sternberg's three aspects of love is likely to shift through the course of a relationship. A healthy dose of all three components–found in consummate love–typifies, for many of us, an ideal marriage. At the outset of marriage, passions may be strong but intimacy weak. Couples may only just be getting to know each other's innermost thoughts and feelings. Time alone does not cause intimacy and commitment to grow, however. Some couples are able to peer into each other's deeper selves and form meaningful commitments at relatively early stages in their relationships. Other long-married couples may remain distant or waver in their commitment. Some couples experience only a faint flickering of passion early in the relationship. Then it becomes quickly extinguished. For some, the flames of passion burn ever bright. Yet many married couples find that passion tends to fade while intimacy and commitment grow stronger.

Knowing about these components of love may help couples avoid pitfalls. Couples who recognize that passion exerts a strong pull early in a relationship may be less likely to rush into marriage. Couples who recognize that it is normal for passions to fade may avoid assuming that their love is at an end when it may simply be changing into a deeper, more intimate and committed form of love. This knowledge may also encourage couples to focus on finding ways of rekindling the embers of romance, rather than looking to escape at the first sign that the embers have cooled.

desire, but not by intimacy and commitment. The partners may each feel passionate love for the other, or such feelings may go unrequited.

Liking is a basis for friendship. It consists of feelings of closeness and emotional warmth without passion or commitment. Liking is not felt toward passing acquaintances. It is reserved for people to whom one feels close enough to share one's innermost feelings and thoughts. We sometimes develop these intimate relationships without making the commitment to maintaining a long-term relationship that typifies other types of love. Liking may develop into a passionate love, however, or into a more committed form of friendship called *companionate love* by many writers, including Sternberg (1988), Clyde and Susan Hendrick (2003), and Elaine Hatfield (Hatfield & Rapson, 2002).

Can lovers also be friends, or shall the twain never meet? There is no reason why people in love should not become good friends—perhaps even the best of friends. Sternberg's model recognizes that the intimacy we find in true friendships and the passion we find in love are blended in two forms of love: romantic love and consummate love. These types of love differ along the dimension of commitment, however.

Romantic love has both passion and intimacy but lacks commitment. Romantic love may burn brightly and then flicker out. Or it may develop into a more complete love, called *consummate love*, in which all three components flower. Desire is accompanied by a deeper intimacy and commitment. The flames of passion can be stoked across the years, even if they do not burn quite so brightly as they once did. Consummate love is most special, and it certainly is an ideal toward which many Westerners strive.

In *empty love*, by contrast, there is nothing *but* commitment. Neither the warm, emotional embrace of intimacy nor the flame of passion exists. With empty love, one's lover is a person whom one tolerates and remains with because of a sense of duty. People often remain in an empty-love relationship because of either personal prescription or social prescription (Cox et al., 1997). *Personal prescription* is based on the belief that one should persist in a relationship. *Social prescription* is based on the belief that one's friends or family members believe that it is right to persist in a relationship.

Sometimes a love relationship has both passion and commitment but lacks intimacy. Sternberg calls this *fatuous (foolish) love.* Fatuous love is associated with whirlwind courtships that burn brightly but briefly as the partners come to realize that they are not well matched. Intimacy can develop in such relationships, but couples who rush into marriage often find that the realities of marriage give the lie to their expectations.

In *companionate love,* finally, intimacy and commitment are strong, but passion is lacking. This form of love typifies long-term (so-called platonic) friendships and those marriages in which passion has ebbed but a deep and abiding friendship remains (Hatfield & Rapson, 2002).

In this chapter, we have discussed interpersonal attraction—the force that initiates social contact. In the next chapter, we follow the development of social contacts into intimate relationships.

Summing Up

A number of factors determine interpersonal attraction.

Physical attractiveness is a major determinant of sexual attraction. In our culture, slenderness is in style. Both genders consider smiling faces more attractive. Socially dominant men, but not dominant women, are usually found attractive. Women place greater emphasis on such traits as vocational status and earning potential, whereas men give more consideration to physical attractiveness. Some evolutionary psychologists believe that evolutionary forces favour such gender differences in preferred traits because these traits offer reproductive advantages.

According to the similarity–attraction hypothesis, people tend to develop romantic relationships with people who are similar to themselves.

Through reciprocation of positive words and actions, neutral or mild feelings may be stoked into feelings of attraction.

The Greeks had four concepts related to the modern meanings of love: storge, agape, philia, and eros.

Western culture has a long tradition of idealizing the concept of romantic love. Most people in Canada see romantic love as a prerequisite to marriage. Early in a relationship, infatuation and more enduring forms of romantic love may be indistinguishable.

Researchers are now applying the scientific method to the study of love.

Berscheid and Hatfield define romantic love in terms of intense physiological arousal and cognitive appraisal of that arousal as love.

Hendrick and Hendrick suggest that there are six styles of love among college students: romantic love, game-playing love, friendship, logical love, possessive love, and selfless love.

Sternberg suggests that there are three distinct components of love: intimacy, passion, and commitment. Various combinations of these components typify different kinds of love. Romantic love is characterized by the combination of passion and intimacy.

Test Yourself

Multiple-Choice Questions

1. **Research suggests that**
   a. smaller waist-to-hip ratios in women are generally considered more attractive
   b. heavier females are considered more attractive
   c. there are universal standards of attractiveness
   d. shorter males are considered more attractive

2. **University men on average think that their physique is**
   a. too heavy to appeal to women
   b. not muscular enough to appeal to women
   c. close to ideal
   d. less attractive than that of their friends

3. **Female university students generally see themselves as**
   a. attractive enough to "get" most men
   b. smaller than they actually are
   c. much heavier than the ideal
   d. more attractive than their friends

4. **A number of studies have shown that**
   a. men are more attracted to socially dominant women
   b. women are more attracted to socially dominant men

c. there are no gender differences in attraction
d. social dominance is not important in attraction

5. Research suggests that regardless of ethnicity, men find all of the following attractive in women except
a. large eyes
b. wide-set eyes
c. full lower lips
d. heavy eyebrows

6. In choosing a mate, women generally place greater emphasis than men on ______________, while men place greater emphasis on ____________.
a. earning potential, warmth, and dependability; youth and physical attractiveness
b. physical strength; education and intelligence
c. political and social attitudes; family background
d. men and women have the same preferences

7. The idea that people are more likely to look for romantic relationships with those who are similar to themselves is known as the
a. reciprocity theory
b. similarity-attraction hypothesis
c. love profile
d. intimacy theory

8. The ancient Greeks distinguished between ____________ varieties of love.
a. one
b. two
c. three
d. four

9. Sternberg's triangular theory of love includes intimacy, passion, and ______________.
a. reciprocity
b. sexuality
c. commitment
d. delight

10. In the early stages of a relationship, love and ____________________ may be difficult to distinguish.
a. infatuation
b. friendship
c. empty love
d. fatuous love

Answers to the Test Yourself questions in each chapter are found on page 509.

Critical Thinking Questions

1. Have you ever been in love? How could you distinguish between love and infatuation?
2. What traits or characteristics are most important to you when you think about a potential date? A marriage partner? Are they the same or different? Why?
3. Would you date someone of another religion or ethnic group? Why or why not? How do you think your friends and family would react?
4. Would you consider a relationship with someone you have only met online in a chatroom? Why or why not? What would you be most concerned about?

Visit MyPsychKit at www.mypsychkit.com, where you can do quizzes and link to additional resources on topics discussed in this text.

CHAPTER SEVEN

Relationships, Intimacy, and Communication

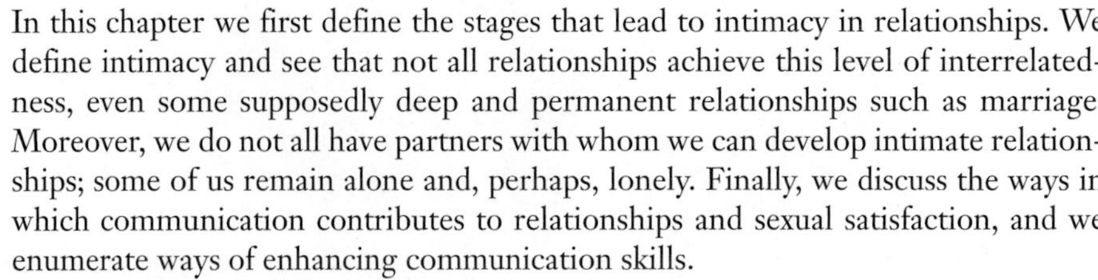

In this chapter we first define the stages that lead to intimacy in relationships. We define intimacy and see that not all relationships achieve this level of interrelatedness, even some supposedly deep and permanent relationships such as marriage. Moreover, we do not all have partners with whom we can develop intimate relationships; some of us remain alone and, perhaps, lonely. Finally, we discuss the ways in which communication contributes to relationships and sexual satisfaction, and we enumerate ways of enhancing communication skills.

Social exchange theory The view that the development of a relationship reflects the unfolding of social exchanges—that is, the rewards and costs of maintaining the relationship as opposed to those of ending it.

ABCDE model Levinger's view, which approaches romantic relationships in terms of five stages: Attraction, Building, Continuation, Deterioration, and Ending.

The ABC(DE)'s of Romantic Relationships

Romantic relationships, like people, undergo stages of development. According to **social exchange theory**, this development reflects the unfolding of social exchanges, which involve the rewards and costs of maintaining the relationship, compared with the rewards and costs of dissolving it. During each stage, positive factors sway partners toward maintaining and enhancing their relationship. Negative factors incline them toward letting it deteriorate and end.

Numerous investigators have viewed the development of romantic relationships in terms of phases or stages (Berscheid & Reis, 1998; Dindia & Timmerman, 2003; Hendrick & Hendrick, 2000; Honeycutt & Cantrill, 2001; Levinger, 1980). From their work, we can build a five-stage **ABCDE model** of romantic relationships: (1) *A*ttraction, (2) *B*uilding, (3) *C*ontinuation, (4) *D*eterioration, and (5) termination, or *E*nding.

Attraction occurs when two people become aware of each other and find one another appealing or enticing. We may find ourselves attracted to an enchanting person "across a crowded room," in a nearby office, or in a new class. We may meet others through blind dates, introductions by mutual friends, computer match-ups, or by "accident."

The internet has become one of the most popular places to meet potential dating and sexual partners. In Canada there are numerous online sites promoting dating and sexual relationships for people of all sexual orientations and preferences. One of the newest sites is **lavalifePRIME.com** which is for people over the age of 40.

There are also virtual dating sites where people can go on virtual dates with someone before deciding whether to date offline. Toronto-based **OmniDate.com** provides avatars (virtual characters) that go on dates with other avatars. Persons using OmniDate choose an avatar and then decide where to go on a virtual date. Through their interactions with the avatars, people reveal their personalities to their online partners (Rao, 2008).

In a survey of gay and bisexual men in Ontario, 35% reported they had met a sexual partner online within the previous six months. However, by far the most common meeting place was the gay bar (Myers et al., 2004).

While men are more likely than women to go online to meet potential dating partners, women are more likely than men to sign up with introduction agencies. Susan Kates, the owner of **Dinnerworks.ca**, a company that organizes dinner parties for singles in Toronto, reports that 70% of her clients are women ("Two girls . . . ," 2004).

How do you feel about the idea of meeting a potential dating partner on the internet? Do you think more people will be meeting on the internet in future?

For people who are uncomfortable about meeting online, there are many other options. In particular, there are numerous events focused on bringing singles together. In Toronto, one of the largest events for singles is the "Playing for Matches" fundraiser for a local hospital. This event, which attracts almost 2000 singles, has everyone complete a questionnaire ahead of time in an attempt to match up people with similar interests.

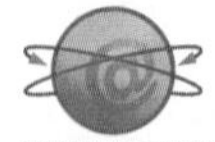

Dating Websites

www.lavalife.com

www.perfectmatch.com

www.date.com

www.personals.yahoo.com

www.eharmony.com

www.plentyoffish.com

www.canadamatchmaker.net

www.gaymatchescanada.com

A Closer Look

REELING IN A DATE

If Markus Frind's example is anything to go by, the best way to earn a few cool million is to do not much at all, and certainly, much less than your competitors. Frind, 30, runs one of the world's busiest dating sites out of his home in Vancouver. Operating in New Zealand, Australia, the United States, the United Kingdom and Canada, he has single-handedly managed to become a major player in the world of on-line matchmaking.

Frind started PlentyofFish.com in March 2003. He wanted to create a free dating site in a market that usually charges members between $20 and $60 per month.

Dating sites are usually very niche. If you are a member of a particular group, have a sexual fetish, or an obscure hobby or interest, there is likely a dating site for you. There's TrekPassions.com (for Trekkies), BikerKiss.com, LoveMeLoveMyPets.com, BlackPlanet.com, Prescription4Love.com (for people with everything from Tourette's syndrome to herpes), SeniorFinder.com, and AshleyMadison.com, which is strictly for adulterers. Mostly, the clients self-select, but some sites build in barriers to weed out those who don't fit the target demographic. For example, Match.com requires a lengthy and involved 400-item questionnaire that can take several hours to complete, says Evan Marc Katz, a dating coach and author of *I Can't Believe I'm Buying This Book: A Commonsense Guide to Successful Internet Dating*. The quiz is designed to discourage those who aren't serious about relationships. Then there's ItsJustLunch.com—exclusively for busy professionals. The $1600 cost of arranging 14 lunch dates, excluding the meal cost, is supposed to turn off anyone who can't afford to pick up the tab.

Plenty of Fish has taken the opposite approach. The registration process is deliberately short, and open to everyone. It aims to attract large numbers of people from a broad cross-section of society. The downside, critics say, is that the site inevitably draws the type of person who prefers not to spend any money in their search for companionship. In Canada, the average age is 38. In the U.S., it's 39, but in both countries persons in their twenties as well as seniors are also well-represented. "It's brilliant because it is really easy to use," explains Bonny Albo, who writes About.com's "Guide to Dating." "People really like it, especially because it's free."

While many other dating websites offer a range of video and messaging functions, Plenty of Fish offers the bare basics. Rather than requiring compatibility tests and offering referrals, visitors to Plenty of Fish search for their own dates. Instead of video clips, profiles are accompanied by simple head shots. If you run into problems, there's no customer service number to call. You can send an email, although the site warns that there are only a couple of people reading what you write, so responses often take days. There is no banner advertising because Plenty of Fish relies on word of mouth for traffic and Google ads for revenue.

"They let people do their own thing," Katz explains. "There is no real quality control or filter on who is joining the site. If you want to find what you are looking for, you probably have to sift through a lot of people. It's a big, sloppy, under-managed site that's very laissez-faire."

It may be laissez-faire but it works, argues Frind. The site posts thousands of photos, testimonials and thank you letters from couples who have met their partner or spouse through the service. And in sheer volume and traffic, it remains No. 1. With 18 million hits per month in Canada, and 58 million worldwide, it is the nation's most popular dating site. Roughly 1.2 million people visit the site every month in Canada. Lavalife is a distant second with 752 000 people for the same duration, according to Comscore. Revenues total about $10 million per year, says Frind, compared to annual operating costs of about $1 million, covering advertising, site maintenance and the cost of employing two customer service staffers. The rest of the profits go to Frind, who works about 10 hours per week, and is planning to expand into Brazil and Germany next. In the dating site world, growth can feed off itself, explains Katz. "If you throw two billion people in a barrel, you don't have to do much for some of them to meet and hit it off. Plentyoffish.com does well mainly because of the law of averages."

Source: Shimo, A. (2008, July 16) "Reeling in a date: Plenty of Fish has become the dating site for the masses." The Toronto Star.

Building a relationship follows initial attraction. Factors that motivate us to try to build relationships include similarity in the level of physical attractiveness, similarity in attitudes, and mutual liking and positive evaluations. Factors that may deter us from trying to build relationships include lack of physical appeal, dissimilarity in attitudes, and negative mutual evaluations.

NOT SO SMALL TALK: AN AUDITION FOR BUILDING A RELATIONSHIP In the early stages of building a relationship, we typically look for common ground in the form of overlapping attitudes and interests, and we check out our feelings of attraction. At this point, the determination of whether to strive to develop

Innovative Canadian Research

DATING ONLINE

Robert Brym from the University of Toronto and Rhonda Lenton of McMaster University have conducted a study of the online dating experiences of 7700 Canadians (Brym & Lenton, 2001). They found there were twice as many male as female online daters. About one-third of the respondents had not met anyone in person, almost one-half had met between one and five people, and the remainder had met more than five. The majority had talked on the phone and exchanged pictures before agreeing to meet. Most people said that they used online dating sites primarily to find dating partners and to establish a long-term relationship. However, more than twice as many men (53%) as women (20%) said that they dated online in order to find a sexual partner. Among online daters who had met dates in person, about two-thirds had had sex with at least one. Sixty percent had formed at least one long-term friendship and about one-quarter said they had met someone they came to regard as a partner.

Brym and Lenton (2001) believe that online dating will become more popular in the future for the following reasons:

- The number of singles in the population is rapidly increasing.
- Increasing time pressures lead people to look for more efficient ways of meeting others for intimate relationships.
- Increasing mobility means that single people are finding it harder to meet others for dating.
- Concerns about sexual harassment make it more difficult to date someone at work.

The workplace does not seem to be as popular a meeting place for potential mates as used to be the case—probably because of concerns over possible sexual harassment. An online survey of 34 000 workers on the **Monster.ca** career website found some interesting cultural differences in attitude. Europeans (65%) were the most accepting of office romances while Americans (30%) were the least accepting and Canadians (43%) were in the middle (Prashad, 2004).

Safety is one of people's main concerns about online dating. However, only 10% of those who went on a date with someone they met online reported that they had been frightened by the experience (Brym & Lenton, 2001).

Applied Knowledge

BEWARE OF ROMANCE SCAMS ON THE INTERNET

It is prudent to be cautious when meeting people on the internet. The reality is that some people misrepresent themselves. In Kitchener, Ontario, a man referred to as "Online Casanova" was sentenced by a judge to three years in prison for defrauding 13 women of $150 000 (Wood, 2006). This man, posing as a lawyer on the dating site **PlentyofFish.com**, persuaded the women to give him money for various reasons. Once the women gave him money, he would stop contacting them. Additionally some of the women got a sexually transmitted disease from him and three got pregnant (Wood, 2006).

Men can also be victims of the internet. A 38-year-old Toronto woman met men on the internet and on the street. She used several different identities. Several men said that she pretended to be a medical student at the University of Toronto and claimed she needed money for tuition fees, rent, etc. In 1998 she defrauded several men out of $350 000 and in 2005 she defrauded two men out of $50 000. She was twice convicted of fraud (Roberts, 2005).

In an international internet dating scam, based in Africa, men claimed they were from the U.S. and working overseas. They used photos stolen from dating sites to portray themselves. In their search for potential victims, thousands of women were contacted. Once a relationship was established with a woman via the internet, the men tried to obtain as much information as possible from that woman. In particular, they asked about what kind of man the woman desired. Using this information as a guide, the man quickly began to profess love for the female victim. Shortly after, he would give hardship stories as a basis for requesting money.

This scam and many others are discussed on the website **www.romancescams.org**. This site was created in 2005 to inform the public of the various types of online romance scams in existence. It provides useful tips on how to avoid being scammed, such as not giving money to someone met on the internet—regardless of the reason for the request. Additionally, the site provides counselling support to victims of romance scams.

the relationship is often made, at least in part, on the basis of **small talk**. Small talk allows an exchange of information but stresses breadth of topic coverage rather than in-depth discussion. Engaging in small talk may seem "phony," but premature self-disclosure of intimate information may repel the other person, as we shall see.

Small talk is a trial balloon for friendship. Successful small talk encourages a couple to venture beneath the surface. At a cocktail party, people may flit about from person to person, exchanging small talk, but now and then a couple finds common ground and pairs off.

What Do You Say When You're Meeting Someone New? Do you make small talk? About what? Do you use an opening line? Which one? Are you genuine? Are you phony? Are you tense? At ease? Small talk actually isn't so small at all. People use it to search for common ground and test possible feelings of attraction.

THE "OPENING LINE": HOW DO YOU GET THINGS STARTED? One kind of small talk is the greeting, or opening line. We usually precede verbal greetings with eye contact and decide to begin talking if this eye contact is reciprocated. Avoidance of eye contact may mean that the person is shy, but it could also signify lack of interest. If you would like to progress from initial attraction to surface contact, try a smile and direct eye contact. If the eye contact is reciprocated, choose an opening line, or greeting. Because your opening line can be important, you may prefer to say something more meaningful than "one, two, one, two."

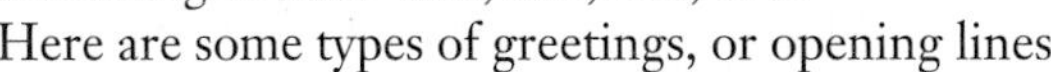

Here are some types of greetings, or opening lines:

- Verbal salutes, such as "Good morning."
- Personal inquiries, such as "How are you doing?"
- Compliments, such as "I like your outfit."
- References to your mutual surroundings, such as "What do you think of that painting?" or "This is a nice apartment house, isn't it?"
- References to people or events outside the immediate setting, such as "How do you like this weather we've been having?" (Opening gambits about the weather may work best when accompanied by a self-deprecating grin to acknowledge how corny the remark might seem.)
- References to the other person's behaviour, such as "I couldn't help noticing you were sitting alone," or "I see you out on this track every Saturday morning."
- References to your own behaviour, or to yourself, such as "Hi, my name is Allan Felix" (feel free to use your own name, if you prefer).

The simple "Hi" or "Hello" is very useful. A friendly glance followed by a cheerful hello ought to give you some idea of whether the attraction is reciprocated. If the hello is returned with a friendly smile and inviting eye contact, follow it up with another greeting, such as a reference to your surroundings, the other person's behaviour, or your name.

EXCHANGING "NAME, RANK, AND SERIAL NUMBER" Early exchanges are likely to include name, occupation, marital status, and hometown. Each person seeks a sociological profile of the other to discover common ground that may provide a basis for pursuing the conversation. An unspoken rule seems to be at work: "If I provide you with some information about myself, you will reciprocate

Small talk A superficial kind of conversation that allows exchange of information but stresses breadth of topic coverage rather than in-depth discussion.

How Will She Get Rid of Him?
Perhaps she will give him a phony email address. Some women now use email as a method of avoiding seeing people they do not want to go out with. They may give out their actual email addresses but never respond, or they may give out seldom used or erroneous email addresses. It's like giving out the wrong phone number. (Bye bye.)

by giving me an equal amount of information about yourself. Or 'I'll tell you my hometown if you tell me yours'" (Knapp & Vangelista, 2000). If the other person is unresponsive, she or he may not be attracted to you, and you may wish to try someone else. But you may also be awkward in your approach or perhaps turn the other person off by disclosing too much about yourself at once.

SELF-DISCLOSURE: YOU TELL ME AND I'LL TELL YOU . . . CAREFULLY Opening up, or **self-disclosure**, is central to building intimate relationships. But just what sort of information is safe to disclose upon first meeting someone? If you refuse to go beyond name, rank, and serial number, you may look uninterested or as though you are trying to keep things under wraps. If, on the other hand, you blurt out the fact that you have a terrible rash on your thigh, it's likely that you have disclosed too much too soon.

Research suggests that we should refrain from disclosing certain types of information too rapidly if we want to make a good impression (Punyanunt-Carter, 2006). We may say we value openness and honesty in our relationships, but it may be a social mistake to open up too soon.

SELF-DISCLOSURE ON DATING WEBSITES On the other hand, rapid self-disclosure seems to be something of a new norm when people meet in cyberspace (Ben-Ze'ev, 2003). Cyberspace allows for relative anonymity and enables people to control what they want to reveal—to safeguard their privacy even as they increase their emotional closeness and openness. The very nature of privacy changes in cyberspace.

Self-disclosure The revelation of personal—perhaps intimate—information.

If the surface contact provided by small talk and initial self-disclosure has been mutually rewarding, partners in a relationship tend to develop deeper feelings of

Innovative Canadian Research

SEXUALLY DIRECT APPROACHES IN SINGLES BARS

While most people follow traditional strategies for meeting potential partners, in some situations initial approaches are more explicitly sexual. In a survey of female students at the University of Guelph who went to singles bars, more than 80% reported that men had approached them using a sexually overt approach behaviour (Huber & Herold, 2006). About half of the women had themselves initiated such behaviours with someone they did not know. The specific behaviours were buttock touching over clothes, breast/chest touching over clothes, genital touching over clothes, grinding pelvis to pelvis, and grinding from behind. The grinding behaviours were the most commonly experienced, while breast and genital touching were the least experienced. About 90% said they would be bothered by breast and/or genital approaches, and about half said they would be bothered by buttock touching or grinding.

Sexually overt approaches are far less common in other contexts. Indeed, in most other contexts, these behaviours would be almost universally defined as sexual harassment or sexual assault. However, in the bar context only about one-quarter of the women defined buttock touching or grinding approaches as harassment while about three-quarters saw breast or genital touching as harassment.

Although there is a broader acceptability of certain types of behaviours in a singles bar than in other contexts, there still are certain limitations. At a Guelph bar, a University of Windsor student pleaded guilty to assault after having ground against a woman from behind. The woman complained to police after the man ejaculated on her (Mercury Staff, 2007).

Robin Milhausen and Michael Cho were hosts of the Canadian television series Sex, Toys and Chocolate. *Unlike most Canadians, the guests on this show were extremely open in disclosing their sexual preferences and behaviours.*

liking for each other (Abell et al., 2006). Self-disclosure may continue to build gradually through the course of a relationship as partners come to trust each other enough to share confidences and more intimate feelings.

While sexual disclosure can be very rewarding as a means of strengthening relationships, it may also be costly to oneself and one's relationship. In revealing personal information, people are highly aware that the listener might evaluate it negatively and even use it to hurt the person. For example, in a much-publicized case, Canadian writer Evelyn Lau, a former lover of the novelist W. P. Kinsella, wrote a magazine article in which she discussed and critiqued his sexual performance. He sued her, claiming that she had violated his privacy (Canadian Press, 1999).

The media have become very bold in discussing the sex lives of public figures such as politicians and celebrities. For example, newspapers around the world openly printed explicit details of the affair between Monica Lewinsky and former U.S. president Bill Clinton: the thong underwear, the oral sex, the cigar.

In Canada, real people have openly discussed their sex lives on programs such as *Sex with Sue; Sex, Toys and Chocolate;* and *Kink.* Even the more conservative CBC television show *Newsworld* has shown the documentary *Sex, Truth and Video*, which involved 30 women of various ages speaking openly and explicitly about their own sexuality. The openness of participants on these programs is in direct contrast to the reticence of most Canadians.

The internet, because of its anonymity, facilitates self-disclosure. Frank sexual self-disclosure is seen on many sex blog sites. Amy Muise (2006), a University of Guelph researcher, has conducted a qualitative analysis of female sex blog sites. Muise gives examples of how the women describe their sexual fantasies and sexual behaviours in lustful detail. Most of the women also provide insight into their feelings and reactions regarding the development of their sexuality. Some refer to this process as "releasing their inner slut." In general, the women state that they are much more revealing about their sex lives on the web than they are in real life (see Chapter 15 for more discussion of this).

Apparent disclosure is not always honest. Some people select information carefully to manipulate others, and even invent the stories they "disclose." Researchers at

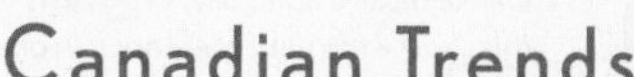

Canadian Trends

SEXUAL SELF-DISCLOSURE TO CLOSE FRIENDS

The belief that women are open and men tight-lipped appears to be something of a myth. Overall, researchers find that women are only slightly more revealing about themselves than men. When Canadians were asked in the Compas (1998) survey about how much detail they shared about their sexual life with their close friends, close to as many females (43%) as males (50%) said they did not share any information. Hardly any of the females (6%) or males (4%) said that they shared a lot of details. As shown in Figure 7.1, age was a much stronger predictor of disclosure than gender. Among those 18 or 19, 86% disclosed to their friends compared with only 16% of those aged 60 and older.

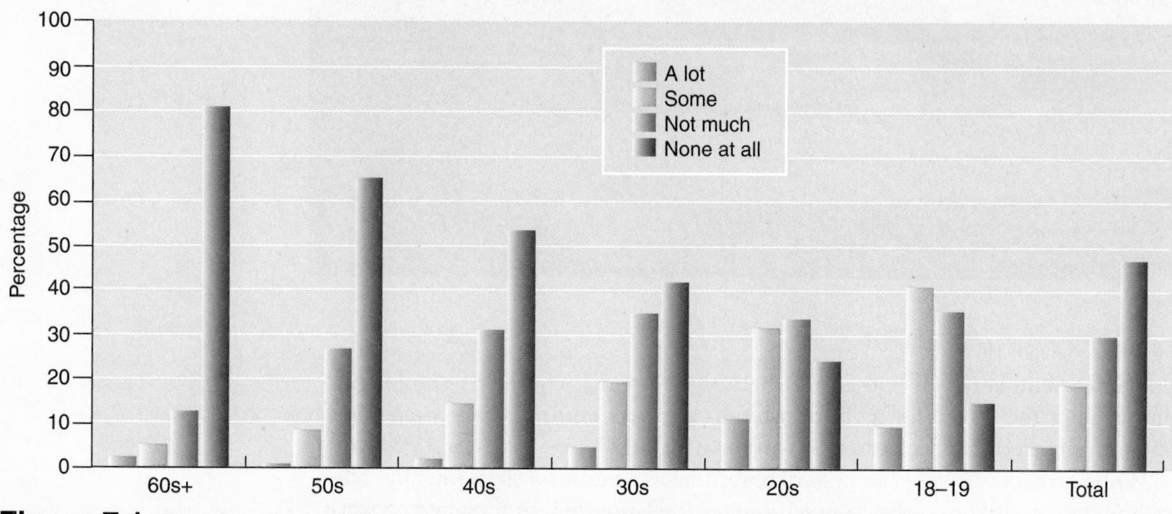

Figure 7.1 Disclosure of Sexual Details to Close Friend, by Age.

According to the Compas (1998) study, young Canadian adults are far more disclosing about their sexuality than those in their sixties.

Source: Compas (1998). Modern life survey of the Canadian adult population.

Queen's University found that men with higher scores on a test of psychopathy were more likely to use deception both in sexual and nonsexual situations. These men were also more likely to have a history of unstable sexual relationships (Seto et al., 1997).

SEX DIFFERENCES IN SELF-DISCLOSURE A woman complains to a friend: "He never opens up to me. It's like living with a stone wall." Women commonly declare that men are loath to express their feelings. Researchers find that masculine-typed individuals, whether male or female, tend to be less willing to disclose their feelings, perhaps in adherence to the traditional "strong and silent" masculine stereotype. A study by Susan Basow and Kimberly Rubenfeld (2003) found that feminine-typed individuals are more likely to be empathetic and to listen to other people's troubles than masculine-typed individuals, regardless of their anatomic sex.

A New Brunswick study of students in dating relationships found that women disclosed slightly more information about both sexual and nonsexual issues than did men (Byers & Demmons, 1999). However, in a more recent study at Trent University (Humphreys & Newby, 2007), there were no gender differences in sexual self-disclosure.

In the New Brunswick study, the students disclosed to their dating partners more about nonsexual than sexual issues and more about their sexual likes than their sexual dislikes. Those who were more disclosing about nonsexual issues were also more disclosing about sexual issues (although most did not fully reveal all their true sexual feelings). A key factor in the amount of disclosure was whether the partner was also disclosing. Those who were more open were more satisfied with their level of sexual communication, and ultimately with their sexual relationship.

In another New Brunswick study, the process by which sexual self-disclosure related to sexual satisfaction seemed to differ for men and women (MacNeil, 2004). For men, there was a direct relationship between sexual disclosure and sexual satisfaction. For women, disclosing about nonsexual issues seemed to be more important: Women who could freely disclose about other aspects of their relationship were more satisfied with their relationship in general, and this accounted for their greater sexual satisfaction. In other words, it seems that for women, relationship satisfaction is a key factor in sexual satisfaction.

In an earlier study, female students at the University of Guelph were asked how much they disclosed about eight sexual topics (Herold & Way, 1988). The least disclosed topics were masturbation and sexual thoughts. The women were divided about revealing their sexual past, with less than half believing that "a woman who truly loves her partner should be willing to tell him about all her previous sexual experience."

Those who felt guilty about their sexuality were less disclosing. People who feel guilty worry about the judgments of others, and might feel even more guilty if they reveal their sexual thoughts and experiences to others (Herold & Way, 1988).

SEXUAL INITIATION Initiating sex is stereotypically considered to be the male's role. In a study of cohabiting and married individuals in New Brunswick (Byers & Heinlein, 1989), men initiated sex twice as often as did the women. As well, the men considered initiating sex but did not do so more often than did the women. Contrary to the stereotype that men are always available for sex, men refused invitations to have sex proportionally as often as did the women. Similarly, the women accepted sexual initiations as often as did the men.

In a follow-up study of dating individuals, O'Sullivan and Byers (1992) again found that men initiated sex more often than women. The invitations were mainly in the form of either nonverbal gestures or indirect verbal offers. Only in a minority of situations was a direct verbal request used.

What about situations where the woman wants to have sex but has a reluctant partner? How does she influence her partner to have sex? To answer this question, researchers at the University of Waterloo (Clements-Schreiber & Rempel, 1995) surveyed a community sample of married and single women. About half the women said they would directly ask their partner to have sex. The most common strategies, which more than 90% said they would use, included arranging an opportunity to be alone with him, paying a lot of attention to him, and touching him affectionately. The next most common strategies, indicated by 70% or more of the women involved, were kissing him passionately, setting a romantic mood with candlelight and music, dressing in a seductive way, rubbing his back and shoulders, and letting their hands wander around his body.

Making a Commitment

Numerous studies find that men tend to be more reluctant than women to make commitments. David Popenoe, co-director of the National Marriage Project at Rutgers University in New Jersey, conducted a study with 60 unmarried heterosexual men and found that the commonness of cohabitation is one reason why they are reluctant to make a commitment. In cohabitation, sex—traditionally a key reason for

Innovative Canadian Research

OBTAINING SEXUAL CONSENT

A great deal has been written about the necessity of obtaining sexual consent before initiating sexual relations with a partner. However, there has been limited research on this topic (Beres, 2007).

At the University of Guelph, students were asked how they ask for and give sexual consent (Humphreys, 2004). Only about one-third said that they explicitly asked for sex. The three most common nonverbal behaviours used by both genders were kissing the partner, moving closer, and touching him or her sexually. The most common ways in which two-thirds of both males and females indicated consent for sex were by not stopping their partner from kissing and sexual touching, kissing their partner, moving closer, and touching their partner sexually. About half said they gave consent by *not* saying no. About half the men and one-third of the women indicated giving consent by saying yes. The study clearly indicated that young people find directly asking for sex to be problematic, with two-thirds agreeing that verbally asking for sexual consent is awkward.

When asked how consent should be obtained, more than half (65% of females and 53% of males) preferred that one should ask first before engaging in any sexual activity. But a large minority (35% of females, 47% of males) preferred to assume consent and to continue with the sexual behaviour until their partner indicated otherwise. Interestingly, although sexual consent has been stressed in many campus educational programs, only about half of the students had discussed the topic with their friends.

It should be noted that methodologically a major contribution of this research was the development of scales measuring sexual consent attitudes and sexual consent behaviours. These scales have solid reliability and validity (Humphreys & Herold, 2007).

In a follow-up study, Humphreys (2007a) found that students believed it was not as necessary to obtain sexual consent in longer-term relationships as it was at the beginning of a relationship. This was true for sexual behaviours ranging from hugging to sexual intercourse. The one exception was anal intercourse, where students felt that explicit consent was required regardless of the status of the relationship. Humphreys speculates students felt this way because most had not engaged in anal intercourse.

A controversial policy developed by Antioch College in Ohio requires that verbal consent be obtained at every step of a sexual encounter. For example, if a woman wanted to kiss her partner, according to the policy, she would need to directly ask if she could kiss him. Later, if he wished to touch her breasts, he would need to ask directly if he could do so and she would have to say yes, verbally. When asked their opinion about this policy, students at the University of Guelph felt this type of consent procedure was not practical and would not be followed by the great majority of young people (Humphreys & Herold, 2003).

In Banff, Alberta, Melanie Beres (2006) interviewed young men and women about how they communicated sexual consent with a casual sex partner. In her analysis of the interviews, Beres found that three main themes emerged. First, the respondents said that they simply "knew" whether the other person was interested in having casual sex. Thus they felt it was not necessary to make a formal request to initiate sexual activity.

The second theme involves communicating about not wanting to engage in casual sex. Here there were variations on the idea of "'no' means 'no.'" Rather than directly saying "no," women would use a diversity of tactics, such as saying that they had a boyfriend. Also, women would show their discomfort with proceeding by pulling away or by letting their bodies become tense and stiff. In the absence of these kinds of signals, a man assumed that the woman was interested in having sex.

The third theme was that "'yes' means 'yes.'" Here, again, the respondents relied on subtle cues. For example, it was assumed that if the other person was willing to leave a bar setting and go to a more private location, such as one's home, that this behaviour indicated an interest in engaging in casual sex. Other indications were pulling the partner closer and listening to physical signs such as sighing, heavy breathing, and moaning. However, the respondents agreed that despite these signals, it was possible that at any stage the other person (usually the woman) could change his or her mind and decide not to have sex (Beres, 2006).

In conclusion, these studies on sexual consent demonstrate the complexity of the process of obtaining and granting sexual consent. In reality, for most people, the process is more subtle than blatant.

men to marry—is readily available. Popenoe (cited in Hussain, 2002) notes that "In a sense, with cohabitation he gets a quasi-wife without having to commit."

In committed relationships, a delicate balance exists between individuality and mutuality. In healthy unions, a strong sense of togetherness does not eradicate individuality. Partners in such relationships remain free to be themselves. Neither seeks to dominate the other or to submerge himself or herself into the personality of the other. Each partner maintains individual interests, likes and dislikes, needs, and goals.

Factors that can throw continuing relationships into a downward spiral include boredom, as in falling into a rut in leisure activities or sexual practices. Yet boredom does not always end relationships. Consider a study of 12 men who admitted to experiencing sexual boredom in long-term heterosexual relationships (Tunariu & Reavey, 2003). The men were not happy with sexual boredom, particularly in a culture in which men are viewed as highly sexual and romantic love is supposed to remain passionate. On the other hand, they viewed their boredom as a normal trade-off for so-called true love and long-term companionship.

Other factors that contribute to the discontinuation of a relationship include evidence of negative evaluation (such as bickering, and forgetting anniversaries and other important dates or pretending that they do not exist), lack of fairness in the relationship (such as one partner's always deciding how the couple will spend their free time), jealousy, and general dissatisfaction.

Jealousy: Is the World a Real-Life *Temptation Island*?

Anthropologists find evidence of jealousy in all cultures, although it may vary in amount and intensity across and within cultures. It appears to be more common and intense among cultures with a stronger *machismo* tradition, in which men are expected to display their virility. It is also powerful in cultures in which men view a woman's infidelity as a threat to their honour.

Sexual jealousy is aroused when we suspect that an intimate relationship is threatened by a rival. Lovers can become jealous when others show sexual interest in their partners or when their partners show an interest (even a casual or nonsexual interest) in another. Jealousy can lead to loss of feelings of affection, to feelings of insecurity and rejection, to anxiety and loss of self-esteem, and to mistrust of one's partner and potential rivals. Jealousy is a common reason why relationships fail.

Feelings of possessiveness, which are related to jealousy, can also subject a relationship to stress. In extreme cases, jealousy can cause depression or give rise to spousal abuse, suicide, or murder. But milder forms of jealousy are not necessarily destructive to a relationship. They may even serve the positive function of revealing how much one cares for one's partner.

What causes jealousy? Experience and personality variables play roles. People may become mistrustful of their partners because former partners had cheated. People with low self-esteem may experience sexual jealousy because they become overly dependent on their partners. They may fear that they will not be able to find another partner if their present partner leaves.

How do we explain feelings of jealousy? What does jealousy do to an intimate relationship?

JEALOUSY AND FACEBOOK Facebook is a popular social networking site. Facebook allows one access to information about one's partner that might otherwise not be known. In a University of Guelph study, three-fourths of students reported that they and their partners had previous romantic or sexual partners as Facebook "friends" (Muise et al., 2008). Also, 92% said their partner had Facebook friends whom they did not know. Correspondence with or seeing photos of these persons was found to trigger feelings of jealousy, especially among partners who already had jealous feelings. Also, those who spent the most time on Facebook were likely to be the most jealous (Muise et al., 2008).

JEALOUSY AND EVOLUTIONARY THEORY Sex differences in jealousy appear to support evolutionary theory. Males seem to be more upset by sexual infidelity, females by emotional infidelity (Shackelford et al., 2002). That is, males are made more insecure and angry when their partners have sexual relations with someone else. Females are made more insecure and angry when their partners become emotionally attached to someone else. Why? Evolutionary theory hypothesizes that sexual jealousy was shaped by natural selection as a method of assuring males that their female partner's offspring is their own, and of assuring females that their male partners will continue to provide resources to facilitate child-rearing (Buss, 2003, 2005; Harris, 2003).

LACK OF SEX DIFFERENCES IN RESPONSES TO SAME-SEX AFFAIRS Interestingly, the hypothesized gender difference in reactions to infidelity disappears when one's partner has an affairs with someone of his or her own sex (Sagarin et al., 2003). Is it because the affair carries no threat of impregnation (a view that would be consistent with evolutionary theory)?

Or is it because the victim consoles himself or herself by thinking that he or she really isn't competing in the same arena with the intruder? Are both explanations and other explanations possible?

A COGNITIVE PERSPECTIVE In recent years, cognitive theory has gained importance in many areas of the behavioural sciences, and sexual jealousy is no exception. In two studies, Stacie Bauerle and her colleagues (2002) presented 156 college undergraduates and 128 members of the general population with various scenarios in which their partners were unfaithful. By and large, jealousy increased when the individuals attributed their partner's infidelity to *internal* causes, such as clear personal choice. When they attributed the infidelity to *external* causes, such as alcohol or social pressure, the individuals in the study reported feeling significantly less jealous. ("Don't blame me; it was the alcohol.")

Responses to Deterioration of a Relationship

A relationship begins to fail when it becomes less rewarding than it was. Couples can respond to deterioration in active or passive ways. Active means of response include doing something that may enhance the relationship (such as working on improving communication skills, negotiating differences, or seeking professional help) or deciding to end the relationship. Passive methods of responding include merely waiting for something to happen, doing little, or doing nothing. People can sit back and wait for the relationship to improve on its own (occasionally it does) or for the relationship to deteriorate to the point where it ends. ("Hey, these things happen.")

It is irrational (and damaging to a relationship) to assume that good relationships require no investment of time and effort. No two people are matched perfectly. When problems arise, it is better to work to resolve them than to act as though they don't exist and hope that they will just disappear.

Breaking Up

According to social exchange theory, relationships draw to a close when negative forces hold sway—when the partners find little satisfaction in the affiliation, when the barriers to leaving the relationship are low (that is, the social, religious, and financial constraints are manageable), and especially when alternative partners are available. Problems in communication and jealousy are among the most common reasons for ending a relationship (Zusman & Knox, 1998). The availability of alternatives decreases one's commitment to and investment in a relationship (Rusbult et al., 1998).

People Who Have Been Rejected Sometimes Stalk Their Former Partners
Stalking includes behaviours such as breaking into their email. (Hint: Change your passwords from time to time.)

This fact has been widely recognized throughout the ages, which is one reason why patriarchal cultures like to keep their women locked up as much as possible.

Some people obviously take breaking up better than others. A study of more than 5000 people who responded to a survey on the internet found that anxious people were more likely to be highly preoccupied with the lost partner, to suffer more physical and emotional distress, to attempt to re-establish the relationship, and to be angry and vengeful (Davis et al., 2003). Emotionally secure individuals were most likely to seek social support among their friends and their families. Insecure individuals were most likely to turn to alcohol and drugs.

Breaking up is sometimes followed by **stalking**, or other "unwanted pursuit behaviours," such as unwelcome phone calls or emails, asking third parties about the person who dissolved the relationship, and following, threatening, or attacking that person or new partners of that person (Davis et al., 2002; Langhinrichsen–Rohling et al., 2002). Jealousy, abusiveness, and physical violence in relationships are key predictors of unwanted pursuit (Puente & Cohen, 2003). Stalkers and violent individuals also tend to have a strong need to control others (Dye & Davis, 2003).

On the other hand, the swan song of a relationship—moving on—can be a sign of healthful decision making, not a sign of failure. When people are highly incompatible, and when genuine attempts to preserve the relationship have failed, ending the relationship can offer both partners a chance for happiness with someone else.

Stalking Following or observing a person persistently, especially because of obsession with the person; can occur online as well as in person, as when a person breaks into someone else's email.

Intimacy Feelings of closeness and connectedness that are marked by sharing of innermost thoughts and feelings.

Intimacy: Sharing Innermost Thoughts and Feelings

Intimacy consists of feelings of emotional connectedness with another person and the desire to share one's innermost thoughts and feelings (Yela, 2006). Partners in the throes of romantic love usually want to disclose everything to and know everything about one another (Kito, 2005; Vaculík & Hudecek, 2005). Along with sex, intimacy is one of the key ingredients in passionate relationships (Firestone et al., 2006; Korobov & Thorne, 2006). Feelings of intimacy and affection tend to grow as romantic relationships develop (Nieder & Sieffge–Krenke, 2001). Relationships also develop from being more casual and superficial to being relatively committed

Working on the Relationship.
When one partner works on the relationship, the other partner is more motivated to reciprocate. Why did one partner give this gift? "Just because."

(Nieder & Sieffge–Krenke, 2001). As couples age, intimacy becomes one of the most valued—if not *the* most valued—components of the relationship (Villar et al., 2005). Intimate relationships are also characterized by trust, caring, and acceptance.

Sternberg's (2004) triangular theory of love regards intimacy as a basic component of romantic love, but people can be intimate and not in love, at least not in romantic love. Close friends and family members become emotionally intimate when they care deeply for each other and share their feelings and experiences.

People need not be *sexually* intimate to be emotionally intimate. Nor does sexual intimacy automatically create emotional intimacy. People who are sexually involved may not achieve emotional closeness. People can be more emotionally intimate with friends than with lovers.

Because intimacy involves the sharing of one's innermost thoughts and feelings, honesty is a core feature of intimacy. A person need not be an "open book" to

Canadian Trends

HONESTY, TRUTH, AND LIES

While honesty is desired in relationships, total honesty can devastate a relationship (Finkenauer & Hazam, 2000). In a national survey of 3000 Canadians sponsored by Harlequin Romance publications, two-thirds of respondents said that it was okay to sometimes lie, even though one-half believed that honesty and truth were most important in a good relationship (Van der Voort, 2008).

In the same survey, more than one-third of Canadians reported having sent sexually explicit extramarital emails, but only 17% said they would confess to having done so. Only 30% said they would tell their partners about kissing someone else and only one-quarter of the men said they would admit to an extramarital affair. Almost one-half (45%) of women and 41% of men would admit to flirting with someone else (Van der Voort, 2008).

develop and maintain intimacy, however. Some aspects of experience are better kept even from one's most intimate partners, especially when they are embarrassing or threatening (Finkenauer & Hazam, 2000; Korobov & Thorne, 2006).

Intimacy is important not only to interpersonal relationships but also to one's health. Researchers have found that intimacy fosters well-being and that its absence can be psychologically and physically harmful (Driver et al., 2003).

Research also shows that people come to trust their partners when they see that their partners have made sincere investments in the relationship, as evidenced, for example, by making sacrifices to be with them, such as incurring the disapproval of their family (Rusbult & Van Lange, 2003; Wieselquist et al., 1999). Commitment and trust in a relationship can be seen as developing according to a model of **mutual cyclical growth**:

Mutual cyclical growth The view that the need for one's partner promotes commitment, and commitment promotes acts that enhance the relationship; these acts build trust, increasing one's partner's commitment to the relationship.

- Feeling that one needs one's partner promotes commitment to and dependence on the relationship.
- Commitment to the relationship encourages partners to do things that are good for the relationship.
- One's partner perceives the pro-relationship acts.
- Perception of pro-relationship acts enhances the partner's trust in the other partner and in the relationship.
- Feelings of trust increase the partner's willingness to depend on the relationship.

Caring is an emotional bond that allows intimacy to develop. Caring means that partners try to satisfy each other's needs, gratify each other's interests, and make sacrifices, if necessary.

Communication Skills for Enhancing Relationships and Sexual Relations

Relationship counsellors and sex therapists might be less busy if more couples communicated with each other about their sexual feelings. Unfortunately, when it comes to sex, the most overlooked four-letter word may be *talk*.

Many couples suffer for years because one or both partners are unwilling to speak up. Or problems arise when one partner misinterprets the other. One partner might interpret the other's groans or grimaces of pleasure as signs of pain and pull back during sex, leaving the other frustrated. Improved communication may be no panacea, but it helps. Clear communication can take the guesswork out of relationships, avert misunderstandings, relieve resentments and frustrations, and increase both sexual and general satisfaction with the relationship.

In a study of communication about sexual health issues such as HIV and pregnancy prevention at the University of Guelph (Cleary et al., 2002), female students typically reported that they did not discuss these issues prior to engaging in sexual intercourse for the first time with a new partner. Generally, the women reported feeling uncomfortable about initiating discussion about sexual health topics and sensed that their partner was uncomfortable as well. They feared offending their partner and possibly risking a negative reaction from him.

There is considerable variation among people with regard to how comfortable they are in communicating with a partner about sexual matters. Carleton University researchers Melanie Kristel Oates and Alia Offman (2007) found that persons who had higher levels of sexual self-esteem were better able to communicate their sexual desires to a partner. Sexual self-esteem was measured by statements such as "I feel self-assured about my sexual abilities." Sexual self-esteem was a stronger predictor of sexual communication than was general self-esteem. Researchers at Trent University

(Humphreys & Newby, 2007) found that students who felt more positive feelings about their sexuality were more likely to use a diversity of verbal and nonverbal tactics when wanting to ask their partner to try something new sexually. Also, those who had more previous partners were more willing to make verbal requests to try new sexual activities.

Obstacles to Sexual Communication

Why is it so difficult for couples to communicate about sex? Here are some possibilities:

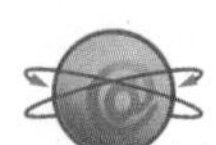

Selfhelp Magazine
Features articles on relationship issues, such as effective communication and finding a partner.
www.selfhelpmagazine.com

IS SEX TALK VULGAR? Vulgarity, like beauty, is to some degree in the eye of the beholder. One couple's vulgarity may be another couple's pillow talk. Some people may maintain a Victorian belief that no talk about sex is fit for mixed company, even between intimate partners. Sex, that is, is something you may do, but not something to be talked about. Other couples may be willing in principle to talk about sex, but find the reality difficult because they lack an agreeable, common language.

How, for example, are they to refer to their genitals or to sexual activities? One partner may prefer to use coarse words to refer to them. (As the forbidden fruit is often the sweetest, some people feel sexually aroused when they or their partners "talk dirty.") The other might prefer more clinical terms. A partner who likes to use slang for the sex organs might be regarded by the other as vulgar or demeaning. One who uses clinical terms, such as *fellatio* or *coitus*, might be regarded as, well, clinical. Some couples compromise and try to use terms that are neither vulgar nor clinical. They might speak, for example, of "doing it" rather than "screwing" (and the like) at one extreme or of "engaging in sexual intercourse" at the other. Or they might speak of "kissing me down there" rather than of "eating me" or of "practising fellatio or cunnilingus."

Active Listening.
Effective communication requires listening to the other person's view of things. You can listen actively by maintaining eye contact and modifying your facial expression to show that you understand your partner's feelings and ideas. You can ask helpful questions, such as "Did I disappoint you when I . . . ?"

IRRATIONAL BELIEFS Many couples also harbour irrational beliefs about relationships and sex, such as the notion that people should somehow *know* what their partners want without having to ask. Men, in particular, seem burdened with the stereotype that they should have a natural expertise at sex. Women may feel it is "unladylike" to talk openly about their sexual needs and feelings. Both partners may hold the idealized romantic notion that "all you need is love" to achieve sexual happiness. But such knowledge does not arise from instinct or from love. It is learned—or it remains unknown.

A related irrational belief is that one's partner will read one's mind. We may erroneously assume that if our partner truly loved us, they would somehow know what types of sexual stimulation we desire. Unfortunately—or fortunately—others cannot read our minds. We must assume the responsibility for communicating our preferences.

Some people communicate more effectively than others, perhaps because they are more sensitive to others' needs or because their parents served as good models as communicators. But communication skills can be acquired at any time. Learning takes time and work, but the following guidelines should prove helpful if you want to enhance your communication skills. The skills can also improve communication in areas of intimacy other than the sexual.

Getting Started

How do you broach sexual topics? Here are some ideas.

You can admit that it is difficult to talk about sex. You can say that your sexual relationship is important to you and that you want to do everything you can to enhance it. Gently probe your partner's willingness to set aside time to talk about sex, preferably when you can dim the lights and avoid interruptions.

Applied Knowledge

ARE YOU SEXUALLY COMPATIBLE?

Because many couples find it difficult to discuss sexual issues openly, they may not learn whether or not they are sexually compatible until much later in their relationship. Guy Grenier (2007), a sex therapist in London, Ontario, believes it is essential that couples determine whether or not they are sexually compatible before they commit themselves to a long-term relationship. Grenier notes that sexual incompatibility can lead to serious conflict and also the end of relationships. Carleton University researchers Alia Offman and Kimberly Matheson (2005) found that couples who were sexually compatible had higher levels of sexual satisfaction,

In his book *The 10 Conversations You Must Have Before You Get Married (And How To Have Them)*, Grenier outlines how couples can determine whether or not they sexually suit each other. He presents several topics that can be indicators of sexual compatibility, such as feelings about monogamy. Another is desired frequency of sex. Other indicators include: what you want to know about your partner's past sexual history, how to signal that you are in the mood for sex, when do you prefer to have sex, what type of foreplay you prefer, and whether it is always necessary to have intercourse when you start a sexual encounter.

Additionally, Grenier believes that partners should indicate what they like and do not like regarding specific sexual activities. Here is Grenier's list of sexual behaviours for couples to consider:

Describe for your partner your thoughts and feelings about engaging in each of the following activities:

a. Manually stimulating a partner's genitals
b. Sexual intercourse
c. Giving oral sex
d. Receiving oral sex
e. Anal sex (again, talk about giving *and* receiving)
f. Mutual masturbation
g. Intercourse during menstruation
h. Using enticing clothing (or costumes) to enhance arousal
i. Using sexually explicit material to enhance arousal
j. Recording your own sexual behaviour (i.e., using still or video cameras) to enhance arousal
k. Having three-person (or more) sex
l. Having sex in public or risky places (i.e., where you might be discovered by others)
m. Using food for sex play
n. Using sex toys
o. Wearing each other's clothing or clothing of the other gender (i.e., cross-dressing)
p. Having phone sex
q. Sharing personal sexual fantasies
r. Being tied up or restrained during sex
s. Using various types of pain to enhance sensual and sexual feelings
t. Viewing sexual performances (e.g., strip or sex shows)
u. Attending sex shows or clubs

Grenier emphasizes that it is not essential that partners be in complete agreement regarding these behaviours. Nevertheless, strong disagreements about the desirability of some of the behaviours could indicate sexual incompatibility and lead to conflict and dissatisfaction in the relationship.

Source: Grenier, G. (2007). The 10 Conversations You Must Have Before You Get Married (And How To Have Them). *Toronto: Key Porter.*

The "right time" may be when both of you are relaxed, rested, and not pressed for time. The "right place" can be any place where you can enjoy privacy and talk undisturbed. Sex talk need not be limited to the bedroom. Couples may feel more comfortable talking about sex over dinner, when cuddling on the sofa, or when just relaxing together.

Another possibility is to request permission to raise an issue. You can say something like this: "There's something on my mind. Do you have a few minutes? Is now a good time to tell you about it?" Or you can say, "There's something that we need to talk about, but I'm not sure how to bring it up. Can you help me with it?"

You can tell your partner that it is okay to point out ways in which you can become a more effective lover. For example, you can say, "I know that you don't want to hurt my feelings, but I wonder if I'm doing anything that you'd rather I didn't do?"

Applied Knowledge

COMMUNICATING SEXUAL NEEDS

Listening is basic to learning about another person's needs, but sometimes it helps to go a few steps further.

Asking Questions to Draw the Other Person Out You can ask open-ended questions that allow for a broader exploration of issues, such as these:

- "What do you like best about the way we make love?"
- "Do you think that I do things to bug you?"
- "Does it bother you that I go to bed later than you do?"
- "Does anything disappoint you about our relationship?"
- "Do you think that I do things that are inconsiderate when you're studying for a test?"

Closed-ended questions that call for a limited range of responses tend to be most useful when you're looking for a simple yes-or-no type of response. ("Would you rather make love with the stereo off?")

Using Self-Disclosure Self-disclosure is essential to developing intimacy. You can also use self-disclosure to learn more about your partner's needs, because communicating your own feelings and ideas invites reciprocation. For example, you might say, "There are times when I feel that I disappoint you when we make love. Should I be doing something differently?"

Granting Permission for the Other Person to Say Something That Might Upset You You can ask your partner to level with you about an irksome issue. You can say that you recognize that it may be awkward to discuss it but that you will try your best to listen conscientiously and not get too disturbed. You can also limit communication to one such difficult issue per conversation. If the entire emotional dam were to burst, the job of mopping up could be overwhelming.

Providing Information There are many skillful ways of communicating information, including "accentuating the positive" and using verbal and nonverbal cues. When you want to get something across, remember that it is irrational to expect that your partner can read your mind. He or she can tell when you're wearing a grumpy face, but your expression does not provide much information about your specific feelings. When your partner asks, "What would you like me to do?" responding with "Well, I think you can figure out what I want" or "Just do whatever you think is best" is not very helpful. Only you know what pleases you. Your partner is not a mind reader.

Accentuating the Positive Let your partner know when he or she is doing something right! Speak up or find another way to express your appreciation. Accentuating the positive is rewarding and also informs your partner about what pleases you. In other words, don't just wait around until your partner does something wrong and then seize the opportunity to complain!

Using Verbal Cues Sexual activity provides an excellent opportunity for direct communication. You can say something like "Oh, that's great" or "Don't stop." Or you can ask for feedback, as in "How does this feel?" Feedback provides direct guidance about what is pleasing. Partners can also make specific requests and suggestions.

Using Nonverbal Cues Sexual communication also occurs without words. Couples learn to interpret each other's facial expressions as signs of pleasure, anxiety, boredom, even disgust. Our body language also communicates our likes and dislikes. Our partner may lean toward us or away from us when we touch them, or they may relax or tense up; in any case, they speak volumes in silence.

The following exercises may help couples use nonverbal cues to communicate their sexual likes and dislikes. Similar exercises are used by sex therapists to help couples with sexual dysfunctions.

1. *Taking turns petting.* Taking turns petting can help partners learn what turns each other on. Each partner takes turns caressing the other, stopping frequently enough to receive feedback by asking questions like "How does that feel?" The recipient is responsible for giving feedback, which can be expressed either verbally ("Yes, that's it–yes, just like that" or "No, a little lighter than that") or nonverbally, such as by making certain appreciative or disapproving sounds. Verbal feedback is usually more direct and less prone to misinterpretation. The knowledge gained through this exercise can be incorporated into the couple's regular pattern of lovemaking.
2. *Directing your partner's hand.* Gently guiding your partner's hand–to show your partner where and how you like to be touched–is a most direct way of communicating sexual preferences. While taking turns petting, and during other acts of lovemaking, one partner can gently guide the other's fingers and hands through the most satisfying strokes and caresses. Women might show their partner how to caress the breasts or clitoral shaft in this manner. Men might cup their partner's hands to show them how to stroke the penile shaft or caress the testes.
3. *Signalling.* Couples can use agreed-upon nonverbal cues to signal sexual pleasure. For example, one partner may rub the other in a certain way, or tap the other, to signal that something is being done right. The recipient of the signal takes mental notes and incorporates the pleasurable stimulation into the couple's lovemaking. This is a sort of "hit or miss" technique, but even near misses can be rewarding.

Canadian Trends

MAKING SEXUAL REQUESTS

A basic part of improving relationships or lovemaking is asking partners to change their behaviour–to do something differently or to stop doing something that hurts or is no longer gratifying. As shown in Table 7.1, almost half of Canadians (46%) report that they are "very comfortable" in asking a sexual partner to try something new or different in their sexual relationship, with only 17% saying that they are not comfortable (Compas, 1998). Those aged 50 and over were the least comfortable about this. Table 7.2 shows some interesting regional differences, with people in Quebec being the most likely to say they are "very comfortable" requesting something new sexually and those in the Prairies the least likely.

TABLE 7.1
How Comfortable Canadians Are With Asking a Partner to Try Something New in Their Sexual Relationship

	Males	Females	Total
Very	45.2%	46.5%	45.8%
Somewhat	39.8	34.5	37.2
Not really	10.2	11.5	10.8
Not at all	4.8	7.5	6.1

Source: Compas (1998). Modern life survey of the Canadian adult population.

TABLE 7.2
Regional Differences in Comfort Asking a Partner to Try Something New

Region	Atlantic	Quebec	Ontario	Prairies	B.C.	Total
Very	44.6%	58.5%	41.2%	36.9%	46.4%	45.8%
Somewhat	37.5	28.8	40.5	42.9	36.8	37.2
Not really	12.5	6.8	10.9	15.0	10.0	10.8
Not at all	5.4	5.9	7.4	5.1	6.8	6.1

Source: Compas (1998). Modern life survey of the Canadian adult population

Listening Effectively

Listening involves such skills as active listening, paraphrasing, the use of reinforcement, and valuing your partner even when the two of you disagree.

To listen actively rather than passively, first adopt the attitude that you may actually learn something—or perceive things from another vantage point—by listening. Second, recognize that even though the other person is doing the talking, you shouldn't just sit there. In other words, it is not helpful to stare off into space while your partner is talking. Instead, you can listen actively by maintaining eye contact and modifying your facial expression to show that you understand his or her feelings and ideas. For example, nod your head when appropriate.

Listening actively also involves asking helpful questions, such as "Would you please give me an example?"

Good listeners do not interrupt, change the topic, or walk away when their partners are speaking.

Paraphrasing shows that you understand what your partner is trying to say. In paraphrasing, you recast or restate the speaker's words to confirm that you have understood correctly. For example, suppose your partner says, "You hardly ever say anything when we're making love. I don't want you to scream or make obligatory grunts or do something silly, but sometimes I wonder if I'm trying to make love to a brick wall." You can paraphrase this comment by saying something like: "So it's sort of hard to know if I'm really enjoying it."

Even when you disagree with what your partner is saying, you can maintain good relations and keep channels of communication open by saying something like "I really appreciate your taking the time to try to work this out with me" or "I hope you'll think it's okay if I don't see things entirely in the same way, but I'm glad that we had a chance to talk about it."

When you disagree with your partner, do so in a way that shows that you still value your partner as a person. In other words, say something like "I love you very much, but it annoys me when you . . ." rather than "You're really contemptible for . . . ." By so doing, you encourage your partner to disclose sensitive material without risk of attack or of losing your love or support.

Summing Up

Many Canadians use the internet to meet possible dating partners. However, one needs to be cautious of internet romance scams.

Levinger proposes an ABCDE model of romantic relationships. The letters refer to five stages: attraction, building, continuation, deterioration, and ending.

The major promoter of attraction is propinquity.

Similarity in the level of physical attractiveness, similarity in attitudes, and liking motivate us to build relationships.

Factors such as variety, caring, positive evaluations, lack of jealousy, perceived fairness in the relationship, and mutual feelings of satisfaction encourage us to continue relationships.

The factors that foster deterioration include failure to invest time and energy in the relationship, deciding to put an end to it, and simply permitting deterioration to proceed unchecked.

Relationships tend to end when the partners find little satisfaction in the affiliation, when alternative partners are available, when couples are not committed to preserving the relationship, and when they expect it to falter.

Intimacy involves feelings of emotional closeness with another person and the desire to share each other's innermost thoughts and feelings.

Intimate relationships require trust, caring, and tenderness.

Honesty is a core feature of intimacy.

Communication is a two-way street. It embraces sending *and* receiving messages. We often express feelings through nonverbal channels such as tone of voice, gestures, body posture, and facial expressions.

Couples may find it difficult to talk about sex because of the lack of an agreeable common language. Many couples also harbour irrational beliefs about relationships and sex.

Ways of getting started in communicating include talking about talking, requesting permission to raise an issue, and granting one's partner permission to say things that might be upsetting.

Skilled listening involves elements such as active listening, paraphrasing, the use of reinforcement, and valuing your partner even when you disagree.

A basic part of improving relationships or lovemaking is asking partners to change their behaviour.

Test Yourself

Multiple-Choice Questions

1. **Which internet dating site uses avatars?**
   a. Lavalife
   b. eharmony
   c. Perfectmatch
   d. OmniDate

2. **Research has shown that**
   a. women are much more likely to disclose their feelings than men
   b. men are much more likely to disclose their feelings than women
   c. there are few gender-based differences in self-disclosure
   d. older people are much more likely to disclose their feelings than younger people

3. **All of the following encourage the continuation of relationships except**
   a. maintaining interest
   b. evidence of caring
   c. mutual satisfaction
   d. jealousy

4. **All of the following can cause jealousy except**
   a. having a former partner cheat on you
   b. a lack of self-confidence
   c. a fear of not being able to find another partner
   d. a high level of independence

5. **Recent research has shown that men are more upset by __________________ infidelity and women by ________________________ infidelity.**
   a. sexual/emotional
   b. emotional/sexual
   c. sexual/sexual
   d. emotional/emotional

6. **Social exchange theory suggests that relationships may end when**
   a. barriers to leaving the relationship are high
   b. the couple stops having sex
   c. alternative partners are available
   d. family pressures are too strong

7. **Which of the following statements is true about emotional intimacy?**
   a. It is necessary to be sexually intimate in order to have emotional intimacy.
   b. It is necessary to be emotionally intimate in order to have sexual intimacy.
   c. Some people may share greater emotional intimacy with friends than with partners.
   d. Emotional intimacy between friends is seen as wrong in Canada.

8. **Which of the following is *not* one of the irrational beliefs about communication that are described in the text?**
   a. Men should have a natural expertise at sex.
   b. People should know what their partners want without having to ask.
   c. Good communication can enhance all aspects of a relationship
   d. It is "unladylike" for women to talk about their sexual needs and feelings.

9. **Which of the following is *not* one of the suggestions described in the text to learn about your partner's needs?**
   a. using self disclosure
   b. asking open-ended questions
   c. giving permission for the other person to say something that might upset you
   d. criticizing your partner's performance in bed

10. **The most successful intimate relationships are characterized by**
   a. total honesty about past sexual experiences
   b. secrecy about past sexual experiences
   c. totally honest criticism
   d. discretion in revealing details of past relationships

Answers to the Test Yourself questions in each chapter are found on page 509.

Critical Thinking Questions

1. Have you ever signed up with an online dating service? How did the experience turn out? Would you do it again? If you haven't, would you? Why or why not?
2. Have you ever had a partner who was extremely jealous? What was the most difficult part of the relationship? How did you deal with the jealousy?
3. Have you ever met someone online and then met face to face? Was this a successful experience? Did your impressions of this person change after you met face to face?
4. Have you ever sat next to someone on a bus or a plane and disclosed to them details of your life that you would not share with a friend? How did you feel about this afterwards? Why do many people find it easy to talk like this to total strangers?
5. Have you ever been in a relationship that had problems in communication? How did this affect the relationship?

Visit MyPsychKit at www.mypsychkit.com, where you can do quizzes and link to additional resources on topics discussed in this text.

CHAPTER EIGHT

Sexual Techniques and Behaviour Patterns

This is the chapter that describes sexual techniques and statistical breakdowns of "who does what with whom." There is great variety in human sexual expression. Some of us practise few, if any, of the techniques in this chapter. Some of us practise most or all of them. Some of us practise some of them some of the time. Our knowledge of the prevalence of these techniques comes from sex surveys. Of course, surveys are plagued by problems such as nonrepresentative sampling, social desirability, and volunteer bias. Therefore, we must be cautious in generalizing on the basis of their results. Surveys provide our best "guesstimate" of the prevalence of sexual behaviours. They do not provide precise figures.

Readers of this textbook are as varied in their sexual values, preferences, and attitudes as is society in general. Some of the techniques discussed may thus strike some readers as indecent. Our aim is to provide information about the diversity of sexual expression. We are not seeking consensus on what is acceptable. Nor do we pass judgments or encourage readers to expand their sexual repertoires.

The human body is sensitive to many forms of sexual stimulation. Yet we reiterate the theme that biology is not destiny: A biological capacity does not impose a behavioural requirement. Cultural expectations, personal values, and individual experience—not only our biological capacities—determine our sexual behaviour. What is right for you is right for you, but not necessarily for your neighbour.

We begin by reviewing the techniques that people practise by themselves to derive sexual pleasure: masturbation and sexual fantasy. We then consider techniques that involve a partner.

Solitary Sexual Behaviour

Various forms of sexual expression do not require a partner or are not generally practised in the presence of a partner. Masturbation, which involves direct stimulation of the genitals, is one of the principal forms of one-person sexual expression. Other forms of individual sexual experience, such as thinking about sex and sexual fantasy, may or may not be accompanied by genital stimulation.

Sexual Fantasy

People may use sexual fantasies when they are alone or to heighten sexual excitement with a partner. Some couples find it sexually arousing to share fantasies or to enact them with their partners. Sexual fantasies may be experienced without sexual behaviour, as in erotic dreams or daydreams. Masturbators often require some form of cognitive stimulation, such as indulging in a favourite fantasy or reading or viewing erotica, to increase their arousal to the point of orgasm.

Canadian Trends

THINKING ABOUT SEX

According to a national survey conducted by Compas polling, Canadian men report thinking about sex much more often than women do—a gender difference found across all ages and educational levels (Fischtein & Herold, 2002). About half of men (46%) but only 11% of women think about sex several times a day. Those who are younger and who are university educated think about sex more often than those who are older and who have not completed high school. Among women, 49% of those in their twenties think about sex once a day or more compared with 10% of women in their sixties. Among men, 90% of those in their twenties have sexual thoughts at least once a day compared with 35% of men in their sixties.

How common are sexual fantasies? At an Ontario university, 97% of the female students reported having experienced sexual fantasies (Pelletier & Herold, 1988). Of those who had masturbated, 87% fantasized during masturbation, with 57% always fantasizing during masturbation. Of those with intercourse experience, 73% had fantasized during intercourse, but only 10% usually or always fantasized during intercourse. Most had also fantasized in nonsexual situations (84%). Interestingly, the women experienced a greater number of different types of fantasies in nonsexual situations than in sexual ones. This suggests that in sexual situations, women focus on those fantasies they find to be the most arousing. Table 8.1 presents a complete breakdown of these data.

That the most common fantasy was about one's boyfriend is not consistent with studies of married women (Davidson & Hoffman, 1986), who reported commonly fantasizing about other men rather than their husband. It appears that when women

TABLE 8.1
Sexual Fantasies of University Females

	Situation During Which Fantasy Occurred			
Fantasy	**Masturbation**	**Coitus**	**Nonsexual**	**Total**
Sex with boyfriend	54%	49%	69%	90%
Undressed by male	46	39	54	79
Previous sexual experience	44	31	58	78
Intercourse in exotic place	33	43	55	72
Undressing a male	26	28	54	71
Cunnilingus	48	46	41	66
Intercourse with male friend	31	14	47	60
Forced sex with male	30	26	31	51
Fellatio	21	28	34	49
Intercourse with male stranger	24	9	34	46
Intercourse with famous person	19	6	34	38
Doing striptease	15	10	26	37
Male masturbating	32	12	19	33
Sex with many men	26	11	17	29
Sex with objects	25	9	13	23
Sex with other watching	20	11	6	21
Female masturbating	18	4	7	18
Sex with female	15	4	9	18
Forced sex with more than one male	15	9	9	18
Anal sex	9	12	9	17
Group sex with males and females	10	3	9	16
Sex with relative	3	0	12	14
Sex with animal	8	3	4	9
Sadomasochistic sex	1	4	4	7

Note: The percentages in the Masturbation and Coitus columns are based on those who had experienced the fantasies while engaged in those behaviours. The percentage in the Total column represents those who had experienced that fantasy in one or more of the situations.

Source: Pelletier, L. A., & Herold, E. S. (1988). The relationship of age, sex guilt and sexual experience with female sexual fantasies. Journal of Sex Research, 24, 250–256.

become involved in long-term relationships, the object of their fantasy switches to other men.

Partners are often reluctant to share their fantasies, or even to admit to having them. This is especially true when the fantasy is about someone other than one's partner. The fantasizer might fear being accused of harbouring extramarital desires. Any perceived merits of self-disclosure are best weighed against one's partner's potential reactions to coital fantasies.

In the Ontario study of female students, one-half of the women had forced-sex fantasies (Pelletier and Herold, 1988). It is important to note that this does *not* mean that they want in reality to be sexually assaulted. In the fantasy situation, the women are the ones who are actually in control.

About one-quarter of the women had sexual fantasies once a day or more often, and about one-half fantasized a few times a week. When asked why they fantasized, three-quarters said it was a pleasant way to pass the time. About one-half said they fantasized to become aroused, and 30% to help achieve orgasm. Interestingly, 30% used fantasy to help them fall asleep.

One stereotype about fantasies holds that people who are sexually deprived fantasize the most about sex. In fact, Pelletier and Herold found that the women with the most sexual experience and who had the most sexual partners fantasized about sex more often and had a greater number of more explicit sexual fantasies. For example, those with oral sex experience fantasized more about oral sex than women who had not experienced oral sex. Those women who felt guilty about sex fantasized less.

Among university students in British Columbia, males had more fantasies than females (Meston et al., 1996). Males in particular fantasized more than females about having many partners and about engaging in oral and anal sex.

Sexual fantasies can be experienced as either positive or negative, or both. In a study of students at the University of New Brunswick, positive types of feelings were experienced more often than negative ones (Renaud & Byers, 1999). More positive feelings were experienced for fantasies involving a loved one and more negative feelings were experienced for fantasies involving casual sex. Having intercourse with a loved one was the most common fantasy of both genders. Men were more likely than women to have fantasies of anonymous sex and sex with multiple partners.

Evolutionary theorists conjecture that women are relatively more likely to fantasize about the images of familiar lovers because female reproductive success in ancestral times was more likely to depend on an emotionally close, protective relationship with a reliable partner (Goleman, 1995). Women can bear and rear relatively few offspring. Thus, they would have a relatively greater genetic investment than men in each reproductive opportunity.

As already mentioned, fantasizing about forcing someone into sexual activity, or about being victimized, does not mean that one wants these events to occur (Leitenberg & Henning, 1995). Women who imagine themselves being sexually coerced remain in control of their fantasies. Real assault victims are not in control. Nor is it unusual for heterosexual people to have episodic fantasies about sexual activity with people of their own gender, or for gay males or lesbians to fantasize about sexual activity with people of the other gender. In neither case does the person necessarily intend to act out the fantasy.

Why do people fantasize when they masturbate? Masturbation fantasies serve several functions. For one, they increase or facilitate sexual arousal. Sex therapists encourage clients to use sexual fantasies to enhance sexual arousal (e.g., Heiman & LoPiccolo, 1987). Sexual fantasies are highly arousing, in part because fantasizers can command the imagined sexual encounter. They may imagine that people who will not give them the time of day find them irresistible and are willing to fulfill their sexual desires. Or fantasizers may picture improbable or impossible arousing situations, such as sexual activity on a commercial airliner or while skydiving. Some masturbation fantasies may be arousing because they permit us to deviate from traditional gender roles. Women might fantasize about taking an aggressive role or forcing someone into sexual activity. Men, by contrast, may imagine being overtaken by a horde of sexually aggressive women. Other fantasies involve sexual transgressions or "forbidden" behaviours, such as exposing oneself, doing a striptease before strangers, engaging in sexual activity with strangers, or sadomasochistic sex (S&M).

Sexual Fantasies of Lesbian, Gay, and Bisexual (LGB) Individuals

A survey of 129 women (85 lesbian, 44 bisexual) who were in same-sex relationships that had lasted 5 to 10 years found connections between satisfaction in the relationship and the nature of sexual fantasies (Robinson & Parks, 2003). By and large, the happier the women were with their relationships, the more likely they were to fantasize about common activities with their partners. If their relationships were not going so well, they were relatively more likely to fantasize about things they used to do with their partners or things they did with former partners.

A study in India compared the sexual fantasies of 30 heterosexual males with those of 30 gay males (Bhugra et al., 2006). The heterosexual males appeared to be more limited in the sphere of their fantasies, restricting them to more standard sexual activities with females. The gay males were more open to fantasizing about a wider range of sexual behaviours.

Sexual Dreams

There has been limited research regarding sexual dreams. Researchers at Trent University (Humphreys et al., 2007) found that sexual dreams are common among university students, with most having sexual dreams at least once a week. Almost all of the students rated their sexual dreams as being pleasurable, with many saying that their dreams were as pleasurable as having sexual intercourse. The activities most commonly dreamed about were kissing and sexual intercourse. Rarely did anyone dream about masturbation. Students generally dreamed about behaviours they had engaged in with a partner rather than untried behaviours. The females were more likely to dream about a current partner, whereas the males were more likely to dream about someone other than their partner.

Masturbation

Some older dictionaries define masturbation as "self-abuse." This definition provides clues to historical cultural attitudes toward the practice. **Masturbation** may be practised by manual stimulation of the genitals, perhaps with the aid of artificial stimulation, such as a vibrator. It may employ an object, such as a pillow or a **dildo**, that touches the genitals. Even before we conceive of sexual experiences with others, we may learn early in childhood that touching our genitals can produce pleasure.

Within the Judeo-Christian tradition, masturbation has been strongly condemned as sinful (Allen, 2000). Early Judeo-Christian attitudes toward masturbation reflected the censure that greeted nonprocreative sexual acts.

Until very recently, the history of cultural attitudes toward masturbation in Western society has been one of almost continual condemnation of the practice on moral and religious grounds—and even on medical grounds. In the 1830s the Reverend Sylvester Graham developed a cracker, since called the graham cracker, to help people control their sexual impulses. One of the more influential writers was the superintendent of the Battle Creek Sanatorium in Michigan, Dr. J. H. Kellogg (1852–1943), the creator of the breakfast cereal. Kellogg believed that sexual desires could be controlled by sticking to a diet of simple foods, especially grains, including the corn flakes that have since borne his name.

Masturbation Sexual self-stimulation.

Dildo A penis-shaped object used in sexual activity.

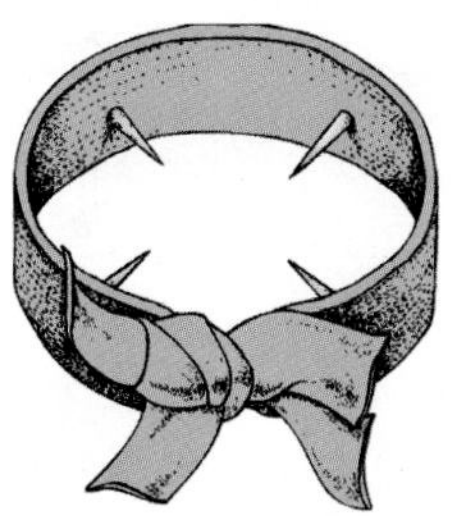
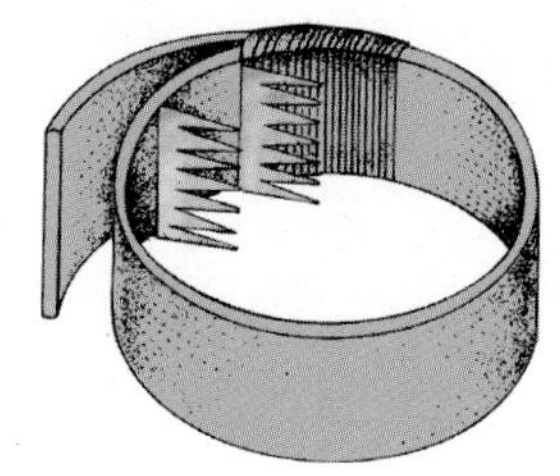

Figure 8.1 Devices Designed to Curb Masturbation.

Because of widespread beliefs that masturbation was harmful, various contraptions were introduced in the nineteenth century to prevent the practice in children. Some of the devices were barbarous.

Many nineteenth-century physicians also advised parents to take measures to prevent their children from masturbating. Kellogg suggested that parents bandage or cage their children's genitals or tie their hands. Some of the contraptions devised to prevent masturbation were barbarous (see Figure 8.1).

Despite this history, there is no scientific evidence that masturbation is harmful, save for rare injuries to the genitals from rough stimulation. Sex therapists have even found that masturbation has therapeutic benefits. It has emerged as a treatment for women who have difficulty reaching orgasm.

Of course, people who consider masturbation wrong, harmful, or sinful may experience anxiety or guilt if they masturbate or wish to masturbate. These negative emotions are linked to their attitudes toward masturbation, not to masturbation per se (Ortega et al., 2005).

Until recently, masturbation was considered such a taboo topic that it was avoided by the mass media. Now Hollywood is openly presenting masturbation, as seen in such hit films as *American Pie*, *There's Something About Mary*, and *American Beauty*. In Canada, the producers of the Discovery Channel series *The Sex Files* presented an entire show on masturbation during prime-time television viewing. The program included a sequence involving a group of women learning how to reach orgasm with a vibrator.

Another indication of masturbation's coming of age is that May has been declared Masturbation Month. This first began at the Good Vibrations sex shop in San Francisco in 1995 with the objective of promoting the benefits of masturbation. Many sex shops across North America have joined this annual promotion. In May 2005, Toronto's Come As You Are held a Masturbate-A-Thon for which people solicited pledges for sex-oriented charities, with donations based on the number of minutes the volunteer masturbated.

Surveys indicate that most people masturbate at some time, including many married people. The incidence of masturbation is generally greater among men than women. However, there are women who masturbate frequently and men who rarely if ever do so (Michael et al., 1994).

A survey of university students in British Columbia found that nearly twice as many men (80%) as women (48%) reported some experience with masturbation

Innovative Canadian Research

ONLINE MASTURBATION

In a survey of university students, University of Victoria researcher Sylvain Boies (2002) found that many had engaged in masturbation while online at the computer (72% of males and 21% of females). Among those who had actually viewed sexually explicit material online, 83% of the men and 55% of the women had masturbated while online. Those who approved of these materials were more likely to masturbate online than those who disapproved. Not surprisingly, 80% of those who found online sexually explicit material to be arousing had masturbated while online compared with only 25% of those who said that this material was not arousing.

A World of Diversity

NATIONAL SURVEY OF MASTURBATION IN BRITAIN

In a large national survey conducted in Britain (Gerressu et al., 2008), twice as many men (73%) as women (37%) reported masturbating in the weeks prior to participating in the survey. Men who reported more frequently having vaginal sex had lower rates of masturbation. In contrast, women who had more sexual activity (more vaginal sex, more oral sex, and more sexual partners) had higher rates of masturbation. It seems that for men masturbation is a compensation for having less vaginal sex, whereas for women, having more partnered sex increases the desire to masturbate. Both men and women having same-sex partners were more likely to masturbate.

Despite the sexual revolution, women may still find masturbation less pleasurable or acceptable than men do. Women may still be subject to traditional socialization pressures that teach that sexual activity for pleasure's sake is more of a taboo for women than for men. In the British study (Gerressu et al., 2008), women who were more religious were less likely to masturbate. Education would appear to be a liberating influence on masturbation. For both genders, people with more education reported more frequent masturbation (Gerressu et al., 2008). Perhaps better-educated people are less likely to believe the old horror stories about masturbation or to be subject to traditional social restrictions. Conservative religious beliefs appear to constrain masturbation.

(Meston, Trapnell, & Gorzalka, 1996). Of those students who had masturbated, men did so more often than did the women. Among female students surveyed at an Ontario university, 69% had masturbated (Pelletier & Herold, 1988). (Only students in senior-level classes [mean age of 21.5] were surveyed, which may account for why these percentages are higher than those of the B.C. study. As age increases, so does the proportion of people who masturbate.) About one-third of the students felt guilty about masturbation.

At another Ontario university, more men (84%) than women (62%) had first masturbated before the age of 16 (Rye, 2001). More than 90% of the students had fantasized during masturbation, with 27% of the women and 7% of the men using mechanical aids such as a vibrator. While 75% of the women and 92% of the men reported having had an orgasm in more than half of their masturbation experiences, more women (17%) than men (6%) said they had more than one orgasm in more than half of these experiences (Rye, 2001).

There appears to be a link between attitudes toward masturbation and orgasmic potential. A study of women revealed more negative attitudes toward masturbation among a group of 21- to 40-year-olds who had never achieved orgasm than among a comparison group of women who had (Kelly et al., 1990). Adolescent masturbation probably also sets the stage for sexual satisfaction with a partner by yielding information about the types of stimulation people need to obtain sexual gratification.

In our efforts to correct misinformation about masturbation, we do not wish to leave the impression that there is anything wrong with people who choose *not* to masturbate. Nor do we wish to imply that people *should* masturbate. Rather, we believe that it is up to the individual to decide for themselves.

MASTURBATION TECHNIQUES USED BY MALES

> Sex is like bridge—if you don't have a good partner, you'd better have a good hand.
>
> —Bathroom graffiti

Although masturbation techniques vary widely, most men report that they masturbate by manual manipulation of the penis (see Figure 8.2). Men tend to grip the penile shaft with one hand, jerking it up and down in a milking motion. Some men

Figure 8.2 Male Masturbation.

Masturbation techniques vary widely, but most men report that they masturbate by manual manipulation of the penis. They tend to grip the penile shaft with one hand and jerk it up and down in a milking motion.

move the whole hand up and down the penis, while others use just two fingers, generally the thumb and index finger. Men usually shift from a gentler rubbing action during the flaccid or semi-erect state of arousal to a more vigorous milking motion once full erection takes place. Men are also likely to stroke the glans and frenulum lightly at the outset, but their grip tightens and their motions speed up as orgasm nears. At orgasm, the penile shaft may be gripped tightly, but the glans has become sensitive, and contact with it is usually avoided. (Likewise, women usually avoid stimulating the clitoris directly during orgasm because of increased sensitivity.)

Some men use soapsuds (which may become irritating) as a lubricant for masturbation during baths or showers. Other lubricants, such as petroleum jelly or K-Y jelly, may also be used to reduce friction and to simulate the moist conditions of coitus.

A few men prefer to masturbate by rubbing the penis and testicles against clothing or bedding. A few men rub their genitals against inflatable dolls sold in sex shops. These dolls may come with artificial mouths or vaginas that can be filled with warm water to mimic the sensations of coitus. Artificial vaginas are also for sale.

MASTURBATION TECHNIQUES USED BY FEMALES Techniques of female masturbation also vary widely. In fact, Masters and Johnson reported never observing two women masturbating in precisely the same way. Even when the general technique was similar, women varied in the tempo and style of their self-caresses. But some general trends have been noted. Most women masturbate by massaging the mons, labia minora, and clitoral region with circular or back-and-forth motions (Hite, 1976). They may also straddle the clitoris with their fingers, stroking the shaft rather than the glans (see Figure 8.3). In a study of university women, half (53%) preferred stimulation of the external part of the genitals when masturbating to orgasm, while 36% preferred using both external and internal stimulation (Maisel & Meggars, 2007). Only 11% preferred internal stimulation of the vagina.

The glans may be lightly touched early during arousal, but because of its exquisite sensitivity, it is rarely stroked for any length of time during masturbation. Women typically achieve clitoral stimulation by rubbing or stroking the clitoral shaft or pulling or tugging on the vaginal lips. Some women also massage other sensitive areas, such as their breasts or nipples, with their free hand. Many women, like men, fantasize during masturbation.

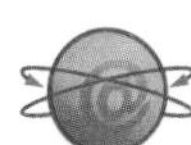

Come As You Are
This Toronto sex shop offers information and courses on a variety of sex topics, such as self-pleasuring, anal play, and sex toys.

www.comeasyouare.com

Figure 8.3 Female Masturbation.

Techniques of female masturbation vary so widely that Masters and Johnson reported never observing two women masturbating in precisely the same way. Most women, however, masturbate by massaging the mons, labia minora, and clitoral region, either with circular or back-and-forth motions.

Sex shops sell dildos, which women can use to rub their vulvas or to insert vaginally. Penis-shaped vibrators may be used in a similar fashion. Many women masturbate during baths, some by spraying their genitals with water-massage showerheads.

Handheld electric vibrators (see Figure 8.4) provide a constant massaging action against the genitals that can be erotic. Women who use vibrators often experiment with different models to find one with the shape and intensity of vibration that suits them.

Figure 8.4 Electric Vibrators.

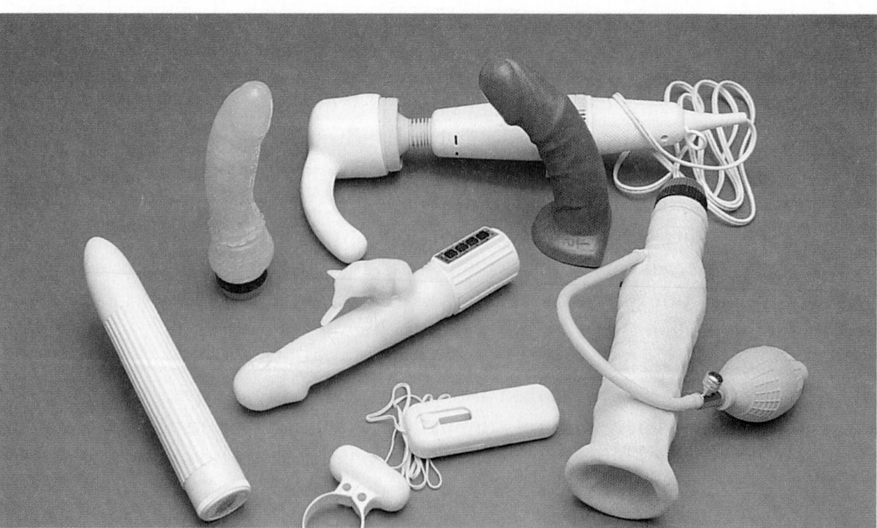

Sexual Behaviour With Others

Foreplay Physical interactions that are sexually stimulating and set the stage for intercourse.

Partners' feelings for one another, and the quality of their relationships, may be stronger determinants of their sexual arousal and response than the techniques that they employ. Partners are most likely to experience mutually enjoyable sexual interactions when they are sensitive to each other's sexual needs and incorporate techniques with which they are both comfortable. As with other aspects of sharing relationships, communication is the most important "sexual" technique.

Foreplay

Various forms of noncoital sex, such as cuddling, kissing, petting, and oral–genital contact, are used as **foreplay**. The pattern and duration of foreplay varies widely within and across cultures.

Because women usually require a longer period of stimulation during sex with a partner to reach orgasm, increasing the duration of foreplay may increase female coital responsiveness.

Kissing, genital touching, and oral–genital contact may also be experienced as ends in themselves, not as preludes to coitus. Many people behave as though all sexual contact has to lead to coitus, perhaps because of the importance that our culture places on it.

TANTRIC SEX Tantric sex is a type of sexual lovemaking that emphasizes prolonged foreplay. It is based on Eastern spiritual philosophies that promote the integration of the mind and the body. Tantric sex focuses on sexual union as a spiritual connection leading to heightened sexual pleasure and ecstasy. The techniques include deep breathing, a slowing down of the sexual process, and delayed ejaculation for men. Some tantric sex instructors teach men how to have orgasms without ejaculating. There are numerous variations of tantric sex.

Kissing

Kissing is almost universal in our culture, but it occurs less often among the world's cultures than manual or oral stimulation of the genitals (Frayser, 1985). Couples may kiss for its own enjoyment or as a prelude to intercourse, in which case it is a part of foreplay. In *simple kissing*, the partners keep their mouths closed. Simple kissing may develop into caresses of the lips with the tongue or into nibbling of the lower lip. In what Kinsey called *deep kissing*, which is also called French kissing or soul kissing, the partners part their lips and insert their tongues into each other's mouths. Some prefer the lips parted slightly. Others open their mouths widely.

Innovative Canadian Research

DESIRED DURATION OF FOREPLAY

In a study of heterosexual couples, Andrea Miller and Sandra Byers (2004) of the University of New Brunswick found that the men and women were similar in their desired duration of foreplay. However, the women underestimated both their partner's and the average male's desired duration. Perhaps women are influenced by societal stereotypes that men are mainly interested in intercourse. Interestingly, the men were accurate in estimating how much time their partner, and the average woman, wanted to spend in foreplay. However, like the women, the men underestimated how much time the average man would like to spend.

Kissing.
Kissing is almost universal in our culture, but is less practised in some other cultures.

Kissing is not limited to the partner's mouth. Other parts of the body are also often kissed, including the hands and feet, the neck and earlobes, the breasts, the insides of the thighs, and the genitals themselves.

Touching

Touching or caressing erogenous zones with the hands or other parts of the body can be highly arousing. Even simple hand-holding can be sexually stimulating for couples who are sexually attracted to one another. The hands are very rich in nerve endings.

Touching is a common form of foreplay. Both men and women generally prefer manual or oral stimulation of the genitals as a prelude to intercourse. Women generally prefer that direct caressing of the genitals be focused around the clitoris but not directly on the extremely sensitive clitoral glans. Men sometimes assume (often

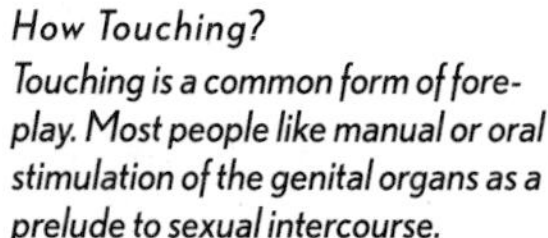

How Touching?
Touching is a common form of foreplay. Most people like manual or oral stimulation of the genital organs as a prelude to sexual intercourse.

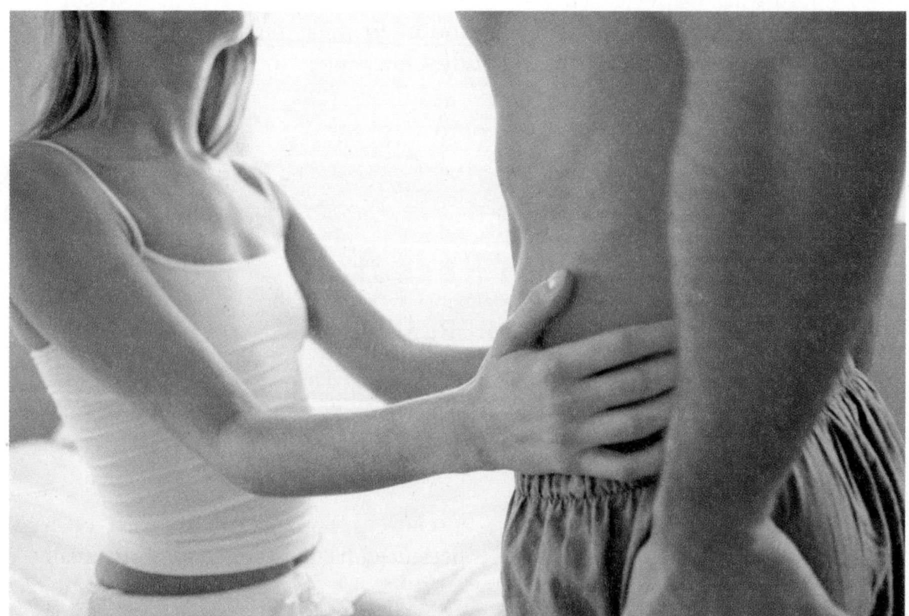

Applied Knowledge

TECHNIQUES OF MANUAL STIMULATION OF THE GENITALS

Here again, variability in technique is the rule, so partners need to communicate their preferences. The man's partner may use two hands to stimulate his genitals. One may be used to fondle the scrotum, by gently squeezing the skin between the fingers (taking care not to apply pressure to the testes themselves). The other hand may circle the coronal ridge and engage in gentle stroking of the penis, followed by more vigorous up-and-down movements as the man becomes more aroused.

The penis may also be gently rolled back and forth between the palms as though one were making a ball of clay into a sausage, increasing pressure as arousal progresses. Note that men who are highly aroused or who have just had an orgasm may find direct stimulation of the penile glans uncomfortable.

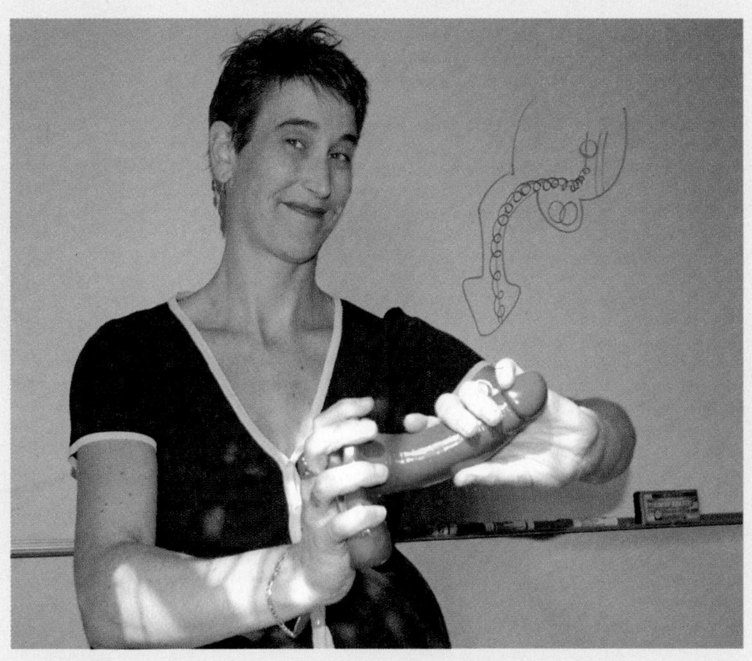

Carlyle Jansen at Good For Her in Toronto gives a course called The Art and Joy of a Hand Job. She uses a dildo to illustrate manual sex techniques.

The woman may prefer that her partner approach genital stimulation gradually, following stimulation of other body parts. Genital stimulation may begin with light, stroking motions of the inner thighs and move on to the vaginal lips (labia) and the clitoral area. Women may enjoy pressure against the mons pubis from the heel of the hand, or they may like tactile stimulation of the labia, which are sensitive to stroking motions. Clitoral stimulation can focus on the clitoral shaft or the region surrounding the shaft, rather than on the clitoris itself, because of the extreme sensitivity of the clitoral glans to touch.

Moreover, the clitoris should not be stroked if it is dry, lest it become irritated. Because it produces no lubrication of its own, a finger may enter the outer portion of the vagina to apply some vaginal lubrication to the clitoral region.

Some, but not all, women enjoy having a finger inserted into the vagina, which can stroke the vaginal walls or simulate thrusting of the penis. Vaginal insertion is usually preferred, if at all, only after the woman has become highly aroused. Many women desire that their partners discontinue stroking motions while they are experiencing orgasm, but others want stimulation to continue. Men and women may physically guide their partners' hands or otherwise indicate what types of strokes they find most pleasurable.

If a finger is to be inserted into the vagina, it should be clean. Fingernails should be well trimmed. Inserting into the vagina fingers that have been in the anus is dangerous. The fingers may transfer microbes from the woman's digestive tract, where they do no harm, to the woman's reproductive tract, where they can cause serious infections.

Across Canada some sex educators (mainly those associated with sex toy stores) offer practical courses for adults on enhancing sexual pleasure, including techniques of manual and/or oral stimulation of the genitals. Good For Her (**www.goodforher.com**) in Toronto also offers courses on kissing, stripping for your lover, and anal sex.

mistakenly) that their partners want them to insert their finger or fingers into the vagina as a form of foreplay. But not all women enjoy this form of stimulation.

Some women go along with it because it's what their partners want or something they *think* their partners want. Ironically, men may do it because they assume that their *partners* want it. When in doubt, it would not hurt to ask. If you are not sure what to say, you can always blame us: "Listen, I read this thing in my human sexuality text, and I was wondering . . . ." Among students at an Ontario university, more than 90% reported that they had experienced having their genitals manually stimulated by their partner (Rye, 2001).

Figure 8.5 Lesbians Holding One Another.

This position enables lesbians to hug one another and to reach one another's genitals. If they draw a bit closer, they can rub against one another's genitals.

Men typically prefer direct stroking of their genitals by their partner early in lovemaking. Women, however, tend to prefer that their partners caress their genitals after a period of general body contact that includes holding, hugging (Figure 8.5), and nongenital massage. This is not a hard and fast (or slow) rule, but it concurs with other observations that men tend to be more genitally oriented than women.

Stimulation of the Breasts

Men are more likely to stimulate women's breasts than to enjoy having their own breasts fondled, even though the breasts (and especially the nipples) are erotically sensitive in both sexes. Most, but not all, women enjoy stimulation of the breasts. Some women are capable of achieving orgasm from stimulation of the breasts alone.

The hands and the mouth can be used to stimulate the breasts and the nipples. The desired type and intensity of stimulation of the breasts varies from person to person, so partners need to communicate their preferences.

In general, women usually prefer several minutes of body contact and gentle caresses before they want their partner to kiss their breasts or suck or lick their nipples. Many women also usually do not prefer a hard sucking action unless they are highly aroused. Often women are reluctant to tell their partners if sucking hurts, because they do not want to interfere with their partner's pleasure.

Among male university students in British Columbia, 77% of the non-Asian Canadians had kissed a female's breasts, compared with 61% of Asian Canadians. Among the women, 83% of the non-Asian Canadians had had their breasts kissed by a male, compared with 55% of the Asian Canadian women (Meston et al., 1996).

GAY MALES AND STIMULATION OF THE BREASTS Gay men apparently make more use of stimulation of their partner's nipples than heterosexual women do. Gay male couples tend to engage in sexual activities such as kissing, hugging, petting, mutual masturbation, fellatio, and anal intercourse. Masters and Johnson's (1979) laboratory observations of sexual relations between gay males showed that gay males spent a good deal of time caressing their partners' bodies before approaching the genitals (Figure 8.6). After hugging and kissing, 31 of 42 gay male couples observed by Masters and Johnson used oral or manual nipple stimulation.

Although some heterosexual men enjoy having their breasts and nipples stimulated by their partners, many do not. Many men are unaware that their breasts are erotically sensitive.

Figure 8.6 Gay Males Hugging.

Masters and Johnson's observations suggest that gay males are likely to spend more time than heterosexual males in hugging their partners. Gay males are also more likely than heterosexual males to want their nipples to be caressed.

Oral-Genital Stimulation

Oral stimulation of the male genitals is called **fellatio**. Fellatio is referred to by slang terms such as *blow job*, *sucking*, *sucking off*, or *giving head*. Oral stimulation of the female genitals is called **cunnilingus**, which is referred to by slang expressions such as *eating* (a woman) or *going down* on her.

The popularity of oral–genital stimulation has increased dramatically since Kinsey's research in the 1940s and '50s. Carleton University researchers Alan Hunt and Bruce Curtis (2006), in analyzing marriage and sex advice manuals over the twentieth century, found a number of changes in advice about oral sex. From being a taboo subject, oral sex became viewed as a normal activity over time with first cunnilingus becoming accepted and then fellatio. Initially, oral sex was seen as a way of arousing the couple, especially the woman, in preparation for intercourse and later it became accepted as a means of sexual pleasure in its own right. Recently, considerable anxiety has been raised among parents because of sensationalized media reports of group oral sex parties among youth.

Like touching, oral–genital stimulation can be used as a prelude to intercourse or as a sexual end in itself. If orgasm is reached through oral–genital stimulation, a woman may be concerned about tasting or swallowing a man's ejaculate. There is no scientific evidence that swallowing semen is harmful to one's health, unless the man is infected with a sexually transmitted disease in which semen can act as a conduit of infections. Note that oral–genital contact with the genitals of an infected partner, even without contact with semen, may transmit harmful organisms. Couples are thus advised to practise "safer sex" techniques unless they know that they and their partners are free of sexually transmitted diseases.

Despite the popularity of oral sex, some people abstain from it. Some people view the genitals as "dirty" because of their proximity to the urinary and anal openings. Concerns about offensive odours or cleanliness may be relieved by thoroughly

Fellatio Oral stimulation of the male genitals.

Cunnilingus Oral stimulation of the female genitals.

Canadian Trends

ORAL SEX EXPERIENCE

The Compas poll has been the only national survey of Canadians to date to ask about oral sex. Although almost all the participants in that survey responded to these questions, they had the highest refusal rates, with three times as many women (15%) as men (5%) refusing to answer the question (Fischtein & Herold, 2002). The majority of both men (89%) and women (78%) reported having experienced giving and/or receiving oral sex, a gender difference that may be at least partially accounted for by the women's higher refusal rate. Interestingly, the proportion who had received oral sex was almost the same as for those who gave it.

Research with gay and bisexual men in Ontario found that almost all of the men surveyed had engaged in oral sex in the previous three months (Myers et al., 2004). Of those who engaged in insertive oral sex with a regular partner, about 80% did not use a condom. Similarly, most heterosexual couples do not use condoms when having oral sex.

The age differences in oral sex experience among Canadians reveal a much greater acceptance of oral sex among the younger age groups (see Table 8.2). The most notable differences are those between people in their sixties and in their fifties. One explanation is that those who are in their fifties experienced their adolescence at the time of the sexual revolution, when many changes in sexual behaviours were occurring. Changes in the acceptance of oral sex behaviours were so dramatic that they have been referred to as the second stage in the sexual revolution, with the first stage having focused on changes in rates of premarital intercourse (Herold, 1984).

Canadians who have not completed high school are the least likely to have experienced oral sex. This is especially true for women, with half of those who have not completed high school saying that they have not experienced oral sex (Fischtein & Herold, 2002). The data on oral sex as well as other sexual practices suggests that those with less education are less experimental and perhaps more concerned about the "normality" of these practices.

In a more recent study at the University of Guelph, Tanya Hill (2005) found that 89% of female students had engaged in oral sex with their most recent partner. About one-half reported they engaged in oral sex most of the time when having sexual relations with their partner.

TABLE 8.2
Oral Sex Experience Among Canadians, by Age

Age Cohort	Males	Females
60s	54%	28.8%
50s	85.9	77.8
40s	91.1	81.1
30s	93.5	90.0
20s	97.9	92.4

Source: Fischtein, D. S., & Herold, E. S. (2002, June). Gender differences in sexual attitudes and behaviours among Canadian adults: A national survey. Poster session presented at the annual meeting of the International Academy of Sex Research, Hamburg, Germany. Based on the Compas poll.

Applied Knowledge

ORAL SEX TECHNIQUES

Techniques of Fellatio

Although the word *fellatio* is derived from a Latin root that means "to suck," a sucking action is generally not highly arousing. The up-and-down movements of the penis in the partner's mouth, and the licking of the penis, are generally the most stimulating. Gentle licking of the scrotum may also be highly arousing.

The mouth is stimulating to the penis because it contains warm, moist mucous membranes, as does the vagina. Muscles of the mouth and jaw can create varied pressure and movements. Erection may be stimulated by gently pulling the penis with the mouth (being careful never to touch the penis with the teeth) and simultaneously providing manual stimulation, as described earlier.

Higher levels of sexual arousal or orgasm can be promoted by moving the penis in and out of the mouth, simulating the motion of the penis in the vagina during intercourse. The speed of the motions can be varied, and manual stimulation near the base of the penis (firmly encircling the lower portion of the penis or providing pressure behind the scrotum) can also be stimulating.

Some people may gag during fellatio, a reflex that is triggered by pressure of the penis against the back of the tongue or against the throat. Gagging may be avoided if the man's partner grasps the shaft of the penis with one hand and controls the depth of penetration. Gagging is less likely to occur if the partner performing fellatio is on top, rather than below, and if there is verbal communication about how deep the man should penetrate. Gagging may also be overcome by allowing gradually deeper penetration of the penis over successive occasions while keeping the throat muscles relaxed.

Techniques of Cunnilingus

Women can be highly aroused by their partner's tongue because it is soft, warm, and well lubricated. In contrast to a finger, the tongue can almost never be used too harshly. A woman may thus be more receptive to direct clitoral contact by a tongue. Cunnilingus provides such intense stimulation that many women find it to be the best means for achieving orgasm. Some women cannot reach orgasm in any other way.

In performing cunnilingus, the partner may begin by kissing and licking the woman's abdomen and inner thighs, gradually nearing the vulva. Gentle tugging at or sucking of the labia minora can be stimulating, but the partner should take care not to bite. Many women enjoy licking of the clitoral region, and others desire sucking of the clitoris itself. The tongue may also be inserted into the vagina, where it may imitate the thrusts of intercourse.

"69"

The term *sixty-nine* describes simultaneous oral-genital stimulation (see Figure 8.7). The numerals 6 and 9 are used because they resemble two partners who are upside-down and facing each other.

The "69" position has the psychologically positive feature of allowing couples to experience simultaneous stimulation, but it can be awkward if two people are not similar in size. Some couples avoid "69" because it deprives each partner of the opportunity to focus fully on receiving or providing sexual pleasure. The "69" technique may be practised side by side or with one partner on top of the other. But here again there are no strict rules, and couples often alternate positions.

Figure 8.7 Simultaneous Oral–Genital Contact.

The "69" position allows partners to engage in simultaneous oral–genital stimulation.

washing the genitals beforehand. Others may worry whether oral sex is morally acceptable by their religion.

Some women prefer not to taste or swallow semen because they find the ejaculate "dirty," sinful, or repulsive. Others are put off by the taste or texture. Semen has a salty taste and a texture similar to that of an egg white. If couples are to engage in unprotected oral sex, open discussion of feelings can enhance pleasure and diminish anxiety. For example, the man can be encouraged to warn his partner or remove his penis from her mouth when he is nearing ejaculation.

Sexual Intercourse: Positions and Techniques

Sexual intercourse, or *coitus*, is sexual activity in which the penis is inserted into the vagina. Intercourse may take place in many different positions. Each position, however, must allow the genitals to be aligned so that the penis is contained by the vagina. In addition to varying positions, couples vary the depth and rate of thrusting (in-and-out motions) and the sources of additional sexual stimulation.

Missionary position The coital position in which the man is on top. Also termed the *male-superior position.*

Though the number of possible coital positions is virtually endless, we will focus on four of the most commonly used positions: the male-superior (man-on-top) position, the female-superior (woman-on-top) position, the lateral-entry (side-entry) position, and the rear-entry position. We shall also discuss anal intercourse, a sexual technique used by both male–female and male–male couples.

THE MALE-SUPERIOR (MAN-ON-TOP) POSITION The male-superior position (this "superiority" simply reflects the couple's body positions, but it has sometimes been taken as a symbol of male domination) has also been called the **missionary position**. In this position the partners face each other. The man lies above the woman, perhaps supporting himself on his hands and knees rather than resting his full weight on his partner (see Figure 8.8). Even so, it is easier for the man to move than for the woman, which suggests that he is responsible for directing their activity.

Many sex therapists suggest that it is preferable for the woman to guide the penis into the vagina, rather than having the man do so. The idea is that the woman can feel the location of the vaginal opening and determine the proper angle of entry. To accomplish this, the woman must feel comfortable "taking charge" of the couple's lovemaking. With the breaking down of the traditional stereotype of the female as passive, women are feeling more comfortable taking this role. The male-superior position has the advantage of permitting the couple to face one another so that kissing is easier. The woman may run her hands along her partner's body, stroking his buttocks and perhaps cupping a hand beneath his scrotum to increase stimulation as he reaches orgasm.

But the male-superior position makes it difficult for the man to caress his partner while simultaneously supporting himself with his hands. Therefore, the position may not be favoured by women who enjoy having their partners provide manual clitoral stimulation during coitus.

Figure 8.8 The Male-Superior Coital Position.

In this position the couple face each other. The man lies above the woman, perhaps supporting himself on his hands and knees rather than allowing his full weight to press against his partner. The position is also (somewhat disparagingly) referred to as the missionary position. (Primitive peoples have supposedly reported that this position never occurred to them until Western visitors described it.)

Figure 8.9 The Female-Superior Coital Position.

The woman straddles the male from above, controlling the angle of penile entry and the depth of thrusting. The female-superior position puts the woman psychologically and physically in charge. The woman can ensure that she receives adequate clitoral stimulation from the penis or the hand. This position also tends to be less stimulating for the male and may thus help him to control ejaculation.

THE FEMALE-SUPERIOR (WOMAN-ON-TOP) POSITION In the female-superior position, the couple face each other with the woman on top. The woman straddles the male from above, controlling the angle of penile entry and the depth of thrusting (see Figure 8.9). Some women maintain a sitting position; others lie on top of their partners. Many women vary their position.

In the female-superior position, the woman is psychologically—and to some degree physically—in charge. She can move as rapidly or as slowly as she wishes with little effort, adjusting her body to vary the angle and depth of penetration. The woman can, in effect, guarantee that she receives adequate clitoral stimulation, either by the penis or manually by his hand or her own. This position thus facilitates orgasm in the woman.

THE LATERAL-ENTRY (SIDE-ENTRY) POSITION In the lateral-entry position, the man and woman lie side by side, facing each other (see Figure 8.10). This position has the advantages of allowing each partner relatively free movement and easy access to the other. The man and woman may kiss freely, and they can stroke each other's bodies with a free arm. The position is not physically taxing, because both partners are resting easily on the bedding. Thus it is an excellent position for prolonged coitus, for older couples, and when couples are somewhat fatigued. The lateral position is useful during pregnancy (at least until the final stages, when the distension of the woman's abdomen may make lateral entry difficult).

THE REAR-ENTRY POSITION In the rear-entry position, the man faces the woman's rear. In one variation (see Figure 8.11), the woman supports herself on her hands and knees while the man supports himself on his knees, entering her from behind. In another, the couple lies alongside one another and the woman lifts one

Figure 8.10 The Lateral-Entry Coital Position.

In this position, the couple face each other side by side. Each partner has relatively free movement and easy access to the other. Because both partners rest easily on the bedding, it is an excellent position for prolonged coitus and for coitus when couples are fatigued.

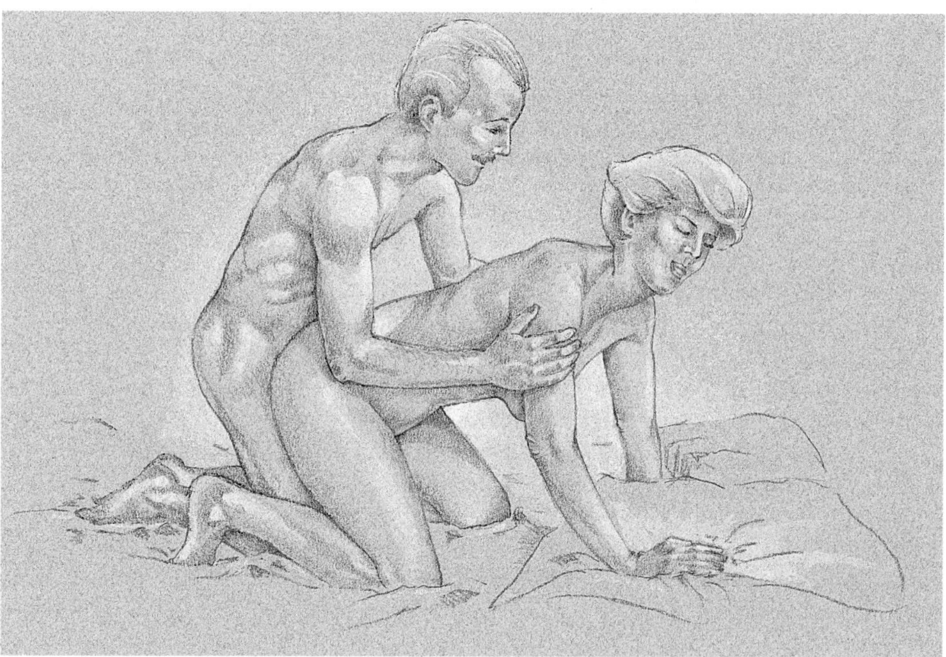

Figure 8.11 The Rear-Entry Coital Position.

The rear-entry position is highly erotic for men who enjoy viewing and pressing their abdomen against their partner's buttocks. However, some couples feel uncomfortable about the position because of its association with animal mating patterns. The position is also impersonal in that the partners do not face each other. Moreover, some couples dislike the feeling that the man is psychologically in charge because he can see his partner but she cannot readily see him.

leg, draping it backward over her partner's thigh. The latter position is particularly useful during the later stages of pregnancy.

The rear-entry position may be highly stimulating for both partners. Men may enjoy viewing and pressing their abdomen against their partner's buttocks. The man can reach around or underneath to provide additional stimulation of the clitoris or

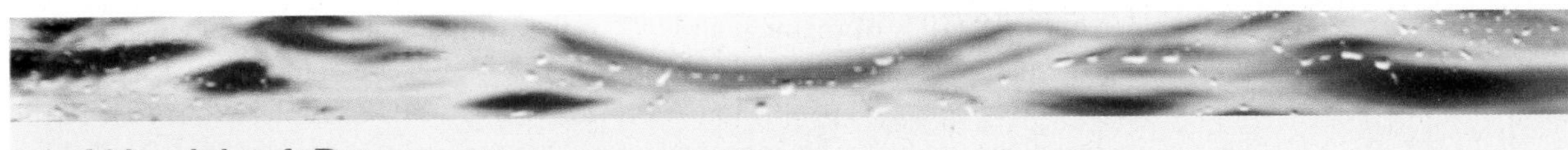

A World of Diversity

POPULAR SEXUAL POSITIONS AMONG ASIAN AND NON-ASIAN STUDENTS

In a study among students at a university in British Columbia, the two most popular positions were the male superior and the female superior and the least popular was the lateral entry (Meston et al., 1996). Table 8.3 provides a breakdown of how Asian and non-Asian students responded.

TABLE 8.3
Intercourse Positions Used by Asian and Non-Asian Students in British Columbia

	Male		Female	
Position	**Non-Asian**	**Asian**	**Non-Asian**	**Asian**
Male above	63%	35%	69%	36%
Female above	58	34	66	33
From rear	45	27	60	22
Sitting	41	28	57	28
Side by side	36	19	50	19

Note: The sample included both those who had experienced sexual intercourse and those who had not. If this analysis had included only the former group, the percentages for each sexual position would have been higher.

Source: Adapted from Meston, C. M., Trapnell, P. D., & Gorzalka, B. B. (1996). Ethnic and gender differences in sexuality: Variations in sexual behavior between Asian and non-Asian university students. Archives of Sexual Behavior, *25, 33-72.*

breasts, and she may reach behind (if she is on her hands and knees) to stroke or grasp her partner's testicles.

Some couples may feel uncomfortable about using the position because of its association with animal mating patterns. The position is also impersonal in the sense that the partners do not face each other, which may create a sense of emotional distance.

ANAL INTERCOURSE Anal intercourse can be practised by male–female couples and male–male couples. It involves insertion of the penis into the rectum.

The rectum is richly endowed with nerve endings and is thus highly sensitive to sexual stimulation. Anal intercourse is also referred to as "Greek culture," or lovemaking in the "Greek style," because of bisexuality in ancient Greece among males. Both women and men may reach orgasm through receiving the penis in the rectum.

In anal intercourse, the penetrating male usually situates himself behind his partner. (He can also lie above or below his partner in a face-to-face position.) The receiving partner can supplement anal stimulation with manual stimulation of the clitoral region or penis to reach orgasm. Because the rectum produces no natural lubrication, people engaging in anal intercourse are advised to use an artificial lubricant, such as K-Y jelly.

Some people want their partner's fingers in the anus at the height of passion or at the moment of orgasm. A finger in the rectum during orgasm can heighten sexual sensation because the anal sphincters contract during orgasm.

Many couples are repulsed by the idea of anal intercourse. They view it as unnatural, immoral, or risky. Yet others find anal sex to be an enjoyable sexual variation, though perhaps not a regular feature of their sexual diet.

The NHSLS (National Health and Social Life Survey of Americans) found that one man in four (26%) and one woman in five (20%) reported having engaged in anal sex at some time during their lives (Laumann et al., 1994). Yet only about one person in 10 (10% of the men and 9% of the women) had engaged in anal sex during the past year. As with oral sex, there was a higher incidence of anal sex among more highly educated people in the NHSLS survey. For example, about 30% of the male college graduates had engaged in anal sex, as compared with 23% of male high school graduates. About 29% of the women with advanced college degrees had engaged in anal sex, as compared with about 17% of the women who had graduated only from high school (Laumann et al., 1994). In a more recent national U.S. study of young adults, who were 18 to 26 years old and in long-term relationships, 22% were having anal sex (Kaestle, 2007).

Not all gay males enjoy or practise anal intercourse. Of those who do, most alternate between being the inserter and being the insertee. Interviews with 51 gay men suggest that playing the inserter role in anal intercourse is sometimes associated with fantasies of domination, and the insertee role with fantasies of submission (Kippax & Smith, 2001). But some gays who practised anal intercourse denied that sex had anything to do with power and with a dimension of activity–passivity; they felt that sex was about sharing.

Some individuals engage in the sexual practice called "fisting." Fisting is the insertion of the fist or hand into the vagina or the rectum. Fisting is more common among male–male than among male–female couples, and it carries the risk of infection or injury to the rectum or anus. A survey of 75 gay men in Australia found that fisting was usually done with gloves, although fingering was not (Richters et al., 2003).

Some couples kiss or lick the anus in their foreplay. This practice is called **anilingus**. Oral–anal sex carries a serious health risk, however, because micro-organisms that cause intestinal diseases and various sexually transmitted diseases can be spread through oral–anal contact.

Many couples today hesitate to engage in anal intercourse because of the fear of AIDS and other sexually transmitted infections (STIs). The AIDS virus and other micro-organisms that cause STIs, such as gonorrhea, syphilis, and hepatitis, can be spread by anal intercourse, because small tears in the rectal tissues may allow the microbes to enter the recipient's blood system. Women also run a greater risk of contracting HIV, the virus that causes AIDS, from anal intercourse than from vaginal intercourse—just as receptive anal intercourse in gay men carries a high risk of infection (Voeller, 1991). However, partners who are both infection-free are at no risk of contracting STIs through any sexual act.

Anilingus Oral stimulation of the anus.

Canadian Trends

INCIDENCE OF ANAL INTERCOURSE

In a study of university students in British Columbia, 19% of the non-Asian females reported engaging in anal intercourse compared with 3% of the Asian females; 5% of the non-Asian men and 6% of the Asian men engaged in anal intercourse (Meston et al., 1996). More of the students had engaged in caressing of the anal area. About half (45%) of the non-Asian women reported having their anal area caressed compared with 28% of the non-Asian men. About one-fifth of the Asian men and women had experienced caressing of the anal area.

At the University of Waterloo, more students had engaged in anal intercourse without a condom (15%) than with a condom (9%) (Rye, 2001). Among female students at the University of Guelph, 13% had engaged in anal intercourse with their most recent partner. However, of those who had engaged in anal sex, most said that they rarely did this (Hill, 2005).

Anal intercourse is more common among gay males than among heterosexual couples. In a study of almost 5000 gay males from across Canada, 62% had engaged in anal intercourse in the previous three months (Myers et al., 1996).

A World of Diversity

SEXUAL BEHAVIOURS AT MOST RECENT HETEROSEXUAL ENCOUNTER IN AUSTRALIA

In a national Australian survey involving 19 307 respondents between the ages of 16 and 59, researchers (Richters et al., 2006) asked heterosexuals about which sexual behaviours they had engaged in the last time they had sex with a partner. An important contribution of this study is that the researchers analyzed combinations of behaviours rather than considering behaviours in isolation. Almost all of the encounters (95%) included vaginal intercourse. However, engaging in vaginal intercourse by itself involved only 12% of the encounters. The most common combinations of behaviours were intercourse and manual stimulation of the man's and/or woman's genitals (49%) and intercourse and manual and oral stimulation (32%). Only 1% had anal intercourse, and 17% of the men and 14% of the women reported digital anal stimulation during their last sexual encounter.

Men had an orgasm in 95% of the encounters and women had an orgasm in 69%. Women were more likely to reach orgasm when the encounters included more sexual practices, especially cunnilingus.

Sexual Behaviours of Gay Men and Lesbians

In an Ontario survey of Canadian gay and bisexual men, more than half of the men reported having sex in the three months prior to the survey, with at least one regular partner (that is, someone the respondent had sex with more than once). Also, more than half had engaged in sex during this time with at least one casual partner (someone he had sex with only once) (Myers et al., 2004). The most common sexual activities reported were deep tongue kissing, oral sex without a condom, and mutual masturbation. Table 8.4 lists the types of sexual behaviours experienced by the respondents. The types of sexual behaviours experienced were fairly similar for both regular and casual partners, with the exception of anal sex without a condom, which

TABLE 8.4

Sexual Behaviours of Gay and Bisexual Men in Ontario Over a Period of Three Months

	With Regular Male Partner	With Casual Male Partner
Mutual masturbation	81%	78%
Oral sex—no condom (I)	86	80
Deep tongue kissing	86	78
Oral sex—no condom (R)	80	73
Anal sex with condom (I)	44	47
Oral-anal sex	53	40
Anal sex—no condom (I)	41	21
Anal sex with condom (R)	36	35
Anal sex—no condom (R)	34	6

Note: I = Insertive, R = Receptive

Source: Myers, T., & Allman, D. (2004). Ontario men's survey. Ottawa: Canadian Public Health Association.

Like heterosexual women, lesbians are less genitally oriented and less fixated on orgasm than are men.

was experienced twice as often with a regular partner than with a casual partner. Forty-four percent said they had never engaged in receptive anal intercourse without a condom.

Sexual techniques practised by lesbians vary. Lesbian couples report kissing, manual and oral breast stimulation, and manual and oral stimulation of the genitals. Manual genital stimulation is a common and frequent sexual activity among lesbian couples. Many lesbian couples also engage in genital apposition. That is, they position themselves so as to rub their genitals together rhythmically. Like gay males, lesbians spend a good deal of time holding, kissing, and caressing each other's bodies before they approach the breasts and genitals By contrast, heterosexual males tend to move quickly to stimulate their partners' breasts or start directly with genital stimulation (Masters & Johnson, 1979).

There has been far less research regarding the sexual behaviours of lesbians than those of gay men and heterosexuals. One of the more recent detailed surveys was taken in Australia (Richters, 2007). Almost all of the women had engaged in manual and oral sex (see Table 8.5).

This survey also asked about the use of dental dams for oral sex as a means of preventing infection of sexually transmitted diseases. Only

TABLE 8.5

Sexual Behaviours With Another Woman Experienced by Lesbians in Sydney, Australia

Behaviours Experienced	Percent
Fingers on external genitals	96%
Fingers inside vagina	94
Oral sex giving	85
Oral sex receiving	81
Sex toy used on external genitals	56
Sex toy used in vagina	57
Fingers inside anus	31
Rimming (her mouth, your anus)	15
Rimming (your mouth, her anus)	16
Sex toy inside anus	14

Source: Richters, J. (2007). Researching sex between women. Paper presented at the World Congress of Sexology, Sydney, Australia.

Innovative Canadian Research

HOW TO HAVE GREAT SEX: SEXUAL ADVICE IN POPULAR MAGAZINES

University of Ottawa researchers Dana Menard and Peggy Kleinplatz (2008) analyzed the advice given in popular men's and women's magazines for achieving "great sex." Five categories of advice emerged from the analysis:

1. Technical, mechanical, and physical factors: Recommendations included improving sexual techniques and/or positions, learning new ones, and having sex for the appropriate length of time. Factors also included improving physical health through diet or exercise.
2. Variety: Readers were encouraged to experiment sexually, try "mild kink," watch steamy movies or porn, or engage in "rough" female-initiated sex.
3. Relationship factors: Suggestions included improving communication about sexual desires and becoming more emotionally intimate.
4. Personal and psychological improvements: This involved relaxation during sex, focus on sexuality both during and outside of sex, improved female body image, and increased self-knowledge (usually through masturbation).
5. Preparing for sex: Recommendations involved making oneself more physically attractive and making the sexual setting more seductive.

Most of the advice centred on the first two categories of improving sexual techniques and increasing the variety of sexual experiences.

The magazines relied on a number of gender stereotypes in their advice, such as the belief that men preferred "quickies" whereas women preferred long drawn-out sex. The magazines also relied on traditional scripts, that is, recommending regular partners but not casual partners. Sometimes messages were contradictory, for example, one magazine might suggest that couples view pornography whereas another magazine would discourage this. Sexual advice was more common in women's than in men's magazines with the exception of *Men's Health*.

7% of the women reported they had ever used a dental dam when having oral sex with a woman. Of the women who had used a dental dam, three-quarters said they had used it only once (Richters, 2007).

Feelings About Sexual Behaviours

The fact that people engage in certain behaviours does not necessarily mean they have positive feelings about those behaviours. McGill University researchers Eric Ochs and Yitzchak Binik (1999) surveyed 70 couples about their experience with 68 sexual behaviours, including how comfortable they felt about each of them. Women rated themselves as more comfortable than did the men on the least sexually explicit behaviours (cuddling, hugging, and dancing). The men were more comfortable than the women with fellatio, anal intercourse, woman-on-top intercourse, and vaginal rear-entry intercourse.

In this chapter, we have observed many of the variations in human sexual expression. No other species shows such diversity in sexual behaviour.

Summing Up

Sexual fantasies are often incorporated during masturbation or during sex with another person to heighten sexual response.

Masturbation may be practised by means of manual stimulation of the genitals, perhaps with the aid of an electric vibrator or an object that provides tactile stimulation. Surveys indicate that most people have masturbated at some point in their lives.

The pattern and duration of foreplay varies widely within and across cultures. Couples kiss for its own enjoyment or as a prelude to intercourse.

Touching or caressing erogenous zones with the hands or other parts of the body can be highly arousing. Men typically prefer direct stroking of their genitals by their partner early in lovemaking. Women, however, tend to prefer that their partners caress their genitals after a period of general body contact.

Most, but not all, women enjoy stimulation of the breasts. The popularity of oral–genital stimulation has increased dramatically since Kinsey's day.

Four of the most commonly used coital positions are the male-superior position, the female-superior position, the lateral-entry position, and the rear-entry position.

Most gay males and a significant minority of heterosexuals engage in anal sex. There has been limited research on the sexual behaviours of lesbians.

Test Yourself

Multiple-Choice Questions

1. **Women who have fantasies about being sexually coerced**
   a. have been sexually abused as children
   b. believe that men should be sexually dominant
   c. have sadomasochistic tendencies
   d. remain in control, unlike women who are sexually assaulted

2. **The most common sexual fantasy reported by both men and women is**
   a. having intercourse with a colleague or classmate
   b. having intercourse with a loved one
   c. having a same-sex sexual encounter
   d. having sex with more than one person

3. **Masturbation is more common among**
   a. less-educated men
   b. men than women
   c. younger adults than older adults
   d. women than men

4. **The finding that men find masturbation more pleasurable than women is most likely due to**
   a. differences in socialization between men and women
   b. ethnocentricity
   c. the greater variety of sexual behaviours available to men
   d. women's lack of visual acuity

5. **Most men report that they masturbate by**
   a. using electric devices such as vibrators
   b. manual stimulation of the penis
   c. using sex dolls or artificial vaginas
   d. rubbing the penis against a pillow

6. **Masters and Johnson reported that**
   a. most women masturbate by constant stroking of the clitoris
   b. all women touch their breasts during masturbation
   c. no two women were observed masturbating in exactly the same way
   d. there was an absence of fantasy during masturbation in women

7. **The varieties of physical contact that occur before sexual intercourse are collectively called**
   a. prologue
   b. foreplay
   c. othercourse
   d. afterplay

8. **According to the text, most women prefer ________________ as a prelude to intercourse**
   a. inserting fingers into the anus
   b. hard sucking on the breasts
   c. inserting fingers into the vagina
   d. caressing the area around the clitoris

9. **Which statement is true about breast stimulation?**
   a. Most men's breasts are not erotically sensitive.
   b. Some women are able to reach orgasm from breast stimulation alone.
   c. Men are more likely to touch their own breasts than their partners'.
   d. Women prefer manual stimulation of the breasts to manual stimulation of the clitoris.

10. **Oral sex is more common among**
    a. people in lower-paying jobs
    b. couples living together
    c. dating couples
    d. people with more education

Answers to the Test Yourself questions in each chapter are found on page 509.

Critical Thinking Questions

1. Have you ever wondered if your sexual fantasies are "normal"?
2. While you were growing up, did you receive negative messages about masturbation from your parents? From your friends? Has this affected how you view this behaviour?
3. How do you feel about masturbating to online sexual images? If you do so, would you tell your best friend? Your girlfriend or boyfriend? Why or why not?
4. Were you ever punished severely for masturbating as a child? Do you think that this has affected your behaviour as an adult? Explain.

Visit MyPsychKit at www.mypsychkit.com, where you can do quizzes and link to additional resources on topics discussed in this text.

CHAPTER NINE

Sexual Orientation

Getting Oriented Toward Sexual Orientation

Sexual orientation The directionality of one's sexual interests—toward members of the same sex, the other sex, or both.

Heterosexual orientation Erotic attraction to, and preference for developing romantic relationships with, members of the other sex.

Homosexual orientation Erotic attraction to, and preference for developing romantic relationships with, members of one's own sex.

Sexual orientation refers to one's erotic attractions toward, and interests in developing romantic relationships with, members of one's own or the other sex. A **heterosexual orientation** refers to an erotic attraction to, and preference for developing romantic relationships with, members of the other sex. (Many homosexual people refer to heterosexual people as *straights*, and to heterosexuality as *being straight*.)

A **homosexual orientation** refers to an erotic attraction to, and interest in forming romantic relationships with, members of one's own sex. The term *homosexuality* denotes sexual interest in members of one's own anatomic sex and applies to both men and women. Homosexual men are often referred to as *gay males*. Homosexual women are often called *lesbians*. Gay males and lesbians may also be referred to collectively as *gays* or *gay people*. The term *bisexuality* describes an orientation in which one is sexually attracted to, and interested in forming romantic relationships with, both males and females.

Coming to Terms With Terms

Now that we have defined homosexuality, let us note that the term is somewhat controversial. Some gay people object to it, because they feel that it draws attention to sexual behaviour. Moreover, the term bears a social stigma. It has also been historically associated with concepts of deviance and mental illness. In addition, the term is often used to refer to men only. It thus renders lesbians invisible. For these reasons, many people would prefer terms such as *gay male* or *lesbian sexual orientation* (Savin-Williams, 2006).

Holly Devor (2002)—now Aaron Devor—argues that transgendered people (discussed in Chapter 5) should also be included under the topic of sexual orientation. Devor reasons that, since transgendered people have been the most visible minority among people engaged in same-sex practices, they face many of the same issues and concerns as do gay, lesbian, and bisexual people. Yet transgendered people lack the legal protection granted to gay males and lesbians. It should be

Brokeback Mountain.
In the film Brokeback Mountain, *Jake Gyllenhaal and Heath Ledger portray two cowboys who begin a love affair in Wyoming in 1963. Neither understands what it means to have a gay sexual orientation.*

A World of Diversity

NINA'S UNSTOPPABLE! DESIRE TO BE HERSELF

Arsenault's drive to become glamorous included 60 surgeries that cost $160 000.

As a child growing up in a Beamsville trailer park, Rodney Arsenault was shown pictures of the beautiful, naked women in Playboy by some other kids.

There was instant attraction—of a very different sort.

There were no pre-pubescent sexual stirrings, but a desire by Rodney to become one of those "gorgeous, glamorous women" he admired, because he was "a little girl trapped in a little boy's body."

By age 24, Rodney had two master's degrees and was one of the youngest course instructors at York University, teaching acting, but was ready to jettison that promising career and his male identity for a female one.

Rodney changed his name to Nina while still at York and let nothing—not money, pain, negative social attitudes or medical concerns—deter "her" from that goal, which was achieved after nine years and about 60 cosmetic surgeries and procedures costing $160 000, financed by working in the sex trade.

It's that determination that has Arsenault being cited for this year's Unstoppable! theme award at the annual Pride Gala in Toronto, one of eight persons to be honoured for their achievements in different categories.

"Knowing that Pride Toronto selects one Canadian queer who embodies the event's theme every year, I'm really honoured that it's me. I know so many unstoppable people," Arsenault says.

"I had this long-term vision in my head of the type of woman I wanted to be and that sort of woman doesn't blend in very well. I'm kind of over the top in my gender expression—with all my cosmetic surgeries, the way I wear my hair and my flashy clothes. But I walk down the street every day with dignity."

Arsenault believes that revealing the most intimate details of her life, on TV shows such as *Kink* and in her former T-Girl (T as in transsexual or tranny) column in *fab* magazine, helps contribute to a better understanding of transgendered people.

"There are many who misunderstand us, are afraid of us, are threatened by us or don't like us and I think it's because they really don't know anything about us. The girls and guys that I know are just an amazing community of people who've been through so much."

David Anderson, co-chair of Pride Toronto's board of directors and a member of the awards panel, describes Arsenault as "a remarkable individual we think embodies that spirit of being unstoppable in the courage that she has shown to be completely who she believes herself to be . . . even in the face of obstacles."

Nina Arsenault was a winner of the 2007 Toronto Pride Gala's Unstoppable! award. Most organizations that represent gay males and lesbians also include transgender people.

Among the more radical procedures, Arsenault's testicles were removed at a Mexican clinic to block the production of testosterone, but the penis remains. Her rib cage was also reshaped.

"I'm not planning on having any more plastic surgeries, but I'm still transitioning psychologically. I don't think the transition ever stops."

Source: (2007, June 14). Nina's Unstoppable! desire to be herself. Toronto Star. *p. 5. Reprinted with permission – Torstar Syndication Services.*

noted, however, that some within the transgendered community identify themselves as "trans," and view their issues as related to gender, not to sexual orientation.

Currently, most organizations that represent gay males and lesbians also include transgender people, although this was not true in the past. As a sign of inclusivity, many organizations have adopted the label *LGBTQ* (lesbian, gay, bisexual, transgender, and queer). The formerly derogatory term *queer* has been reclaimed in Canada by several gay, lesbian, and bisexual organizations as a means of encompassing such previously excluded groups as transgender people (Devor, 2002). However, some lesbians are uncomfortable with the term *queer* and worry that the general use of that term may serve to hide some of the particular issues facing lesbians. For example, Alberta therapists Bonita Decaire and Deborah Foster (in press) believe that because of sexism, lesbians have more in common with other women regarding issues such as power inequities and discrimination than they do with gay men.

Sexual Orientation and Gender Identity

When heterosexuals think about homosexuals, they tend to focus almost exclusively on the sexual aspects of male–male and female–female relationships. But the relationships of homosexuals, like those of heterosexuals, involve more than sex. In a study of Ontario men, Barry Adam (2000b) at the University of Windsor found that for gay men the concept of "gay" centred on the possibility for emotional involvement and relationships with other people who felt the same way rather than on sexual behaviour. Homosexuals, like heterosexuals, spend only a small amount of time in sexual activity. More basic to a gay male or a lesbian sexual orientation is the formation of romantic attachments with members of one's own sex. These attachments, like male–female attachments, provide a framework for love and intimacy. Sexual orientations are not defined by sexual activity per se, but rather by the direction of one's romantic interests and erotic attractions (Mosher et al., 2005).

Kevin Alderson, at the University of Calgary, has for several years been researching the concept of sexual orientation. His findings have resulted in a new scale, the Sexuality Questionnaire. Alderson (2007) concluded that sexual orientation should be conceptualized and measured as a combination of the following factors: sexual attraction, sexual fantasies, sexual preference, sexual partners, tendency to fall in love romantically, and experience of falling in love romantically. The scale also measures one's self-identified sexual identity.

Classification of Sexual Orientation: Is Yes or No Enough?

Determining a person's sexual orientation might seem to be a clear-cut task. Some people are exclusively gay and limit their sexual activities to partners of their own sex. Others are strictly heterosexual and limit their sexual activities to partners of the other sex. Some people fall in between.

It is possible, indeed not unusual, for heterosexual people to have had sexual experiences with people of their own sex (Mosher et al., 2005; Savin–Williams, 2006). In the absence of heterosexual outlets, adolescents and those in isolated populations (such as prison inmates) may have sexual experiences with people of their own sex while they maintain their heterosexual identities.

Gay males and lesbians, too, may engage in male–female sexual activity while maintaining a gay sexual orientation. In the Ontario Men's Survey of gay and bisexual men, 83% of respondents identified themselves as gay, yet 61% reported having had sex with a woman in the past (Myers et al., 2004). Some gay males and lesbians marry members of the other sex, but harbour unfulfilled desires for members of their own sex. Then, too, some people are bisexual but may not act on their attraction to members of their own sex (Edser & Shea, 2002).

Sexual orientation is not necessarily expressed in sexual behaviour. Many people see themselves as gay or heterosexual long before they ever have sex with members of their own sex (Diamond, 2003b; Savin–Williams & Diamond, 2000). Some people, gay and heterosexual alike, adopt a celibate lifestyle for religious or ascetic reasons.

People's erotic interests and fantasies may also shift over time. Gay males and lesbians may experience sporadic **heteroerotic** interests. Heterosexual people may have occasional **homoerotic** interests. Women's sexual orientations are apparently somewhat more flexible or plastic than men's, with women being somewhat more dependent on social experience (Diamond, 2003a). Lisa M. Diamond (2003b) conducted a survey of lesbian and bisexual women that involved three interviews over a five-year period. She found that more than 25% of the women relinquished their lesbian or bisexual orientation as time went on. Half of these relabelled themselves as heterosexual, and the other half renounced any effort at self-labelling.

Heteroerotic Of an erotic nature and involving members of the other sex.

Homoerotic Of an erotic nature and involving members of one's own sex.

Figure 9.1 The Kinsey Continuum.

Kinsey and his colleagues conceived of a seven-point heterosexual–homosexual continuum that classifies people according to their homosexual behaviour and the magnitude of their attraction to members of their own gender.

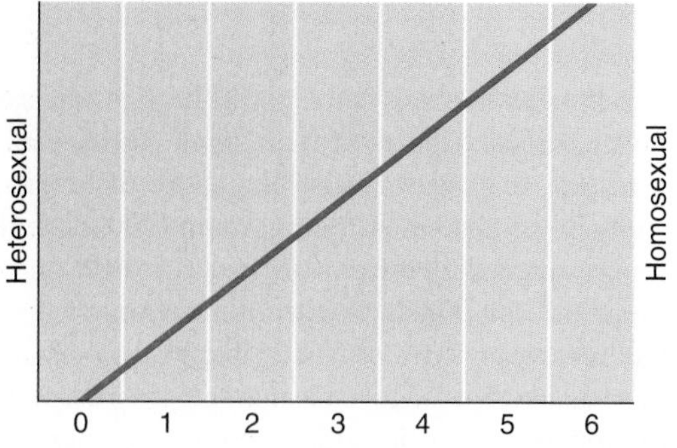

Chivers and Bailey (2005) exposed men and women to visual male and female sexual stimuli. They measured both their genital responses and their self-reports of sexual arousal. Male heterosexuals responded genitally only to the female stimuli, and gay males showed the reverse pattern. Their genital responses bore out their verbal reports. The women, both heterosexual and lesbian, were more likely to be aroused by both male and female sexual stimuli. Chivers and Bailey's findings are consistent with research showing that women's sexual orientations are more flexible than men's and apparently more intertwined with their social experience (Bailey, 2003a; Diamond, 2003b).

Attraction to people of the other sex and people of one's own sex may thus not always be mutually exclusive. People may have various degrees of sexual interest in, and sexual experience with, people of either sex. Kinsey and his colleagues recognized that the boundaries between gay male and lesbian sexual orientations on the one hand, and a heterosexual orientation on the other, are sometimes blurry.

Kinsey and his colleagues (1948, 1953) found evidence of a continuum of sexual orientation among the people they surveyed, with bisexuality representing a midpoint between exclusively heterosexual and exclusively homosexual sexual orientations (Figure 9.1). People are located on the continuum according to their patterns of sexual attraction and behaviour. People in category 0 are considered exclusively heterosexual. People in category 6 are considered exclusively gay.

Kinsey and his colleagues reported that about 4% of men and 1% to 3% of women in their samples were exclusively gay (six points on their scale). A larger percentage of people were considered predominantly gay (four or five points) or predominantly heterosexual (one or two points on their scale). All in all, Kinsey's data suggested that close to 10% of the U.S. population was gay or predominantly gay, a number that dramatically exceeds current estimates. Some were classified as equally gay and heterosexual in orientation and could be labelled bisexual (three points). Most people were classified as exclusively heterosexual (zero points).

Statistics concerning past sexual activity with a member of one's own sex can be misleading. They may represent a single episode or a brief period of adolescent experimentation. Half the men who reported male–male sexual activity in Kinsey's sample limited it to the age of 12 to 14. Another third had male–male sexual experience by the age of 18, but not again.

Kinsey's research also showed that sexual behaviour patterns can change, sometimes dramatically so. Sexual experiences or feelings involving people of one's own sex are common, especially in adolescence, and do not necessarily mean that one will engage in sexual activity exclusively with people of one's own sex in adulthood (Diamond, 2003a).

ESTIMATES OF SEXUAL ORIENTATION The controversy regarding how many people are gay continues. Research in the United States, Britain, France, and Denmark finds that about 3% of men surveyed identify themselves as gay (Mosher et al., 2005; Savin-Williams, 2006). About 1% to 2% of the U.S. women surveyed identify themselves as lesbians (Mosher et al., 2005; Savin-Williams, 2006). Similar results were found in a sample of 8000 university and college students in Canada and the United States, with 3% of the males identifying themselves as gay or bisexual and 2% of the females identifying themselves as lesbian or bisexual (Ellis et al., 2005).

The approach that is used to measure sexual orientation strongly influences the results. In a study of men who have sex in parks in Ottawa, Huber and Kleinplatz (2002) found that 80% identified themselves as gay, 17% as bisexual, and only 3% as heterosexual. Similar results were found when they surveyed men in bathhouses. And in a large Canadian study of gay and bisexual men, 81% described themselves as gay and about 15% said they were bisexual, with the rest saying they were heterosexual or other (Myers, Godin, et al., 1993). However, in terms of actual experience with men or women, less than half (44%) had had sex only with men in their lifetime, 13% had had sex with both men and women in the past year, and 41% said they were currently gay but had had sex with women in the past.

The 1998 Compas survey asked Canadians, "In general, whom are you most attracted to?" As shown in Table 9.1, about 8% of males and 10% of females said they were attracted to the same sex. However, less than 2% of the men said they were attracted only to men and less than 1% of the women said they were attracted only to women.

In the Canada Youth and AIDS Survey (Boyce, 2003), students were asked to indicate their sexual orientation, as indicated by their physical attraction to members of the same sex, the other sex, or both sexes. Girls were more likely to admit to a same-sex attraction. In grade 11, more males (1.5%) and females (3%) indicated being physically attracted to both sexes than to their own sex exclusively (0.9% of males and 1.7% of females).

In a survey of Canadians aged 13 to 29 (designed by Kris Wells of the University of Alberta), 3.5% of respondents identified themselves as *GLBT* (gay, lesbian, bisexual, or transgendered) (Youthography Ping Survey, 2004). Slightly more males than females identified themselves this way (Wells, 2008).

In 2003 Statistics Canada for the first time included a question on sexual orientation as part of its Canadian Community Health Survey. Among the 135 000 respondents aged 18 to 59, 1.0% reported that they were gay or lesbian and 0.7% said they were bisexual. Twice as many men (1.3%) as women (0.7%) reported they were homosexual. However, more women (0.9%) than men (0.6%) reported they were bisexual (Statistics Canada, 2004b).

Another approach to determining sexual orientation involves measuring physiological responses to sexual stimuli. Researchers in Quebec have devised a method of measuring sexual preference in virtual reality (Renaud et al., 2002). This involves measuring a respondent's computer interaction with an image of a naked woman as a measure of his or her sexual preference.

TABLE 9.1
Sexual Attraction Preferences of Canadian Men and Women

	Males	**Females**
Only men	1.6%	90.1%
Mostly men	0.5	6.7
Both men and women	1.9	2.2
Mostly women	4.5	0.1
Only women	91.4	0.8

Source: Based on analysis of Compas (1998) Modern life survey of the Canadian population.

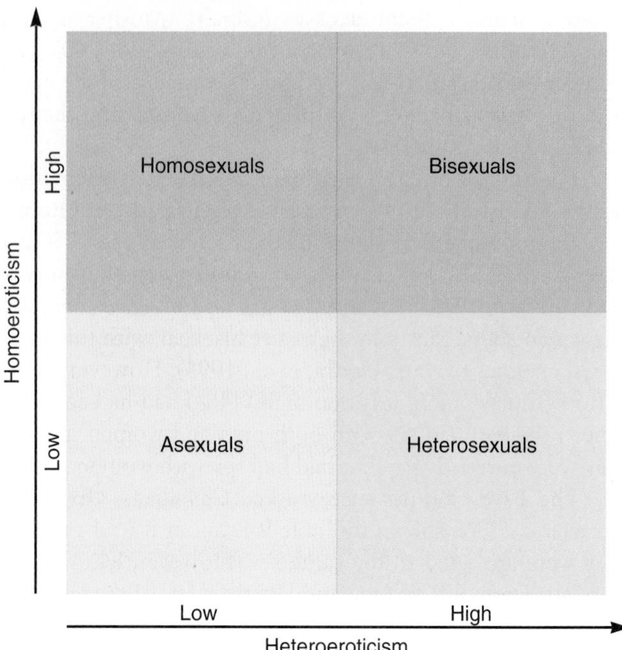

Figure 9.2 Heterosexuality and Homosexuality as Separate Dimensions.

According to this model, homosexuality and heterosexuality are independent dimensions. One can thus be high or low on both dimensions at the same time. Most people are high on one dimension. Bisexuals are high on both dimensions. People who are low on both are considered asexual.

CHALLENGES TO THE KINSEY CONTINUUM Alfred Kinsey believed that exclusive heterosexual and gay sexual orientations lay at opposite poles of one continuum. Therefore, the more heterosexual a person is, the less gay that person is, and vice versa.

Using the self-reporting of the content of erotic fantasies as an indication of sexual orientation, Storms (1980) found evidence that there are separate dimensions of responsiveness to male–female sexual stimulation (heteroeroticism) and sexual stimulation that involves someone of the same sex (homoeroticism), as shown in Figure 9.2. According to this model, bisexuals are high in both dimensions, whereas people who are low in both are essentially asexual. According to Kinsey, bisexual individuals would be less responsive to stimulation by people of the other sex than heterosexual people, but more responsive to stimulation by people of their own sex. But the two-dimensional model allows for people to be as responsive to stimulation by people of the other sex as heterosexual people, and as responsive to stimulation by people of their own sex as gay people.

Bisexuality

Bisexual people are sexually attracted to both males and females. Yet many have a somewhat stronger attraction to people of one sex than the other. In fact, Weinrich and Klein (2002) speak of bisexuals as being bi–gay, bi–straight, or bi–bi, meaning that some have a stronger leaning toward people of their own sex (bi–gays), some toward people of the other sex (bi–straights), and still others appear to be equally attracted to people of their own sex and the other sex (bi–bis).

About 1% of the people (0.8% of the men and 0.9% of the women) surveyed in the American NHSLS study (Laumann et al., 1994) reported having a bisexual identity. About 4% said they were sexually attracted to both women and men. However, the Canadian studies discussed in the previous section reported higher percentages for bisexual experience and attraction (Compas, 1998; Myers et al., 1993).

Some gay people (and some heterosexual people) believe that claims to bisexuality are a "cop-out" that people use to deny being gay. Perhaps they fear leaving their spouses or "coming out" (declaring their gay male or lesbian sexual orientation publicly). Others view bisexuality as a form of sexual experimentation with people of one's own sex by people who are mostly heterosexual. Surveys of more than 600 college undergraduates confirm that **biphobia**, or hatred of bisexuals, can be found in both the heterosexual and the homosexual populations (Mulick & Wright, 2002). To assist bisexuals in dealing with these issues, groups such as Bisexual Women of Toronto provide counselling and support. One of its objectives is to educate community service groups about the effects of prejudice and discrimination against bisexuals.

Biphobia Negative attitudes and feelings toward bisexual people, including intolerance, hatred, and fear.

Many avowed bisexuals and researchers assert that bisexuals can maintain erotic interests in, and romantic relationships with, members of both sexes. They insist that bisexuality is an authentic sexual orientation with its own developmental patterns, and is not just a "cover" for a gay male or lesbian sexual orientation (Brown, 2002; Weinrich & Klein, 2002).

Some bisexual people follow lifestyles that permit them to satisfy their dual inclinations. Others feel pressured by heterosexual and gay people alike to commit themselves one way or the other (Edser & Shea, 2002). Some gay people also mask their sexual orientation by adopting a bisexual lifestyle. That is, they get married but also enter into clandestine sexual liaisons with members of their own sex.

Asexuality

Anthony Bogaert (2006a) from Brock University in Ontario argues that asexuality should be considered a sexual orientation. He defines asexuals as people who have a low sexual attraction for both sexes; that is, they are low on both heteroeroticism and homoeroticism. However, they might be romantically attracted to others. Most have a low interest in any kind of sexual stimulation, including masturbation. In a survey, Bogaert asked respondents if "they have never felt sexual attraction to anyone at all." One percent replied "yes." However, one-third of these said they were in a long-term marital or cohabiting relationship and another 11% had been in such a relationship in the past. Some of the asexual people still engaged in sexual activity with a partner, but the frequency was very low. Bogaert suggests that some have sex just to please their partner.

Bogaert (2006a) notes that his definition of asexuality is narrow in scope in that it does not take into account whether someone is romantically attracted to another person or is engaging in sexual activity. In his conclusion, Bogaert argues that asexuality is not pathological in that asexual people can live a happy life.

Perspectives on Gay Male and Lesbian Sexual Orientations

Gay male and lesbian sexual orientations have existed throughout history. Attitudes toward them have varied widely. They have been tolerated in some societies, and openly encouraged in others, but condemned in most.

Historical and Religious Perspectives

Some ancient societies such as the Greeks were openly accepting of male–male sexual behaviour (see Chapter 1). Many famous people throughout history, such as Alexander the Great, have been gay. Yet most cultures have held negative attitudes toward homosexuality.

Jews and Christians have traditionally referred to male–male sexual activity as the sin of Sodom, hence the term *sodomy*, which generally denotes anal intercourse (and sometimes oral–genital contact). According to the Book of Genesis, the city of Sodom was destroyed by God. Yet it is unclear what behaviour incurred God's

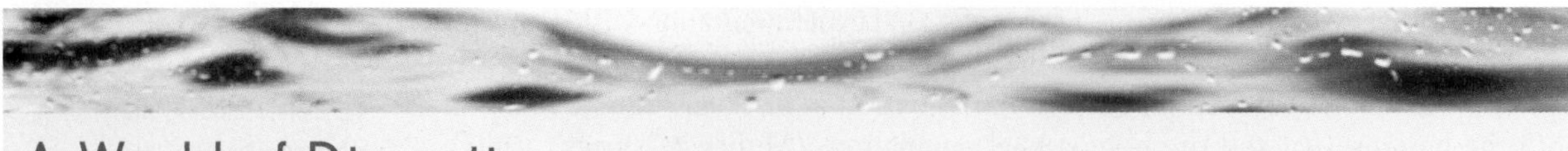

A World of Diversity

THE NEW GAY TEENAGER

Professor Ritch Savin-Williams of Cornell University, in his controversial book *The New Gay Teenager*, argues that today's urban teenagers no longer accept the traditional gender and sexual orientations. In the preface he states:

> Gay people have historically too readily accepted the inevitability and desirability of divisions based on sexual categories. It's not that same-sex attractions are disappearing—indeed, they appear to be on the upswing as young people more freely share with each other their same-sex feelings. They're not embarrassed by gayness, don't consider it deviant, and see it all around them—on television, in movies, in songs, in cultural icons, among their friends.

In his interviews with urban American teenagers, Savin-Williams discovered that many no longer consider gender categories as being important. Rather they view themselves as "pansexuals" or bisexuals who reject gender labels. Savin-Williams believes that the media have played a key role in changing the gender perspectives of young people by normalizing same-sex attraction in television and in films. Also, in large urban centres such as New York and Los Angeles, school boards have introduced programs intended to increase students' acceptance of a range of sexual orientations.

Savin-Williams is highly critical of social scientists who in their research force the participants to label themselves as either gay or straight. Bisexuals are typically ignored or forced into one of these categories. Also, the researchers do not allow for broader choices such as polysexual or multiple identities, such as bi-lesbian.

Savin-Williams argues that the standard image of gay youth presented by researchers as being depressed, isolated, drug-dependent, and suicidal is overly exaggerated. He believes many of these studies were flawed in that they purposely oversampled troubled teens. From his own research, he concludes that most gay males and lesbians are psychologically healthy and in this regard no different from heterosexual youth.

In analyzing the trends and conclusions reported by Savin-Williams, we need to consider if they are only applicable to a small minority of sophisticated urban youth or whether these trends are indeed accurately representative of what is occurring among youth.

The New Gay Teenager *is a book by Ritch Savin-Williams.*

Kristopher Wells (2008), of the University of Alberta, reports on a Canadian study that found similar trends among gay youth. According to Wells, Canadian youth are challenging the traditional stereotypes of sexuality and gender and are reluctant to have their sexual identities forced into narrow categories.

Source: Savin-Williams, R. C. (2005). The New Gay Teenager. *Cambridge, Massachusetts: Harvard University Press.*

wrath. Pope Gregory III was not ambiguous, however, in his eighth-century account of the city's obliteration as a punishment for sexual activity with members of one's own sex.

Despite the history of opposition to gay male and lesbian sexual orientations, some churches today are performing marriages of gay couples—or at least "blessing" these relationships. The Metropolitan Community Church has many gay male and lesbian parishioners in Canada. The first Canadian church to perform formal marriage ceremonies for same-sex couples was the Metropolitan Church in Toronto. Since then an increasing number of churches have performed same-sex marriages.

Many Canadian churches allow for the ordination of gay male and lesbian clergy, providing they remain celibate. Some churches, however, such as the Unitarian and the United Church of Canada, do accept clergy who are involved in same-sex relationships. Yet the more conservative churches continue to oppose equal rights, including same-sex marriages, for anyone whose sexual orientation is not heterosexual.

Today a major international legal and political struggle over gay rights is taking place based on two opposing values: gay equality versus religious freedom. At the

United Nations, a coalition of mainly Islamic countries has been leading a campaign for the development of international laws that would prohibit "defamation of religions" such as Islam (Savage, 2008). One intent of this movement is to deter international organizations such as the UN from discussing issues such as gay rights, because this would be viewed by Islamic countries as an affront to their religious beliefs and accordingly an act of religious discrimination (Savage, 2008).

Some countries still harshly punish people convicted of engaging in homosexual acts. For example, in 2008, five men in Egypt were sentenced to three years in prison for "debauchery," which is the term used in Egypt for homosexual sex acts (Associated Press, 2008).

Cross-Cultural Perspectives

Male–male sexual behaviour has been practised in many preliterate societies. In their review of the literature on 76 preliterate societies, Ford and Beach (1951) found that in 49 societies (64%), male–male sexual interactions were viewed as normal and deemed socially acceptable for some members of the group. The other 27 societies (36%) had sanctions against male–male sexual behaviour. Nevertheless, male–male sexual activity persisted.

Sexual activities between males are sometimes limited to rites that mark the young male's initiation into manhood. In some preliterate societies, semen is believed to boost strength and virility. Older males thus transmit semen to younger males through oral or anal sexual activities. Among the Sambian people of New Guinea, a tribe of warlike headhunters, 9- to 12-year-old males leave their parents' households and live in a "clubhouse" with other prepubertal and adolescent males. There they undergo sexual rites of passage. To acquire the fierce manhood of the headhunter, they perform fellatio on older males and drink "men's milk" (semen) (Bailey, 2003b). By the age of 19, however, young men are expected to take brides and enter exclusively male–female sexual relationships.

These practices of Sambian culture might seem to suggest that the sexual orientations of males are fluid and malleable. The practices involve behaviour, however, not sexual orientation. Male–male sexual behaviour among Sambians takes place within a cultural context that bears little resemblance to consensual male–male sexual activity in Western society. The prepubertal Sambian male does not seek sexual liaisons with other males. He is removed from his home and thrust into male–male sexual encounters by older males (Baldwin & Baldwin, 1989).

Sambian culture presents a different perspective on gay identity than is found in Western societies. Also, Tarik Bereket, at the University of Toronto, and Barry D. Adam, at the University of Windsor (2006), found that Turkish men who have same-sex relations do not share the Western concept of gay identity as held by Westerners. For example, men who assume the inserter role in anal intercourse do not consider themselves as being gay.

Little is known about female–female sexual activity in non-Western cultures. Evidence of female–female sexual behaviour was found by Ford and Beach in only 17 of the 76 societies they studied. Perhaps female sexual behaviour in general, not just sexual activity with other females, was more likely to be repressed.

Cross-Species Perspectives

Biologists have observed male–male and female–female sexual behaviour in at least 450 different animal species in every part of the world (Hird, 2006).

A male baboon may present his rear and allow himself to be mounted by another male. This behaviour may resemble anal intercourse among gay men. But is the behaviour sexually motivated? Mounting behaviour among male baboons may represent a type of dominance ritual in which lower-ranking males adopt a submissive (feminine) posture to ward off attack from dominant males (Nadler, 1990).

A World of Diversity

ETHNICITY AND SEXUAL ORIENTATION

Because of societal prejudices, it is difficult for many young people to come to terms with an emerging lesbian or gay male sexual orientation. You might assume that people who have been subjected to prejudice and discrimination—members of ethnic minority groups—would be more tolerant than others of people with a lesbian or gay male sexual orientation. However, such an assumption might not be warranted.

By and large, a lesbian or gay male sexual orientation is rejected by many ethnic minority groups in Canada. For example, about 80% of First Nations people in Ontario believe that homosexuality is wrong (Myers et al., 1993). The Ethnocultural Communities Facing AIDS study sponsored by Health Canada found that both the Chinese and the South Asian communities strongly disapprove of same-sex relationships, which they view as abnormal. Because they fear bringing shame to their families, lesbians and gay males in those communities feel pressured to keep their sexual orientations a secret or to move to communities where they can live openly without sanction.

In her study of gay male Vietnamese immigrants in Toronto, Cynthia Vo (2001), a graduate student at the University of Guelph, found that only a small minority of the gay men chose to come out to their parents. Many felt their parents would no longer be proud of them. They were worried about bringing shame to the family and causing their parents to lose face in the community.

If any generalization is possible, it may be that lesbians and gay men find more of a sense of belonging in the gay community than in their ethnic communities. Yet members of some minority groups may feel that their issues are not addressed by mainstream gay male and lesbian organizations. Among Vietnamese gay men in Toronto, for example, some stated that they felt more discrimination from the white gay community than they did from Canadian society at large (Vo, 2001). As a result, gay Asians have formed their own groups, including Gay Asians of the Vancouver Area and the Bubble Tea Lounge community in Toronto.

Paul Vasey of the University of Lethbridge has done considerable research on sexual preference and orientation in female Japanese macaques. Vasey (2002) has found that these females routinely engage in sexual behaviours with both males and females. Often female Japanese macaques will choose to have sex with other females even if willing male partners are available. In another study, Vasey et al. (2006) found that the female macaques did not mount other females in the same way that males did. Rather the mounting styles of the females were more varied than that of the males and were done in such a way as to provide greater genital pleasure to the females. This physical drive for sexual pleasure with another female supports the assumption that this behaviour is sexual and indicates a bisexual orientation (Vasey et al., 2006).

Current Attitudes Toward Sexual Orientation

Historically speaking, negative attitudes toward gay people have pervaded our society. Today, however, there is far greater acceptance in Canadian society of equal rights for gay people. According to University of Manitoba professor Bob Altemeyer (2001), a major factor in this acceptance has been increased contact with persons known to be gay, brought about by the fact that gays and lesbians have been increasingly open about revealing their sexual orientation. Similarly, in a survey of civic leaders in Hamilton, McMaster professor Rhoda Howard-Hassmann (2001) found that learning a relative, neighbour, co-worker, or client was gay not only made people more accepting of gays but humanized gays in their mind.

Approximately three-quarters of both teenagers and adults feel that homosexuals should be entitled to the same rights as other Canadians. Older adults, however, are less accepting of equal rights than younger Canadians (Bibby, 2001). Slightly more than half of Canadians approve of homosexual relationships (adults 60% and

Innovative Canadian Research

MEASURES OF HOMONEGATIVITY

Waterloo, Ontario, researchers (Rye et al., 2008) analyzed three measures of homonegativity to determine which instrument best measured negative attitudes toward homosexuals. The three scales were: Attitudes Toward Lesbians and Gay Men (ATLG) by Herek, Modern Homonegativity by Morrison and Morrison, and Index of Homophobia by Hudson and Ricketts. All three scales were found to be good measures of homonegativity. For a sample of university students, each of the scales determined that attitudes were more positive than negative toward homosexuals. The ATLG and Modern Homonegativity scales did the best job of assessing both cognitive and emotional reactions, whereas the Index of Homophobia mainly focused on emotional reactions. The Modern Homonegativity Scale had a slight edge over the two other scales with its stronger psychometrics.

teenagers 54%). And, compared with when they were teenagers, more than half of Canadian adults report that they have become more approving of homosexuality, with fewer than 10% having become less approving. Women tend to be somewhat more approving of homosexuality than men are (Bibby, 2001).

Despite opposition by a vociferous minority, most Canadians accept same-sex marriage. In a 2003 national survey conducted by the Centre for Research and Information on Canada, 61% of Canadian adults approved of same-sex marriage (Hurst, 2003). In a separate national survey of Canadian young people, only a minority (23%) disapproved of same-sex marriage and even fewer (15%) said they would never vote for a gay or lesbian political candidate (Youthography Ping Survey, 2004).

HOMOPHOBIA **Homophobia** takes many forms, including

- Use of derogatory names (such as queer, faggot, and dyke).
- Telling disparaging "queer jokes."
- Barring gay people from housing, employment, or social opportunities.
- Taunting (verbal abuse).
- **Gay bashing** (physical abuse, sometimes lethal).

Although homophobia is more common among heterosexuals, gay people can also be homophobic.

Although some psychologists link homophobia to fear of a gay male or lesbian sexual orientation within oneself, homophobic attitudes may also be embedded within a cluster of stereotypical gender-role attitudes (Cotten-Huston & Waite, 2000). People who have a strong stake in maintaining stereotypical gender roles may feel more readily threatened by the existence of the gay male or lesbian sexual orientation, because gay people appear to confuse or reverse these roles. Homophobic attitudes are more common among males who identify with a traditional male gender role and a conservative political orientation (Cotten–Huston & Waite, 2000), and those who hold a fundamentalist religious orientation (Davies, 2004). But those who actually engage in violence against gay males, and especially those who kill, tend to be criminal psychopaths (Parrot et al., 2006).

A widely publicized incident of gay bashing occurred in Oshawa, Ontario, in November 2008. A lesbian mother and her female partner were physically and verbally assaulted by a man while waiting for their son outside his school.

Some homophobic men may have homoerotic impulses of which they are unaware. Denial of these impulses may be connected with their fear and disapproval of gay males. Henry Adams and his colleagues (1996) showed men sexually explicit

Homophobia A cluster of negative attitudes and feelings toward gay people, including intolerance, hatred, and fear.

Gay bashing Violence against homosexuals.

Canadian Trends

HARASSMENT OF LGBTQ YOUTH

In a national survey of Canadian youth conducted by the Ping marketing organization, 28% of those between the ages of 15 and 19 reported witnessing an act of violence or verbal abuse directed toward an LGBTQ youth (Wells, 2008).

Results from the first phase of Egale Canada's 2008 National Survey on homophobia and transphobia in Canadian schools reveal that over two-thirds of those students who self-identify as LGBTQ feel unsafe at school. Almost half have had rumours spread about them at school and close to a third have had rumours spread about them on the internet or through text messages (Egale, 2008). "Forty-one percent had been sexually harassed compared to 19 percent of those who identified as straight," said Dr. Catherine Taylor of the University of Winnipeg and the survey's principal investigator. Over a quarter reported being physically harassed, because of their orientation, and fewer than half felt comfortable talking to their parents about the issue (Eagle Canada, 2008).

Canadian and U.S. studies have also found that LGBTQ youth are more likely than heterosexual youth to have been physically and sexually abused both by family members and by people outside of the family (Saewyc et al., 2006b).

videotapes of male–female, female–female, and male–male sexual activity and measured their sexual response by means of the penile plethysmograph. (The plethysmograph measures size of erection.) Subjects were also asked to report how sexually aroused they felt in response to the videos. The men were also evaluated for their attitudes toward gay males. Men who were not homophobic were sexually aroused, according to their penile circumference, only by videos of male–female and female–female sexual activity. The homophobic viewers were also aroused in terms of penile circumference by the video of male–male sexual activity. However, the homophobic men reported that they did not feel aroused by the male–male sexual activity. Were they out of touch with their biological response or was their biological response misleading?

HETEROSEXISM Heterosexism, also known as heterosexual bias, is the tendency or assumption in society to view the world in heterosexual terms, namely, that heterosexual relationships are "normal." This perspective devalues other kinds of relationships, such as same-sex, and tends to make these other relationships invisible. For lesbians and gay males, heterosexism is often a greater concern than homophobia, because it is so pervasive in society.

SEXUAL ORIENTATION AND CANADIAN LAW The fight for legal equality by gays and lesbians has progressed considerably. The first major breakthrough came in 1969 when Parliament passed an amendment to the Criminal Code that decriminalized same-sex behaviour between consenting adults. Since then other major pieces of legislation have benefited gay males and lesbians:

- In 1995, the federal government passed the Hate Crimes Act, which imposes harsh penalties on those who assault members of minority groups such as gay males and lesbians.
- In 1996, Parliament added the words "sexual orientation" as a prohibited ground of discrimination in the Canadian Human Rights Act.
- In 2003, the House of Commons extended hate-crimes protection to gay males and lesbians.
- In 2005, the House of Commons and the Senate passed legislation to extend civil marriage rights to same-sex couples. In 2006, Stephen Harper's Conservatives reopened the issue of same-sex marriage; however, the majority of the members in the House of Commons voted against changing the 2005 law.

The national lobby group Equality for Gays and Lesbians Everywhere (EGALE) is at the forefront in fighting for equality through the legal system. Other significant advances for gay rights have come from court rulings under the Charter of Rights and Freedoms and the Canadian Human Rights Act:

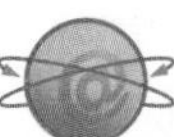

Equality for Gays and Lesbians Everywhere (Egale)
www.egale.ca

- In 1992, the Supreme Court of Canada ruled that the Canadian Armed Forces cannot discriminate against gay males and lesbians and must allow them the right to join the military.
- In 1998, the Supreme Court of Canada ordered the Alberta government to include protection for gay males and lesbians under Alberta human rights legislation.
- In 1999, the Supreme Court of Canada ruled that the province of Ontario's definition of spouse violated the Charter of Rights and Freedoms because it applied only to heterosexuals and not to gay males and lesbians.
- In 2002, when Marc Hall, a gay student in Toronto, was refused the right by the Catholic school board to take his partner to his high school prom, he went to court to appeal the board's decision. The Ontario Supreme Court judge ruled that Hall could go to the prom because the school board had violated his constitutional right to equality. (This case is discussed further in Chapter 12.)
- In 2002, the Ontario Supreme Court ruled that because the legal definition of marriage is discriminatory, it should be changed to include same-sex couples. (This is discussed further in Chapter 12.)
- In 2004, the Supreme Court of Canada ruled that Parliament has the authority to redefine marriage to include same-sex couples.
- Many provinces have allowed only a mother and a father to be registered on a birth certificate. In 2008, an Ontario court ruled that two women can be registered, and in another case, the Ontario Court of Appeal held that two women and a man could be registered.

GAY ACTIVISM During the past generation, gay people have organized effective political action to fight discrimination. In a comprehensive analysis of the history of same-sex relationships and of the gay rights movement in Canada, Gary Kinsman (1996) of Laurentian University argues that, by challenging heterosexuality as the societal norm and affirming their right to sexual self-determination, gay males and lesbians are also helping other groups achieve greater sexual freedom.

The AIDS epidemic has had a profound effect on the political agenda of gay-rights organizations. Most Canadian cities have AIDS organizations, with the largest being the AIDS committee of Toronto. These organizations combat the AIDS epidemic on several fronts:

1. They lobby for increased funding for AIDS research and treatment.
2. They educate the gay and wider communities on the dangers of high-risk sexual behaviour.
3. They encourage gay men and others to adopt safer sex practices, including the use of condoms.
4. They protect the civil rights of people with AIDS and carriers of HIV (the virus that causes AIDS) with respect to employment, housing, and medical and dental treatment.
5. They provide counselling and support services for people with HIV/AIDS.

Svend Robinson, former MP.
Svend Robinson was the first member of Canada's Parliament to openly acknowledge that he was gay.

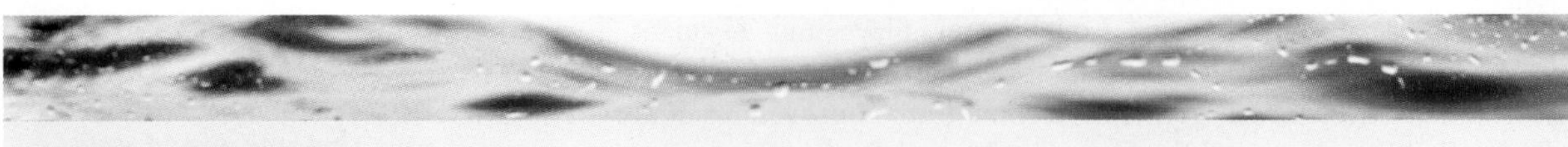

A World of Diversity

LESBIAN AND GAY MALE ACTIVISM IN TORONTO

In 1981, a large-scale police raid on Toronto bathhouses resulted in the arrest of 300 men, making it the second-largest mass arrest in Canada. The police raid shocked the lesbian and gay community, and thousands of gay men and lesbians gathered in downtown Toronto in the first major Canadian gay rights protest. Like the Stonewall riots in 1969, when the gay community in New York protested against police raids on the Stonewall gay bar, the protest was a major turning point for the development of gay rights activism in Canada.

The first Lesbian and Gay Pride Day was held in Toronto in 1981. In the early years of gay pride celebrations, many politicians did not want to be seen as supporting these events. In the mid-1980s, for example, Toronto mayor Art Eggleton refused to publicly recognize gay pride celebrations, by not proclaiming Pride Week. By the later 1980s and the 1990s, however, gay pride celebrations, especially the parade, became increasingly accepted by the public and by politicians, and in 1991 Mayor Eggleton officially proclaimed Pride Week for the first time. The events celebrating Gay Pride Day have grown enormously over the years; several hundred thousand people now attend the Toronto parade. In fact, the parade has become so mainstream that by 1998 politicians such as Toronto mayor Mel Lastman took part in it. In 2005, the Toronto police chief rode in the parade for the first time. Many large corporations sponsor the parade, and the website for Tourism Toronto features a link to gay activities in the city. Today a number of Canadian cities hold gay pride parades, including smaller cities such as Windsor and Fredericton.

But despite the many gains in human rights, the struggle continues. In 2000, for example, the lesbian community in Toronto was angered when the Toronto police raided an all-female bathhouse event entitled the "Pussy Palace." In the ensuing court case, the judge condemned the manner in which the raid had been carried out by male police officers and dismissed the charges against the two women who held the liquor licence for the event.

The mayor of Edmonton, Bill Smith, had for several years refused to proclaim Gay Pride Week. However, when the Alberta Human Rights Commission ruled against his stand in 2003, Smith relented.

STEREOTYPES AND SEXUAL BEHAVIOUR Among heterosexual people, sexual aggressiveness is linked to the masculine gender role. Sexual passivity is linked to the feminine role. Some heterosexual people assume (often erroneously) that in gay male and lesbian relationships, one partner consistently assumes the masculine role in sexual relations, and the other the feminine role.

Many gay couples, however, vary the active and passive roles. Among gay male couples, for example, roles in anal intercourse (inserter versus insertee) and in fellatio often alternate. Contrary to popular assumptions, sexual behaviour between lesbians seldom reflects distinct **butch–femme** gender roles. Most lesbians report both providing and receiving oral–genital stimulation. Typically, partners alternate roles or simultaneously perform and receive oral stimulation. Many gay people claim that the labels masculine and feminine represent only "the straight community's" efforts to pigeonhole them in terms that "straights" can understand.

What Determines Sexual Orientation?

Biological Perspectives

Biological perspectives focus on the possible roles of evolution, genetics, and hormonal influences in shaping sexual orientation.

Butch A lesbian who assumes a traditional masculine gender role.

Femme A lesbian who assumes a traditional feminine gender role.

THE EVOLUTIONARY PERSPECTIVE It might seem odd that evolutionary theorists have endeavoured to explain gay male and lesbian sexual orientations. After all, gay males and lesbians are not motivated to engage in sexual activity with members of the other sex. How, then, can these sexual orientations confer any evolutionary advantage?

To answer this question, we must look to the group or the species rather than the individual. Kirkpatrick (2000) suggests that male–male and female–female sexual behaviours derive from individual selection for reciprocal altruism. That is, strong male–male and female–female alliances have advantages for group survival in that they bind group members together emotionally. This hypothesis remains speculative.

According to evolutionary theory, heterosexual men seek younger female partners for fertility reasons. However, a recent study, comparing partner preferences between homosexual and heterosexual men in the U.S. and Canada who place internet ads, questions this assumption (Gobrogge et al., 2007). More homosexual than heterosexual men explicitly sought sexual encounters, which is a reflection of the greater acceptance of casual sex in the gay male community. However, regardless of sexual orientation, men who wanted a casual sex partner were willing to accept a wider age range of partners than men who wanted a longer-term relationship. The findings indicate that evolutionary theories need to take into account the type of desired relationship. Also, the fact that both homosexual and heterosexual men prefer someone close to their own age for a longer-term relationship suggests that reasons other than procreation, such as wanting a partner who is more socially compatible, are also important (Gobrogge et al., 2007).

GENETICS AND SEXUAL ORIENTATION Considerable evidence exists that gay male and lesbian sexual orientations run in families (Mustanskiet et al., 2005). In one study, for example, 22% of the brothers of a sample of 51 predominantly gay men were either gay or bisexual themselves. This is nearly four times the proportion expected in the general population (Pillard & Weinrich, 1986). Although such evidence is consistent with a genetic explanation, families also share a common environment.

Twin studies also shed light on the possible role of heredity (Bailey, 2003b; Kendler et al., 2000). **Monozygotic (MZ) twins**, or identical twins, develop from a single fertilized ovum and share 100% of their heredity. **Dizygotic (DZ) twins**, or fraternal twins, develop from two fertilized ova. Like other brothers and sisters, DZ twins share only 50% of their heredity. Thus, if a gay male or lesbian sexual orientation were transmitted genetically, it should be found about twice as often among identical twins of gay people as among fraternal twins. Because MZ and DZ twins who are reared together share similar environmental influences, differences in the degree of concordance for a given trait between the types of twin pairs are further indicative of genetic origins.

CONCORDANCE AGREEMENT Several studies have looked at gay men with twin brothers (Kendler et al., 2000). In one of the most carefully conducted twin studies, about 52% of identical (MZ) twin pairs were found to be "concordant" (in agreement) for a gay male sexual orientation, compared with 22% of fraternal (DZ) twins and only 11% of adoptive brothers (Bailey, 2003a). Bear in mind that MZ twins are more likely than DZ twins to be dressed alike and treated alike. Thus, their greater concordance for a gay sexual orientation may at least in part reflect environmental factors (Kendler et al., 2000).

Researchers have found evidence linking a region on the X sex chromosome to a gay male sexual orientation (Bailey et al., 1999). One group of researchers (Hamer et al., 1993) found that gay males were more likely than the general population to have gay male relatives on their mother's side of the family. Yet they did not have a greater than expected number of gay male relatives on the paternal side of the family. This pattern of inheritance is consistent with genetic traits, such as hemophilia, that are linked to the X sex chromosome, which men receive from their mothers.

The researchers then examined the X sex chromosome in 40 pairs of gay male, non-twin brothers. In 33 of the pairs, the brothers had identical DNA markers on the end tip of the X chromosome. For brothers overall in the general population, about half would be expected to have inherited this chromosomal structure. It is

Monozygotic (MZ) twins Twins who develop from the same fertilized ovum; identical twins.

Dizygotic (DZ) twins Twins who develop from different fertilized ova; fraternal twins.

Activating effects Those effects of sex hormones that influence the level of the sex drive, but not sexual orientation.

suspected, therefore, that this chromosomal region may hold a gene that predisposes men to a gay male sexual orientation.

HORMONAL INFLUENCES AND SEXUAL ORIENTATION Sex hormones strongly influence the mating behaviour of other species (Crews, 1994). Researchers have thus looked into the possible role of hormonal factors in determining sexual orientation in humans.

Testosterone is essential to male sexual differentiation. Thus, levels of testosterone and its by-products in the blood and urine have been studied as possible influences on sexual orientation. Research has failed to connect sexual orientation in either sex with differences in the levels of either male or female sex hormones in adulthood (Friedman & Downey, 1994). In adulthood, testosterone appears to have **activating effects**. That is, it affects the intensity of sexual desire, but not the preference for partners of the same or the other sex.

Sari van Anders and Elizabeth Hampson (2005) at the University of Western Ontario found that women who were not strictly heterosexual had superior spatial ability relative to heterosexual women. They suggest that the relationship between increased spatial abilities and heteroflexible sexual orientation may be affected by high levels of androgens prior to birth.

Innovative Canadian Research

BIRTH ORDER AND SEXUAL ORIENTATION

Ray Blanchard and colleagues at the Centre for Addiction and Mental Health-Clarke Institute in Toronto have conducted several studies analyzing the relationship of birth order to sexual orientation. Blanchard et al. (2002) built upon their previous findings that the odds of a man's being gay increase in proportion to the number of his older brothers. They concluded that a gay male with three or more older brothers can attribute most of the origin of his sexual orientation to that effect. They also concluded that femininity in male children tends to be predictive of homosexuality. (However, not all gay men were feminine boys.) In their 2002 study they analyzed a sample of feminine boys, who they assumed on the basis of previous research were likely to be gay, and confirmed that those who had two or more older brothers weighed less at birth than heterosexual males who had older brothers. Blanchard et al. concluded that prenatal factors increase the odds of homosexuality in later-born males. In explaining this finding, the researchers hypothesized that the process is immunologic—that anti-male antibodies are produced by the mothers in response to immunization by male fetuses—and that this could decrease the birth weight of later male fetuses as well as increase the odds of their becoming gay. In effect, this process influences aspects of sexual differentiation in the brain of the fetus.

In 2004, Blanchard analyzed data from a total of 10 143 respondents and again found that homosexuality in males was predicted by a higher number of older brothers, but not by numbers of older or younger sisters or younger brothers. This relationship between older brothers and sexual orientation has not been found among females. Similarly, Anthony Bogaert (2005b) at Brock University reported that fraternal birth order is more influential than sibling sex ratio in affecting men's sexual orientation. Blanchard and Bogaert (2004) estimate that about one in four gay men can attribute their sexual orientation to this fraternal birth order effect. In a more recent study, Bogaert (2006b) found that the effect of having older brothers only applied to genetically related brothers and not to those who had stepbrothers or adopted brothers. These findings strongly support a prenatal biological basis for sexual orientation.

Further evidence for prenatal influences is seen in the literature review by Lalumiere et al. (2000) regarding handedness and sexual orientation. Based on their review they concluded that "non right handedness" is related to homosexual orientation. More recently, Blanchard and Lippa (2007) extended this line of research by analyzing the relations among fraternal birth order, hand preference, and sexual orientation in a large British internet sample. They found that having older brothers increases the odds of being homosexual for right-handed males but not for non-right-handed males. These findings were replicated in another study (Blanchard et al., 2006), which also found that, among men with no older brothers, homosexuals are more likely to be non-right-handed than heterosexuals. They also found that, among men with one or more older brothers, homosexuals are less likely to be non-right-handed than heterosexuals.

THE STRUCTURE OF THE BRAIN AND SEXUAL ORIENTATION Researchers at the Stockholm Brain Institute (Savic & Lindstrom, 2008) have found structural differences between the brains of heterosexuals and homosexuals. These researchers used MRIs and PET scans to examine the functioning of a part of the brain called the amygdala. The researchers focused on the amygdala because it is less likely to be affected by social conditioning than other parts of the brain. Brain size was also considered, as both sides of a woman's brain are usually similar, while the right side of a man's brain is usually larger than the left side. There were 50 homosexual and 40 heterosexual participants in the study. The researchers found similarities between the brains of the gay men and the heterosexual women and between those of the lesbians and the heterosexual men. For the lesbians and heterosexual men, the right hemisphere of the brain was larger than the left. For the gay men and heterosexual women, both sides of the brain were about the same size. Also, the functioning of the amygdala was similar for the lesbians and heterosexual men and it was also similar for the gay men and heterosexual women. The findings suggest that the organization of someone's brain differs according to sexual orientation as well as by gender, thus also suggesting that biology predisposes someone to be either homosexual or heterosexual. Additional research is needed to confirm these findings.

THE FINAL WORD ON BIOLOGY Researchers in the U.S. and Canada (Mustanski, Chivers, & Bailey, 2003) conducted a comprehensive review of the research relating to the role of biology in determining sexual orientation. These researchers concluded that to some degree sexual orientation is influenced by biological factors. These factors seem to play a stronger role for men than for women. Biological factors play a key role prior to birth as indicated by the handedness research and the older brothers research, referred to above. Also, genetic factors are an important influence. Finally, brain differences between gay and heterosexual men as well as between lesbian and heterosexual women suggest biological influences.

Considerably more sophisticated research has been carried out recently and these studies further support the conclusions of Mustanski et al. (2003). If anything, they present an even stronger case for the role of biology in sexual orientation.

Psychological Perspectives

Do family relationships play a role in the origins of sexual orientation? What are the effects of childhood sexual experiences? Psychoanalytic theory and learning theory provide two of the major social–psychological approaches to understanding the origins of sexual orientation.

PSYCHOANALYTIC VIEWS Sigmund Freud, the originator of psychoanalytic theory, believed that children enter the world open to all forms of sexual stimulation. However, through proper resolution of the Oedipus complex, a boy will forsake his incestuous desires for his mother and come to identify with his father. As a result, his erotic attraction to his mother will eventually be transferred onto more appropriate female partners. A girl, through proper resolution of her Electra complex, will identify with her mother and seek erotic stimulation from men when she becomes sexually mature.

In Freud's view, a gay male or lesbian sexual orientation results from failure to resolve the Oedipus complex successfully by identifying with the parent of the same sex. In men, faulty resolution of the Oedipus complex is most likely to result from the so-called classic pattern of an emotionally "close-binding" mother and a "detached-hostile" father. A boy reared in such a family may come to identify with his mother and even to "transform himself into her" (Freud, 1922/1959, p. 40). He may thus become effeminate and develop sexual interests in men.

Freud believed that the mechanism of unresolved **castration anxiety** plays a role in a gay male sexual orientation. During the throes of the Oedipus complex,

Castration anxiety In psychoanalytic theory, a man's fear that his genitals will be removed. Castration anxiety is an element of the Oedipus complex and is implicated in the directionality of erotic interests.

Penis envy In psychoanalytic theory, the girl's wish to have a penis.

the boy unconsciously comes to fear that his father, his rival in love for the mother, will retaliate by removing the organ that the boy has come to associate with sexual pleasure. His fear causes him to repress his sexual desire for his mother and to identify with the potential aggressor—his father. The boy thus overcomes his castration anxiety and is headed along the path of adult heterosexuality. If the Oedipus complex is not successfully resolved, castration anxiety may persist. When sexually mature, the man will not be able to tolerate sex with women. Their lack of a penis will arouse unconscious castration anxiety within him. The supposed Electra complex in little girls follows a somewhat different course. Freud believed that little girls become envious of boys' penises because they lack their own. This concept of **penis envy** was one of Freud's most controversial beliefs. In Freud's view, jealousy leads little girls to resent their mothers, whom they blame for their anatomic "deficiency," and to turn from their mothers to their fathers as sexual objects. They now desire to possess the father, because the father's penis provides what they lack. But incestuous desires bring the girl into competition with her mother. Motivated by fear that her mother will withdraw her love if these desires persist, the girl normally represses them and identifies with her mother. She then develops traditional feminine interests and eventually seeks erotic stimulation from men. She supplants her childhood desire for a penis with a desire to marry a man and bear children. The baby, emitted from between her legs, serves as the ultimate penis substitute.

A nagging problem in assessing the validity of Freudian theory is that many of its concepts, such as castration anxiety and penis envy, are believed to operate at an unconscious level. As such, they lie beyond the scope of scientific observation and measurement.

LEARNING THEORIES Learning theorists agree with Freud that early experiences play an important role in the development of sexual orientation. They focus, however, on the role of reinforcement of early patterns of sexual behaviour rather than on the resolution of unconscious conflicts. People generally repeat pleasurable activities and discontinue painful ones. Thus, people may learn to engage in sexual activity with people of their own sex if childhood sexual experimentation with them is connected with sexual pleasure.

Although learning may play a role in the development of a gay male or lesbian sexual orientation, learning theorists have not identified specific learning experiences that would lead to these orientations. Moreover, most adolescent encounters with people of the same sex, even if they are pleasurable, do not lead to an adult gay male or lesbian sexual orientation. Many heterosexual people have had adolescent encounters with members of their own sex without affecting their adult orientations. This is true even of people whose early sexual interactions with the other sex were fumbling and frustrating. Moreover, the overwhelming majority of gay males and lesbians were aware of sexual interest in people of their own sex before they had sexual encounters with them, pleasurable or otherwise (Savin-Williams & Diamond, 2000).

GENDER NONCONFORMITY Gender nonconformity means not behaving in a way that is consistent with the gender-role stereotype associated with one's anatomic sex in a given culture. On average, gay males tend to be somewhat feminine and lesbians to be somewhat masculine, but there is a good deal of variation within each group (Dawood et al., 2000). Thus it seems that stereotypes of the effeminate gay male and the masculine lesbian are exaggerated. Gender nonconformity is rooted in childhood; gay males and lesbians are more likely than heterosexuals to report childhood behaviour stereotypical of the other sex (Bailey & Zucker, 1995). Many gay males and lesbians recall acting and feeling "different" from their childhood peers.

Gay males are more likely to recall feeling more sensitive than their peers during childhood (Isay, 1990). They had more artistic interests. As well, gay males are more likely than their heterosexual counterparts to have preferred "girls' toys" (Dawood et al., 2000).

According to University of British Columbia researchers, this childhood gender nonconformity found in many gay males often leads to social rejection by parents and peers (Landolt et al., 2004). This rejection is a major factor in the difficulty many gay males have in accepting their sexual orientation.

There is also evidence of masculine-typed behaviour among lesbians as children (Bailey & Zucker, 1995). Lesbians are more likely than heterosexual women to perceive themselves as having been "tomboys." They were more likely to prefer rough-and-tumble games to playing with dolls and enjoyed wearing boys' clothing rather than "cutesy" dresses.

An important study by Devendra Singh and colleagues (1999) relates gender nonconformity in lesbians to the butch–femme dimension and biological factors. The investigators compared self-identified butch and femme lesbians on various personality, behavioural, and biological measures. They found that butch lesbians were significantly more likely than femme lesbians to recall gender-atypical behavioural preferences in childhood. Butch lesbians also had higher waist-to-hip ratios and higher testosterone levels in their saliva, both of which are more typical of males. The Singh group suggests that their findings support the validity of the butch–femme distinction and that the distinction may be caused by differences in exposure to prenatal androgens (male sex hormones).

How might extreme childhood effeminacy lead to a gay male sexual orientation? Green (1987) speculates that the social detachment of these boys from male peers and role models (especially fathers) creates strong, unfulfilled cravings for male affection. This craving then leads them to seek males as partners in sex and love relationships in adolescence and adulthood.

Of course, there is another possibility, as suggested in research by J. Michael Bailey and his colleagues (Bailey et al., 2000; Dawood et al., 2000): Gender nonconformity appears to be somewhat heritable. Moreover, if a tendency toward homosexuality is inherited, gender nonconformity could well be that tendency.

Coming Out: Coming to Terms With Being Gay

Gay men and lesbians usually speak of the process of accepting their sexual orientation as "coming out" or as "coming out of the closet." Coming out is a two-pronged process: coming out to oneself (recognizing one's gay male or lesbian sexual orientation) and coming out to others (declaring one's orientation to the world). Coming out can create a sense of pride in one's sexual orientation and foster the ability to form emotionally and sexually satisfying relationships with gay male or lesbian partners.

Coming Out to Oneself

According to Ritch Savin-Williams and Lisa Diamond (2000), the development of sexual identity in gay males and lesbians involves four steps or features: attraction to members of the same sex, self-labelling as gay or lesbian, sexual contact with members of the same sex, and disclosure of one's sexual orientation to other people. The researchers by and large found a 10-year gap between initial attraction to members of one's own sex, which tended to occur at about the age of eight or nine, and disclosure of one's orientation to other people, which usually occurred at about age 18. In keeping with sex differences noted in Chapter 5, females were more likely to focus on the emotional or romantic aspects of their budding feelings. Males were more likely to focus on the sexual aspects. Males—who are generally more open than females to sexual experimentation—were likely to become involved in sexual activity with other males before they labelled themselves as gay. Females, on the other hand, were more likely to label themselves as lesbians before pursuing relationships with other females.

> Sexual orientation emerges strongly during early adolescence. Youths with emerging identities that are gay, lesbian, or bisexual, living in generally hostile climates, face particular dilemmas. They are well aware that in many secondary schools the words "fag" and "dyke" are terms of denigration and that anyone who is openly gay, lesbian, or bisexual is open to social exclusion and psychological and physical persecution. Some of their families too will express negative feelings about people who are gay, lesbian, or bisexual; youths in such families may be victimized if they disclose that they are not heterosexual (Bagley & D'Augelli, 2000).

For some people, coming to recognize and accept a gay male or lesbian sexual orientation involves gradually stripping away layers of denial. For others it may be a sudden awakening. Alberta professors Kevin Alderson and Ronna Jevne (2003) have explored the psychic conflict that is involved in the coming out process and have conceptualized this as a struggle between catalysts that push gay males to acknowledge their sexual orientation and hindrances that block the acceptance of their identity. They identify the major catalyst as developing an increased awareness of being gay and gay culture and the major hindrance as fear and condemnation of homosexuals. Alderson and Jevne believe that a person will self-identify as gay only when the catalysts overpower the hindrances.

Alderson (2003) is highly critical of fixed-stage models of gay identity acquisition, such as those proposed by Savin-Williams and Diamond (2000), which assume that all people coming out go through a series of well-defined stages. He charges that they fail to take into account environmental influences.

Applied Knowledge

SUPPORT PROGRAMS FOR LESBIANS AND GAY MALES

Some cities offer support and counselling for gay males and lesbians through programs such as the Sexual Orientation and Youth Project of Central Toronto Youth Services. Telephone hotline services also provide information to gay, lesbian, and bisexual youth. The supportive contact with other lesbians and gay youth provided by these kinds of services is an important factor in helping young people to accept their sexual orientation. For those who struggle with the process of coming out, the internet provides valuable information and access to resources.

Some school boards have included discussion of sexual orientation in their school curricula. In 1992, the Toronto Board of Education approved the first Canadian high school curriculum guide on the topics of homosexuality and homophobia (Barrett et al., 1997). Since then many school boards and teachers' associations in Canada have adopted policies and programs designed to reduce homophobia and make schools safer and more accepting places for gay and lesbian youth. Education faculty and students at the University of Alberta have played a major role in initiating these policies and programs. In particular, they have encouraged the development of gay-straight student alliances.

The Toronto School Board has developed a Triangle program for lesbian, gay, bisexual, and transgender (LGBT) students. This innovative program offers Canada's only classroom for LGBT students. The internet also plays an important role in introducing LGBT students to various resources and support groups.

Applied Knowledge

COUNSELLING GAY MALES AND LESBIANS

Karine Blais and colleagues (2004) at the University of Montreal have outlined some key issues relating to sexual orientation about which therapists need to be knowledgeable. These include

- homophobia
- HIV
- the lack of conjugal role models
- the "coming out" process

However, it is also important for therapists to recognize that gay and lesbian couples face many of the issues faced by heterosexual couples. The Toronto Centre for Addictions and Mental Health has prepared a handbook, *Asking the Right Questions*, to guide therapists who counsel gay and lesbian clients.

Alderson (2003) has developed an ecological model of gay male identity that incorporates both external (social and environmental) and internal psychological influences that lead to a gay self-definition. In his model, cognitive dissonance about being gay plays a key role in the movement toward identity development. Alderson believes that his ecological model provides clinicians with a useful framework for counselling gay males and in particular helping those who are questioning their sexual identities.

In a survey of 14 Canadian universities, Alderson (2003) also found that graduate students in clinical psychology and counselling received little training on issues facing lesbians, gays, and bisexuals. Graduates of these programs feel that they are not prepared to work with sexual minority clients.

Recognition of a gay sexual orientation may be only the first step in a lifelong process of sexual identity formation. Acceptance of being gay becomes part of one's self-definition (Isay, 1990). The term *gay identity*, or *homosexual identity*, refers to the subjective sense of being gay.

Coming out to one's parents can be a scary thing, and many lesbians and gay males avoid it for years, or even for a lifetime.

Coming Out to Others

There are different patterns of coming out to others. Coming out occasionally means making an open declaration to the world. Some individuals inform only one or a few select people. Others may tell friends but not family members.

In Ontario, Brock University researchers Anthony Bogaert and Luanne Jamieson (2008) analyzed several factors to determine which ones might predict the age of coming out among gay and bisexual men. The researchers found that attractive men and those who believed in a just world were more likely to come out at a younger age. Those who had more feminine behavioural traits in childhood tended to delay coming out.

Many gay men and lesbians remain reluctant to declare their sexual orientation, even to friends and family. Disclosure is fraught with the risk of loss of jobs, friendships, and social standing (Bagley & D'Augelli, 2000). Gay men and lesbians often anticipate that family members will have negative reactions, including denial, anger, and rejection (Bagley & D'Augelli, 2000).

Parents and Friends of Lesbians and Gays (Canada)
Promotes the health and well-being of gay, lesbian, bisexual, and transgendered persons and their families and friends through support and education.

www.pflag.ca

Parents, children, neighbours, and friends of lesbians deny, or compartmentalize, or struggle with their knowledge in the same way the women themselves do.

> My parents know I've lived with my partner for six years. She goes home with me. We sleep in the same bed there. The word *lesbian* has never been mentioned. I told my mother and she said, "Well, now that's over with. We don't need to mention it again." She never has, and that was ten years ago. I don't know if she ever told my father. (Barrett, 1990, p. 52)

Some families are more accepting. They may in fact have had suspicions and prepared themselves for such news. Then, too, many families are initially rejecting but often eventually come to at least grudging acceptance that a family member is gay.

Dave Vervoort (1999), a University of Guelph graduate student, conducted an online survey of gay fathers, almost all of whom lived in Canada or the U.S. Most of the fathers had their children living with them or had joint custody. In coming out to their children about their sexual orientation, the fathers reported that the response was generally more positive than anticipated. Only about 10% of the children were clearly upset about the disclosure. Older children were more negative. However, over time even many of these children became more positive in their acceptance of their father's gay status.

Another University of Guelph graduate student, Daniel Mahoney (1994), interviewed parents who belong to the support group Parents, Friends and Family of Lesbians and Gays (PFLAG) to discover how they reacted when they found out their children were gay or lesbian. All the parents reported that their initial reactions were highly emotional, involving "shock, denial, guilt and shame." Each felt that he or she now had to deal with the new identity of being a parent of a lesbian or gay child. However, all the parents in the study felt that it was essential to accept their son's or daughter's sexual orientation, since they feared that otherwise they might lose their child. Acceptance was a way of expressing their unconditional love. Of course, some parents are not as accepting as those included in Mahoney's study.

Patricia Vanderheyden (2005), a therapist in London, Ontario, produced a video, *Diary of a Lipstick Lesbian*, which documents the coming-out process and is based on personal interviews. (She may be contacted at p.vanderheyden@rogers.com.)

Adjustment of Gay Males and Lesbians

Carefully controlled studies have found that gay males and lesbians are more likely than heterosexuals to experience feelings of anxiety and depression and that they are more prone to suicide (Bagley & D'Augelli, 2000; Savin-Williams, 2001).

In a large-scale British Columbia study of students in grades 7 to 12, gay males, lesbians, and bisexuals had much higher rates of psychological and social difficulties than did heterosexual females and males (The McCreary Centre Society, 2007). For example, compared to heterosexual youth, LGB youth:

- Were more likely to have experienced physical and sexual abuse, harassment in school, and discrimination in the community.
- Were more likely to have run away from home once or more in the past year.
- Were more likely to be sexually experienced, and more likely either to have been pregnant or to have gotten someone pregnant.
- Were more likely to have reported emotional stress, suicidal thoughts, and suicide attempts.
- Were less likely to participate in sports and physical activity, and reported higher levels of spending time on the computer.

- Felt less cared about by parents and less connected to their families than heterosexual teens, and for lesbian and bisexual females, less connected to school.
- Who reported high family and school connectedness had a much lower probability of suicide attempts than that for bisexual teens with lower connectedness, even when they were strongly at risk of committing suicide, because of, for example, a history of sexual abuse and symptoms of emotional distress.

A key reason for adjustment problems among gays and lesbians is the stress of societal oppression and rejection. Lesbian, gay, and bisexual youth are less likely to have supportive family and school environments than heterosexual youth have (Saewyc, 2006a). For some, adjustment is related to conflict over their sexual orientation (Simonsen et al., 2000). Yet it is important to acknowledge that many gay males and lesbians are well adjusted. Those who accept their sexual orientation and, in particular, those who are openly gay are more likely to be well adjusted.

Most gay males and lesbians who share close relationships with their partners are satisfied with the quality of their relationships. Researchers have found that heterosexual and gay couples report similar levels of satisfaction with their relationships (Kurdek, 2005). Gay males and lesbians in enduring relationships generally report high levels of love, attachment, closeness, caring, and intimacy.

Differences in Sexual Relationships Between Gay Males and Lesbians

Researchers have consistently found that gay males are more likely than lesbians to engage in casual sex with many partners. Lesbians more often confine their sexual activity to a committed, affectionate relationship. These differences parallel those found for heterosexuals. As discussed in Chapter 5, heterosexual men are more likely than heterosexual women to report engaging in casual sex and to report having sex with more partners.

University of Guelph graduate student Melanie Beres conducted an internet study of men who have sex with men (MSM) and women who have sex with women (WSW). The study participants were located mainly through university websites, and most lived in Canada and the United States. Beres et al. (2004) found that the number of partners was much higher for the men, with 32% of the MSM having

Applied Knowledge

INCREASING RESILIENCE AMONG LGBTQ YOUTH

Kristopher Wells (2008), in reviewing studies of the social adjustment of LGBTQ youth, concludes that the following protective factors are crucial in providing a social environment that will result in greater resiliency and consequently fewer adjustment problems:

- Positive representations of LGBTQ people in the media and in the classroom.
- Family acceptance and support.
- School support programs, including gay-straight alliances.
- School policies that explicitly prohibit discrimination on the grounds of sexual orientation.
- Support networks of other LGBTQ youth.
- Inclusive nonjudgmental sexual health education that challenges negative stereotypes associated with specific sexual identities.

Innovative Canadian Research

RELATIONSHIP INNOVATION IN GAY MALE RELATIONSHIPS

Barry Adam (2006), of the University of Windsor, interviewed 70 gay men in Toronto who were in coupled relationships regarding their management of sexual inclusivity. Monogamy was most common among younger men and/or men newly involved in gay relationships. Also, monogamy was more accepted among men from cultural settings where they were not exposed to, or had limited exposure to, autonomous gay scenes such as gay bars. However, the majority of these couples were involved in sexually open relationships that allowed for sexual experiences with other men. These couples wanted to have the emotional security of a committed love relationship and at the same time be able to experience sexual pleasure with other men. To achieve this, couples agreed that their couple relationship was the primary or most important one, and they negotiated rules for having sex with others. Sexual exclusivity was typically practised during the first two years of the relationship. This allowed for the development of mutual trust in the relationship. Some couples were monogamous for longer periods, but for most monogamy was a passing phase of their relationship. Adam notes that his sample consisted of men who were in successful relationships, but that there are many other gay men engaging in casual sex who wish that they could develop a deeply emotional relationship with another man.

had 22 or more partners, compared with only 2% of the WSW. And 80% of the WSW reported six or fewer partners, compared with only 31% of the MSM. In the survey of gay and bisexual men in Ontario (Myers et al., 2004), only 24% reported having had sex with just one partner the previous year, while 10% had sex with 30 or more partners.

In the same survey, respondents were asked where they had looked for sex with men during the previous year (Myers et al., 2004). By far the most common place was a gay bar (60%) and the next most common places included the internet (35%) and bathhouses (31%). In an Ontario study of bathhouse culture (Haubrich et al., 2004), gay men were asked their reasons for going to a bathhouse. Most stated that the predominant reason was for sexual release in an environment that they considered personally safe. They did not expect to develop a relationship with someone they met there.

In another bathhouse study, Ontario researchers (Holmes et al., 2007) focused on how the architecture and design of three gay men's bathhouses in two different cities promoted conditions for heightening sexual desire and pleasure while facilitating casual sex encounters. Each of the bathhouses had lounges, saunas, steam rooms, and showers where men could meet and talk with other patrons and bathhouse staff. However, most men at the bathhouses did not engage in verbal conversation. Rather, communication was mainly through body language which would indicate if they were interested in having sex and what kinds of sexual activity they wished to engage in. Each bathhouse also had private rooms with beds and dark rooms where the men could not see each other. Gay pornographic videos were shown in the public areas and/or in the private rooms. Finally, each facility had "glory holes"—small holes cut into adjacent walls at waist level allowing a man to insert his genitals into the adjacent room. The rest of his body would be hidden from the person in the adjacent room, thus facilitating completely anonymous sex.

Bathhouses typically provide free condoms and advertisements providing information about, and encouraging, safer sex practices. Additionally, members of AIDS organizations regularly visit bathhouses to provide counselling about safer sex. Accordingly, Holmes et al. (2007) argue that bathhouses are safer venues for casual sex than other locations such as parks, washrooms, etc.

Bathhouses for casual sex have traditionally not been a part of lesbian culture. However, for some lesbians this appears to be changing. A few times a year, a group of lesbians and bisexual women rent a gay men's bathhouse in Toronto to engage in casual sex with other women. (This was discussed in Chapter 5.)

In an earlier Canadian survey, 57% of gay men said they attended gay bars at least once a week while only 7% said they went to bathhouses that often (Myers et al., 1993). In the study by Beres (2002), three-quarters of both MSM and WSW in Canada and the U.S. met partners through friends. The MSM (65%) were also more likely than the WSW (29%) to use the internet to find partners.

Despite the advent of AIDS, some gay men, like some heterosexual people, continue high-risk behaviour. For example, they engage in unprotected anal intercourse and sexual activity with multiple partners. Montreal researchers (Engler et al., 2005) found that bisexual men in Quebec who had sex with both men and women were less likely to wear a condom when engaging in anal intercourse with a male.

Another Canadian survey of gay and bisexual men found that, of the men who had engaged in anal intercourse during the previous three months, 23% had not used a condom each time (Myers et al., 1993). Since the early 1990s, it seems that the level of sexual risk-taking has increased. In the Ontario study (Myers et al., 2004), 40% of the men who had engaged in anal sex in the previous three months had not used a condom each time. When asked why they hadn't used a condom the last time they had unprotected anal intercourse, half of the men said they were having sex with a regular partner. About one-quarter said they were HIV-negative, the sex was too exciting to put on a condom, or putting on a condom makes them lose their erection.

An international study of lesbian, gay, and bisexual youth in Canada, New Zealand, and the U.S. found that those who had experienced being stigmatized because of their sexual orientation were more likely to engage in HIV risky sexual behaviours (Meininger et al., 2007). The findings indicate that helping sexual minority youth to deal with stigmatization could help to lower sexual risk-taking among this population.

In a British Columbia study, gay/lesbian and bisexual youth were also more likely to engage in HIV risky behaviour than were heterosexuals (Saewyc et al., 2006b). In each sexual orientation group, those who had experienced sexual abuse had higher risk scores. The findings indicate that because sexual minority youth experience greater sexual abuse, they are more likely to engage in risky sexual behaviour than heterosexual youth.

A study of gay men in Ontario (Calzavara et al., 2003) found that half were not putting on condoms when engaging in anal sex until they were about to ejaculate. These men are at risk of HIV infection because the human immunodeficiency virus can be present in pre-ejaculatory fluid. In fact, the study found that those men who delayed putting on the condom until just before they ejaculated were six times as likely to become infected with HIV as those who put them on early (Calzavara et al., 2003). These findings clearly demonstrate the importance of applying a condom prior to anal penetration.

In a study of older gay males in Toronto, some of the men felt that when they had sex with a younger man they would not insist that he use a condom (Murray & Adam, 2001). Because the older men perceived themselves as less desirable, they felt they had to go along with whatever the younger man desired. As well, many older men find that wearing a condom makes it more difficult to get and keep an erection.

Three-fourths of the respondents in the Ontario survey had been tested for the HIV antibody. The Ontario study was the first major survey conducted in the gay community to determine the rate of HIV infection based on obtaining a biological specimen. Among the 77% of men who provided a saliva specimen, 6% tested HIV-positive. Of those who tested HIV-positive, about one-quarter either did not know their HIV status or chose not to disclose it in this study (Myers et al., 2004).

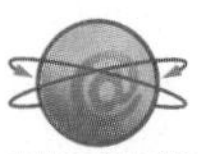

The Advocate
This magazine for gay males and lesbians contains up-to-date news, profiles of notable people (gay and straight), reviews of media events, and articles about the adjustment of gay males and lesbians.
www.advocate.com

Gay Lifestyles

One of the mistakes that laypeople (and some researchers) make is to treat gay people as though they are all the same. Variations in sexual expression exist within and across sexual orientations. Descriptions of gay and heterosexual lifestyles must consider individual differences.

University of Lethbridge researchers Doug VanderLaan and Paul Vasey (2008) compared homosexual and heterosexual couples regarding strategies they used to "retain their mates" in the relationship. They found that in a number of aspects the gay males and heterosexual males were typical of their sex, whereas homosexual females were less so. For example, homosexual women and both homosexual and heterosexual men were not as concerned about the economic status of their partners as were heterosexual women. Also, heterosexual women were the most concerned of the three groups about their physical appearance. Heterosexual women were also the most likely to be concerned about a partner spending time away and were most likely to threaten to end the relationship if the partner were to have sex with someone else. Heterosexual men were more likely than homosexual men or homosexual women to threaten to end the relationship because of infidelity. However, homosexual men were more likely to denigrate potential competitors to their relationship than were heterosexual women.

Gay men and lesbians in larger urban centres can usually look to gay communal structures to provide services and support. These include gay-rights organizations and gay-oriented newspapers, magazines, bookstores, housing cooperatives, medical services, and other support services. The gay community provides a sense of acceptance and belonging that gay people do not typically find in society at large.

Not all gay people, however, feel that they are a part of the "gay community" or participate in gay rights organizations. For many, their sexual orientation is a part of their identity but not a dominant theme that governs their social and political activities. Homosexuals, like heterosexuals, have many different styles of life. Things are no simpler in the gay world than in the straight world.

In closing this chapter on sexual orientation, we wish to acknowledge a study of human sexuality textbooks including this one that contained a chapter devoted to sexual orientation. The researchers—Glenn Meaney of Wilfrid Laurier University and B. J. Rye of the University of Waterloo (2008)—concluded that each of the textbooks provided adequate and accurate information about homosexuality and promoted more positive attitudes toward homosexuals.

Summing Up

Sexual orientation describes the directionality of one's sexual and romantic interests—toward members of the same sex, members of the other sex, or both. Gay male and lesbian sexual orientations denote sexual and romantic interest in members of one's own sex.

Gay males and lesbians have a gender identity that is consistent with their chromosomal and anatomic sex.

Kinsey and his colleagues found evidence of degrees of homosexuality and heterosexuality, with bisexuality representing a midpoint between the two.

Bisexual people are attracted to both males and females.

Throughout much of Western history, gay people have been deemed sinful and criminal.

Male–male sexual behaviour is practised by at least some members of many preliterate societies.

Many animals engage in behaviours that resemble male–male and female–female contacts among humans, but we must be cautious in ascribing motives to animals.

Attitudes toward gay people have shifted, though homophobia persists. The majority of Canadians now approve of same-sex relationships.

Evidence of a genetic contribution to sexual orientation is accumulating. Prenatal sex hormones may also play a role in determining sexual orientation in humans.

Psychoanalytic theory connects sexual orientation with unconscious castration anxiety and improper resolution of the Oedipus complex. Learning theorists focus on the role of reinforcement of early patterns of sexual behaviour.

Coming out is a two-pronged process: coming out to oneself and coming out to others.

Many gay males and lesbians fear rejection if they disclose their sexual orientation. Some families struggle with the knowledge; others are more accepting.

Evidence has failed to show that gay males, lesbians, and bisexuals are more emotionally unstable or more subject to psychiatric disorders than heterosexual people are.

Gay males are more likely than lesbians to engage in casual sex with many partners. Lesbians more often confine sexual activity to a committed, affectionate relationship.

Gay people do not adopt a single, stereotypical lifestyle.

Test Yourself

Multiple-Choice Questions

1. **Sexual orientation is**
   a. completely genetically determined
   b. fixed and unchanging
   c. an excellent predictor of sexual behaviour
   d. not necessarily a good predictor of sexual behaviour

2. **Gay people**
   a. always wish they were the other sex
   b. have a gender identity consistent with their anatomical sex
   c. often wish they were the other sex
   d. always behave like the other sex in childhood

3. **According to Statistics Canada, more men than women report that they are ________________ and more women than men report that they are ________________.**
   a. bisexual; homosexual
   b. homosexual; bisexual
   c. homosexual; asexual
   d. asexual; homosexual

4. **Psychologist Michael Storms suggests that**
   a. heterosexuality and homosexuality are at opposite ends of a continuum of sexual orientation
   b. asexuality is a completely separate dimension
   c. homosexuality and heterosexuality are separate and independent dimensions
   d. bisexual individuals are at the midpoint of the continuum between heterosexuality and homosexuality

5. **In preliterate societies, sexual activity between males may be limited to men who are**
   a. uneducated
   b. being initiated into manhood
   c. outcasts
   d. unable to find an appropriate bride

6. **A 2003 poll of adult Canadians found that ________________ favoured same-sex marriages.**
   a. 21%
   b. 41%
   c. 61%
   d. 81%

7. **Which of the following most accurately explains how a learning theorist would explain a homosexual orientation?**
   a. A young child has a pleasurable same-sex experience.
   b. A child is exposed to gay and lesbian issues in a sexuality class at school.
   c. A young adult goes to a gay pride parade and experiments with a gay lifestyle.
   d. A young teenager reads about homosexuality, which then influences him to become gay himself.

8. **Strongly held negative attitudes toward homosexuality are referred to as**
   a. homeopathy
   b. homophilia
   c. homophobia
   d. homoerotic

9. **Traditional Western religions are most likely to condemn homosexuality as "unnatural" because**
   a. homosexuality is closely associated with Eastern religions
   b. homosexuality does not lead directly to procreation
   c. homosexuals seduce children
   d. homosexual couples corrupt heterosexual couples

10. **Doug VanderLaan and Paul Vasey, in comparing homosexual and heterosexual couples, found that ________________ were most likely to be concerned about the economic status of their partner.**
    a. heterosexual women
    b. gay men
    c. lesbians
    d. heterosexual men

Answers to the Test Yourself questions in each chapter are found on page 509.

Critical Thinking Questions

1. What messages did you receive about homosexuality from your parents? Were they positive or negative? Did you receive different messages from your friends?
2. Why do you think men tend to be more homophobic than women?
3. People who believe that sexual orientation is biological tend to be more tolerant of homosexuality than those who do not. How would you explain this?
4. If you are a gay male or a lesbian, have you come out to your family? Your friends? If so, how did you find the experience? If not, why not?
5. If you are heterosexual, has a close friend or family member ever come out to you, telling you that they are gay or lesbian? What was your initial reaction? Why do you think you reacted this way?

Visit MyPsychKit at www.mypsychkit.com, where you can do quizzes and link to additional resources on topics discussed in this text.

CHAPTER TEN

Conception, Pregnancy, and Childbirth

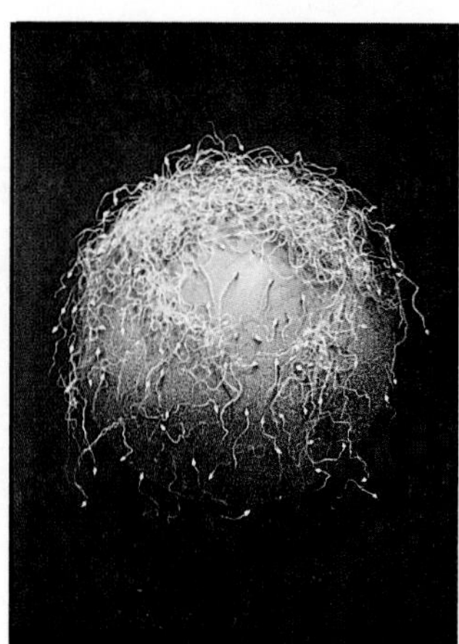

Figure 10.1 Human Sperm Swarming Around an Ovum in a Fallopian Tube.

Fertilization normally occurs in a fallopian tube, not in the uterus.

When Elaine had used her ovulation-timing kit the previous morning, it showed that she was about to ovulate. So later that night, Elaine and Dennis had made love, hoping that Elaine would conceive. Dennis ejaculated hundreds of millions of sperm within Elaine's vagina. Only a few thousand survived the journey through the cervix and uterus to the fallopian tube that contained the ovum, released just hours earlier (Figure 10.1). Of these, a few hundred remained to bombard the ovum. One succeeded in penetrating the ovum's covering, resulting in conception.

Conception

Conception is the union of a sperm cell and an ovum. On the one hand, conception is the beginning of a new human life. On the other hand, conception is the end of a fantastic voyage, in which a viable ovum—one of only several hundred that will mature and ripen during a woman's lifetime—unites with one of several hundred *million* sperm produced by a man in the average ejaculate.

Ova carry X sex chromosomes. Sperm carry either X or Y sex chromosomes. Girls are conceived from the union of an ovum and an X-bearing sperm, boys from the union of an ovum and a Y-bearing sperm. The 200 to 400 million sperm in an average ejaculation may seem excessive, given that only one can fertilize an egg. Only 1 in 1000 will ever arrive in the vicinity of an ovum, however. Millions deposited in the vagina simply flow out of the woman's body because of gravity, unless she remains prone for quite some time. Normal vaginal acidity kills many more. Many surviving sperm swim (against the current of fluid coming from the cervix) through the os and into the uterus. Surviving sperm may reach the fallopian tubes 60 to 90 minutes after ejaculation. About half the sperm end up in the wrong tube—that is, the one that does not contain the egg. Perhaps some 2000 sperm find their way into the right tube. Fewer still manage to swim the final 5 cm (2 in.) against the currents generated by the cilia that line the tube.

The journey of sperm may be blind but not random. Ova secrete a chemical that attracts sperm. Because sperm cells have odour receptors, it is thus conceivable (pardon the pun) that sperm are attracted to ova through a variation of the sense of smell.

Innovative Canadian Research

LIFE AFTER TEENAGE MOTHERHOOD

Teenage motherhood has generally been associated with negative and long-term socioeconomic consequences for women, but it does not necessarily condemn them to a life in low income, according to a new study.

The study, Life After Teenage Motherhood, published in *Perspectives on Labour and Income*, used the Survey of Labour and Income Dynamics to examine the personal and long-term socioeconomic characteristics of women aged 30 to 39 who gave birth as teenagers.

Specifically, it compared women who were teen moms with those who were adult mothers on the basis of educational outcome, long-term labour force participation, and low-income status.

Overall, teenage mothers in Canada had a lower probability than their adult counterparts of completing high school and post-secondary education, even after controlling for family background and other characteristics.

But the study also found that education may help counter the negative impact that being a teen mother had on labour force participation and low-income status.

Overall, women with similar education levels, regardless of when they had their first child, also had a similar likelihood of being in full-year, full-time employment.

Teen moms and adult mothers with less than high school education were both less likely to be working in a full-time job for the full year.

On the other hand, teenage mothers who completed postsecondary studies were actually more likely than their adult counterparts to work full-time.

The study found similar results for the probability of living at a low income. One-fifth (21%) of families of women who were teenage mothers had income below Statistics Canada's low-income measure (LIM) compared with just 12% of adult mother families.

But education made a big difference. Teenage moms and adult mothers who both had less than high school were more likely to be living below the LIM than adult mothers with a high school diploma.

Likewise, women who were teenage mothers and adult mothers who had completed postsecondary studies were less likely to fall below the LIM.

The study suggested that other unobserved characteristics—such as family support, social network and a variety of other resources, psychological traits, and other factors—may also influence socioeconomic outcomes.

Family background remains an influence even in the long run. Women whose mothers finished high school or postsecondary studies were five percentage points more likely to work full-year, full-time than women whose mothers had less than high school.

About half of teenage mothers married in their teens, compared with only 8% of adult mothers. But only 20% of teenage mothers were married prior to the birth of their first child, compared with 72% of adult mothers. Teenage mothers were more likely to live in common-law relationships, but they were still more likely to separate or divorce. Furthermore, teenage mothers were almost three times more likely to report marrying more than once.

Source: Statistics Canada. (2008x). The Daily, *May 23, Study: Life After Teenage Motherhood. [online]. Available:* ***www.statcan.ca/Daily/English/080523/d080523c.htm***

Fertilization normally occurs in a fallopian tube. (Figure 10.1 shows sperm swarming around an egg in a fallopian tube.) Ova contain chromosomes, proteins, fats, and nutritious fluid and are surrounded by a gelatinous layer called the **zona pellucida**. This layer must be penetrated if fertilization is to occur. Sperm that have completed their journey secrete the enzyme **hyaluronidase**, which briefly thins the zona pellucida, enabling one sperm to penetrate. Once a sperm has entered, the zona pellucida thickens, locking other sperm out. The corresponding chromosomes in the sperm and ovum line up opposite each other. Conception occurs as the chromosomes from the sperm and ovum combine to form 23 new pairs, which carry a unique set of genetic instructions.

Zona pellucida A gelatinous layer that surrounds an ovum.

Hyaluronidase An enzyme that briefly thins the zona pellucida, enabling one sperm to penetrate.

TEENAGE PREGNANCY Fertility rates have been declining among teenage girls almost steadily since 1991. In 2004, there were 31 611 teenage pregnancies in Canada, which represented 4.2% of total births. Canada's birth rate among teenagers of 13.6 for every 1000 teenage girls in 2004 remained far below the birth rate of 41.1 for every 1000 teenage girls in the United States.

However, it was still almost seven times higher than the rate in Sweden, which has one of the lowest teenage birth rates of all developed countries (Statistics Canada, 2008c).

About half of teenage pregnancies end in an abortion. Of those teenagers who go to term, about four-fifths choose to keep their babies (Maticka-Tyndale et al., 2001). Researchers in Nova Scotia have determined that a number of community and familial factors—such as single-parent families, lower levels of education, and low levels of church attendance—increase the possibility of teenage pregnancy occurring. Higher rates of teen pregnancy also occur in communities with higher proportions of First Nations and black people (Langille, Flowerdew, & Andreou, 2004).

More attention has been focused on teenage mothers, but young fathers bear an equal responsibility for teenage pregnancies. A U.S. survey based on a nationally representative sample of 1880 young men aged 15 through 19 showed that socio-economically disadvantaged young men in particular appeared to view paternity as a source of self-esteem and were consequently more likely than more affluent young men to say that fathering a child would make them feel like a real man and that they would be pleased—or at least not as upset—with an unplanned pregnancy (Marsiglio, 1993a). Thus, poor young men were less likely to have used an effective contraceptive method during their most recent sexual experience.

SEXUAL ORIENTATION AND TEENAGE PREGNANCY A study of 74 000 teenagers in British Columbia led by Elizabeth Saewyc (2007) at the University of British Columbia found that pregnancy rates are higher among sexually active gay, lesbian, and bisexual teenagers than among heterosexual teenagers (see Table 10.1). According to Saewyc, many gay and lesbian youth, fearing stigmatization because of

Preventing Teenage Pregnancy. Even with the recent decline in the rate of pregnancy among teenagers, several thousand Canadian girls become pregnant each year.

TABLE 10.1

Sexual Orientation and Pregnancy Rates Among Sexually Active Teenagers in British Columbia

Sexual Orientation	Males*	Females
Gay	17%	
Lesbian		13%
Bisexual	17%	9%
Heterosexual	5%	5%

*Note: Male percentages refer to teenage males who had a heterosexual partner who became pregnant.

Source: Saewyc, E. M., Poon, C., Wang, N., Homma, Y., Smith, A., & the McCreary Centre Society. (2007). Not yet equal: The health of lesbian, gay & bisexual youth in BC. *Vancouver, BC: McCreary Centre Society.*

Canadian Trends

BIRTH TRENDS

Birth rates in Canada have varied considerably over time. Following the Second World War, the Canadian birth rate dramatically rose to its highest level since the previous high in 1921. In 1947, Canada's fertility rate was 3.6 children per woman. In the mid-1960s, along with the introduction of the birth control pill, the number of births dropped sharply and reached an all-time low in 2000. Since then, the number of births has increased, mainly because of the increase in the birth rate among women 30 years of age and older. The average age at which women have their first baby has climbed from 25.9 in 1980 to 29.2 in 2005. Women aged 30 to 34 have the highest proportion of births (Statistics Canada, 2007b).

Nevertheless the number of births is below the level needed to replace the population (an average of 2.1 children per woman). Canadian women have an average of 1.54 children. As shown in Figure 10.2, the lowest birth rates are in Newfoundland and Labrador and the highest are in Nunavut and the Northwest Territories (Statistics Canada, 2007c.)

The provinces and territories with the highest birth rates also have the largest proportion of First Nations people. Birth rates of First Nations people are much higher than those of the general population.

Why is the birth rate so low? Why are women giving birth later in life? There are a number of reasons:

- Women are marrying later.
- More women are completing higher education.
- Women are entering the workforce later.
- Changing values emphasize individual happiness and career achievement rather than having children.
- Material possessions are more socially valued at the same time as the cost of raising children is rising.

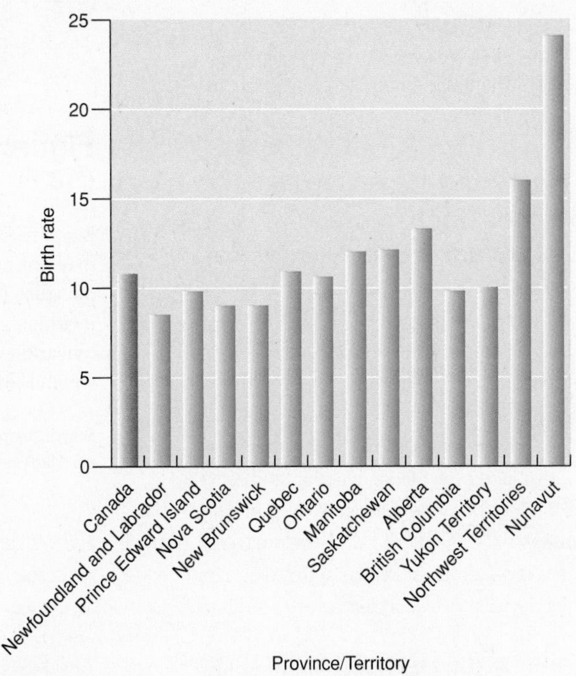

Figure 10.2 Canadian Birth Rates by Province and Territory (2006/2007).

Note: From July 1 of one year to June 30 of the next year.

Source: Statistics Canada, CANSIM, tables (for fee) 051-0001 and 051-0004, and Catalogue no. 91-213-X.

Applied Knowledge

OPTIMIZING THE CHANCES OF CONCEPTION

Some couples may wish to optimize their chances of conceiving during a particular month so that birth occurs at a desired time. Others may have difficulty conceiving and wish to maximize their chances for a few months before consulting a fertility specialist. Some fairly simple procedures can dramatically increase the chances of conceiving for couples without serious fertility problems.

The ovum can be fertilized for about 4 to 20 hours after ovulation (Wilcox et al., 2000). Sperm are most active within 48 hours after ejaculation. So one way of optimizing the chances of conception is to engage in coitus within a few hours of ovulation. There are a number of ways to predict ovulation.

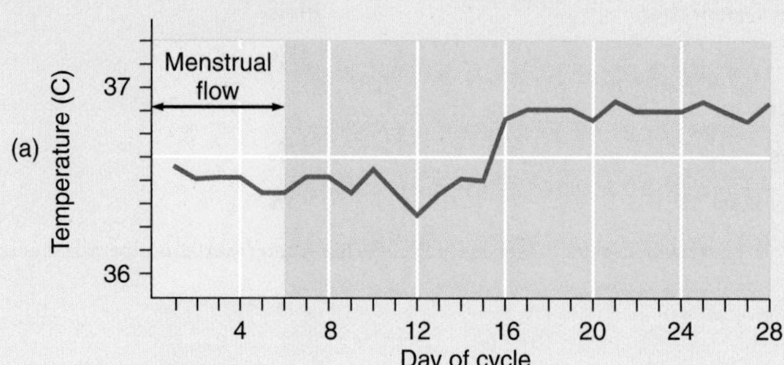

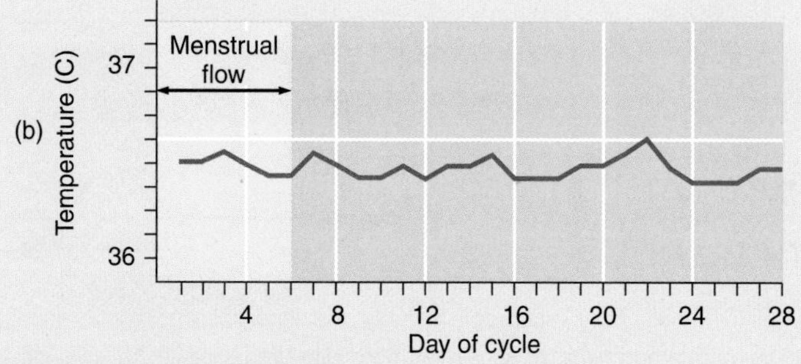

Figure 10.3 A Basal Body Temperature (BBT) Chart.

Because most women have somewhat irregular menstrual cycles, they may not be able to predict ovulation perfectly. The basal body temperature (BBT) chart helps them to do so. Part (a) represents a cycle in which a sustained elevation in temperature occurred following ovulation on day 15. Part (b) shows no substantial temperature rise, which is indicative of an absence of ovulation in this cycle.

Source: Adapted from R.C. Kolodny, W.H. Masters, and V.E. Johnson. Textbooks of Sexual Medicine.

Using the Basal Body Temperature Chart

Few women have perfectly regular cycles, so they can only guess when they are ovulating (Wilcox et al., 2000). A basal body temperature (BBT) chart (Figure 10.3) may help provide a more reliable estimate.

As shown in Figure 10.3, body temperature is fairly even before ovulation, and early-morning body temperature is generally below 37°C (98.6°F). But just before ovulation, basal temperature dips slightly. Then, on the day after ovulation, temperature tends to rise by about 0.2°C to 0.4°C (0.4°F to 0.8°F) and to remain higher until menstruation. In using the BBT method, a woman attempts to detect these temperature changes by tracking her temperature just after awakening each morning but before rising from bed. Thermometers that provide finely graded readings, such as electronic digital thermometers, are best suited for determining these minor changes. The couple records the woman's temperature and the day of the cycle (as well as the day of the month) and indicates whether they have engaged in coitus. With regular charting for six months, the woman may learn to predict the day of ovulation more accurately—assuming that her cycles are fairly regular.

Opinion is divided as to whether it is better for couples to have coitus every 24 hours or every 36 to 48 hours for the several-day period during which ovulation is expected. More frequent coitus around the time of ovulation gives more chances for conception. Less frequent coitus (that is, every 36 to 48 hours) leads to a higher sperm count during each ejaculation. Most fertility specialists recommend that couples seeking to conceive a baby have intercourse once every day or two during the week in which the woman expects to ovulate. However, men with lower than normal sperm counts may be advised to wait 48 hours between ejaculations.

Analyzing Urine or Saliva for Luteinizing Hormone

Over-the-counter kits are more accurate than the BBT method and predict ovulation by analyzing the woman's urine or saliva for the surge in luteinizing hormone (LH) that precedes ovulation by about 12 to 24 hours (Peris, 2006).

Applied Knowledge (Continued)

Tracking Vaginal Mucus

Women can track the thickness of their vaginal mucus during the phases of the menstrual cycle by rolling it between their fingers and noting changes in texture. The mucus is thick, white, and cloudy during most phases of the cycle. It becomes thin, slippery, and clear for a few days preceding ovulation. A day or so after ovulation, the mucus again thickens and becomes opaque.

Additional Considerations

Coitus in the male-superior position allows sperm to be deposited deeper in the vagina and minimizes leakage of sperm out of the vagina due to gravity. Women may improve their chances of conceiving by lying on their backs and drawing their knees close to their breasts after ejaculation. This position, perhaps aided by the use of a pillow beneath the buttocks, may prevent sperm from dripping out quickly and elevate the pool of semen in relation to the cervix. It thus makes gravity work for, rather than against, conception. Women may also lie as still as possible for about 30 to 60 minutes after ejaculation to help sperm move toward the cervical opening.

Women with severely retroverted, or "tipped," uteruses may profit from supporting themselves on their elbows and knees and having their partners enter them from behind. Again, this position helps prevent semen from dripping out of the vagina.

The man should penetrate the woman as deeply as possible just before ejaculation, hold still during ejaculation, and then withdraw slowly in a straight line to avoid dispersing the pool of semen.

their sexual orientation, engage in heterosexual sex to mask their sexual preferences. Some want to experiment to see if they can "cure" themselves of their same-sex orientation. Others may use pregnancy as a means of "proving" to their peers that they are heterosexual. Sexual assault can also lead to pregnancy among lesbian youth (Saewyc et al., 2007).

Infertility and Assisted Reproductive Technology

For couples who want children, few problems are more frustrating than the inability to conceive. Physicians often recommend that couples try to conceive on their own for six months before seeking medical assistance. The term **infertility** is usually not applied until the failure to conceive has persisted for more than a year.

Because the likelihood of infertility increases with age, the current somewhat elevated incidence of infertility is partially the result of a rise in the number of couples who postpone childbearing until their thirties and forties (Shevell et al., 2006). All in all, about 15% of couples in North America have fertility problems (American Fertility Association, 2006). However, about half of them eventually succeed in conceiving a child. Many treatment options are available, ranging from drugs to stimulate ovulation to newer reproductive technologies, such as in vitro fertilization.

Infertility treatments can be very costly. In 2008, the Ontario government appointed an expert panel for advice on how to make infertility treatments more affordable. The panel was also asked to recommend ways of making the adoption process easier.

Male Fertility Problems

Although most concerns about fertility have traditionally centred on women, the problem lies with the man in about 30% of cases. In about 20% of cases, problems are found in both partners (Hatcher et al., 2006).

Infertility Inability to conceive a child.

Motility Self-propulsion. A measure of the viability of sperm cells.

Autoimmune response The production of antibodies that attack naturally occurring substances that are (incorrectly) recognized as being foreign or harmful.

Artificial insemination The introduction of sperm into the reproductive tract through means other than sexual intercourse.

Fertility problems in the male reflect abnormalities such as:

1. Low sperm count
2. Irregularly shaped sperm—for example, malformed heads or tails
3. Low sperm **motility**
4. Chronic diseases such as diabetes, as well as infections such as sexually transmitted infections
5. Injury to the testes
6. An **autoimmune response**, in which antibodies produced by the man deactivate his own sperm
7. A pituitary imbalance and/or thyroid disease

Problems in producing normal, abundant sperm may be caused by genetic factors, advanced age, hormonal problems, diabetes, injuries to the testes, varicose veins in the scrotum, drugs (alcohol, narcotics, marijuana, and/or tobacco), antihypertensive medications, environmental toxins, excess heat, and emotional stress.

Low sperm count (or the absence of sperm) is the most common problem. Sperm counts of 40 million to 150 million sperm per millilitre of semen are considered normal. A count of less than 20 million is generally regarded as low. Sperm production may be low among men with undescended testes that were not surgically corrected before puberty. Frequent ejaculation can reduce sperm counts. Sperm production may also be impaired in men whose testicles are consistently one or two degrees above the typical scrotal temperature of 34°C to 35°C (94°F to 95°F) (Leary, 1990). Sometimes the sperm count is adequate, but prostate, hormonal, or other factors deprive sperm of motility or deform them. Motility can also be hampered by scar tissue from infections. Scarring may prevent sperm from passing through parts of the male reproductive system, such as the vas deferens.

Sperm counts have been increased by surgical repair of the varicose veins in the scrotum. Microsurgery can also open blocked passageways that prevent the outflow of sperm (Schroeder-Printzen et al., 2000). Researchers are also investigating the effects on sperm production of special cooling undergarments. Most men whose infertility is the result of higher-than-normal scrotal temperatures show increased sperm counts and quality when they wear such undergarments.

ARTIFICIAL INSEMINATION The sperm of men with low sperm counts can be collected and quick-frozen. The sperm from multiple ejaculations can then be injected into a woman's uterus at the time of ovulation. This is one kind of **artificial insemination**. The sperm of a man with low sperm motility can also be injected into his partner's uterus, so that the sperm begin their journey closer to the fallopian tubes. Sperm from a donor can be used to artificially inseminate a woman whose partner is completely infertile or has an extremely low sperm count. The child then bears the genes of one of the parents, the mother. A donor can be chosen who resembles the man in physical traits and ethnic background. A variation of artificial insemination has been used with some men with very low (or zero!) sperm counts in the semen, immature sperm, or immotile sperm. Immature sperm can be removed from a testicle by a thin needle and then directly injected into an egg in a laboratory dish.

In 2002, the Canadian health minister introduced legislation that would require the creation of a databank on sperm donors (Minister of Health, 2002). Offspring of the donors would be allowed to obtain medical information regarding the donor, although the identity of the donor would be revealed only with his consent.

ASSISTED PARENTHOOD FOR GAY MEN AND LESBIANS Many gay men and lesbians use reproductive technologies to become parents. At some fertility clinics in Toronto about a third of the clients are gay men or lesbians (Epstein, 2008). Of course, a key difference between gays and lesbians and heterosexuals who are clients of fertility clinics is that the majority of same-sex couples do not have infertility problems. Rather they are seeking access to donor sperm and ova. Thus their counselling needs are different from those of heterosexuals. A major concern of same-sex couples is that many fertility clinics have a heterosexual focus and are not able to provide proper counselling for them (Epstein, 2008).

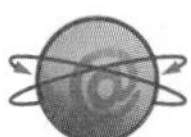

Sherbourne Health Centre
Sherbourne Health Centre provides information and advice regarding assisted conception and the use of reproductive technologies for gay men and lesbians who wish to become parents.
www.sherbourne.on.ca

Female Fertility Problems

The major causes of infertility in women are:

1. Irregular ovulation, including failure to ovulate
2. Obstructions or malfunctions of the reproductive tract, which are often caused by infections or diseases involving the reproductive tract
3. Endometriosis
4. Declining hormone levels of estrogen and progesterone that occur with aging and may prevent the ovum from becoming fertilized or remaining implanted in the uterus

From 10% to 15% of female infertility problems stem from failure to ovulate. Many factors can play a role in failure to ovulate, including hormonal irregularities, malnutrition, genetic factors, stress, and chronic disease. Failure to ovulate may occur in response to low levels of body fat, as in the cases of athletes and women with eating disorders (Frisch, 2002).

Ovulation may often be induced by the use of fertility drugs such as *clomiphene* (Clomid). Clomiphene stimulates the pituitary gland to secrete FSH and LH, which in turn stimulate maturation of ova. Clomiphene leads to conception in the majority of cases of infertility that are due *solely* to irregular or absent ovulation. But because infertility can have multiple causes, only about half of women who use clomiphene become pregnant. Another infertility drug, Pergonal, contains a high concentration of FSH, which directly stimulates maturation of ovarian follicles. Like clomiphene, Pergonal has a high success rate with women whose infertility is due to lack of ovulation. Clomiphene and Pergonal have been linked to multiple births, including quadruplets and even quintuplets (Shevell et al., 2005). McGill University researchers found that 41% of patients at an infertility clinic actually preferred to have multiple births so that they could have an "instant" family (Child, Henderson, & Tan, 2004). This desire was especially strong among couples who had no children and had been infertile for a long time.

Local infections that scar the fallopian tubes and other organs impede the passage of sperm or ova. Such infections include pelvic inflammatory disease—an inflammation of the woman's internal reproductive tract that can be caused by various infectious agents, such as the bacteria responsible for gonorrhea and chlamydia (see Chapter 14).

In **endometriosis**, cells break away from the uterine lining (the endometrium) and become implanted and grow elsewhere. When they develop on the surface of the ovaries or fallopian tubes, they may block the passage of ova or impair conception. About one in six cases of female sterility is believed to be due to endometriosis. Hormone treatments and surgery sometimes reduce the blockage to the point where the woman can conceive. A physician may suspect

Endometriosis An abnormal condition in which endometrial tissue is sloughed off into the abdominal cavity rather than out of the body during menstruation. The condition is characterized by abdominal pain and may cause infertility.

Laparoscopy A medical procedure in which a long, narrow tube (laparoscope) is inserted through an incision in the navel, permitting the visual inspection of organs in the pelvic cavity.

In vitro fertilization A method of conception in which mature ova are surgically removed from an ovary and placed in a laboratory dish along with sperm.

Gamete intrafallopian transfer (GIFT) A method of conception in which sperm and ova are inserted into a fallopian tube to encourage conception.

Zygote intrafallopian transfer (ZIFT) A method of conception in which an ovum is fertilized in a laboratory dish and then placed in a fallopian tube.

Donor IVF A variation of in vitro fertilization in which the ovum is taken from one woman, fertilized, and then injected into the uterus or fallopian tube of another woman.

Embryonic transfer A method of conception in which a woman volunteer is artificially inseminated by the male partner of the intended mother, after which the embryo is removed from the volunteer and inserted within the uterus of the intended mother.

Intracytoplasmic sperm injection A method of contraception during which a single sperm is injected directly into an ovum.

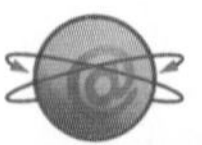

The Infertility Awareness Association of Canada
www.iaac.ca

endometriosis during a pelvic exam, but it is diagnosed with certainty by **laparoscopy**. A long, narrow tube is inserted through an incision in the navel, permitting the physician to inspect the organs in the pelvic cavity visually. The incision is practically undetectable.

Several methods help many couples with problems such as blocked fallopian tubes bear children.

IN VITRO FERTILIZATION When Louise Brown was born in England in 1978 after being conceived by **in vitro fertilization** (IVF), the event made headlines around the world. Louise was dubbed the world's first "test-tube baby." Conception actually took place in a laboratory dish (not a test tube), and the embryo was implanted in the mother's uterus, where it developed to term. Before in vitro fertilization, fertility drugs stimulate ripening of ova. Ripe ova are then surgically removed from an ovary and placed in a laboratory dish along with the father's sperm. Fertilized ova are then injected into the mother's uterus to become implanted in the uterine wall.

A variation of IVF is vitrification, which involves the freezing of a woman's ova. With this procedure the ova are rapidly frozen to prevent ice crystals from forming. Rapid freezing ensures that a far higher proportion of the ova will survive. This procedure appeals to women who want to delay becoming mothers until they are older but want to preserve their young ova to improve their fertility chances. The McGill (University) Reproductive Centre in Montreal has pioneered research on this procedure (Ogilvie, 2008).

GIFT In **gamete intrafallopian transfer (GIFT)**, sperm and ova are inserted together into a fallopian tube for fertilization. Conception occurs in a fallopian tube rather than in a laboratory dish.

ZIFT **Zygote intrafallopian transfer (ZIFT)** involves a combination of IVF and GIFT. Sperm and ova are combined in a laboratory dish. After fertilization, the zygote is placed in the mother's fallopian tube to begin its journey to the uterus for implantation.

DONOR IVF "I tell her mommy was having trouble with, I call them ovums, not eggs," says a 50-year-old female therapist in Los Angeles (cited in Stolberg, 1998a). "I say that I needed these to have a baby, and there was this wonderful woman and she was willing to give me some, and that was how she helped us. I want to be honest that we got pregnant in a special way."

That special way is termed **donor IVF**, which is a variation of the IVF procedure in which the ovum is taken from another woman, fertilized, and then injected into the uterus or fallopian tube of the intended mother. The procedure is used when the intended mother does not produce ova. The number of births brought about by this method has been mushrooming in recent years (Stolberg, 1998a).

EMBRYONIC TRANSFER A similar method for women who do not produce ova of their own is **embryonic transfer**. In this method, a woman volunteer is artificially inseminated by the male partner of the infertile woman. Five days later the embryo is removed from the volunteer and inserted within the uterus of the mother-to-be, where it is hoped that it will become implanted.

INTRACYTOPLASMIC SPERM INJECTION **Intracytoplasmic sperm injection** (ICSI) can be used when a man has too few sperm for IVF, or when IVF

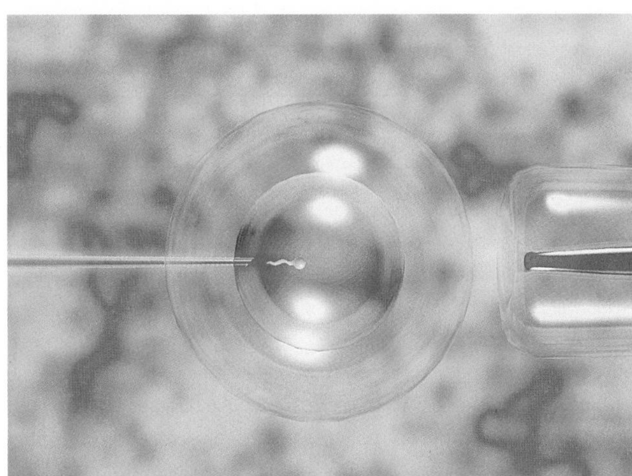

Intracytoplasmic Sperm Injection.
ICSI is sometimes used when the man has too few sperm for IVF, or when IVF fails. As shown in the photograph, a thin (very thin!) needle injects a single sperm directly into an ovum.

Surrogate mother A woman who is impregnated with the sperm of a prospective father via artificial insemination, carries the embryo and fetus to term, and then gives the child to the prospective parents.

fails. ICSI injects a sperm cell directly into an ovum. However, these methods may be associated with an increase in birth defects, such as heart, stomach, kidney, and bladder problems; cleft palate; hernia; and, in boys, malformation of the penis (Shevell et al., 2005).

SURROGATE MOTHERHOOD A **surrogate mother** is artificially inseminated by the husband of the infertile woman and carries the baby to term.

FUTURE REPRODUCTIVE TECHNOLOGIES The journal *Nature* (Pearson, 2008) asked experts in reproductive medicine to predict future developments in reproductive technologies. Three potential technologies were discussed:

- The creation of sperm and ova in the laboratory. Sperm and ova from stem cells would be combined to initiate the development of human embryos.
- Correcting diseases. To protect people from genetic diseases, physicians would insert corrective genetic material into embryos.
- Artificial wombs. Scientists would develop artificial wombs to help fetuses grow outside of the body. This would be particularly helpful in ensuring that premature babies could continue to develop safely in a womb-like atmosphere.

ADOPTION Adoption is yet another way for people to obtain children. Despite the occasional conflicts in which adoptive parents are pitted against biological parents who change their minds about giving their children up for adoption, most adoptions result in the formation of loving new families.

In Canada, adolescent mothers are the most common providers of babies for adoption (Daly & Sobol, 1994). However, because most young women who experience unwanted pregnancies today either keep the baby or have an abortion, there are far fewer Canadian babies available for adoption.

Daly and Sobol (1994) found that the major restriction on adoption placement was sexual orientation, with only about 4% of agencies stating that they would place a child with a same-sex couple without any reservations. In the 1990s, however, court rulings and provincial legislation that provided greater equality for same-sex couples paved the road for an increase in same-sex adoptions. In 1995, for example, an Ontario lesbian went to court seeking the right to adopt her partner's child. The judge ruled that the Ontario adoption law defining a spouse as a person of the opposite sex was unconstitutional, and that the woman should be able to adopt (Gower & Philp, 2002a). In 1996, British Columbia

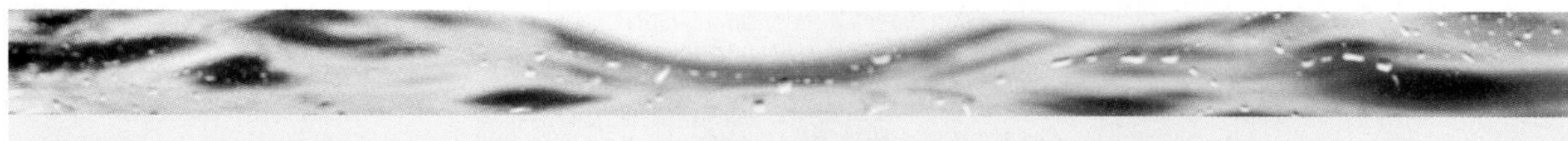

A World of Diversity

WOMBS FOR RENT

Pushpa Pandye still sometimes cries when she thinks of the baby. She didn't eat for a month after she gave him up, a little boy weighing 5 lb. 4 oz. who came into the world last April in a utilitarian delivery room at the Kaival Maternity Home & Surgical Hospital in Anand, India. "He was so cute," she says ruefully. After she gave birth, she nursed the infant in her room at Kaival for two weeks. Her husband and two children met him; her eight-year-old still remembers the baby who lived in her mother's tummy for safekeeping. And then Pandye handed him over to his rightful owners and genetic parents, a couple from the Indian city of Bangalore, some 1400 km away.

Another nine or ten months from now, assuming the pregnancy "takes," she plans to go through the entire exercise again, this time for an Indian immigrant couple settled in the U.S. Already she dreads the delivery date. But her stint as a paid surrogate has given her an opportunity she couldn't otherwise have dreamed of: the chance to escape the lower-middle-class ghetto in what remains one of the most rigid class-bound democracies in the world. For her last pregnancy, Pandye was paid 150 000 rupees, or $390—a sum that would take her years to earn in her job as a clerk at an incense store or with her occasional work as a government security guard. She used the money to purchase a two-bedroom flat. The money from the next pregnancy will allow her to send her kids to a better school—where they can learn English and work with computers—and then to college. Her heart's desire is that her daughter will become a doctor, or else a pilot.

Pandye is a bright, high-spirited 28-year-old from this town in the state of Gujarat, in the western tip of India. She possesses only a high school education—an abiding regret, since her ambition was to become a teacher—but her geographic location has given her an unusual and spectacularly lucrative career option unthinkable in another time: she's part of a cottage industry of Indian surrogate mothers who have given hope to dozens of infertile couples all over the world, and new life to this dusty town.

These days husbandry of a different sort draws visitors here, and it takes place just a kilometre or so away from the Amul complex, in the salmon-coloured stucco building where Pandye gave birth. The woman who delivered the baby and presides over the hospital is an obstetrics and infertility specialist named Dr. Nayana Patel. Nayana-*ben*, as she's known in this region (*ben* means *sister*, a term of respect), vaulted to fame and into the reproductive tourism business a few years ago, after she facilitated a rather unorthodox surrogacy arrangement. She was contacted by a U.K.-based couple on behalf of their son and daughter-in-law, Aakash and Lata Nagla, who were desperate for a child. Infertility threatened to break up the marriage, and the parents begged Dr. Patel to do something. She did. The problem was with Lata's uterus—she didn't have one. But her eggs and ovaries were perfectly functional. So Dr. Patel removed some eggs, fertilized them in a petri dish with the husband's sperm, and transplanted the resulting embryo into another woman's womb: Lata's mother's. In February 2004, 44-year-old Vidhya Valand gave birth to her grandchildren, a twin boy and girl, to great media hoopla, and some social outrage.

Within months, Dr. Patel had overseen her first commercial surrogate birth, and had inquiries for others. Grandmothers-in-waiting are not always a reliable option, and Dr. Patel began seeking out paid surrogates. She has since arranged more than 70 surrogates for couples from India and from as far away as Japan, Finland, Germany, the U.S., and Canada. She has created a gainful if not exactly desirable career niche for dozens of impoverished women in neighbouring villages and towns and indeed across India. And she has helped launch a national boom estimated at $200 million around a process that raises a tangle of ethical questions: is it moral to pay the world's poor to have our children? Have we opened the door to shady practitioners who are exploiting women? Does surrogacy, as critics suggest, turn the parent-child relationship into a matter of property rights?

In the three years since Vidhya Valand carried her daughter's twins, the number of IVF clinics in India has doubled. There are now an estimated 600; of these, 200 are thought to offer surrogacy (numbers are hard to track because clinics don't have to be accredited). Nonetheless, the phenomenon dubbed "rent-a-womb" or "outsourcing pregnancy" is so controversial many of the women who volunteer for it don't tell their families or friends. Of course, Dr. Patel has a catchphrase of her own, a positive spin on the arrangement. "This is the globalization of reproduction," she told a roomful of Indian reporters at a February press conference to mark her latest hand-off: a Korean-American baby, born in Anand to a surrogate from Kolkata. One doesn't become an international medical superstar without some media savvy.

Source: Subramanian, S. (2007, July 2). Wombs for rent. Maclean's. *pp. 40–47. Reprinted with permission.*

became the first province to pass legislation granting same-sex couples the same rights to adopt as those of heterosexual couples. Since then, most other provinces have passed similar legislation. Consequently, Canada has become a world leader in facilitating adoptions for gays and lesbians. However, this does not mean that same-sex couples are not still facing prejudice by adoption agencies.

Attitudes of university students about gay and lesbian adoption have been studied by Rye and Meaney (2008). While the students were generally positive about homosexuals being able to adopt, they were still more positive about heterosexual adoption. Women were more accepting than men of adoption by homosexual parents.

Canadian Legislation Governing Reproductive Technologies

In 2004, the Canadian Parliament passed legislation to regulate reproductive technologies. This legislation came 12 years after the first commission on reproductive technologies was established, a fact that highlights just how contentious are the issues relating to these technologies. The main provisions of the Act Respecting Assisted Human Reproduction include:

- Banning the cloning of humans
- Banning the selection of a baby's sex for non-medical purposes
- Making it illegal to pay women to be surrogate mothers
- Making it illegal to pay for sperm donations

After the act was passed, there were fewer sperm donations in Canada and infertility clinics had to import sperm from the United States. The United States allows for payment to sperm donors and to surrogate mothers.

One of the most controversial provisions was the permitting of research using stem cells from embryos left over from infertility treatment. Leaders of the pro-life movement are critical of the legislation, arguing that the use of embryos in this way diminishes the value of human life. Proponents of the research argue that stem cells can play a vital role in helping to provide cures for such diseases as cancer, diabetes, and Parkinson's disease.

In December 2006, the Conservative government of Stephen Harper named eight people to the board responsible for implementing polices that would guide the work of the Assisted Human Reproduction Agency of Canada. The board members included people who have spoken out against abortion and stem-cell research. The board did not appear to include any stem-cell scientists or fertility experts. Critics of the board appointees were concerned that the government intended to use the board as a means of adopting policies that would appeal to religious conservatives rather than focus on the scientific aspects of reproductive technologies (Abraham, 2006).

Gay Adoption.
Robert Gibson and Thomas Jones of Brampton, Ontario, adopted two half-brothers with the help of the Children's Aid Society of Toronto. They are among a growing number of gay couples in Canada who are applying to adopt.

Pregnancy

Women react to becoming pregnant in different ways. For those who are psychologically and economically prepared, pregnancy may be greeted with joyous celebration. On the other hand, an unwanted pregnancy may evoke feelings of fear and hopelessness.

In this section we examine biological and psychological aspects of pregnancy: signs of pregnancy, prenatal development, complications, effects of drugs and sex, and the psychological experiences of pregnant women and fathers.

Early Signs of Pregnancy

For many women the first sign of pregnancy is missing a period. But some women have irregular menstrual cycles or miss a period because of stress. Missing a period is thus not a fully reliable indicator. Some women also experience cyclic bleeding or spotting during pregnancy, although the blood flow is usually lighter than normal. If a woman's basal body temperature remains high for about three weeks after ovulation, there is reason to suspect pregnancy even if she spots two weeks after ovulation.

Pregnancy Tests

You may have heard your parents say that they learned your mother was pregnant by means of the "rabbit test," in which a sample of the mother's urine was injected into a laboratory animal. This procedure, which was once commonly used to confirm pregnancy, relied on the fact that women produce **human chorionic gonadotropin** (HCG) shortly after conception. HCG causes rabbits, mice, and rats to ovulate.

Today, pregnancy can be confirmed in minutes by tests that directly detect HCG in the urine as early as the third week of pregnancy. A blood test—the *beta subunit HCG radioimmunoassay* (RIA)—can detect HCG in the woman's blood as early as the eighth day of pregnancy, about five days preceding her expected period.

Over-the-counter home pregnancy tests are also available. They too test the woman's urine for HCG and are intended to be used as early as one day after a missed period. Laboratory-based tests are considered 98% or 99% accurate. Home-based tests performed by laypeople are somewhat less accurate. Women are advised to consult their physicians if they suspect that they are pregnant or wish to confirm a home pregnancy test result.

Early Effects of Pregnancy

Just a few days after conception, a woman may note tenderness of the breasts. Hormonal stimulation of the mammary glands may make the breasts more sensitive and cause sensations of tingling and fullness.

The term **morning sickness** refers to the nausea, food aversions, and vomiting that many women experience during pregnancy. Although called morning sickness, it is not a "sickness" at all, but rather a perfectly normal part of pregnancy (Flaxman & Sherman, 2000).

In some cases, morning sickness is so severe that the woman cannot eat regularly and must be hospitalized to ensure that she and the fetus receive adequate nutrition. In milder cases, having small amounts of food in the stomach throughout the day is helpful. Many women find that eating a few crackers at bedtime and before getting out of bed in the morning is effective. Other women profit from medication. Morning sickness usually—but not always—subsides by about the twelfth week of pregnancy.

Pregnant women may experience greater-than-normal fatigue during the early weeks, sleeping longer and falling asleep more readily than usual. Frequent urination, which may also be experienced, is caused by pressure from the swelling uterus on the bladder.

Human chorionic gonadotropin A hormone produced by women shortly after conception, which stimulates the corpus luteum to continue to produce progesterone. The presence of HCG in a woman's urine indicates that she is pregnant.

Morning sickness Symptoms of pregnancy, including nausea, aversions to specific foods, and vomiting.

Miscarriage (Spontaneous Abortion)

Miscarriage A spontaneous abortion.

Miscarriages have many causes, including chromosomal defects in the fetus and abnormalities of the placenta and uterus. Miscarriage is more prevalent among older mothers (Stein & Susser, 2000). About three in four miscarriages occur in the first 16 weeks of pregnancy, and the great majority of these occur in the first seven weeks. Some miscarriages occur so early that the woman is not aware she was pregnant.

After a miscarriage, a couple may feel a deep sense of loss and undergo a period of mourning. Emotional support from friends and family often helps the couple cope with the loss. In most cases, women who miscarry can carry subsequent pregnancies to term.

Sex During Pregnancy

Most health professionals concur that coitus is safe throughout the course of pregnancy until the start of labour, provided that the pregnancy is developing normally and the woman has no history of miscarriages. Women who experience bleeding or cramps during pregnancy may be advised by their obstetricians not to engage in coitus.

There is often an initial decline in sexual interest among pregnant women during the first trimester. There is increased interest during the second trimester and another decline in interest during the third. Many women show declines in sexual interest and activity during the first trimester because of fatigue, nausea, or misguided concerns that coitus will harm the embryo or fetus. Also during the first trimester, vasocongestion may cause tenderness of the breasts, discouraging fondling and sucking. One study found that 90% of 570 women were engaging in coitus at five months into their pregnancies (Byrd et al., 1998). Researchers in Israel reported a gradual decline in sexual interest and frequency of intercourse and orgasm during pregnancy among a sample of 219 women. The greatest decline occurred during the third trimester (Hart et al., 1991). Pain during intercourse is also commonly reported, especially in the third trimester.

As the woman's abdominal region swells, the popular male-superior position becomes unwieldy. The female-superior, lateral-entry, and rear-entry positions are common alternatives. Manual and oral sex can continue as usual.

Psychological Changes During Pregnancy

A woman's psychological response to pregnancy reflects her desire to be pregnant, her physical changes, and her attitudes toward these changes. Women with the financial, social, and psychological resources to meet the needs of pregnancy and child rearing may welcome pregnancy. Some describe it as the most wondrous experience of their lives. Other women may question their ability to handle their pregnancies and childbirth. Or they may fear that pregnancy will interfere with their careers or their mates' feelings about them. In general, women who want to have a baby and choose to become pregnant are better adjusted during their pregnancies. The first trimester may be difficult for women who are ambivalent about pregnancy. At that stage symptoms like morning sickness are most pronounced, and women must come to terms with being pregnant. The second trimester is generally less tempestuous. Morning sickness and other symptoms have largely vanished. It is not yet difficult to move about, and the woman need not yet face the delivery. Women first note fetal movement during the second trimester, and for many the experience is stirring:

> I was lying on my stomach and felt—something, like someone lightly touching my deep insides. Then I just sat very still and . . . felt the hugeness of having something living growing in me. Then I said, No, it's not possible, it's too early yet, and then I started to cry . . . That one moment was my first body awareness of another living thing inside me (Boston Women's Health Book Collective, 2005).

Men, like women, respond to pregnancy according to the degree to which they want the child. Many men are proud and look forward to the child with great anticipation. In such cases, pregnancy may bring parents closer together. But fathers who are financially or emotionally unprepared may consider the pregnancy a "trap."

Prenatal Development

We can date pregnancy from the onset of the last menstrual cycle before conception, which makes the normal gestation period 280 days. We can also date pregnancy from the date at which fertilization was assumed to have taken place, which normally corresponds to two weeks after the beginning of the woman's last menstrual cycle. In this case, the normal gestation period is 266 days.

Once pregnancy has been confirmed, the delivery date may be calculated by *Nagele's rule:*

- Jot down the date of the first day of the last menstrual period.
- Add seven days.
- Subtract three months.
- Add one year.

Few babies are born exactly when they are due, but the great majority are delivered during a 10-day period that spans the date.

The Germinal Stage

Within 36 hours after conception, the zygote divides into two cells. It then divides repeatedly, becoming 32 cells within another 36 hours as it continues its journey to the uterus. It takes the zygote perhaps three or four days to reach the uterus. This mass of dividing cells then wanders about the uterus for perhaps another three or four days before it begins to become implanted in the uterine wall. Implantation takes about another week. This period from conception to implantation is termed the **germinal stage** or the **period of the ovum** (see Figure 10.4).

Several days into the germinal stage, the cell mass takes the form of a fluid-filled ball of cells, which is called a **blastocyst**. Already some cell differentiation has begun. Cells begin to separate into groups that will eventually become different structures.

Implantation may be accompanied by some bleeding, which results from the usual rupturing of some small blood vessels that line the uterus. Bleeding can also be a sign of a miscarriage—although most women who experience implantation bleeding do not miscarry but go on to have normal pregnancies and deliver healthy babies.

The Embryonic Stage

The period from implantation to about the eighth week of development is called the **embryonic stage**. The major organ systems of the body begin to differentiate during this stage.

The embryo—and later the fetus—develops within a protective environment in the mother's uterus called the **amniotic sac**, which is surrounded by a clear membrane. The embryo or fetus is suspended within the sac in **amniotic fluid**. The amniotic fluid acts like a shock absorber. It cushions the embryo from damage that might result from the mother's movements.

Nutrients and waste products are exchanged between mother and embryo (or fetus) through a mass of tissue called the **placenta**. The placenta is unique in origin. It develops from material supplied by both mother and embryo. The fetus is connected to the placenta by the **umbilical cord**.

Ultimately, the placenta passes from the woman's body after delivery. For this reason it is also called the afterbirth.

Germinal stage The period of prenatal development before implantation in the uterus.

Period of the ovum Germinal stage.

Blastocyst A stage of embryonic development within the germinal stage of prenatal development, at which the embryo is a sphere of cells surrounding a cavity of fluid.

Embryonic stage The stage of prenatal development that lasts from implantation through the eighth week and is characterized by the differentiation of the major organ systems.

Amniotic sac The sac containing the fetus.

Amniotic fluid Fluid within the amniotic sac that suspends and protects the fetus.

Placenta An organ connected to the fetus by the umbilical cord. The placenta serves as a relay station between mother and fetus, allowing the exchange of nutrients and wastes.

Umbilical cord A tube that connects the fetus to the placenta.

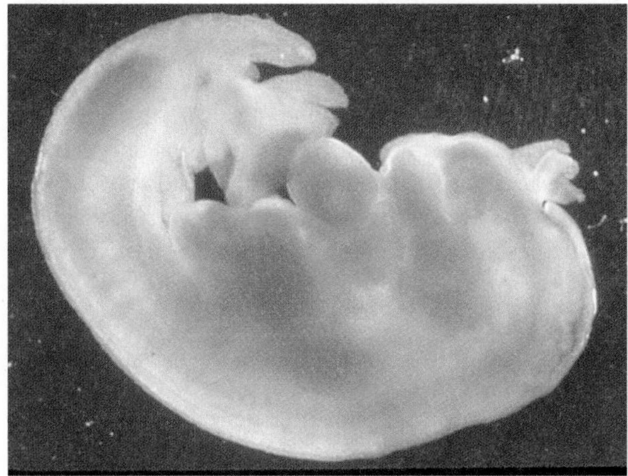

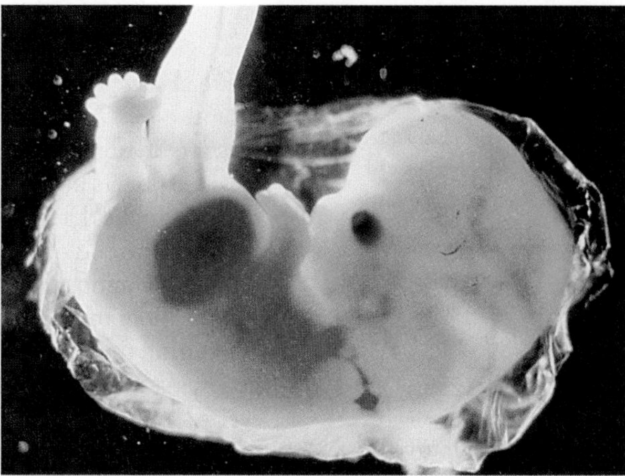

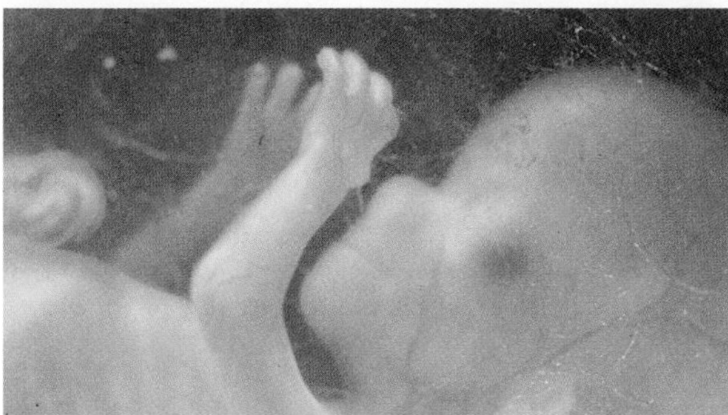

Prenatal Development. Developmental changes are most rapid and dramatic during prenatal development. Within a few months, a human embryo and then fetus advances from weighing a gram to several kilograms, and from one cell to billions of cells.

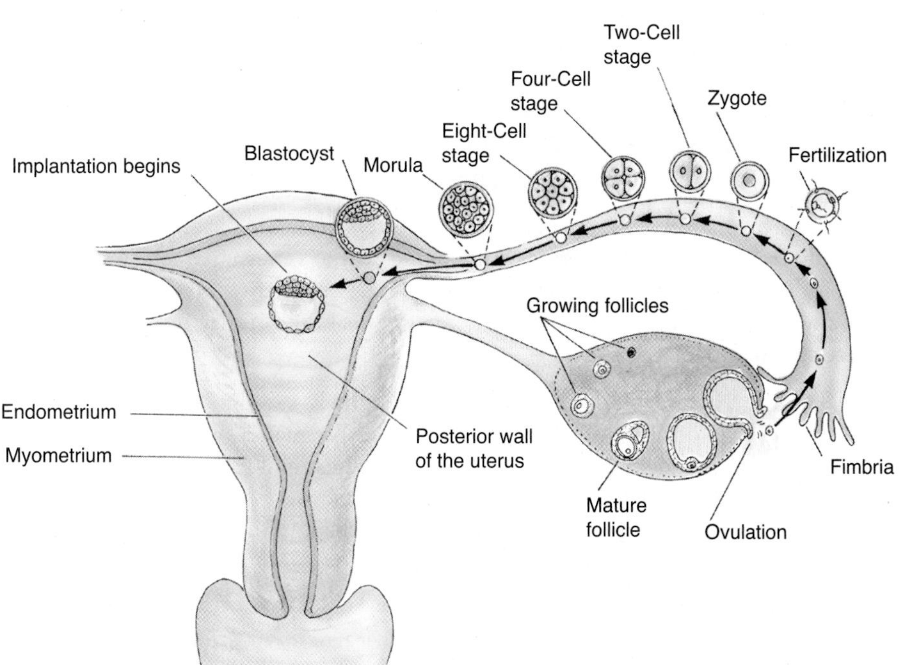

Figure 10.4 The Ovarian Cycle, Conception, and the Early Days of the Germinal Stage.

The zygote first divides about 36 hours after conception. Continuing division creates the hollow sphere of cells termed the blastocyst. The blastocyst normally becomes implanted in the wall of the uterus.

Age of viability The age at which a fetus can sustain independent life.

Teratogens Environmental influences or agents that can damage an embryo or fetus.

Critical period of vulnerability A period of time during which an embryo or fetus is vulnerable to the effects of a teratogen.

Rubella A viral infection that can cause mental retardation and heart disease in an embryo. Also called *German measles.*

Syphilis A sexually transmitted disease caused by a bacterial infection.

Stillbirth The birth of a dead fetus.

Acquired immunodeficiency syndrome (AIDS) A sexually transmitted infection that destroys white blood cells in the immune system, leaving the body vulnerable to various "opportunistic" infections.

The Fetal Stage

The fetal stage begins by the ninth week and continues until birth. By about the ninth or tenth week, the fetus begins to respond to the outside world by turning in the direction of external stimulation. By the end of the first trimester, the major organ systems, the fingers and toes, and the external genitals have been formed. The gender of the fetus can be determined visually. The eyes have become clearly distinguishable.

Near the end of the second trimester the fetus approaches the **age of viability**. Still, only a minority of babies born at the end of the second trimester who weigh under a kilogram will survive—even with intense medical efforts.

During the final months of pregnancy, the mother may become concerned that the fetus seems to be less active than before. Most of the time, the change in activity level is normal. The fetus has merely grown so large that it is cramped, and its movements are restricted.

Environmental Influences on Prenatal Development

We focus in this next section on the environmental factors that affect prenatal development.

THE MOTHER'S DIET Malnutrition in the mother can adversely affect fetal development. Pregnant women who are adequately nourished are more likely to deliver babies of average or above-average size. Their infants are also less likely to develop colds and serious respiratory disorders. However, maternal *obesity* is linked with a higher risk of stillbirth (Cnattingius et al., 1998).

MATERNAL DISEASES AND DISORDERS Environmental influences or agents that can harm the embryo or fetus are called **teratogens**. These include drugs taken by the mother, such as alcohol and even Aspirin, as well as substances produced by the mother's body, such as Rh-positive antibodies. Other teratogens include the metals lead and mercury, radiation, and disease-causing organisms such as viruses and bacteria. Although many disease-causing organisms cannot pass through the placenta to infect the embryo or fetus, some extremely small organisms, such as those that cause syphilis, measles, mumps, and chicken pox, can.

CRITICAL PERIODS OF VULNERABILITY The times at which exposure to particular teratogens can cause the greatest harm are termed **critical periods of vulnerability**. Critical periods correspond to the times at which the structures most affected by the teratogens are developing. The heart, for example, develops rapidly from the third to the fifth week after conception. It may be most vulnerable to certain teratogens at this time.

RUBELLA (GERMAN MEASLES) **Rubella** is a viral infection. Women who contract rubella during the first month or two of pregnancy, when rapid differentiation of major organ systems is taking place, may bear children who are deaf or who develop mental retardation, heart disease, or cataracts.

Most Canadian women have either had rubella as children or been vaccinated against it. Women who do not know whether they are immune to rubella may be tested. If they are not immune, they can be vaccinated *before pregnancy.*

SYPHILIS Maternal **syphilis** may cause miscarriage or **stillbirth**, or it may be passed along to the child in the form of congenital syphilis. Congenital syphilis can impair the vision and hearing, damage the liver, or deform the bones and teeth.

Routine blood tests early in pregnancy can diagnose syphilis. The fetus will probably not contract syphilis if an infected mother is treated successfully with antibiotics before the fourth month of pregnancy.

HIV/AIDS **Acquired immunodeficiency syndrome (AIDS)** is caused by the *human immunodeficiency virus* (HIV). HIV is blood-borne and is sometimes transmitted through the placenta to infect the fetus. The rupturing of blood vessels in mother and baby during childbirth provides another opportunity for transmission of HIV. *However, the majority of babies born to mothers who are infected with HIV do not become infected themselves.* Using antiviral medication can minimize the probability of transmission (see Chapter 14). HIV can also be transmitted to children by breastfeeding.

TOXEMIA **Toxemia**, a life-threatening condition characterized by high blood pressure, may afflict women late in the second trimester of pregnancy or early in the third. If left untreated, it can lead to maternal or fetal death. Babies born to women with toxemia are often undersized or premature.

ECTOPIC PREGNANCY In an **ectopic pregnancy**, the fertilized ovum implants itself somewhere other than in the uterus. Most ectopic pregnancies occur in a fallopian tube ("tubal pregnancies"). If ectopic pregnancies do not abort spontaneously, they must be removed by surgery or use of medicines.

RH INCOMPATIBILITY In **Rh incompatibility**, antibodies produced by the mother are transmitted to a fetus or newborn infant. *Rh* is a blood protein found in some people's red blood cells. Rh incompatibility occurs when a woman who does not have this blood factor, and is thus *Rh-negative*, is carrying an *Rh-positive* fetus, which can happen if the father is Rh-positive. However, it becomes a problem only in a minority of the resulting pregnancies.

MEDICATIONS TAKEN BY THE MOTHER (AND THE FATHER) Some widely used drugs, including nonprescription drugs, are linked with birth abnormalities. Several antibiotics may harm a fetus, especially if they are taken during certain periods of fetal development.

Acne drugs such as Accutane can cause physical and mental handicaps in up to 50% of the children of women who take these drugs during pregnancy. Hoffman La Roche Limited Canada, which makes Accutane, warns women of childbearing age on its website **rochecanada.com** against pregnancy as there is an "extremely high risk that your baby will be deformed."

If you are pregnant or suspect that you are, it is advisable to consult your obstetrician before taking any and all drugs, not just prescription drugs.

VITAMINS Many pregnant women are prescribed daily doses of multivitamins to maintain their own health and to promote the development of a healthy pregnancy. "Too much of a good thing," however, may be hazardous. High doses of vitamins such as A, B_6, D, and K have been linked to birth defects.

NARCOTICS Maternal use (and sometimes paternal use) of illegal drugs can also place the fetus at risk. Narcotics such as heroin and methadone can readily pass from mother to fetus through the placental membrane. Narcotics are addictive. Fetuses of mothers who use them regularly during their pregnancies can become addicted in utero.

ALCOHOL Mothers who drink during pregnancy expose the fetus to greater risk of birth defects, infant mortality, sensory and motor problems, and mental retardation. Nearly 40% of children whose mothers drink during pregnancy develop **fetal alcohol syndrome** (FAS). FAS is a cluster of symptoms typified by developmental lags and characteristic facial features, such as an underdeveloped upper jaw, flattened nose, and widely spaced eyes. Infants with FAS are often smaller than average and have a smaller-than-average brain.

Although research suggests that light drinking is unlikely to harm the fetus in most cases, FAS has been found even among the children of mothers who drank only 60 mL (2 oz.) of alcohol a day during the first trimester (Astley & Clarren, 2001).

A high proportion of children in Canada who are in foster homes waiting to be adopted have FAS. For example, it is estimated that about half of the permanent wards of the Winnipeg Child and Family Services have FAS (Gower & Philp, 2002b). Yet, few adoptive parents are aware of FAS or that their adopted children are at high risk of having been damaged in the womb by alcohol.

Toxemia A life-threatening condition that is characterized by high blood pressure.

Ectopic pregnancy A pregnancy in which the fertilized ovum becomes implanted somewhere other than in the uterus.

Rh incompatibility A condition in which antibodies produced by a pregnant woman are transmitted to the fetus and may cause brain damage or death.

Fetal alcohol syndrome Caused by maternal alcohol consumption during pregnancy, a cluster of symptoms in the infant typified by developmental lags, characteristic facial features, and smaller than average overall size and brain size.

Don't Do It! Smoking cigarettes and pregnancy do not mix.

CIGARETTE SMOKING Cigarette smoke contains chemicals (such as carbon monoxide and the stimulant nicotine) that are transmitted to the fetus. It also lessens the amount of oxygen received by the fetus. Maternal smoking increases the risk of spontaneous abortion and complications during pregnancy such as premature rupturing of the amniotic sac, stillbirth, premature birth, low birth weight, and early infant mortality (Cnattingius, 2004; Secker-Walker & Vacek, 2003). These risks increase with the amount smoked (Bernstein et al., 2005). Low birth weight is a common risk factor for infant disease, mortality, and problems in learning in school (O'Keeffe et al., 2003).

The combination of smoking and drinking alcohol places the child at greater risk of low birth weight than either practice alone (Spencer, 2006). Maternal smoking affects the fetal heart rate and increases the risk of sudden infant death syndrome (SIDS) (Gordon et al., 2002; Pollack, 2001). Maternal smoking has also been linked to reduced lung function in newborns and asthma in childhood. Evidence also points to reduced attention spans, hyperactivity, and lower IQs and achievement test scores in children exposed to maternal smoking during and after pregnancy.

Smoking by the father (or other household members) may be dangerous to a fetus because secondary smoke (smoke exhaled by the smoker or emitted from the tip of a lit cigarette) may be absorbed by the mother and passed along to the fetus. Passive exposure to second-hand smoke during infancy is also linked to increased risk of SIDS (Gordon et al., 2002).

Many women do not suspend alcohol or cigarette use until they learn that they are pregnant, which may not occur until weeks into the pregnancy (Cnattingius, 2004). It may be easier for women to quit if they consider quitting as limited to the term of their pregnancy rather than as permanent. Then, of course, if they should remain abstinent after delivery, perhaps they will not be disappointed.

Chromosomal and Genetic Abnormalities

Not all of us have the normal complement of chromosomes. Some of us have genes that threaten our health or our existence.

On the basis of information about a couple's medical background and family history of genetic defects, genetic counsellors help couples assess the risks of passing along genetic defects to their children. Some couples who face a high risk of passing along genetic defects to their children decide to adopt. Other couples decide to have an abortion if the fetus is determined to have certain abnormalities. Various medical procedures are used to detect the presence of these disorders in the fetus.

Parental blood tests can suggest the presence of problems such as sickle-cell anemia, Tay–Sachs disease, and neural tube defects. Still other tests examine fetal DNA and can indicate the presence of Huntington's chorea, cystic fibrosis, and other disorders. Blood tests also now allow detection of Down syndrome during the first trimester.

Childbirth

Early in the ninth month of pregnancy, the fetus's head settles in the pelvis. This shift is called "dropping" or "lightening." The woman may actually feel lighter because of lessened pressure on the diaphragm. About a day or so before the beginning of labour, the woman may notice blood in her vaginal secretions because fetal pressure on the pelvis may rupture superficial blood vessels in the birth canal.

Canadian Trends

REDUCING HEALTH RISK FACTORS FOR PREGNANT TEENS

The rates of teen pregnancy and low birth weights in Northern Ontario are higher than for the rest of the province. These concerns led health units in the districts of Sudbury, Manitoulin, and Algoma to conduct a three-year teen prenatal study (PHERO, 1999) involving 397 pregnant teens aged 14 to 19 years.

Before they knew they were pregnant, 90% of these teens smoked, 90% drank alcohol, and about two-thirds used illicit drugs. During the period of the study, alcohol and drug use was reduced dramatically to 8% and 5%, respectively. However, it was more difficult to reduce smoking, with 60% continuing to smoke. Those who continued to smoke, drink alcohol, and take drugs were less likely than those who stopped to believe that these practices were harmful to the baby. As well, barriers to quitting included the addictive nature of tobacco, the use of cigarettes as a means of dealing with stress, and the fact that people around them smoked. About four-fifths of the teenagers studied reported that they tried to improve their eating habits, with about half taking prenatal vitamins. The main barrier to improved nutrition was the lack of sufficient money to pay for proper food.

Those who continued with risky health practices had more problematic births:

- Those who smoked during pregnancy were more than twice as likely as nonsmokers to have low-birth-weight and/or premature babies.
- Those who drank during pregnancy were more than twice as likely as nondrinkers to have low-birth-weight babies.
- Those who had inadequate nutrition were more than twice as likely as those who ate well to have low-birth-weight babies.
- Drug users were more than three times as likely as non-users to have premature babies.

This study of high-risk teenage mothers shows that, when given proper health education along with supportive counselling, the majority of teen mothers do make significant changes in their alcohol consumption, drug use, and nutritional habits. Most really do want to do "what is best for the baby." Unfortunately, the addictive nature of tobacco makes it more difficult to quit smoking, and in this area greater efforts need to be made.

Tissue that had plugged the cervix, possibly preventing entry of infectious agents from the vagina, becomes dislodged. There is a resultant discharge of bloody mucus. At about this time, 1 woman in 10 also has a rush of warm "water" from the vagina. The "water" is amniotic fluid, and it means that the amniotic sac has burst. Labour usually begins within a day after rupture of the amniotic sac. For most women the amniotic sac does not burst until the end of the first stage of childbirth. Labour begins with the onset of regular uterine contractions.

The first uterine contractions are relatively painless and are called **Braxton–Hicks contractions**, or false labour contractions. They are "false" because they do not widen the cervix or advance the baby through the birth canal. They tend to increase in frequency but are less regular than labour contractions. Real labour contractions, by contrast, become more intense when the woman moves around or walks.

The Stages of Childbirth

Childbirth begins with the onset of labour and has three stages.

In the first stage, uterine contractions **efface** and **dilate** the cervix to about 10 cm (4 in.) in diameter, so that the baby may pass. Stretching of the cervix causes most of the pain of childbirth. A woman may experience little or no pain if her cervix dilates easily and quickly. The first stage may last from a couple of hours to more than a day. Twelve to 24 hours of labour is considered about average for a first pregnancy. In later pregnancies labour takes about half this time.

The initial contractions are usually mild and spaced widely, at intervals of 10 to 20 minutes. They may last 20 to 40 seconds. As time passes, contractions become more frequent, long, strong, and regular.

Transition is the process that occurs when the cervix becomes almost fully dilated and the baby's head begins to move into the vagina, or birth canal. Contractions usually

Braxton-Hicks contractions So-called false labour contractions that are relatively painless.

Efface To become thin.

Dilate To open or widen.

Transition The process during which the cervix becomes almost fully dilated and the head of the fetus begins to move into the birth canal.

Episiotomy A surgical incision in the perineum that widens the birth canal, preventing random tearing during childbirth.

Perineum The area between the vulva and the anus.

come quickly during transition. Transition usually lasts about 30 minutes or less and is often accompanied by feelings of nausea, chills, and intense pain.

The second stage of childbirth follows transition and begins when the cervix has become fully dilated and the baby begins to move into the vagina and first appears at the opening of the birth canal. The second stage is shorter than the first stage. It lasts from a few minutes to a few hours and ends with the birth of the baby.

Each contraction of the second stage propels the baby farther along the birth canal (vagina). When the baby's head becomes visible at the vaginal opening, it is said to have *crowned.* The baby typically emerges fully a few minutes after crowning.

An **episiotomy** may be performed on the mother when the baby's head has crowned. The purpose is to prevent the random tearing of the **perineum** that can occur if it becomes extremely effaced. Episiotomies are controversial, however (Roberts, 2000). Physicians generally agree that an episiotomy should be performed if the baby's shoulders are too wide to emerge without causing tearing or if the baby's heartbeat drops for an extended period of time (Eason & Feldman, 2000).

In Canada the number of episiotomies is decreasing. In 1991, episiotomies were performed in almost half of vaginal births. By 2001, this occurred in only about one-quarter of vaginal births. Rates have also fallen in the United States and other countries (Canadian Institute for Health Information, 2004).

The third, or placental, stage of childbirth may last from a few minutes to an hour or more. During this stage, the placenta is expelled. Detachment of the placenta from the uterine wall may cause some bleeding. The uterus begins the process of contracting to a smaller size. The attending physician sews up the episiotomy or any tears in the perineum.

IN THE NEW WORLD As the baby's head emerges, mucus is cleared from its mouth by means of suction aspiration to prevent the breathing passageway from being obstructed. Aspiration is often repeated once the baby is fully delivered. Once the baby is breathing adequately, the umbilical cord is clamped and severed about 7.5 cm (3 in.) from the baby's body. The stump of the umbilical cord dries and falls off in its own time, usually in 7 to 10 days.

While the mother is in the third stage of labour, the caregiver may perform procedures on the baby, such as placing drops of silver nitrate or an antibiotic ointment into the eyes. This procedure is required to prevent bacterial infections in the newborn's eyes.

Methods of Childbirth

Until the twentieth century, childbirth was usually an event that happened at home and involved the mother, a midwife, family, and friends. These days, women in Canada typically give birth in hospitals attended by physicians who use surgical instruments and anesthetics to protect mothers and children from infection, complications, and pain. Medical procedures save lives but also make childbearing more impersonal. Social critics argue that these procedures have medicalized a natural process, usurping control over women's bodies and, through the use of drugs, denying many women the experience of giving birth.

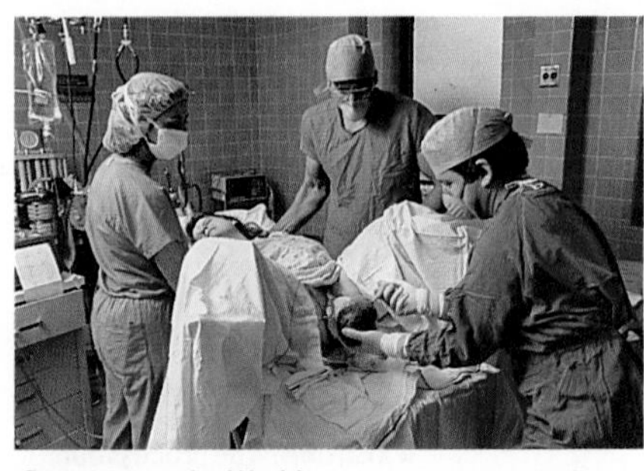

Coming into the World.
Childbirth progresses through three stages. In the first stage, uterine contractions efface and dilate the cervix so that the baby can pass through. The second stage lasts from a few minutes to a few hours and ends with the birth of the baby. During the third stage, the placenta is expelled.

ANESTHETIZED CHILDBIRTH During the past two centuries, science and medicine have led to the expectation that women should experience minimal discomfort during childbirth. Today some anesthesia is used to minimize or eliminate pain in most Canadian deliveries.

Anesthetic drugs, as well as tranquillizers and narcotics, decrease the strength of uterine contractions during delivery. They may thus delay the process of cervical dilation and prolong labour. They also reduce the woman's ability to push the baby through the birth canal.

And because they cross the placental membrane, they also lower the newborn's overall responsiveness. However, there is little evidence that medicated childbirth has serious, long-term consequences for children.

PREPARED CHILDBIRTH: THE LAMAZE METHOD The French obstetrician Fernand Lamaze visited the Soviet Union in 1951 and found that many Russian women bore babies without anesthetics and without reporting a great deal of pain. Lamaze returned to Western Europe with some of the techniques the women used; they are now termed the **Lamaze method**, or *prepared childbirth*. Lamaze (1981) argued that women can learn to conserve energy during childbirth and reduce the pain of uterine contractions by associating the contractions with other responses, such as thinking of pleasant mental images such as beach scenes, or engaging in breathing and relaxation exercises.

A pregnant woman typically attends Lamaze classes with a "coach"—usually the father or partner—who will aid her in the delivery room by timing contractions, offering emotional support, and coaching her in the breathing and relaxation exercises. The partner is integrated into the process, and many couples report that their relationships are strengthened as a result.

The Lamaze method is flexible about the use of anesthetics. Many women report some pain during delivery and obtain anesthetics. However, the Lamaze method appears to help women to gain a greater sense of control over the delivery process.

CAESAREAN SECTION In a **caesarean section**, the baby is delivered through surgery rather than naturally through the vagina. In a caesarean section (C-section for short) the woman is anesthetized, and incisions are made in the abdomen and uterus so that the surgeon can remove the baby. The incisions are then sewn up and the mother can begin walking, often on the same day, although generally with some discomfort for a while.

C-sections are most likely to be advised when normal delivery is difficult or threatening to the health of the mother or child. Vaginal deliveries can become difficult if the baby is large, the mother's pelvis is small or misshapen, or the mother is tired, weakened, or aging. Herpes and HIV infections in the birth canal can be bypassed by C-section. C-sections are also likely to be performed if the baby presents for delivery in the breech position (feet downward) or the **transverse position** (lying crosswise) or if the baby is in distress.

Use of the C-section has mushroomed. In Canada, in 2006, C-section rates reached an all-time high of 26.3% of in-hospital deliveries compared with 17% in 1993 (The Canadian Institute for Health Information, 2007). More Canadian women are having C-sections the first time they give birth and fewer are delivering vaginally after having a previous C-section birth (The Canadian Institute for Health Information, 2004).

The Society of Obstetricians and Gynecologists of Canada (SOGC) is concerned by the rising trend of C-sections. The Society urges women to opt for C-sections only when medically necessary. Previously the Society had recommended that pregnant women should be allowed to choose to have a C-section even if there were no medical reasons for it (The Society of Obstetricians and Gynecologists of Canada, 2008).

According to the SOGC, women considering C-sections should be informed that having a C-section is potentially more dangerous for healthy mothers than a vaginal delivery. Women who have C-sections take substantially longer to recover. C-sections present greater risks of complications such as infection, bleeding, scarring, chronic pelvic pain, and damage to the intestines or bladder. C-sections also increase the risks during subsequent pregnancies, making a repeat C-section more likely (The Society of Obstetricians and Gynecologists of Canada, 2008).

However, do not forget that sometimes there are excellent reasons for having C-sections. It makes no sense to avoid a C-section if vaginal delivery might put the mother or the baby at risk.

Lamaze method A childbirth method during which women learn about childbirth, learn to relax and to breathe in patterns that conserve energy and lessen pain, and have a coach (usually the father) present at childbirth; also termed *prepared childbirth*.

Caesarean section A method of childbirth in which the fetus is delivered through a surgical incision in the abdomen.

Transverse position A crosswise birth position.

The Society of Obstetricians and Gynecologists of Canada

www.sogc.org

Preterm Born before 37 weeks of gestation.

Birth Problems

Most deliveries are uncomplicated, or "unremarkable" in the medical sense—although childbirth is the most remarkable experience of many parents' lives. Problems can and do occur, however.

PRETERM AND LOW-BIRTH-WEIGHT CHILDREN A neonate is considered to be premature, or **preterm**, if it is born before 37 weeks of gestation. The normal period of gestation is 40 weeks. Prematurity is generally linked with low birth weight, because the fetus normally makes dramatic gains in weight during the last weeks of pregnancy.

Regardless of the length of its gestation period, a newborn baby is considered to have a low birth weight if it weighs less than about two kilograms. Preterm and low-birth-weight babies face a heightened risk of infant mortality from causes ranging from asphyxia and infections to sudden infant death syndrome (SIDS) (Berger, 2000; Kramer et al., 2000). Neurological and developmental problems are also common among preterm infants, especially those born at or prior to 25 weeks of gestation (Wood et al., 2000).

Preterm infants usually remain in the hospital for a time. There they can be monitored and placed in incubators that provide a temperature-controlled environment and offer some protection from infection. If necessary, they may also receive oxygen. Although remarkable advances are being made in our ability to help preterm babies survive, the likelihood of developmental disabilities continues to increase dramatically for babies who are born at 25 weeks of gestation or earlier (Cole, 2000).

STILLBIRTH Stillbirth, in which the baby is born dead, is the gravest of birth problems. Stillbirth is connected with fetal abnormalities, infection, medical conditions of the mother, and pregnancy complications such as pre-eclampsia and problems with the placenta (Pasupathy & Smith, 2005). Yet the majority of cases have no clear cause and are considered unexplainable. In Canada there are about 2200 stillbirths each year (6.4 stillbirths for every 1000 total births; Statistics Canada, 2007b). Stillbirth has a deep psychological impact on parents, leading, in many cases, to post-traumatic stress disorder (PTSD), which is characterized by rumination about the loss, intrusive thoughts, and nightmares (Born et al., 2006). When a baby still within the mother is declared dead, she

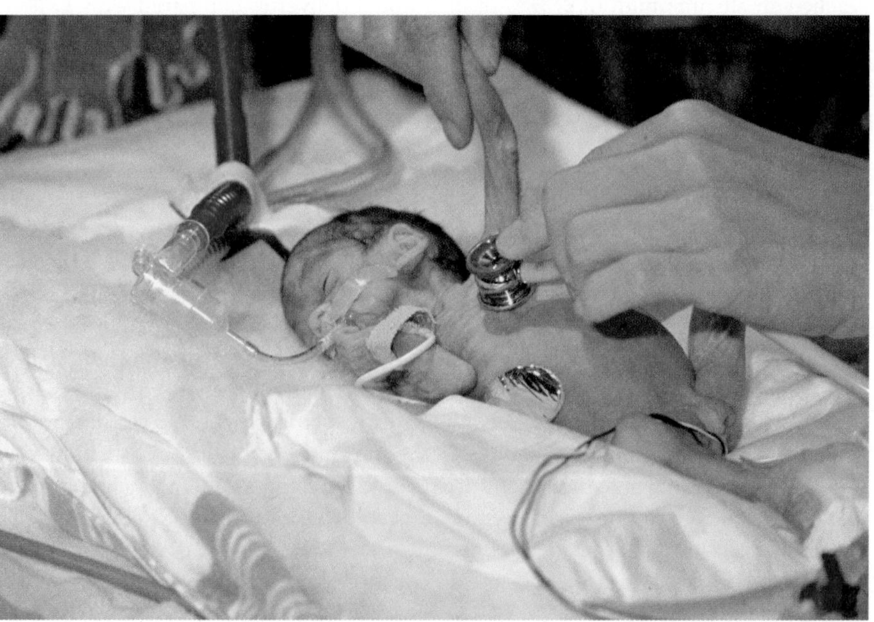

Too Early.
A baby is considered premature if it is born before 37 weeks of gestation. Premature babies are vulnerable to various developmental problems.

A World of Diversity

MATERNAL AND INFANT MORTALITY AROUND THE WORLD

Contemporary medicine has made great contributions to the safety of childbirth and infancy, but they are not distributed equally throughout the world. Save the Children, a nonprofit relief and development organization, tracks the likelihood that women will die during pregnancy and childbirth (maternal mortality) and that infants will die during their first year (infant mortality).

These mortality rates reflect factors such as the percentage of births that are attended by trained people, the literacy rate of women (a measure of women's education), and participation of women in government (a measure of women's empowerment). The safest place for childbirth and infancy is Sweden, where a woman's chance of dying in childbirth is about 1 in 30 000, and only 3 in 1000 infants die before their first birthday. Sweden also has close to a 100% adult female literacy rate, provides trained personnel to assist in all births, and has the greatest participation rate (45%) by women in national government. The most dangerous place is Afghanistan, where 1 woman in 6 will die during pregnancy or delivery, and 165 children of 1000 will die before their first birthday. Only 21% of Afghan women can read; 12% are assisted in birth by a professional; and, in this patriarchal society, women have almost no voice in government. There is also little if any prenatal care in Afghanistan.

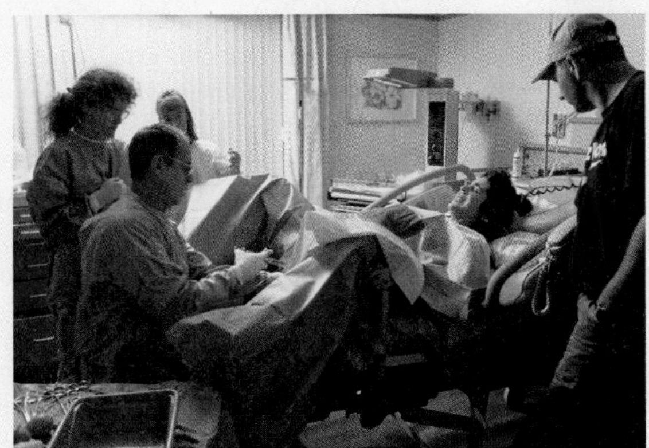

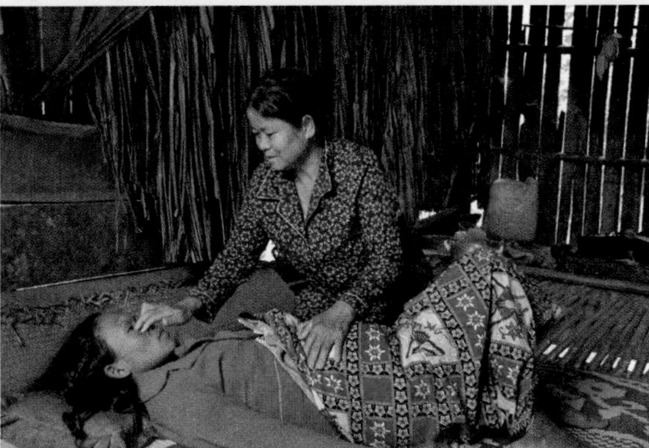

A Mother's Safety Depends on Where She's Having Her Child. It's not just the medical care. It's the wider issue of whether the culture empowers women.

Source: Adapted from the Complete Mothers' Index 2004 in Children Having Children: State of the World's Mothers 2004. *Reprinted by permission of Save the Children USA.*

may need a few hours before labour is induced to adjust to the fact (Trulsson & Rådestad, 2004).

The Postpartum Period

The weeks after delivery are called the **postpartum** period. The first few days postpartum are frequently happy ones. The long wait is over, as are the discomforts of childbirth. However, about 70% of new mothers have periods of tearfulness, sadness, and irritability that the American Psychiatric Association (2000) refers to as "baby blues." Baby blues and other postpartum mood problems are so common that they are statistically normal (Gavin et al., 2005).

Postpartum After Childbirth

Postpartum Following birth.

Baby blues affect the majority of women in the weeks after delivery. Researchers believe they are common because they are caused by the hormonal changes that

Prolactin A pituitary hormone that stimulates production of milk. (From roots that mean "for milk.")

Lactation Production of milk by the mammary glands.

accompany and follow delivery (Bloch et al., 2006; Morris, 2000). They last for about 10 days and are not severe enough to impair the mother's functioning. As many as 1 in 5 to 10 women encounter a more serious mood disorder called postpartum depression (PPD). PPD begins within four weeks after delivery and may linger for weeks or months. PPD is symptomized by serious sadness, feelings of hopelessness and helplessness, feelings of worthlessness, difficulty concentrating, and major changes in appetite (usually loss of appetite) and sleep patterns (frequently insomnia). There can also be severe fluctuations in mood, from depression to elation and then back to depression. Some women show obsessive concern with the well-being of their babies at this time.

Some researchers suggest that PPD is caused by the interactions of biological (mainly hormonal) factors, including that precipitous drop-off in estrogen (Johnstone et al., 2001), and psychological factors, such as

- Concerns about the life changes that motherhood creates
- Concerns about whether one will be a good mother
- Marital problems
- Having a sick or unwanted baby

But the focus today is on the biological, because there are major changes in body chemistry during and after pregnancy, and because women around the world seem to experience similar disturbances in mood, even when their life experiences and support systems are very different from those we find in Canada and the United States (Cohen et al., 2006).

Women who experience PPD may benefit from psychotherapy or drugs. Drugs that increase estrogen levels or antidepressants may help. Most women recover from PPD on their own. At the very least, women need to know that the problem is not unusual and does not necessarily mean that there is something seriously wrong with them or that they are not living up to their obligations.

LESBIAN MOTHERS Lesbian mothers are also at risk for maternal depression. University of Toronto researcher Lori Ross, in reviewing the research literature, concluded that lesbian mothers may experience more stress because of less support from their own parents and because of societal prejudices. On the other hand, there are also factors reducing stress and the likelihood of postpartum depression. For example, lesbian pregnancies are more likely to be planned, and there is more of an equal division of labour in childcare in lesbian couples (Ross, 2005).

Breastfeeding

Breastfeeding reduces the baby's general risk of infections by transmitting the mother's antibodies to the baby. Breastfeeding also reduces the incidence of allergies in babies, particularly in allergy-prone infants (Barisic, 1998). On the other hand, HIV (the AIDS virus) can be transmitted to infants via breast milk. According to U.N. estimates, one-third of the infants with HIV around the world were infected via breast milk (United Nations Special Session on AIDS, 2001). Moreover, when undernourished mothers in developing countries breastfeed their babies, the babies too can become malnourished.

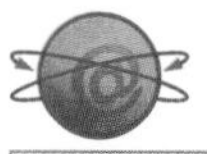

La Leche League International
Provides information, support, and encouragement to women who want to breastfeed.
www.lalecheleague.org

The hormones prolactin and oxytocin are involved in breastfeeding. **Prolactin** stimulates production of milk, or **lactation**, two to three days after delivery. Oxytocin causes the breasts to eject milk and is secreted in response to suckling. When an infant is weaned, secretion of prolactin and oxytocin is discontinued, and lactation comes to an end.

Uterine contractions that occur during breastfeeding help return the uterus to its typical size, leading the belly to flatten more quickly. Because of the expenditure of energy, breastfeeding may also help women lose the extra weight of pregnancy

Canadian Trends

BREASTFEEDING VERSUS BOTTLE-FEEDING

In 2003 the Canadian Community Health Survey of women who had given birth in the previous five years found that 85% of Canadian mothers breastfeed their newborns. This represents a marked increase from the mid-1960s, when only about 25% of Canadian women breastfed. Canadian public health guidelines call for exclusive breastfeeding for at least the first six months. However, only 17% of Canadian women breastfeed that long (Miller & McLean, 2005).

As shown in Table 10.2, breastfeeding rates are lower in the Atlantic provinces and Quebec than in the rest of Canada.

Researchers at McMaster University (Callen & Pinelli, 2004) conducted a comparative literature review of breastfeeding patterns in Canada, the United States, Europe, and Australia. Rates and duration of breastfeeding of infants were higher in Europe and Australia than in Canada and the United States. Across all four countries, breastfeeding incidence and duration were highest among women who were older, were married, were better educated, and had higher incomes.

In the 2003 Canadian Community Health Survey, immigrants were more likely to breastfeed than Canadian-born women, and women in urban areas were more likely to breastfeed than women in rural areas.

The most common reason Canadian mothers give for breastfeeding is that it is better for the baby. When asked why they did not breastfeed, common answers were:

- There was not enough breast milk
- The baby weaned himself or herself
- The mother returned to work or school
- It was inconvenient or tiring (Statistics Canada, 2005d)

Health Canada recommends that mothers breastfeed their babies for at least six months. In 2001, the Canadian federal government extended maternity leave from six months to one year. This resulted in more women breastfeeding for a longer time. The proportion of women breastfeeding for at least six months increased from 20% to 28% (Statistics Canada, 2007d).

TABLE 10.2

Percentage of Canadian Women Who Breastfeed at Birth and at Six Months

Province	At Birth	At Six Months
Newfoundland and Labrador	63%	9%
Prince Edward Island	77	12
Nova Scotia	76	14
New Brunswick	64	8
Quebec	76	10
Ontario	87	18
Manitoba	89	18
Saskatchewan	86	18
Alberta	90	22
British Columbia	93	28

Source: Statistics Canada, Canadian Community Health Survey, 2003.

Reactions to breastfeeding vary. Many women enjoy the emotional intimacy of breastfeeding. Some find it physically enjoyable. Others find it unpleasant and a nuisance. Some appreciate the convenience of having nothing to buy, stir, warm, refrigerate, and cart along. Others are embarrassed at uncovering their breasts in public or find it constraining to have the baby with them most of the time. Some choose to share feeding chores with the father, who is equally equipped to prepare and hold a bottle, but not, of course, to breastfeed (although he can give a baby expressed milk in a bottle when the mother is not available).

Most Canadians are supportive of breastfeeding. However, in a study of longer-term breastfeeding, Brock University researcher Lynn Rempel (2004) found that mothers who were breastfeeding at nine months perceived that approval for breastfeeding declined as the baby got older.

more quickly. Breastfeeding also delays resumption of normal menstrual cycles. Breastfeeding is not a completely reliable birth-control method, however.

DOES BREASTFEEDING AFFECT SEXUAL BEHAVIOUR? In an analysis of the research literature, researchers at the University of British Columbia found that women who breastfeed are more likely than those who bottle-feed to experience decreased sexual desire, decreased frequency of sexual intercourse, and painful intercourse because of lack of vaginal lubrication (LaMarre et al., 2003).

LaMarre et al. (2003) conclude that breastfeeding decreases both androgen levels, leading to decreased sexual desire, and estrogen levels, leading to vaginal

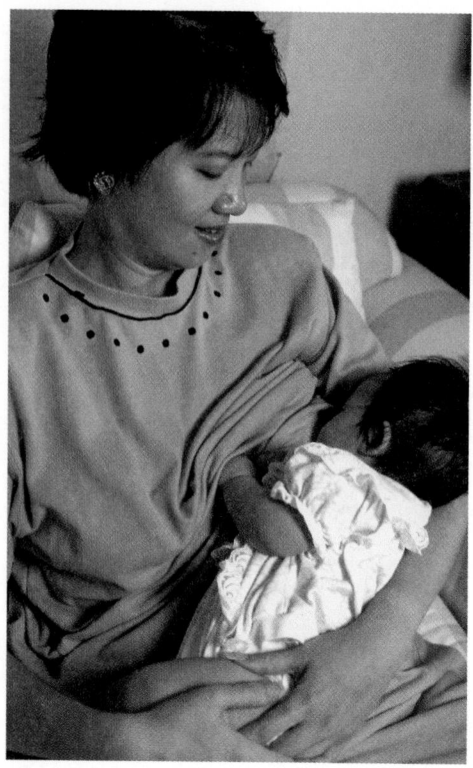

Breastfeeding Seems to Be the "Gold Standard" for Mothers in Canada Today. Why? Is it always possible? Under what circumstances should women not breastfeed their children?

dryness. Also, breastfeeding mothers are more fatigued from having to get up at night to breastfeed their child. However, differences in sexuality between breastfeeders and bottle-feeders diminish considerably after 12 months.

Should a woman breastfeed her baby? The issue has become highly politicized (Law, 2000). Much of the vast literature on breastfeeding has little to do with the advantages of breast milk or formula, but with occupational and domestic arrangements, day care, mother–infant bonding, and the politics of domestic decision making. Although breastfeeding has benefits for both mother and infant, each woman must weigh these benefits against the difficulties breastfeeding may pose for her.

Resumption of Ovulation and Menstruation

For close to a month after delivery, women experience a reddish vaginal discharge called **lochia**. A non-nursing mother does not resume actual menstrual periods until two to three months postpartum. The first few cycles are likely to be irregular. Many women incorrectly assume that they will resume menstruating after childbirth by first having a menstrual period and then ovulating two weeks later. In most cases the opposite is true. Ovulation precedes the first menstrual period after childbirth. Thus a woman may become pregnant before the menstrual phase of her first postpartum cycle. Some women, but not all, who suffered premenstrual syndrome before their pregnancies find that their periods give them less discomfort after the birth of their children.

Resumption of Sexual Activity

The resumption of coitus depends on a couple's level of sexual interest, the healing of episiotomies or other injuries, fatigue, the recommendations of physicians, and, of course, tradition. Obstetricians usually advise a six-week waiting period for safety and comfort. One study of 570 women found that they actually resumed sexual intercourse an average of seven weeks after childbirth (Byrd et al., 1998).

Lochia A reddish vaginal discharge that may persist for a month after delivery.

Women typically prefer to delay coitus until it becomes physically comfortable, generally when the episiotomy or other lacerations have healed and the lochia has ended. This may take several weeks. Women who breastfeed may also find that they

Applied Knowledge

WHERE TO GET HELP BREASTFEEDING

During pregnancy, women tend to romanticize breastfeeding, assuming that this natural function will be pleasant and trouble-free. But many women encounter problems, ranging from local irritation to difficulty maintaining the flow of milk. As noted by lactation consultant Corky Harvey (2000), breastfeeding can be painful, inconvenient, and stressful, especially at first.

Harvey suggests that women who are having problems breastfeeding call the hospital where they delivered and ask whether it has a lactation consultant or can refer them to one. Or call your pediatrician or obstetrician or a friend or relative who has successfully breastfed.

The internet can also be helpful: Try **www.breastfeeding.org**, **www.breastfeeding.com**, **www.lalecheleague.org**, or **www.ILCA.org**, the site for the International Lactation Consultants Association.

have less vaginal lubrication, and the dryness can cause discomfort during coitus. K-Y jelly or other lubricants may help in such cases. Couples may enjoy other forms of sexual activity earlier; as soon as both partners are interested and comfortable.

The return of sexual interest and resumption of sexual activity may take longer for some couples than for others. Sexual interest depends more on psychological than on physical factors. Many couples encounter declining sexual interest and activity in the first year following childbirth, generally because childcare can sap energy and limit free time. Generally speaking, couples whose sexual relationships were satisfying before the baby arrived tend to show greater sexual interest and to resume sexual activity earlier than those who had less satisfying relationships beforehand. (No surprise.)

Summing Up

Conception is the union of a sperm cell and an ovum. Fertilization normally occurs in a fallopian tube.

Optimizing the chances of conception means engaging in coitus at the time of ovulation. Ovulation can be predicted by calculating the woman's basal body temperature, analyzing the woman's urine for luteinizing hormone, or tracking the thickness of vaginal mucus.

Fertility problems in the male include low sperm count, irregularly shaped sperm, low sperm motility, certain chronic or infectious diseases, trauma to the testes, an autoimmune response to sperm, and pituitary imbalances and/or thyroid disease.

The major causes of infertility in women include irregular ovulation, obstructions or malfunctions of the reproductive tract, endometriosis, and the decline of hormone levels with age. Failure to ovulate may often be overcome by fertility drugs. Methods for overcoming other female fertility problems include in vitro fertilization, GIFT, ZIFT, donor IVF, embryonic transfer, and surrogate motherhood.

In Canada, the federal government act respecting assisted human reproduction and related research, whose short title is the Assisted Human Reproduction Act, includes a controversial provision that would allow researchers to use stem cells from embryos left over from infertility treatment.

Early signs of pregnancy include a missed period and the presence of human chorionic gonadotropin (HCG) in the blood or urine.

Pregnancy tests detect the presence of HCG in the woman's urine or blood.

Miscarriages have many causes, including chromosomal defects in the fetus and abnormalities of the placenta and uterus.

Most health professionals concur that, in most cases, coitus is safe until the start of labour.

A woman's psychological response to pregnancy reflects her desire to be pregnant, her physical changes, and her attitudes toward these changes.

The germinal stage is the period from conception to implantation.

The embryonic stage begins with implantation, extends to about the eighth week of development, and is characterized by differentiation of the major organ systems.

The fetal stage begins by the ninth week, continues until the birth of the baby, and is characterized by continued maturation of the fetus's organ systems and dramatic increases in size.

Environmental factors that affect prenatal development include the mother's diet, maternal diseases and disorders, and drugs. Maternal malnutrition has been linked to low birth weight and infant mortality. Exposure to particular teratogens causes the greatest harm during critical periods of vulnerability.

Chromosomal and genetic abnormalities can lead to birth defects.

In the first stage of childbirth, uterine contractions efface and dilate the cervix so that the baby may pass through. The second stage begins when the cervix is fully dilated and ends with the birth of the baby. During the third stage, the placenta is expelled.

Contemporary methods for facilitating childbirth include anesthetized childbirth, natural childbirth, the Lamaze method, and caesarean section.

Prenatal anoxia can cause brain damage and mental retardation in the child. Preterm and low-birth-weight babies have a heightened risk of infant mortality.

Many new mothers experience transient mood changes after childbirth. Women with postpartum depression experience lingering depression following childbirth.

Breastfeeding is associated with fewer infections and allergic reactions in the baby than bottle-feeding.

Obstetricians usually advise waiting about six weeks after childbirth before resuming coitus. Couples need not wait this long to enjoy other forms of sexual activity.

Test Yourself

Multiple-Choice Questions

1. According to Statistics Canada, in 2005, the average age of Canadian women having their first baby was ________________ years of age.

a. 25.2
b. 27.2
c. 29.2
d. 31.2

2. ________________ may carry either X or Y chromosomes.

a. sperm
b. ova
c. gametes
d. blastocysts

3. The most common cause of fertility problems in males is ________________.

a. sexually transmitted infections
b. injury to the testes
c. low sperm count
d. old age

4. All of the following can cause infertility in females except

a. failure to ovulate
b. sexually transmitted infections
c. declining levels of estrogen
d. use of illicit drugs

5. Which of the following statements is true?

a. Surrogate motherhood is becoming more common in Canada.
b. Surrogate motherhood contracts must specify the amount of financial support that will be provided.
c. Surrogate motherhood is legal if both parties agree to it.
d. It is illegal to pay a woman to be a surrogate mother.

6. The first stage of prenatal development is the ________________ stage.

a. embryonic
b. placental
c. fetal
d. germinal

7. Most ectopic pregnancies occur in the ________________.

a. ovary
b. cervix
c. fallopian tubes
d. uterus

8. Which stage of childbirth ends with the birth of the baby?

a. the first stage
b. the second stage
c. the third stage
d. the fourth stage

9. Approximately ____________ of women experience some sadness, irritability, or low mood following the birth of a baby.

a. 25%
b. 40%
c. 50%
d. 70%

10. Which statement about postpartum depression (PPD) is false?

a. Women who lack social support are more likely to suffer from PPD.
b. PPD can involve feelings of extreme sadness and apathy.
c. PPD may be caused by a combination of physiological and psychological factors.
d. Women with PPD are always a danger to their babies.

Answers to the Test Yourself questions in each chapter are found on page 509.

Critical Thinking Questions

1. Today's reproductive technologies make it possible for infertile couples to have children, for women to have babies after menopause, and for women to give birth to their own grandchildren using eggs donated by their daughters. It might even be possible for parents to choose to have a child of a particular genetic makeup in order to provide bone marrow or other tissue to save another of their children. However, the development of these technologies has leapfrogged ahead of society's efforts to grapple with their ethical, moral, and legal implications. Where should the line be drawn in determining how far medical science should go in these matters?
2. A good friend of yours is pregnant. You notice that she is still drinking alcohol and smoking cigarettes. Would you confront her about these behaviours? Why or why not?
3. You read a news report that doctors can determine whether a fetus is likely to be heterosexual or homosexual. Should parents have the right to choose the sexual orientation of their children, even to the extent of aborting a "gay" or "lesbian" fetus (or, perhaps for a gay couple, a "heterosexual" fetus)? Why or why not?

Visit MyPsychKit at www.mypsychkit.com, where you can do quizzes and link to additional resources on topics discussed in this text.

CHAPTER ELEVEN

Contraception and Abortion

History of Contraception Museum.
This museum was established in Toronto by the pharmaceutical firm Janssen-Ortho, Inc. One of the artifacts on display is the caecum (intestinal pouch) of a sheep, which was used by early Egyptian males as a form of condom.

Condom A sheath made of animal membrane or latex that covers the penis during coitus and serves as a barrier to sperm following ejaculation.

People have been devising means of contraception since they became aware of the relationship between coitus and conception. Greek and Roman women placed absorbent materials within the vagina to absorb semen. The use of sheaths or coverings for the penis has a long history. Sheaths worn over the penis as decorative covers can be traced to ancient Egypt (1350 B.C.). Sheaths of linen were first described in European writings in 1564 by the Italian anatomist Fallopius (from whom the name of the fallopian tube is derived). The term **condom** was not used to describe penile sheaths until the eighteenth century. At that time, sheaths made of animal intestines became popular as a means of preventing sexually transmitted infections and unwanted pregnancies.

Condoms made of rubber (hence the slang "rubbers") were introduced shortly after Charles Goodyear invented vulcanization of rubber in 1843. Many other forms of contraception were also used widely in the nineteenth century, including withdrawal, vaginal sponges, and douching.

Contraceptive Use Among Canadian Adolescents

In the 2005–2006 Canadian Health Behaviour in School-Aged Children study, about a quarter of the students in grade 10 had experienced sexual intercourse (Boyce et al., 2008). Among these sexually experienced youth, the most common contraceptive methods used at last intercourse were condoms (males, 47%; females, 40%) and the birth-control pill (males, 25%; females, 33%). Withdrawal was the third most common method (males, 8%; females, 14%).

Canadian Trends

CONTRACEPTIVE USE IN CANADA

In 2002, Bill Fisher of the University of Western Ontario, along with Richard Boroditsky of the University of Manitoba and Brian Morris at the University of Toronto, conducted their fourth national survey on the contraceptive attitudes and behaviours of Canadian women aged 15 to 44 (Fisher et al., 2004a, 2004b). In total, 1582 responses were received for a response rate of 47%, down from 70% in the 1984 Canadian Fertility Study.

Almost all of the women were familiar with oral contraceptives (96%) and condoms (93%). Only around one-half were familiar with other methods such as sterilization (62%), withdrawal (59%), the morning-after pill (57%), and intrauterine devices (50%). Oral contraceptives were by far the preferred method, with 63% favouring them and 31% currently using them. In second place were condoms and sterilization; 38% had a very favourable opinion of condoms and 21% were currently using them, while 39% had a very positive view of male sterilization and 15% said their male partner had been sterilized. Nine percent of the respondents reported they did not use contraception. In analyzing contraceptive trends since 1993, Fisher et al. concluded:

- Canadian women consistently rate oral contraceptives highly and continue to use them more than any other contraceptive.
- Approval ratings for condoms have risen slightly, while actual condom use has declined.
- Female sterilization and IUDs have fallen out of favour.
- Women frequently switch their methods of contraception.
- Younger women are more likely to use oral contraceptives and condoms, while older women are more likely to use sterilization.

Relatively few studies of contraceptive use have focused on immigrant groups in Canada. One exception is a study of ethnic Chinese women in Vancouver who wanted to have an abortion (Wiebe et al., 2002). There was a clear difference between the Chinese women born in Canada and new immigrants. The Chinese immigrant women had more negative attitudes toward the birth-control pill. In particular, single female immigrants linked using oral contraceptives with promiscuity and "bad women." Some were also concerned about weight gain and infertility.

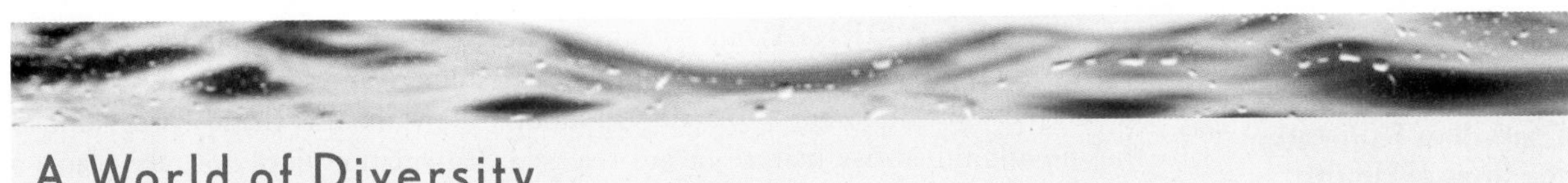

A World of Diversity

HISTORY OF BIRTH CONTROL IN CANADA

Birth control was legal in Canada until the nineteenth century, when laws were introduced forbidding the use of birth control and abortion. It was even illegal to provide information about birth control. Because contraceptives were associated with loose morals and prostitution, it was considered unacceptable for doctors to discuss birth control with their patients.

The movement to legalize contraception in Canada began in the 1920s with female activists in Vancouver, who formed the Canadian Birth Control League. In the following years, several women's groups from across Canada also began to lobby politicians to change the law that prohibited the use of birth control. A few men also joined the cause.

Despite protests by some physicians, Mary Hawkins established the first Canadian birth control clinic in Hamilton, Ontario, in the early 1930s. In 1937, clinics were also set up in Windsor and Kitchener. A prominent supporter of birth control education at that time was A. R. Kaufman, a wealthy Kitchener businessman who hired women to deliver birth control information door to door.

The first major legal challenge to the law forbidding the dissemination of birth control information came with the arrest of Dorothea Palmer (an employee of Kaufman) for promoting birth control in the poorer districts of the Ottawa region. Her arrest sparked protests and support by birth control activists, including Kaufman, who helped to win her acquittal in court. This victory helped to legitimize birth-control education and spurred the birth control movement to make greater efforts in the struggle to legalize all birth control activities.

By the 1960s, the use of contraceptives (particularly the birth-control pill) had become so widespread that most Canadians did not realize that contraceptives were still illegal. The 1960 arrest of Harold Fine, a Toronto pharmacist, for selling condoms enraged many Canadians. As a result, in 1961 Barbara and George Cadbury established the Planned Parenthood Association of Toronto with the objective of amending the Criminal Code. And in 1965 another leader in the birth control movement, Dr. Marion Powell, opened the first city-funded public health clinic (focused on family planning) in Scarborough, Ontario.

It was not until 1969, under the leadership of Prime Minister Pierre Trudeau, that contraception became legal and abortion was allowed under restricted conditions. Today, contraceptives are widely advertised in popular magazines and openly displayed on pharmacy shelves.

The use of **artificial contraception** continues to be opposed by many groups, including the Roman Catholic Church. Yet many individual Catholics, including many priests, hold liberal attitudes toward contraception.

Sources: The Planned Parenthood Federation of Canada (1999), A History of Birth Control in Canada; *Liu, K. E., and Fisher, W.A. (2002). Canadian Physician's Role in Contraception from the 19th Century to Now.* Journal of Obstetrics and Gynaecology Canada, *24(3), 239–44.*

A large-scale study of teenagers in British Columbia (Saewyc et al., 2007) found that condom use during last intercourse increased from 1992 to 2003 (64% to 75% among males, and 53% to 64% among females). As teenagers get older and form longer-term relationships, they switch from using condoms to using the pill.

Methods of Contraception

Oral Contraceptives ("the Pill")

An **oral contraceptive** is commonly referred to as a birth-control pill or simply "the pill." However, there are many kinds of birth-control pills that vary in the type and dosages of hormones they contain. Birth-control pills fall into two major categories: combination pills and minipills.

Combination pills contain a combination of synthetic forms of the hormones estrogen and progesterone (progestin). Most combination pills provide a steady dose of synthetic estrogen and progesterone. Other combination pills, called *multiphasic* pills, vary the dosage of these hormones across the menstrual cycle to reduce the overall dosages to which the woman is exposed and possible side effects. The **minipill** contains synthetic progesterone (progestin) only.

Artificial contraception A method of contraception that applies a human-made device.

Oral contraceptive A contraceptive, consisting of sex hormones, that is taken by mouth.

Combination pill A birth-control pill that contains synthetic estrogen and progesterone.

Minipill A birth-control pill that contains synthetic progesterone but no estrogen.

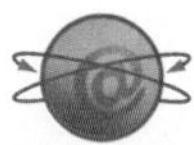

Canadian Federation for Sexual Health
Formerly the Planned Parenthood Federation of Canada, this organization is dedicated to promoting sexual and reproductive health.

www.cfsh.ca

HOW THEY WORK Women cannot conceive when they are already pregnant because their bodies suppress maturation of egg follicles and ovulation. The combination pill fools the brain into acting as though the woman is already pregnant, so that no additional ova mature or are released. If ovulation does not take place, a woman cannot become pregnant.

In a normal menstrual cycle, low levels of estrogen during and just after the menstrual phase stimulate the pituitary gland to secrete FSH, which in turn stimulates the maturation of ovarian follicles. The estrogen in the combination pill inhibits FSH production, so follicles do not mature. The progesterone (progestin) inhibits the pituitary's secretion of LH, which would otherwise lead to ovulation. The woman continues to have menstrual periods, but there is no unfertilized ovum to be sloughed off in the menstrual flow.

The combination pill is taken for 21 days of the typical 28-day cycle. Then, for seven days, the woman does not take a pill or takes an inert placebo pill to maintain the habit of taking a pill a day. The sudden drop in hormone levels causes the endometrium to disintegrate and menstruation to follow three or four days after the last pill has been taken. Then the cycle is repeated.

The progestin in the combination pill also increases the thickness and acidity of the cervical mucus. The mucus thus becomes a more resistant barrier to sperm and inhibits development of the endometrium. Therefore, even if an egg were somehow to mature and become fertilized in a fallopian tube, sperm would not be likely to survive the passage through the cervix. Even if sperm were somehow to succeed in fertilizing an egg, the failure of the endometrium to develop would mean that the fertilized ovum could not become implanted in the uterus. Progestin may also impede the progress of ova through the fallopian tubes and make it more difficult for sperm to penetrate ova.

The minipill contains progestin but no estrogen. Minipills are taken daily through the menstrual cycle, even during menstruation. They act in two ways. They thicken the cervical mucus to impede the passage of sperm through the cervix, and they render the inner lining of the uterus less receptive to a fertilized egg. Thus, even if the woman does conceive, the fertilized egg will pass from the body rather than becoming implanted in the uterine wall.

EFFECTIVENESS The failure rate of the birth-control pill associated with perfect use is very low: 0.5% or less, depending on the type of pill. The failure rate increases to 3% in typical use. Failures can occur when women forget to take the

Canadian Trends

USE OF ORAL CONTRACEPTIVES

Oral contraceptives (OCs) are used by 31% of women in Canada (Fisher et al., 2003). The great majority of Canadian women (83%) use the pill at some time, and, on average, women begin using the pill at age 17. Thirty-four percent of women begin taking the pill before initiating intercourse and 15% start pill use and having intercourse at the same time.

Half of Canadian women believe that it is easy to forget to take the pill every day. Sixty-two percent of current OC users report they had missed taking at least one pill during the previous six months (Fisher et al., 2003).

Canadian women who use the pill are more likely to report a history of STIs than are condom users. Typically, women stop using condoms when they begin using the pill (Fisher et al., 2003).

Canadian women overestimate negative side effects and underestimate positive effects. Many women are not aware that the pill can make periods lighter and reduce the risk of certain cancers (Fisher et al., 2003).

pill for two days or more, when they do not use backup methods when they first go on the pill, and when they switch from one brand to another.

In 2004 the World Health Organization (WHO) issued new guidelines regarding missed pills. First, a woman who misses taking a pill should take one as soon as possible and then continue taking one each day. However, a woman who misses three or more combination pills in a row should use condoms or abstain from sexual intercourse until she has taken pills for seven days in a row. With the lowest-dose pills, a woman should take extra precautions after missing two (Info Reports, 2005).

REVERSIBILITY The use of oral contraceptives may temporarily reduce fertility after they are discontinued but is not associated with permanent infertility. Nearly all women begin ovulating regularly within three months of suspending use. When a woman appears not to be ovulating after going off the pill, a drug like clomiphene is often used to induce ovulation.

ADVANTAGES AND DISADVANTAGES The great advantage of oral contraception is that when used properly, it is nearly 100% effective. Unlike many other forms of contraception, such as the condom or diaphragm, its use does not interfere with sexual spontaneity or diminish sexual sensations.

Birth-control pills may also have some *healthful* side effects. They appear to reduce the risk of pelvic inflammatory disease (PID), benign ovarian cysts, and fibrocystic (benign) breast growths. The pill regularizes menstrual cycles and reduces menstrual cramping and premenstrual discomfort.

Oral contraceptive pills in Canada are approved for a 28-day cycle, meaning that a woman takes a hormone-containing pill each day for 21 days in a row and then takes a sugar (placebo) pill, or stops taking the pill, for the next seven days. Some physicians have prescribed these oral contraceptives (mainly multiphasics) for extended cycles for women who have difficulties with their periods, for example, women with heavy periods, crampy periods, or endometriosis. However, the recently introduced Seasonale is the only oral contraceptive pill that has been specifically approved by Health Canada for an extended cycle of 91 days. For 84 days, a woman takes an active pill, containing ethinyl estradiol and levonorgestrel, and then takes a sugar (placebo) pill, or stops taking Seasonale, for seven days. Taking the pill in this way means fewer menstrual cycles, typically four periods per year.

The pill may also be helpful in the treatment of iron-deficiency anemia and facial acne. The combination pill reduces the risks of ovarian and endometrial cancer, even for a number of years after the woman has stopped taking it (Hatcher et al., 2006).

The pill does have some disadvantages. It confers no protection against STIs. Moreover, it may reduce the effectiveness of antibiotics used to treat STIs. Going on the pill requires medical consultation, so a woman must plan to begin using the pill at least several weeks before becoming sexually active or before discontinuing the use of other contraceptives.

The main drawbacks of birth-control pills are potential side effects and possible health risks. Although a good deal of research suggests that the pill is safe for healthy women, in 2006 the American College of Obstetricians and Gynecologists released a bulletin suggesting caution in women with various pre-existing medical conditions. These include hypertension, diabetes, migraine headaches, fibrocystic breast tissue, uterine fibroids, and elevated cholesterol level.

The estrogen in combination pills may produce side effects such as nausea and vomiting, fluid retention (feeling bloated), weight gain, increased vaginal discharge, headaches, tenderness in the breasts, and dizziness. Many of these are temporary. When they persist, women may be switched from one pill to another, perhaps to one with lower doses of hormones. Pregnant women produce high estrogen levels in the corpus luteum and placenta. The combination pill artificially raises levels of estrogen, so it is not surprising that some women who use it have side effects that mimic the early signs of pregnancy, such as weight gain or nausea ("morning sickness"). Weight gain can result from estrogen (through fluid retention) or progestin (through increased appetite and development of muscle) (Hatcher et al., 2006). Women who encounter problems with high blood pressure from taking the pill are usually advised to switch to another form of contraception.

Many women experience hormone withdrawal symptoms during periods when they do not take the pill (Sulak et al., 2000). These include headaches, pelvic pain, bloating, and breast tenderness.

Many women have avoided using the pill because of the risk of blood clots. The lower dosages of estrogen found in most types of birth-control pills today are associated with much lower risk of blood clots than was the case in the 1960s and 1970s, when higher dosages were used (Hatcher et al., 2006). Still, women who are at increased risk for blood clotting, such as women with a history of circulatory problems or stroke, are typically advised not to use the pill.

Women who are considering using the pill need to weigh the benefits and risks with their physicians. For the great majority of young, healthy women in their twenties and early thirties, the pill is unlikely to cause blood clots or other cardiovascular problems (Hatcher et al., 2006). Although research has found the pill to be safe for most women who do not smoke and are younger than 35, pill users may have a slightly higher chance than nonusers of developing blood clots in the veins and lungs, having a stroke, or having a heart attack (Rako, 2003).

Some women should not be on the pill at all (Hatcher et al., 2006). These include women who have had circulatory problems or blood clots and those who have suffered a heart attack or stroke or have a history of coronary disease, breast or uterine cancer, undiagnosed genital bleeding, liver tumours, or sickle-cell anemia (because of associated blood-clotting problems). Because of their increased risk of cardiovascular problems, caution should be exercised when the combination pill is used with women over 35 years of age who smoke (Hatcher et al., 2006). Nursing mothers should also avoid using the pill; the hormones may be passed to the baby in the mother's milk.

The pill may also have psychological effects. Some users report depression or irritability. Switching brands or altering doses may help. Evidence is lacking concerning the effects of lower-estrogen pills on sexual desire.

Irregular bleeding, or so-called breakthrough bleeding, between menstrual periods is a common side effect of the minipill. Irregular bleeding should be brought to the attention of a health professional. Because they can produce vaginal dryness, minipills can hinder vaginal lubrication during intercourse, decreasing sexual sensations and rendering sex painful.

Results from several large-scale studies show no overall increase in the rates of breast cancer among pill users (Hatcher et al., 2006). The evidence linking use of the pill to increased risk of cervical cancer is mixed, with some studies showing such a link and others showing none (Hatcher et al., 2006).

Women considering the pill are advised to have a thorough medical evaluation to rule out pre-existing conditions that might make its use unsafe. Women who begin to use the pill, regardless of their age or risk status, should pay attention to changes in their physical condition, have regular checkups, and promptly report any physical complaints or unusual symptoms to their physician.

EMERGENCY CONTRACEPTION (EC) Emergency contraception (the so-called morning-after pill) is taken after unprotected sexual intercourse or when contraception fails. The most recommended EC pill is levonorgestrel, also known as Plan B. It is not generally considered an abortion pill because it cannot end an established pregnancy. Rather, Plan B prevents pregnancy by preventing the joining of sperm and egg and by preventing a fertilized egg from attaching to the uterine wall. About half of Canadian women report being familiar with the morning-after pill (Fisher et al., 2003).

Innovative Canadian Research

USE OF EMERGENCY CONTRACEPTION

In British Columbia, Soon et al. (2005) studied EC use both before and after the treatment was provided without a prescription. The key findings were:

- EC use was highest among women aged 20 to 24 years; the second-highest users were 15- to 19-year-olds.
- More than half of users (56%) obtained EC within 24 hours of having unprotected intercourse, and almost all (98%) within 72 hours.
- Very few women used EC on a regular basis, with only 2.5% receiving EC three or more times a year and 1.1% obtaining EC for future use.
- More than half of women receiving EC (56%) reported using a method of birth control that had failed.
- The provision of EC without a doctor's prescription significantly increased the use of EC.

The researchers concluded that the provision of EC without a prescription will be an important factor in reducing unwanted pregnancies and abortions in Canada.

EC should be taken as soon as possible after unprotected intercourse. It is most effective when taken within 72 hours. More recent research suggests it may still be effective even if taken within 120 hours. An alternative EC is the Yuzpe regimen, which consists of two doses of combined estrogen-levonorgestrel with the second dose taken 12 hours after the first. Another option is a copper IUD, which can be inserted up to seven days after unprotected intercourse.

In 2005, Health Canada allowed pharmacists to provide Plan B without a prescription. However, pharmacies were required to keep supplies of Plan B behind the counter, and women wanting to obtain Plan B had to first consult with a pharmacist. In British Columbia, more than half of the women who obtained the morning-after pill from a pharmacist did so during evenings or weekends (PPFC, 2002). In 2008, Health Canada permitted Plan B to be available on customer-accessible pharmacy shelves rather than being kept behind the counter. Along with this change, it was expected that women would no longer need to consult a pharmacist about its use. However, some pharmacists have resisted this change and have kept Plan B behind the counter, as they believe that their customers should be counselled on the proper use of this medication.

EC pills have a higher hormone content than most birth-control pills. For this reason, nausea is a common side effect. Nausea is usually mild and passes within a day or two after treatment, but it can be treated with antinausea medication.

THE CONTRACEPTIVE PATCH The contraceptive patch is another method of delivering estrogen and progestin to prevent ovulation and implantation. The patch is thin and measures about 5 cm by 5 cm (2 in. by 2 in.). It is worn on the abdomen, buttocks, upper arm, or upper torso but not on the breasts. The patch contains a week's worth of hormones and releases them gradually into the bloodstream. The patch is worn weekly for three weeks and the fourth week is patch-free to allow for menstrual bleeding. It can be worn in water.

Like the birth control pill, when used correctly, the patch is more than 99% effective. Women who use the patch need not think about contraception daily. Also like the pill, the patch doesn't interrupt sex. Its side effects and potential hazards are similar to those of the pill.

THE VAGINAL RING The vaginal ring delivers hormones through the skin. Shaped like a diaphragm, the ring contains a combination of estrogen and progestin. A doctor's prescription is needed to obtain the ring from a pharmacy.

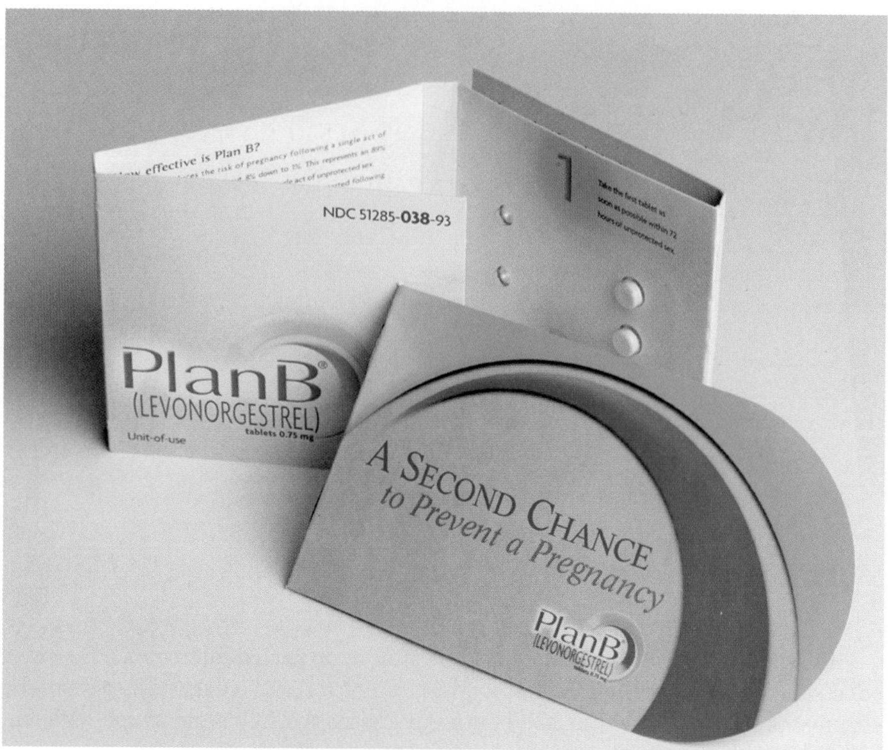

Plan B.
The morning-after pill is available in Canada without a prescription.

The ring is inserted into the vagina and worn for three consecutive weeks, followed by a ring-free week to allow menstruation. At the end of the ring-free week, the woman inserts another ring to begin a new cycle. The ring should be left in place during sex. If it does slip out of the vagina, it can be reinserted. Most men and women do not notice it during intercourse, although some women may experience vaginal discomfort. The ring is as effective as the birth control pill, and it may be more effective if a woman has trouble remembering to take her pill every day. More research is needed on both the ring and the patch to determine if there are long-term side effects.

INJECTABLE CONTRACEPTION Depo-Provera is an injectable hormone solution available by prescription. It contains progestin only. Depo-Provera prevents ovulation and is 99.7% effective in preventing pregnancy. It is administered by a needle in the muscle of the arm or buttocks every 12 weeks, and each injection prevents pregnancy for three months.

Depo-Provera has the advantage of permitting spontaneous sex, and remaining effective without being taken every day. Its side effects are similar to those of other types of hormonal contraceptives, but in addition it causes loss of bone density. Because of this, Depo-Provera is usually only recommended for people who are unable to take other contraceptive methods. When a woman stops using Depo-Provera, it takes on average about nine months for her to begin ovulating again.

Intrauterine Devices (IUDs)

Intrauterine device (IUD)
A small object that is inserted into the uterus and left in place to prevent conception.

Intrauterine devices (IUDs) are small objects of various shapes that are inserted into the uterus by a physician or nurse practitioner. Fine plastic threads or strings hang down from the IUD into the vagina, so that the woman can check to be sure it is still in place.

Currently there are two main intrauterine devices and systems available in Canada: copper IUDs (Flexi-T 300 or Nova-T) and a levonorgestrel-releasing IUD system (Mirena). These devices are about 99% effective for up to five years. The IUD prevents sperm from fertilizing an egg. If sperm does fertilize the egg, the IUD

Canadian Trends

IUD USE

IUDs achieved their greatest popularity in Canada in the 1960s and 1970s. A sharp drop-off in their use during the 1980s occurred after a popular model, the Dalkon Shield, was linked to a high incidence of pelvic infections and tubal infertility (Hatcher et al., 2006). IUDs are used by only 1% of sexually active women of child-bearing age in Canada (Fisher et al., 2003).

prevents the fertilized egg from implanting in the uterus. Women who use IUDs are advised to check the string several times a month to ensure that the IUD is in place.

IUDs may be removed readily by professionals. About 9 out of 10 former IUD users who wish to do so become pregnant within a year. A major advantage of the Mirena IUD system is that it reduces the amount of menstrual bleeding and cramping (Hatcher et al., 2006).

IUDs are highly effective and relatively "maintenance-free." Then why are they not more popular? One reason is side effects. The most common side effects are excessive menstrual cramping, irregular bleeding (spotting) between periods, and heavier-than-usual menstrual bleeding (Hatcher et al., 2006). A more serious concern is the possible risk of pelvic inflammatory disease (PID), a serious disease that can become life-threatening if left untreated (Hatcher et al., 2006). PID can produce scar tissue that blocks the fallopian tubes, causing infertility. Women with pelvic infections should not use an IUD (Hatcher et al., 2006). Women who have risk factors for PID may also wish to consider the advisability of an IUD. Risk factors include a recent episode of gonorrhea or chlamydia. IUD users are also at greater risk for ectopic pregnancies.

Diaphragm A shallow rubber cup or dome, fitted to the contour of a woman's vagina, that is coated with a spermicide and inserted prior to coitus to prevent conception.

The Diaphragm

The **diaphragm** is a shallow cup or dome made of thin latex rubber (see Figure 11.1). The rim is a flexible metal ring covered with rubber. Diaphragms come in different sizes to allow a precise fit.

Diaphragms are available by prescription and must be fitted to the contour of the vagina by a health professional. Several sizes and types of diaphragms may be tried during a fitting.

HOW IT WORKS The diaphragm is inserted and removed by the woman, much like a tampon. It is akin to a condom in that it forms a barrier against sperm when placed snugly over the cervical opening. Yet it is unreliable when used alone. Thus, the diaphragm should be used in conjunction with a spermicidal cream or jelly.

HOW IT IS USED The woman or her partner places a tablespoonful of spermicidal cream or jelly on the inside of the cup and spreads it inside the rim. The woman opens the inner lips of the vagina with one hand and folds the diaphragm with the other by squeezing the ring. She inserts the diaphragm against the cervix, with the inner side facing upward (see Figure 11.2). The diaphragm should be left in place *at least six hours* after intercourse to allow the spermicide to kill any remaining sperm in the vagina (Hatcher et al., 2006).

EFFECTIVENESS If it is used consistently and correctly, the failure rate of the diaphragm is estimated to be 6% during the first year of use. In typical use, however, the failure rate is believed to be three times as high—18%. Some women become pregnant because they do not use the diaphragm during every coital experience.

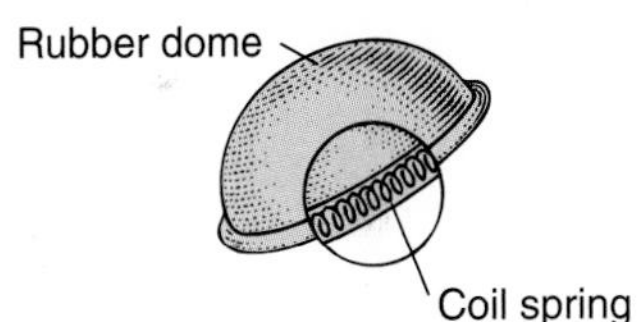

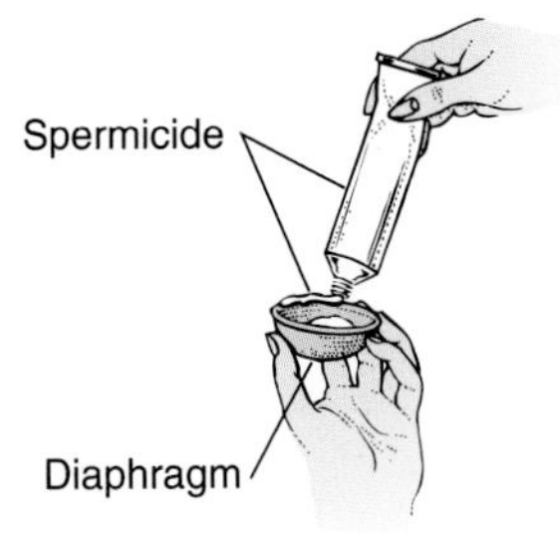

Figure 11.1
A Diaphragm.

The diaphragm is a shallow cup or dome made of latex. Diaphragms must be fitted to the contour of the vagina by a health professional. The diaphragm forms a barrier to sperm but should be used in conjunction with a spermicidal cream or jelly.

Figure 11.2
Inserting and Checking the Diaphragm.

Women are instructed in the insertion of the diaphragm by a health professional.

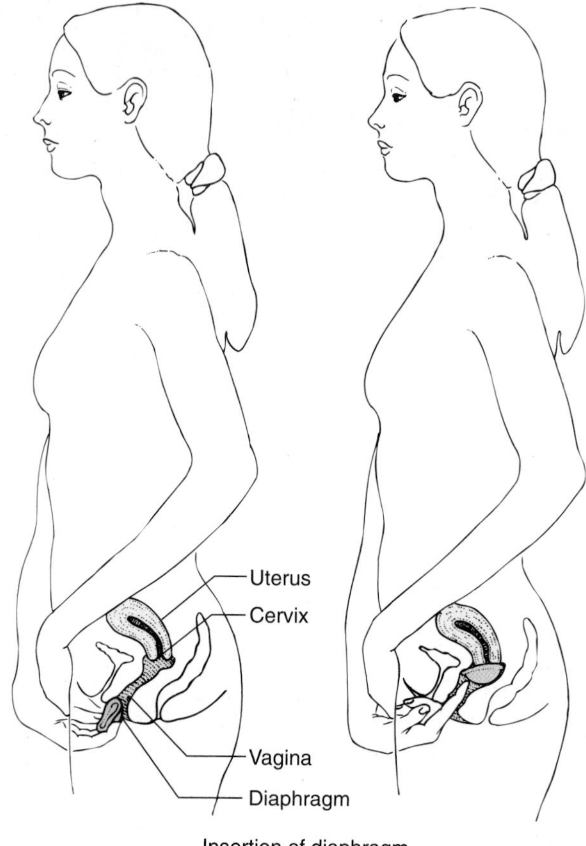

Effectiveness is also seriously compromised when the diaphragm is not used along with a spermicide.

ADVANTAGES AND DISADVANTAGES The major advantage of the diaphragm is that when used correctly, it is a fairly effective means of birth control. The diaphragm can be used as needed, whereas the pill must be used daily. The major disadvantage is the high pregnancy rate associated with typical use. Nearly one in five typical users (18%) of the diaphragm combined with spermicidal cream or jelly become pregnant during the first year of use (Hatcher et al., 2006). Another disadvantage is the need to insert the diaphragm prior to intercourse, which the couple may find disruptive.

The Cervical Cap

The cervical cap is a dome-shaped rubber cup. It comes in different sizes and must be fitted by a health professional. It is smaller than the diaphragm, however—about the size of a thimble—and is meant to fit snugly over the cervical opening.

Like the diaphragm, the cap is intended to be used with a spermicide applied inside it (Hatcher et al., 2006). When inserting it, the woman (or her partner) fills the cap about a third full of spermicide. Then, squeezing the edges together, the woman inserts the cap high in the vagina, so that it presses firmly against the cervix. It should be left in place for at least eight hours after intercourse. The cap provides continuous protection for upwards of 48 hours without the need for additional spermicide. The failure rate in typical use is estimated to be high, ranging from 18% in women who have not borne children to 36% in women who have (Hatcher et al., 2006).

Some women find the cap uncomfortable. Side effects include urinary tract infections and allergic reactions or sensitivities to the rubber or spermicide.

Spermicides

Spermicides coat the cervical opening, blocking the passage of sperm and killing sperm by chemical action. They come in different forms, including jellies and creams, suppositories, and aerosol foam. Spermicides should be left in place in the vagina (no douching) for *at least six to eight hours* after coitus. Spermicidal jellies, creams, and foam should be used no more than 60 minutes preceding coitus to provide maximum effectiveness (Hatcher et al., 2006).

In typical use, the first-year failure rate of spermicides used alone is 21% (Hatcher et al., 2006). When used correctly and consistently, the failure rate is estimated to drop to about 6% All forms of spermicide are more effective when they are combined with other forms of contraception, such as the condom.

Spermicides occasionally cause vaginal or penile irritation. Some partners find the taste of spermicides unpleasant. (Couples can engage in oral sex before applying spermicides.)

THE CONTRACEPTIVE SPONGE The contraceptive sponge is a soft, disposable device. Unlike the diaphragm, the sponge does not need to be fitted. Like the diaphragm, it provides a barrier that holds a spermicide, but the spermicide is built in. The sponge can also be inserted into the vagina several hours before coitus and has the additional advantage of absorbing sperm. It provides 12-hour protection, and sexual intercourse can be repeated during this time. On the negative side, about 1 user in 20 (male and female) is mildly irritated by the spermicide. The pregnancy failure rate of the sponge is between 9% and 20%. The failure rate can be reduced to 2% when used in combination with the male condom.

The Condom.
Condoms were once considered a man's domain. Today many Canadian women are insisting on their use, and often it is the woman who buys and carries them.

Male Condom

Some condoms are made of latex rubber and others are made of polyurethane. Thinner, more expensive condoms ("skins") are made from the intestinal membranes of lambs. The latter allow greater sexual sensation but do not protect so well against STIs. Others have nipples or reservoirs (see Figure 11.3) that catch semen and may help prevent the condom from bursting during ejaculation.

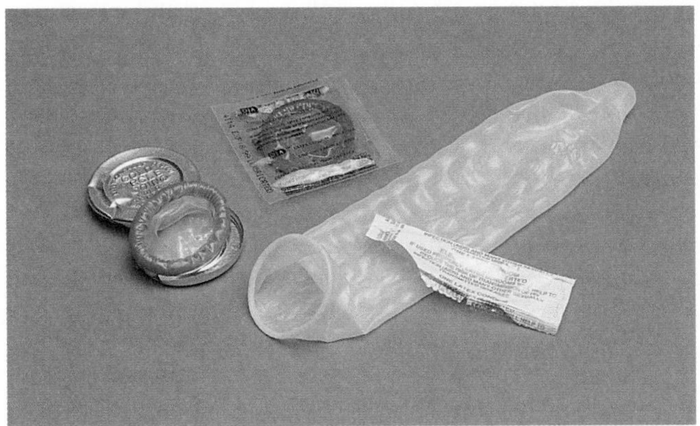

Figure 11.3 Condoms.

Some condoms are plain-tipped, whereas others have nipples or reservoirs that catch semen and may help prevent the condom from bursting during ejaculation. Latex condoms form effective barriers to the tiny AIDS virus.

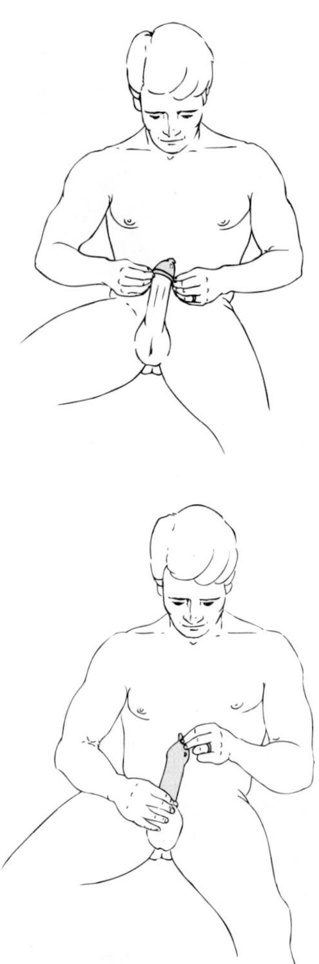

Figure 11.4 Applying a Condom.

First the rolled-up condom is placed on the head of the penis, and then it is rolled down the shaft of the penis. If a condom without a reservoir tip is used, a 1 cm (0.5 in.) space should be left at the tip for the ejaculate to accumulate.

Condoms come in different sizes. Men with larger penises should use larger condoms to lessen the chances of condom breakage. Also, the tight fit of the smaller regular-size condoms is uncomfortable for men with larger penises; thus they may be less likely to use a condom if they are not aware that larger-size condoms are available.

HOW THEY WORK A condom is a cylindrical sheath that serves as a barrier, preventing the passage of sperm and disease-carrying micro-organisms from the man to his partner. It also helps prevent infected vaginal fluids (and micro-organisms) from entering the man's urethral opening or penetrating through small cracks in the skin of the penis.

HOW THEY ARE USED The condom is rolled onto the penis once erection is achieved and before contact between the penis and the vagina (see Figure 11.4). If the condom is *not* used until moments before the point of ejaculation, sperm-carrying fluid from the Cowper's glands or from preorgasmic spasms may already have passed into the vagina. Nor does the condom afford protection against STIs if it is fitted after penetration. In a study of condom users at Indiana University, 43% of the males reported that sometimes they did not put the condom on until after they started having intercourse and 15% sometimes removed the condom before they had finished intercourse (Crosby et al., 2002).

EFFECTIVENESS In typical use, the failure rate of the male condom is estimated at 12%. This rate drops dramatically if the condom is used correctly and combined with the use of a spermicide (Hatcher et al., 2006).

ADVANTAGES AND DISADVANTAGES Condoms offer protection against STIs that is unparalleled among contraceptive devices. Toronto researcher Alex McKay from the Sex Information and Education Council of Canada has extensively analyzed studies of condom effectiveness. He concludes that in providing an impermeable barrier to STI/HIV pathogens, the proper and consistent use of latex condoms substantially reduces the risk of STI/HIV infections (McKay, 2007).

Both partners can share putting on the condom, which makes it an erotic part of their lovemaking, not an intrusion. The use of textured or ultrathin condoms may increase sensitivity, especially for the male. It is tempting to claim that the condom has a perfect safety record and no side effects. Let us settle for "close to perfect." Some people have allergic reactions to the spermicides with which some lubricated condoms are coated or that the woman may apply. In such cases the couple may need to use a condom without a spermicidal lubricant or stop using supplemental spermicides. Some people are allergic to latex. Condoms also sometimes slip off, break or tear, allowing sperm to leak through.

A major disadvantage of the condom is that it may render sex less spontaneous. The couple must interrupt lovemaking to apply the condom. Condoms may also lessen sexual sensations. Some men experience erectile difficulties when using a condom. In a study of heterosexual university males, one-fifth lost their erection before the condom was put on and one-fifth lost their erection after the condom was on and intercourse had begun (Crosby et al., 2002). Men who reported erection loss when using condoms were less likely to use condoms. Similarly, among HIV-positive gay men, an Australian study found that those who had difficulty achieving or maintaining an erection sometimes decided not to use a condom (Richters et al., 2003). Some males take Viagra as a means of overcoming this problem. Unfortunately, the problem of erection loss with condoms is not given serious consideration by some sex educators, but this issue should be discussed in educational and counselling situations.

Interestingly, although health educators emphasize the importance of using condoms in preventing STI/HIV infection, many people who use condoms do so for pregnancy prevention. In a sample of men and women from Ottawa, more than two-thirds said that the most important reason they used condoms was to prevent pregnancy (Edgley, 2002). And in the Canadian contraceptive study, only 7% of the

Canadian Trends

CONDOM USE REPORTED BY WOMEN

Most Canadian women (76%) have used a condom at least once, and 21% indicate that the condom is their current method of contraception (Fisher et al., 2003). Among those who report using only condoms, 70% indicated using condoms every time they have intercourse.

Typically Canadian women use condoms when first beginning a sexual relationship with a new partner and then switch to oral contraceptives. The most common reasons given for discontinuing condom use are that the woman has only one partner (47%), or that she knows and trusts her partner (46%). Other reasons are decreased sexual sensation for the partner (19%) or for the woman (14%). Only 4% of women say they stopped using a condom because their partner refused to use them; however, 14% say it would be difficult to get their partner to use condoms.

Usually, discussions about condoms and sexual pleasure focus on male sexual pleasure. However, among Canadian women who have used condoms, about as many say that condoms make sex less enjoyable for women (30%) as for men (33%) (Fisher et al., 2003).

Applied Knowledge

USING A CONDOM EFFECTIVELY

To use a condom most effectively and to help prevent it from either breaking or falling off, a couple should observe the following guidelines:

- Use a condom each and every time you have intercourse. Inexperienced users should also practise putting on a condom before they have occasion to use one with a partner.
- Handle the condom carefully, making sure not to damage it with your fingernails, teeth, or sharp objects.
- Place the condom on the erect penis before it touches the vulva.
- Uncircumcised men should pull back the foreskin before putting on the condom.
- If you use a spermicide, put some inside the tip of the condom before placing the condom on the penis. You may also wish to use additional spermicide applied by an applicator inside the vagina to provide extra protection, especially in the event that the condom breaks.
- For a condom without a reservoir tip, leave a small empty space—about 1 cm (0.5 in.)—at the end of the condom to hold semen, yet do not allow any air to be trapped at the tip. Some condoms come equipped with a reservoir (nipple) tip that will hold semen.
- Unroll the condom all the way to the base of the penis.
- Ensure that adequate vaginal lubrication is present during intercourse, using lubricants if necessary. But use only water-based lubricants such as contraceptive jelly or K-Y jelly. Never use an oil-based lubricant that can weaken the latex material, such as petroleum jelly (Vaseline), cold cream, baby oil or lotion, mineral oil, massage oil, vegetable oil, Crisco, hand or body lotions, and most skin creams.
- If the condom breaks during intercourse, withdraw the penis immediately, put on a new condom, and use more spermicide.
- After ejaculation, carefully withdraw the penis while it is still erect.
- Hold the rim of the condom firmly against the base of the penis as the penis is withdrawn, to prevent the condom from slipping off.

Because condoms can be eroded by exposure to body heat or other sources of heat, they should not be kept for any length of time in a pocket or the glove compartment of a car. Nor should a condom be used more than once. Here are some other things you should *never* do with a condom:

- Never use a condom after its expiration date.
- Condoms that are sticky, gummy, discoloured, brittle, or showing other signs of deterioration should be considered damaged.
- Never use a condom if the sealed packet containing the condom is damaged, cracked, or brittle; the condom itself may be damaged or defective.
- Do not open the sealed packet until you are ready to use the condom.
- Never use the same condom twice.

Innovative Canadian Research

ATTITUDES TOWARD SUGGESTING A CONDOM

One of the stereotypes about condom use is that people are reluctant to suggest using a condom for fear of offending their partner. In a study of Ontario university students, Davidson-Harden et al. (2000) surveyed attitudes toward people who initiate condom use within the context of exclusive dating relationships. Both men and women rated individuals of either gender who initiated condom use more favourably than unfavourably. The researchers concluded that it has become less socially acceptable to engage in sexual intercourse without using a condom.

In an Ontario study of patrons of singles bars, Herold and Mewhinney (1993) asked about attitudes and intentions toward condom use with someone the person had just met. Almost all the men (96%) and women (98%) said they would have no objection if their partner suggested using a condom, and only about a quarter of the respondents said they would be uncomfortable suggesting condom use to a new partner. Women were more likely than men to say they would insist on condom use; 85% of the women and 57% of the men said they would insist on condom use even if the partner didn't agree, and fewer women (12%) than men (22%) said they would have intercourse if the partner refused to use a condom.

These results suggest that, faced with the prospect of using a condom with a partner one has just met, men are more influenced by the partner's attitudes than are women, perhaps because women worry more than men about getting infected with an STI or the AIDS virus (Herold & Mewhinney, 1993). And given that half of the women and three-quarters of the men said they might be less likely to use a condom in the heat of passion, factors other than partner reluctance, especially the level of arousal, might be more important in explaining the nonuse of a condom.

A study among aboriginal youth in Saskatchewan found that assertively communicating about using a condom to a partner was related to self-efficacy of condom use. Thus youth who felt comfortable insisting on using a condom with a partner were more likely to feel confident that they would actually use a condom during sex (Shercliffe et al., 2007).

women said they chose to use condoms primarily to protect against STIs or HIV (Fisher & Black, 2007).

There are many factors that might influence the decision to use condoms. Concerns about partner reaction when initiating condom use is discussed in the nearby Innovative Canadian Research feature.

Female Condom

The female condom consists of a polyurethane (plastic) sheath that is used to line the vagina during intercourse. It is held in place at each end by a flexible plastic ring. The female condom provides a secure but flexible shield that barricades against sperm but allows the penis to move freely within the vagina during coitus. It can be inserted as much as eight hours before intercourse but should be removed immediately afterward (Hatcher et al., 2006). A new one must be used for each act of intercourse. The female condom (brand name: Reality) carries a warning label that it appears to be less effective than the male latex condom in preventing pregnancies and transmission of STIs. During test trials, the pregnancy rate was estimated to range between 21% and 26%, but it is estimated to be as low as 5% among cautious users (Hatcher et al., 2006). Many women complain that the female condom is bulky and difficult to insert. The female condom costs several times as much as the male condom. Fisher and his colleagues (2004) found that only 34% of Canadian women had heard of the female condom, and only 6% had a very favourable opinion of it.

Douche To rinse or wash the vaginal canal by inserting a liquid and allowing it to drain out.

Douching

Many couples believe that if a woman douches shortly after coitus, she will not become pregnant. Women who **douche** for contraceptive purposes often use

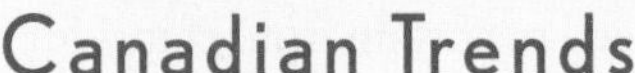

Canadian Trends

USE OF FERTILITY AWARENESS METHODS

Fertility awareness methods are used by about 2% of sexually active Canadian women aged 15 to 44. While 40% of Canadian women are aware of these methods, only 7% have very favourable opinions of them and only 2% report using them (Fisher et al., 2003).

syringes to flush the vagina with water or a spermicidal agent. Douching is ineffective, however, because large numbers of sperm move beyond the range of the douche seconds after ejaculation.

Regular douching may also alter the natural chemistry of the vagina, increasing the risk of vaginal infection. In short, douching is a "nonmethod" of contraception.

Withdrawal

In using withdrawal, the man removes his penis from the vagina before ejaculating. Withdrawal has a first-year failure rate among typical users of about 20% (Hatcher et al., 2006). There are several reasons for these failures. The man may not withdraw in time. Even if the penis is withdrawn just before ejaculation, some ejaculate may still fall on the vaginal lips, and sperm may find their way to the fallopian tubes. Active sperm may also be present in the *pre*-ejaculatory secretions of fluid from the Cowper's glands, a discharge the man is usually unaware of and cannot control. Despite the risks of using withdrawal as a method of birth control, 6% of Canadian women report using this method (Fisher et al., 2003).

Fertility Awareness Methods

Fertility awareness methods, or *rhythm* methods, rely on awareness of the fertile segments of the woman's menstrual cycle. Terms such as *natural birth control* and *natural family planning* also refer to these methods. The essence of such methods is that coitus is avoided on days when conception is most likely. Because the rhythm method does not employ artificial devices, it is acceptable to the Roman Catholic Church.

HOW THEY WORK A number of rhythm methods are used to predict the likelihood of conception. They are the mirror images of the methods that couples use to increase their chances of conceiving (see Chapter 10). Methods for enhancing the chances of conception seek to predict the time of ovulation so that the couple can arrange to have sperm present in the woman's reproductive tract at about that time. As methods of birth control, rhythm methods seek to predict ovulation so that the couple can abstain from coitus when the woman is fertile.

THE CALENDAR METHOD The **calendar method** assumes that ovulation occurs 14 days prior to menstruation. The couple abstains from intercourse during the period that begins three days prior to day 13 (because sperm are unlikely to survive for more than 72 hours in the female reproductive tract) and ends two days after day 15 (because an unfertilized ovum is unlikely to remain receptive to fertilization for longer than 48 hours). The period of abstention thus covers days 10–17 of the woman's cycle.

When a woman has regular 28-day cycles, predicting the period of abstention is relatively straightforward. Women with irregular cycles are generally advised to

Calendar method A fertility awareness (rhythm) method of contraception that relies on prediction of ovulation by tracking menstrual cycles, typically for a 10- to 12-month period, and assuming that ovulation occurs 14 days before menstruation.

chart their cycles for 10 to 12 months to determine their shortest and longest cycles. The first day of menstruation counts as day 1 of the cycle. The last day of the cycle is the day preceding the onset of menstruation.

Most women who follow the calendar method need to abstain from coitus for at least 10 days during the middle of each cycle. Moreover, the calendar method cannot ensure that the woman's longest or shortest menstrual cycles will occur during the 10- to 12-month period of baseline tracking. Some women, too, have such irregular cycles that the range of "unsafe" days cannot be predicted reliably even if baseline tracking is extended.

THE BASAL BODY TEMPERATURE (BBT) METHOD In the **basal body temperature (BBT) method**, the woman tracks her body temperature upon awakening each morning to detect the small changes that occur directly before and after ovulation. A woman's basal body temperature sometimes dips slightly just before ovulation and then tends to rise between 0.2°C and 0.4°C (0.4°F and 0.8°F) just before, during, and after ovulation. It remains elevated until the onset of menstruation. Thermometers that provide finely graded readings, such as electronic thermometers, are best suited for determining minor changes. A major problem with the BBT method is that it does not indicate the several *unsafe* pre-ovulatory days during which sperm deposited in the vagina may remain viable. Rather, the BBT method indicates when a woman *has* ovulated. Thus many women use the calendar method to predict the number of "safe" days prior to ovulation and the BBT method to determine the number of "unsafe" days after. A woman would avoid coitus during the "unsafe" pre-ovulatory period (as determined by the calendar method) and then for three days when her temperature rises and remains elevated. A drawback of the BBT method is that changes in body temperature may also result from factors unrelated to ovulation, such as infections, sleeplessness, and stress. This is why some women triple-check themselves by also tracking their cervical mucus.

THE CERVICAL MUCUS (OVULATION) METHOD The **ovulation method** tracks changes in the **viscosity** of the cervical mucus. Following menstruation, the vagina feels rather dry. There is also little or no discharge from the cervix. These dry days are relatively safe. Then a mucus discharge appears in the vagina that is first thick, sticky, and white or cloudy in colour. Coitus (or unprotected coitus) should be avoided at the first sign of any mucus. As the cycle progresses, the mucus discharge thins and clears, becoming slippery or stringy, like raw egg white. These are the **peak days**. This mucus discharge, called the *ovulatory mucus*, may be accompanied by a feeling of vaginal lubrication or wetness. Ovulation takes place about a day after the last peak day (about four days after this ovulatory mucus first appears). Then the mucus becomes cloudy and tacky once more. Intercourse may resume four days following the last peak day.

One problem with the mucus method is that some women have difficulty detecting changes in the mucus discharge. Such changes may also result from infections, certain medications, or contraceptive creams, jellies, or foam. Sexual arousal may also induce changes in viscosity.

OVULATION-PREDICTION KITS Predicting ovulation is more accurate with an ovulation-prediction kit. These kits enable women to test their urine daily for the presence of luteinizing hormone (LH). LH levels surge about 12 to 24 hours prior to ovulation. Some couples use the kits to enhance their chances of conceiving a child by engaging in coitus when ovulation appears imminent. Others use them as a means of birth control to find out when to avoid coitus.

EFFECTIVENESS The estimated first-year failure rate in typical use is 20%. Fewer failures occur when these methods are applied conscientiously, when a combination of rhythm methods is used, and when the woman's cycles are quite regular.

Basal body temperature (BBT) method A fertility awareness method of contraception that relies on prediction of ovulation by tracking the woman's temperature during the course of the menstrual cycle.

Ovulation method A fertility awareness method of contraception that relies on prediction of ovulation by tracking the viscosity of the cervical mucus.

Viscosity Stickiness, consistency.

Peak days The days during the menstrual cycle when a woman is most likely to be fertile.

ADVANTAGES AND DISADVANTAGES Because they are a natural form of birth control, rhythm methods appeal to many people who, for religious or other reasons, prefer not to use artificial means. No devices or chemicals are used, so there are no side effects. Rhythm methods are inexpensive, except for ovulation-prediction kits. A disadvantage is the fact that the reliability of rhythm methods is low. Rhythm methods may be unsuitable for women with irregular cycles. Women with irregular cycles who ovulate as early as a week after their menstrual flows can become pregnant even if they engage in unprotected intercourse only when they are menstruating, because some sperm remaining in a woman's reproductive tract may survive for up to eight days and fertilize an ovum that is released at that time. Moreover, the rhythm method requires abstaining from coitus for several days, or perhaps weeks, each month.

Sterilization Surgical procedures that render people incapable of reproduction without affecting sexual activity.

Vasectomy The surgical method of male sterilization in which sperm are prevented from reaching the urethra by cutting each vas deferens and tying it back or cauterizing it.

Sterilization

Many people decide to be sterilized when they plan to have no children or no more children. With the exception of abstinence, sterilization is the most effective form of contraception. Yet the prospect of **sterilization** arouses strong feelings because a person is transformed all at once, and presumably permanently, from someone who might be capable of bearing children to someone who cannot. This transformation often involves a profound change in self-concept. These feelings are especially strong in men and women who link fertility to their sense of masculinity or femininity.

MALE STERILIZATION The male sterilization procedure used today is the **vasectomy**.

A vasectomy is usually carried out in a doctor's office, under local anesthesia, in 15 to 20 minutes. Small incisions are made in the scrotum. Each vas is cut, a small segment is removed, and the ends are tied off or cauterized (to prevent them from growing back together) (see Figure 11.5). Now sperm can no longer reach the urethra. Instead, they are harmlessly reabsorbed by the body.

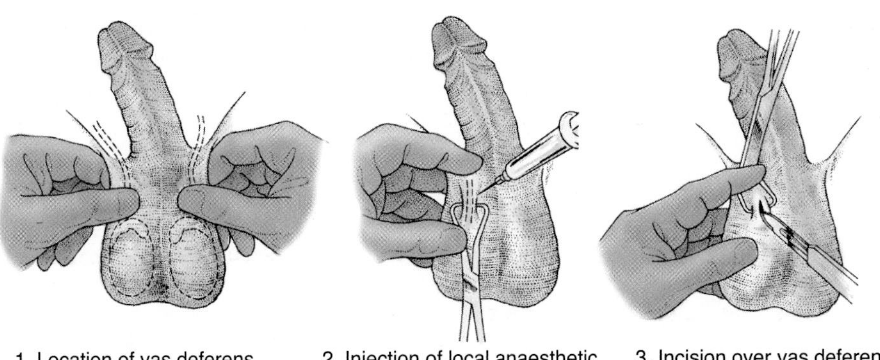

1. Location of vas deferens
2. Injection of local anaesthetic
3. Incision over vas deferens

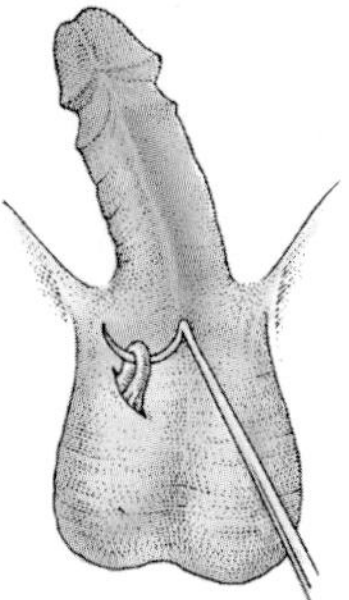

4. Isolation of vas from surrounding tissue

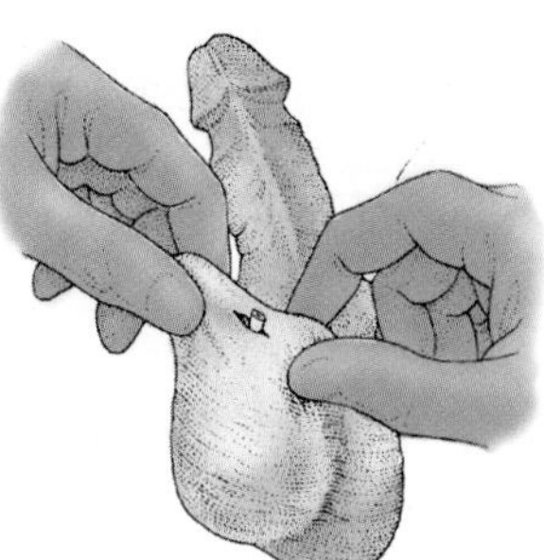

5. Removal of segment of vas; tying of ends

6. Return of vas to position; incision is closed and process is repeated on the other side

Figure 11.5
Vasectomy.

Small incisions are made in the scrotum. Each vas deferens is cut, and the ends are tied off or cauterized to prevent sperm from reaching the urethra. The vasectomy is nearly 100% effective. The few failures stem from sperm remaining in the male's genital tract shortly after the operation or from the growing together of the segments of a vas deferens.

Vasovasotomy The surgical method of reversing vasectomy in which the cut or cauterized ends of the vas deferens are sewn together.

Tubal sterilization The most common method of female sterilization, in which the fallopian tubes are surgically blocked to prevent the meeting of sperm and ova. Also called *tubal ligation.*

Minilaparotomy A kind of tubal sterilization in which a small incision is made in the abdomen to provide access to the fallopian tubes.

Laparoscopy Tubal sterilization by means of a *laparoscope,* which is inserted through a small incision just below the navel and used to cauterize, cut, or clamp the fallopian tubes. Sometimes referred to as "belly-button surgery."

According to guidelines established by the World Health Organization in 2004, men are advised to wait three months after a vasectomy before relying on it for contraception. This advice is based on an analysis of several studies which found that for the great majority of men, vasectomies are completely effective after three months (Info Reports, 2005).

Vasectomy does not diminish sex drive or result in any change in sexual arousal, erectile or ejaculatory ability, or sensations of ejaculation. Male sex hormones and sperm are still produced by the testes. Without a passageway to the urethra, however, sperm are no longer expelled with the ejaculate. Sperm account for only about 1% of the ejaculate, so the volume of the ejaculate is not noticeably different.

Minor complications are reported in 4% or 5% of cases. They typically involve temporary local inflammation or swelling after the operation. Ice packs and anti-inflammatory drugs, such as Aspirin, may help reduce swelling and discomfort. More serious but rarer medical complications include infection of the epididymis.

Reversibility is simple in concept but not in practice. Thus, vasectomies should be considered permanent. In an operation to reverse a vasectomy, called a **vasovasotomy**, the ends of the vas deferens are sewn together, and in a few days they grow together. Estimates of success at reversal, as measured by subsequent pregnancies, range from 16% to 79% (Hatcher et al., 2006).

FEMALE STERILIZATION While the male sterilization rate is increasing, the rate of female sterilization in Canada is decreasing (Fisher et al., 2004b).

Tubal sterilization, also called *tubal ligation*, is the most common method of female sterilization. Tubal sterilization prevents ova and sperm from passing through the fallopian tubes. The two main surgical procedures for tubal sterilization are *minilaparotomy* and *laparoscopy.* In a **minilaparotomy**, a small incision is made in the abdomen, just above the pubic hairline, to provide access to the fallopian tubes. Each tube is cut and either tied back or clamped with a clip. In a **laparoscopy** (see Figure 11.6), sometimes called "belly-button surgery," the fallopian tubes are approached through a small incision in the abdomen just below the navel. The surgeon uses a narrow, lighted viewing instrument called a *laparoscope* to locate the tubes. A small section of each of the tubes is cauterized, cut, or clamped. The woman usually returns to her

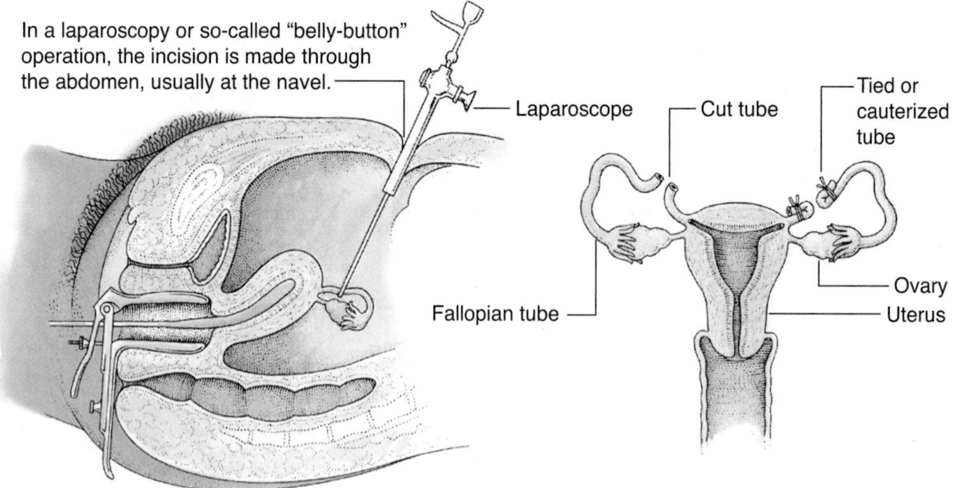

Figure 11.6 Laparoscopy.

In this method of female sterilization, the surgeon approaches the fallopian tubes through a small incision in the abdomen just below the navel. A narrow instrument called a *laparoscope* is inserted through the incision, and a small section of each fallopian tube is cauterized, cut, or clamped to prevent ova from joining with sperm.

Canadian Trends

STERILIZATION

Sterilization is the most widely used form of birth control among Canadian married couples aged 35 to 44. Among Canadian women in this group, 32% report that their male partner has been sterilized while 14% report that they themselves have been sterilized (Fisher et al., 2003). Married women in Canada are more likely to rely on a permanent method of contraception (tubal sterilization or vasectomy) than are single women.

daily routine in a few days and can resume coitus when it becomes comfortable. In an alternative sterilization procedure, a **culpotomy**, the fallopian tubes are approached through an incision in the back wall of the vagina.

Culpotomy A kind of tubal sterilization in which the fallopian tubes are approached through an incision in the back wall of the vagina.

Hysterectomy Surgical removal of the uterus. (*Not* appropriate as a method of sterilization.)

None of these methods disrupts sex drive or sexual response. The menstrual cycle is undisturbed. The unfertilized egg is simply reabsorbed by the body, rather than being sloughed off in the menstrual flow.

A **hysterectomy** also results in sterility. A hysterectomy is a major operation that is commonly performed because of cancer or other diseases of the reproductive tract; it is inappropriate as a method of sterilization. Hysterectomy carries the risks of major surgery, and when the ovaries are removed along with the uterus, it induces a "surgical menopause" because the woman no longer produces female sex hormones.

Female sterilization is highly effective in preventing pregnancy, although slightly less effective than male sterilization. Overall, about one woman in 200 (0.4%) is likely to become pregnant in the first year following a tubal sterilization (Hatcher et al., 2006); this is most likely to result from a failed surgical procedure or a pregnancy undetected at the time of the procedure. Like vasectomy, tubal ligation should be considered irreversible. Reversals are successful, as measured by subsequent pregnancies, in 43% to 88% of cases (Hatcher et al., 2006). Reversal is, however, difficult and costly.

ADVANTAGES AND DISADVANTAGES OF STERILIZATION The major advantages of sterilization are effectiveness and permanence. Sterilization is nearly 100% effective. Following surgery, the couple need not do anything more to prevent conception. The permanence is also its major drawback, however. People sometimes change their minds about wanting to have children.

Sterilization procedures create varying risks of complications following surgery, and women generally incur greater risks than men.

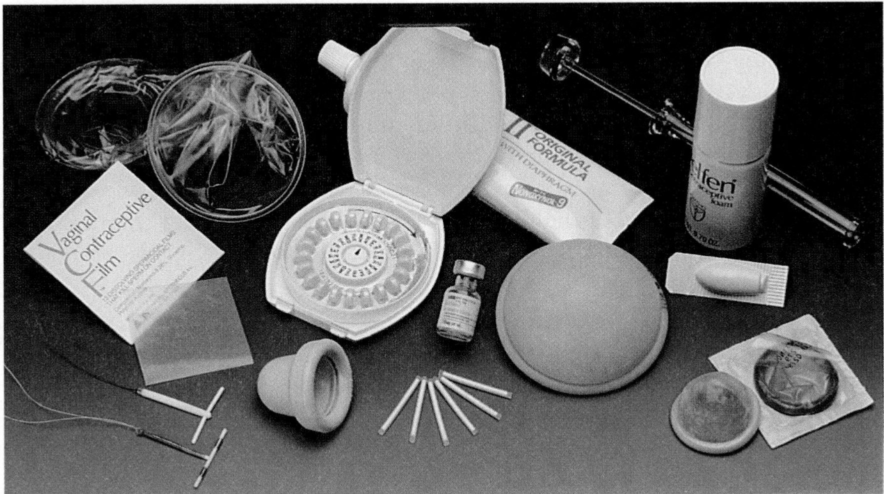

Selecting a Method of Contraception.
Should you and your partner use contraception? If so, how can you determine which method is right for you?

Applied Knowledge

SELECTING A METHOD OF CONTRACEPTION

Should you and your partner use contraception? If so, how can you determine which method is right for you? There is no simple answer. What is right for your friends may be wrong for you. You and your partner will make your own selections, but there are some issues you may want to consider:

1. *Convenience.* Is the method convenient? The convenience of a method depends on a number of factors. Does it require a device that must be purchased in advance? If so, can it be purchased over the counter as needed, or is a consultation with a doctor and a prescription required? Will the method work at a moment's notice, or, as with the birth-control pill, will it require time to reach maximum effectiveness?
2. *Moral acceptability.* A method that is morally acceptable to one person may be objectionable to another.
3. *Cost.* Methods vary in cost.
4. *Sharing responsibility.* Most forms of birth control place the burden of responsibility largely, if not entirely, on the woman. Some couples prefer methods that allow for greater sharing of responsibility, such as alternating use of the condom and diaphragm. A man can also share the responsibility for the birth-control pill by accompanying his partner on her medical visits, sharing the expense, and helping her remember to take her pill.
5. *Safety.* How safe is the method? What are the side effects?
6. *Reversibility.* In most cases the effects of birth control methods can be fully reversed by discontinuing their use. One form of contraception, sterilization, should be considered irreversible, although many attempts at reversal have been successful.
7. *Protection against sexually transmitted infections (STIs).* Birth control methods vary in the degree of protection they afford against STIs.
8. *Effectiveness.* Techniques and devices vary widely in their effectiveness in actual use. The failure rate for a particular method refers to the percentage of women who become pregnant when using the method for a given period of time, such as during the first year of use. Most contraceptive methods are not used correctly all or even much of the time. Thus it is instructive to compare the failure rate among people who use a particular method or device *perfectly* (consistently and correctly) with the failure rate among *typical* users. Failure rates among typical users are often considerably higher because of incorrect, unreliable, or inconsistent use.

The Search Goes On

sexualityandU.ca
Developed by the Society of Obstetricians and Gynaecologists of Canada, this site provides reliable information on contraception.
www.sexualityandu.ca

Even now, in the third millennium, the ideal contraceptive does not yet seem to be within our grasp. However, it does appear that we will be making new advances in mechanical and chemical barrier methods, systems for delivering hormones, intrauterine devices (IUDs), and systemic methods for men (such as a male pill).

It seems that many women are not comfortable with the idea of a male pill; 63% of young Canadian women (aged 18–24) in a 2004 Ipsos-Reid poll said that they would not trust a man to take a pill every day.

A major contraceptive breakthrough was announced in 2008 by Canadian and European researchers regarding the discovery of a gene (Lrh1) that controls ovulation (Duggavathi et al., 2008). When this gene was removed in mice, the mice stopped ovulating. The gene works mainly through follicle cells surrounding an ovum. The discovery of the gene may be useful in treating infertility as well as in contraception.

Abortion

Induced abortion The purposeful termination of a pregnancy before the embryo or fetus is capable of sustaining independent life.

An **induced abortion** (in contrast to a *spontaneous abortion*, or miscarriage) is the purposeful termination of a pregnancy. Perhaps more than any other contemporary social issue, induced abortion (hereafter referred to simply as abortion) has divided neighbours and family members into opposing camps.

Abortion is rarely used as a primary means of birth control. It usually comes into play when other methods have failed. The many reasons why women have abortions include psychological factors as well as external circumstances. Abortion is often motivated by a desire to reduce the risk of physical, economic, psychological, and social disadvantages that the woman perceives for herself and her present and future children should she take the pregnancy to term. Moral concerns about abortion often turn on the question of when human life begins. However, the question of when *human* life begins is a matter of definition that is apparently unanswerable by science.

Canadian Abortion Rights Action League
Canada's pro-choice volunteer organization works to ensure that all women have reproductive freedom to exercise the right to safe, accessible abortion.
www.caral.ca

Historical and Legal Perspectives on Abortion

Attitudes toward abortion have varied across cultures and times in history. Abortion was permitted in ancient Greece and Rome. The Bible does not specifically prohibit abortion (Sagan & Dryan, 1990). For much of its history, the Roman Catholic Church held to Thomas Aquinas's belief that ensoulment of the fetus did not occur for at least 40 days after conception. In 1869, Pope Pius IX declared that human life begins at conception. Thus an abortion at any stage of pregnancy became murder in the eyes of the Church and grounds for excommunication.

The right-to-life (pro-life) movement asserts that human life begins at conception and thus views abortion as the murder of an unborn child. Some in the pro-life movement brook no exception to their opposition to abortion. Others would permit abortion to save the mother's life or when a pregnancy results from rape or incest. The pro-choice movement contends that abortion is a matter of personal choice and that the government has no right to interfere with a woman's right to terminate a pregnancy. Pro-choice advocates argue that women are free to control what happens within their bodies, including pregnancies.

The National Right to Life Committee
Contains the organization's views on when human life begins, the negative aspects of abortion, and so on.
www.nrlc.org

Many people in the pro-choice movement argue that if abortions were to be made illegal again, thousands of women, especially poor women, would die or suffer serious physical consequences from botched or nonsterile abortions. People in the pro-life movement counter that alternatives to abortion, such as adoption, are available to pregnant women. Pro-choice advocates argue that the debate about abortion should be framed not only by notions of the mother's right to privacy but also by the issue of the quality of life of an unwanted child. They argue that minority and physically or mentally disabled children are often hard to place for adoption. These children often spend their childhood being shuffled from one foster home to another. Pro-life advocates counter that killing a fetus eliminates any potential that it might have, despite hardships, of living a fruitful and meaningful life.

At Canadian universities there have been a number of clashes between student unions and student anti-abortion groups over whether the latter groups should be allowed to operate on campus as official student organizations. The anti-abortion groups argued that the student unions were violating their constitutional human rights regarding free speech and were discriminating against religious beliefs. The student unions countered that these groups threatened a woman's right to have an abortion (Brean, 2008).

Although Canadians are divided in their opinions on abortion, most accept abortion under certain circumstances. Reginald Bibby (2001) of the University of Lethbridge found that most Canadian adults (90%) and teenagers (84%) believe that abortion should be legal when rape is involved, but fewer (adults 43%, teenagers 55%) believe it should be legal for any reason.

Methods of Abortion

The two most common methods of abortion used in Canada are vacuum aspiration, and dilation and evacuation.

VACUUM ASPIRATION **Vacuum aspiration**, or suction curettage, is the safest and most common method of abortion in Canada. It is relatively painless and

Vacuum aspiration Removal of the uterine contents via suction. In the procedure, the cervix is usually dilated first by insertion of progressively larger curved metal rods, or "dilators," or by insertion, hours earlier, of a stick of seaweed called *Laminaria digitata*. *Laminaria* expands as it absorbs cervical moisture, providing a gentler means of opening the os. Then an angled tube connected to an aspirator (suction machine) is inserted through the cervix into the uterus. The uterine contents are then evacuated (emptied) by suction.

Canadian Trends

HISTORY OF ABORTION IN CANADA

Abortion was illegal in Canada until 1969, when Parliament amended the Criminal Code so that abortion could be performed under limited circumstances. Abortions could be performed only in accredited hospitals with the approval of a Therapeutic Abortion Committee. It had to be shown that the abortion was justified, in that continuation of the pregnancy would endanger the woman's life or health. The struggle continued between pro-life groups, which sought greater restrictions on abortion, and the pro-choice movement, which sought to make abortion available to any Canadian woman who wanted one.

Both pro-life and pro-choice groups have heavily lobbied politicians to support their cause. Some pro-life groups use such tactics as picketing hospitals and clinics where abortions are performed as well as the homes of physicians who perform abortions. Three Canadian physicians have been shot in their homes by anti-abortion extremists. The harassing tactics used by some of these groups have led provinces such as Ontario and British Columbia to restrict picketing outside abortion clinics.

Dr. Henry Morgentaler, the leader of the pro-choice movement in Canada, challenged the law by establishing private abortion clinics. Dr. Morgentaler has won several legal challenges against provincial governments that wanted to close his clinics (although in 1974 he was imprisoned for 10 months by the Quebec government after the Quebec Court of Appeal overturned a jury's acquittal). Juries refused to convict Morgentaler because they believed he was providing an important medical service for women. He was also supported by such pro-choice groups as the Canadian Abortion Rights Action League (CARAL).

Morgentaler was awarded the Order of Canada in 2008 for his commitment to increased health-care opportunities for women and his efforts to influence public policy. The giving of this award to Morgentaler was strongly opposed by pro-life groups and caused considerable controversy. Nevertheless, in a national Ipsos-Reid poll, taken in July 2008, 65% of Canadians supported the awarding of Canada's highest civilian honour to Dr. Morgentaler.

Choosing Sides.
Pro-choice and pro-life advocates confront each other.

Dr. Henry Morgentaler.
Dr. Henry Morgentaler fought numerous court battles to secure Canadian women greater access to abortions.

The Supreme Court of Canada overturned the abortion law in 1988, stating that it violated the Charter of Rights and Freedoms, and there has been no federal law restricting abortion since then. And in 1989, after a Quebec man went to court in an attempt to prevent his former girlfriend from having an abortion, an important precedent was set when the Supreme Court of Canada ruled that he could not stop the abortion because the law does not recognize a father's right to do so.

Despite these legal decisions, today only a minority of hospitals perform abortions and these are located only in urban areas. In 2007 only 16% of general hospitals in Canada provided abortion services (Shaw, 2007). Prince Edward Island does not offer any abortion services, and some provinces, such as New Brunswick, restrict women's access to abortions at public hospitals and do not pay for abortions performed at private abortion clinics. In 2008 Morgentaler launched a court challenge against New Brunswick's refusal to fund private abortion clinics in that province.

Women who live in rural or northern areas of Canada often have to travel long distances to obtain abortion services (Shaw, 2007). Additionally, when Ottawa researcher Jessica Shaw phoned hospitals that did offer abortions, asking to talk to someone about abortion, she was often given misinformation and/or had to talk to someone at the hospital who was opposed to abortions.

The federal Conservative party under the leadership of Stephen Harper has been opposed to abortion. In 2008 Conservative Member of Parliament Ken Epp introduced a private member's bill (C-484) "to protect fetuses from violence" that would in effect award the fetus legal rights from the time of conception. Critics of the bill stated that if it were passed, the bill would lead the way to restricting abortions in Canada. The Quebec government was so concerned about this bill that all members of the National Assembly in Quebec voted to ask the federal government not to pass it. To stem this controversy, during the 2008 federal election campaign, the Harper government stated that it would not reopen the debate on abortion. Instead it proposed a new law that would force judges to take into account whether a woman who was injured or killed in an attack was pregnant at the time (Woods, 2008).

Canadian Trends

INDUCED ABORTIONS IN 2005 BY PROVINCE

In recent years, the number of abortions among Canadian women has been declining, and the decline occurred mostly among women under 20 years of age.

A total of 96 815 induced abortions were performed on Canadian women in 2005, down from 105 154 in 2002. Induced abortion rates fell in all age groups, except among women aged 35 to 39, for whom the rate remained the same. Teenage women, under the age of 20, experienced the largest decline in rates. The induced abortion rate for these women has declined gradually since 1996, when it peaked at 18.9 induced abortions per 1000 women in the age group, to 13.0 induced abortions per 1000 women in 2005.

Induced abortions continue to be the most common among women in their early twenties. This age group accounted for 31% of all women who obtained an induced abortion in 2005. On average, 28 women out of every 1000 aged 20 to 24 obtained an induced abortion.

TABLE 11.1
Induced Abortions in 2005 by Province

	Number of Abortions	Rate per 1000 Women
Total	96 815	14.1
Newfoundland and Labrador	883	8.1
Prince Edward Island	126	4.4
Nova Scotia	1 897	9.7
New Brunswick	941	6.1
Quebec	29 259	18.8
Ontario	33 546	12.3
Manitoba	2 236	9.2
Saskatchewan	1 824	9.1
Alberta	10 859	14.8
British Columbia	14 444	15.9
Yukon, Northwest Territories, and Nunavut	615	24.9
Residence unknown	185	...

Note: Users should be aware of certain limitations with the Therapeutic Abortion Survey. Data for 2005 cover induced abortions performed in hospitals and clinics in provinces and territories, except those performed in Manitoba clinics, which have been unavailable since 2004. As of 2004, induced abortions obtained by Canadian women in some American states are no longer collected. Also, the survey does not include abortions performed in doctors' offices.

Source: Statistics Canada. (2008d). The Daily, *May 21, Induced Abortions. [online]. Available:* **www.statcan.ca/Daily/English/080521/d080521c.htm**

inexpensive. It can be done with little or no anesthesia in a medical office or clinic, but only during the first trimester. Later, thinning of the uterine walls increases the risks of perforation and bleeding.

Dilation and evacuation (D&E) After dilation of the cervix, a suction tube and forceps are used to remove the uterine contents. The uterine wall may be scraped to ensure that the lining has been removed fully.

DILATION AND EVACUATION (D&E) The **dilation and evacuation (D&E)** is used most commonly during the second trimester, when vacuum aspiration alone would be too risky. First the cervix is dilated. The cervix must also be dilated more fully than with vacuum aspiration to allow for passage of the larger fetus. Then a suction tube is inserted to remove some of the contents of the uterus. But suction alone cannot safely remove all uterine contents, so the remaining contents are removed with forceps. A blunt scraper may also be used to scrape the uterine wall to make sure that the lining has been removed fully. The D&E is usually performed in a hospital under general anesthesia.

ABORTION DRUGS RU-486 was approved in France in the late 1980s. It has not yet been approved for use in Canada, although it is available in several European countries and the United States. The chemical mifepristone induces early abortion by blocking the effects of progesterone. Progesterone is the hormone that stimulates proliferation of the endometrium, allowing implantation of the fertilized ovum.

The pill was developed in France, and nearly half of French women who seek abortion prefer RU-486 to surgical methods (Christin-Maitre et al., 2000). Supporters of RU-486 argue that it offers a safe, noninvasive substitute for more costly and unpleasant abortion procedures (Christin-Maitre et al., 2000). RU-486's introduction in Canada is being delayed largely because of opposition by pro-life groups. Opponents argue that RU-486 makes abortions more accessible and difficult to regulate. Pro-life groups consider abortion to be murder, whether it is induced by surgery or by a pill.

Psychological Consequences of Abortion

The woman who faces an unwanted pregnancy may experience a range of negative emotions, including fear, anger directed inward ("How could I let this happen?"), guilt ("What would my parents think if they knew I was having an abortion?"), and ambivalence ("Will I regret it if I have an abortion? Will I regret it more if I don't?")

Women's reactions depend on various factors, including the support they receive from others (or the lack thereof) and the strength of their relationships with their partners. Women with greater support from their male partners or parents tend to show a more positive emotional reaction following an abortion (Williams, 2001). Generally speaking, the sooner the abortion occurs, the less stressful it is. Women who have a difficult time reaching an abortion decision, who blame the pregnancy on their character, who have lower coping ability, and who have less social support experience more distress following abortion.

Innovative Canadian Research

WOMEN WHO HAVE REPEAT ABORTIONS

In Canada, about a third of induced abortions are for women who have had previous abortions. University of Western Ontario researchers led by William Fisher (2005) conducted a study to determine the characteristics of women who have repeat abortions. Contrary to the stereotype, most of these women were not using abortion as a method of birth control. About one-half of the women undergoing repeat abortions reported that they or their partner were using a method of birth control at the time of conception. In fact, they were more likely to be using birth control than a comparison group of women who were having their first abortion. The key finding of the study was that women having repeat abortions were significantly more likely to have experienced physical abuse by a male partner, or sexual abuse or coercion. The findings indicate that women seeking an abortion should be screened for experience with physical or sexual abuse. This could result in counselling that might help to avert subsequent abuse and possibly help to prevent a future abortion (Fisher et al., 2005).

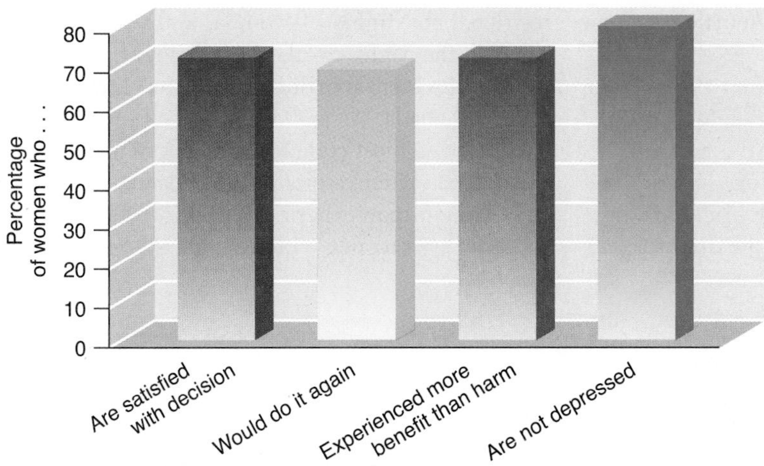

Figure 11.7 Women's Psychological Adjustment Two Years After Having Had an Abortion.

Of several hundred respondents to an *Archives of General Psychiatry* survey, 72% of those who had had an abortion reported being satisfied with their decision two years after the fact. How do you interpret the finding? Do you focus on the finding that the great majority of women are satisfied with their choice or on the finding that significant numbers of women (28%) are not?

Consider one survey of several hundred women reported in *Archives of General Psychiatry* (Major et al., 2000) who showed up at one of three sites for a first-trimester abortion. Of these 882, 442 were actually followed for two years. As shown in Figure 11.7, the majority (72%) said they were satisfied with their decision to have the abortion. A majority said they would make the same decision if they had it to do over (69%) and that they had experienced more benefit than harm from having the abortion (72%). Moreover, 80% were *not* depressed.

Summing Up

The provision of contraceptive information and services was illegal in Canada until 1969.

Birth-control pills include combination pills and minipills. Combination pills contain estrogen and progestin and fool the brain into acting as though the woman is already pregnant, so that no additional ova mature or are released. Minipills contain progestin, thicken the cervical mucus to impede the passage of sperm through the cervix, and render the inner lining of the uterus less receptive to a fertilized egg. "Morning-after" pills prevent implantation of a fertilized ovum in the uterus.

The intrauterine device (IUD) is highly effective, but there are possible troublesome side effects and the potential for serious health complications.

The diaphragm covers the cervix and should be used with a spermicidal cream or jelly.

Spermicides block the passage of sperm and kill sperm. Their failure rate is high.

Latex condoms afford protection against STIs as well as protect against pregnancy.

Withdrawal requires no special equipment but has a high failure rate.

Rhythm methods rely on awareness of the fertile segments of the woman's menstrual cycle. Rhythm methods include the calendar method, the basal body temperature method, and the cervical mucus method. Their failure rate is high in typical use.

Sterilization methods should be considered permanent, although they can be reversed in many cases.

Less commonly used methods include methods of delivering hormones, such as Depo-Provera (injections), the skin patch, and the vaginal ring; barrier/spermicide methods such as the cervical cap, the female condom, and the contraceptive sponge.

Moral concerns about abortion often turn on the question of when human life begins—a question of definition.

Societal attitudes toward abortion have varied across cultures and times in history. In 1988, the Supreme Court of Canada ruled that the abortion law restricted the rights of women, and women were thus allowed the right to abortion without restriction. In reality, however, abortion services are limited in many parts of Canada.

The two most common methods of abortion used in Canada are vacuum aspiration and dilation and evacuation.

Women may experience distress after an abortion, but most are satisfied with their decision to have one.

Test Yourself

Multiple-Choice Questions

1. **Over the course of a lifetime, more Canadian women use ____________________________ than any other method of contraception.**
   a. intrauterine devices
   b. sterilization
   c. oral contraceptives
   d. diaphragms

2. **Which statement about birth-control pills is true?**
   a. They fool the brain into thinking the woman is already pregnant.
   b. If used correctly, they are 100% effective.
   c. They ensure ovulation on day 21 of the woman's menstrual cycle.
   d. They offer excellent protection against sexually transmitted infections.

3. **Recent research suggests that Canadian women ________________ the disadvantages and ________________ the advantages of oral contraceptives.**
   a. underestimate/overestimate
   b. overestimate/underestimate
   c. overestimate/overestimate
   d. underestimate/underestimate

4. **All of the following are potential side effects of birth-control pills except**
   a. nausea and vomiting
   b. low blood pressure
   c. fluid retention
   d. weight gain

5. **Emergency contraception (the morning-after pill)**
   a. is illegal in Canada
   b. is available without a prescription
   c. contains higher levels of testosterone than the pills available in Europe
   d. is available only to victims of sexual assault

6. **Which of the following statements about intrauterine devices is true?**
   a. The percentage of Canadian women using IUDs has decreased since 1980.
   b. IUDs are less effective than condoms.
   c. Approximately 10% of Canadian women currently use this method of birth control.
   d. IUDs offer significant protection against sexually transmitted infections.

7. **What percentage of Canadian women say that they have used a condom at least once?**
   a. 41%
   b. 51%
   c. 76%
   d. 91%

8. **Among married couples aged 35–44, __________________________ is/are the most commonly used form of contraception.**
   a. diaphragms
   b. oral contraceptives
   c. condoms
   d. sterilization

9. **There has been no federal law restricting abortions in Canada since the Supreme Court ruling in**
   a. 1965
   b. 1977
   c. 1988
   d. 2004

10. **The safest and most common method of abortion is**
    a. dilation and evacuation (D&E)
    b. intra-amniotic infusion
    c. dilation and curettage (D&C)
    d. vacuum aspiration

Answers to the Test Yourself questions in each chapter are found on page 509.

Critical Thinking Questions

1. Have you ever discussed the use of birth control with a partner or potential partner? If not, why not? If you have, did you find it difficult to talk about? Why or why not?
2. If you are female, have you ever been faced with an unintended pregnancy? If so, what did you do about it? What factors influenced your decision? Were your friends supportive of your choice? Your partner? Your family?
3. If you are male, has a sexual partner of yours ever been faced with an unintended pregnancy? If so, what was done about it? Were you part of the decision-making process? Why or why not?
4. A friend of yours, who you know does not want a child, tells you that she is sexually active but not using any birth control. Would you discuss this behaviour with her? Why or why not?

Visit MyPsychKit at www.mypsychkit.com, where you can do quizzes and link to additional resources on topics discussed in this text.

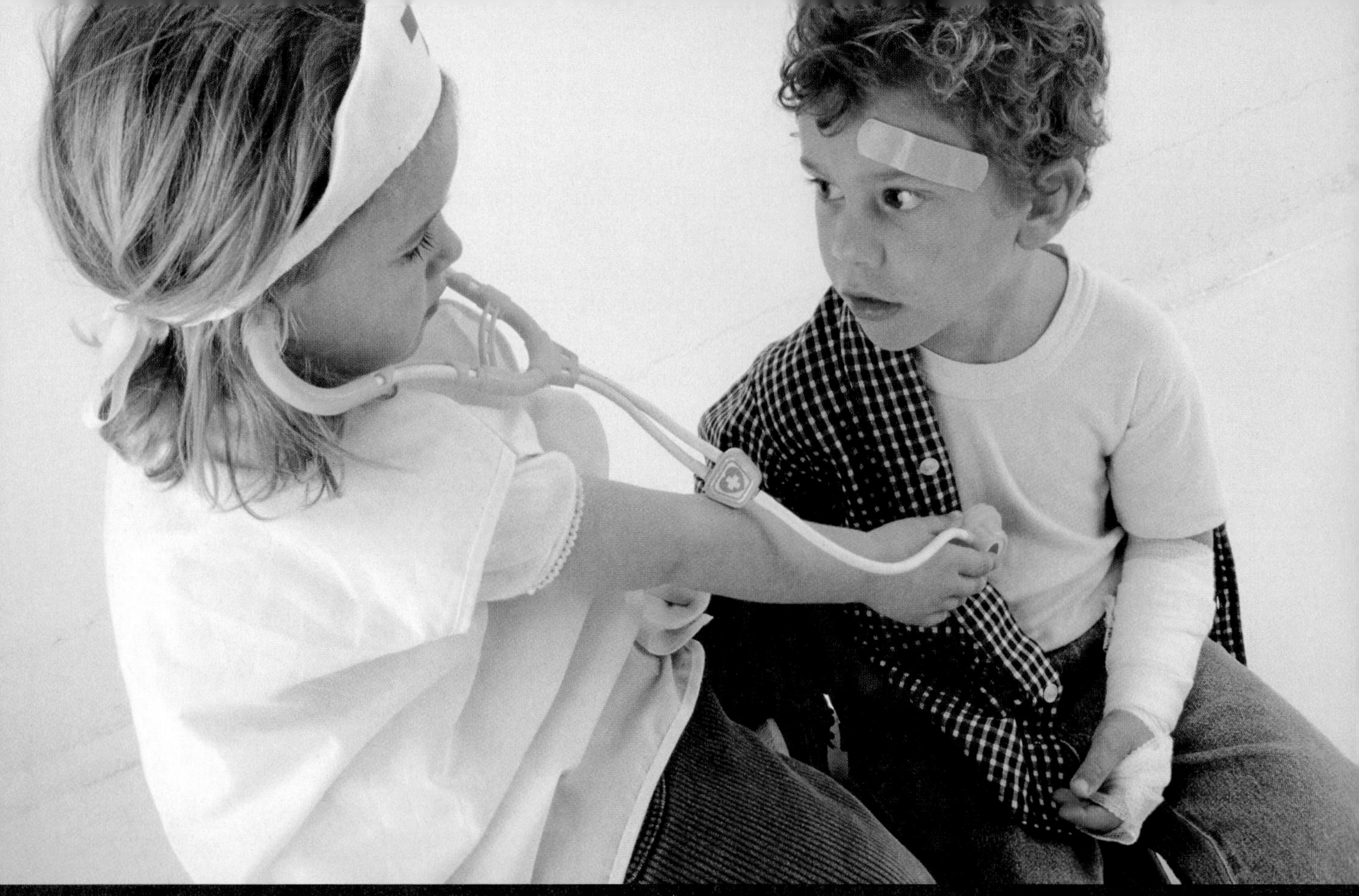

CHAPTER TWELVE

Sexuality Across the Life Cycle

In this chapter we discuss sexuality across the life cycle. Within children's personal and social experiences lie the seeds of later sexual competence and self-esteem—or the seeds of incompetence, guilt, and shame. While people experience changes in their sexuality throughout their lives, many continue to enjoy sexual relations well into old age. Given concerns over issues such as teen pregnancy and sexually transmitted infections, much research has been conducted in Canada on adolescent sexuality. Accordingly, in this chapter we will present a wealth of Canadian data on young people, including statistics from major national surveys.

Hardly any research has been conducted on childhood sexuality, with the exception of child sexual abuse. As a result, we know far more about childhood sexual abuse in Canada than we do about normal childhood sexual development.

Infancy (Birth to Two Years): The Search for the Origins of Human Sexuality

Infants—and fetuses!—engage in a variety of "sexual" behaviours, although the "meaning" of these behaviours, if there is one, is a matter for speculation. Imaging techniques such as ultrasound have shown, for example, that male fetuses have erections. Fetuses of both sexes suck their fingers. The sucking reflex allows babies to obtain nourishment, but infants also appear to reap pleasure from sucking fingers, pacifiers, nipples, or whatever else fits into the mouth. None of this is surprising, given the sensitivity of the mouth's mucous lining.

Stimulation of the genitals in infancy can also produce pleasure. Parents who touch their infants' genitals while changing or washing them may discover the infants smiling or becoming excited. Infants discover the pleasure of self-stimulation (*masturbation*) for themselves when they gain the ability to manipulate their genitals with their hands.

The Infant's Capacity for Sexual Response

Boys not only have erections in utero, but many boys are, in fact, born with erections. Erection is a reflex that begins to operate early in life. Most boys have erections during the first few weeks. Signs of sexual arousal in infant girls, such as

Applied Knowledge

HOW SHOULD PARENTS DEAL WITH THEIR CHILDREN OBSERVING THEM IN THE NUDE/ SHOWERING TOGETHER OR HAVING SEX?

Sigmund Freud referred to observing parents having sex as the "primal scene," and he thought it could lead to all sorts of psychological problems. However, many sex educators say it's just part of a child's sex education. Let us suggest that observing nudity, parental or otherwise, is not in itself a problem. Are we going to "protect" our children from the greatest works of art in the greatest museums? And observing parents or stepparents engaged in sexual activity is not the end of the world either. A child can simply be told, "That's a way we express our love (or affection) for one another." If necessary, the child can also be told, preferably with a smile, "We prefer our privacy when we do that, you know." But then, parents also have to be willing to respect the child's privacy. Warning: If parents act as if the child has caught them doing something bad, the message is: We were doing something bad.

vaginal lubrication, are less readily detected. Yet evidence of lubrication and genital swelling has been reported (Mazur, 2006).

But do not interpret children's reflexes according to adult concepts of sexuality. The reflexes of lubrication and erection do not necessarily signify "interest" in sex. We cannot say what, if anything, infants' sexual reflexes "mean" to them.

PELVIC THRUSTING Pelvic thrusting is observed in infant monkeys, apes, and humans. These observations led ethologist John Bowlby (1969) to suggest that infantile sexual behaviour may be the rule in mammals, not the exception. Thrusting has been observed in humans at eight to 10 months of age and may be an expression of affection. Typically, the infant clings to the parent, then nuzzles, thrusts, and rotates the pelvis for several seconds.

At What Age Does Curiosity About Sex Develop? Children are naturally inquisitive about sexual anatomy and sexual behaviour. Much curiosity is triggered when they become aware that males and females differ in anatomy.

ORGASM At least some infants seem capable of involuntary muscular contractions that closely resemble orgasm. Kinsey and his colleagues (1953) noted that baby boys show behaviours that resemble orgasm as early as five months, baby girls as early as four months. Orgasms in boys are similar to those in men, but lack ejaculation. Ejaculation occurs only after puberty.

Masturbation

Masturbation is typical for infants and young children and may start as early as five months of age (Health24.com, 2006; Narchi, 2003). Infants may masturbate by rubbing their genitals against a soft object, such as a towel, bedding, or a doll. As they mature and develop sensorimotor coordination, infants may prefer manual stimulation of the genitals.

Masturbation to orgasm is rare until the second year (Reinisch, 1990). Some children begin masturbating to orgasm later. Some never do. All in all, however, orgasm from masturbation is found frequently among children, as among adults (Reinisch, 1990).

Sexual Curiosity

Children frequently develop sexual curiosity as early as 12 to 15 months of age. They play "doctor" and show their curiosity about the

A Lesbian Couple and Their Child.
Many lesbian couples, such as this one, have children. Sometimes the children derive from earlier marriages. Sometimes they are adopted. Some lesbians are artificially inseminated or else engage in sexual intercourse for the purpose of becoming pregnant.

sexual anatomy of other people in other ways, such as wanting to watch a parent take a shower or bath (Health24.com, 2006; Pike, 2005).

Genital Play

Children in Canada typically do not engage in genital play with others until about the age of two. Then, as an expression of their curiosity about their environment and other people, they may investigate other children's genitals or may hug, cuddle, kiss, or climb on top of them. None of this need cause concern. There is no reason to infer that children are seeking sexual gratification. Rough-and-tumble play, including touching the genitals, is common among children.

Lesbian and Gay Parents

Questions have been raised about the effects—if any—of being reared by gay parents. There has been relatively little research on lesbian and gay couples and parenting. Deborah Foster (2005a), a therapist in Alberta, has provided a comprehensive analysis of the research on lesbian families. She notes that most lesbian families were formed as a result of the birth mother having had children in a heterosexual relationship, leaving that relationship, and then living in a lesbian relationship. Foster has summarized key findings based on comparison of children raised in lesbian families with those raised in heterosexual families. She found that children raised in lesbian families:

- Develop normal gender identities and gender roles;
- Develop normal peer relationships;
- Exhibit normal emotional/behavioural development;
- Have fewer issues regarding their sexual identity; and,
- Are no more likely to grow up gay or lesbian than children raised in heterosexual families. (Foster, 2005a, pp. 291–292)

Foster states that a key factor of the tendency for children in lesbian families to have a normal development is that lesbian families tend to be equalitarian, nurturing, and empathic (Foster, 2005b). Foster concludes that children raised in lesbian families are just as well adjusted, if not more so, than those raised in heterosexual families. Similar findings have been reported for children raised by gay male parents (Vervoort, 1999).

Early Childhood (Three to Eight Years)

> *Susan:* Once my younger sister and I were over at a girlfriend's house playing in her bedroom. For some reason she pulled her pants down and exposed her rear to us. We were amazed to see she had an extra opening down there we didn't know about. My sister reciprocated by pulling her pants down so we could see if she had the same extra opening. We were amazed at our discovery, our mothers not having mentioned to us that we had a vagina!
>
> *Christopher:* Nancy was a willing playmate, and we spent many hours together examining each other's bodies as doctor and nurse. We even once figured out a pact that we would continue these examinations and watch each other develop. That was before we had started school. (Morrison et al., 1980, p. 19)

These recollections from early childhood illustrate children's interest in sexual anatomy and behaviour. Children in early childhood often show each other their bodies (Pike, 2005). The unwritten rule seems to be, "I'll show you mine if you'll show me yours."

Masturbation

> *Kim:* I began to masturbate when I was three years old. My parents . . . tried long and hard to discourage me. They told me it wasn't nice for a young lady to have her hand between her legs.
>
> When I was five I remember my mother discovering that I masturbated with a rag doll I slept with. She was upset, but she didn't make a big deal about it. She just told me in a matter-of-fact way, "Do you know that what you're doing is called masturbating?" That didn't make much sense to me, except I got the impression she didn't want me to do it. (Morrison et al., 1980, pp. 4–5)

Because of the difficulties in conducting research into childhood sexuality, statistics on masturbation and other sexual activities are largely speculative (Bancroft, 2003). Parents may not wish to answer questions about their children's sexual behaviour. Or they may want to present their children as little "gentlemen" and "ladies" by underreporting their sexual activity. Their biases may lead them not to perceive genital touching as masturbation. Many parents will not even allow their adolescents to be interviewed about sex (Kaiser Family Foundation et al., 2003), let alone younger children. And when we try to look back as adults, our memories may be cloudy.

A study by William Friedrich (1998) of the Mayo Institute relied on interviews with the mothers of more than 1100 children. The goal of the study was to establish what kinds of sexual behaviours can normally be expected in childhood to help

Some children sexualize their Barbies.

TABLE 12.1
Some Common Sexual Behaviours During Childhood

	Boys	Girls
Ages 2-5		
Touches or tries to touch mother's or other women's breasts	42.4%	43.7%
Touches private parts when at home	60.2	43.8
Tries to look at people when they are nude or undressing	26.8	26.9
Ages 6-9		
Touches private parts when at home	39.8	20.7
Tries to look at people when they are nude or undressing	20.2	20.5
Ages 10-12		
Is very interested in the opposite sex	24.1	28.7

Source: Friedrich, W. M., Fisher, J., Broughton, D., Houston, M., & Shafran, C. R. (1998). Normative sexual behaviour in children: A contemporary sample. Pediatrics, *101(4) e9 [electronic article].*

educators and other professionals determine when sexual behaviour might be suggestive of childhood sexual abuse. The study did not provide data about masturbation per se, but, as shown in Table 12.1, it offered some insight into how many children touch their "private parts." Friedrich (1998) suggests that behaviour that occurs in at least 20% of children is normal from a statistical point of view.

Let's listen in on a woman describing her memories when she was on the cusp of preadolescence:

> When I was 8 and had just learned about menstruation, I fashioned a small sanitary napkin for [my Barbie doll] out of neatly folded tissues. Rubber bands held it in place. "Look," said my bemused mother, "Barbie's got her little period. Now she can have a baby." I was disappointed, but my girlfriends snickered in a way that satisfied me. You see, we all wanted Barbie to be, well. Dirty . . .
>
> Our Barbies had sex, at least our childish version of it. They hugged and kissed the few available boy dolls we had—clean-cut and oh-so-square Ken, the more relaxed and sexy Allan. Our Barbies also danced, pranced, and strutted, but mostly they stripped. An adult friend tells me how she used to put her Barbie's low-backed bathing suit on backward, so the doll's breasts were exposed. I dressed mine in her candy-striped babysitter's apron—and nothing else. Girls respond intuitively to the doll's sexuality, and it lets them play out those roles in an endlessly compelling and yet ultimately safe manner. (McDonough, 1998, p. 70).

The "childish version" of things has a way of shaping a lifetime of sexual experiences. As we see in the saga of the Barbie dolls, children tend to play at sex for many years before they are ready for "real" sex.

Male-Female Sexual Behaviour

> *Alicia:* On my birthday when I was in the second grade, I remember a classmate, Tim, walked home with a friend and me. He kept chasing me to give me kisses all over my face, and I acted like I didn't want him to do it, yet I knew I liked it a lot; when he would stop, I thought he didn't like me anymore (Morrison et al., 1980, pp. 21, 29).

Three- and four-year-olds commonly express affection through kissing. Curiosity about the genitals increases in this stage. Sex games like "show" and playing "doctor" may begin earlier, but they become common between the ages of 6 and 10 (Pike, 2005). Much of this sexual activity takes place in same-sex groups, although mixed-sex sex games are not uncommon. Children may show their genitals to each other, touch each other's genitals, or masturbate together.

Male-Male and Female-Female Sexual Behaviour

> *Arnold:* When I was about five, my cousin and I . . . went into the basement and dropped our pants. We touched each other's penises, and that was it. I guess I didn't realize the total significance of the secrecy in which we carried out this act. For later . . . my parents questioned me . . . and I told them exactly what we had done. They were horrified and told me that that was definitely forbidden (Morrison et al., 1980, p. 24).

Despite Arnold's parents' "horror," same-sex sexual play in childhood does not foreshadow adult sexual orientation (Reinisch, 1990). It may, in fact, be more common than heterosexual play. It typically involves handling the other child's genitals, although it may include oral or anal contact. It may also include an outdoor variation of the game of "show" in which boys urinate together and see who can reach farthest or highest.

Preadolescence (Nine to Thirteen Years)

Some preadolescent behaviours are sexually related rather than sexual per se. For example, preadolescents typically form a relationship with a "best friend" of the same sex that enables them to share secrets and confidences. Preadolescents also tend to socialize with larger networks of friends in sex-segregated groups. At this stage, boys are likely to think that girls are "dorks." To girls at this stage, "dork" is too nice an epithet to apply to most boys.

Preadolescents grow increasingly preoccupied with, and self-conscious about, their bodies. Peers pressure preadolescents to conform to dress codes, the "proper" slang, and group norms concerning sex and drugs. Peer disapproval can be an intense punishment.

Sexual urges are experienced by many preadolescents but may not emerge until adolescence (O'Sullivan, 2003).

Masturbation

Kinsey and his colleagues (1948, 1953) reported that masturbation is the primary means of achieving orgasm during preadolescence for both boys and girls. They found that 45% of males and 15% of females masturbated by age 13. Although the frequencies of masturbation reported by Kinsey and his colleagues are suspect, other studies agree that adolescent males are more likely to masturbate than adolescent females (Pinkerton et al., 2002). As noted by Steven Pinkerton and his colleagues (2002), the frequency of masturbation is connected with social norms that appear to hold that masturbation is more acceptable or normal for males than for females.

Male-Female Sexual Behaviour

Preadolescent sex play often involves mutual display of the genitals, with or without touching. Such sexual experiences are quite common and do not appear to affect future sexual adjustment (www.guttmacher.org, 2006; Health24.com, 2006).

Although preadolescents tend to socialize in same-sex groups, interest in the other sex among heterosexuals tends to increase gradually as they approach puberty. Group activities and mixed-sex parties often provide preadolescents with their first exposure to heterosexual activities (Connolly et al., 2004). However, couples may not begin to pair off until middle adolescence.

Male-Male and Female-Female Sexual Behaviour

Much preadolescent sexual behaviour among members of the same sex is simply exploration. Some incidents reflect lack of availability of partners of the other sex. As with younger children, preadolescent experiences with children of the same sex may be more common than heterosexual experiences (www.guttmacher.org, 2006; Health24.com, 2006). These activities are usually limited to touching each other's genitals or mutual masturbation. Because preadolescents generally socialize with peers of their own sex, their sexual explorations are also often with peers of their own sex. Most same-sex sexual experiences involve single episodes or short-lived relationships and do not always reflect one's sexual orientation.

Sources of Information About Sex

We can learn about sex from many different sources. In the 2003 Canada Youth and AIDS Survey, students were asked for their main sources of information about sex and birth control (Boyce et al., 2003). About 45% of grade 9 students said that school was their main source of information. More girls than boys listed friends and mother as their main sources of sex information, whereas more boys than girls said the school and the internet were. Only 5% said medical professionals were their main source and hardly any (less than 2%) said that fathers were.

Many people believe that parents should have the main responsibility for providing sex education. In the Canada Youth and AIDS Survey, about a quarter of the boys said they could talk openly about sex with their father or mother, while 37% of girls said they could talk to their mother and far fewer (12%) said they could talk to their father (Boyce et al., 2003). Yet about two-thirds of high school students in a New Brunswick survey rated the sex education they received from parents as good to excellent. However, about one-half did not want their parents to talk to them more about sexuality (Byers et al., 2003).

In Regina, most high school students said they preferred learning about topics such as pregnancy and STI prevention from school. However, when the topics were dating and relationships, most preferred learning from personal experience, friends, and parents (Hampton et al., 2005).

The popular media are especially important for providing information about topics that are not covered in school programs, such as sexual techniques and pleasure. A study of women at an Ontario university found that women's magazines were a common source of sexuality information (Bielay & Herold, 1995). The most frequently read magazine (by 79%) was *Cosmopolitan*. (Students with more liberal sexual attitudes read the magazine more often than did students having more conservative values.) The women reported that, out of the 34 sexuality topics included in the survey, *Cosmopolitan* was their major magazine source of information for 25.

Although *Cosmopolitan* has an emphasis on sexual content, it is not considered a "sex" magazine but rather a "women's" magazine. This distinction is important in providing greater legitimacy both for the women who read it and for the stores that sell it (Bielay & Herold, 1995).

Websites have been developed by health, education, and social agencies to provide sex information. One of the most comprehensive is **www.sexualityandu.ca**, sponsored by the Society of Obstetricians and Gynaecologists of Canada. Developed by William Fisher at the University of Western Ontario, the site is based on Fisher's Information-Motivation-Behavioural Skills theoretical model (IMB), which emphasizes the motivation and behavioural skills required by individuals to act in a sexually healthy manner. In addition to providing information specifically for adolescents, the site has modules for adults, parents, and health-care providers. A similar innovative website has been developed by Alberta teachers and health professionals at **www.teachingsexualhealth.ca**. Teachers can browse and download lesson plans for teaching sex education by grade level and by topic.

sexualityandu.ca: Your Link to Sexual Well-Being
This website provides comprehensive sex information on a range of topics such as contraception and sexually transmitted infections.

www.sexualityandu.ca

Formal Sources of Sexuality Education

Because education in Canada is the responsibility of the provinces and the territories, the quality of sex education varies tremendously both across provinces and within them. And rather than being taught as a separate subject, sex education is usually included in health courses, often with a focus on its biological/reproductive aspects.

During the 1970s teenage pregnancy was a major concern in Canada, a fact that encouraged many school boards to incorporate sex education topics, particularly contraception, into the curriculum. Until that time contraception had not been taught in the schools, primarily because contraceptives were illegal until 1969. The spread of HIV in the 1980s further encouraged the teaching of sex education, especially the teaching about condoms.

Over the years, some religiously based groups have opposed sex education in Canadian schools and have pressured school boards to adopt programs that teach only sexual abstinence and that avoid subjects such as contraception and homosexuality. For the most part, these groups have not been influential in Canada. However, in the United States, conservative religious groups have had a strong voice in influencing the U.S. Congress to spend hundreds of millions of dollars on abstinence-only sex education programs. These programs are not permitted to discuss the benefits of contraception. In contrast, the Canadian federal government does not support abstinence-only programs. Most formal evaluations of abstinence-only programs indicate that they do not reduce rates of sexual behaviour (Bennett & Assefi, 2005).

The Alberta Teachers' Association
Provides resources for building awareness of sexual orientation and gender identity issues. Click on Diversity, Equity and Human Rights under Issues in Education.
www.teachers.ab.ca

Most Canadians support sex education in the schools, including contraceptive methods (Maticka-Tyndale et al., 2001). In a study of 4200 parents in New Brunswick, 94% agreed that sexual health education should be provided by schools. Most of the parents supported the teaching of a broad range of topics, including homosexuality, masturbation, and sexual pleasure (Weaver et al., 2002).

Most Canadian provinces require that sex education be taught as a component of health education at least at the grade 9 level. However, in 2005, the Quebec government no longer mandated sex education.

Unfortunately, sex education is not seen as a major priority in most Canadian school systems and the time allocated for instruction on sexual health is minimal. Thus many students are disappointed with the quality of sex education they receive. In a survey of New Brunswick high school students, only 13% rated their sexual health education as very good or excellent (Byers et al., 2003). Also, in Newfoundland and Labrador, most adolescents felt that they had only limited access to sex education and service (Johns & Lush, 2004). Moreover, Canadian students in 2002 were found to be less knowledgeable about STI and HIV transmission than were students in 1989 (Boyce et al., 2003).

A major criticism of school-based sex education programs is that they focus on harm. In an interview study, young adults in British Columbia and Nova Scotia expressed dissatisfaction with their sex education for neglecting the emotional and potentially positive aspects of sex. They stated that these programs were concerned only with providing information about pregnancy and STI prevention (Shoveller et al., 2004).

Sue Johanson.
The most popular sex educator in Canada presents down-to-earth information in a humorous manner to youth and to adults. Johanson has given sex education talks in every part of Canada to a wide diversity of audiences.

MEETING THE NEEDS OF GAY, LESBIAN, AND BISEXUAL YOUTH Many sex education programs do not address the needs of gay, lesbian, and bisexual youth. University of Alberta researchers Andre Grace and Kristopher Wells (2007) have analyzed many of the difficulties faced by these youth, such as feelings of isolation, fear of humiliation, and lack of social support. Grace and Wells (2006) have developed a series of teacher professional-development workshops designed to address sexual minority issues in schools. In recent years several initiatives have been made to make schools more inclusive. For example, the Toronto District School Board established a Triangle program for lesbian, gay, bisexual, and transgendered (LGBT) youth.

Gay high school youth are playing an important activist role in challenging heterosexism and homophobia in schools. They are promoting inclusivity through such strategies as creating gay–straight student alliances, initiating positive-space campaigns, and sharing of LGBTQ resources (Grace & Wells, 2007).

Teachers' organizations across Canada have adopted policies that are supportive of LGBT youth. The Alberta Teachers' Association has been in the forefront in fighting discrimination based on sexual orientation. Under the leadership of the University of Alberta teaching faculty, guides have been developed for creating safe, caring, and inclusive schools and developing gay–straight alliances.

Kristopher Wells (2006) has written a *Gay–Straight Student Alliance Handbook*, published by the Canadian Teachers Federation. Its primary objective is to assist Canadian educators in creating safe, inclusive, and welcoming spaces for LGBT youth. Gay–straight student alliances (student-run and teacher-supported groups) are an important means of achieving this objective. The Canadian Teachers Federation has also published *Challenging Silence, Challenging Censorship* (Schrader & Wells, 2007), which discusses practical resources to help educators and decision-makers challenge discrimination and promote positive change for sexual minorities.

SEXUAL VALUES While Canadians want sex education in the schools, they differ about what values should be taught. Among 130 Ontario mothers of school-aged children, for example, 91% believed that the schools should teach sex education and 70% agreed that schools should teach contraceptive methods. Asked whether an important objective of sex education was to discourage premarital sex, however, 45% disagreed, 36% agreed, and 19% were undecided. The strongest predictor of attitudes to sex education was the mothers' attitudes to premarital sex. Those who were opposed to premarital sex were the least supportive of sex education and wanted the schools to teach conservative values (Marsman & Herold, 1986).

Alex McKay, in his 1998 book *Sexual Ideology and Schooling*, gives an insightful analysis of the battle over values. He discusses a range of sexual values along a continuum from restrictive to permissive and clearly shows how a particular sexual ideology can influence the objectives and content of sexuality education. McKay argues that students should be informed about the differing values perspectives so that they are better prepared to decide which sexual ideology they should choose for themselves.

CANADIAN GUIDELINES FOR SEXUAL HEALTH EDUCATION

To facilitate the development of comprehensive education programs for healthy sexuality, Health Canada sponsored the Canadian Guidelines for Sexual Health Education. These guidelines, developed by experts in sexual health under the coordination of the Sex Information and Education Council of Canada (SIECCAN), not only focus on the prevention of sexual problems such as HIV/AIDS, but also promote sexual health enhancement, for example by promoting positive self-image and non-exploitative sexual satisfaction. These guidelines clearly illustrate how Canadian attitudes differ from American attitudes.

One of the guiding principles of the Canadian Guidelines is that effective sexual health education should be available to everyone, from young children to senior adults. Moreover, promoting healthy sexuality is not simply a matter of providing information, but also involves the development of motivations, insight, and skills so that people can establish and maintain sexual health. To encourage sexually active adolescents to use condoms, the guidelines maintain that schools should not only provide instructions on how to use a condom, but also explain why they are a good idea, help students to communicate about them, and consider ways to make them more accessible. (Some Canadian schools, for example, have health clinics providing contraceptives; others have condom dispensers in the washrooms.)

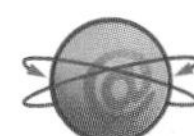

Sex Information and Education Council of Canada (SIECCAN)

www.sieccan.org

The Canadian Guidelines can be viewed at the website of the Sex Information and Education Council of Canada (SIECCAN). The SIECCAN site also provides information on many of the commonly asked questions about sex education programs, such as "Are abstinence-only programs an appropriate form of school-based sexual health education?"

SEX EDUCATION CURRICULUM AND RESOURCES A wide variety of sex education programs and resources have been developed across Canada. In Ontario, Skills for Healthy Relationships is a sexual health curriculum for grade 9 students developed by the Social Program Evaluation Group at Queen's University. This curriculum provides a practical example of the Canadian Guidelines and follows many of its principles. When the program was evaluated in a two-year follow-up with 6750 students from four provinces, the results showed that students who took the curriculum were less likely to have experienced first intercourse in the two years after the program than students who did not. However, they did not differ from students who had not taken the program with respect to condom use. Within both groups, 41% reported that they always used condoms (Maticka-Tyndale, 2001).

Another curriculum—Girl Time: Grade 7/8 Healthy Sexuality Program, based on the Canadian Guidelines—was developed and tested by an Ontario group led by University of Waterloo researcher B. J. Rye (2008). The objectives were to encourage young girls to delay sexual intercourse until they were mature enough and to practise safer sex when they were having sex. Girls participating in the program were more likely than nonparticipants to discuss sexual topics with their parents, to feel confident in being able to have safer sex such as by obtaining condoms, and to intend to engage in safer sex practices such as abstaining from sexual intercourse (Rye et al., 2008).

Community agencies such as public health units, sexual health centres, and Planned Parenthood groups provide valuable assistance and resources to schools. For example, the Calgary Sexual Health Centre provides comprehensive sexuality education to youth throughout Calgary, to students as well as to youth and adults who are not in school.

Nova Scotia has made improving the sexual health of youth a key priority and has launched an integrated approach that involves sexual health education, and services and support systems for youth. The program is based on a document called "Framework for Action: Youth Sexual Health in Nova Scotia." A key aspect of this program is that youth in Nova Scotia are participating in every phase, including the development of content for schools' sex-education programs. The Department of Health Promotion and Protection consulted with 500 youth in developing a sex education book, *Sex—A Healthy Sexuality Resource*. Young people were asked what they "wanted to know, needed to know or wish they had been told" in order to make decisions about healthy sexuality. Consultations were also held with parents, teachers, and experts in sexual health. The book is colourful and presents practical information, such as how to avoid getting STIs and how to talk to one's parents about sex.

Alberta educators and researchers have developed and evaluated the use of a theatrical play for 14- to 16-year-olds (Esmail et al., 2007). *Are We There Yet?* is a theatre-based sexual education program based on learning theory. It uses a student-centred approach to present real-life situations that students can relate to. This encourages greater student participation in the play. Student evaluations indicate that the play is an effective means of providing sex education to youth (Esmail et al., 2007).

TRAINING OF SEXUAL HEALTH PROFESSIONALS A major limit to the effectiveness of sex education programs is the lack of training for teachers. Many teachers and therapists have not received adequate training in sexuality. For example, two-thirds of New Brunswick elementary and middle school teachers report that they have not received training to teach sex education (Cohen et al., 2004). Although many Canadian universities offer undergraduate courses in human sexuality, a surprising number have no sexuality courses. Few offer graduate programs.

Applied Knowledge

TALKING WITH YOUR CHILDREN ABOUT SEX

"Daddy, where do babies come from?"

"What are you asking me for? Go ask your mother."

Most children do not find it easy to talk to their parents about sex. Yet most young children are curious about where babies come from, about how girls and boys differ, and so on (Pike, 2005). Parents who avoid discussing these matters convey their own uneasiness about sex and may teach children that sex is something to be ashamed of.

Parents need not be sex experts to talk to their children about sex. Parents can turn to books or surf the internet to fill gaps in knowledge, or turn to books written for parents to read to children. They can admit they do not know all the answers. Children often respect such honesty.

In answering children's questions, parents need to think about what children can understand (Pike, 2005). The four-year-old who wants to know where babies come from is probably not interested in sexual details. It may be enough to say, "From Mommy's uterus" and then point to the abdominal region. Why say "tummy"? "Tummy" is wrong and confusing.

Sex educators offer pointers about discussing sex with children:

- Be "askable." Be willing to answer questions about sex.
- Use appropriate language. Children need to learn the correct names of their sex organs and that the "dirty words" others use to refer to the sex organs are not acceptable in most social settings. Nor should parents use silly words like "pee-pee" or "privates" to describe sex organs.
- Give advice in the form of information that the child can use to make sound decisions, not as an imperial edict. Parents who "lay down the law" may be less effective than parents who provide information and encourage discussion.
- Share information in small doses. Pick a time and place that feels natural for these discussions, such as when the child is preparing for bed or when you are in the car.
- Encourage the child to talk about sex. Children may feel embarrassed about talking about sex, especially with family members. Children's books about sex can be left around or given to the child with a suggestion such as "I thought you might be interested in this book about sex. If you want to read it, we can talk about it."

Talking With Children About Sex. ***Answer the questions truthfully. Use language the child will understand, but don't make it silly child language. In other words, don't talk about pee-pees and wee-wees and Mommy's tummy. Try penis, vagina, and uterus. Get a book with drawings or pictures.***

- Respect privacy rights. Most of us, parents and children alike, value privacy at times. A parent who feels uncomfortable sharing a bathroom with a child can tell the child. The parent might explain, "I like privacy when my door is closed. If you knock, I'll tell you whether you may come in. I'll knock when your door is closed too." Fair is fair.

The Université du Québec à Montréal offers both undergraduate and graduate degree programs (in French) in human sexuality. St. Jerome's University at the University of Waterloo offers an undergraduate program in sexuality, marriage, and family studies, directed by Dr. B. J. Rye. Programs are also offered at York University and the University of Toronto. Other Canadian universities, such as the University of Guelph, provide undergraduate and graduate courses and/or research specialization opportunities in sexuality. The largest annual conference on human sexuality in Canada is offered by the University of Guelph.

Adolescence

Adolescence is bounded by the advent of puberty at the earlier end and the capacity to take on adult responsibilities at the later end. Adults see adolescents as impulsive and as needing to be restricted for "their own good." Given these restrictions, a sex drive that is heightened by surges of sex hormones, and media inundation with sexual themes, it is not surprising that many adolescents are in conflict with their families about going around with certain friends, about sex, and about using the family car.

Puberty The stage of development during which reproduction first becomes possible. Puberty begins with the appearance of *secondary sex characteristics* and ends when the long bones make no further gains in length.

Secondary sex characteristics Physical characteristics that differentiate males and females and that usually appear at puberty but are not directly involved in reproduction, such as the bodily distribution of hair and fat, the development of muscle mass, and deepening of the voice.

Primary sex characteristics Physical characteristics that differentiate males and females and are directly involved in reproduction, such as the sex organs.

Critical fat hypothesis The view that girls must reach a certain body weight to trigger pubertal changes such as menarche.

Menarche (men-AR-kee) The onset of menstruation; first menstruation. Girls experience menarche between the ages of 10 and 18. In the 1890s, Canadian girls typically reached menarche by about 14.8 years. Since then, the age of menarche has declined sharply, probably as a result of improved nutrition and health care. The average age of menarche in Canada is now between 12 and 13 (Wyshuk & Frisch, as cited by Maticka-Tyndale, 2001).

Anovulatory Without ovulation.

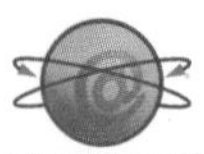

Scarleteen
A sex education website for teenagers.
www.scarleteen.com

Puberty

Puberty begins with the appearance of **secondary sex characteristics** and ends when the long bones make no further gains in length. The appearance of strands of pubic hair is often the first visible sign of puberty. Puberty also involves changes in **primary sex characteristics**. Once puberty begins, most major changes occur within three years in girls and within four years in boys.

Toward the end of puberty, reproduction becomes possible. The two principal markers of reproductive potential are menarche in the girl and the first ejaculation in the boy. But these events do not generally herald immediate fertility.

The **critical fat hypothesis** suggests that girls must reach a certain body weight (perhaps 47–50 kg) to trigger pubertal changes such as menarche, and children today tend to achieve larger body sizes sooner. According to this hypothesis, body fat plays a crucial role because fat cells secrete leptin, a chemical that then signals the body to secrete a cascade of hormones that increases the levels of estrogen in the body. It is known that menarche comes later to girls who have a lower percentage of body fat, such as athletes (Frisch, 1997).

Brock University researcher Anthony Bogaert (2005a) found that age of puberty was related to father absence. Both females and males at the age of 14 whose father was absent had earlier signs of puberty such as menarche or voice change. However, having an absent mother had no effect on the age of puberty. The findings suggest that certain psychosocial factors such as father absence may affect the growth development of both girls and boys (Bogaert, 2005).

PUBERTAL CHANGES IN THE FEMALE First menstruation, or **menarche**, is the most obvious sign of puberty in girls. Yet other less obvious changes have already set the stage for menstruation. Between 8 and 14 years of age, release of FSH by the pituitary gland causes the ovaries to begin to secrete estrogen. Estrogen has several major effects on pubertal development. For one, it stimulates the growth of breast tissue ("breast buds"), perhaps as early as age eight or nine. The breasts usually begin to enlarge during the tenth year.

Estrogen also promotes the growth of the uterus, thickening of the vaginal lining, and the growth of fatty and supporting tissue in the hips and buttocks. This tissue and the widening of the pelvis causes the hips to become rounded and permit childbearing. But growth of fatty deposits and connective tissue varies considerably. Some women may have pronounced breasts; others may have relatively large hips.

Small amounts of androgens produced by the female's adrenal glands, along with estrogen, stimulate development of pubic and underarm hair, beginning at about age 11. Excessive androgen production can darken or thicken facial hair.

Estrogen causes the labia to grow during puberty, but androgens cause the clitoris to develop. Estrogen stimulates growth of the vagina and uterus. Estrogen typically slows down the female growth spurt some years before that of the male. Estrogen production becomes cyclical in puberty and regulates the menstrual cycle. Following menarche, a girl's early menstrual cycles are typically **anovulatory**—without ovulation. Girls cannot become pregnant until ovulation occurs, and ovulation may lag behind menarche by as much as two years. As well, ovulation may not be reliable at first, so a girl may be relatively infertile. Some teenagers, however, are highly fertile soon after menarche.

PUBERTAL CHANGES IN THE MALE At puberty the hypothalamus signals the pituitary to increase production of FSH and LH. These releasing hormones

Adolescence.
Adolescents have a sex drive that is heightened by surges of hormones.

stimulate the testes to increase their output of testosterone. Testosterone prompts growth of the male genitals: the testes, scrotum, and penis. It fosters differentiation of male secondary sex characteristics: the growth of facial, body, and pubic hair and the deepening of the voice. Testicle growth, in turn, accelerates testosterone production and pubertal changes. The testes continue to grow, and the scrotal sac becomes larger and hangs loosely from the body. The penis widens and lengthens, and pubic hair appears.

Nocturnal emission Involuntary ejaculation of seminal fluid while asleep.

Larynx A structure of muscle and cartilage that lies at the upper end of the trachea and contains the vocal cords; the voice box.

By age 13 or 14, erections become frequent. Indeed, many junior high school boys dread being caught between classes with an erection or being asked to stand before the class. Under the influence of testosterone, the prostate and seminal vesicles—the organs that produce semen—increase in size, and semen production begins. Boys typically experience their first ejaculation by age 13 or 14, most often through masturbation. About a year after their first ejaculation, boys may begin to experience **nocturnal emissions**, which are also called wet dreams because usually nocturnal emissions accompany erotic dreams.

Underarm hair appears at about age 15. Facial hair is at first a fuzz on the upper lip. A beard does not appear for another two or three years. Only half of boys shave (of necessity) by age 17. The beard and chest hair continue to develop past the age of 20. At age 14 or 15, the voice deepens because of the growth of the **larynx** and the lengthening of the vocal cords.

Boys and girls undergo general growth spurts during puberty. Girls usually shoot up before boys. Individuals differ, however, and some boys spurt sooner than some girls.

Increases in muscle mass produce increases in weight. The shoulders and the circumference of the chest widen. At the age of 18 or so, men stop growing taller because estrogen prevents the long bones from making further gains in length. Males normally produce some estrogen in the adrenal glands and testes. Nearly one in two boys experiences temporary enlargement of the breasts during puberty; this also is caused by estrogen.

With all these dramatic physical changes occurring so quickly, it is no surprise that body image can be of great concern to both male and female adolescents. Adolescent girls are typically more concerned about body image issues than are boys. Among Canadian teenagers, more girls (45%) than boys (21%) report that they are troubled a lot by their weight, although almost as many boys (45%) as girls report that they are troubled a lot by their looks (Bibby, 2001).

Masturbation

Masturbation is a major sexual outlet during adolescence. Yet many Canadian teens, especially girls, have negative attitudes toward masturbation. In the 2002 Canadian schools study, only 32% of grade 11 girls compared with 63% of boys approved of masturbation (Boyce et al., 2003).

Male-Female Sexual Behaviour

DATING In his study of 3500 Canadian youth aged 15 to 19, Reginald Bibby (2001), a sociologist at the University of Lethbridge in Alberta and one of Canada's foremost experts on adolescents, found that dating is an important part of the lives of most adolescents. Twenty-five percent of the girls and 17% of the boys reported that they had conflicts with their parents over dating, suggesting that Canadian parents are more concerned about the dating of their daughters than of their sons.

Twice as many boys (53%) as girls (27%) reported they weren't dating anyone (Bibby, 2001), probably owing to the fact that many adolescent girls date older males. About one-quarter of adolescents report that they are seriously involved in a dating relationship with one person. It should be noted that, although researchers use the concept of dating for the sake of consistency, young people today are more likely to use terms such as *seeing each other* instead of dating and *going together* instead of steady dating (Larson, Goltz, & Munro, 2000).

In recent years there have been major changes in dating norms. For example, in the past it was expected that it was up to the boy to ask a girl for a date. However, in the 2002 Canadian schools survey, more than 90% of boys and girls agreed that it is acceptable for a girl to ask someone out on a date (Boyce et al., 2003).

Canadian adolescents generally agree that as the level of dating increases, the acceptability of more intimate sexual behaviours also increases (Bibby, 2001). Almost all agree that kissing is acceptable after a few dates and more than two-thirds agree that it is acceptable on the first date. More than 80% feel that petting is acceptable after a few dates (or earlier). There are major gender differences in the acceptability of sexual intercourse, with far more males (68%) than females (36%) saying that it is okay to have sex after a few dates. These differing standards can lead to sexual conflict and tension between dating partners.

PETTING Many adolescents use petting to express affection, satisfy their curiosity, heighten their sexual arousal, and reach orgasm while avoiding pregnancy and maintaining virginity.

In the 2002 Canadian schools survey, students were asked if they had engaged in touching above the waist and below the waist. Two-thirds of the grade 9 students and four-fifths of the grade 11 students had engaged in touching above the waist. Among the grade 7 students, 46% of boys reported this behaviour, compared with 34% of girls (Boyce et al., 2003).

Fewer of the students had engaged in touching below the waist, with about half of the grade 9s reporting this behaviour, compared with three-fourths of the grade 11s. Among the grade 7 students, more boys (33%) reported experiencing this behaviour than girls (23%).

ORAL SEX More Canadian youth experience oral sex than have sexual intercourse. About one-third of Canadian students in grade 9 and one-half in grade 11 report having experienced oral sex (Boyce et al., 2003).

There have been several newspaper articles on the topic of teenage girls performing oral sex on boys. One of the most publicized stories occurred in Charlottetown, Prince Edward Island, where two boys aged 17 and 18 were convicted of having sexual contact with two girls under the age of 14 (which is the legal age of consent in Canada). The girls testified that they voluntarily performed oral sex on the boys and that they had no other physical contact such as kissing or sexual touching. One girl who was 12 at the time of the incident said that performing oral sex was not a "big deal" (Armstrong, 2003).

In an earlier study of Ontario female university students, 61% had performed oral sex on a male and 68% had received oral sex stimulation from a male (Herold & Way, 1983). One-half of the women had brought their partners to orgasm through oral sex and one-half had themselves had an orgasm while receiving oral sex. Among those who had not experienced coitus, one-third had engaged in oral sex.

ATTITUDES TO PREMARITAL INTERCOURSE The most significant changes in sexual attitudes in Canada occurred in the late 1960s and early 1970s. Prior to that time societal attitudes were firmly opposed to premarital sex (Herold, 1984). Canadian youth are more accepting of premarital sex than are older people.

Canadian Trends

SEXUAL INTERCOURSE EXPERIENCE OF CANADIAN YOUTH

In 2006, researchers from Queen's and Carleton universities (Boyce, Craig, & Elder, 2008) conducted a large-scale health survey of Canadian school students (aged 11 to 15) from across Canada. This was part of a larger international survey involving 40 countries. One-quarter of the boys and girls in grade 10 reported having experienced sexual intercourse. This figure was unchanged from the 2002 survey.

A decrease in sexual intercourse was found in surveys of students from grades 7 to 12 in British Columbia between 1992 and 2003 (Saewyc et al., 2008). In 2003, intercourse rates were 23% for boys and 24% for girls compared with 1992 rates of 34% of boys and 29% for girls. There was also a slight decrease in the number of students reporting three or more lifetime sexual partners (boys: 42% in 1992 and 39% in 2003; girls: 36% in 1992 and 32% in 2003). Among students aged 17 and over, the intercourse rate decreased from 55% in 1992 to 47% in 2003. Saewyc et al. attribute the decrease in sexual experience to a reduction in the incidence of sexual abuse or forced intercourse.

Canadian street youth have more sexual experience than those in high school. In a British Columbia study, 82% of street youth have had sexual intercourse (Smith et al., 2007). Two-thirds had intercourse at age 14 or younger.

Data on sexual intercourse were also obtained by Statistics Canada (2008e) in the 1996 and 2005 Canadian Community Health Surveys. The proportions of youth reporting that they had experienced intercourse are shown in Table 12.2. The main change over that period was that fewer girls had experienced intercourse, while the rates were unchanged for boys. In 2005, identical proportions of girls and boys had experienced intercourse (43%). The proportion of youth having intercourse increases with age. Two-thirds of those aged 18 or 19 had intercourse, compared with about one-third of those aged 15 to 17. The highest percentage of sexually experienced youth were in the provinces of Quebec and Newfoundland and Labrador, with the next highest in New Brunswick. (Statistics Canada, 2008e).

TABLE 12.2

Percentage of Canadian Youth (15–19 Years Old) Who Have Experienced Sexual Intercourse

Experienced Intercourse	1996	2005
Boys	43%	43%
Girls	51%	43%

Source: Data from Statistics Canada. (2008e). Trends in teen sexual behaviour and condom use. Health Reports, *Vol. 19, no. 3 (82-003-XWE).*

A large majority of adolescents (82%) approve of premarital sex if the two people love each other, and over half (58%) approve if the two people like each other (Bibby, 2001).

A study of high school students in Regina found that most students perceived their parents as disapproving of their having sexual intercourse. Females were more likely than males to believe that their father would disapprove (Hampton et al., 2005). No relationship was found between whether the students perceived their parents disapproved of their having sex and whether the students actually were having sex. Only one-third of the students were comfortable talking to their parents about sex and these students were more likely to inform their parents that they were having sex (Hampton et al., 2005).

Most parents do not believe that their children have had intercourse. In a national survey sponsored by *Maclean's* magazine in 2002, parents of 13- to 18-year-olds were asked if their teens had experienced sex. Only 23% of parents in Quebec and hardly any parents outside of Quebec (4%) said they had (Dreidger, 2002). Parents were also asked "Should your teens be allowed to spend the night together in your home with their sex partner?" Most parents responded that this was unacceptable, with 41% of Quebec parents and only 14% of parents outside of Quebec approving (Dreidger, 2002).

How accepting are young people if a potential marriage partner has had considerable sexual experience with others? University students were asked to rate the suitability of potential partners, taking into account the target person's sexual experience (Garcia, 2006). Both men and women rated someone who had engaged in a high number of sexual activities with a high number of sexual partners as not being a desirable marriage partner. They worried that this person would not be monogamous.

FACTORS RELATED TO AGE OF FIRST SEXUAL INTERCOURSE

Various social factors are predictive of intercourse at a young age. According to the 2001 National Longitudinal Survey of Children and Youth, Canadian adolescents who begin having sex at younger ages tend to also begin smoking by the age of 12 or 13, indicating that they do not conform to societal norms in general. Drinking alcohol at age 12 or 13 was associated with early age of intercourse for girls but not for boys. There was a striking gender difference in the role of self-esteem. Girls with a weak self-concept were more likely to have early intercourse, whereas boys with a *strong* self-concept were more likely to engage in early intercourse. Physical characteristics also played a stronger role with girls: Girls who reached puberty at a young age and who were not overweight were more likely to have early intercourse (Statistics Canada, 2005d). In the 2002 Canadian schools survey, poor school attachment and poor relationships with parents were also predictive of early sexual intercourse (Boyce et al., 2003). Also, among students in Regina, having male and female peers who were having sex was strongly predictive of intercourse experience among both females and males (Hampton et al., 2005).

Among high school girls in Nova Scotia, Donald Langille (2002) of Dalhousie University found that the strongest predictors of having sexual intercourse at a young age were:

- not living with both parents
- father's low level of education
- infrequent church attendance

In British Columbia the following factors were related to both boys and girls having sexual intercourse at a young age (Saewyc et al., 2008):

- low connectedness to family
- low connectedness to school
- having peers who are sexually permissive

ADAMANT VIRGINS, POTENTIAL NONVIRGINS, AND NONVIRGINS When studying factors related to sexual experience, most researchers categorize their sample into those who are and those who are not sexually experienced. However, in order to better understand the interaction of attitudes and behaviour, Herold and Goodwin (1981) differentiated students according to three categories: adamant virgins, potential nonvirgins, and nonvirgins. Adamant virgins believe that they should not have sex until marriage. They tend to be very religious, and have friends who are opposed to premarital sex. Potential nonvirgins have not experienced coitus but do not believe they should wait until marriage to have sexual intercourse. They are similar to the nonvirgins in accepting the idea of premarital sex; however, they are less likely to have sexually experienced friends and less likely to be in a love relationship. When asked why they have not had intercourse, they are likely to say that they have not met the right person or that they are not yet ready for sex (Herold & Goodwin, 1981).

These beliefs are reflected in a national survey of Canadian adolescents who were asked if sex before marriage is acceptable when the two people love each other (Bibby, 2001). Almost all of those who attended religious services less than weekly felt that it was (91%), compared with fewer than half of those who attended on a weekly basis (49%). However, the sexual attitudes and behaviour of most Canadian youth are not influenced by religion. Although about three-quarters say they identify with a particular religious group, only 22% attend religious services at least once a week (Bibby, 2001).

Innovative Canadian Research

THE FIRST TIME

For most Canadian young people, having sexual intercourse for the first time is one of the most significant events in their lives. The event also is of interest to society in general because of concerns about unwanted pregnancy, sexually transmitted infections, and sexual coercion. For many religious and ethnic groups, having sexual intercourse outside of the marital bond is seen as a serious violation of cultural norms and family honour. Consequently, first intercourse for most young people is an important decision.

Because of the double standard, first intercourse has traditionally been seen as the woman giving a gift to the man. Trent University researcher Terry Humphreys (2007b) found that twice as many university females (40%) as males (21%) viewed their first intercourse experience as giving their partner the gift of their virginity. On the other hand, about three times as many men (22%) as women (6%) viewed their virginity status as a stigma or an embarrassment that they were glad to rid themselves of when they had intercourse for the first time. Students who perceived virginity as a stigma were more likely to lose their virginity with a stranger or a friend rather than with a love partner. More than half of both genders viewed first intercourse as a naturally occurring process that was a desirable and inevitable transition to adulthood.

University of Alberta researchers Lily Tsui and Elena Nicoladis (2004), in surveying university students, found that while there were some differences in the physical response of the genders, there were similarities in social-psychological aspects. The two main gender differences concerned pain and orgasm. About half of the women but only 5% of the men reported experiencing pain at first intercourse. Most men (76%) experienced orgasm at first intercourse compared with only 12% of women. Not surprisingly, then, more men (62%) than women (35%) reported being physically satisfied after first intercourse.

In terms of emotional context, more women (63%) than men (43%) believed they were in love when they first had intercourse. However, about half of both genders said they were emotionally satisfied after first intercourse, and almost all said that they had sex again with the same partner and stayed together as a couple or became a couple after. They were also similar in reporting no regrets over first intercourse (males 76%, females 72%) and in rating the experience positively (males 72%, females 62%).

That most women rated their first intercourse experience positively is interesting, considering that half of them experienced pain and few had an orgasm. This suggests that many women do not focus only on physical sensations. Often women as well as men report satisfaction that in "doing it" they have achieved a major step toward adulthood.

In the 2002 Canadian schools survey, only 11% of girls and 5% of boys in grade 9 gave wanting to be a virgin until marriage as a reason for not having sexual intercourse. Only 3% of boys and 4% of girls gave religious beliefs as a reason for not having sex. The most common reasons for not having intercourse were not being ready, not having had the opportunity, and not having met the right person (Boyce et al., 2003).

SEXUAL FREQUENCY AND NUMBER OF SEXUAL PARTNERS

Having experienced sexual intercourse does not mean that one is currently having sexual relations. In fact, only a minority of Canadian adolescents are having sexual relations on a frequent basis, with 25% reporting that they have sex at least once a week (Bibby, 2001). As well, it should be noted that studies such as Bibby's have a methodological weakness in that they refer to *sex* rather than *sexual intercourse*. Bibby cautions that while most teens use the word *sex* to refer to sexual intercourse, not all of them do.

Typically, males report having more sexual partners than do females; 21% of adolescent males in Bibby's 2001 Canadian survey report having two or more partners during the current year, compared with 13% of females (Bibby, 2001). In the 2002 Canadian schools survey, about one-half of the grade 11 students reported having only one sexual partner (males 43%, females 54%). Only a small minority of boys (15%) and girls (9%) reported six or more partners (Boyce et al., 2003). The number of partners was lower than reported in the 1989 schools survey.

Age of first intercourse is a significant predictor of number of partners, with those beginning sexual intercourse at younger ages having more partners (Rotermann, 2005). Having more than one partner does not necessarily mean, however, that one is engaging in casual relations. The pattern for most youth is serial monogamy, whereby a person has sex within the context of a committed love relationship; when that relationship ends then he or she has sex in another committed relationship.

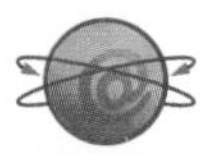

Sponsored by Planned Parenthood Toronto, this website provides teenagers with information on sexual health, decision making, and relationships.

www.spiderbytes.ca

MOTIVES FOR INTERCOURSE Having sexual intercourse is motivated by a number of factors. In the 2002 Canadian schools survey, the most common reason given for having sexual intercourse was "love for the person," with more girls than boys giving this reason. The second most common reason was "curiosity/experimentation" (Boyce et al., 2003).

This quote from a 19-year-old Ontario university student typifies the motivations of many young women:

> Sexual intercourse was for me mainly an expression of the love I felt for my partner whom I wanted to satisfy. Also, in a more minor way it satisfied an intense curiosity I had about sexual intercourse. (Herold, 1984, p. 19)

YOUNG PEOPLE AND CASUAL SEX Generally, males are more in favour of casual sex than are females. In the 2002 Canadian schools survey, twice as many grade 11 boys (66%) approved of casual sex as did girls (32%) (Boyce et al., 2003). A study of high school students in Vancouver, British Columbia, and Amherst, Nova Scotia, found that girls were judged more negatively for engaging in casual sex than were boys. However, those girls who displayed greater self-confidence and whose parents were from higher social classes were less likely to be judged negatively (Shoveller et al., 2004).

The AIDS epidemic and concern over sexual health risk-taking behaviours have led to an increasing number of studies on casual sex. Rates of casual sex are difficult to determine, however, because there are so many differing definitions. Some researchers have focused on the time between first meeting someone and having sex with them (Herold & Mewhinney, 1993), while others have considered the lack of emotional involvement with the partner (Townsend, 1995). Further complicating the study of casual sex is the fact that young people today are using a variety of terms to describe it, such as "hooking up," "friends with benefits," "booty call," and "fuck friends."

In a study of 230 Ontario female university students, four different measures of casual sex were used (Weaver & Herold, 2000). The results showed how choosing a particular indicator has a strong impact on determining the percentage of people who are considered to be engaging in casual sex. Only 13% of the female students reported they had engaged in sexual intercourse with someone they had met the same day or night, but three times as many (36%) reported they had had sexual intercourse with someone they were not in a committed relationship with. The rates of casual sex jumped substantially when noncoital sexual experiences were measured. One-half had engaged in hand–genital and/or oral sex with someone they had met that day and three-quarters had experienced these behaviours with someone they were not in a committed relationship with. Most reported having only one or two casual sex partners, however.

More of the women in the Ontario study who had experienced any of the casual sex behaviours thought casual sex was enjoyable (76%) than those who had not (57%). When asked what aspects of casual sex were appealing, one-third said there was nothing appealing. Sexual pleasure was by far the most common reason given for having casual sex. Other reasons were to live it up, to fulfill sexual fantasies, the novelty of new partners, to improve sexual technique, doing the forbidden, heightened self-esteem, feeling good about one's body, and the thrill of attracting new partners.

When asked which factors might prevent them from engaging in casual sex, more than 90% of the women surveyed responded that they were concerned about AIDS, STIs, and pregnancy. The next major concerns related to morality, guilt, loose reputation, and fear of being physically harmed. Those who had not experienced casual sex were far more concerned about the moral issue than those who had.

Most studies of casual sex have used university samples. However, in one study, 169 people at singles bars were surveyed to see if they would have higher rates of casual sex than samples of university students (Herold & Mewhinney, 1993). Indeed, more of the females (49%) reported engaging in sexual intercourse the same day they met someone than in the above study of university females (13%) (Weaver & Herold, 2000).

The singles bar study revealed significant gender differences. More males than females reported casual sex experience, and the males were more likely to anticipate ahead of time that they might engage in casual sex. They enjoyed casual sex more, and felt less guilt about having casual sex. The women were more concerned with the risks, with 52% of the females compared with 7% of the males saying that they were worried about being physically harmed when alone with someone they had just met. The women were also more concerned about AIDS and STIs (Herold & Mewhinney, 1993).

Sexual Behaviour and Sexual Orientation

Lesbian, gay, and bisexual (LGB) youth in grades 7 to 12 in British Columbia were surveyed along with heterosexual youth in the Adolescent Health Surveys completed in 1992, 1998, and 2003. The surveys were conducted by the McCreary Centre Society. The proportion of LGB students in the surveys varied between 2% and 4%. The surveys asked about the gender of one's sexual partner and whether sexual intercourse with an opposite-sex partner had been experienced. Unfortunately, the survey was mainly focused on heterosexual behaviours and did not ask questions about same-sex behaviours (Saewyc et al., 2007).

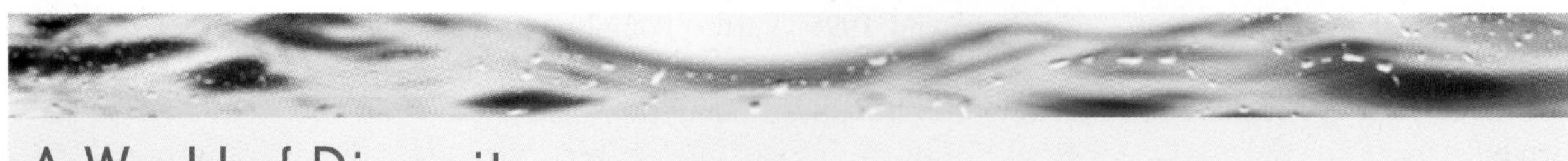

A World of Diversity

SEX ON SPRING BREAK

Every winter, thousands of Canadian college and university students travel to Florida and other destinations in search of fun and relaxation. Researchers Eleanor Maticka-Tyndale, Edward Herold, and Dawn Mewhinney have done extensive research on students going on spring break in Florida. Since relatively few studies have looked at how particular contexts can reduce people's inhibitions, a major goal of the research was to determine how the situational context of spring break may influence sexual attitudes and behaviour. (Nonetheless, those who went away on spring break were not representative of students in general; they were more sexually experienced and drank more alcohol at home than those who did not go on spring break.)

In a preliminary study of university students' perceptions of spring-break norms, two-thirds agreed that students on spring break are more likely to have casual sex than they are while at school (Mewhinney, Herold, & Maticka-Tyndale, 1995). In a second study, which involved 151 students who were on their way to spring break and 681 who completed questionnaires during or after spring break, five main themes emerged (Maticka-Tyndale & Herold, 1997):

- travelling with a group of friends
- perpetual party atmosphere
- high alcohol consumption
- sexually suggestive contests and displays
- perception that casual sex is common

It was accepted that people would engage in types of behaviour, such as wet T-shirt contests, that they might not engage in at home, and that most did not expect to form long-lasting relationships with the opposite sex (Maticka-Tyndale & Herold, 1997).

Many more men (55%) than women (11%) went on spring break with the intention of engaging in casual sex. However, there was no actual difference in the percentage of men (15%) and women (13%) who actually engaged in sexual intercourse while on spring break with someone they had not known previously. Of those who did not have sexual intercourse, about half engaged in sexual "fooling around" with someone new. The fact that more men than women were interested in having casual sex meant that it was far easier for women to meet potential partners (Maticka-Tyndale, Herold, & Mewhinney, 1998).

As shown in Table 12.3, many of the LGB youth had opposite-sex as well as same-sex partners. A small minority (14% of bisexual males and 5% of bisexual females) had only same-sex partners in the past year. In comparison, 55% of gay males and 29% of lesbians reported having only same-sex partners in the past year. More LGB youth than heterosexual youth reported having experienced sexual intercourse with an opposite-sex partner. Highest rates of intercourse were among bisexual females and males (Saewyc et al., 2007).

TABLE 12.3
Sexual Orientation and Gender of Sexual Partners in the Past Year

	Opposite Gender Only	Both Genders	Same Gender Only
MALE			
Bisexual	55%	32%	14%
Gay	26	19	55
FEMALE			
Bisexual	62	33	5
Lesbian	15	56	29

Source: Saewyc, E., Poon, C., Wang, N., Homma, Y., Smith, A., and the McCreary Centre Society. (2007). Not Yet Equal: The Health of Lesbian, Gay, & Bisexual Youth in BC. *Vancouver, BC: McCreary Centre Society. Courtesy of McCreary Centre Society.*

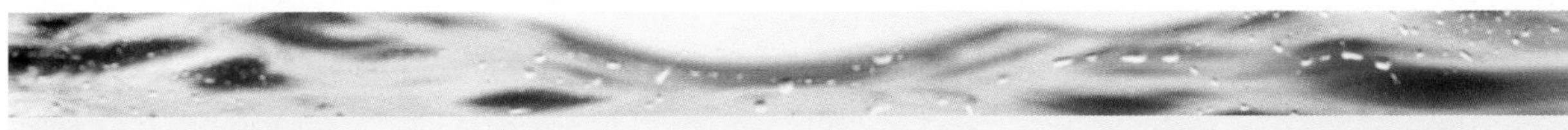

A World of Diversity

GAY PROM DATE

They danced the night away.

Marc Hall, the shy, blue-coiffed 17-year-old Oshawa student who wouldn't take no for an answer when told he couldn't take his boyfriend to his high-school prom, won a major court victory for Catholic students yesterday.

In a comprehensive and clear decision granting Hall's request for an injunction, Mr. Justice Robert MacKinnon of the Superior Court of Justice said a ban on same-sex dates at the prom was a clear violation of Hall's constitutional rights, and ordered the Durham Catholic School Board to allow Hall and Jean-Paul Dumond, 21, to attend the dance.

School board chair Mary Ann Martin said while the board was "extremely disappointed" with the ruling, Hall and his date would be allowed to attend the prom "if they wish."

Hall, in a white tuxedo and blue tie, said he "was very happy and so excited that we won." When he first heard the news from his lawyer at his home in Oshawa, he said, "I was jumping up and down and everybody was shouting."

"I feel at ease now knowing that we are free of discrimination," said the grade 12 student at Monsignor John Pereyma Catholic High School.

Source: Josey, S. (2002, May 11). From "Gay Prom Battle Ends with a Waltz." Toronto Star.

Gay Date at School Prom.
Marc Hall, 17, heads to his Toronto school prom with Jean-Paul Dumond, 21. Coming to terms with adolescence is often a difficult struggle, but it is frequently more intense for gay people.

In a national Canadian survey of students in grades 9 and 11, Stephen Fergus (2006), at Queen's University, compared the sexual experience of students who felt attraction to the same sex with those who had opposite-sex attraction. Those having same-sex attraction were more likely to be sexually experienced and to have first had sex at a younger age. They were also more likely to have been pressured to engage in sex and to have had a sexually transmitted disease.

Adulthood

Canadians entering adulthood today face a wider range of sexual choices and lifestyles than did earlier generations. An increasing number of young people choose to remain single as a way of life, not merely as a way station preceding the arrival of Mr. or Ms. Right.

In this section, we discuss diverse forms of adult sexuality in Canada today, including singlehood, marriage, and alternative lifestyles.

Singlehood

Recent years have seen a sharp increase in the number of single young people in our society. "Singlehood," not marriage, is now the most common lifestyle among people in their twenties. Several factors contribute to the increased proportion of singles. For one thing, more people are postponing marriage to pursue educational and career goals. Many young people are deciding to "live together" (cohabit), at least for a while, rather than get married.

Figure 12.1 Average Age of First Marriage in Canada.

The age at first marriage has substantially increased in Canada, partly because many adults live together before getting married.

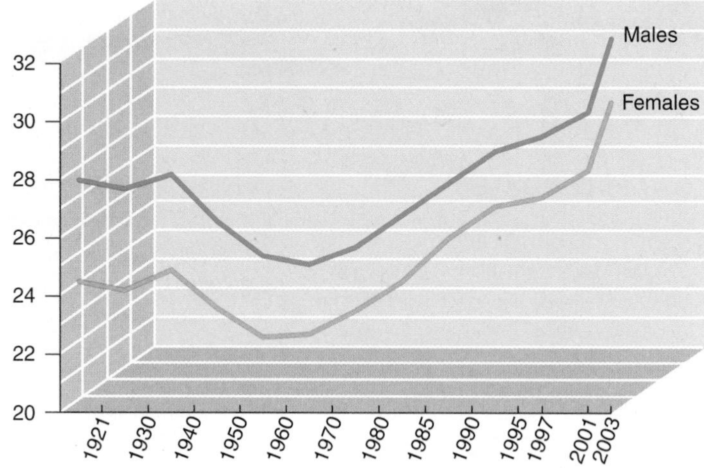

For single heterosexual women, much has been written about a "man shortage." According to the 2006 Census, for every 100 Canadian women, there are 96 men (Bonoguore, 2007). The sex ratio gap is largest in major Canadian cities such as Toronto. However, there are more men than women in Canada's north, rural Alberta, and skiing towns, such as Whistler.

As you can see in Figure 12.1, people are getting married later. In 2003, the typical man in Canada got married for the first time at 30.8, compared with 25 in 1960. The typical woman got married at 28.5, compared with 22 in 1960 (Statistics Canada, 2007). The average age at marriage is highest in Quebec and lowest in Saskatchewan.

Many young adults in Canada live in the parental home, especially males. Two-thirds of men aged 20 to 24 live with their parents compared with about half the women of that age (Statistics Canada, 2002). Many young adults live with their parents when they are going to university or when they are trying to find a job. And, because of the high cost of rental housing, many cannot afford to rent their own apartment.

Singles.
There is no single "singles scene." Although some singles meet in singles bars, many meet in more casual settings, such as the neighbourhood laundromat. Some singles advertise online or in newspapers or magazines.

Many single people do not choose to be single. Some remain single because they have not yet found Mr. or Ms. Right. However, many young people see singlehood as an alternative, open-ended way of life, not just a temporary stage that precedes marriage. Now that career options for women have expanded, they are not as financially dependent on men as were their mothers and grandmothers. A number of career women, like young career-oriented men, choose to remain single (at least for a time) to focus on their careers.

In the 2001 General Social Survey on family and marital history, Canadian singles were asked if they expected to marry. Statistics Canada (2005e) focused its analysis on "mature singles" who do not expect to marry. Mature singles were older than the average age at which Canadians first marry (28 for women, 30 for men) but younger than 55. Mature singles who did not expect to marry placed less importance on love and being part of a couple and/or being married. Among the mature singles, francophones in Quebec were far less likely to expect they would get married than anglophones outside of Quebec. Also, those who had less education, earned less income, and were single parents had the lowest expectations of ever getting married (Statistics Canada, 2005e).

TABLE 12.4
Canadians' Feelings About Being Single

	Males	Females	Total
Exciting	6.2%	8.5%	7.3%
Fun	15.4	14.3	14.9
Confusing	14.7	14.3	14.5
Lonely	17.5	12.4	15.1
Dangerous	3.8	7.0	5.3
Frustrating	9.6	9.7	9.6
Freedom	29.8	32.6	31.1
None of the above	3.1	2.1	2.6

Note: Respondents could list up to three words. This table reports only the first word chosen.

Source: Compas (1998). Modern life survey of the Canadian population.

Singlehood is not without its problems. Many single people are lonely. Some singles express concern about their lack of a steady, meaningful social relationship. Others, usually women, worry about their physical safety. Some people living alone find it difficult to satisfy their needs for intimacy, companionship, sex, and emotional support. Despite these concerns, most singles are well adjusted and content. Singles who have a greater number of friends and a supportive social network tend to be more satisfied with their lifestyles.

The 1998 Compas survey asked single Canadians to indicate from a list of words which one best reflects their feelings about being single. The responses indicate a range of both positive and negative feelings. The most common response (31%) was "freedom" (see Table 12.4).

Three-quarters of both men and women said that women were more choosy in selecting a dating partner (Compas, 1998), yet almost equal percentages of women (80%) and men (76%) found it difficult to find a good dating partner (Compas, 1998). Adding to the challenge, 42% of single Canadians (and more women than men) were not comfortable asking for a date (see Table 12.5).

People are also uncertain about what dating guidelines they should follow. Fein and Schneider's 1990s book *The Rules* advised women that they needed to follow more traditional guidelines if they wanted to get a desirable man to marry them. When Canadian singles were asked their opinions about these rules, most disagreed with those such as "She should always let the man ask her on date" (68% disagreed) and "She should not accept any invitation for a Saturday date received after the previous Wednesday" (85% disagreed). However, 66% agreed with the rule "She should not be sexually available for at least a few weeks after the first date" (Compas, 1998). This last rule was most strongly endorsed in the Maritimes and least endorsed in Quebec.

There is no one "singles scene." Single people differ in their sexual interests and lifestyles. Many achieve emotional and psychological security through a network of intimate relationships with friends. Most are sexually active and practise **serial monogamy**. Other singles have a primary sexual relationship with one steady partner but occasional brief flings. A few are "swinging singles." That is, they pursue casual sexual encounters, or "one-night stands."

Serial monogamy A pattern of becoming involved in one exclusive relationship after another, as opposed to engaging in multiple sexual relationships at the same time.

Although the stereotype of the "swinging single" is pervasive, 50% of Canadian singles are not even dating (Compas, 1998). Here there are some interesting gender and age differences. Among people in their twenties almost twice as many men (46%) as women (27%) are not dating, whereas among singles in their fifties, more women (79%) than men (64%) are not dating. Single men are more open to the idea of the

A World of Diversity

CANADIAN FEMALE TOURISTS AND BEACH BOYS IN THE DOMINICAN REPUBLIC

In recent years, some researchers have begun to study how social context can affect sexual behaviour. One such context is that of vacation travel, which is often associated with "sun, sand, and sex." Typically, people on vacation are in a party mood, drink more alcohol, and are open to meeting new people.

A Canadian study analyzed how the social context of the vacation structured the interpersonal dynamics that occurred in the Dominican Republic between Canadian female tourists and local men who were commonly known as "beach boys" (referred to locally as "sanky panky") (Herold, Garcia, & Demoya, 2001). While the female tourists had more economic power, the men were more knowledgeable about how to use the local cultural context to their advantage to obtain wanted resources from the women. The crossing of traditional racial boundaries added another layer of complexity.

The female tourists in the study often met beach boys—men who work as tour guides, waiters, or bartenders, or in beach or sports equipment rental, or lottery ticket or condominium timeshare sales—since their jobs provided the men a legitimate excuse for approaching female tourists and made it easy to initiate social contact. The beach boys were usually younger, ranging in age from 17 to 25, and in good physical shape.

For some beach boys, particularly the younger ones, the sexual conquest of tourists was a major objective. However, the main reason given by the professional beach boys for their involvement with female tourists was economic. Their material goals ranged from free meals and entertainment, driving a current-model rental car, and buying new clothes or jewellery, to buying a motorcycle or starting a small business, trips to Canada and other countries, or being sponsored through marriage to live and work there.

Most first-time female tourists did not anticipate becoming involved with a local male. (Interestingly, more francophone tourists from Quebec than anglophone tourists from Ontario anticipated that they would.) Of those who did become involved, most viewed their relationship as romantic rather than sexual (*first-time romantic tourists*). A minority of first-time tourists did anticipate involvement, however, and focused on the sexual aspects (*first-time sex tourists*). Generally, these women had heard about the experiences of other women who had been to the Dominican Republic, and in particular about the sexual prowess of the local men. Of those women who had been to the Dominican Republic before and had had a romantic relationship with a local man, many returned because they wished to maintain this love relationship (*romantic returnees*). A minority of the women returned with the objective of maximizing their sexual pleasure. Most of these women sought to have sex with one partner with whom they wished to spend most of their time (*romantic sex tourists*), while some preferred to have casual sex with a number of partners (*adventurer sex tourists*).

Which female tourists were pursued by the beach boys depended on the men's motivations. Those who sought only sexual conquest preferred young, attractive, preferably blonde women—women who were unlikely to provide money. (Having a relationship with this kind of woman also enhanced a beach boy's reputation among his peers.) But for the majority of beach boys who were primarily interested in making money, the main target groups were women past the age of 40 or younger, overweight women. In selecting these women, the beach boys were conscious of playing on female vulnerability. Many of these women may not have been used to having males pay romantic attention to them; this may have been a new experience or one they had not had in a long time.

TABLE 12.5

How Comfortable Are Canadians in Asking for a Date?

	Males	Females	Total
Very	25.3%	16.4%	21.2%
Somewhat	40.3	32.4	36.6
Not really	26.6	24.0	25.4
Not at all	7.8	27.2	16.8

Source: Compas (1998). Modern life survey of the Canadian population.

According to the beach boys, these vulnerable women fell in love more readily and were usually more open about their financial situation, and thus likely to provide more money than other women. The men who chose overweight women believed that, since Canadian males prefer thin women, the overweight women had had few sexual partners and thus were less likely to pass on a sexually transmitted infection. The men also reported that overweight or older women were less embarrassed to be seen with them.

What Are the Dynamics of This Relationship? *Many Canadian female tourists in the Dominican Republic and on other islands in the Caribbean develop sexual and/or romantic relationships with local men, often referred to as "beach boys."*

The men aimed to provide a total relationship involving a diversity of experiences, including sightseeing, going dancing, and going to restaurants. If a relationship developed, most preferred to be with the same woman during the entire time she was on her vacation. (Of course, beach boys were more likely to receive a monetary or gift reward if they remained with one woman.) The beach boys usually took their dates to places where they were well known so that the women would quickly notice they were popular, thus adding to their appeal.

The beach boys continually attempted to refine their seduction skills. They often compared their different techniques of seduction with other beach boys and provided one another with specific examples. The younger beach boys looked up to the older ones for words of wisdom about the seduction process.

The men commented that tourists who were sexual adventurers differed significantly from other women, including Dominican women, in their sexual practices and expectations. These women were uninhibited, and were more likely to take the initiative in sexual advances and to suggest a diversity of sexual activities. They typically urged the man to be more sexually assertive, and were more responsive during sex. One beach boy cited this example of being in a hotel room with a woman: "She was screaming so loudly at orgasm that the hotel watchman knocked on the door, believing that I was hurting her."

Most of the beach boys said they didn't like using condoms because it reduced their sexual pleasure, and further reasoned that overweight women were unlikely to have an STI since they had not had much sexual experience. (The men also believed that if a woman was overweight she was in a healthy condition and not infected with an STI.) Indeed, because they felt confident they could judge by a woman's appearance alone whether she had AIDS or an STI, many believed it was not necessary for them to use a condom. Most of the female tourists insisted that the man wear a condom, however. A condom was typically used when the couple first had intercourse, but was discontinued after a few times. Only about a third of the beach boys reported that they used a condom every time they had sexual intercourse with a tourist. Some of the men commented on the frequent breakage of condoms, which may be attributed to their lack of knowledge of how to use them properly.

Inherent in the results of this study is the issue of exploitation. Do you think the female tourists used their wealthier status to exploit the beach boys? Do you think the men used tactics of manipulation to exploit the female tourists? Or was neither group exploited?

"swinging singles" than are women. When asked if they would have sexual intercourse with an attractive person they just met (if that person was free of infection), 55% of Canadian men but only 8% of Canadian women said that they would (Compas, 1998).

Some singles remain celibate, either by choice or for lack of opportunity. People choose **celibacy** for a number of reasons. Nuns and priests do so for religious reasons. Others believe that celibacy allows them to focus their energies and attention on work or to commit themselves to an important cause. They see celibacy as a temporary accommodation to other pursuits. Others remain celibate because they view sex outside of marriage as immoral. Still others remain celibate because they find the prospects of sexual activity aversive or unalluring, or for fear of contracting STIs.

Celibacy Complete sexual abstinence. (Sometimes used to describe the state of being unmarried, especially in the case of people who take vows to remain single.)

In her book *A History of Celibacy*, Elizabeth Abbott (1999), the dean of women at Trinity College, University of Toronto, discusses her own reasons for becoming celibate after her divorce. She emphasizes that her decision was based on personal

Cohabitation Living together as though married but without legal sanction.

growth rather than on moralistic reasons. In particular, she finds that celibacy makes her life less stressful and allows her greater freedom: "Much as I once reveled in sexual indulgence, I realized that at this stage of my life, I value even more the independence and serenity chaste solitude brings me" (Abbott, 1999, p. 9).

Cohabitation

Social scientists believe that **cohabitation** has become accepted within the social mainstream. Among Canadians, 84% approve of cohabitation (Bibby, 2001). We seldom hear cohabitation referred to as "living in sin" or "shacking up," as we once did. People today are more likely to refer to cohabitation with value-free expressions such as "living together."

There are considerable differences among Canadians of various ethnic backgrounds in the acceptability of cohabitation. Acceptance is higher among those of British origin than among South Europeans. The Chinese are less accepting, and the Indo-Canadian community is the least accepting (Michell, 2001).

REASONS FOR COHABITATION Why do people cohabit? Cohabitation, like marriage, is an alternative to the loneliness that can accompany living alone. Romantic partners may have deep feelings for each other but not be ready to get married. Some couples prefer cohabitation because it provides a consistent relationship without the legal entanglements of marriage.

Economic factors come into play as well. Emotionally committed couples may decide to cohabit because of the economic advantages of sharing household expenses. Some older people live together rather than marry because of resistance from adult children. Some children fear that a parent will be victimized by a needy senior citizen.

COHABITATION FIRST AND MARRIAGE LATER: BENEFIT OR RISK? Cohabiting couples may believe that cohabitation will strengthen their eventual marriage by helping them iron out the kinks in their relationship. Yet cohabitors who later marry also run a serious risk of getting divorced. In Canada, married people who live together prior to their marriage are twice as likely to separate as those who did not first live together (Statistics Canada, 2002c). Among those

Canadian Trends

COHABITATION TRENDS IN CANADA

Since the 1970s, the proportion of Canadians who are not married but who live together as a couple has significantly increased. In 2001, about 1.2 million couples were cohabiting (Statistics Canada, 2002c). The legal term for this is *common-law union*. The proportion of Canadians living in common-law relationships is about double that of the United States.

Based on findings from the 2001 Census, Statistics Canada (2002c) estimated that 53% of Canadians who are between the ages of 20 and 29 will experience their first living-together arrangement as a common-law relationship. These types of relationships are especially popular in Quebec, which has the highest proportion of couples beginning their first union as a common-law one. About 30% of all couples in Quebec live in a common-law relationship, one of the highest rates in the world. These relationships are less likely to lead to marriage. Among Quebec women in their thirties who started living in a common-law relationship, only one-third had married their partner at the time of the 2001 Census, compared with 59% of women in the rest of Canada (Statistics Canada, 2002c).

Most Canadians living common-law do marry, however. About two-fifths of those in their thirties first live in a common-law relationship and about 80% of them will eventually marry someone. Children are common in cohabiting households, as nearly half of cohabiting couples have children in the household (Statistics Canada, 2002c).

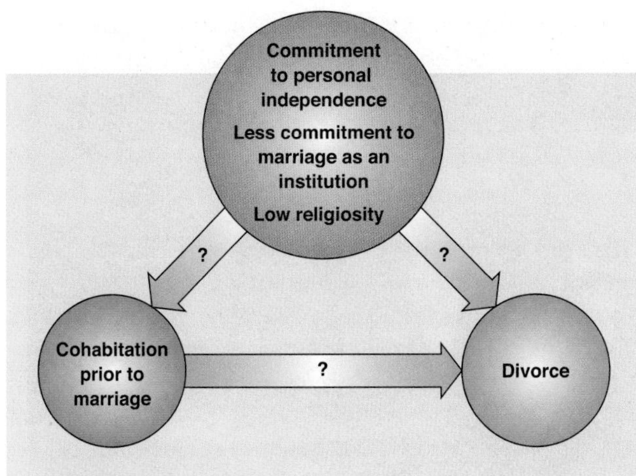

Figure 12.2 Does Cohabitation Prior to Marriage Increase the Risk of Eventual Divorce?

There is a correlational relationship between cohabitation prior to marriage and the risk of divorce later on. Does cohabitation increase the risk of divorce, or do other factors—such as a commitment to personal independence—contribute both to the likelihood of cohabitation and to eventual divorce?

in their thirties who live together prior to marriage, 63% separate, compared with 30% of those who do not first live together. Why might cohabiting couples run a greater risk of divorce than couples who did not cohabit prior to marriage? Cohabitors tend to be more committed to personal independence than noncohabitors (Bumpass, 1995). They also tend to be less traditional and less religious. All in all, people who cohabit prior to marriage tend to be less committed to the values and interests traditionally associated with the institution of marriage. The attitudes of cohabitors, and not cohabitation itself, may thus account for their higher rates of marital dissolution (see Figure 12.2).

Marriage

Marriage is found in all human societies. Most people in every known society—sometimes nearly all—get married at least once. Marriage is our most common lifestyle. Statistics Canada (2005e) estimates that three-quarters of Canadians who are in their thirties will marry at some point in their lives. Most people see marriage as permanent.

Same-Sex Marriage

Traditionally, societies have defined marriage as applying only to heterosexual couples. This definition was challenged by same-sex couples in Canada, who argued that not allowing same-sex marriage restricted their freedom. In July 2002, the Ontario Superior Court ruled that the traditional definition of marriage was discriminatory to lesbians and gays and ordered governments to redefine the term *marriage* to include recognition of same-sex couples. In this landmark decision, the judges argued that prohibiting same-sex couples from marrying was a violation of the Canadian Charter of Rights and Freedoms. In 2005, the Canadian Parliament passed legislation allowing same-sex couples to marry. (Same-sex marriages are also discussed in Chapters 1 and 9.)

In recent years there has been considerable analysis and debate surrounding gay and lesbian marriage. Certainly, the changes in Canadian law that allowed gay marriages to take place have accelerated discussion of these topics.

In 2001, the Canadian Census obtained data for the first time about same-sex couples. Same-sex couples represented 0.5% of all couples, with 34 200 same-sex couples being counted (Statistics Canada, 2002f); 85% of the male couples and 75% of the female couples live in the larger urban areas of Canada. About 15% of female same-sex couples have children living with them, compared with 3% of male couples.

Lawyer Douglas Elliott, second from left, and partner Greg Lawrence, centre, are congratulated by guests after their wedding in Toronto. Elliot was one of the leading lawyers in the fight to make gay marriage legal in Canada. The couple had been together for 32 years before they married.

The 2006 Census counted 75 770 same-sex common-law partners, an increase of 11% over the past five years. The 2006 Census measured same-sex marriage for the first time and counted 15 000 persons living as same-sex married couples (Statistics Canada, 2007). Two Canadian studies have analyzed married lesbian and gay male couples (Alderson, 2004; MacIntosh & Reissing, in press). The couples surveyed reported the following benefits of being married:

- social sanction; greater acceptance and normalization of their relationship by friends and family
- feeling equal to heterosexuals with regard to making decisions for an ill partner, caring for children, and receiving benefits related to inheritance and insurance
- feeling closer to their partner and more secure about their relationship
- decrease in feelings of internalized homophobia
- more openness to the idea of having children in their relationship

The Foundation for Equal Families
Offers up-to-date developments on issues relating to gay and lesbian unions in Canada.
www.ffef.ca

It should be noted that not everyone in the gay community supports same-sex marriage. Those who are opposed tend to criticize marriage as a patriarchal heterosexual institution. However, married same-sex couples do not share this view and argue that the legalization of marriage offers the freedom of choice. These married couples also opposed the proposal of the Conservative Party of Canada to offer civil unions instead of marriage, believing that civil unions are not equal to marriage (MacIntosh & Reissing, in press).

WHY DO PEOPLE MARRY? Marriage meets personal and cultural needs. It legitimizes sexual relations and provides a legal sanction for deeply committed relationships. It permits the maintenance of a home life and provides an institution in which children can be supported and socialized into adopting the norms of the family and the culture at large. Marriage restricts sexual relations so that a man can be assured—or at least can assume—that his wife's children are his. Marriage also permits the orderly transmission of wealth from one family to another and from one generation to another.

Notions such as romantic love, equality, and the very radical concept that men as well as women would do well to aspire to the ideal of faithfulness are recent additions to the structure of marriage in Western society. Not until the nineteenth century did the notion of love as a basis for marriage become widespread in Western culture.

When Canadians were asked why people should get married, almost all (95%) said for love (Compas, 1998). The next common reasons were for companionship (83%) and to have children (82%). Two-thirds cited having a regular and safe sex partner. In another national survey, Canadians were asked about the importance of marriage (Canadian Press, 2007). There was a major discrepancy regarding the importance of marriage in their own lives and the perception of its importance in society. When asked for their personal attitudes toward marriage, 42% said it had become more important in their own lives and only 17% said less important, with 39% saying it had not changed. However, only 13% believed that marriage had become more important in society, while 53% felt it had become less important. Three-quarters said that making a marriage work was harder today than in the past (Canadian Press, 2007).

TYPES OF MARRIAGE There are two major types of marriage: monogamy and polygamy. In **monogamy**, a husband and wife are wed only to each other. But let us not confuse monogamy, which is a form of matrimony, with sexual exclusivity. People who are monogamously wedded often do have extramarital affairs, as we shall see, but they are considered to be married to only one person at a time. In **polygamy**, a person has more than one spouse and is permitted sexual access to all of them.

The Vanier Institute of the Family
Contains educational material and research on Canadian families.
www.vifamily.ca

In Bountiful, British Columbia, a religious group has been openly practising polygamy since the 1950s. The group is a breakaway sect of the Mormon Church. Teenage girls are often forced to marry much older men who already have wives. The British Columbia government has been reluctant to charge community members with violating Canada's anti-polygamy law, however, because the Canadian Charter of Rights protects religious freedom (Canadian Press, 2005b). Yet, in 2009, after 20 years of investigations, the British Columbia government brought charges of polygamy against two leaders of the community, Winston Blackmore and James Oler.

Some Muslims in Canada also have plural wives. Inman Aly Hindy at an Islamic centre in Toronto stated that he has officiated at more than 30 polygamous marriages over a five-year period (Javed, 2008). Islam allows men to marry up to four wives, whereas the Mormon sect in British Columbia allows an unlimited number of wives. A key difference between the two religions is that the sect in Bountiful, B.C., requires polygamous marriages, because it is believed that this is necessary to get to heaven, whereas the Muslim religion permits polygamy but does not require it. In fact, the great majority of Muslim men have only one wife (Javed, 2008).

Polygyny is by far the most prevalent form of polygamy among the world's preliterate societies (Frayser, 1985). **Polyandry** is practised only rarely. In polygynous societies, men are permitted to have multiple wives if they can support them; more rarely, a man will have one wife and one or more concubines. Economic factors and the availability of prospective mates usually limit the opportunities for men to wed more than one woman at a time, however. In many cases, only wealthy men can afford to support multiple wives and the children of these unions. In addition, few if any societies have enough women to allow most men to have two or more wives (Harris & Johnson, 2000; Whitten, 2001). For these reasons, even in societies that prefer polygyny, fewer than half of the men at any given time actually have multiple mates (Ford & Beach, 1951).

Monogamy Marriage to one person.

Polygamy Simultaneous marriage to more than one person.

Polygyny A form of marriage in which a man is married to more than one woman at the same time.

Polyandry A form of marriage in which a woman is married to more than one man at the same time.

ARRANGED MARRIAGE In Western cultures, mate selection is presumably unrestricted. Parents today seldom arrange marriages, although they may still encourage their child to date that wonderful son or daughter of the solid churchgoing couple who live down the street. However, among recent immigrants to Canada from the Middle East and East Asia, arranged marriages are relatively common.

WHOM WE MARRY The universal incest taboo proscribes matings between close relatives. Societal rules and customs also determine which people are desirable mates and which are not.

Arranged Marriage in Canada. *A number of ethnic groups in Canada still engage in the practice of arranging marriages. Often they have arranged marriages with partners from their country of origin.*

Homogamy The practice of marrying someone who is similar to oneself in social background and standing.

Because we make choices, we tend to marry people who attract us. These people are usually similar to us in physical attractiveness and attitudes, and even in minute details. We are more often than not similar to our mates in characteristics such as height, weight, personality traits, and intelligence (Buss, 1994). The people we marry also seem likely to meet our material, sexual, and psychological needs.

The concept of "like marrying like" is termed **homogamy**. We usually marry people of the same racial/ethnic background, educational level, and religion. However, with the increased cultural diversity in Canada, the number of people who choose a partner outside of their racial or ethnic group is increasing. In 2001, there were 452 000 individuals who formed mixed couples—a 35% increase from 1991. Mixed unions comprise 3.2% of all couples in Canada. In the 20–29 age group, the proportions of mixed unions were 13% in Vancouver, 11% in Toronto, and 6% in Montreal. Japanese Canadians are the most likely to choose a partner from outside of their ethnic group, and South Asian Canadians are the least likely (Statistics Canada, 2004c).

Marriages between individuals who are alike may stand a better chance of survival, because the partners are more likely to share their values and attitudes.

We also tend to follow *age homogamy*. Age homogamy is the selection of a partner who falls in one's own age range. Bridegrooms tend to be two to five years older than their wives, on the average, in European, North American, and South American countries (Buss, 1994). Persons who marry late or who remarry tend not to select partners so close in age.

When it comes to picking a mate, men tend to be the romantics, women the pragmatists. When Canadians were asked "Who is more choosy in selecting a marriage partner?" both men and women (57%) were more likely to say that women are (Compas, 1998). Considerably fewer believed that men are more choosy (28%) or that the genders are equally choosy (15%). In her study of male–female relationships in Canada and the United States, Dennis (1992) concludes that women have raised their expectations so high that many will never meet their ideal man and thus will have to decide whether to lower their standards or to remain single.

Marital Sexuality

Patterns of marital sexuality vary across cultures, yet anthropologists have noted some common threads (Harris & Johnson, 2000; Whitten, 2001). Privacy for sexual relations is valued in nearly all cultures. Most cultures also place restrictions on coitus during menstruation, during at least some stages of pregnancy, and for a time after childbirth.

We usually think of the sexual revolution in terms of the changes in sexual behaviours and attitudes that occurred among young, unmarried people. Indeed, most Canadians accept the idea that spouses will have had premarital sex with another person. Only 18% believe that "the ideal marriage partner should never have had any previous sexual partners" (Compas, 1998), with three-quarters agreeing that "the ideal marriage partner has had some but not too many partners."

The sexual revolution, however, also ushered in profound changes in marital sexuality. In particular, it helped dislodge the view that sexual pleasure is meant only for men and that it is the duty of women to satisfy their husbands' sexual needs.

How frequently do married couples engage in coitus? As shown in Table 12.6, Canadian adults most commonly report having sex once or twice a week. People who are married or in common-law relationships have sex more often than singles, and those who are in common-law relationships have sex more often than those who are married. These data certainly call into the question the image of the "swinging single."

The frequency of sexual relations declines with age (Compas, 1998). Regardless of a couple's age, sexual frequency also appears to decline with years of marriage.

In coitus, as in foreplay, the marital bed since Kinsey's day has become a stage on which the players act more varied roles. In a study among Montreal couples, the male-superior and female-superior were the two most popular positions (Ochs & Binik, 1999).

Canadians report that their sexual encounters last 39 minutes on average (*Maclean's*/CTV Poll, 1994). In a study of 77 cohabiting or married individuals in New Brunswick (Byers & Heinlein, 1989), sexual episodes were reported to last about half an hour on average (ranging from five minutes to two hours). Intercourse itself on average lasted about a quarter of an hour (ranging from two minutes to 1.25 hours).

SEXUAL SATISFACTION Researchers at the University of New Brunswick found that perceptions of rewards and costs are related to feelings of sexual satisfaction (Lawrence & Byers, 1995). (Rewards include the amount of fun experienced

TABLE 12.6

Frequency of Sexual Intercourse During Previous Four Weeks by Relationship Status

Frequency	Single	Married	Common-Law	Total
Did not have sex	47.5%	11.3%	8.1%	25.3%
Less than once a week	12.5	15.0	12.9	13.8
Once or twice a week	21.9	52.9	41.1	39.3
Three to four times a week	14.4	17.8	29.0	17.7
Five or more times a week	3.7	3.0	8.9	3.9

Note: Single includes never married, divorced, and widowed.

Source: Compas (1998). Modern life survey of the Canadian population.

Figure 12.3 Relationship Status and Level of Sexual Satisfaction.

According to the Compas study (1998), married Canadians experience higher levels of satisfaction than those who are single (including divorced and widowed) or living common-law. Those who were married also reported the highest sexual frequency. Do these results mean that married people are more satisfied, or are they just more likely to report that they are satisfied?

Source: Compas (1998).

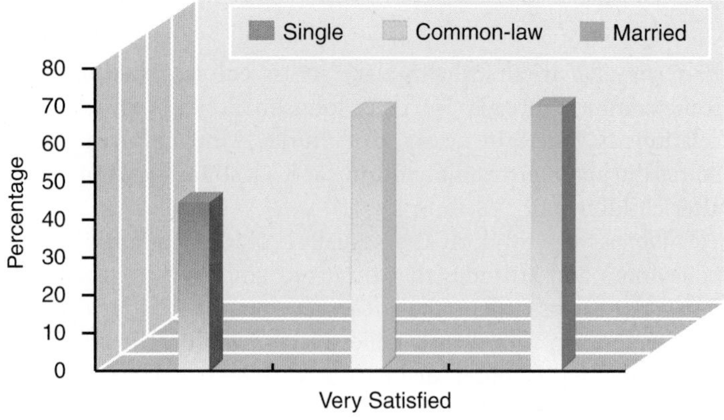

during sex, pleasurable physical sensations from touching and caressing, and feeling comfortable with one's partner. Costs include too-infrequent sexual activity and poor sexual communication with one's partner.) People who believe they are getting many sexual rewards and low sexual costs are likely to have a high level of sexual satisfaction. This is especially true when the rewards are greater and the costs lower than originally expected.

Other researchers have found that wives who talk openly to their husbands about their sexual feelings and needs report higher levels of sexual satisfaction. Among both men and women in New Brunswick who were in long-term relationships, sexual satisfaction was higher for those who could tell their partners about their sexual likes and dislikes (MacNeil & Byers, 1997). Interestingly, satisfaction was also higher for those who could openly communicate about nonsexual topics.

Couples who are in more committed relationships report higher levels of sexual satisfaction than those who are in noncommitted relationships. When asked how satisfied they are with their sex lives, two-thirds of Canadians who are married or in common-law relationships say they are very satisfied, compared with 44% of those who are single (Compas, 1998) (see Figure 12.3).

SEXUAL CONFLICT Couples can experience conflict over any number of sexual issues. In a study of couples in New Brunswick, one-quarter of the men were concerned that "I like to do things my partner does not" and one-third of the women were concerned that my "partner chooses inconvenient times for sex" (MacNeil & Byers, 1997). More than one-third of Canadians have conflicts over sex at least once a month, with those in common-law relationships having conflicts more often than married couples (Compas, 1998) (see Table 12.7).

TABLE 12.7

Frequency of Conflicts Canadians Experience With Their Partner Over Sex

	Males		Females	
	Common-Law	**Married**	**Common-Law**	**Married**
Often	1.4%	1.4%	3.6%	2.5%
Several times a month	4.2	3.5	8.9	7.8
Once or twice a month	39.4	30.1	35.7	28.6
Never	54.9	65.1	51.8	61.2

Source: Compas. (1998). Modern life survey of the Canadian population.

B. J. Rye (2001) at the University of Waterloo found that 21% of students were often having serious and frequent disagreement about the occurrence of sex. Almost three times as many males (45%) as females (15%) were concerned that their partner's sexual desire was lower than what the respondent would like.

Sexual Orientation and Relationship Satisfaction

Numerous researchers have studied the factors that predict satisfaction in a relationship or the deterioration and ending of a relationship. Much of this research has sought to determine whether there are differences in the factors that satisfy heterosexual and homosexual couples, and the interesting finding is that we are hard-pressed to find differences. One difference is that gay and lesbian couples tend to distribute household chores evenly and not in terms of gender-role stereotypes (Kurdek, 2005, 2006). Now for the similarities: Sexual satisfaction is tied to satisfaction with the relationship in both heterosexual and lesbian women (Mathews et al., 2006; Twist, 2005). Gay, lesbian, and male–female couples are all more satisfied when they receive social support from their partners, there is sharing of power in the relationship, they fight fairly, and they perceive their partners to be committed

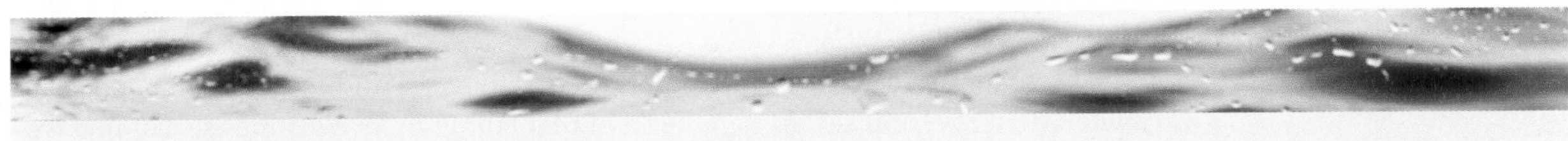

A World of Diversity

MATING IN CAPTIVITY

Do love and intimacy lead to hot sex? In her best-selling book *Mating in Captivity,* New York therapist Esther Perel offers a provocative analysis that challenges commonly held views of the relationship between intimacy and sex. The book stems from Perel's counselling heterosexual and gay couples who have a secure, caring relationship but a dull, unsatisfactory sex life. Using case studies, she illustrates how the desire for intimacy and security can stifle marital lust. Perel argues that the human desire for safety and closeness in a long-term relationship conflicts with the desire for novelty, excitement, and risk-taking. In particular, she believes that too much closeness can feel like an imprisonment. Desire needs freedom to thrive. People are most sexually attracted to a partner who is seen as a separate individual. This requires the ability to not totally rely on one's partner to satisfy all of one's emotional needs.

The women and men discussed in Perel's book long for a more vibrant, exciting sex life with their partner. In response, Perel states that couples need to unlock their erotic intelligence by removing the restraints they have placed on their lustful imagination. This requires a movement away from the security of dull but comfortable ways of having sex and an acceptance of the risk-taking involved in having adventurous sex. Sexual desire, response, and pleasure are heightened by the erotic elements of anticipation, surprise, and mystery.

One of Perel's most controversial conclusions is that hot sex requires not only that one feels a sense of independence from the partner but also that each person is more sexually aroused and alive when they have the freedom to objectify the other.

> We are socialized to control ourselves, to restrain our impulses, to tame the animal within. So as dutiful citizens and spouses we edit ourselves and mask our ravenous appetites and conceal our fleeting need to objectify the one we love. To my thinking cultivating a sense of ruthlessness in our intimate relationships is an intriguing solution to the problem of desire. While it may appear at first glance to be detached and even uncaring, it is in fact rooted in the love and security of our connection. It is a rare experience of trust to be able to let go completely without guilt or fretfulness, knowing that our relationship is vast enough to withstand the whole of us. We reach a unique intimacy in the erotic encounter. It transcends the civility of the emotional connection and accommodates our unruly impulse and primal appetites. The flint of rubbing bodies gives off a heat not easily achieved through tamer expressions of love (Perel, 2006, pp. 122-123).

Note: Esther Perel was a plenary speaker at the June 2008 University of Guelph Annual Conference on Human Sexuality. The primarily female audience, comprising sex educators, therapists, and health professionals from across Canada and the U.S., was so impressed by the challenging insights Perel presented that they gave her a standing ovation.

to the relationship. But there are a couple of differences that favour stability in the relationships of male–female couples: They are more likely to have the support of their families and less likely to be stigmatized by society at large.

Extramarital Sex

Why do people engage in extramarital sex? Some people engage in extramarital sex for variety (Lamanna & Riedmann, 2005). Some have affairs to break the routine of a confining marriage. Others enter affairs for reasons similar to the nonsexual reasons why adolescents often have sex: as a way of expressing hostility toward a spouse or retaliating for injustice. Husbands and wives who engage in affairs often report that they are not satisfied with or fulfilled by their marital relationships. Curiosity and desire for personal growth are often more prominent motives than marital dissatisfaction. Middle-aged people may have affairs to boost their self-esteem or to prove that they are still attractive.

Many times the sexual motive is less pressing than the desire for emotional closeness. Some women say they are seeking someone they can talk to or communicate with (Lamanna & Riedmann, 2005). There is a notable gender difference here: 77% of women who have had affairs, compared with 43% of the men, cite love as their justification (Townsend, 1995). Men who have had affairs are more likely than women to cite a need for sexual excitement as a justification—75% versus 55% (Glass & Wright, 1992).

Men are more likely than women to "separate sex and love; women appear to believe that love and sex go together and that falling in love justifies sexual involvement" (Glass & Wright, 1992, p. 361). Men (whether single, married, or cohabiting) are also generally more approving of extramarital affairs than women are (Glass & Wright, 1992). But note that these are all *group* differences. Many individual men are interested primarily in the extramarital relationship rather than the sex per se. Similarly, many women are out for the sex and not the relationship.

PATTERNS OF EXTRAMARITAL SEX Let us begin with a few definitions. **Extramarital sex** (an "affair") is usually conducted without the spouse's knowledge or approval. Secret affairs are referred to as **conventional adultery**, infidelity, or simply "cheating." Conventional adultery runs the gamut from the "one-night stand" to the affair that persists for years. In **consensual adultery**, extramarital relationships are conducted openly—that is, with the knowledge and consent of the partner. In what is called **swinging, comarital sex**, or mate swapping, the partner participates.

In a 1994 poll by *Maclean's*, fewer Canadians admitted to having an extramarital affair (14% of men, 7% of women) than has been reported in American surveys. The rates for extramarital sex are higher in Quebec than for any other province. Similar rates were found in a 2005 Compas poll, in which 10% of married Canadians said that an extramarital affair had occurred in their marriage.

In the 2005 Compas survey, about half of respondents believed that in Canadian society being faithful is not as important as it once was. One reflection of this belief might be the popularity of the Toronto-based website (**www.ashleymadison.com**) for attached people who want to have sexual flings. The Ashley Madison agency claims that more than half a million people have signed up as members since the site was launched in 2002.

Some people who suspect that their spouse is having an affair collect DNA samples from bed sheets, underwear, cigarette butts, etc., and send them for DNA testing. Paragon Genetics in Toronto receives such samples from across North America and Europe. Forty percent of the samples test positive, indicating that the DNA is from someone other than the spouse (White, 2008).

ATTITUDES TOWARD EXTRAMARITAL SEX Most married couples embrace the value of monogamy as the cornerstone of their marital relationship.

Extramarital sex Sexual relations between a married person and someone other than his or her spouse.

Conventional adultery Extramarital sex that is kept hidden from one's spouse.

Consensual adultery Extramarital sex that is engaged in openly with the knowledge and consent of one's spouse.

Swinging A form of consensual adultery in which both spouses share extramarital sexual experiences. Also referred to as *mate swapping*.

Comarital sex Swinging; mate swapping.

TABLE 12.8

Percentage of Canadians Who Would Be Bothered If Their Partner Had Sexual Intercourse With Someone Else

	Males		Females	
	Common-Law	**Married**	**Common-Law**	**Married**
Very	93.0	89.6	100.0	92.4
Somewhat	4.2	8.7	0.0	6.1
Not really	2.8	0.7	0.0	0.6
Not at all	0.0	0.0	0.0	0.9

Source: Compas. (1998). Modern life survey of the Canadian population.

As shown in Table 12.8, almost all Canadians in married or common-law relationships say that they would be bothered if their partner had sexual intercourse with someone else. However, about one-half of Canadians are accepting of their partner having a "very close but nonsexual relationship" with someone of the opposite sex (Compas, 1998).

In a 2005 Compas survey, Canadians were asked if an act of unfaithfulness by their partner would mean the end of their relationship. Less than half (41%) said it definitely would and 27% said it probably would.

EFFECTS OF EXTRAMARITAL SEX The discovery of infidelity can evoke a range of emotional responses. The spouse may be filled with anger, jealousy, or even shame. Feelings of inadequacy and doubts about one's attractiveness and desirability may surface. Infidelity may be seen by the betrayed spouse as a serious breach of trust and intimacy. Marriages that are not terminated in the wake of the disclosure may survive in a damaged condition.

The harm an affair does to a marriage may reflect the meaning of the affair to the individual and his or her spouse. Deborah Lamberti, director of a counselling and psychotherapy centre in New York City, points again to women's traditional intertwining of sex with relationships and argues that "Men don't view sex with another person as a reason to leave a primary relationship" (1997, pp. 131–132). Women may recognize this and be able to tell themselves that their husbands are sleeping with someone else just for physical reasons. But women are more concerned about remaining monogamous. Therefore, if a woman is sleeping with another man, she may already have a foot out the door, so to speak. Alterman (1997) also notes that a wife's affair may be an unforgivable blow to the husband's ego or pride. A woman may be more likely to see the transgression as a threat to the structure of her life.

If a person has an affair because the marriage is deeply troubled, the affair may be one more factor that speeds its dissolution. The effects on the marriage may depend on the nature of the affair. It may be easier to understand that a spouse has fallen prey to an isolated, unplanned encounter than to accept an extended affair. In some cases the discovery of infidelity stimulates the couple to work to improve their relationship.

SWINGING Swinging—also called "mate swapping" or comarital sex—is a form of consensual adultery in which both partners openly share sexual experiences with other people. Most swingers seek to avoid emotional entanglements with their swinging partners, but they may fail to separate their emotions from their sexual activity. Emotional intimacy between swinging partners can be even more threatening to the swingers' primary relationships than sexual intimacy.

Until recently, Canadians who engaged in swinging or ran swingers' clubs could be charged with various offences under the Criminal Code, usually with

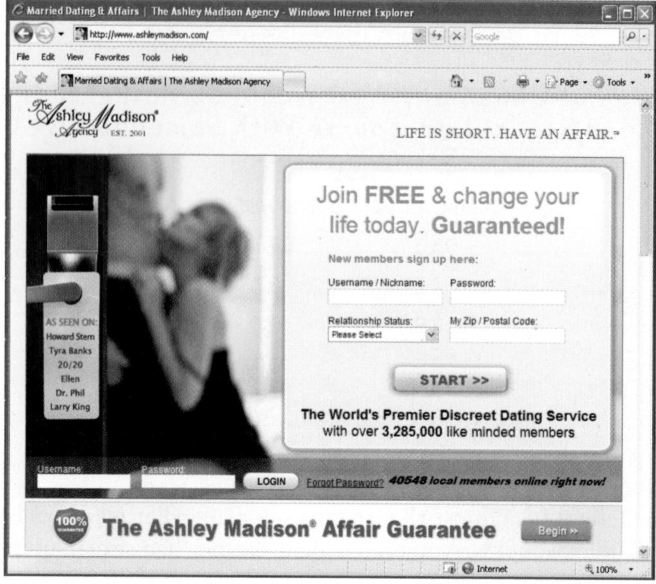

A Website for Flings.
The Ashley Madison website attracts many people who are in relationships but who also want to have flings. The site claims that more than half a million people have subscribed to it. This claim suggests that more Canadians might be having affairs than are willing to admit to infidelity to researchers.

having sex in a public place (public indecency) or with running a common bawdy house (a place used for prostitution or for acts of indecency). However, in 2005 the Supreme Court of Canada ruled that swinging was not illegal. The case, which involved the owners of two Montreal swingers' clubs, turned on the concept of indecency. The Court declared that sexual activity of consensual swingers was not harmful to Canadian society, and was therefore not indecent. The Supreme Court's verdict is highly significant because it used the criteria of harm to society, rather than community standards of morality, as a test for indecent behaviour.

Polyamory

A term that is commonly used today in referring to different forms of non-monogamy is *polyamory*. **Polyamory** is a general concept that covers the various forms of extramarital relationships. It refers to open relationships that allow for consensual sexual and/or emotional interactions with more than one partner. It is based on the view that people's needs for intimacy are unlikely to be gratified through one relationship. Proponents argue that the core marriage can be enhanced if the partners have the opportunity to develop emotionally intimate relationships with others.

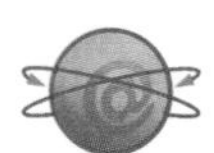

The Polyamory Society
This nonprofit organization promotes and supports the interests of individuals of multipartner relationships and families.

www.polyamorysociety.org

Divorce

> My wife and I were considering a divorce, but after pricing lawyers we decided to buy a new car instead.
>
> —Henny Youngman

More than one-third of Canadians divorce within 30 years of marriage (Statistics Canada, 2005f). The divorce rate in 2003 was about three times as high as in 1968. The peak was reached in 1987 in response to changes in the Divorce Act in 1985, which made it easier to obtain a divorce. There has also been a significant increase in the number of people experiencing their second divorce. In 2003, 16.2% of divorces involved men who had been previously divorced, compared with only 5.4% in 1973 (Statistics Canada, 2005). Interestingly, divorces are most likely to occur after three to four years of marriage. Quebec has the highest rate of divorce and Newfoundland and Labrador has the lowest (Statistics Canada, 2005).

With the increasing acceptance of cohabitation, more and more divorced people choose to live common-law instead of remarrying (Statistics Canada, 2005f). However, the rate of breakups in common-law relationships is much greater than for married couples.

Polyamory Any form of open relationship that allows for consensual sexual and/or emotional interactions with more than one partner.

Should They Remain Together "For the Sake of the Children?" The research seems to suggest that children may fare better when parents who are in regular conflict separate.

The greater number of divorces has resulted in a large increase in the number of stepfamilies. In 2001, there were about 500 000 stepfamilies in Canada, an increase of 17% from 1995 (Statistics Canada, 2005f).

Canada's no-fault divorce laws allow a divorce to be granted without a finding of marital misconduct. The increased economic independence of women has also contributed to the rising divorce rate. More women today have the economic means of breaking away from a troubled marriage. Today, more people consider marriage an alterable condition than in prior generations.

People today hold higher expectations of marriage than did their parents or grandparents. They expect marriage to be personally fulfilling as well as to function as an institution for rearing children. Many demand the right to be happy in marriage. The most common reasons given for a divorce today are problems in communication and a lack of understanding. When it is the woman who seeks to end a marriage today, her reasons often include a husband's criticism, defensiveness, contempt, and stonewalling—not lack of support (Carrère et al., 2000).

SAME-SEX DIVORCE The first same-sex divorce happened in 2004. Two lesbians in Ontario divorced after five days of marriage (Tyler, 2004). In 2005, a Vancouver judge granted a divorce to a woman on the basis that her husband had engaged in adultery with another man. The judge decided that she had the authority to change the legal definition of adultery, which had been limited to people of the opposite sex (Canadian Press, August 31, 2005).

THE COST OF DIVORCE Divorce often causes financial and emotional problems. When a household splits, the resources often cannot maintain the earlier standard of living for both partners. Financially speaking, divorce hits women harder than men. Divorced mothers often face the combined stress of being solely responsible for rearing their children and needing to increase their income to make ends meet. Divorced fathers may find it difficult to pay alimony and child support while attempting to establish a new lifestyle.

Divorce can also prompt feelings of failure as a spouse and parent, loneliness and uncertainty about the future, and depression. Married people appear to be better able to cope with the stresses and strains of life, perhaps because they can rely on each other for emotional support. Divorced and separated people have the highest rates of physical and mental illness in the population, and divorced people have higher rates of suicide than married people (Carrère et al., 2000). On the other hand, divorce can be a catalyst for personal growth and renewal. It can provide an opportunity for people to take stock of themselves and establish a new, more rewarding life.

Children are often the biggest losers when parents get a divorce (Ellis, 2000). On the other hand, chronic marital conflict or fighting is also connected with serious psychological distress in children and adolescents (Ellis, 2000).

Researchers attribute children's problems after divorce not only to the divorce itself but also to a subsequent decline in the quality of parenting. Children's adjustment is enhanced when parents maintain their parenting responsibilities and set aside their differences long enough to agree on child-rearing practices (Wallerstein & Blakeslee, 1989). Children of divorce also benefit when divorced parents encourage each other to continue to play important roles in their children's lives and avoid saying negative things about each other in their children's presence.

Sex in the Later Years

According to Statistics Canada (2007x), more than 4.3 million people in Canada are senior citizens, and their number is growing twice as fast as that of the general population (Statistics Canada, 2007x). People are also living longer. According to the 2006 Census, the average age at death is now 74 years for men and 77 years for women (Statistics Canada, 2008x). This "greying" of the population may have a profound effect on our views of older people, especially concerning their sexuality. Many people in our culture see sexual activity as appropriate only for the young. This belief falls within a constellation of unfounded cultural myths about older people, which includes the notions that older people are sexless, that older people with sexual urges are abnormal, and that older males with sexual interests are "dirty old men."

You're Never Too Old!
A common sexual myth in Canada is that the elderly, especially women, are not interested in sex. Sonia McMahon, 69, stakes out first place in a lineup of hundreds awaiting the arrival of Toronto firefighters for their 2002 charity calendar signing in the men's underwear department of the Bay. Obviously no one told Sonia that she's too old to be interested in sexually attractive men.

Researchers find that sexual daydreaming, sex drive, and sexual activity tend to decline with age. In the 1998 Compas survey of Canadians, only 20% of men over the age of 60 said they thought about sex several times a day, compared with 65% of men in their twenties (see Chapter 8). Among women over 60, only 3% thought about sex several times a day compared with 15% of women in their twenties. One-third of women in their sixties said they never thought about sex compared with only 3% of women in their twenties.

The Compas survey also found that people over 50 were *less* likely than younger people to do the following:

- feel comfortable asking their sexual partner to try something new
- share any information about their sex lives with their friends
- have conflicts with their partner over sex
- engage in oral sex
- use condoms

Sexuality in Late Adulthood.
Are older people sexually active? If they are, are they abnormal or deviant? Although young people often find it difficult to imagine older people engaging in sexual activity, it is normal to retain sexual interest and activity for a lifetime.

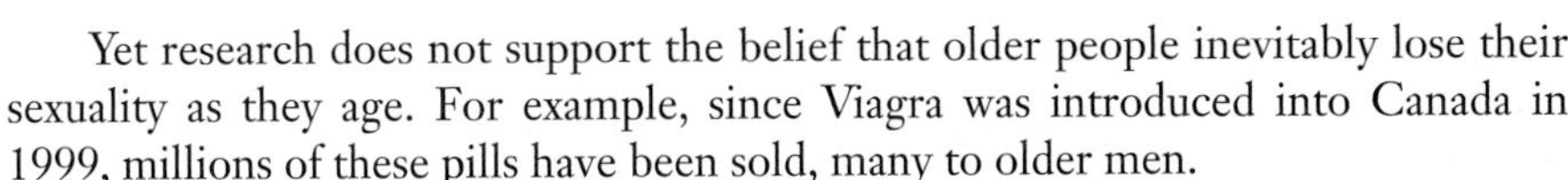

Yet research does not support the belief that older people inevitably lose their sexuality as they age. For example, since Viagra was introduced into Canada in 1999, millions of these pills have been sold, many to older men.

Stephen Katz and Barbara Marshall (2003) from Trent University in Ontario analyzed the role of Viagra in changing our perceptions of sexual functioning in older men. Katz and Marshall state that declining sexual function in older men used to be seen as a normal part of the aging process—a process that men were encouraged to accept as inevitable.

Today, our society is encouraged by marketers to believe that many of the limitations of aging can be overcome. Erectile dysfunction is no longer seen as a natural accompaniment to aging but rather a sexual problem that most men can remedy—simply by taking a pill. Indeed, advertising for Viagra suggests that any older man can be just as sexually functional as a 20-year-old.

Sexual activity among older people, as among other groups, is influenced not only by physical structures and changes but also by psychological well-being, feelings of intimacy, and cultural expectations.

Physical Changes

Although many older people retain the capacity to respond sexually, physical changes do occur as the years pass (see Table 12.9). If we are aware of them, we will not view them as abnormal or find ourselves unprepared to cope with them. Many potential problems can be averted by adjusting our expectations or making some changes to accommodate the aging process.

Let's not start this section with a deeply biological focus on changes in cells, hormones, and the like. Let's talk, first, about what happens when we look in the mirror. Many of us are dismayed by visible changes that occur as we age. We develop wrinkles. Our hair turns grey. Our muscle tone decreases. We tend to put on weight, especially if we do not exercise regularly. All in all, we are likely to feel less attractive than we did. And the fact is that our partners may find us to be less attractive. Nevertheless, in enduring intimate relationships, feelings of love, intimacy, and sharing life can outweigh those changes and feelings. However, if we are single in our later years, perhaps because of divorce or becoming widowed, the future, including the sexual future, may look bleak.

TABLE 12.9

Changes in Sexual Arousal Often Associated With Aging

Changes in the Female	Changes in the Male
Reduced myotonia (muscle tension)	Longer time to erection and orgasm
Reduced vaginal lubrication	Need for more direct stimulation for erection and orgasm
Reduced elasticity of the vaginal walls	Less semen emitted during ejaculation
Smaller increases in breast size during sexual arousal	Erections may be less firm
Reduced intensity of muscle spasms at orgasm	Testicles may not elevate as high into the scrotum
	Less intense orgasmic contractions
	Lessened feeling of a need to ejaculate during sex
	Longer refractory period

CHANGES IN THE FEMALE Many of the physical changes in women stem from decline in the production of estrogen around the time of menopause. The vaginal walls lose much elasticity and the thick, corrugated texture of the childbearing years. They grow paler and thinner. Thus coitus may become irritating. The thinning of the walls may also exert greater pressure on the bladder and urethra during coitus, leading in some cases to urinary urgency and burning urination that may persist for days.

The vagina also shrinks in size. The labia majora lose much of their fatty deposits and become thin. The introitus becomes relatively constricted, and penile entry may become somewhat difficult. This "problem," however, has a positive aspect: Increased friction between the penis and vaginal walls may heighten sexual sensations. The uterus decreases in size after menopause and no longer becomes so congested during sexual arousal. Following menopause, women also produce less vaginal lubrication, and the lubrication that is produced may take minutes, rather than seconds, to appear. Lack of adequate lubrication is also a major reason for painful coitus.

Many of these changes may be slowed or reversed through estrogen-replacement therapy (see Chapter 3) or topical application of estrogen-containing cream. Natural lubrication may also be increased through more elaborate foreplay. The need for more foreplay may encourage the man to become a more considerate lover. (Older men too are likely to need more time to become aroused.) An artificial lubricant can also ease problems posed by difficult entry or painful thrusting.

Women's breasts show smaller increases in size with sexual arousal as they age, but the nipples still become erect. Because the muscle tone of the urethra and anal sphincters decreases, the spasms of orgasm become less powerful and fewer in number. Thus orgasms may feel less intense. The uterine contractions that occur during orgasm become discouragingly painful for some postmenopausal women. Despite these changes, women can retain their ability to achieve orgasm well into their advanced years.

CHANGES IN THE MALE Age-related changes tend to occur more gradually in men than in women and are not clearly connected with any one biological event, as they are with menopause in the woman. Male adolescents may achieve erection in a matter of seconds through sexual fantasy alone. After about age 50, men take progressively longer to achieve erection. Erections become less firm, perhaps because of lowered testosterone production. Older men may require minutes of direct stimulation of the penis to achieve an erection. Couples can adjust to these changes by extending the length and variety of foreplay.

Most men remain capable of erection throughout their lives. Erectile dysfunction is not inevitable with aging. Men generally require more time to reach orgasm as they age, however, which may also reflect lowered testosterone production. In the eyes of their sex partners, however, delayed ejaculation may make them better lovers.

Testosterone production usually declines gradually from about age 40 to age 60 and then begins to level off. However, the decline is not inevitable and may be related to the man's general health. Sperm production tends to decline as the seminiferous tubules degenerate, but viable sperm may be produced quite late in life. Men in their seventies, eighties, and even nineties have fathered children.

Nocturnal erections tend to diminish in intensity, duration, and frequency as men age, but they do not normally disappear in healthy men (Perry et al., 2001). The refractory period tends to lengthen with age. An adolescent may require only a few minutes to regain erection and ejaculate again after a first orgasm, whereas a man in his thirties may require half an hour. Past age 50, the refractory period may increase to several hours.

Older men produce less ejaculate, and it may seep rather than shoot out. The contractions of orgasm become weaker and fewer. Still, an older male may enjoy orgasm as thoroughly as he did at a younger age. Attitudes and expectations can be as important as the contractions themselves.

In sum, most physical changes do not bring a man's or a woman's sex life to a grinding halt. People's attitudes, sexual histories, and partners are usually more important factors in sexual behaviour and enjoyment.

Patterns of Sexual Activity

Despite the decline in certain physical functions, older people can continue to lead a vibrant, fulfilling sex life. In fact, years of sexual experience may more than compensate for any diminution of physical responsiveness (Laumann et al., 2006).

Innovative Canadian Research

EFFECTS OF AGING ON GAY MALES AND LESBIANS

Only limited research has been carried out on the effects of aging on gay males. James Murray of the AIDS Committee of Toronto and Barry Adam of the University of Windsor (2001) conducted interviews in Toronto with gay and bisexual men aged 40 and over to find out some of their concerns about aging in the context of HIV. A common concern was that, because the gay community values youth and attractiveness, older men are at a disadvantage in finding sexual partners. Consequently, older gay men often see themselves as "invisible" and rejected by younger men. Clearly, several of the men believed they were no longer seen as desirable and consequently felt unwelcome in gay social gatherings. Feelings of isolation and loneliness were common themes, especially for those who had lost their partner and close friends to AIDS.

Positive aspects of aging were also expressed, however. For some, the attainment of an intimate relationship outweighed diminished sexual prowess. And because the sex drive was now less urgent, some men felt that they could be in greater control of their sexuality. Finally, those who were most involved in gay community organizations felt that the social connections they established there would be a source of support as they aged (Murray & Adam, 2001).

Montreal researchers have found that older lesbians as well as gay males experience feelings of exclusion within gay and lesbian organizations because of age discrimination (Brotman et al., 2003). In addition, the older age groups feel doubly discriminated against in their interactions with health agencies in the broader society, because of both their sexual orientation and their age. Many from the older generation have not been open in society about their sexual orientation and experience considerable fear when dealing with health and social agencies. Not surprisingly, most agencies do not know how to respond to the unique needs of older lesbians and gay males. This is especially true in settings such as nursing homes where workers may be homophobic (Brotman et al., 2003).

Canadian Trends

SEXUAL INTERCOURSE AMONG OLDER CANADIANS

In the 1998 Compas survey of Canadians, 65% of men and 39% of women over the age of 60 reported that they were having sexual intercourse. Among this group, 74% of men and 39% of women were having sex at least once a week. These gender differences can be explained by the fact that, because women outlive men, more older women than men do not have a sexual partner, and thus have less opportunity to have sex. Among Canadians 65 years of age and older, 61% of the men live with a spouse or partner compared with only 35% of the women (Statistics Canada, 2002h).

Several factors play a role in declining sexual activity, including physical problems, boredom, and cultural attitudes toward sex among the aging. Among Canadians 50 years and over, four-fifths report that general health problems negatively affect their sex life (Compas, 1998).

Unfortunately, people who overreact to expected changes in sexual response may conclude that their sex lives are over and give up on sexual activity or even on expressing any physical affection (Dunn, 1998).

Despite general trends, sexuality among older people is variable. Some become disgusted by sex; others simply lose interest. In contrast, some older people engage in intercourse, oral sex, and masturbation at least as often as when they were younger.

One of the most recent comprehensive studies of sex and aging was conducted by researchers at the University of Chicago, who sampled more than 3000 adults in the U.S. between the ages of 57 and 85 (Tessler Lindau et al., 2007). The key findings were:

- Sexual relations declined with age.
- Having sex with a partner in the previous year was reported by
    - 73% of those aged 57–64
    - 53% of those aged 65–74
    - 26% of those aged 75–85
- Among the sexually active, the average frequency was two to three times a month.
- Because more women than men were widowed, women were less likely to have sexual relations than were men.
- People in good health were twice as likely to be sexually active as those in poor health.
- Among the sexually active, half reported one or more sexual problems, yet most had not discussed these problems with a doctor since they turned 50.
- Fourteen percent of men used Viagra or other supplements to improve their sexual functioning.
- Only a minority felt that sex was "not all that important" (males: 13%, females: 35%) (Tessler Lindau et al., 2007).

In another study of mid-life women, aged 35 to 55, researchers found that body image has a more important influence than menopause on sexual functioning and satisfaction (Koch et al., 2005). One-fifth of the respondents could not think of their having even one attractive feature and reported an overall sense of dissatisfaction with their bodies. The features that the women considered least attractive were the stomach/abdomen, hips, and thighs and legs. The more a woman perceived herself as less attractive, the more likely there was a decline in her sexual desire or activity over the past 10 years. Two-thirds of the women reported one or more changes in their sexual response, such as desiring sex less and engaging in sex less often. However, some women had improved sexual response. When the women did have sex, there was a high level of enjoyment (Koch et al., 2005).

Taking a different approach, researchers at the University of Ottawa focused on couples experiencing optimal sexuality rather than sexual problems. Peggy Kleinplatz and Dana Menard (2007) found that for some couples "great sex" did not occur until they were in mid-life. This change required a recognition that conventional sexual scripts were not working and that a more creative approach to their sexual relationship was necessary.

Couples may accommodate to the physical changes of aging by broadening their sexual repertoire to include more diverse forms of stimulation such as oral–genital sex, sexual fantasy, sexually explicit materials, anal stimulation, vibrators, and other sexual techniques. Sexual satisfaction may be derived from manual or oral stimulation, cuddling, caressing, and tenderness, as well as from intercourse to orgasm.

Summing Up

Stimulation of the genitals in infancy may produce sensations of pleasure. Masturbation may begin as early as 6 to 12 months. Some infants seem capable of sexual responses that closely resemble orgasm.

In early childhood, children show curiosity about the genitals.

Preadolescent sex play often involves mutual display of the genitals, with or without touching. Much preadolescent same-sex sexual behaviour involves sexual exploration and is short-lived.

Pubertal changes are ushered in by sex hormones. Once puberty begins, most major changes in primary sex characteristics occur within three years in girls and within four years in boys.

Masturbation is a major sexual outlet during adolescence.

Many adolescents use petting as a way of achieving sexual gratification without becoming pregnant or relinquishing one's virginity.

Most adolescent same-sex sexual encounters are transitory. Coming to terms with adolescence is often more intense for gay males and lesbians, largely because gay male and lesbian sexual orientations are stigmatized in our society.

Recent years have seen a sharp increase in the number of single young people in our society. Some couples prefer cohabitation because it provides a consistent intimate relationship without the legal and economic entanglements of marriage.

Cohabitors who later marry may run a greater risk of divorce than noncohabitors, perhaps because cohabitors are a more liberal group.

Throughout history, marriage has legitimized sexual relations, sanctioned the permanence of a deeply committed relationship, provided for the orderly transmission of wealth, and established a setting for child rearing. People in Canada tend to marry within their geographical area and social class. They tend to marry people similar to themselves in physical attractiveness, people whose attitudes are similar to their own, and people who seem likely to meet their material, sexual, and psychological needs.

Married couples today engage in coitus more frequently and for longer durations of time than in Kinsey's day. They engage in a greater variety of sexual activities.

In most cases, extramarital relationships are conducted without the spouse's knowledge or approval. People may have affairs for sexual variety, to punish their spouses, to achieve emotional closeness, or to prove that they are attractive. Extramarital sex continues to be viewed negatively by the majority of married people in our society.

Polyamory includes arrangements such as open marriages and group marriages that permit intimate relationships with people outside the marriage.

About one-third of the marriages in Canada end in divorce. Reasons include relaxed restrictions on divorce, greater financial independence among women, and wider acceptance of the idea that marriages should be happy.

Physical changes as the years pass can impair sexual activity. Many potential problems can be averted by altering expectations and making changes to accommodate the aging process.

Sexual activity tends to decline with age, but continued sexual activity can boost self-esteem and be an important source of gratification.

Test Yourself

Multiple-Choice Questions

1. Children frequently develop sexual curiosity as early as __________ of age.

a. 12 months
b. 24 months
c. 36 months
d. 48 months

2. Sex games like "show me yours" and "playing doctor" become more common between the ages of

a. 2 and 3
b. 5 and 8
c. 6 and 10
d. 12 and older

3. Same-sex sexual play in childhood

a. is a sign that the child will grow up gay or lesbian
b. is much more common in boys than in girls
c. is much more common in girls than in boys
d. does not predict adult sexual orientation

4. Which of the following is not one of the effects of estrogen during puberty?

a. thickening of the vaginal lining
b. enlargement of the labia
c. growth of the vagina and uterus
d. development of the clitoris

5. Most adolescent males experience their first ejaculation through

a. sexual intercourse
b. nocturnal emissions
c. masturbation
d. oral sex

6. The website "sexualityandu" is based on

a. learning theory
b. information-motivation-behavioural skills model
c. peer education models
d. queer theory

7. Alberta researchers found that at first intercourse males and females most differed from each other with regard to

a. having regrets
b. rating the experience positively
c. being emotionally satisfied
d. being physically satisfied

8. The average age of marriage is highest in the province of

a. Nova Scotia
b. Quebec
c. Ontario
d. Alberta

9. The proportion of Canadians living in common-law relationships is ______ that of the United States.

a. the same as
b. double
c. one-half
d. slightly less than

10. The Canadian divorce rate increased sharply in the late 1980s due to

a. the sexual revolution
b. an increase in the number of people having extramarital affairs
c. a relaxation of legal restrictions
d. the feminist movement

Answers to the Test Yourself questions in each chapter are found on page 509.

Critical Thinking Questions

1. Would you characterize your own background as sexually permissive or restrictive? Why?
2. If you have not had a consensual sexual experience with another person, under what circumstances do you think this will take place? Are you waiting for the right person, for love, or for marriage?
3. If you have had a consensual sexual experience with another person, recall the first time it happened. What were your reasons? How old were you? How did you find the experience?
4. Would you consider cohabiting with someone? Why or why not? What would your parents think about it? Your grandparents?
5. Have you ever had a partner who "cheated" on you? How did you handle it? What effect did this have on the relationship?

Visit MyPsychKit at www.mypsychkit.com, where you can do quizzes and link to additional resources on topics discussed in this text.

CHAPTER THIRTEEN

Sexual Dysfunctions

Sexual dysfunctions Persistent or recurrent difficulties in becoming sexually aroused or reaching orgasm.

Sexual dysfunctions are recurring difficulties in becoming sexually aroused or reaching orgasm. Many of us are troubled by sexual problems from time to time. Men occasionally have difficulty achieving an erection or ejaculate more rapidly than they would like. Most women occasionally have difficulty achieving orgasm or becoming sufficiently lubricated. People are not considered to have a sexual dysfunction, however, unless the problem is persistent and causes distress.

People with sexual dysfunctions may avoid sexual opportunities for fear of failure. They may anticipate that sex will result in frustration or physical pain rather

Canadian Trends

SEXUAL PROBLEMS IN CANADA

Because many people are reluctant to admit to sexual problems, we do not have precise figures on their frequencies. The best current information we have in Canada is based on the Canadian Contraceptive Survey (Fisher et al., 2004b). The survey asked women if they had experienced five possible types of sexual difficulties: low sexual desire, painful intercourse, lack of orgasm during intercourse, partner's erectile difficulties, and partner's premature ejaculation. About half of the women had experienced at least one of these problems. More married women reported sexual difficulties than did single women.

The most common problem reported by Canadian women (43%) was diminished sexual desire. Married women (57%) were twice as likely to report low desire as unmarried women (26%). The second most common problem was difficulty with orgasm, with 24% of women saying that they do not usually have an orgasm during intercourse. Painful intercourse was a problem reported by 15% of women. The percentages of Canadian women reporting these sexual problems are similar to those reported by American women (Laumann et al., 1994).

In the Fisher et al. (2003) Contraceptive Survey, very few women reported that their partners have problems with either ejaculating too soon (7%) or maintaining an erection (6%). However, in another national survey of Canadians, 11.7% of women reported that their partners had experienced erectile dysfunction in the previous six months, with 10.4% of men reporting this dysfunction (Auld & Brock, 2002). These percentages are similar to those found in a national U.S. survey, in which 10% of men said that they had problems maintaining an erection during intercourse and 29% that they ejaculated too soon (Laumann et al., 1994). In the Canadian study, the rate of erectile dysfunction was determined by combining those who said they had experienced erectile dysfunction in the previous six months with those who had a low score measuring erectile dysfunction on the Sexual Health Inventory for Men (SHIM). Using these combined scores, Auld and Brock concluded that 27% of Canadian men experience erectile dysfunction. Obviously, the reported rate of this dysfunction is strongly influenced by the measures used.

The Compas survey (1998) asked Canadians to indicate which factors have a negative impact on their sex life. The two most common factors were being too tired and being too busy. (These are obviously a reflection of the hectic lives that many Canadians lead.) More women (41%) than men (26%) reported that their own lack of desire had a negative impact. Similarly, 42% of the men and only 18% of the women said that their partner's lack of desire had a negative impact on their sex life.

Married people (75%) were more likely than singles (51%) to report that being tired, or their partner's being too tired, has a negative effect on their sex life. As well, more of those who were married (41%) than single (21%) said that having children in the household had a similar negative effect (Compas, 1998).

In a more recent national survey of Canadians between the ages of 40 and 64, more than half said they were often too tired to have sex, 42% said they were too stressed, and 40% said they did not have the time (Reuters, 2006).

To what extent do people find their sexual problems to be frustrating? Tanya Hill (2005) conducted an online survey of 236 University of Guelph females (aged 17–24). Traditionally, it was believed that women did not get sexually frustrated because of the stereotype that sexual pleasure was not important to women. Contrary to this belief, three-quarters of the female students said that they felt sexually frustrated at least some of the time and 9% said they often felt frustrated.

The most frustrating situations for the women were

- not experiencing an orgasm during intercourse
- partner not being affectionate
- partner being unavailable
- partner refusing to have sex

Despite the prevalence of sexual problems, many people are reluctant to seek professional advice. Only a third of Canadian women reported that they have asked their doctor about sexual issues (Fisher et al., 2003). In another study of women at an Ontario clinic, only 16% of those who had experienced sexual problems had discussed these with a doctor (Fisher et al., 2004b).

than pleasure and gratification. Because of the emphasis that our culture places on sexual competence, people with sexual dysfunctions may feel inadequate or incompetent, feelings that diminish their self-esteem. They may experience guilt, shame, frustration, depression, and anxiety.

Dyspareunia A sexual dysfunction characterized by persistent or recurrent pain during sexual intercourse.

Vaginismus A sexual dysfunction characterized by involuntary contraction of the muscles surrounding the vaginal barrel, preventing penile penetration or rendering penetration painful.

Types of Sexual Dysfunctions

The most widely used system of classification of sexual dysfunctions is based on the American Psychiatric Association's *Diagnostic and Statistical Manual of Mental Disorders* (the DSM) of 2000. The DSM groups sexual dysfunctions into four categories:

1. *Sexual desire disorders.* These involve lack of interest in sex or aversion to sexual contact.
2. *Sexual arousal disorders.* Sexual arousal is mainly characterized by erection in the male and vaginal lubrication and swelling of the external genitalia in the female. In men, sexual arousal disorders involve difficulty in obtaining or sustaining erections sufficient to engage in sexual intercourse. In women, they typically involve insufficient lubrication.
3. *Orgasmic disorders.* Men or women may have difficulty reaching orgasm or reach orgasm more quickly than they would like. Women are more likely to encounter difficulties reaching orgasm. Men are more likely to reach orgasm too quickly (have premature ejaculation).
4. *Sexual pain disorders.* Both men and women may suffer from **dyspareunia** (painful intercourse). Women may experience **vaginismus**, or involuntary contraction of muscles that surround the vaginal barrel, preventing penetration by the penis or making penetration painful.

Sexual dysfunctions are classified as lifelong or acquired. (Acquired dysfunctions follow a period of normal functioning.) Dysfunctions are also classified as generalized or situational. *Generalized* dysfunctions occur in all situations. *Situational* dysfunctions affect sexual functioning only in some situations, as during intercourse but not masturbation, or with one partner but not another. If a man has never been able to obtain an erection during sexual relations with a partner but can do so during masturbation, his dysfunction is lifelong and situational.

Sexual Desire Disorders

Sexual desire disorders involve lack of sexual desire or aversion to genital sexual activity. People with little or no sexual interest or desire are said to have *hypoactive sexual desire disorder.* The problem is more common among women than men. Nevertheless, the belief that men are always eager for sex is a myth.

Lack of sexual desire does not imply that a person is unable to get an erection, lubricate adequately, or reach orgasm. Some people with low sexual desire can become sexually aroused and reach orgasm when stimulated adequately. Many enjoy sexual activity, even if they are unlikely to initiate it. Many appreciate the affection and closeness of physical intimacy but have no interest in genital stimulation.

Hypoactive sexual desire is one of the most commonly diagnosed sexual dysfunctions. Yet there is no clear consensus among clinicians and researchers concerning the definition of low sexual desire. How much sexual interest or desire is "normal"? There is no standard level of sexual desire, and lack of desire is usually considered a problem when couples recognize that their level of sexual interest has gotten so low that little remains. Sometimes the lack of desire is limited to one partner. When one member of a couple is more interested in sex than the other, sex therapists often recommend that couples try to compromise. They also attempt to uncover and resolve problems in the relationship that may dampen the sexual ardour.

Vasocongestion Engorgement of blood vessels with blood, which swells the genitals and breasts during sexual arousal.

Male erectile disorder Persistent difficulty getting or maintaining an erection sufficient to allow the man to engage in or complete sexual intercourse. Also termed *erectile dysfunction.*

When is lack of sexual desire among women a dysfunction (Basson, 2002)? The literature on gender differences strongly suggests that women, in general, are less interested in sex than men are (Peplau, 2003). This is not to suggest that there is anything wrong with women who experience strong, regular sexual urges. Keep in mind that lack of desire usually does not come to the health practitioner's attention unless one partner is more desirous of sex than the other.

SEXUAL AVERSION DISORDER People with low sexual desire may have little or no interest in sex, but they are not repelled by genital contact. Some people, however, find sex disgusting or aversive and avoid genital contact.

A history of erectile problems can cause sexual aversion in men. A history of sexual trauma, such as rape or childhood sexual abuse or incest, often figures prominently in cases of sexual aversion, especially in women.

Sexual Arousal Disorders

When we are sexually stimulated, our bodies normally respond with **vasocongestion**, which produces erection in the male and vaginal lubrication in the female. People with sexual arousal disorders, however, fail to achieve or sustain the lubrication or erection necessary to facilitate sexual activity. Or they lack the subjective feelings of sexual pleasure or excitement that normally accompany sexual arousal.

MALE ERECTILE DISORDER Sexual arousal disorder in the male is called **male erectile disorder** or *erectile dysfunction.* It is characterized by persistent difficulty in getting or maintaining an erection sufficient to allow the completion of sexual activity. In most cases the failure is limited to sexual activity with partners, or with some partners and not others. It can thus be classified as *situational.* In rare cases the dysfunction is found during any sexual activity, including masturbation. In such cases, it is considered *generalized.* Some men with erectile disorder are unable to attain an erection with their partners. Others can achieve erection but not sustain it.

The Canadian Erectile Difficulties Resource Centre
www.edhelp.ca

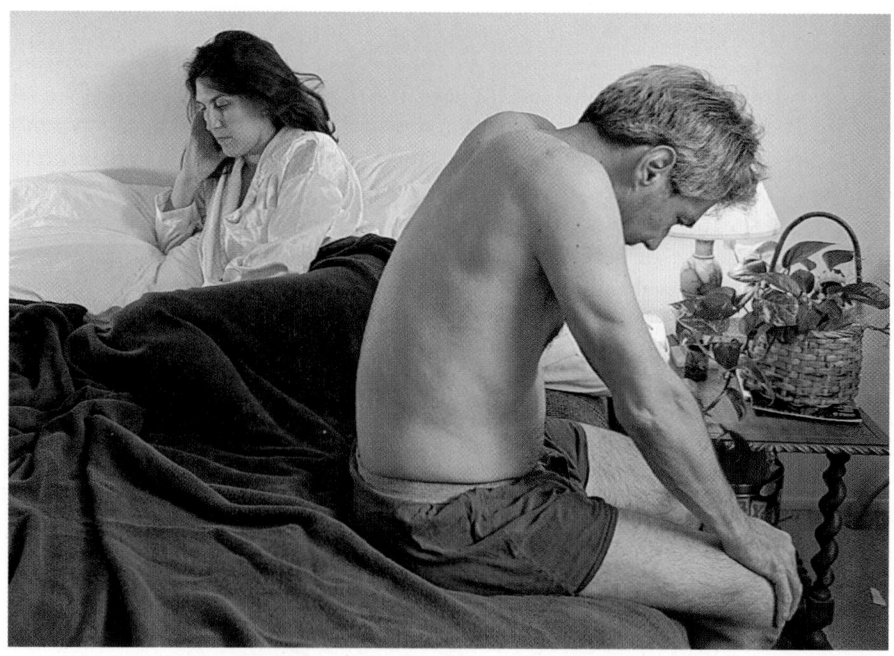

The Emotional Toll of Erectile Dysfunction.
Male erectile disorder, or erectile dysfunction, is characterized by persistent difficulty in getting or maintaining an erection sufficient to allow the completion of sexual activity. Occasional erectile problems are common and may be caused by fatigue, alcohol, or anxiety about a new partner. But fear of recurrence can create a vicious circle, in which anxiety leads to failure, and failure heightens anxiety.

Performance anxiety Anxiety concerning one's ability to perform behaviours, especially behaviours that may be evaluated by other people.

The incidence of erectile disorder increases with age although there is disagreement as to how many men are affected. Occasional problems in getting or maintaining an erection are quite common. Fatigue, alcohol, anxiety over impressing a new partner, and other factors may account for a transient episode. Even an isolated occurrence, however, can lead to a persistent problem if the man fears recurrence. The more anxious and concerned the man becomes about his sexual ability, the more likely he is to suffer **performance anxiety**. This anxiety can contribute to repeated failure, and a vicious circle of anxiety and failure may develop.

A man with erectile problems may try to "will" an erection, which can compound the problem. Each failure may further demoralize and defeat him. He may ruminate about his sexual inadequacy, setting the stage for yet more anxiety. His partner may try to comfort and support him by saying things like "It can happen to anyone," "Don't worry about it," or "It will get better in time." But attempts at reassurance may be to no avail. As one client put it,

> I always felt inferior, like I was on probation, having to prove myself. I felt like I was up against the wall. You can't imagine how embarrassing this [erectile failure] was. It's like you walk out [naked] in front of an audience that you think is a nudist convention and it turns out to be a tuxedo convention.
>
> —The Authors' Files

The vicious circle of anxiety and erectile failure may be interrupted if the man recognizes that occasional problems are normal and does not overreact. However, the emphasis in our culture on men's sexual prowess may spur them to view occasional failures as catastrophes rather than transient disappointments. Viewing occasional problems as an inconvenience, rather than a tragedy, may help avert the development of persistent erectile difficulties.

Performance anxiety is a prominent cause of erectile disorder. So are other psychological factors such as depression, lack of self-esteem, and problems in the relationship. Biological factors can also play a causal role, as we shall see.

A common belief regarding the sexual arousal of men is that the process is much simpler than it is for women. However, a recent focus group study (Jansen et al., 2008) suggests that men's sexual arousal is also complex and there is considerable variation among men regarding what they find sexually arousing. For example, the older men in the study reported that emotional connection with their partner was now more important than physical attractiveness in their sexual arousal. Some men reported that if a woman had low self-esteem, they were less likely to be aroused by her even if she was physically attractive.

FEMALE SEXUAL AROUSAL DISORDER Women may encounter persistent difficulties becoming sexually excited or sufficiently lubricated in response to sexual stimulation. In some cases these difficulties are lifelong. In others they develop after a period of normal functioning. In some cases difficulties are pervasive and occur during both masturbation and sex with a partner. More often they occur in specific situations. For example, they occur with some partners and not with others, or during coitus but not during oral–genital sex or masturbation.

According to Vancouver therapist Rosemary Basson (2004), most women with arousal disorder experience little or no subjective arousal or sexual excitement. These women can be categorized into two groups. In the first are women who experience no subjective arousal and do not feel any genital response (combined arousal disorder). In the second group are women who are aware of their genitals physically responding to stimulation yet feel no subjective arousal (subjective arousal disorder).

There is also a minority of women who can become aroused by many different kinds of stimuli but do not find stimulation of their genitals to be arousing (genital arousal disorder). Women with this disorder can still have a high interest in sex and become subjectively aroused providing there is non-genital stimulation (Basson, 2004).

Female sexual arousal disorder, like its male counterpart, may have physical causes. A thorough evaluation by a medical specialist (a urologist in the case of a male, a gynecologist in the case of a female) is recommended. Any neurological, vascular, or hormonal problem that interferes with the lubrication or swelling response of the vagina to sexual stimulation may contribute to female sexual arousal disorder. For example, diabetes mellitus may lead to diminished sexual excitement in women because of the degeneration of the nerves servicing the clitoris and the blood vessel (vascular) damage it causes. Reduced estrogen production can also result in vaginal dryness.

Another interesting line of research suggests that the skin of some women with sexual arousal problems is not as sensitive to touch as the skin of women who do not have such problems (Frohlich & Meston, 2005). In such cases, the woman might seek to increase sexual stimulation—psychological as well as physical.

Female sexual arousal disorder more commonly has psychological causes. In some cases, women harbour deep-seated anger and resentment toward their partners. In other cases, sexual trauma is implicated. Survivors of sexual abuse often find it difficult to respond sexually to their partners. Childhood sexual abuse is especially prevalent in cases of female sexual arousal disorder (Bean, 2002).

Feelings of helplessness, anger, or guilt—or even flashbacks of the abuse—may surface when the woman begins sexual activity, undermining her ability to become aroused. Other psychosocial causes include anxiety or guilt about sex and ineffective stimulation by the partner (Bean, 2002).

At the opposite end of the sexual arousal continuum are those women who experience persistent and intense genital sexual arousal (Leiblum & Chivers, 2007). This condition is extremely distressing to some of the women who experience it. (This is discussed in Chapter 4.)

Orgasmic Disorders

Orgasmic disorders include (1) female orgasmic disorder, (2) male orgasmic disorder, and (3) premature or rapid ejaculation. In female or male orgasmic disorder, the woman or man is persistently delayed in reaching orgasm or does not reach orgasm at all, despite achieving sexual stimulation that would normally be of sufficient intensity to result in orgasm. The problem is more common among women than men. In some cases, a person can reach orgasm without difficulty while engaging in sexual relations with one partner, but not with another.

FEMALE ORGASMIC DISORDER Women with female orgasmic disorder are unable to reach orgasm or have difficulty reaching orgasm following what would usually be an adequate amount of sexual stimulation. Women who have never reached orgasm through any means are sometimes labelled **anorgasmic** or *preorgasmic*.

A woman who reaches orgasm through masturbation or oral sex may not necessarily reach orgasm dependably during coitus with her partner. Penile thrusting during coitus may not provide sufficient clitoral stimulation to facilitate orgasm. University of Waterloo researcher B. J. Rye (2001) found that 93% of university women sometimes or usually need direct clitoral stimulation during intercourse in order to have an orgasm. Only 46% of the women surveyed have an orgasm during at least half of their intercourse experiences, and 49% say that it often takes them a long time to have an orgasm.

Anorgasmic Never having reached orgasm.

MALE ORGASMIC DISORDER Male orgasmic disorder has also been termed *delayed ejaculation*, *retarded ejaculation*, and *ejaculatory incompetence*. The problem may be lifelong or acquired, generalized or situational. There are very few cases of men who have never ejaculated. In most cases the disorder is limited to coitus. The man may be capable of ejaculating during masturbation or oral sex but may find it difficult, if not impossible—despite high levels of sexual excitement—to ejaculate during intercourse. There is a myth that men with male orgasmic disorder and their female partners enjoy this condition, because it enables them to "go on forever" (Dekker, 1993). Actually, the experience is frustrating for both partners.

Male orgasmic disorder may be caused by physical problems, such as multiple sclerosis or neurological damage, that interfere with neural control of ejaculation. It may also be a side effect of certain drugs. Various psychological factors may also play a role, including performance anxiety, sexual guilt, and hostility toward one's partner.

Premature ejaculation A sexual dysfunction in which ejaculation occurs with minimal sexual stimulation and before the man desires it.

PREMATURE EJACULATION Men with **premature ejaculation** ejaculate too rapidly to permit their partners or themselves to enjoy sexual relations fully. The degree of prematurity varies. Some men ejaculate during foreplay, even at the sight of their partner disrobing. But most ejaculate either just before or immediately after penetration or following a few coital thrusts.

Guy Grenier and Sandra Byers (2001) of the University of New Brunswick studied the ejaculatory behaviour of a community sample of men. In this study the term *rapid ejaculation* (RE) was used instead of *premature ejaculation* (PE). The men reported that intercourse typically lasted about eight minutes before they ejaculated. They also reported that ejaculation happened more quickly than they desired in about one-third of their acts of sexual intercourse. The men attempted to delay the timing of their ejaculation during about half of their intercourse experiences.

The percentage of men experiencing RE varies widely (between 4% and 61%) depending on what criteria are used (Grenier & Byers, 2001); 23% of the men in the study identified themselves as having a problem with premature ejaculation. These men ejaculate sooner than other men, perceive less control over the timing of ejaculation, and are more concerned over ejaculating sooner than desired.

Just what constitutes *prematurity?* There is no clear cutoff. Some scholars argue that the focus should be on whether the couple is satisfied with the duration of coitus rather than on a specific time period.

In another study of 52 New Brunswick couples, Byers and Grenier (2003) compared the men's and women's reports of the man's ejaculatory behaviour. There was only moderate agreement between the men and women. The women tended to underestimate how seriously the male partner viewed RE. However, both the men and women reported lower sexual satisfaction in response to the man's problem with RE (Byers & Grenier, 2003).

Helen Singer Kaplan (1974) suggested that the label *premature* should be applied to cases in which men persistently or recurrently lack voluntary control over their ejaculations. This may sound like a contradiction in terms, given that ejaculation is a reflex, and reflexes need not involve thought or conscious control. Kaplan means that a man may control his ejaculation by learning to regulate the amount of sexual stimulation he experiences so that it remains below the threshold at which the ejaculation reflex is triggered.

Sexual Pain Disorders

For most of us, coitus is a source of pleasure. For some of us, however, coitus gives rise to pain and discomfort.

DYSPAREUNIA Traditionally, dyspareunia was defined as painful coitus. However, it also includes those women who have persistent pain with attempted vaginal intercourse (Basson, 2004). According to Caroline Pukall of Queen's University, some therapists and researchers believe a more accurate term is "vulvodynia" (Pukall et al., 2003).

Dyspareunia is one of the most common sexual dysfunctions and is also a common complaint of women seeking gynecological services. The location of the pain can vary. For example, it can be at the entrance to the vagina, in the vagina, or in the pelvic region (Pukall et al., 2003). Painful intercourse is less common in men and is generally associated with genital infections that cause burning or painful ejaculation.

Unfortunately, many women are too embarrassed to talk about genital pain and do not seek treatment. Also, few doctors or therapists are properly trained regarding the diagnosis of dyspareunia and thus many women suffering from this condition do not receive adequate care (Pukall et al., 2005). Queen's University researchers have developed a vulvalgesiometer, which can measure the degree of pain severity experienced by women (Pukall et al., 2007).

Pain is a sign that something is wrong—physically or psychologically. Dyspareunia may result from physical causes, emotional factors, or an interaction of the two (Binik, 2005). The most common cause of coital pain in women is inadequate lubrication. In such a case, additional foreplay or artificial lubrication may help. Vaginal infections and sexually transmitted infections (STIs) may also produce coital pain. Allergic reactions to spermicides, even the latex material in condoms, can give rise to coital pain or irritation. Pain during deep thrusting may be caused by endometriosis or pelvic inflammatory disease (PID), by other diseases, or by structural disorders of the reproductive organs. Psychological factors such as unresolved guilt or anxiety about sex or the lingering effects of sexual trauma may also be involved. These factors may inhibit lubrication and cause involuntary contractions of the vaginal musculature, making penetration painful or uncomfortable.

Researchers in Montreal (Binik et al., 2002) have extensively studied dyspareunia in women and evaluated various treatment strategies. They found that women with dyspareunia had lower tolerance for pain, not only in the vaginal area but also on the upper arm, suggesting that a generalized hypersensitivity may contribute to this problem in some women (Pukall et al., 2002).

Based on these findings, Binik (2005) argues that dyspareunia should be categorized as a pain disorder rather than a sexual dysfunction as defined by the American Psychiatric Association (DSM-IV) and should be assessed and treated like other pain disorders. Binik's recommendations have caused considerable controversy. Kenneth Zucker, editor of *Archives of Sexual Behavior*, asked 18 experts to comment on them in the February 2005 edition of the journal. There was only limited support for Binik's proposals.

Binik (2005) believes that every case of dyspareunia has both physiological and psychological components. Interestingly, the researchers found that women who believe their pain is due to psychosocial factors report higher levels of pain and more sexual problems than women who believe their pain is due to physical causes. Because of the complexity (both physical and psychological) surrounding the problem of dyspareunia, Binik et al. (2002) believe that multidisciplinary teams should be established to deal with it. They note that for many women the pain arising from dyspareunia cannot be totally eliminated, and that these women need to be taught coping strategies for managing the pain.

VAGINISMUS Vaginismus involves an involuntary contraction of the pelvic muscles that surround the outer third of the vaginal barrel. Avoidance of penetration seems to be the key factor differentiating vaginismus from dyspareunia (Bergeron & Lord, 2003). Vaginismus occurs reflexively during attempts at vaginal penetration, making entry by the penis painful or impossible. These muscle contractions are accompanied by a deep-seated fear of penetration (Beck, 1993). Some women with vaginismus are unable to tolerate penetration by any object, including a finger, a tampon, or a physician's speculum.

Women with vaginismus often have histories of sexual trauma, sexual assault, or botched abortions that resulted in vaginal injuries. They may desire sexual relations. They may be capable of becoming sexually aroused and achieving orgasm. However, fear of penetration triggers an involuntary spasm of the vaginal musculature at the point of penile insertion. Vaginismus can also be a cause or an effect of dyspareunia. Women who experience painful coitus may develop a fear of penetration. Fear then leads to the development of involuntary vaginal contractions. Vaginismus and dyspareunia may also give rise to, or result from, erectile disorder in men. Feelings of failure and anxiety come to overwhelm both partners.

Some researchers in Montreal (Reissing et al., 2004) disagree that vaginismus is easily diagnosed and easily treated. Instead they propose that cases diagnosed as vaginismus should be reconceptualized as either an aversion to vaginal penetration or as a genital pain disorder. These distinctions are important in suggesting different courses of treatment.

VULVODYNIA

> The pain has lasted for months. You're so uncomfortable you can hardly sit. Having sex is unthinkable. Nothing alleviates the pain, burning, and irritation, at least not for long.
>
> —Mayo Clinic, 2006

This is a description of vulvodynia, posted by the Mayo Clinic (2006). Vulvodynia is a gynecological condition characterized by vulval pain, particularly chronic burning sensations, irritation, and soreness (Lotery et al., 2004; Masheb et al., 2004). Although vulvodynia and related conditions, such as vestibulitis, can give rise to painful intercourse, they are not in themselves considered sexual dysfunctions (Kaler, 2005).

Vulvar vestibulitis (VV) is pain that can be experienced through both sexual and nonsexual contact at the entrance of the vagina (the vulvar vestibule, which is bordered by the inner vaginal lips). Women with VV usually seek treatment because they experience pain when intercourse is attempted. Unlike VV, vulvodynia does not require some kind of external contact for pain to be triggered (Pukall et al., 2005).

Vulvar vestibulitis may be caused by various factors, such as repeated yeast infections, hormonal changes, and genetics. Other possibilities are STIs, allergies, urinary infections, and sexual abuse. Psychological factors such as low sexual esteem, anxiety, and hypervigilance (obsessional focus on pain) may also contribute to VV (Pukall et al., 2005).

Innovative Canadian Research

SEXUAL AROUSAL AND VULVAR VESTIBULITIS

Some therapists believe that VV is associated with insufficient sexual arousal. To test this theory, an experimental study was conducted at McGill University. Two samples of women (one with VV and the other a healthy group) were shown both an erotic and a non-erotic film (Payne et al., 2007). Both groups were sexually aroused in response to the erotic film. Genital arousal (specifically, of the labia minora) was measured with a labial thermistor clip.

The group with VV did not report subjective arousal but exhibited greater pain than did the control group in both genital and nongenital areas. The findings indicate that women with VV are not lacking in sexual arousal. However, lack of subjective feelings of arousal may contribute to experiencing vulvar pain during intercourse (Payne et al., 2007).

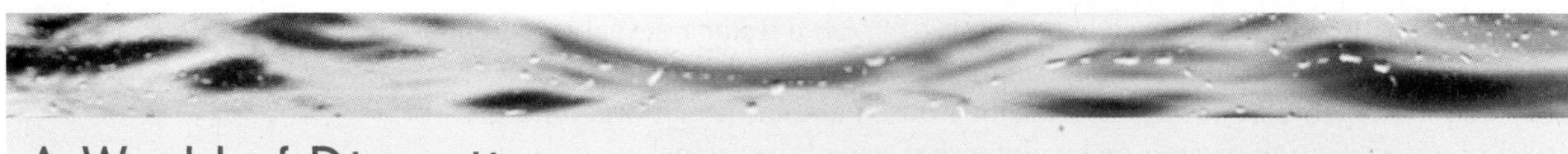

A World of Diversity

A NEW VIEW OF WOMEN'S SEXUAL DYSFUNCTIONS?

By Lori A. Brotto, PhD, Assistant Professor, Department of Obstetrics and Gynaecology, University of British Columbia

The classification of sexual dysfunctions in *the Diagnostic and Statistical Manual of Mental Disorders* (American Psychiatric Association, 2000) is based on the Human Sexual Response Cycle model of Masters and Johnson (1966). This classification has been criticized because of (1) the specific wording of these sexual dysfunction criteria, and (2) the overall taxonomic system for classifying sexual dysfunctions in women. These criticisms resulted in attempts to establish new classification systems. Yet these revisions continued to use the Masters and Johnson medical model, which is symptom-focused on problems relating to desire, arousal, orgasm, and pain.

Leonore Tiefer, a clinical psychologist and activist, convened a group of feminist social scientists in 2000 to propose a new diagnostic system that was intended to be free of the pharmaceutical conflicts of interest and the medical model on which it is based. Specifically, there was concern over the creation of a "Female Sexual Dysfunction (FSD)" diagnosis by pharmaceutical companies that would then be in a profitable position to develop and market a drug to treat this "disease." Thus, the "New View Campaign" was formed.

The New View classification system is a radical departure from the existing American Psychiatric Association's (DSM-IV) taxonomic structure. It is based on feminist theories attributing women's sexual problems to cultural and relational factors (Tiefer, 2001). The system deliberately avoids specifying any particular "normal" pattern of sexual response. Instead, the resulting four-part classification system focuses on the causes of sexual problems, defined as "discontent or dissatisfaction with any emotional, physical, or relational aspect of sexual experience." It does not differentiate among the problematic symptoms of desire, arousal, orgasm, or other sexual complaints.

The causes of women's sexual problems are classified by Tiefer (2001) into four main groupings:

- Sexual problems due to sociocultural, political, or economic factors
- Sexual problems relating to a partner or a relationship
- Sexual problems due to psychological factors
- Sexual problems due to medical factors

The New View classification is an improvement over the DSM-IV perspective of sexual response, which is based on a medical model of men's sexuality. However, empirical data supporting the usefulness and validity of the new classification system has not been collected. Moreover, this radical departure from the DSM-IV system means that there is no continuity of research between the two systems. Also, an overriding question exists: Is it useful to diagnose sexual dysfunction on the basis of causes rather than on the basis of symptoms? Moreover, with a new system, we need to start all over again in determining the prevalence of sexual difficulties. What we previously knew about the rates of sexual desire, arousal, orgasm, and genital pain complaints would thus be lost.

Origins of Sexual Dysfunctions: A Biopsychosocial Approach

Human beings are complex, with complex bodies as well as complex mental processes. We are also reared in families within cultural settings. For these reasons, we need to consider possible biological, psychological, and social factors in sexual dysfunctions (Brown & Haaser, 2005). For example, biological and psychosocial factors—hormonal deficiencies, depression, dissatisfaction with one's relationship, and so on—contribute to lack of desire. Moreover, these factors can interact in a number of ways. Researchers refer to such an approach as a **biopsychosocial model**.

Biopsychosocial model An approach to explaining dysfunctions that refers to the interactions of biological, psychological, and social/cultural factors.

Biological Causes

Among the medical conditions that diminish sexual desire are testosterone deficiencies, thyroid overactivity or underactivity, and temporal lobe epilepsy. Sexual desire is stoked by testosterone, which is produced by men in the testes and both men and women in the adrenal glands (Tuiten et al., 2000). Women may experience less sexual desire when their adrenal glands are surgically removed. Low sexual interest, along with erectile difficulties, is also common among men with **hypogonadism**, which is treated with testosterone (Lue, 2000).

Hypogonadism An endocrine disorder that reduces the output of testosterone.

The reduction in testosterone levels that occurs in middle and later life may in part explain a gradual decline in sexual desire among men (Janssen, 2006; Janssen et al., 2006). However, women's sexual desire may also decline with age, because of physical and psychological changes, as we will see (Goldstein et al., 2006). Some medications, especially those used to control anxiety or hypertension, may also reduce desire. Changing medications or doses may increase the person's level of desire.

Fatigue may lead to erectile disorder and orgasmic disorder in men, and to inadequate lubrication and orgasmic disorder in women, but these will be isolated incidents unless the person attaches too much meaning to them and becomes concerned about future performance. Painful sex, however, often reflects underlying infections (Binik, 2005; Schultz et al., 2005). Medical conditions that affect sexual response include heart disease (Thompson et al., 2005), diabetes mellitus, multiple sclerosis, spinal cord injuries, complications from surgery (such as removal of the prostate in men), hormonal problems, and use of some medicines, such as those used to treat hypertension and psychiatric disorders (Byerly et al., 2006; Olfson et al., 2005; Taylor et al., 2005).

A SPECIAL WARNING ABOUT SSRI DRUGS AND SEXUAL RESPONSE People and physicians need to be aware of the sexual side effects of some drugs used to treat depression. So-called selective serotonin reuptake inhibitors—SSRIs for short—are widely prescribed not only for depression, but also for panic disorder, obsessive–compulsive disorder, anorexia nervosa, and other ills. Most physicians are aware that these drugs have "some" sexual side effects in "some" patients. However, the fact of the matter is that they almost completely impair sexual arousal in many patients, especially older patients (Clayton et al., 2006; Williams et al., 2006). Moreover, even when the patients discontinue the drugs, sexual functioning does *not* necessarily bounce back (Bolton et al., 2006; Csoka & Shipko, 2006).

The "good" news is that some drugs that are helpful with depression are less likely to impair sexual functioning. Wellbutrin, as a matter of fact, can have a positive effect on sexual functioning and is sometimes prescribed along with an SSRI to help prevent sexual side effects. Ask your physician.

A recent experimental study of depressed women using an SSRI found that for some of these women, taking Viagra helped to restore their sexual functioning (Nurnberg et al., 2008).

Researchers find that health problems can contribute to all kinds of sexual dysfunctions in men, but mostly to sexual pain in women (Barsky et al., 2006; Binik, 2005; Schultz et al., 2005). Even when biological factors are involved in sexual dysfunctions, psychological factors such as anger and depression can prolong or worsen them (Goldstein & Alexander, 2005; Mohan & Bhugra, 2005).

Cardiovascular problems can lead to erectile disorder by affecting the flow of blood to and through the penis, a problem that becomes more common as men age. Damage to the nerves involved in erection can also play a role (Goldstein, as cited in Kolata, 1998; Goldstein, as cited in Norton, 2000). Erectile problems can arise when clogged or narrow arteries leading to the penis deprive the penis of oxygen (Thompson et al., 2005). For example, erectile disorder is common among men with diabetes mellitus, a disease that can damage blood vessels and nerves. Eric Rimm (2000), of the Harvard School of Public Health, studied 2000 men and found that erectile dysfunction was connected with a large waist, physical inactivity, and drinking too much alcohol (or not having any alcohol!). The common condition among these men may be high cholesterol levels. Cholesterol can impede the flow of blood to the penis just as it impedes the flow of blood to the heart. Another study connects erectile dysfunction with heart disease and hypertension (Johannes et al., 2000). Exercise, weight loss, and eating less animal fat help lower cholesterol levels.

Similarly, aging can affect the sexual response of women. Perimenopausal and postmenopausal women usually produce less vaginal lubrication than younger women, and the vaginal walls thin—changes that can render sex painful (Dennerstein & Goldstein, 2005; Dennerstein & Hayes, 2005; Hayes & Dennerstein, 2005). These physical changes, along with negative stereotypes of older women and men, can create performance anxiety and fumbling performances, and discourage both partners from attempting sexual activity (McCabe, 2005; McCarthy & Fucito, 2005; Schultz et al., 2005). In such cases, artificial lubrication can supplement the woman's own production, and estrogen replacement may halt or reverse some of the sexual changes of aging (Goldstein & Alexander, 2005). However, partners also need to have realistic expectations and consider enjoyable sexual activities they can engage in without discomfort or high demands (McCarthy & Fucito, 2005; Mohan & Bhugra, 2005).

Middle-aged and older men might try weight control and regular exercise. The findings of the Massachusetts Male Aging Study suggest that men who exercise regularly seem to ward off erectile dysfunction (Derby, 2000). Men who burned 200 calories or more a day in physical activity—an amount that can be achieved by walking briskly for three kilometres (two miles)—cut their risk of erectile dysfunction almost in half. Exercise seems to prevent clogging of arteries, keeping them clear for the flow of blood into the penis.

Nerve damage resulting from prostate surgery may impair erectile response. Erectile disorder may also result from multiple sclerosis (MS), a disease in which nerve cells lose the protective coatings that facilitate transmission of neural messages. MS has also been implicated in male orgasmic disorder.

The bacteria that cause syphilis, an STI, can invade the spinal cord and affect the cells that control erection, resulting in erectile dysfunction. Chronic kidney disease, hypertension, cancer, emphysema, and heart disease can all impair erectile response. So can endocrine disorders that impair testosterone production (Ralph & McNicholas, 2000).

Women also develop vascular or nervous disorders that impair genital blood flow, reducing lubrication and sexual excitement, rendering intercourse painful, and reducing their ability to reach orgasm. As with men, these problems become more likely as women age.

People with sexual dysfunctions are generally advised to undergo a physical examination to determine whether their problems are biologically based. Men with erectile disorder may be evaluated in a sleep centre to determine whether they attain erections while asleep. The technique is termed *nocturnal penile* **tumescence** (NPT). Healthy men usually have erections during REM sleep, which occurs every 90 to 100 minutes. Men with biologically based erectile disorder often do not have nocturnal erections.

Prescription drugs and illicit drugs account for many cases of erectile disorder. Antidepressant medication and antipsychotic drugs may impair erectile functioning and cause orgasmic disorders (Olfson et al., 2005; Taylor et al., 2005). Tranquilizers like Valium and Xanax may cause orgasmic disorder in either sex. Some drugs used to treat high blood pressure can impair erectile response (Ralph & McNicholas, 2000). Switching to other blood pressure drugs or adjusting dosages may help. Other drugs that can lead to erectile disorder include adrenergic blockers, diuretics, cholesterol-lowering drugs ("statins"), anticonvulsants, anti-Parkinsonian drugs, and dyspepsia and ulcer-healing drugs (Ralph & McNicholas, 2000).

Central nervous system depressants such as alcohol, heroin, and methadone can reduce sexual desire and impair sexual arousal (Brown et al., 2005). Narcotics also depress testosterone production, thereby reducing sexual desire and leading to erectile failure. Marijuana use has been associated with reduced sexual desire and performance (Wilson et al., 2000).

Tumescence Swelling; erection.

Regular use of cocaine can cause erectile disorder or male orgasmic disorder and may reduce sexual desire in both women and men (Rawson et al., 2002). Some people report increased sexual pleasure from the initial use of cocaine, but repeated use can lead to dependency on the drug for sexual arousal. Long-term use may compromise the ability to experience sexual pleasure. Despite the fact that alcohol can impair sexual arousal on a given occasion, Edward Laumann and his colleagues (1999) found no general relationship between alcohol consumption and sexual dysfunctions.

HIV AND SEXUAL DYSFUNCTIONS There is little doubt that HIV/AIDS is associated with sexual dysfunction in both men and women. Men with HIV are also more likely to have hypogonadism and erectile dysfunction, which are apparently worsened by antiretroviral therapy (Crum et al., 2005). Antiretroviral therapy increases levels of estrogen in men (Lamba et al., 2004). A study of 78 seropositive gay males found a host of sexual dysfunctions, ranging from loss of interest in sex to delayed ejaculation and erectile disorder (Cove & Petrak, 2004). Because the men were more capable of obtaining and maintaining erections without condoms than with condoms, many of them used condoms inconsistently.

HIV-seropositive women, too, show various sexual dysfunctions, from lack of interest to sexual arousal disorders to orgasmic dysfunction (Florence et al., 2004). Researchers attribute the dysfunctions to psychological factors—anxiety, irritability, and depression—and to the effects of HIV.

Psychosocial Causes

Abrupt changes in sexual desire are more often explained by psychological and interpersonal factors such as depression, stress, and problems in the relationship (Bodenmann et al., 2006; Moore & Heiman, 2006). Psychological problems can contribute to low sexual desire (Bancroft et al., 2005b, 2005c). Anxiety is the most commonly reported factor. Anxiety may dampen sexual desire, including performance anxiety (anxiety over being evaluated negatively), anxiety involving fears of pleasure or loss of control, and deeper sources of anxiety relating to fears of injury (Janssen & Bancroft, 2006). Depression is also a common cause of lack of desire (Frohlich & Meston, 2002; Kuffel & Heiman, 2006; Lykins et al., 2006). A history of sexual assault has also been linked to low sexual desire (McCarthy et al., 2006).

Psychosocial factors connected with sexual dysfunctions include cultural influences, economic problems, psychosexual trauma, being gay within a heterosexual marriage, dissatisfaction with one's relationship, lack of sexual skills, irrational beliefs, and performance anxiety (Bancroft et al., 2005b; McCabe, 2005).

CULTURAL INFLUENCES Children reared in sexually repressive cultural or home environments may learn to respond to sex with feelings of anxiety and shame, rather than anticipation and pleasure (Nobre & Pinto-Gouveia, 2006). People whose parents instilled in them a sense of guilt over touching their genitals may find it difficult to accept their sex organs as sources of pleasure (McCarthy et al., 2006).

In most cultures, sexual pleasure has traditionally been a male preserve. Young women may be reared to believe that sex is a duty to be performed for their husbands, not a source of personal pleasure. Although the traditional double standard has diminished in developed countries (Fugl–Meyer et al., 2006), some girls are still exposed to repressive attitudes. Women are more likely than men to be taught to suppress sexual desires (Nobre & Pinto–Gouveia, 2006). Self-control and vigilance—not sexual awareness and acceptance—become identified as feminine virtues. Women reared with such attitudes may not learn about their sexual potentials or express their erotic desires to their partners.

Many women who are exposed to negative attitudes about sex during childhood and adolescence find it difficult to suddenly view sex as a source of pleasure and satisfaction as adults. A lifetime of learning to turn themselves off sexually may impair sexual arousal and enjoyment when an acceptable opportunity arises (Bean, 2002; Fishman & Mamo, 2001).

PSYCHOSEXUAL TRAUMA Women and men who were sexually victimized in childhood are more likely to experience difficulty in becoming sexually aroused (McCarthy et al., 2006; Mosher et al., 2005). Some learning theorists speak of conditioned anxiety in explaining sexual dysfunctions. Sexual stimuli come to elicit anxiety when they have been paired with traumatic experiences, such as rape, incest, or sexual molestation. Unresolved anger, misplaced guilt, and feelings of disgust also make it difficult for victims of sexual trauma to respond sexually, even years later and with loving partners.

SEXUAL ORIENTATION Some gay males and lesbians test their sexual orientation by developing heterosexual relationships, even by entering "Brokeback marriages," in which they rear children with partners of the other sex. Others may wish to maintain the appearance of heterosexuality to avoid the social stigma attached to a gay sexual orientation. In such cases, problems with heterosexual partners can signify lack of heteroerotic interest (McCarthy et al., 2006).

INEFFECTIVE SEXUAL TECHNIQUES In some relationships, couples fall into a narrow sexual routine because one partner controls the timing and sequence of sexual techniques. A woman who remains unknowledgeable about the erotic importance of her clitoris may be unlikely to seek direct clitoral stimulation. A man who responds to one erectile failure by trying to force an erection may be unintentionally setting himself up for repeated failure. The couple who fail to communicate their sexual preferences or to experiment with new techniques may find themselves losing interest. Brevity of foreplay and coitus may contribute to female orgasmic disorder.

EMOTIONAL FACTORS Orgasm involves a sudden loss of voluntary control. Fear of losing control or "letting go" may block sexual arousal. Other emotional factors, especially depression, are often implicated in sexual dysfunctions (Ralph & McNicholas, 2000). Depression can contribute to lack of sexual desire (Frohlich & Meston, 2002). Stress can also interfere with sexual interest and response.

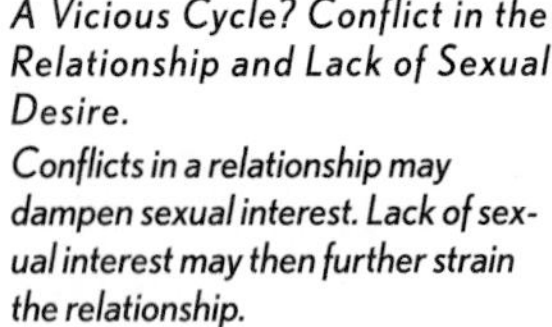

A Vicious Cycle? Conflict in the Relationship and Lack of Sexual Desire.
Conflicts in a relationship may dampen sexual interest. Lack of sexual interest may then further strain the relationship.

Sex therapy A collective term for short-term behavioural models for treatment of sexual dysfunctions.

PROBLEMS IN THE RELATIONSHIP Problems in the relationship are not easily left at the bedroom door (McCarthy et al., 2006; Moore & Heiman, 2006). Heterosexual and homosexual couples alike usually find that sex is no better than other facets of their relationship (Matthews et al., 2006). Partners who have general trouble communicating may also be unable to communicate their sexual desires. Couples who harbour resentments may make sex their combat arena. They may fail to become aroused by their partners or "withhold" orgasm to make their partners feel guilty or inadequate (Firestone et al., 2006b).

The following case highlights how sexual dysfunctions can develop against the backdrop of a troubled relationship:

> After living together for six months, Paul and Petula are contemplating marriage. But a problem has brought them to a **sex therapy** clinic. As Petula puts it, "For the last two months he hasn't been able to keep his erection after he enters me." Paul is 26, and a lawyer; Petula, 24, is a buyer for a large department store. They both grew up in middle-class, suburban families, were introduced through mutual friends and began having intercourse, without difficulty, a few months into their relationship. At Petula's urging, Paul moved into her apartment, although he wasn't sure he was ready for such a step. A week later he began to have difficulty maintaining his erection during intercourse, although he felt strong desires for his partner. When his erection waned, he would try again, but would lose his desire and be unable to achieve another erection. After a few times like this, Petula would become so angry that she began striking Paul in the chest and screaming at him. Paul, who at 200 pounds weighed more than twice as much as Petula, would just walk away, which angered Petula even more.
>
> It became clear that sex was not the only trouble spot in their relationship. Petula complained that he preferred to be with his friends and go to baseball games than to spend time with her. When they were together at home, he would become absorbed in watching sports events on television, and showed no interest in activities she enjoyed—attending the theatre, visiting museums, etc. Since there was no evidence that the sexual difficulty was due to either organic problems or depression, a diagnosis of male erectile disorder was given. Neither Paul nor Petula was willing to discuss their nonsexual problems with a therapist. While the sexual problem was treated successfully with a form of sex therapy modelled after techniques developed by Masters and Johnson [see discussion later in the chapter] and the couple later married, Paul's ambivalence continued well into their marriage, and there were future recurrences of sexual problems as well. (Adapted from Spitzer et al., 1989, pp. 149–150)

LACK OF SEXUAL SKILLS Sexual competency involves sexual knowledge and skills that are acquired through learning. We generally learn what makes us and others feel good through trial and error, and by talking and reading about sex. Some people may not develop sexual competency because of a lack of opportunity to acquire knowledge and experience—even within a committed relationship. People with sexual dysfunctions may have been reared in families in which discussions of sexuality were off limits, and early sexual experimentation was harshly punished. University of Ottawa researchers (Reissing et al., 2005) found that women who had higher sexual self-efficacy (confidence in their sexual abilities) had fewer sexual problems.

IRRATIONAL BELIEFS Irrational beliefs and attitudes may contribute to sexual dysfunctions. We cannot expect our partners to read our minds. We cannot assume that if they truly cared for us, they would know what we need, or want. Communication is one of the keys to sexual satisfaction.

PERFORMANCE ANXIETY Anxiety—especially performance anxiety—plays an important role in sexual dysfunctions (Bancroft et al., 2005b; McCabe, 2005). Performance anxiety occurs when a person becomes overly concerned with how well he or she performs a certain act or task. Performance anxiety may place a dysfunctional individual in a spectator role rather than a performer role. Rather than focusing on erotic sensations and allowing reflexes like erection, lubrication, and orgasm to occur naturally, he or she focuses on self-doubts and thinks, "Will I be able to do it this time? Will this be another failure?"

In men, performance anxiety can inhibit erection and trigger a premature ejaculation as well (Bancroft et al., 2005b; Hellstrom et al., 2006; Janssen & Bancroft, 2006). Erection, mediated by the parasympathetic nervous system, can be blocked by activation of the sympathetic nervous system in the form of anxiety. Because ejaculation, like anxiety, is mediated by the sympathetic nervous system, arousal of this system in the form of anxiety can increase the level of stimulation and thereby heighten the potential for premature ejaculation.

In women, performance anxiety can reduce vaginal lubrication and contribute to orgasmic disorder (Goldstein et al., 2006). Women with performance anxieties may try to force an orgasm, only to find that the harder they try, the more elusive it becomes.

OTHER FACTORS Researchers from the University of Western Ontario (Gruszecki et al., 2005), using data from the Canadian Contraceptive Study, found a number of factors relating to common sexual concerns in women. Higher body weight was associated with low sexual desire and infrequent coital orgasm. These sexual issues could also be due to health as well as self-esteem issues connected to body weight. Married women, older women, and those with higher levels of educations were also more likely to report low desire.

A World of Diversity

SEXUAL DYSFUNCTIONS: CULTURAL COMPARISONS

Researchers conducted an international survey to determine the prevalence of sexual dysfunctions among adults aged 40 to 80 years (Nicolosi et al., 2004). Data were collected from 27 500 men and women in 29 countries. More than 80% of the men and 65% of the women had sexual intercourse during the past year. The most common dysfunctions for men were early ejaculation (14%) and erectile difficulties (10%). Among the women the most frequent were a lack of sexual interest (21%), inability to reach orgasm (16%), and lubrication difficulties (16%). Overall, 28% of the men and 39% of the women said that they were affected by at least one sexual dysfunction. The prevalence of dysfunctions increased with age.

Among the men, problems with early ejaculation were most common in the Asian and South and Central American countries, while erectile difficulties were highest in Asia. The prevalence of erectile difficulties greatly increased with age. Among women, the highest frequencies of sexual problems were in Asia and the Middle East (Nicolosi et al., 2004).

Vancouver researchers Jane Woo and Lori Brotto (in press) found with a sample of university students in British Columbia that Asian Canadians reported more sexual problems such as sexual avoidance and sexual dissatisfaction. Among the women, Asians experienced a greater number of vaginismus and orgasm difficulties. However, those who identified more with Western culture such as by having more open attitudes toward sex were less likely to have these sexual problems. They also could communicate more easily with a partner about sex. These findings suggest that a person's personal beliefs about sexuality can override the general cultural beliefs of one's ethnic group.

Treatment of Sexual Dysfunctions

In sex therapy, the most common models are cognitive and behavioural. Sex therapy aims to modify dysfunctional cognitions (beliefs and attitudes) and behaviour as directly and quickly as possible. Sex therapists also recognize the roles of childhood conflicts and the quality of the partners' relationship. Therefore, they draw upon various forms of therapy as needed (Adams, 2006; Kleinplatz, 2003; Corty, 2006).

Although the particular approaches vary, sex therapies aim to

1. Change self-defeating beliefs and attitudes
2. Teach sexual skills
3. Enhance sexual knowledge
4. Improve sexual communication
5. Reduce performance anxiety

Sex therapy usually involves both partners, although individual therapy is preferred in some cases. Therapists find that granting people "permission" to experiment sexually or discuss negative attitudes about sex helps many people overcome sexual problems without the need for more intensive therapy. Some therapists encourage their clients to view educational sex videos as an enhancement to the therapy program. Ottawa therapist Peggy Kleinplatz (1997) believes that these videos can help couples to communicate more effectively about their sexual desires and problems.

Today, biological treatments have also been emerging for various sexual dysfunctions. Since 1998, most public attention has been focused on Viagra, a drug that is helpful in most cases of erectile dysfunction. But biological treatments are also emerging for premature ejaculation, female orgasmic dysfunction, and lack of sexual desire.

An important issue in therapy is gender. Many therapists have adopted feminist perspectives in their practice in order to challenge sexist ways of thinking. Calgary therapists Mary Valentich and James Gripton (1992) have broadened this approach to encompass a gender-sensitive practice. This involves analyzing gender issues facing both women and men and critiquing how traditional gender roles restrict the sexual fulfillment of both genders. Such analysis encourages people to find their own ways of expressing love and sex so that they don't have to follow the traditional gender scripts.

Use of Explicit Videos in Sex Therapy.
Some sex therapists encourage clients to view instructional sex videos to enhance their lovemaking skills. This video, The Joy of Erotic Massage, *is part of the Better Sex Video Library produced by the Sinclair Institute (www.sinclairwholesale.com).*

Sensate focus exercises Exercises in which sex partners take turns giving and receiving pleasurable stimulation in nongenital areas of the body.

In the next section we will explore both psychological and behavioural approaches to the treatment of sexual dysfunctions. Let us begin with the groundbreaking work of Masters and Johnson.

The Masters-and-Johnson Approach

Masters and Johnson pioneered the use of direct behavioural approaches to treating sexual dysfunctions (Masters & Johnson, 1970). A female–male therapy team focuses on the couple as the unit of treatment during a two-week residential program. Masters and Johnson consider the couple, not the individual, dysfunctional. A couple may describe the husband's erectile disorder as the problem, but this problem is likely to have led to problems in the couple by the time they seek therapy. Similarly, a man whose wife has an orgasmic disorder is likely to be anxious about his ability to provide effective sexual stimulation.

Anxieties and resentments are aired, but the focus of treatment is behavioural change. Couples perform daily sexual homework assignments, such as **sensate focus exercises**, in the privacy of their own rooms.

Sensate focus sessions are carried out in the nude. Partners take turns giving and receiving stimulation in nongenital areas of the body. Without touching the breasts or genitals, the giver massages or fondles the receiving partner in order to provide pleasure under relaxing and nondemanding conditions. Because genital activity is restricted, there is no pressure to "perform." The giving partner is freed to engage in trial-and-error learning about the receiving partner's sensate preferences. The receiving partner is freed to enjoy the experience without feeling rushed to reciprocate or obliged to perform by becoming sexually aroused. The receiving partner's only responsibility is to direct the giving partner as needed. In addition to these general sensate focus exercises, Masters and Johnson used specific assignments designed to help couples overcome particular sexual dysfunctions.

Integration of Sex Therapy and Psychotherapy

Sex therapy, as noted, has cognitive components, for example, addressing self-defeating attitudes and expectations, and sex education. Because sexual activity is so often embedded in relationships, many therapists (e.g., Coyle, 2006; McCarthy et al., 2004, 2006) use psychotherapy and couples therapy to help couples learn how

Working With Lesbians, Gays, and Bisexuals. *Couples therapists who work with LGBs (lesbian, gay, and bisexual couples) will find many problems akin to those of heterosexual couples, but some will reflect the sexual orientations of the members of the couple; for example, LGB identity development, gays as parents, and so on.*

Applied Knowledge

HOW DO YOU FIND A QUALIFIED SEX THERAPIST?

How would you locate a sex therapist if you had a sexual dysfunction? Since the provinces do not regulate use of the term *sex therapist*, it is essential to determine that a sex therapist is a member of a recognized profession (such as psychology, social work, medicine, or marriage and family counselling) and has had training and supervision in sex therapy. Professionals are usually licensed or certified by their provinces. (All provinces require licensing of psychologists and physicians, but some provinces do not license social workers or marriage counsellors.) Only physicians are permitted to bill their provincial health plans for providing sex therapy services.

If you are uncertain how to locate a qualified sex therapist in your area, try your university or college psychology department, health department, or counselling centre; a medical or psychological association; a marriage and family therapy association; a family physician; or your instructor.

Relatively few people in Canada have been trained as specialists in sex therapy. The only Canadian organization that certifies sex therapists is the Board of Examiners in Sex Therapy and Counselling in Ontario (BESTCO), comprising professionals from diverse backgrounds with clinical expertise in human sexual concerns.

Some Canadian therapists are also certified by American-based organizations such as the American Association of Sex Educators, Counselors, and Therapists (AASECT) and the Society for Sex Therapy and Research (SSTAR).

Ethical professionals are not annoyed or embarrassed if you ask them (1) what their profession is, (2) where they earned their advanced degree, and (3) whether they are licensed or certified, or if you inquire about (4) their fees, (5) their plans for treatment, and (6) their training in human sexuality and sex therapy. These questions are important because there is such a wide diversity in the professional background and training of sex therapists. Accordingly, the type of treatments and services that are available vary enormously (Kleinplatz, 2003). If the therapist becomes uncomfortable, asks why you are asking such questions, or fails to provide a direct answer, beware.

Professionals are also prohibited, by the ethical principles of their professions, from engaging in unethical practices, such as sexual relations with their clients. Any therapist who makes a sexual overture toward a client, or tries to persuade a client to engage in sexual relations, is acting unethically.

to share the power in relationships, how to improve sexual communication, and how to negotiate differences. The combination of sex therapy and couples therapy appears to be a powerful tool for enhancing relationships as well as sex lives.

Helen Singer Kaplan (1974) combined sex therapy with psychoanalytic methods. She saw sexual dysfunctions as having *immediate* causes and *remote* causes (conflicts that date to childhood). As a sex therapist, Kaplan focused on improving the couple's sexual communication, eliminating performance anxiety, and fostering sexual skills and knowledge. As a psychoanalyst, she used insight-oriented therapy when it appeared that remote issues impaired response to sex therapy. By so doing, she aimed to bring to awareness unconscious conflicts that might have stifled the person's sexual desire or response.

Let us now consider some of the specific techniques that sex therapists have introduced in treating several of the major types of sexual dysfunctions.

Treatment of Sexual Desire Disorders

Some sex therapists help kindle the sexual appetites of people with hypoactive sexual desire by prescribing self-stimulation exercises combined with erotic fantasies. Sex therapists may also assist dysfunctional couples by prescribing sensate focus exercises, enhancing communication, and expanding the couple's repertoire of sexual skills. Sex therapists recognize that hypoactive sexual desire is often a complex problem that requires more intensive treatment than problems of the arousal or orgasm phases. Helen Singer Kaplan (1987) argues that insight-oriented approaches are especially helpful in the treatment of hypoactive sexual desire and sexual aversion to uncover and resolve deep-seated psychological conflicts.

Some cases of hypoactive sexual desire in men involve hormonal deficiencies, especially deficiencies in testosterone. But testosterone replacement therapy works with only about half of men who have low testosterone levels (Rakic et al., 1997). Among women, as among men, lack of sexual desire can be connected with low levels of androgens, and testosterone shows promise in heightening desire (Tuiten et al., 2000).

Researchers (van Anders et al., 2005) in London, Ontario, found that testosterone-treated women showed a significant increase in sexual desire for both masturbation and partner sex. Sexual desire increased even among women who did not have hormonal deficiency.

When lack of desire is connected with depression, sexual interests may rebound when the depression lifts. Treatment in such cases may involve psychotherapy or chemotherapy, not sex therapy per se. When problems in the relationship are involved, marital or couples therapy may be indicated to improve the relationship. Once interpersonal problems are ironed out, sexual interest may return.

Treatment of sexual aversion disorder may involve a multifaceted approach, including biological treatments, such as the use of medications to reduce anxiety, and psychological treatments designed to help the individual overcome the underlying sexual phobia. Couples therapy may be used in cases in which sexual aversions arise from problems in relationships (Gold & Gold, 1993). Sensate focus exercises may be used to lessen generalized anxiety about sexual contact. But fears of specific aspects of the sexual act may need to be overcome through behavioural exercises in which the client learns to manage the stimuli that evoke fears of sexual contact:

> Bridget, 26, and Bryan, 30, had been married for four years but had never consummated their relationship because Bridget would panic whenever Bryan attempted coitus with her. Although she enjoyed foreplay and was capable of achieving orgasm with clitoral stimulation, her fears of sexual contact were triggered by Bryan's attempts at vaginal penetration. The therapist employed a program of gradual exposure to the feared stimuli to allow Bridget the opportunity to overcome her fears in small, graduated steps. First she was instructed to view her genitals in a mirror when she was alone—this in order to violate her long-standing prohibition against looking at and enjoying her body. This exercise initially made her feel anxious, but with repeated exposure she became comfortable performing it and then progressed to touching her genitals directly. When she became comfortable with this step, and reported experiencing pleasurable erotic sensations, she was instructed to insert a finger into the vagina. She encountered intense anxiety at this step and required daily practice for two weeks before she could tolerate inserting her finger into her vagina without discomfort. Her husband was then brought into the treatment process. The couple was instructed to have Bridget insert her own finger in her vagina while Bryan watched. When she was comfortable with this exercise, she then guided his finger into her vagina. Later he placed one and then two fingers into her vagina, while she controlled the depth, speed, and duration of penetration. When she felt ready, they proceeded to attempt penile penetration in the female-superior position, which allowed her to maintain control over penetration. Over time, Bridget became more comfortable with penetration to the point where the couple developed a normal sexual relationship. (Adapted from Kaplan, 1987, pp. 102–103)

Treatment of Sexual Arousal Disorders

Men with chronic erectile disorder may believe that they have "forgotten" how to have an erection. Erection, however, is an involuntary reflex, not a skill.

Figure 13.1 The Training Position Recommended by Masters and Johnson for Treatment of Erectile Disorder and Premature Ejaculation.

By lying in front of her partner, who has his legs spread, the woman has ready access to his genitals. In one part of a program designed to overcome erectile disorder, she repeatedly "teases" him to erection and allows the erection to subside. Thus she avoids creating performance anxiety that could lead to loss of erection. Through repeated regaining of erection, the man loses his fear that loss of erection means it will not return.

In sex therapy, women who have trouble becoming lubricated and men with erectile problems learn that they need not "do" anything to become sexually aroused. As long as their problems are psychologically and not organically based, they need only receive sexual stimulation under relaxed circumstances so that anxiety does not inhibit their natural reflexes.

In order to reduce performance anxiety, the partners engage in nondemanding sexual contacts—contacts that do not demand lubrication or erection. They may start with nongenital sensate focus exercises in the style of Masters and Johnson. After a couple of sessions, sensate focus extends to the genitals. The position shown in Figure 13.1 allows the woman easy access to her partner's genitals. She repeatedly "teases" him to erection and allows the erection to subside. Thus she avoids creating performance anxiety that could lead to loss of erection. By repeatedly regaining his erection, the man loses the fear that loss of erection means it will not return. He learns also to focus on erotic sensations for their own sake. He experiences no demand to perform, because the couple is instructed to refrain from coitus.

Even when the dysfunctional partner can reliably become sexually excited (denoted by erection in the male and lubrication in the female), the couple does not immediately attempt coitus; this might rekindle performance anxiety. Rather, the couple engages in a series of nondemanding, pleasurable sexual activities, which eventually culminate in coitus.

In Masters and Johnson's approach, the couple begin coitus after about 10 days of treatment. The woman teases the man to erection while she is sitting above him, straddling his thighs. When he is erect, *she* inserts the penis (to avoid fumbling attempts at entry) and moves slowly back and forth in a *nondemanding way.* Neither attempts to reach orgasm. If erection is lost, teasing and coitus are repeated. Once the couple become confident that erection can be retained—or reinstated if lost—they may increase coital thrusting gradually to reach orgasm.

BIOLOGICAL APPROACHES TO TREATMENT OF ERECTILE DISORDER The world's attention has recently been focused on biological approaches to treating erectile disorder. Biological or biomedical approaches are helpful in treating erectile disorder, especially when organic factors are involved.

Oral medications are by far the most popular biological treatment of erectile problems. Oral forms of several compounds—sildenafil (Viagra), vardenafil (Levitra), and tadalafil (Cialis)—relax the muscles that surround the small blood vessels in the penis, allowing them to dilate so that blood can flow into them more freely. After taking the drug, the man must still be aroused through manual or oral stimulation, and so on, for an erection to occur. The amount of time that it takes for the drug to become effective varies with the drug. Viagra can become effective within half an hour and is effective for up to four hours. The oral form of tadalafil (Cialis) becomes effective in about half an hour and lasts up to 36 hours. Users in France dubbed it "the weekend pill."

The most common side effects of these drugs are facial flushing, stuffy nose, and headaches including in some cases migraine headaches. These drugs should not be used by individuals taking any type of nitrate drug, such as nitroglycerine, due to the risk of developing potentially life-threatening low blood pressure.

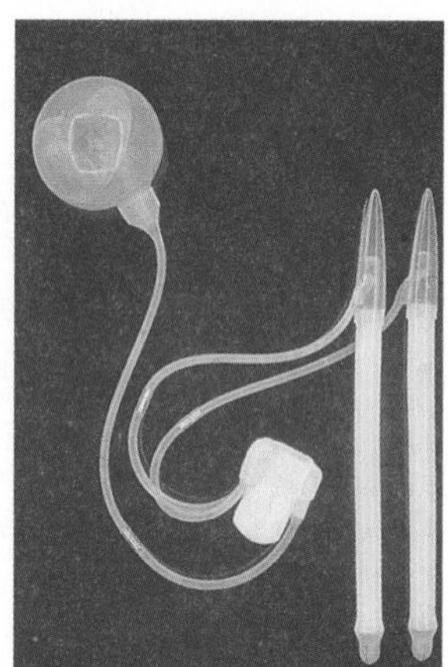

Figure 13.2 A Penile Implant.

Penile implants provide erection when the man's cardiovascular system does not do the job. This implant consists of cylinders that are implanted in the penis. A fluid reservoir (top left) is placed near the bladder. A pump (lower middle) is typically inserted in the scrotum. Squeezing the pump forces fluid into the cylinders, inflating the penis. Tripping a release valve later returns the fluid to the reservoir, deflating the penis.

Viagra was hailed as a miracle drug when it hit the market in early 1998. It sold faster than any new drug had ever sold. A study published in the *New England Journal of Medicine* tested the effects of Viagra on more than 800 men with erectile dysfunction due both to psychological causes and to a number of organic causes (Goldstein et al., 1998). In one phase of the study, 69% of attempts to engage in intercourse were successful for men taking Viagra, compared to 22% for men taking a placebo. A Canadian study (Carrier et al., 2005) found that Viagra was still effective after three years.

In a study by Bill Fisher of the University of Western Ontario and colleagues (2005), many women whose partners had erectile dysfunction reported that they also experienced diminished sexual desire, arousal, orgasm, and sexual satisfaction. A significant proportion of women whose partners used an erection drug experienced increased sexual desire, arousal, and orgasm.

Next in popularity to oral medications are hormone treatments. Testosterone helps restore the sex drive and erectile ability in many men with abnormally low levels of testosterone (Lue, 2000; Rakic et al., 1997). There is no evidence that hormone therapy helps men who already have normal hormone levels.

Various other treatments are available, such as vascular surgery of the penis, penile implants (Figure 13.2), penile injections, penile suppositories, and a vacuum pump held over the penis to increase blood flow. However, relatively few men use these techniques as they are not very practical or comfortable to use.

FEMALE SEXUAL AROUSAL DISORDER Psychological treatments for female sexual arousal disorder parallel those for orgasmic disorder and are discussed in the following pages. Here let us briefly note that they involve sex education (labelling the parts, discussing their functions, and explaining how to arouse them), searching out and coping with possible cognitive interference (such as negative sexual attitudes), creating nondemanding situations in which sexual arousal may occur, and—when appropriate—working on problems in the relationship.

Applied Knowledge

THINKING CRITICALLY ABOUT BUYING VIAGRA AND OTHER DRUGS ONLINE

Viagra, Levitra, and Cialis are prescription drugs. Many men who might otherwise use these drugs are reluctant to discuss erectile dysfunction with their physicians. The anonymity of doing things on the net is a lure—you don't have to admit your personal worries to your doctor face to face. Some men, unfortunately, do not even have a regular physician. What to do?

Many have discovered that by searching *Viagra* on the net, they can find many websites where they can "consult" with online physicians, obtain a prescription, and order the drug for home delivery. Easy! A few questions and a fee, and they've got it. But is it wise? Perhaps, perhaps not.

Prescriptions are needed for various drugs because physicians are better equipped than most laypeople to diagnose an individual's health problems, understand the chemical nature and side effects of the drugs available for treatment, and predict how the drugs will affect the individual patient. The physicians are also usually prepared to deal with the unexpected effects of the drugs, and there can be many.

So ask yourself what kind of physician will prescribe drugs online, without personally knowing the patient. Is it possible that some of them would have difficulty establishing a private practice or getting a job in a hospital? If you have a question about the drug once you use it, will you be able to get back to the prescriber easily for an answer, or will you wind up making an embarrassed call to your own physician—or a trip to the emergency room?

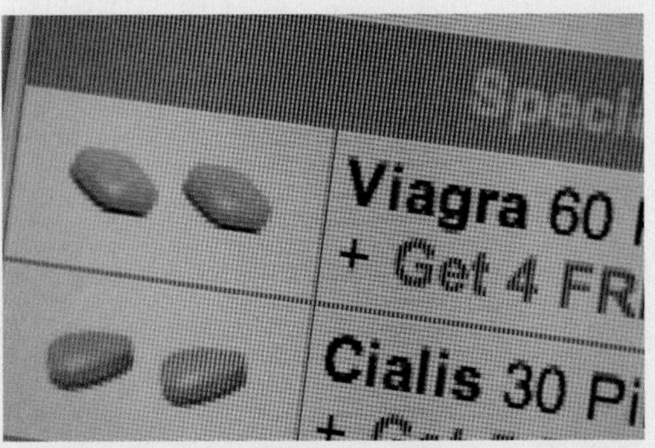

Should You Buy Viagra Online?
Many websites enable men to consult with physicians and order Viagra online. Is it wise to purchase Viagra—or other prescription drugs—online? Prescriptions are needed for drugs when the person's diagnosis is in question and when the drugs have side effects. Physicians are better equipped than most laypeople to diagnose health problems, understand the chemical composition and effects of drugs, and predict how drugs will affect the individual.

While surfing the net, you will also come across sites that claim to have "natural" preparations (including a variety of herbs) that are as effective as Viagra, but without the side effects and without the need to get a prescription. Use some critical thinking: Are you convinced of the effectiveness and safety of these preparations? Because they are foods (sort of) rather than drugs, they escape the scrutiny of government regulators. That is, the government is not watching over them. Be warned.

In sum, even if it is convenient to buy a drug online, you are well advised to get your prescription face to face—from a doctor you know and trust.

Yet many cases of female sexual arousal disorder reflect impaired blood flow to the genitals, just as in erectile disorder. Female sexual arousal involves vaginal lubrication, which permits sexual intercourse without a great deal of pain-causing friction. Lubrication is made possible by vasocongestion—the flow of blood into the genitals. Lack of lubrication can reflect the physical effects of aging, menopause, or surgically induced menopause.

Sometimes all that is necessary to deal with lack of lubrication is an artificial lubricant such as K-Y Jelly. But lessened blood flow to the genitals can also sap sexual pleasure and, as a consequence, lessen a woman's desire for sex.

Just as biological treatments for erectile disorder are mushrooming, so are biological treatments for female sexual arousal disorder. For example, drugs identical or similar to those used for men are being investigated for use with women.

In a study with 35 women, Berman (2000) found they reported greater vaginal lubrication and stronger orgasms after using Viagra. However, in a large survey of estrogen-deficient women, Basson and her colleagues (2002) found that Viagra was not effective in increasing sexual desire. Likewise, in a separate laboratory study of 35 postmenopausal women, British Columbia researchers Rosemary Basson and

Figure 13.3 A Clitoral Device That Stimulates Genital Vasocongestion in Women by Creating (Gentle) Suction Over the Clitoris.

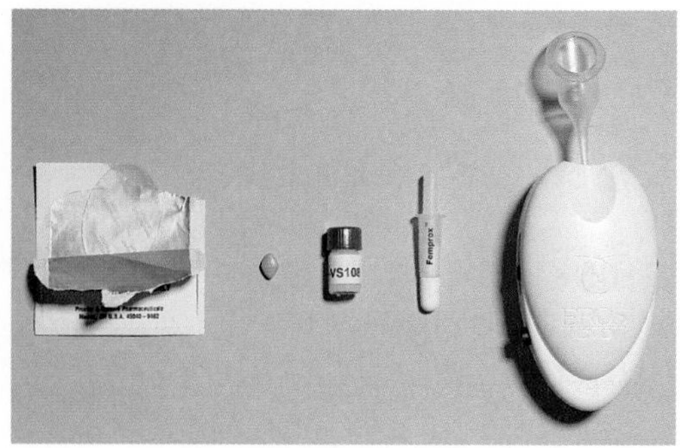

Lori Brotto (2003) found that in general, Viagra did not help those with sexual arousal and orgasm problems. However, improvement was seen among a subgroup who did not have vaginal engorgement during sexual arousal. More research needs to be done to determine the effect of drugs such as Viagra on women's sexual functioning.

Other treatments for women include, for example, testosterone injections. There is even a device—Eros—that creates "gentle" suction over the clitoris, increasing vasocongestion and sexual sensations (see Figure 13.3).

Canadian sex therapists Peggy Kleinplatz (2003) and Rosemary Basson (2000) have been very vocal in their opposition to what they view as the "medicalization of female sexuality." Indeed, it is important to note that there are often other factors involved in cases of sexual dysfunction, such as intimacy and relationship issues, and that if these are not addressed the sexual problem will likely persist.

Orgasmic Disorders

Women who have never experienced orgasm often harbour negative sexual attitudes that cause anxiety and inhibit sexual response. Treatment in such cases may first address these attitudes.

Masters and Johnson use a couples-oriented approach in treating anorgasmic women. They begin with sensate focus exercises. Then, during genital massage and later during coitus, the woman guides her partner in the caresses and movements that she finds sexually exciting. Taking charge helps free the woman from the traditional stereotype of the passive, subordinate female role.

Innovative Canadian Research

SEX THERAPY ON THE INTERNET

Eric Ochs and Yitzchak Binik of McGill University (2000) developed a computer program called Sexpert that provides online sexual counselling for couples. The Sexpert program asks couples detailed questions about their sexual behaviours, including initiation, foreplay, intercourse positions, and afterplay, and nonsexual aspects of their relationship. This interactive program gives couples feedback about their responses and provides information about related aspects of sexual functioning.

In their evaluative studies of Sexpert, Ochs and Binik (2000) found that although participants' initial reactions to the idea were negative, couples who used the program reported positive changes in foreplay activities and improved communication about sex. These couples rated the program more highly than sex education books or videos, but less highly than a therapist.

Applied Knowledge

PROMOTING EROTICISM IN SEX THERAPY

Ottawa sex therapist Peggy Kleinplatz (2003) has developed an innovative approach to sex therapy. She argues that most sex therapy is too focused on treating symptoms and solving problems. Instead, therapists should focus on personal growth, which includes enhancing sexual relationships and erotic potential. Kleinplatz is especially concerned about the focus on pills and devices. The medical model emphasizes performance measures such as frequency and firmness of erections and ignores the quality of interactions (e.g., satisfaction, intimacy). Kleinplatz presents a more thorough critique of the field of sex therapy in her 2001 book, *New Directions in Sex Therapy: Innovations and Alternatives*.

Kleinplatz believes that many therapists are personally uncomfortable with promoting eroticism, and attempt only to enable couples to engage in the mechanics of sexual intercourse rather than helping them maximize sexual pleasure (Kleinplatz, 2001). This mechanical approach results in sexual boredom for many couples, who come to rely on specific routines for achieving orgasm and then are afraid to risk trying new, and possibly more fulfilling, approaches.

According to Kleinplatz (2003), many couples want to excite their partners and establish a deep, sensual connection that will bring more intense sexual ecstasy. Eroticism, in Kleinplatz's view, is the key to maintaining sexual desire. The erotic encounter should focus on pleasure for its own sake rather than the tension release of orgasm (Kleinplatz, 2003).

Masters and Johnson recommend a training position (see Figure 13.4) that gives the man access to his partner's breasts and genitals. She can guide his hands to show him the types of stimulation she enjoys. The genital play is *nondemanding*. The goal is to learn to provide and enjoy effective sexual stimulation, not to reach orgasm. The clitoris is not stimulated early, because doing so may produce a high level of stimulation before the woman is prepared.

After a number of occasions of genital play, the couple has coitus in the female-superior position (see Figure 13.5). This position allows the woman freedom of movement and control over her genital sensations. She is told to regard the penis as her "toy." The couple engage in several sessions of deliberately slow thrusting to

Figure 13.4 The Training Position for Nondemanding Stimulation of the Female Genitals.

This position gives the man access to his partner's breasts and genitals. She can guide his hands to show him what types of stimulation she enjoys.

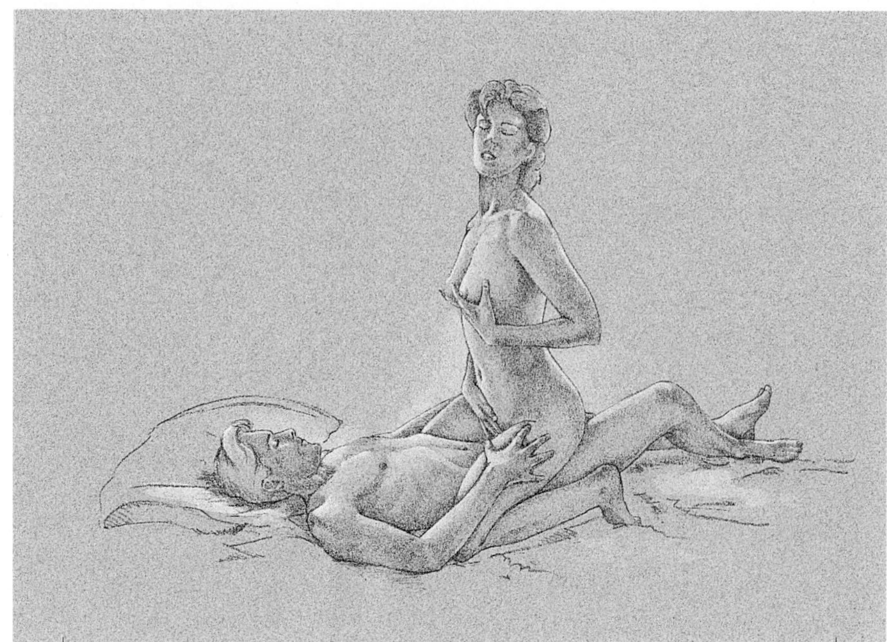

Figure 13.5 Coitus in the Female-Superior Position.

In treatment of female orgasmic disorder, the couple undertake coitus in the female-superior position after a number of occasions of genital play. This position allows the woman freedom of movement and control over her genital sensations. She is told to regard the penis as her "toy." The couple engage in several sessions of deliberately slow thrusting to sensitize the woman to sensations produced by the penis and to break the common counterproductive pattern of desperate, rapid thrusting.

sensitize the woman to sensations produced by the penis and break the common counterproductive pattern of desperate, rapid thrusting.

Orgasm cannot be willed or forced. When a woman receives effective stimulation, feels free to focus on erotic sensations, and feels that nothing is being demanded of her, she will generally reach orgasm. Once the woman is able to attain orgasm in the female-superior position, the couple may extend their sexual repertoire to other positions.

Masters and Johnson prefer working with the couple in cases of anorgasmia. Other sex therapists prefer to begin working with the woman individually and suggest masturbation as therapy.

Our focus has been on sexual techniques, but it is worth noting that a combination of approaches that focus on sexual techniques and underlying interpersonal problems may be more effective than focusing on sexual techniques alone, at least for couples whose relationships are troubled.

MALE ORGASMIC DISORDER Treatment of male orgasmic disorder generally focuses on increasing sexual stimulation and reducing performance anxiety. Masters and Johnson instruct the couple to practise sensate focus exercises for several days, during which the man makes no attempt to ejaculate. The couple is then instructed to bring the man to orgasm in any way they can, usually by the woman's stroking his penis. Once the husband can ejaculate in the woman's presence, she brings him to the point at which he is about to ejaculate. Then, in the female-superior position, she inserts the penis and thrusts vigorously to bring him to orgasm.

PREMATURE EJACULATION In the Masters-and-Johnson approach, sensate focus exercises are followed by practice in the training position shown in Figure 13.1. The woman teases her partner to erection and uses the **squeeze technique** when he indicates that he is about to ejaculate. She squeezes the tip of the penis, which temporarily prevents ejaculation. This process is repeated three or four times in a 15- to 20-minute session before the man purposely ejaculates.

Squeeze technique A method for treating premature ejaculation whereby the tip of the penis is squeezed to prevent ejaculation temporarily.

In the squeeze technique (which should be used only following personal instruction from a sex therapist), the woman holds the penis between the thumb and first two fingers of the same hand. The thumb presses against the frenulum. The fingers straddle the coronal ridge on the other side of the penis. Squeezing the

Applied Knowledge

MASTURBATION PROGRAMS FOR WOMEN IN SEX THERAPY

Masturbation provides women with opportunities to learn about their own bodies at their own pace. It frees them of the need to rely on a partner or to please a partner. The sexual pleasure they experience helps counter lingering sexual anxieties. Although there is some variation among therapists, the following elements are commonly found in directed masturbation programs:

1. *Education.* The woman and her partner (if she has one) are educated about female sexuality.
2. *Self-exploration.* Self-exploration is encouraged as a way of increasing the woman's sense of body awareness. She may hold a mirror between her legs to locate her sexual anatomic features.
3. *Self-massage.* The woman creates a private, relaxing setting for self-massage. She begins to explore the sensitivity of her body to touch, discovering and repeating the caresses she finds pleasurable. Non-alcohol-based oils and lotions may be used to enhance the sensuous quality of the massage and to provide lubrication for the external genitalia. To prevent performance anxiety, the woman does not attempt to reach orgasm during the first few occasions.
4. *Giving oneself permission.* The woman may be advised to challenge lingering guilt and anxiety about sex. For example, she might repeat to herself, "This is my body. I have a right to learn about my body and receive pleasure from it."
5. *Use of fantasy.* Arousal is heightened through the use of sexual images, fantasies, and fantasy aids, such as erotic written or visual materials.
6. *Use of a vibrator.* A vibrator may provide more intense stimulation.
7. *Involvement of the partner.* After the woman is capable of regularly achieving orgasm through masturbation, the focus may shift to her sexual relationship with her partner. Nondemanding sensate focus exercises may be followed by nondemanding coitus. The female-superior position is often used so that the woman can control the depth, angle, and rate of thrusting. She thus ensures that she receives the kinds of stimulation she needs to reach orgasm.

thumb and forefingers together fairly hard for about 20 seconds (or until the man's urge to ejaculate passes) prevents ejaculation. The erect penis can withstand fairly strong pressure without discomfort, but erection may be partially lost.

After two or three days of these sessions, Masters and Johnson have the couple begin coitus in the female-superior position because it creates less pressure to ejaculate. The woman inserts the penis. At first she contains it without thrusting, allowing the man to get used to intravaginal sensations. If he signals that he is about to ejaculate, she lifts off and squeezes the penis. After some repetitions, she begins slowly to move backward and forward, lifting off and squeezing as needed. The man learns gradually to tolerate higher levels of sexual stimulation without ejaculating.

The alternating "stop–start" method for treating premature ejaculation was introduced by urologist James Semans (1956). The method can be applied to manual stimulation or coitus. For example, the woman can manually stimulate her partner until he is about to ejaculate. He then signals her to suspend sexual stimulation and allows his arousal to subside before stimulation is resumed. This process enables the man to recognize the cues that precede his point of ejaculatory inevitability, or "point of no return," and to tolerate longer periods of sexual stimulation. When the stop–start technique is applied to coitus, the couple begin with simple vaginal containment with no pelvic thrusting, preferably in the female-superior position. The man withdraws if he feels he is about to ejaculate. As the man's sense of control increases, thrusting can begin, along with variations in coital positions. The couple again stop when the man signals that he is approaching ejaculatory inevitability.

Gay men also face problems with premature ejaculation when engaging in anal sex. Their partners could use either the squeeze technique or the stop–start method.

BIOLOGICAL TREATMENT OF PREMATURE EJACULATION Some drugs that are usually used to treat psychological problems have been helpful in treating premature ejaculation (Bancroft et al., 2005b, 2005c). Clomipramine, which is used to treat people with obsessive–compulsive disorder or schizophrenia, can impair erectile response at high doses. But in a study with 15 couples, low doses helped men engage in coitus five times longer than usual without ejaculating (Althof, 1994). Antidepressant drugs have also been helpful in the treatment of premature ejaculation (Meston & Frohlich, 2000; Waldinger et al., 2001, 2002). (But note the cautions about using SSRIs expressed earlier in the chapter!)

Treatment of Sexual Pain Disorders

DYSPAREUNIA Dyspareunia, or painful intercourse, generally calls for medical intervention to identify and treat any underlying physical problems, such as urinary tract genital infections, that might give rise to pain. When dyspareunia is caused by vaginismus, treatment through the behavioural approach described below may reduce pain.

BESTCO: Board of Examiners in Sex Therapy and Counselling in Ontario
A site about sex therapy and a referral directory for registered sex therapists in Ontario.
www.bestco.info

VAGINISMUS Vaginismus is generally treated with behavioural exercises in which plastic vaginal dilators of increasing size are inserted to help relax the vaginal musculature. A gynecologist may first demonstrate insertion of the narrowest dilator. Later the woman herself practises insertion of wider dilators at home. The woman increases the size of the dilator as she becomes capable of tolerating insertion and containment (for 10 or 15 minutes) without discomfort or pain. The woman herself—not her partner or therapist—controls the pace of treatment. The woman's or her partner's fingers (first the littlest finger, then two fingers, and so on) may be used in place of the plastic dilators, with the woman controlling the speed and depth of penetration. When the woman is able to tolerate dilators (or fingers) equivalent in thickness to the penis, the couple may attempt coitus. Still, the woman should control insertion. Circumstances should be relaxed and nondemanding. The idea is to avoid resensitizing her to fears of penetration. Because vaginismus often occurs among women with a history of sexual trauma, such as rape or incest, treatment for the psychological effects of these experiences may also be in order (Crowley et al., 2006).

Innovative Canadian Research

EFFECTIVENESS OF TREATMENT PROGRAMS FOR DYSPAREUNIA

A team of researchers from Canada and the U.S. led by Sophie Bergeron and Yitzchak Binik of McGill University (Bergeron et al., 2001) have conducted controlled studies of the effectiveness of three types of treatment programs for dyspareunia resulting from vulvar vestibulitis (a sharp, burning pain experienced when direct pressure is applied just inside the vaginal opening). The three approaches were cognitive-behavioural therapy, biofeedback, and surgery involving the excision of the vestibular area. While each of the treatments resulted in pain reduction, the surgery had the highest success rate. The three treatment approaches were equally successful in improving psychological adjustment and sexual functioning. (However, the researchers note that some of the women who were assigned to the surgical treatment refused to go ahead with that intervention.) The findings indicate that both psychological and surgical interventions can be useful in the treatment of dyspareunia.

A follow-up study involving participants from the original sample was carried out later, by Sophie Bergeron and others from the University of Quebec (Bergeron et al., 2008). Treatment gains were still maintained for each of the three interventions. Yet, over this longer period, cognitive-behavioural therapy was found to be as effective as surgery in reducing levels of reported pain during intercourse. Also, women who held negative attitudes toward sex and sexual pleasure responded less favourably to the surgery.

Canadian Trends

SEX THERAPY AND HELPING PROFESSIONALS

Many people who experience sexual dysfunctions do not seek professional help, largely because of feelings of embarrassment. In a survey of Canadian men, only about one-quarter of those who were experiencing erectile difficulties had discussed this with a physician (Auld & Brock, 2002). Twenty-nine percent of those who had talked to a physician about their problem were dissatisfied with the outcome, mainly because their physician had not taken the problem seriously or else was not properly informed about sexual dysfunctions. Only 48% of the men said that they experienced an improvement in their sexual functioning after consulting with their physician.

This is not surprising, as most helping professionals are not adequately trained to provide sex therapy. A survey of clinical psychologists in Ottawa (Di Giulio & Reissing, 2004) found that most had limited sex therapy training and only 22% said they were very comfortable dealing with sexual issues with their clients. Only 14% said they frequently asked clients about their sexual health concerns.

In a survey of Canadian clinical psychology graduate students, fewer than a third felt they had received adequate education about human sexuality topics, with the exception of sexual orientation issues and dealing with victims of sexual violence (Miller & Byers, 2005). However, there is hope for improvements in future training. Almost all of the students (86%) said they would like more sexuality education and 97% believed that it was important for psychology students to receive sexuality education.

A World of Diversity

ALTERNATIVE APPROACHES TO ENHANCING WOMEN'S SEXUALITY: MINDFULNESS, ACUPUNCTURE, AND YOGA

By Lori A. Brotto, PhD, Department of Obstetrics and Gynaecology, University of British Columbia

Treatment approaches designed to assist women dealing with sexual problems have generally focused on improving sexual response. However, a healthy sexual response does not necessarily signify overall sexual satisfaction and lack of sexual distress. Specifically, 5.5% of American women aged 30 to 79 report unsatisfying sexual activity (Lutfey et al., 2008), despite experiencing no difficulties in desire, arousal, and orgasm. In the Global Study of Sexual Attitudes and Behavior (Laumann et al., 2005), 8% to 18% of women aged 40 to 80 reported finding sex not pleasurable. Thus, some women are not sexually satisfied even though the mechanics of sexual response are operating, and these women do not meet the criteria for a "sexual dysfunction" as defined by the DSM-IV (American Psychiatric Association, 2000). These women (Ogden et al., 2007) have described their sexual experiences as boring, dry, and unemotional. In response to this situation, Ogden and others (2007) have called for a non-goal-oriented spiritual element to sexuality.

Eastern techniques, with their origin in the Kama Sutra of the fourth to sixth centuries, might provide some of the spiritual dimensions that traditionally Western approaches have been lacking. Three Eastern techniques that might improve women's sexuality are mindfulness, acupuncture, and yoga.

Mindfulness Meditation. Mindfulness involves nonjudgmental, present-moment awareness. It has roots in Buddhist meditation. Although it is a nonreligious practice, transcending all organized religions, there is a spiritual component to mindfulness (Carmody et al., 2008).

Recently, mindfulness has been incorporated into a brief, psycho-educational treatment program for women with sexual desire and arousal disorders and found to be effective as part of a larger treatment program that included education, cognitive and behavioural skills, and couples therapy exercises. In the study, women who used a combination of in-session and at-home homework exercises evaluated the mindfulness component as the most valuable aspect of treatment (Brotto & Heiman, 2007).

Specifically, mindfulness was introduced to women by giving them instructions on how to be mindful in their nonsexual life. They were introduced to the topic with the following:

> Many of us go through life not living in the present moment. We fluctuate between thinking in the future (worrying, planning, thinking), and living in the past (reviewing past events, conversations, plans). We miss out on valuable and meaningful experiences in the present. We have evolved to multi-task, and this reinforces mindlessness. However, in instances when we wish to be present, such as the sexual scenario, it is difficult if not impossible for us to turn off the cerebral chatter. The net effect is a reduction in arousal, thereby

A World of Diversity (Continued)

making the sexual experience less rewarding and pleasurable.

The heart of mindfulness is in practising the Body Scan exercise, which involves attending to the sensations in specific parts of the body. Women can practise the Body Scan a few times a week, in addition to daily practice (usually 10 minutes) of mindfulness during another activity (e.g., mindfulness while eating, driving, having a conversation, playing a sport or instrument, etc). They are also given a set of body-focused mindfulness exercises to practise at home. The first is a Focusing Exercise. Women are asked to visually attend to their bodies during and after a bath or shower. They are encouraged to describe what they see in nonjudgmental ways, and are given a list of possible statements to repeat during the exercise, such as "my body is my own," "it is alive," and "I appreciate the following aspects of my body." The Self-Observation exercise asks women to use a hand-held mirror to observe their genitals. They are reminded that this is a nonsexual exercise with the goal of allowing women to remain in the present while letting any judgments about themselves, their bodies, or how they are struggling with the exercise to float away. The exercise Self-Observation and Touch asks women to gently touch their own genitals while repeating the Self-Observation exercise. After some weeks of practice, the exercise is modified to include a sexual goal. The woman is encouraged to repeat the self-observation-and-touch exercise, but to also imagine herself as a competent sexual, feminine, and sensual woman. A discussion around incorporating mindfulness while being sexual, either alone or with a partner, then ensues.

Two studies have tested the efficacy of a mindfulness-based sex therapy intervention for women with low desire and arousal, and both studies found a significant improvement in sexual response and a decrease in sexual distress (Brotto, Basson, & Luria, 2008; Brotto et al., 2008). Thus mindfulness techniques show great promise in the treatment of women's sexual concerns and may fill the spiritual gap missing among some women with unsatisfying sexual experiences.

Acupuncture. Acupuncture is a type of treatment within the medical system of traditional Chinese medicine (TCM). It has been practised for thousands of years in China and other Asian countries. According to the TCM theory, there are more than 2000 acupuncture points on the human body connected with 12 main and eight secondary "meridians" or channels. Pain and disease are the result of these channels becoming blocked. To restore healthy energy, thin, sterile needles are inserted into specific points along these meridians.

Acupuncture is a treatment for a variety of pain conditions and internal medicine pathologies, and is often helpful for patients who do not respond to traditional methods (Murray, 1995). The effectiveness of acupuncture has been tested in two empirical studies of women with vestibulodynia. In the first study, 12 women with chronic vestibulodynia responded positively on pain and quality-of-life measures after five once-weekly acupuncture sessions (Powell & Wojnarowska, 1999). In the second study, 11 of 13 women with vestibulodynia rated their sexual pain as being less pronounced, with 10 reporting that they continued to perceive an improvement three months following acupuncture (Danielsson, Sjoberg, & Ostman, 2001). There are also case reports of acupuncture being effective for women with acquired sexual desire difficulties. Although it is impossible to verify how acupuncture positively affects either genital pain or sexual desire, some patients maintain that acupuncture is the critical ingredient. Of course, research substantiating these claims is needed.

Yoga. Yoga is a practice that involves both physical postures and breathing techniques. In addition, there is a cognitive component focusing on meditation and concentration, which aid in achieving the goal of union between the self and the spiritual. Yoga has been found to improve psychological well-being and overall physical health.

Because of these direct effects, one might assume that yoga has a positive influence on sexual functioning. In Tantric and Taoist traditions of yoga, there is an entire subset of yoga called *kundalini* devoted to improving sexuality. In yogic traditions the human body has power centres, known as *chakras,* which reside in different parts of the body. The goal of *kundalini* yoga is to take the sexual energy that exists in the lowest chakra, the *kundalini*, and use body postures and breathing to direct it upward to other chakras through channels that connect body parts. In doing so, kundalini energy is said to increase sexual pleasure and to extend the longevity of sex by facilitating orgasms without ejaculation in men.

To date, there have been no empirical studies of yoga on any aspect of women's sexual functioning or sexual satisfaction, although among men, yoga has been found to be as effective as medical management in prolonging ejaculation in men with premature ejaculation.

Conclusion

What do these Eastern approaches of mindfulness, acupuncture, and yoga offer that Western approaches do not? Some might argue that they force a unity between mind and body that has become ignored by more contemporary sex therapy techniques. In this era of sexual pharmaceuticals and the quest for the quick fix, attending to the spiritual domains of sexuality is ignored. A humanistic element, with a focus on mind-body connection (Tiefer, 2006), perhaps captured by some of these Eastern approaches such as mindfulness, acupuncture, and yoga, might be the key for improving women's lack of sexual satisfaction. Of course, research supporting such claims awaits us.

Innovative Canadian Research

OPTIMAL SEXUALITY

Most research on human sexuality focuses on sexual problems rather than sexual pleasure. In contrast, Ottawa researchers Peggy Kleinplatz and Dana Menard (2007) interviewed individuals who reported having "great sex" with the objective of building a conceptual model that would outline the key characteristics of optimal sex. The sample consisted of older individuals who were in long-term relationships. Six major components emerged from the interviews.

Being Present. The most basic characteristic of great sex was that of being totally immersed in and intensely focused on the experience. This led to total surrendering of the body to the experience without there being any other, distracting thoughts.

Authenticity. Participants felt they could be free to be themselves and were open about their own desires. They spoke of feeling totally uninhibited.

Intense Emotional Connection. Regardless of whether the sexual encounter occurred in a long-term or other kind of relationship, there was a powerful sense of intimate engagement. This intense emotional connection lasted throughout the sexual experience. It involved a feeling of mutuality and being desired as well as desiring.

Sexual and Erotic Intimacy. A deep sense of caring for one another was stressed even in brief relationships. Here the partners got to know each other well regarding their erotic desires. They were willing to take risks in their sexual requests because they felt safe enough with one another to be vulnerable in sharing their bodies and emotions.

Communication. They partners were willing to be open about what they found erotically exciting and physically stimulating. They acknowledged the pleasure they were receiving. Some found talking to be a sex act that turned them on, such as by "talking dirty."

Transcendence. Many experienced an altered state of consciousness that felt like a spiritual connection.

It is important to note that the participants emphasized that they had developed their ability to experience great sex over a period of time. Also, their perceptions of great sex changed with experience and personal growth.

Summing Up

Sexual dysfunctions are difficulties in becoming sexually aroused or reaching orgasm.

Sexual desire disorders involve dysfunctions in sexual desire, interest, or drive, in which the person experiences a lack of sexual desire or an aversion to genital sexual contact.

In men, sexual arousal disorders involve recurrent difficulty in getting or sustaining an erection sufficient to engage successfully in sexual intercourse. In women, they typically involve failure to become sufficiently lubricated.

Women are more likely to encounter difficulties reaching orgasm. Men are more likely to have premature ejaculation.

Sexual pain disorders include dyspareunia, vaginismus, and vulvodynia.

Many sexual dysfunctions involve the interaction of organic and psychological factors.

Fatigue may lead to erectile disorder in men and to orgasmic disorder and dyspareunia in women. Dyspareunia often reflects vaginal infections and STIs. Organic factors are believed to be involved in the majority of cases of erectile disorder. Medications and other drugs may also impair sexual functioning.

Psychosocial factors that are connected with sexual dysfunctions include cultural influences, psychosexual trauma, marital dissatisfaction, psychological conflict, lack of sexual skills, irrational beliefs, and performance anxiety. Performance anxiety may place a dysfunctional individual in a spectator rather than a performer role.

Sex therapy aims to modify dysfunctional behaviour directly by changing self-defeating beliefs and attitudes, fostering sexual skills and knowledge, enhancing sexual communication, and suggesting behavioural exercises to enhance sexual stimulation while reducing performance anxiety.

Masters and Johnson pioneered the direct, behavioural approach to treating sexual dysfunctions.

Some sex therapists help kindle the sexual appetites of people with inhibited sexual desire by prescribing self-stimulation exercises combined with erotic fantasies.

Men and women with impaired sexual arousal receive sexual stimulation from their partners under relaxed circumstances so that anxiety does not inhibit their natural reflexes. Biological treatments such as the drug Viagra are also used with male erectile disorder.

Masters and Johnson use a couples-oriented approach in treating anorgasmic women. Other sex therapists prefer a program of directed masturbation to enable women to learn about their own bodies at their own pace and free them of the need to rely on a partner or please a partner. Premature ejaculation is usually treated with the squeeze technique or the stop–start method.

Dyspareunia, or painful intercourse, is generally treated with medical intervention. Vaginismus is generally treated with plastic vaginal dilators of increasing size.

Alternative approaches to sex therapy include mindfulness, acupuncture, and yoga.

Test Yourself

Multiple-Choice Questions

1. **The most commonly reported sexual problem for women, according to the 2003 Canadian Contraceptive Study, was**
   a. partner ejaculating too soon
   b. painful intercourse
   c. low sexual desire
   d. lack of orgasm

2. **In a 2005 survey women reported all of the following situations to be frustrating except**
   a. partner not being affectionate
   b. not achieving orgasm
   c. partner refusing to have sex
   d. too many partners available

3. **____________________ involve a lack of sexual interest or an aversion to sexual activity.**
   a. Sexual arousal disorders
   b. Sexual pain disorders
   c. Sexual desire disorders
   d. Sexual orgasm disorders

4. **According to Peggy Kleinplatz, which of the following is NOT a key component of optimal sexuality?**
   a. using advanced sexual techniques
   b. being present
   c. authenticity
   d. intense emotional connection

5. **____________________ is a common cause of erectile difficulties.**
   a. Orgasm anxiety
   b. Ejaculatory incompetence
   c. Performance anxiety
   d. Hyposensitivity of the penis

6. **An involuntary contraction of the muscles that makes penetration painful or impossible is known as**
   a. dyspareunia
   b. vaginismus
   c. phimosis
   d. anorgasmia

7. **Which of the following is NOT one of the alternative therapies discussed by Lori Brotto?**
   a. mindfulness
   b. acupuncture
   c. yoga
   d. stop-start method

8. **Which of the following is not one of the psychosocial factors associated with sexual dysfunctions?**
   a. dissatisfaction with the relationship
   b. lack of sexual skills
   c. anxiety due to previous negative experience
   d. side effects of prescription drugs

9. **A behavioural approach to treating sex disorders might include all of the following except**
   a. adjusting hormone balance to improve sexual functioning
   b. changing self-defeating beliefs and attitudes
   c. enhancing sexual knowledge
   d. improving communication skills

10. **Treatment for ____________________ and ____________________ has produced high success rates.**
    a. sexual arousal disorders; sexual desire disorders
    b. dyspareunia; erectile disorders
    c. vaginismus; premature ejaculation
    d. ejaculatory incompetence; low sexual desire

Answers to the Test Yourself questions in each chapter are found on page 509.

Critical Thinking Questions

1. Have you ever experienced a sexual problem? How did you react in this situation? How did your partner react? Could you talk about it? Why do you think you reacted the way you did?
2. Why do you think so many people find it difficult to admit that they have had a sexual dysfunction? Do you think it is more difficult for men or women to talk about their sexual problems? Why?
3. Would you buy drugs like Viagra over the internet? Why or why not?

Visit MyPsychKit at www.mypsychkit.com, where you can do quizzes and link to additional resources on topics discussed in this text.

CHAPTER FOURTEEN

Sexually Transmitted Infections

Although AIDS is the most deadly of the **sexually transmitted infections (STIs)**, others are more common. STIs are rampant. The World Health Organization estimates that at least 340 million people around the world are stricken with STIs each year (World Health Organization, 2008). STIs are transmitted through sexual means, such as vaginal or anal intercourse, or oral sex. Some STIs can be spread (and often are) through nonsexual contact as well. For example, AIDS and viral hepatitis may be spread by sharing contaminated needles. And yes, a few STIs (such as "crabs") may be picked up from bedding or other objects—such as moist towels—that harbour the organisms that cause these STIs.

Sexually transmitted infections (STIs) Infections that are communicated through sexual contact. (Some, such as HIV/AIDS, can also be transmitted in other ways.)

Some people have STIs and do not realize it. Ignorance is not bliss, however. As well, there are other people who are not honest about having an STI or HIV. They will purposely mislead potential sex partners by assuring them that they have had few other partners and that there is no need to use condoms.

Some STIs may not produce noticeable symptoms, but they can be harmful if left untreated. STIs can also be painful and, in the cases of AIDS and advanced syphilis, lethal. Overall, STIs are believed to account for 15% to 30% of cases of infertility among women. In addition to their biological effects, STIs exact an emotional toll and strain relationships to the breaking point.

Although the overall increase in STI rates is a concern when choosing a potential partner, having sex with a partner who is infected does not always lead to infection. For example, infection rates are much lower for HIV than for chlamydia. University of Montreal researchers (Rosen et al., 2005), in a national survey of health care professionals, found that most of them overestimated the probability of becoming infected with HIV or chlamydia from engaging in a single act of unprotected vaginal sex. The researchers then raised the question of whether it is ethical or not to inform people of the actual infection risks. The concern is that some people may be more willing to take sexual risks if they feel the probability of infection is low. Yet for the person who does get infected from one act of unprotected sex, probabilities do not matter. There is also the reality that the more times one has unprotected sex with an infected partner, the probability of becoming infected increases.

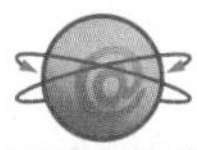

Public Health Agency of Canada
Provides STI information and trends, including the Canadian Guidelines on STI 2006.
www.phac-aspc.gc.ca

Find it hard to do the talking? The website inspot.org has these and other e-cards that can be sent anonymously (or not) to a past sexual partner. Toronto Public Health is encouraging people with STIs to send these cards to encourage past partners to be tested. The website inspot.org was established to help curb a syphilis outbreak in San Francisco. The main clients are men who have sex with men and meet online.

Canadian Trends

SEXUALLY TRANSMITTED INFECTIONS IN CANADA

Canadian rates of STI vary for each type of STI. HPV (genital warts) and genital herpes seem to be relatively common. Unfortunately, we do not have national statistics on them as physicians are not required to report these cases. (The prevalence of HIV/AIDS will be discussed later in the chapter.)

There were over 65 000 reported cases of chlamydia in 2006, with more than twice as many women as men contracting the disease (Public Health Agency of Canada, 2007). Chlamydia is the most commonly reported STI in Canada. Rates of chlamydia declined from 1992 to 1997, but have increased since then. However, Toronto researchers Alex McKay and Michael Barrett (2008) question whether recent rate increases may be attributed to more sensitive testing methods, as is the case in the United States.

Rates of chlamydia and other STI infections vary across Canada (see Table 14.1). The highest STI rates occur in Canada's North and the next highest, in the western provinces, especially in Saskatchewan. This trend is attributed to the higher rates among Canada's First Nations people. (These differences will be discussed in more detail in the section on social factors and STIs near the end of the chapter.)

Gonorrhea was once the most widespread STI in Canada, but it has since been replaced by chlamydia. The rate of infection declined substantially from the mid-1980s through to 1997, apparently

TABLE 14.1

Actual Rate of Chlamydia Infection in Canada for 2006 and Projected Rate for 2007

	Rates: January 1 to December 31	
	2006 Actual Rate[1]	**2007 Projected Rate[2]**
National[3]	202.2	218.8
NL	108.3	100.2
PE	121.3	106.8
NS	188.6	182.1
NB	179.7	161.2
QC	167.6	172.1
ON	150.4	181.8
MB	361.8	431.9
SK	431.4	320.3
AB	309.6	221.4
BC	214.7	232.0
NT	1660.3	1783.7

[1] Rate (per 100 000) based on all reported cases for 2006. Population estimates provided by Statistics Canada. (Source: Statistics Canada, Demography Division, Demographic Estimates Section, July Population Estimates, 2006 revised postcensal.)

[2] Quarter 3 data for Yukon and Nunavut were unavailable at the time of this report. The rates for these two territories have been very high for the previous years.

[3] Rate for 2007 is calculated by projecting the cumulative number of cases reported between January 1 and September 30 and then calculating the rate (per 100 000). Population estimates provided by Statistics Canada. (Source: Statistics Canada. Demography Division, Demographic Estimates Section, July Population Estimates, 2006 preliminary postcensal.)

Source: Surveillance and Epidemiology Section, Community Acquired Infections Division, Centre for Infectious Disease Prevention and Control, Public Health Agency of Canada, 2007. Reproduced with the permission of the Minister of Public Works and Government Services Canada, 2008.

because of safer sexual practices. However, the incidence of gonorrhea doubled between 1997 and 2006. The rate in 1997 was 14.9 per 100 000 population, and in 2007 the projected rate was 33.1. In the first nine months of 2007, there were 8505 reported cases of gonorrhea (Public Health Agency of Canada, 2006).

Because of treatment advances, HIV/AIDS has become less frightening. Thus, people engage in more spontaneous sexual behaviour and the rate of STIs increases.

Syphilis infection rates decreased in Canada with the introduction of penicillin in the 1940s. In recent years the rate of syphilis has been increasing, especially among males. In 2004, males accounted for 88% of the cases (Public Health Agency of Canada, 2006). In the first nine months of 2006, 1011 cases had been reported. This represents a 900% increase since 1997. However, compared with the case numbers for gonorrhea and chlamydia, the number of cases of syphilis is relatively small.

Beginning in 2001, large outbreaks of syphilis occurred in British Columbia (Public Health Agency of Canada, 2006). About half the reported cases have been among sex trade workers and their clients in Vancouver's downtown East Side, which has a high rate of drug use. The remaining cases have involved gay men, heterosexuals who do not use condoms consistently, street youth, and sexually active injection-drug users. Recent outbreaks of syphilis have occurred in several locations across Canada. A number of cases have also been contracted by travellers to Asia and Central America.

The actual rates of STIs are probably much higher than what is reported. Often infections do not show any obvious symptoms and thus are not detected.

Who Is at Risk?
Evidence suggests that young people are more sexually active than ever before. Thus, it is as important as ever that they be aware of the risks involved and take responsibility for their sexual health.

Bacterial Infections

Without the one-celled micro-organisms we call **bacteria**, there would be no wine. Bacteria are essential to fermentation. They also play vital roles in our digestive system. Unfortunately, bacteria also cause many diseases, including the common STIs chlamydia, gonorrhea, and syphilis.

Bacteria Plural of *bacterium,* a class of one-celled micro-organisms that have no chlorophyll and can give rise to many illnesses.

Chlamydia

Chlamydia infections are caused by the *Chlamydia trachomatis* bacterium, a parasitic organism that can survive only within cells. This bacterium can cause several different types of infection, including *nongonococcal urethritis (NGU)* in men and women, *epididymitis* (infection of the epididymis) in men, and *cervicitis* (infection of the cervix), *endometritis* (infection of the endometrium), and *pelvic inflammatory disease (PID)* in women (Hatcher, 2006).

TRANSMISSION Chlamydia is usually transmitted through sexual intercourse—vaginal or anal. Chlamydia may also cause an eye infection if a person touches his or her eyes after handling the genitals of an infected partner. Oral sex with an infected partner can infect the throat.

SYMPTOMS Chlamydia infections usually produce symptoms that are similar to, but milder than, those of gonorrhea. In men, chlamydia can lead to nongonococcal urethritis (NGU). Urethritis is an inflammation of the urethra. NGU refers to forms of urethritis that are not caused by the gonococcal bacterium. (NGU is generally diagnosed only in men. In women, an inflammation of the urethra caused by chlamydia is called a chlamydia infection or simply chlamydia.) NGU was formerly called nonspecific urethritis, or NSU. Many organisms can cause NGU. Chlamydia accounts for about half of the cases among men (Hatcher, 2006).

NGU in men may give rise to a thin, whitish discharge from the penis and some burning or other pain during urination. These symptoms contrast with the yellow-green discharge and more intense pain produced by gonorrhea. There may be soreness in the scrotum and feelings of heaviness in the testes. NGU is about two to three times as prevalent among American men as gonorrhea (Hatcher, 2006).

In women, chlamydial infections usually give rise to infections of the urethra or cervix. Women, like men, may experience burning when they urinate, genital irritation, and a mild (vaginal) discharge. Women are also likely to have pelvic pain and irregular menstrual cycles. The cervix may look swollen and inflamed.

Yet as many as 50% of men and 70% of women infected with chlamydia show no symptoms (Hatcher, 2006). People without symptoms may go untreated and unknowingly pass along their infections to their partners. In women, between 10% and 40% of untreated cases develop into pelvic inflammatory disease (PID) (Public Health Agency of Canada, 2006). An untreated chlamydial infection can spread throughout the reproductive system, leading to PID and to scarring of the fallopian tubes, resulting in infertility. Untreated chlamydial infections can also damage the internal reproductive organs of men.

Chlamydial infections frequently occur together with other STIs, most often gonorrhea. Nearly half of all cases of gonorrhea involve coexisting chlamydial infections (Hatcher, 2006).

DIAGNOSIS AND TREATMENT Various tests can verify a diagnosis of chlamydia in women. The tests analyze cervical or urethral smears. Tests using self-obtained urine samples and vaginal swabs are also highly reliable and are preferred by most women as being less invasive (McKay, 2006b). In men, a swab is inserted through the penile opening, and the extracted fluid is analyzed to detect the presence of chlamydia.

Antibiotics other than penicillin are highly effective in eradicating chlamydia infections. Penicillin, which is effective in treating gonorrhea, is ineffective against chlamydia. Treatment of sex partners is considered critical to prevent the infection from bouncing back and forth (Hatcher, 2006).

Because of the risks that untreated chlamydial infections pose, especially to women, and the high rate of symptom-free infections, many physicians screen young women for chlamydia during regular checkups. However, Toronto researcher Alexander McKay (2006a) found there are also many physicians who do not screen for chlamydia. Male physicians are less likely than female physicians to screen for chlamydia. McKay argues that there is a definite need to make more physicians aware of the need for regular chlamydia screening, especially of sexually active young women living in the economically disadvantaged areas of cities. The STI guidelines provided by Health Canada are an important source of information for physicians and their patients.

Gonorrhea

Gonorrhea is an STI caused by the *Neisseria gonorrhoeae* bacterium and characterized by a discharge and burning urination. Left untreated, gonorrhea can give rise to pelvic inflammatory disease (PID) and infertility.

TRANSMISSION Gonococcal bacteria require a warm, moist environment like that found along the mucous membranes of the urinary tract in both genders and the cervix in women. Outside the body, they die in about a minute. There is no evidence that gonorrhea can be picked up from public toilet seats or by touching dry objects. In rare cases, gonorrhea is contracted by contact with a moist, warm towel or sheet used immediately beforehand by an infected person. Gonorrhea is nearly always transmitted by unprotected vaginal, oral, or anal sexual activity, or from mother to newborn during delivery.

A person who performs oral sex on an infected partner may develop **pharyngeal gonorrhea**, which produces a throat infection. Mouth-to-mouth kissing and cunnilingus are less likely to spread gonorrhea.

A gonorrheal infection may be spread from the penis to the partner's rectum during anal intercourse. A cervical gonorrheal infection can be spread to the rectum if an infected woman and her partner follow vaginal intercourse with anal intercourse. Gonorrhea is less likely to be spread by vaginal discharge than by penile discharge.

Gonorrhea is highly contagious. Women stand nearly a 50% chance of contracting gonorrhea after one exposure. Men have a 25% risk of infection (Hatcher, 2006). The risks to women are apparently greater because women retain infected semen in the vagina. The risk of infection increases with repeated exposure.

Pharyngeal gonorrhea A gonorrheal infection of the pharynx (the cavity leading from the mouth and nasal passages to the larynx and esophagus) that is characterized by a sore throat.

Cervicitis Inflammation of the cervix.

Epididymitis Inflammation of the epididymis.

Pelvic inflammatory disease (PID) Inflammation of the pelvic region—possibly including the cervix, uterus, fallopian tubes, abdominal cavity, and ovaries. Its symptoms are abdominal pain, tenderness, nausea, fever, and irregular menstrual cycles. The condition may lead to infertility.

SYMPTOMS Most men experience symptoms within two to five days after infection. Symptoms include a penile discharge that is clear at first (Figure 14.1). Within a day it turns yellow to yellow-green, thickens, and becomes pus-like. The urethra becomes inflamed, and urination is accompanied by a burning sensation. About 30–40% of males have swelling and tenderness in the lymph glands of the groin. Inflammation and other symptoms may become chronic if left untreated.

The initial symptoms of gonorrhea usually abate within a few weeks without treatment, leading people to think of gonorrhea as being no worse than a bad cold. However, the gonococcus bacterium usually continues to damage the body even though the early symptoms fade.

The primary site of infection in women is the cervix, where gonorrhea causes **cervicitis**. Cervicitis may cause a yellowish to yellow-green pus-like discharge that irritates the vulva. If the infection spreads to the urethra, women may also note burning urination. *However, about 80% of the women who contract gonorrhea have no symptoms during the early stages of the infection.* Because many infected women do not seek treatment until symptoms develop, they may unknowingly infect another sex partner.

When gonorrhea is not treated early, it may spread through the urogenital systems in both genders and strike the internal reproductive organs. In men, it can lead to **epididymitis**, which can cause fertility problems. Swelling and feelings of tenderness or pain in the scrotum are the principal symptoms of epididymitis. Fever may also be present. Occasionally the kidneys are affected.

In women, the bacterium can spread through the cervix to the uterus, fallopian tubes, ovaries, and other parts of the abdominal cavity, causing **pelvic inflammatory disease (PID)**. Symptoms of PID include cramps, abdominal pain and tenderness,

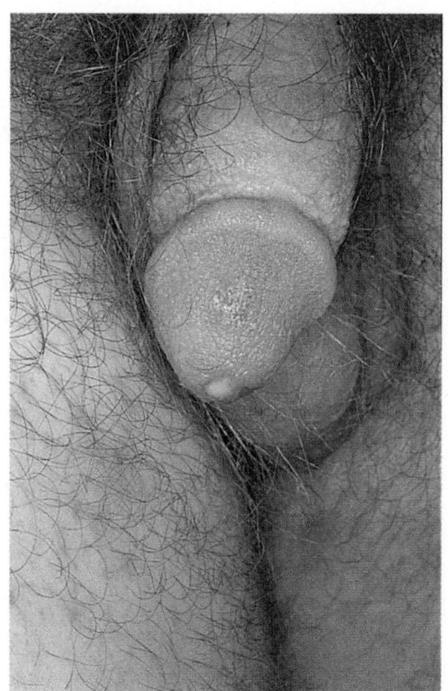

Figure 14.1 Gonorrheal Discharge.

Gonorrhea in the male often causes a thick, yellowish, pus-like discharge from the penis.

Syphilis An STI that is caused by the *Treponema pallidum* bacterium and may progress through several stages of development—often from a chancre to a skin rash to damage to the cardiovascular or central nervous system.

Chancre A sore or ulcer.

Congenital syphilis A syphilis infection that is present at birth.

cervical tenderness and discharge, irregular menstrual cycles, coital pain, fever, nausea, and vomiting. PID may also occur without symptoms. Whether or not there are symptoms, PID can cause scarring that blocks the fallopian tubes, leading to infertility. PID is a serious illness that requires aggressive treatment with antibiotics. Surgery may be needed to remove infected tissue. Unfortunately, many women become aware of a gonococcal infection only when they develop PID. These consequences are all the more unfortunate because gonorrhea, when diagnosed and treated early, clears up rapidly in over 90% of cases.

DIAGNOSIS AND TREATMENT Diagnosis of gonorrhea involves clinical inspection of the genitals by a physician and the culturing and examination of a sample of genital discharge.

Antibiotics are the standard treatment for gonorrhea. Penicillin was once the favoured antibiotic, but the rise of penicillin-resistant strains of *Neisseria gonorrhoeae* has required that alternative antibiotics be used (Hatcher, 2006). An injection of the antibiotic ceftriaxone is often recommended. Other antibiotics for treating gonorrhea include ciprofloxacin and ofloxacin. Because gonorrhea and chlamydia often occur together, people who are infected with gonorrhea are usually also treated for chlamydia through the use of another antibiotic (Hatcher, 2006). Sex partners of people with gonorrhea should also be examined.

Syphilis

In 1905 the German scientist Fritz Schaudinn isolated the bacterium that causes **syphilis**. It is *Treponema pallidum* (*T. pallidum*, for short).

Although syphilis is less widespread than it has been, its effects can be extremely harmful. They can include heart disease, blindness, gross confusion, and death.

TRANSMISSION Syphilis is most often transmitted by vaginal or anal intercourse or by oral–genital or oral–anal contact with an infected person. The spirochete is usually transmitted when open lesions on an infected person come into contact with the mucous membranes or skin abrasions of the partner's body during sexual activity. The chance of contracting syphilis from one sexual contact with an infected partner is estimated at one in three.

Syphilis may also be contracted by touching an infectious **chancre**, but not by using the same toilet seat as an infected person.

Pregnant women may transmit syphilis to their fetus, because the spirochete can cross the placental membrane. Miscarriage, stillbirth, or **congenital syphilis** may result. Congenital syphilis may impair vision and hearing or deform bones and teeth. Blood tests are administered routinely during pregnancy to diagnose syphilis in the mother so that congenital problems in the baby may be averted.

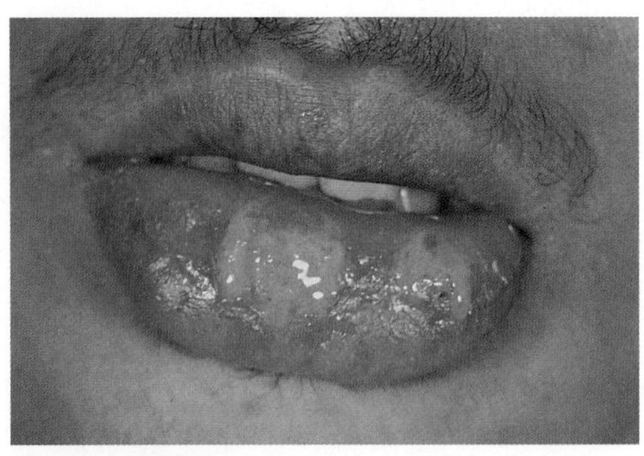

Figure 14.2 Syphilis Chancre.

The first stage, or primary stage, of a syphilis infection is marked by the appearance of a painless sore, or chancre, at the site of the infection.

SYMPTOMS AND COURSE OF ILLNESS Syphilis develops through several stages. In the first stage, or *primary stage*, of syphilis, a painless chancre (a hard, round, ulcer-like lesion with raised edges) appears at the site of infection two to four weeks after contact. When women are infected, the chancre usually forms on the vaginal walls or the cervix. It may also form on the external genitalia, most often on the labia. When men are infected, the chancre usually forms on the penile glans. It may also form on the scrotum or penile shaft. If the mode of transmission is oral sex, the chancre may appear on the lips or tongue (see Figure 14.2). If the infection is spread by anal sex, the rectum may be the site of the chancre. The chancre disappears within a few weeks, but if the infection remains untreated, syphilis will continue to work within the body.

The *secondary stage* begins a few weeks to a few months later. A skin rash develops, consisting of painless, reddish, raised bumps that darken after a while and burst, oozing a discharge. Other symptoms include sores in the mouth, painful swelling of joints, a sore throat, headaches, and fever. A person with syphilis may thus wrongly assume that he or she has the flu.

These symptoms also disappear. Syphilis then enters the *latent stage* and may lie dormant for 1 to 40 years. But spirochetes continue to multiply and burrow into the circulatory system, central nervous system (brain and spinal cord), and bones. The person may no longer be contagious to sex partners after several years in the latent stage, but a pregnant woman may transmit the infection to her newborn at any time.

In many cases the disease eventually progresses to the late stage, or *tertiary stage*. A large ulcer may form on the skin, muscle tissue, digestive organs, lungs, liver, or other organs. This destructive ulcer can often be successfully treated, but still more serious damage can occur as the infection attacks the central nervous system or the cardiovascular system (the heart and the major blood vessels). Either outcome can be fatal. The primary and secondary symptoms of syphilis inevitably disappear. Infected people may thus be tempted to believe that they are no longer at risk and fail to see a doctor. This is unfortunate, because failure to eradicate the infection through proper treatment may eventually lead to dire consequences.

DIAGNOSIS AND TREATMENT Primary-stage syphilis is diagnosed by clinical examination. If a chancre is found, fluid drawn from it can be examined under a microscope. The spirochetes are usually quite visible. Blood tests are not definitive until the secondary stage begins.

Penicillin is the treatment of choice for syphilis, although for people allergic to penicillin, doxycycline and some other antibiotics can be used (Hatcher, 2006). Sex partners of persons infected with syphilis should also be evaluated by a physician.

A New Type of Bacterial Infection

MRSA (FLESH-EATING) BACTERIA A new strain of the MRSA bacteria, multi-drug resistant USA 300, is spreading among gay men in Toronto and large U.S. cities (Graham, 2008). This bacterial strain is resistant to many of the drugs that have been used to treat previous strains. The bacteria are spread by intimate skin-to-skin contact and can lead to infections in the buttocks and genital area, as well as pneumonia. Infection is associated with high-risk sexual behaviours. Washing after having sex may offer some protection against the bacteria.

Vaginal Infections

Vaginitis is any kind of vaginal infection or inflammation. Women with vaginitis may encounter genital irritation or itching and burning during urination, but the most common symptom is an odorous discharge.

Most cases of vaginitis are caused by organisms that reside in the vagina or by sexually transmitted organisms. Organisms that reside in the vagina may overgrow and cause symptoms when the environmental balance of the vagina is upset by factors such as birth-control pills, antibiotics, dietary changes, excessive douching, or nylon underwear or pantyhose. (See Chapter 3 for suggestions on reducing the risk of vaginitis.) Still other cases are caused by sensitivities or allergic reactions to various chemicals.

Vaginitis Any type of vaginal infection or inflammation.

Bacterial vaginosis A form of vaginitis usually caused by the *Gardnerella vaginalis* bacterium.

Candidiasis A form of vaginitis caused by a yeast-like fungus, *Candida albicans.*

The great majority of vaginal infections involve *bacterial vaginosis* (BV), *candidiasis* (commonly called a "yeast" infection), or *trichomoniasis* ("trich"). The microbes that cause vaginal infections in women can also infect the man's urethral tract. A "vaginal infection" can be passed back and forth between sex partners.

Bacterial Vaginosis

Bacterial vaginosis (BV) is most often caused by overgrowth of the bacterium *Gardnerella vaginalis*. The bacterium is transmitted primarily through sexual contact. The most characteristic symptom in women is a thin, foul-smelling vaginal discharge, but infected women often have no symptoms. Diagnosis requires culturing the bacterium in the laboratory. Besides causing troublesome symptoms in some cases, BV may increase the risk of various gynecological problems, including infections of the reproductive tract. Oral treatments are recommended and are effective in most cases. Topical treatments are also effective. Recurrences are common, however.

Questions remain about whether the male partner should also be treated. The bacterium can usually be found in the male urethra but does not generally cause symptoms.

Candidiasis

Also known as *moniliasis, thrush*, or (most commonly) a yeast infection, **candidiasis** is caused by a yeast-like fungus, *Candida albicans.* Candidiasis commonly produces soreness, inflammation, and intense (sometimes maddening!) itching around the vulva that is accompanied by a thick, white, curd-like vaginal discharge (see Figure 14.3). Yeast generally produces no symptoms when the vaginal environment is normal. Yeast infections can also occur in the mouth in both men and women and in the penis in men.

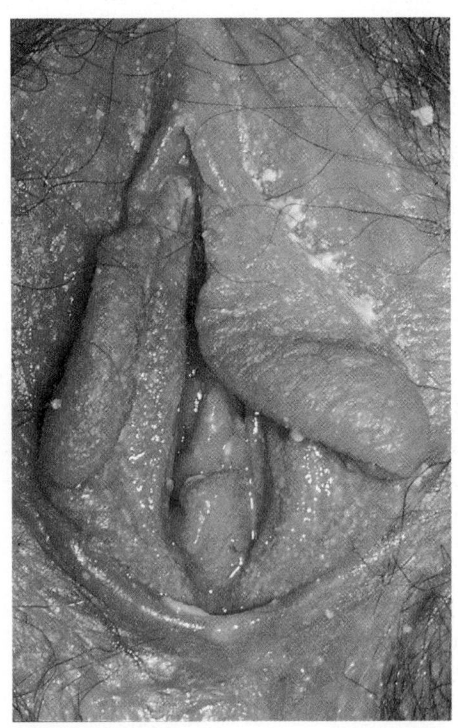

Figure 14.3 Candidiasis.

A "yeast infection" causes soreness, inflammation, and itching around the vulva that is accompanied by a thick, white vaginal discharge.

Infections most often arise from changes in the vaginal environment that allow the fungus to overgrow. Factors such as the use of antibiotics, birth-control pills, or intrauterine devices (IUDs), pregnancy, and diabetes may alter the vaginal balance, allowing the fungus that causes yeast infections to grow to infectious levels. Wearing nylon underwear and tight, restrictive, poorly ventilated clothing may also set the stage for a yeast infection.

Candidiasis can be passed back and forth between sex partners through vaginal intercourse. It can also be passed back and forth between the mouth and the genitals through oral–genital contact and can infect the anus through anal intercourse. However, most infections in women are believed to be caused by an overgrowth of "yeast" normally found in the vagina, not by sexual transmission. Still, it is advisable to evaluate both partners simultaneously. Whereas most men with *Candida* have no symptoms, some may develop NGU or a genital thrush that is accompanied by itching and burning during urination or reddening of the penis. Candidiasis may also be transmitted by nonsexual means, such as between women who share a washcloth.

In Canada, about 75% of women will have at least one episode of candidiasis during their lifetime. It is one of the most common medical problems faced by Canadian women, and accounts for more than 1 million visits to physicians' offices per year (Public Health Agency of Canada, 2005c). About 50% of women have recurrent infections. Recommended treatment is vaginal suppositories or creams (Hatcher, 2006). Many of these treatments are sold over the counter. We recommend that women with vaginal complaints consult their physician before taking any of these medications, to ensure that they receive the proper diagnosis and treatment.

Trichomoniasis

Trichomoniasis ("trich") is caused by *Trichomonas vaginalis. Trichomonas vaginalis* is a one-celled parasite. Trichomoniasis is the most common parasitic STI). Symptoms in women include burning or itching in the vulva, mild pain during urination or coitus, and an odorous, foamy, whitish to yellowish-green discharge. Many women notice that symptoms appear or worsen during, or just after, their menstrual periods. Trichomoniasis facilitates the transmission of HIV and is linked to the development of tubal adhesions that can result in infertility. As with many other STIs, many infected women have no symptoms.

Unlike candidiasis, trichomoniasis is nearly always sexually transmitted. Because the parasite can survive for several hours on moist surfaces outside the body, trich can be communicated from contact with infected semen or vaginal discharges on towels, washcloths, and bedclothes. This parasite is one of the few disease agents that can be picked up from a toilet seat, but it would have to directly touch the penis or vulva.

Trichomonas vaginalis can cause NGU in the male, which can be symptom-free or can cause a slight penile discharge that is usually noticeable prior to first urination in the morning. There may be tingling, itching, and other irritating sensations in the urethral tract. Yet most infected men are symptom-free. Therefore, they can unwittingly transfer the organism to their sex partners. Diagnosis is frequently made by microscopic examination of a smear of a woman's vaginal fluids in a physician's office. Diagnosis based on examination of cultures grown from the vaginal smear is considered more reliable, however. When both partners are treated simultaneously, the success rate approaches 100% (Hatcher, 2006; Wingood & DiClemente, 2002).

Viral Infections

Viruses are tiny particles of DNA surrounded by a protein coating. They are incapable of reproducing on their own. When they invade a body cell, however, they can direct the cell's own reproductive machinery to spin off new viral particles that spread to other cells, causing infection. In this section we discuss several viral STIs: *HIV/AIDS*, *herpes*, *viral hepatitis*, and *genital warts*.

HIV/AIDS

HIV stands for **human immunodeficiency virus**, the virus that causes AIDS. **AIDS** stands for **acquired immunodeficiency syndrome**. HIV attacks and disables the immune system, the body's natural line of defence, stripping it of its ability to fend off disease-causing organisms. AIDS is considered fatal, although many people currently live with HIV/AIDS as a result of the development of powerful antiviral medications. For people in industrialized nations like Canada, HIV/AIDS may become a chronic but manageable condition, like diabetes. But for many millions in developing nations, where medications are too expensive or difficult to deliver, HIV/AIDS may remain a death sentence.

THE IMMUNE SYSTEM AND AIDS AIDS is caused by a virus that attacks the body's **immune system**—the body's natural line of defence against disease-causing organisms. The immune system combats disease in a number of ways. It produces white blood cells that envelop and kill **pathogens** such as bacteria, viruses, and fungi; worn-out body cells; and cancer cells. White blood cells are referred to as **leukocytes**. Leukocytes engage in microscopic warfare. They undertake search-and-destroy missions. They identify and eradicate foreign agents and debilitated cells.

Trichomoniasis A form of vaginitis caused by the protozoan *Trichomonas vaginalis.*

Human immunodeficiency virus (HIV) A sexually transmitted virus that destroys white blood cells in the immune system, leaving the body vulnerable to life-threatening diseases.

Acquired immunodeficiency syndrome (AIDS) A condition caused by the human immunodeficiency virus (HIV) and characterized by destruction of the immune system so that the body is stripped of its ability to fend off life-threatening diseases.

Immune system A term for the body's complex of mechanisms for protecting itself from disease-causing agents such as pathogens.

Pathogen An agent, especially a micro-organism, that can cause a disease.

Leukocytes White blood cells that are essential to the body's defences against infection.

Canadian Trends

HIV/AIDS TRENDS

HIV Trends

According to the Public Health Agency of Canada, from 1985 (when HIV testing began) through December 2005, 60 100 people were diagnosed with HIV (including those with AIDS) in Canada. The number of reported positive HIV tests decreased from 1995 to 2000, but has increased since then. There were an estimated 2300 to 4500 new cases that occurred in 2005 (Public Health Agency of Canada, 2006).

Worldwide, the World Health Organization estimates that there are more than 33 million people living with HIV/AIDS. Most cases occur in sub-Saharan Africa.

In Canada, the proportion of positive HIV tests among women increased from less than 10% in 1995 to over one-quarter of the cases. Among women the largest increase currently is among those 15 to 19 years of age. For both men and women, the proportion of HIV infections acquired through heterosexual contact is increasing and now accounts for a third of all positive HIV tests. A significant proportion of the heterosexual HIV infections originated in countries having high HIV prevalence rates, such as those in Africa. The estimated infection rate among individuals who have immigrated from countries where HIV is endemic is 12.5 times higher than among other Canadians (Public Health Agency of Canada, 2006).

Although the proportion of heterosexually acquired HIV infections is increasing, higher prevalence rates are found among men who have sex with men (MSM). About one-half of new HIV cases are among MSM. The proportion of new infections among MSM declined until 1996 and has increased since then. Greater sexual risk-taking among this group, perhaps because contracting AIDS is less feared, may be related to this increase in new infections (Public Health Agency of Canada, 2006).

Injection-drug users account for 14% of new HIV infections. First Nations people make up a growing percentage of people who test positive for HIV, and injection-drug use is the most common means of HIV transmission among this group. Finally, rates of HIV infection in Canadian prisons are much higher than those in the general population (Public Health Agency of Canada, 2006).

There are also many people living with HIV who are not aware they are infected. These people are thus denied the option of beginning viral therapy treatment that could fight the infection and prolong their lives.

AIDS Trends

From 1979 until the end of 2006, a total of 20 669 cases of AIDS had been reported in Canada (Public Health Agency of Canada, 2007). In 2006, women accounted for 24.2% of the total number of reported AIDS cases, a significant increase from 7% in the pre-1997 period. The most dramatic increase has occurred among women between 15 and 29 years old, who now account for 45% of the female AIDS-related infections. Currently men who have sex with men (MSM) account for about a third of new AIDS cases. This is a major decrease, in that prior to 1994, three-quarters of all AIDS cases were recorded for this group. The development of antiviral drugs has significantly contributed to this decrease. However, since the AIDS epidemic began, MSM account for three-quarters of the total number of AIDS cases in Canada. Of the total reported AIDS cases since 1979, 12% have been reported among Canadians 50 years of age and older. This percentage will increase because, by taking antiviral drugs, more HIV-infected individuals are living longer (Public Health Agency of Canada, 2007).

Leukocytes recognize foreign agents by their surface fragments. The surface fragments are termed **antigens** because the body reacts to their presence by developing specialized proteins, or **antibodies**. Antibodies attach themselves to the foreign bodies, inactivate them, and mark them for destruction. (Infection by HIV may be determined by examining the blood or saliva for the presence of antibodies to the virus.)

Antigen A protein, toxin, or other substance to which the body reacts by producing antibodies. (Combined word formed from *anti*body *gen*erator.)

Antibody Specialized protein that attaches itself to a foreign body, inactivates it, and marks it for destruction.

Rather than mark pathogens for destruction or war against them, special "memory lymphocytes" are held in reserve. Memory lymphocytes can remain in the bloodstream for years, and they form the basis for a quick immune response to an invader the second time around.

EFFECTS OF HIV ON THE IMMUNE SYSTEM Spikes (technically known as "gpl20" spikes) on the surface of HIV allow it to bind to sites on cells in the immune system (Sodroski et al., 1998). Like other viruses, HIV uses the cells it invades to spin off copies of itself. HIV uses the enzyme *reverse transcriptase* to cause the genes in the cells it attacks to make proteins that the virus needs in order to reproduce.

HIV directly attacks the immune system by invading and destroying a type of lymphocyte called the CD4 cell or helper T-cell (see Figure 14.4). The CD4 cell is the quarterback of the immune system. CD4 cells "recognize" invading pathogens and signal B-lymphocytes or B-cells—another kind of white blood cell—to produce antibodies that inactivate pathogens and mark them for annihilation. CD4 cells also signal another class of T-cells, called killer T-cells, to destroy infected cells. By attacking and destroying helper T-cells, HIV disables the very cells on which the body relies to fight off this and other diseases. As HIV cripples the body's defences, the individual is exposed to infections that would not otherwise take hold. Cancer cells might also proliferate. Although the CD4 cells appear to be its main target, HIV also attacks other types of white blood cells.

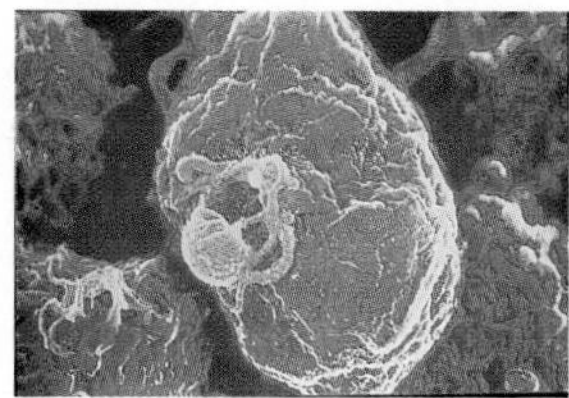

Figure 14.4 HIV (the AIDS Virus) Attacks a White Blood Cell.

HIV progressively weakens the immune system, leaving the body vulnerable to infections and diseases that would otherwise be fended off.

The blood normally contains about 1000 CD4 cells per cubic millimetre. The number of CD4 cells may remain at about this level for years following HIV infection. Many people show no symptoms and appear healthy while CD4 cells remain at this level. Then, for reasons that are not clearly understood, the level of CD4 cells begins to drop off, although symptoms may not appear for a decade or more. As the number of CD4 cells declines, symptoms generally increase, and people fall prey to diseases that their weakened immune systems are unable to fight off. People become most vulnerable to opportunistic infections when the level of CD4 cells falls below 200 per cubic millimetre. Researchers in Vancouver have discovered that treatment for symptoms of AIDS can be started later than previously thought with no difference in health outcomes (Hogg et al., 2001). Specifically, patients can wait until their CD4 cell count drops to 300 instead of 500.

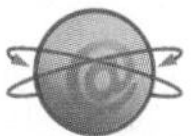

Canadian AIDS Society
Lists a wide range of print resources on HIV/AIDS-related issues.

www.cdnaids.ca

PROGRESSION OF HIV/AIDS HIV follows a complex course once it enters the body. Shortly after infection, the person may experience mild flu-like symptoms—fatigue, fever, headaches and muscle pain, lack of appetite, nausea, swollen glands, and possibly a rash. Such symptoms usually disappear within a few weeks. The infected person may dismiss them as a passing case of flu. People who enter this symptom-free or carrier state generally look and act well and do not realize that they are infectious. Thus they can unwittingly pass the virus along to others.

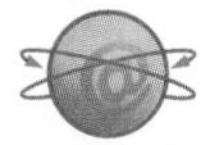

Canadian HIV/AIDS Information Centre
The largest information centre on HIV/AIDS in Canada.

www.aidssida.cpha.ca

Most people who are infected with HIV remain symptom-free for years. Some enter a symptomatic state that is typically marked by chronically swollen lymph nodes and intermittent weight loss, fever, fatigue, and diarrhea. This symptomatic state does not constitute full-blown AIDS, but it shows that HIV is undermining the integrity of the immune system.

The beginnings of full-blown AIDS are often marked by such symptoms as swollen lymph nodes, fatigue, fever, night sweats, diarrhea, and weight loss that cannot be attributed to dieting or exercise.

AIDS is connected with the appearance of diseases such as pneumonia, Kaposi's sarcoma (a form of cancer), toxoplasmosis of the brain (an infection of parasites), and *Herpes simplex* with chronic ulcers. These diseases are termed **opportunistic diseases** because they are not likely to emerge unless a disabled immune system provides the opportunity.

About 10% of people with AIDS have a wasting syndrome. Wasting, the unintentional loss of more than 10% of a person's body weight, is connected with AIDS, some other infections, and cancer. As AIDS progresses, the individual grows thinner and more fatigued. He or she becomes unable to perform ordinary life functions and falls prey to opportunistic infections. If left untreated, AIDS nearly always results in death within a few years.

Opportunistic diseases
Diseases that take hold only when the immune system is weakened and unable to fend them off.

TRANSMISSION HIV can be transmitted by certain contaminated bodily fluids: blood, semen, vaginal secretions, and breast milk. The first three of these may enter the body through vaginal, anal, or oral–genital intercourse with an infected partner. HIV may enter the body through tiny cuts or sores in the mucosal lining of the vagina, the rectum, and even the mouth. These cuts or sores can be so tiny that

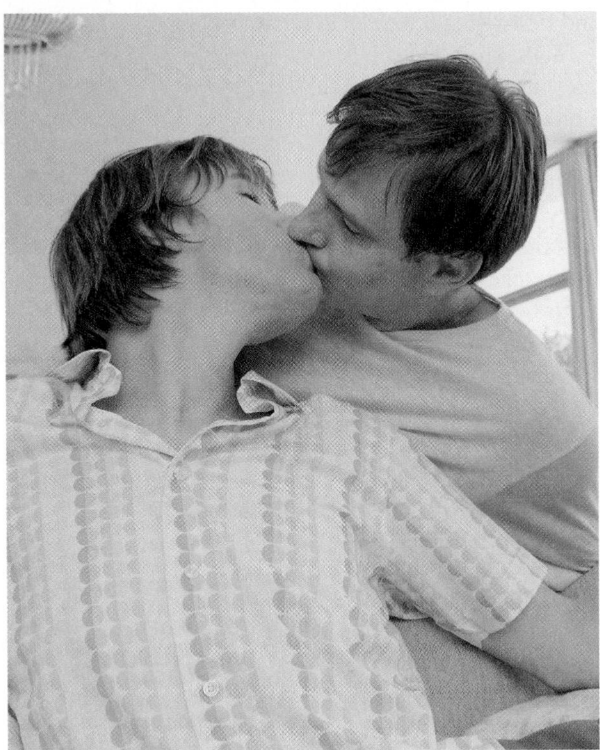

Can Kissing Transmit HIV?
HIV is a blood-borne virus that is transmitted via various bodily fluids, including blood, semen, and vaginal fluids. However, the Centers for Disease Control and Prevention (CDC) have not found that HIV occurs in infectious quantities in saliva.

you are not aware of them. Transmission of HIV through kissing—even prolonged kissing or "French" kissing—is considered unlikely.

Another avenue of infection is sharing a hypodermic needle with an infected person. When a person injects drugs, a small amount of his or her blood remains inside the needle and syringe. If the person is HIV-infected, the virus may be found in the blood remaining in the needle or syringe. Others who use the needle inject the infected blood into their bloodstream. HIV can also be spread by sharing needles used for other purposes, such as injecting steroids, ear piercing, or tattooing.

HIV can also be transmitted from mother to fetus during pregnancy or from mother to child through childbirth or breastfeeding. The transmission of HIV from an HIV-infected mother to her infant through pregnancy and delivery is between 15% and 30% in the absence of intervention. Transmission via breast milk occurs in approximately 10% to 20% of cases (Public Health Agency of Canada, 2007).

In 2004, 163 infants in Canada were born to HIV-positive mothers. However, only 2% of those infants became HIV infected, as 96% of the mothers received antiviral therapy (Public Health Agency of Canada, 2007).

Male-to-female transmission through vaginal intercourse is about twice as likely as female-to-male transmission partly because more of the virus is found in the ejaculate than in vaginal secretions. A man's ejaculate may also remain for many days in the vagina, providing greater opportunity for infection to occur. Male–female or male–male anal intercourse is especially risky, particularly to the recipient, because it often tears or abrades rectal tissue, facilitating entry of the virus into the bloodstream (Caceres & van-Griensven, 1994). Worldwide, male–female sexual intercourse accounts for the majority of cases of HIV/AIDS.

DIAGNOSIS OF HIV/AIDS The most widely used test for HIV infection is the enzyme-linked immunosorbent assay (ELISA), which may take three weeks to yield results. ELISA does not directly detect HIV in the blood. Instead, it reveals HIV antibodies. People may show an antibody response to HIV long before they develop symptoms of infection. A positive (**seropositive**) test result means that antibodies were found and usually indicates that the person is infected with HIV. A negative (**seronegative**) outcome means that antibodies to HIV were not detected.

Seropositive Having a pathogen or antibodies to that pathogen in the bloodstream.

Seronegative Lacking a pathogen or antibodies to that pathogen in the bloodstream.

ELISA can be performed on samples of blood, saliva, or urine. A group of Ontario researchers has demonstrated that the saliva test is almost as accurate as the blood test (Major et al., 1991). A saliva test is less expensive and might encourage people who avoid blood tests to be tested. Although HIV antibodies can be detected in saliva, HIV itself is not found in measurable quantities. This is why kissing is not considered an avenue of transmission of HIV. The saliva is absorbed by a cotton pad on a stick that is placed between the lower gum and the cheek. The saliva in the cotton, like blood, undergoes analysis in a laboratory. When these types of tests show evidence of the presence of HIV antibodies, the presence of the virus itself can be confirmed by more expensive tests, such as the Western blot test or an immunofluorescence assay. HIV tests are not considered accurate until three months have passed since the person's last exposure to the HIV virus. This is generally how long the body takes to produce antibodies.

The most significant change in testing procedures has been the development of rapid testing technologies, so that test results can be given much sooner than previously. In 2007, Ontario was the first province to offer HIV tests that provide results within one minute. The test is available at anonymous HIV- and STI-testing sites and clinics across the province.

Individuals can choose to be tested in a doctor's office or at an anonymous testing site. In a 2003 survey, one-quarter of Canadians reported that they had been tested for HIV. Among men who have sex with men, 71% had been tested (Public Health Agency of Canada, 2007).

HAART (pronounced *HEART*) The acronym for "highly active antiretroviral therapy," which refers to the combination, or "cocktail," of drugs used to treat HIV/AIDS: a protease inhibitor in combination with a couple of other antiretroviral agents.

TREATMENT OF HIV/AIDS For many years, researchers were frustrated by failure in the effort to develop effective vaccines and treatments for HIV/AIDS. There is still no safe, effective vaccine.

Today many drugs are used to combat HIV/AIDS. Drugs that block the replication of HIV, called *protease inhibitors*, target the protease enzyme. A combination, or "cocktail," of antiviral drugs has become the standard treatment of HIV/AIDS. This combination—referred to as **HAART** (for "highly active antiretroviral therapy")—decreases the likelihood that HIV will develop resistance to treatment. It has reduced HIV below detectable levels in many infected people (Lederman & Valdez, 2000). It has also created hope that AIDS will become increasingly manageable—a chronic health problem as opposed to a terminal illness. Haart therapies have a number of negative side effects that make continually taking the antiviral drugs more difficult for HIV-positive people. Also, these therapies can accelerate problems such as depression, memory deficits, and liver and kidney disease.

HAART is expensive, however, and many people who could benefit from it cannot afford it. People in less-developed nations make do, or not, on less expensive medications or on no medication.

HAART has worked many wonders to date in reducing the death rate from AIDS. Yet even when HIV has been reduced to "undetectable levels" by ordinary means, scientists have been able to use methods of close scrutiny to locate it in "resting" (nonreplicating) CD4 cells (Lederman & Valdez, 2000). Therefore, HAART does not appear to be a cure.

In Windsor, Ontario, researchers have studied how the newer HAART therapies for HIV have affected the lives of 31 men and 4 women who are HIV-positive (Adams et al., 2001). While many reported substantial improvement in their health as a consequence of the therapies, some emphasized that their condition was "tolerable." Those who had been recently diagnosed as experiencing symptoms related to HIV were all responding well. Many felt that they could lead more normal lives. Most reported that sexual desire decreased significantly at the time of HIV diagnosis but that sexual desire and activity returned over time. Severity of illness rather than relationship status was the strongest predictor of sexual activity. Most of those who did not have any physical symptoms were sexually active, whereas those who had the most severe physical symptoms were not. However, some avoided sexual activity, because they did not want to put a partner at risk. For those who did not feel comfortable disclosing their HIV status to others, the internet provided a source of

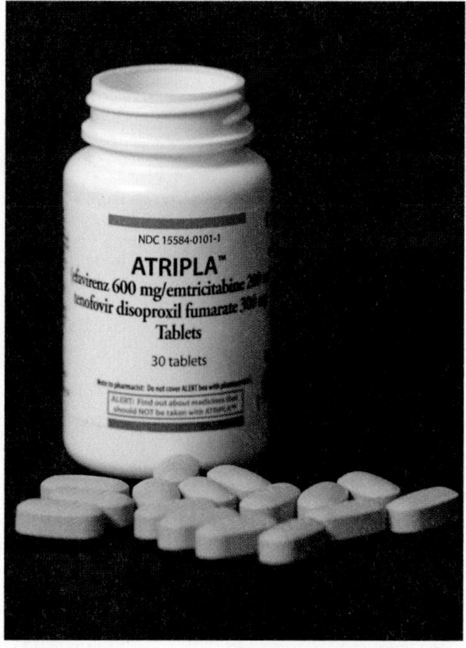

Atripla.
A new three-in-one pill, Atripla, makes it easy to manage the regimen of HAART ("highly active antiretroviral therapy"). Atripla contains a "cocktail" of antiviral drugs that have become the standard treatment of HIV/AIDS in developed countries.

Welcome to Condom Country.
Condom ads based on the ruggedly masculine Marlboro tobacco ads are used by the AIDS Committee of Toronto during Pride Week to encourage gay men to use condoms.

information and friendship. Several were involved in HIV/AIDS support groups.

PREVENTION What can we do to curb the spread of HIV/AIDS? Given that we lack both a vaccine and a cure, prevention is our best hope. Our discussion of prevention will focus on sexual transmission, but other efforts have been made to prevent transmission of HIV from mother to child, through the injection of drugs with shared needles, and through blood transfusions. For example, HIV-infected women are advised to avoid breastfeeding. Zidovudine and other measures, such as C-section, decrease the probability of transmission through childbirth (Ricci et al., 2000). The screening of potential blood donors has rendered the probability of transmission via blood transfusion almost negligible.

Most prevention efforts focus on education. Sexually active people have been advised to alter their sexual behaviour by practising abstinence, by limiting their sexual experiences to a lifelong monogamous relationship, or by practising "safe sex"—which, as we shall see, could more accurately be dubbed "safer sex."

The advent of HIV/AIDS presents the medical, mental health, and educational communities with an unprecedented challenge: to develop programs to contain its spread and to treat people with HIV/AIDS compassionately. Although HIV/AIDS is frightening, it is preventable. For the latest information on HIV/AIDS, call the Toronto AIDS hotline: 1-800-267-6600. The call is free and anonymous. We expand our discussion of prevention of HIV/AIDS in the box entitled "Preventing STIs" later in this chapter.

Herpes

Once you get herpes, it's yours for life. After the initial attack, it remains an unwelcome guest in your body forever. It finds a cozy place to lie low until it stirs up trouble again. It causes recurrent outbreaks that often happen at the worst times, such as around final exams. This is not just bad luck. Stress can depress the functioning of the immune system and heighten the likelihood of outbreaks.

Not only are you stuck with the virus, but you can also pass it along to sex partners for the rest of your life. Flare-ups may continue to recur, sometimes with annoying frequency. On the other hand, some people have no recurrences. Still others have mild, brief recurrences that become less frequent over time.

Herpes simplex virus type 1 The virus that causes oral herpes, which is characterized by cold sores or fever blisters on the lips or mouth. Abbreviated *HSV-1.*

Genital herpes An STI caused by the *Herpes simplex* virus type 2 and characterized by painful, shallow sores and blisters on the genitals.

***Herpes simplex* virus type 2** The virus that causes genital herpes. Abbreviated *HSV-2.*

Different types of herpes are caused by variants of the *Herpes simplex* virus. The most common type, ***Herpes simplex* virus type 1** (HSV-1), causes oral herpes. Oral herpes is characterized by cold sores or fever blisters on the lips or mouth. It can also be transferred to the genitals by the hands or by oral–genital contact (Mertz et al., 1992). **Genital herpes** is caused by a related but distinct virus, the ***Herpes simplex* virus type 2** (HSV-2). This virus produces painful, shallow sores and blisters on the genitals. HSV-2 can also be transferred to the mouth through oral–genital contact. Both types of herpes can be transmitted sexually.

Physicians are not required to report cases of herpes to public health officials, so there are no precise statistics on its prevalence.

Ocular herpes A herpes infection of the eye, usually caused by touching an infected area of the body and then touching the eye.

Prodromal symptoms Warning symptoms that signal the onset or flare-up of a disease.

TRANSMISSION Herpes can be transmitted through oral, anal, or vaginal sexual activity with an infected person. The herpes viruses can also survive for several hours on toilet seats or other objects, where they can be picked up by direct contact. Oral herpes is easily contracted by drinking from the same cup as an infected person, by kissing, and even by sharing towels. But genital herpes is generally spread by coitus or by oral or anal sex.

Many people do not realize that they are infected, and so they can unknowingly transmit the virus through sexual contact. And many of the people who do know they are infected don't realize that they can pass along the virus even when they have no noticeable outbreak (Wald et al., 1995). Although genital herpes is most contagious during active flare-ups, it can also be transmitted when an infected partner has no symptoms (genital sores or feelings of burning or itching in the genitals). Any intimate contact with an infected person carries some risk of transmission of the virus, even if the infected person never has another outbreak. People may also be infected with the virus and have *no* outbreaks, and yet pass the virus along to others.

Herpes can also be spread from one part of the body to another by touching the infected area and then touching another body part. One potentially serious result is a herpes infection of the eye: **ocular herpes**. Thorough washing with soap and water after touching an infected area may reduce the risk of spreading the infection to other parts of the body.

Women with genital herpes are more likely than the general population to have miscarriages. Passage through the birth canal of an infected mother can infect babies with genital herpes, damaging or killing them. Obstetricians thus often perform caesarean sections if the mother has active lesions or **prodromal symptoms** at the time of delivery.

SYMPTOMS Genital lesions or sores appear about six to eight days after infection with genital herpes. At first they appear as reddish, painful bumps, or papules, along the penis or vulva (see Figure 14.5). They may also appear on the thighs or buttocks, in the vagina, or on the cervix. These papules turn into groups of small blisters that are filled with fluid containing infectious viral particles. The blisters are attacked by the body's immune system (white blood cells). They fill with pus, burst, and become extremely painful, shallow sores or ulcers surrounded by a red ring. People are especially infectious during such outbreaks, because the ulcers shed millions of viral particles. Other symptoms may include headaches and muscle aches, swollen lymph glands, fever, burning urination, and a vaginal discharge. The blisters crust over and heal in one to three weeks. Internal sores in the vagina or on the cervix may take 10 days longer than external (labial) sores to heal. Physicians thus advise infected women to avoid unprotected intercourse for at least 10 days after the healing of external sores.

Although the symptoms disappear, the disease does not. The virus remains in the body permanently, burrowing into nerve cells in the base of the spine, where it may lie dormant for years or for a lifetime. The infected person is least contagious during this dormant stage. For reasons that remain unclear, the virus becomes reactivated and gives rise to recurrences in most cases.

Recurrences may be related to infections (such as a cold), stress, fatigue, depression, exposure to the sun, and hormonal changes such as those that occur during pregnancy or menstruation. Recurrences tend to occur within 3 to 12 months of the initial episode and to affect the same part of the body.

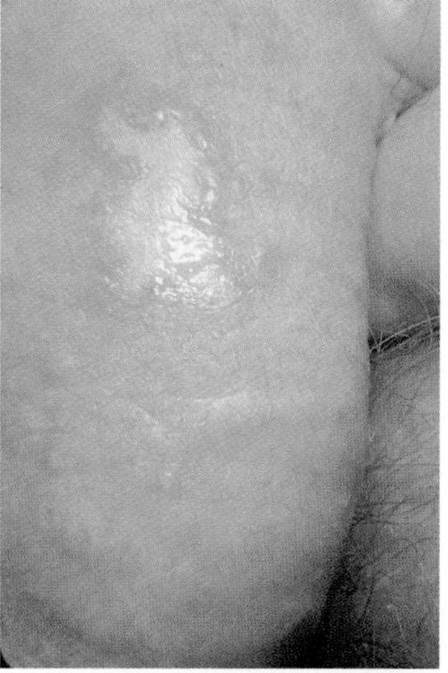

Figure 14.5 Herpes Lesion on the Male Genitals.

Herpes lesions or sores can appear on the genitals in both men and women. In contrast to the syphilis chancre, they can be quite painful. Herpes is most likely to be transmitted during outbreaks of the disease (when the sores are present, that is), but it can be transmitted at other times as well.

The symptoms of oral herpes include sores or blisters on the lips, the inside of the mouth, the tongue, or the throat. Fever and feelings of sickness may occur. The gums may swell and redden. The sores heal over in about two weeks, and the virus retreats into nerve cells at the base of the neck, where it lies dormant between flare-ups.

DIAGNOSIS AND TREATMENT Genital herpes is first diagnosed by clinical inspection of herpetic sores or ulcers in the mouth or on the genitals. A sample of fluid may be taken from the base of a genital sore and cultured in the laboratory to detect the growth of the virus.

Viruses, unlike the bacteria that cause gonorrhea or syphilis, do not respond to antibiotics. Antiviral drugs can relieve pain, speed healing, and reduce the duration of viral shedding (Hatcher, 2006). Oral administration of antiviral drugs may reduce the severity of the initial episode and, if taken regularly, the frequency and duration of recurrent outbreaks (Hatcher, 2006).

There is encouraging news about the development of a vaccine against genital herpes, called Simplirix (Cunningham et al., 2006). In pilot studies, the vaccine is reported to have prevented herpes outbreaks in more than 70% of women who had not previously had cold sores or genital herpes. The herpes virus that causes cold sores ironically confers some protection against genital herpes, but the vaccine does not help women who have already contracted genital herpes. It remains unclear why the vaccine has been ineffective with men.

Warm baths, loosely fitting clothing, Aspirin, and cold, wet compresses may relieve pain during flare-ups. People with herpes are advised to maintain regular sleeping habits and to learn to manage stress.

COPING WITH GENITAL HERPES The psychological problems connected with herpes can be more distressing than the physical effects of the illness. The prospects of a lifetime of recurrences and concerns about infecting one's sex partners exacerbate the emotional impact of herpes.

Most people with herpes learn to cope. Some are helped by support groups that share ways of living with the disease. A caring and trusting partner is important.

The attitudes of people with herpes also play a role in their success in adjusting to it. People who view herpes as a manageable illness or problem, not as a medical disaster or a character deficit, find it easier to cope.

Viral Hepatitis

Hepatitis is an inflammation of the liver that may be caused by such factors as chronic alcoholism and exposure to toxic materials. Viral hepatitis comprises several different types of hepatitis caused by related, but distinct, viruses. The major types are *hepatitis A*, *hepatitis B*, *hepatitis C*, and *hepatitis D*.

Most people with acute hepatitis have no symptoms. When symptoms do appear, they often include **jaundice**, feelings of weakness and nausea, loss of appetite, abdominal discomfort, whitish bowel movements, and brownish or tea-coloured urine. The symptoms of hepatitis B tend to be more severe and long-lasting than those of hepatitis A or C. In about 10% of cases, hepatitis B leads to chronic liver disease. Hepatitis C tends to have milder symptoms but often leads to chronic liver disease such as cirrhosis or cancer of the liver. Hepatitis D occurs only in the presence of hepatitis B. Hepatitis D, which has symptoms similar to those of hepatitis B, can produce severe liver damage and often leads to death.

The hepatitis A virus is transmitted through contact with infected fecal matter found in contaminated food or water, and by oral contact with fecal matter, such as through oral–anal sexual activity (licking or mouthing the partner's anus). (It is largely because of the risk of hepatitis A that restaurant employees are required to wash their hands after using the toilet.) Ingesting uncooked infested shellfish is also a frequent means of transmission of hepatitis A.

Hepatitis An inflammation of the liver.

Jaundice A yellowish discoloration of the skin and the whites of the eyes.

Hepatitis B can be transmitted sexually through anal, vaginal, or oral intercourse with an infected partner; through transfusion with contaminated blood supplies; by the sharing of contaminated needles or syringes; and by contact with contaminated saliva, menstrual blood, nasal mucus, or semen. Sharing razors, toothbrushes, or other personal articles with an infected person can also transmit hepatitis B. Hepatitis C and hepatitis D can be transmitted sexually or through contact with contaminated blood. A person can transmit the viruses that cause hepatitis even if he or she is unaware of having any symptoms of the disease.

In Canada, infection rates for hepatitis A and B declined significantly during the 1990s. However, the rate for hepatitis C has increased, and of the hepatitis viruses, it has by far the highest rate of infection (Health Canada, 2001). In Canada, the incidence of hepatitis B is about 2.3 per 100 000 and is twice as high in men as in women (Public Health Agency of Canada, 2008).

Hepatitis is usually diagnosed by testing blood samples for the presence of hepatitis antigens and antibodies. There is no cure for viral hepatitis. Bed rest and fluids are usually recommended until the acute stage of the infection subsides, generally in a few weeks. Full recovery may take months. A vaccine provides protection against hepatitis B and also against hepatitis D, because hepatitis D can occur only if hepatitis B is present (Hatcher, 2006).

Genital warts An STI that is caused by the human papilloma virus and takes the form of warts that appear around the genitals and anus.

Genital Warts

The *human papilloma virus* (HPV) causes **genital warts**. HPV is a common sexually transmitted infection and approximately 75% of the adult population will have one HPV infection in their lifetime (Health Canada, 2007). Although the warts may appear in visible areas of the skin, in most cases they appear in areas that cannot be seen, such as on the cervix in women or in the urethra in men. Within a few months following infection, the warts are usually found in the genital and anal regions. Women are more susceptible to HPV infection because cells in the cervix divide swiftly, facilitating the multiplication of HPV. It should be noted that HPV infection does not always lead to having warts.

Genital warts are itchy bumps that vary in size and shape. Genital warts are hard and yellow-grey when they form on dry skin, but they take on pink, soft, cauliflower shapes in moist areas such as the lower vagina (see Figure 14.6). In men they appear on the penis, foreskin, and scrotum and in the urethra. They appear on the vulva, along the vaginal wall, and on the cervix in women. They can also occur outside the genital area—for example, in the mouth; on the lips, eyelids, or nipples; around the anus; or in the rectum.

Genital warts may not cause any symptoms and go away without being treated. However, some warts can last for years. Those that form on the urethra can cause bleeding or painful discharges. HPV has been implicated in cancers of the genital organs, particularly cervical cancer and penile cancer. Most cases of cervical cancer are linked to certain strains of HPV. Yet, in most women, HPV does not lead to cervical cancer. Stress seems to play a key role in whether or not HPV leads to cancer. HPV-infected women with higher levels of stress are more likely to develop cervical cancer (Fang, 2008).

Figure 14.6 Genital Warts.

Genital warts are caused by the human papilloma virus (HPV) and may have a cauliflower-like appearance. Many cases occur where they can go visually undetected. HPV is implicated in cervical cancer.

HPV is also linked to throat and anal cancers. Oral sex appears to be a key factor in the relationship between HPV and throat cancer. Since the early 1970s, the proportion of throat cancers attributed to HPV has risen substantially, especially for men. This increase is probably due to an increase in oral-sex behaviours. Contracting an oral HPV infection is strongly related to having a high number of oral-sex partners (Fakhry & Gillison, 2006). The good news is that relatively few people with an oral HPV infection will get throat cancer.

Because of recent publicity surrounding HPV and cancer, some people may mistakenly believe that HPV infection always leads to cancer. The reality is that most

Ectoparasites Parasites that live on the outside of the host's body—in contrast to *endo*parasites, which live within the body.

Pediculosis A parasitic infestation by pubic lice (*Pthirus pubis*) that causes itching.

HPV infections do not lead to cancer. Also, in most cases the cancer when detected can be effectively treated, especially if the cancer is detected early (Barrett, 2006).

HPV can be transmitted sexually through skin-to-skin contact during vaginal, anal, and oral sex. It can also be transmitted by other forms of contact, such as touching infected towels or clothing. The incubation period may vary from a few weeks to a couple of years.

Freezing the wart (*cryotherapy*) with liquid nitrogen is a preferred treatment. One alternative treatment involves painting or coating the warts over several days with a solution, gel, or cream (Hatcher, 2006). An alcohol-based podophyllin solution causes the warts to dry up and fall off. The warts can also be treated by a doctor with electrodes (burning) or surgery (by laser or surgical removal). Unfortunately, although the warts themselves may be removed, treatment does not rid the body of the virus (Hatcher, 2006), and there may be recurrences.

Latex condoms are highly effective in reducing the risk of contracting HPV. In one study, women whose partners always used condoms were 70% less likely to be infected with HPV than those whose partners used them less than 5% of the time (Winer et al., 2006). Condoms do not eliminate the risk entirely, because the virus can be transmitted from areas of the skin not protected by condoms, such as the scrotum. People with active warts should probably avoid sexual contact until the warts are removed and the area heals completely.

VACCINE The most recent advance in the fight against STIs has been the development of a vaccine that immunizes against four particular strains of HPV. These strains are responsible for 90% of the genital warts that cause the majority of cases of cervical, vulvar, and vaginal cancers. The vaccine Gardasil is approved in Canada for females between the ages of 9 and 26. The main target females are those who have not yet been sexually active and thus have never had an HPV infection. The ideal age group for vaccination is girls between 9 and 12. School vaccination programs are being sponsored by the federal and some provincial governments. Three injections of the vaccine are required over a six-month period.

Some parents and religious groups have opposed the vaccine, fearing that it might encourage promiscuity. Some health professionals are concerned about possible long-term adverse effects of the vaccine. There has been considerable media publicity regarding these concerns. Accordingly, only 54% of Ontario parents whose daughters were in grade 8 during the 2007–2008 school year gave permission for their daughters to receive the vaccine (Crawford, 2008).

The pharmaceutical company Merck & Co. is currently applying for government approval to have the vaccine available to women over the age of 26. However, given that by the age of 26, most women will have had an HPV infection, the value of vaccinating women in this age group is questionable. Merck & Co. is also conducting research with males to see if they can benefit from the vaccine.

Figure 14.7 Pubic Lice.

Pediculosis is an infestation by pubic lice (*Pthirus pubis*). Pubic lice are commonly called "crabs" because of their appearance under a microscope.

Ectoparasitic Infestations

Ectoparasites live on the outer surfaces of animals. Ectoparasites are larger than the agents that cause other STIs. In this section we consider two types of STIs caused by ectoparasites: pediculosis and scabies.

Pediculosis

Pediculosis is the name given to an infestation of a parasite whose proper Latin name, *Pthirus pubis* (pubic lice), sounds rather too dignified for these bothersome (dare we say ugly?) creatures that are better known as crabs. Pubic lice are commonly called crabs because, under the microscope, they are somewhat similar in appearance to crabs (see Figure 14.7).

Scabies A parasitic infestation caused by a tiny mite (*Sarcoptes scabiei*) that causes itching.

In the adult stage, pubic lice are large enough to be seen with the naked eye. They are spread sexually but can also be transmitted via contact with an infested towel, sheet, or—yes—toilet seat. They can survive for only about 24 hours without a human host, but they may deposit eggs that can take up to seven days to hatch in bedding or towels. Therefore, all bedding, towels, and clothes that have been used by an infested person must be either dry-cleaned or washed in hot water and dried on the hot cycle to ensure that they are safe. Fingers may also transmit the lice from the genitals to other hair-covered parts of the body, including the scalp and armpits. Sexual contact should be avoided until the infestation is eradicated.

Itching, ranging from the mildly irritating to the intolerable, is the most prominent symptom of an infestation of pubic lice. The itching is caused by the "crabs" attaching themselves to the pubic hair and piercing the skin to feed on the blood of their hosts. (Yecch!) An infestation can be treated effectively with medication.

Scabies

Scabies (short for *Sarcoptes scabiei*) is a parasitic infestation caused by a tiny mite that may be transmitted through sexual contact or contact with infested clothing, bed linen, towels, and other fabrics. The mites attach themselves to the base of pubic hair and burrow into the skin, where they lay eggs and subsist for the duration of their 30-day life span. Like pubic lice, scabies are often found in the genital region and cause itching and discomfort. They are also responsible for reddish lines (created by burrowing) and for sores, welts, or blisters on the skin. Unlike lice, they are too tiny to be seen by the naked eye. Diagnosis is made by detecting the mite or its by-products via microscopic examination of scrapings from suspicious-looking areas of skin (Levine, 1991). Scabies are most often found on the hands and wrists, but they may also appear on the genitals, buttocks, armpits, and feet. They do not appear above the neck—thankfully!

Scabies, like pubic lice, may be treated effectively with medication. To avoid reinfection, sex partners and others in close bodily contact with infected individuals should also be treated. Clothing and bed linen that the infected person has used must be washed and dried on the hot cycle or dry-cleaned. As with "crabs," sexual contact should be avoided until the infestation is eliminated.

Prevention of STIs

Knowledge of STIs and AIDS

A first step in prevention is knowledge. Yet many Canadians lack up-to-date knowledge about STIs and HIV/AIDS. The Canadian Youth, Sexual Health and HIV/AIDS Study asked students a number of questions about these topics (Boyce et al., 2003). One of the disappointing findings was that in 2002 the adolescents were less knowledgeable in some areas than were youth in the 1989 study. For example, fewer students in grade 7 were knowledgeable about the risks of HIV transmission from sharing drug needles, sex without condoms, and multiple partners. Also, fewer adolescents in 2002 knew that it was incorrect to assume HIV/AIDS can be cured if treated early. On the other hand, knowledge had increased about other STIs. As an example, more of the 2002 adolescents knew that chlamydia can lead to serious complications. However, there are some important facts that many youth of today are not aware of. For example, more than 40% of grade 11 students do not know that a person can get genital herpes from having oral sex or that many people with STIs do not show any signs or symptoms (Boyce et al., 2003).

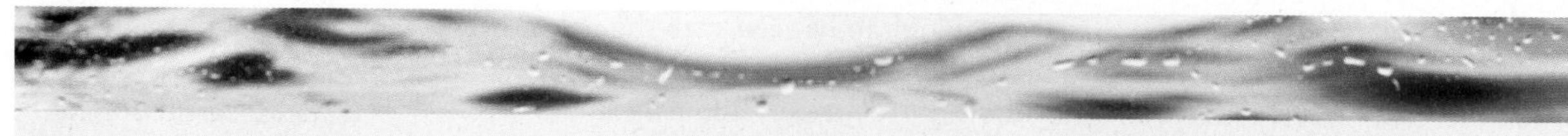

A World of Diversity

QUASI-EXPERIMENTAL EVALUATION OF A NATIONAL PRIMARY SCHOOL HIV INTERVENTION IN KENYA

Eleanor Maticka-Tyndale (2007), of the University of Windsor, has led an international group of researchers in developing and evaluating a primary-school-based HIV prevention program in Kenya. They used a quasi-experimental research procedure along with both quantitative and qualitative research methods. Forty schools received the HIV educational prevention program and the effects were compared with 40 schools that did not receive the program. The research showed a significant impact of the educational program on students aged 11 to 16. The students learned about HIV prevention and how to communicate more openly about HIV. The effects on behaviour were gender specific: the girls delayed engaging in sexual activities and the boys used condoms more frequently. The educational program had its greatest impact on youth who were not yet sexually active. Thus, the researchers concluded that it should be implemented with the youngest age groups possible (Maticka-Tyndale et al., 2007).

Sources of Help

Many different strategies are being used to inform the public about STI/AIDS. All provinces and territories have STI/AIDS telephone information lines that offer anonymous counselling and information about a wide range of sexual health issues. In 2000, the most common questions among the 25 280 calls to the Toronto line related to unprotected sex or condom failure. The type of sexual contact most asked about was vaginal intercourse, and more questions were asked about STIs than about birth control. On the subject of HIV testing, the callers' main concerns were pretest counselling; testing options, including anonymous testing; and incubation/seroconversion time frames (Public Health and Epidemiology Report Ontario, 2002).

Why Is It So Difficult to Eliminate STIs and HIV?

Despite massive educational programs, STIs continue to proliferate. Why is this? Of course an obvious answer is that people are engaging in risky sexual behaviours, such as not using condoms consistently. Current sexual behaviours are definitely related to STI infections. These include having sexual intercourse at a young age and having many sexual partners. These behaviours increase the probability of having sex with someone who has an STI.

In explaining why people engage in behaviours that put them at risk of STI infection, researchers analyze several factors. What are these factors?

In answering this question, we return to the first chapter's discussion of the multidisciplinary nature of human sexuality. You may recall that at the beginning we stated that in order to more fully understand how we function as sexual beings, we need to be aware of the roles played by biological, psychological, and social factors. This multidisciplinary approach certainly is useful when explaining why it is difficult to eliminate STIs.

Biological Factors

BODY LOCATIONS STIs love warm, moist locations such as in genitals and rectums. Thus anyone having unprotected vaginal or anal intercourse with an infected person is at risk. Oral–genital sex is less risky; however, it is not risk-free as many people believe. Proper use of condoms can substantially reduce the risks of STI infection, as using a condom prevents the exchange of body fluids.

The anus provides a convenient port of entry for HIV, because anal sex often results in the tearing or abrading of the rectal lining. In a Toronto study of men who had sex with men who had AIDS, those men who engaged in either insertive or receptive anal intercourse were more likely to be HIV-positive themselves (Coates et al., 1988). Those men who engaged in activities that could damage the lining of the rectum, such as rectal douching, receptive fisting, and placing objects in the anus, were also at greater risk of HIV infection.

AMOUNT OF VIRUS The amount of HIV virus in semen also affects the probability of infection. The quantity of HIV in the semen peaks shortly after initial infection, and when full-blown AIDS develops.

ALREADY HAVING AN STI Some STIs—such as genital warts, gonorrhea, trichomoniasis, and chlamydia—inflame the genital region, which heightens the risk of sexual transmission of other STIs. STIs that produce genital ulcers, such as syphilis and genital herpes, may heighten vulnerability to HIV infection by allowing the virus to enter the circulatory system through the ulcers.

GENDER Biologically, women are more susceptible to STI infection than are men. The warm, moist environment of the vagina is more hospitable to bacteria, viruses, and fungi than the exterior of the male penis. Also, the location of the urethra and bladder in women makes them more susceptible to infection.

LACK OF SYMPTOMS Often infections can occur without there being any obvious symptoms. Thus, unwittingly an infected person can transmit the infection to a partner.

LACK OF VACCINES OR CURES It has been very difficult to develop vaccines to prevent STIs. The HIV virus has been especially resistant to vaccines. Fortunately, an effective vaccine has recently been developed to prevent HPV. Also, there is now a vaccine that appears to be successful in preventing herpes infections.

CIRCUMCISION For men whose penises are not circumcised, the risk of infection may be higher. However, as discussed earlier, there are conflicting research findings. Studies in Africa clearly indicate that these men are more vulnerable to STI/HIV infection, while research in the U.S. and Australia is divided on this issue.

GENETIC FACTORS Genetic factors may also be at work. About 1% of people of Western European descent have inherited a gene from both parents that prevents HIV from entering cells in the immune system, and these people are apparently immune to HIV infection. Perhaps 20% of individuals of Western European descent have inherited this gene from one parent; HIV disease appears to progress more slowly in these people. Some prostitutes in Thailand and Africa, where HIV infection has been running rampant, also appear to be immune to HIV infection (Royce et al., 1997).

Psychological Factors

A number of psychological factors are predictive of sexual risk-taking. These include perceived low risk of infection, myth of personal invulnerability, not being aware if partner is infected, negative attitudes toward condoms, drug and alcohol abuse, and difficulty discussing sexual health issues.

PERCEIVED LOW RISK OF INFECTION One of the major stumbling blocks in promoting safer-sex practices is that many young heterosexuals perceive a low risk of contracting HIV. People who perceive themselves as being at low risk are less likely to alter their behaviour.

Given the relatively low rate of known HIV infections among heterosexuals who do not inject drugs, many heterosexuals may perceive risky sexual practices to be a reasonable gamble. Heterosexuals who have never had a friend or relative with HIV/AIDS may dismiss it as a problem that affects other types of people, but not them.

In the 2002 Canada Youth and AIDS Survey, only 45% of youth said they were worried about catching HIV/AIDS—fewer than in 1989 (Boyce et al., 2003). Montreal researchers Rupert Klein and Barbel Knäuper (2003) found that some young people purposely avoid thinking about STIs and consequently are less likely to discuss safer sex with a partner and less likely to use condoms. In another study (Knäuper et al., 2005), university students felt they were less at risk if they had sex with an appealing rather than an unappealing partner, and thus were less likely to use condoms with an appealing partner.

Gay men may also operate under the "I'm not the type" fallacy and underestimate their personal risks. In a 2002 survey of gay and bisexual men in Ontario, half of the men who had never had an HIV test said that they had never had an HIV test because they believed they were at low risk of infection (Myers et al., 2004a).

MYTH OF PERSONAL INVULNERABILITY Some people believe that they are somehow immune to STIs or AIDS and other diseases. In a national survey, one-half of Canadians distanced themselves from HIV/AIDS. They perceived that only other people could become infected with HIV/AIDS, but not themselves (Rattner et al., 2007). Perceptions of personal invulnerability help to explain why STI/AIDS education does not always translate into behavioural change.

UNAWARE PARTNER IS INFECTED Many people are embarrassed to ask if a partner has an STI infection. Also, some people who do have an infection are reluctant to disclose this for fear disclosure may lead to not having sex and/or the end of a relationship. In casual relationships an infected person may not care about putting the other person at risk. It is not unusual for someone with an STI or HIV infection to hide this information from a partner or even to lie about this condition.

In the 2002 Ontario study of gay and bisexual men, 45% of those with HIV said that in the three months previous to the study, they did not disclose this condition to casual sex partners and another 30% said they sometimes disclosed their status. Unfortunately, we do not have comparable data regarding disclosure among HIV-positive heterosexuals. However, cases brought before the courts indicate there are many HIV-infected heterosexuals who do not disclose their status to sexual partners.

In Kitchener, Ontario, a man pleaded guilty to charges of aggravated assault for infecting four women with the HIV virus. Even though he knew that he was HIV-positive, he had unprotected sex with the women and did not tell them he was infected (Wood, 2002). In Toronto, a man, originally from Trinidad, was charged with aggravated assault and endangering life after his wife died of AIDS-related illnesses, because he had not told her that he was HIV-positive. After the man's arrest, five other women complained to police that he had had sexual contact with them but did not disclose his HIV status (Powell & Chung, 2005). More recently, in 2008, a Windsor, Ontario, man was sentenced to 18 years in prison for not informing his sexual partners that he was HIV-positive. Five of the 15 women he had sex with became infected with HIV. One of the women was 16 years old when she first had sex with him (Loiselle, 2008).

Almost all of the nondisclosure cases have involved HIV-positive men. However, in 2005, an HIV-positive female soldier from Canadian Forces Base Borden, Ontario, was charged with assault after she engaged in unprotected sex with a male soldier without informing him that she had HIV (Verma, 2005).

NEGATIVE ATTITUDES TOWARD CONDOMS Many Canadians fail to use latex condoms consistently, if at all (Fisher et al., 2004a, 2004b). Overall, the percentage of Canadian women currently using condoms declined from 25% in 1995 to

18% in 2002 (Fisher et al., 2003b). However, a large survey of British Columbia adolescents found an increase in condom use from 58% in 1992 to 64% in 2003.

As adolescents get older and form longer-term relationships, they switch from using the condom to using the pill. Although birth-control pills are reliable methods of contraception, they do not prevent the spread of STIs. In the Canadian Contraceptive Study, women using oral contraceptives were more likely to report having had an STI than women who were using condoms (Fisher et al., 2004a, 2004b).

In the 2003 Canadian Community Health Survey, young people between the ages of 20 and 24 were the least likely to use condoms, with 44% saying they did not use a condom at last intercourse. Also, those who began having intercourse at younger ages were less likely to use a condom currently. As well, those who had had only one sex partner in the previous year were less likely to use a condom (Rotermann, 2005).

Researchers at Okanagan University College in British Columbia found that young people in monogamous relationships do not use condoms because they are in love, and trust their partner to be faithful (Netting & Burnett, 2004). The most common reasons Canadian teens give for not using condoms are that they did not expect to have sex, they are using another method of birth control, and they had too much alcohol or drugs (Boyce et al., 2003).

Many factors discourage condom use. Some people feel embarrassed to buy them. For others, the risk of being infected with HIV seems to fly out of their minds whenever the opportunity for sex arises. Some claim that interrupting the sexual act to apply a condom dampens romantic ardour. Some people just regard them as too much of a fuss. Many men as well as some women say that condoms deprive them of sexual pleasure. Unless such obstacles to using condoms are overcome, efforts to stem the tide of HIV infection may be thwarted.

Reasons for not using condoms can be complex. In an Ontario study, high-risk gay and bisexual men gave the following reasons:

- loss of erection
- urgency of passion overcoming fears of infection
- stress and depression overcoming rational prevention
- low self-esteem, leading to indifference about consequences
- relying on intuition to determine that a partner is HIV-negative
- developing a trusting relationship with a partner (Adam et al., 2005)

A common trend among Canadians is to use a condom at the beginning of a relationship and then to stop using it as the relationship continues. As people become more committed to a relationship, they become more trusting of their partner and are less willing to consider the possibility that he or she may have an STI (Maticka-Tyndale, 1997). It has also been found that the more in love a woman is with her partner, the more strongly she comes to believe that she is not at risk for getting an STI from him (Knäuper et al., 2002).

Rupert Klein and Barbel Knäuper (2002) of McGill University found that female university students believe that the use of condoms signifies a lack of commitment and trust in the relationship. To counter this trend, some providers of sexual health services, such as Calgary Health Services, encourage women who are going on the pill to use condoms as well (Wong-Reiger et al., 1996).

ALCOHOL AND DRUG ABUSE Drug and alcohol abuse are also associated with an increased risk of STIs. A study of heterosexuals found that people who abuse drugs or alcohol are more likely than others to engage in risky sexual practices (Lowry et al., 1994). Moreover, certain forms of drug use, such as needle sharing, can directly transmit infectious organisms like HIV.

In a study of men who had sex with a man who was HIV-positive, researchers at the University of Toronto found that safer-sex practices were least likely when the

Innovative Canadian Research

THE ANATOMY OF A FORBIDDEN DESIRE: MEN, PENETRATION, AND SEMEN EXCHANGE

There has been extensive publicity surrounding the HIV risk of a man's having unprotected anal sex with another man (bareback sex). Thus health educators are puzzled as to why some men purposely engage in anal sex without using a condom. Dave Holmes, of the University of Ottawa, and Dan Warner, of Duquesne University in Pittsburgh, Pennsylvania, conducted interviews with gay men in Canada, the U.S., and Europe in order to understand this practice (Holmes & Warner, 2005).

Previous research on this topic has focused on variables such as HIV knowledge, use of drugs, and number of sexual partners. Holmes and Warner chose to focus on the issues of desire, transgression, and pleasure. They found that semen exchange is an important part of the sexuality of barebackers. Many of the men stated that semen exchange was essential to provide a feeling of "connectedness" with the sexual partner. The giving of semen was seen as a "gift." Other respondents felt that a sense of "completion" with the sex act could not occur without the semen exchange. Some interviewees said they had to experience intense feelings of sexual arousal in order to engage in semen exchange. Others stated that it felt more natural to experience semen exchange. In other words, sex also felt more real when ejaculation took place in the anus.

Interestingly, some of the men interviewed did not feel that semen exchange had any special meaning. These men did not allow it to happen.

Holmes and Warner concluded that to understand barebacking, we need to be aware of "the real world of sexual desire." Barebackers are aware of the sexual risks; however, they prefer to focus instead on their sexual desire for semen exchange, so that the sex act can satisfy their emotional needs for connectedness, naturalness, and sexual completion.

Barry Adam (2007), in interviewing Toronto men who engage in barebacking, found they had adopted a different type of moral reasoning to explain why they were not concerned about a partner becoming infected with HIV. Their premise is that each individual is responsible for his own safety. Thus if a potential partner is worried about HIV, then it is up to him to take precautions. For this reason those who engage in barebacking do not feel the need to disclose their HIV status to a partner. However, this practice is contrary to a Supreme Court of Canada decision requiring that HIV-positive people must disclose their HIV status before engaging in sexual relations. Adam states that barebacking is considered irresponsible and is rejected by most gay men.

Although Holmes and Warner focused on gay men, their findings may also be applicable to some heterosexuals. For example, some heterosexuals may feel that they have not really had sex unless the male ejaculates his semen directly in the vagina. The Canadian author of this textbook had a discussion about these issues with an African heterosexual physician at an AIDS conference in Africa. The physician stated that for himself sex had to involve his ejaculating into the woman's vagina. This was essential for him to enjoy sex and outweighed any future probabilities of getting infected with HIV. Obviously, an anecdotal example such as this one is not sufficient to answer the question of whether some heterosexuals have similar feelings regarding semen exchange as do the men in the study reported by Holmes and Warner. Hopefully, in the future, researchers will study this question with samples of heterosexual men and women.

men were drinking or doing drugs (Calzavara et al., 1992). In Toronto, some gay and bisexual men using crystal meth reported that it reduced sexual inhibitions and intensified the sexual experience (Myers et al., 2004b). North American AIDS organizations are concerned that the search for heightened sexual pleasure through the use of crystal meth is contributing to an increase in HIV infections. The AIDS Committee of Toronto warns that taking crystal meth increases sexual risk-taking among gay and bisexual men. Of course, it can also increase risk-taking among heterosexuals.

In addition to the factors discussed above, there can be many other psychological factors that can account for sexual risk-taking. Barry Adam (2006) at the University of Windsor has taken a broader perspective in critiquing the general health perspective of health educators that rational decision making should result in people choosing to avoid risky sexual behaviours. He argues that the drive to satisfy certain emotional needs can often override longer-range safety concerns. For example, someone who is less attractive and/or less secure and/or more needy than his or her partner may not insist on condom use for fear of losing the partner. As well, someone who believes that true sexual intimacy involves ejaculation without a condom may feel unfulfilled emotionally and sexually if a condom is used (see the nearby Innovative Canadian Research box).

DIFFICULTY IN DISCUSSING SEXUAL HEALTH ISSUES In a study of communication about such sexual health issues as HIV and pregnancy prevention at the University of Guelph (Cleary et al., 2002), female students typically reported that they did not discuss these issues prior to engaging in sexual intercourse for the first time with a new partner. Generally, the women reported feeling uncomfortable about initiating discussion about sexual health topics and sensed that their partner was uncomfortable as well. They feared offending their partner and possibly risking a negative reaction from him.

Social Factors

STI rates vary by social factors such as gender, age, sexual orientation, marginalized group membership, province/territory, and negative societal attitudes toward STI-infected people.

GENDER IMBALANCE In Canada among heterosexuals, certain STI infections are much higher among females than among males, especially for chlamydia. However, more men than women have gonorrhea, syphilis, or HIV/AIDS. This gender imbalance is largely accounted for by the higher rate of these STIs among men who have sex with men.

Social factors make heterosexual females vulnerable to HIV/AIDS. Women around the world are more likely to be infected than men, and the numbers of infected women in Canada may be "catching up" with those of men. Violence—or the threat of violence—against women increases their vulnerability to HIV/AIDS and reduces their ability to protect themselves against infection. At the International AIDS Conference held in Toronto in 2006, a key theme was how gender imbalance in many cultures is a key factor in the spread of HIV. Women are more likely than men to be in situations where they lack the right to refuse sex or require that their partners wear a condom. A U.S. study of HIV-positive women found a strong relationship between having an abusive sex partner and never using a condom (Lang, 2007).

AGE Among Canadians, the highest rates for STIs and the largest increases in their transmission are occurring among young people. For example, young people between the ages of 15 and 24 account for about two-thirds of reported cases of chlamydia in Canada (Public Health Agency of Canada, 2006).

Most new STI cases are contracted by males between the ages of 20 and 24 and by females between the ages of 15 and 19 (Public Health Agency of Canada, 2006). This gender difference can be explained by the fact that females generally have sexual partners who are older than themselves.

The major focus for STI educators has been on young people. However, recently, there has been concern raised over the risk-taking of older Canadians. Divorce rates are increasing among baby boomers and many members of this age group are now back on the dating scene engaging in sex with new partners.

SEXUAL ORIENTATION Gay males have the highest STI rates and lesbians have the lowest. One explanation for this is that gay males have a higher number of sexual partners than lesbians and heterosexuals. In the 2002 Ontario survey of gay and bisexual men, 24% reported that they had not had an STI (Myers et al., 2004a). Rates of unprotected sex have been increasing among gay and bisexual men. In the 2002 Ontario Men's Survey (Myers et al., 2004a), 40% of the men reported engaging in unprotected anal sex the previous year, compared with 20% of men in the 1991 Canadian survey (Myers, Godin, et al., 1993).

Men who have sex with men but identify themselves as heterosexual are less likely to use condoms. However, they have fewer partners (Patha et al., 2006).

Innovative Canadian Research

THE INFORMATION-MOTIVATION-BEHAVIOURAL SKILLS MODEL

Simply providing information about AIDS is not enough to decrease the incidence of HIV infection. Bill Fisher of the University of Western Ontario has conducted research into factors affecting the use of safer-sex practices among various groups, including high school and university students, inner-city minority youth, and gay males. Fisher and his colleagues developed a theoretical model (the Information-Motivation-Behavioural Skills Model) to explain what determines behaviours to prevent STIs (Fisher & Fisher, 1992). The model has also been used to explain contraceptive use.

According to this model, people need to be informed not only about causes of STI/AIDS but also about effective means of prevention, including instruction on how to use condoms correctly. The model encourages the development of positive attitudes toward the use of condoms and strong social support for their use. Developing communication skills helps people become more assertive in insisting on condom use, especially with a reluctant partner. Behavioural skills also include gaining experience in going to a pharmacy or sexual health clinic to overcome any embarrassment in obtaining condoms.

Fisher has incorporated the basic principles of this model in the website **www.sexualityandu.ca**.

Based on this model, Fisher (2007) has developed and evaluated The Options Project. Clinicians are taught how to discuss HIV-prevention strategies briefly when first meeting with HIV-positive patients. Follow-up data with 500 patients, a control group, and a group participating in an intervention program showed a dramatic drop in HIV risky behaviours for the patients in the intervention program but an increase in HIV risky behaviours among the control group. This intervention program has been adopted in several clinics in North America and South Africa.

In an international study involving adolescents from Canada, New Zealand, and the U.S., lesbian, gay, and bisexual (LGB) youth were more likely to engage in HIV risk-taking behaviours than were heterosexuals (Meininger et al., 2007). In the three countries, the LGB youth had experienced more discrimination and stigmatization than heterosexual youth. In the Canadian and U.S. samples, this stigmatization had a significant influence on risk-taking regardless of sexual orientation. The researchers concluded that reducing discrimination against LGB youth may reduce sexual risk-taking among this age group.

Similarly, a study of adolescents in British Columbia and Seattle in Washington state found that LGB youth had experienced higher rates of sexual abuse and coercion than had heterosexual youth (Saewyc, 2006). Those who had experienced sexual abuse were more likely to engage in HIV risk-taking behaviours. Having experienced more sexual abuse may also explain some of the higher risk-taking among LGB youth.

A common misperception is that STIs cannot be transmitted between female sex partners. However, there is a high prevalence of bacterial vaginosis (BV) among lesbian women. One study of lesbian and bisexual women found that even though one-half of those between the ages of 18 and 22 had a history of BV, they perceived little risk of STI infection from female partners (Marrazzo, 2005). The women took no precautions with their partners to prevent STIs. In particular, they did not wash their hands before sexual activity, did not use rubber gloves for vaginal or oral penetration, and shared sex toys without washing them or using them with condoms.

MARGINALIZED GROUPS The highest STI rates are among First Nations youth (Shields et al., 2004). According to the 2003 Canadian Community Health Survey, First Nations youth are two-and-a-half times as likely to have an STI as Canadian youth in general (Rotermann, 2005).

Disproportionately high numbers of Canadians who are First Nations or black are living with HIV/AIDS. Prior to 1992, First Nations people accounted for 1.3% of AIDS cases; this increased to 15% in 2004 and 24.4% in 2006 (Public Health Agency of Canada, 2007). Black Canadians accounted for 8% of AIDS cases prior to 1992, and 15.5% in 2004 (Public Agency of Canada, 2005).

A key explanation for higher levels among these racial minorities is the high level of poverty and discrimination they often experience. In a Toronto study, STI

Innovative Canadian Research

THE STIGMA OF HIV/AIDS

Having HIV/AIDS seems to carry more stigma than having any other kind of disease. Heterosexuals appear to worry more about this than gay males. In a Windsor study of HIV-positive people who were taking combination therapies, the heterosexuals were much more secretive about their HIV status, because they perceived they would receive little support from others (Adam et al., 2001). Gay males, on the other hand, felt accepted by their friends and social networks. Adam and colleagues attribute this difference to the perception among heterosexuals that HIV is not a part of their community. However, whether gay or straight, almost all the participants worried that disclosure in the workplace could lead to discrimination and job loss.

In 2006, the Public Health Agency of Canada conducted a national survey of Canadians to determine their attitudes and knowledge related to HIV/AIDS (Rattner et al., 2007). The majority of Canadians (59%) had only low or moderate knowledge of HIV/AIDS. Of even greater concern was the level of discriminatory attitudes toward those with HIV/AIDS. Only one-quarter had a high degree of comfort with people who were infected with HIV/AIDS, and one-fifth did not believe in supporting the rights of people living with HIV/AIDS.

rates were much higher in areas of the city where people were more likely to be living at the poverty level (Hardwick & Patychuck, 1999). Poor people facing a struggle for the everyday basic needs for food and shelter are less able to focus on long-term goals such as the prevention of STIs.

First Nations women are especially at risk. They are more likely to be poor than are other Canadian women and more likely to live in an environment where substance abuse and spousal violence are common (Prentice, 2005).

A study of the perceptions of HIV risk and prevention among black women in Toronto concluded that more attention needed to be given to the structural factors affecting risk. These factors include gender inequality, poverty, racial discrimination in health care, homophobia, and the need for women-controlled prevention methods (Williams et al., 2007).

Marginalization also affects street youth. Rates of infection are extremely high among Canadian youth living on the street. In fact, chlamydia rates are nine times greater among street youth than among youth in general (Shields et al., 2004). Female injection-drug users are also a marginalized group (Open Society Institute, 2007). They are more likely to exchange sex for drugs and for shelter. They also experience high levels of violence from sexual partners and are less able to insist on condom use. They are also subject to infection from contaminated needles. Sex workers are also marginalized and often blamed for the spread of STI infections.

PROVINCE/TERRITORY The infection rates are far higher in the Yukon, Nunavut, and the Northwest Territories than in the rest of Canada, reflecting the higher incidence among First Nations people.

SOCIAL CAPITAL (NETWORKS) University of Windsor researchers (Smylie et al., 2006) found that youth who had strong social ties with family, peers, and community organizations were less likely to engage in risky sexual behaviours. These social networks provide intangible resources that enable youth to make healthier decisions, resulting in fewer social problems for themselves and for society.

NEGATIVE SOCIETAL ATTITUDES TOWARD STI-INFECTED PEOPLE People equate STIs with immoral sexual behaviour and thus negatively regard people with STI/HIV infections. For people infected with an STI, fear of being judged often leads to guilt, which means they will delay seeking treatment and are reluctant to tell others, including their partners, about being infected. This is discussed in more detail in the nearby Innovative Canadian Research box.

Applied Knowledge

PREVENTING STIs

Prevention is the best way to control the spread of STIs, especially those for which there is no cure or vaccine. There are many things that you can do to lower your risk of contracting STIs.

Consider Abstinence or Monogamy

The only fully effective strategies to prevent the sexual transmission of STIs are abstinence and maintaining a monogamous sexual relationship with an uninfected partner.

Be Knowledgeable About the Risks

Many of us try to put the dangers of STIs out of our minds—especially in moments of passion. Make a pact with yourself to refuse to play the dangerous game of pretending that the dangers of STIs do not exist or that you are somehow immune.

Remain Sober and Drug-Free

Alcohol and other drugs increase the likelihood of engaging in risky sexual behaviour.

Inspect Yourself and Your Partner

Inspect yourself and your partner for any discharge, bumps, rashes, warts, blisters, chancres, sores, lice, or foul odours. Do not expect to find telltale signs of an HIV infection, but remember that infected people often have other STIs. Check out any unusual feature with a physician before you engage in sexual activity.

Use Latex Condoms

Latex condoms are effective in blocking nearly all sexually transmissible organisms. Improper or inconsistent use is a common reason for failure.

Use Barrier Devices When Practising Oral Sex (Fellatio or Cunnilingus)

If you decide to practise oral sex, use a condom before practising fellatio and a dental dam (a square piece of latex rubber used by dentists on patients during oral surgery) to cover the vagina before engaging in cunnilingus.

Avoid High-Risk Sexual Behaviours

Avoid unprotected vaginal or anal intercourse (intercourse without the use of a latex condom). Unprotected anal intercourse is one of the riskiest practices. Other behaviours that carry risk include unprotected oral-genital activity, insertion of a hand or fist ("fisting") into someone's rectum or vagina, or any activity in which you or your partner would come into contact with the other's blood, semen, or vaginal secretions. Oral-anal sex, or anilingus (sometimes called rimming), should be avoided because of the potential of transmitting microbes between the mouth and the anus.

Wash the Genitals Before and After Sex

Washing the genitals before and after sex removes a quantity of potentially harmful agents. Do not, however, deceive yourself into believing that washing your genitals is an effective substitute for safer sex.

Have Regular Medical Checkups

Many people are symptomless carriers of STIs, especially of chlamydial infections. Medical checkups enable them to learn about and receive treatment for infections that might otherwise go unnoticed. Many physicians advise routine testing of asymptomatic young women for chlamydial infections to prevent the hidden damage that can occur when the infection goes untreated.

Discuss Whether You and Your Partner Should Undergo Testing Before Initiating Sexual Relations

Some couples reach a mutual agreement to be tested for HIV and other STIs before they initiate sexual relations. (Some people simply insist that their prospective partners be tested before they initiate sexual relations.) However, many people resist testing or feel insulted when their partners raise the issue. People usually assume that they are free of STIs if they are symptom free and have been reasonably selective in their choice of partners. But STIs happen to the "nicest people," and the absence of symptoms is no guarantee of freedom from infection. Unless you have been celibate or involved in a monogamous relationship with an uninfected partner, you should consider yourself at risk of carrying or contracting an infectious STI.

Consult Your Physician If You Suspect That You Have Been Exposed to an STI

If you think that you may have been exposed to an STI, such as HIV, see a doctor as soon as possible. Many STIs are detectable in the early stages of development and can be successfully treated. If HIV is in your bloodstream, there is some chance that it may be eradicated before it infects cells in the immune system. If you are infected with HIV, early treatment may keep virus levels low and prevent you from developing AIDS. Early intervention may also prevent the damage of STIs spreading to vital body organs. Be sensitive to any physical changes that may be symptomatic of STIs. Talk to a health professional when in doubt.

Engage in Noncoital Sexual Activities

Other forms of sexual expression—such as hugging, massage, caressing, mutual masturbation, and rubbing bodies together without vaginal, anal, or oral contact—are low-risk ways of finding sexual pleasure, so long as neither semen nor vaginal fluids come into contact with mucous membranes or breaks in the skin. Many sexologists refer to such activities as **outercourse** to distinguish them from sexual intercourse. Sharing sexual fantasies can be very titillating, as can taking a bath or shower together. Vibrators, dildos, and other "sex toys" may also be erotically stimulating and carry a low risk of infection if they are washed thoroughly with soap and water before use and between uses by two people.

Get to Know Your Partner Before Initiating Sexual Relations

Be selective in your choice of sex partners. Having sex with multiple partners—especially "one-night stands"—increases your risk of sexual contact with an infected person. It also lessens the opportunity to get to know your partner well enough to know whether he or she has participated in high-risk sexual practices or has had many sex partners in the past who practised high-risk behaviours. Remember, with regard to STI risk, you are taking chances not only with your partner but also with all of that person's previous partners.

Be aware though: people are not always truthful about their sexual past. Some people who are infected with an STI or the HIV virus do not disclose this to their partners. Try not to be fooled into taking chances with such a person.

Avoid Other High-Risk Behaviours

Avoid contact with bodily substances (blood, semen, vaginal secretions, fecal matter) from other people. Do not share hypodermic needles, razors, cuticle scissors, or other implements that could contain another person's blood. Be careful when handling wet towels, bed linen, or other material that might contain bodily substances.

Talking About Preventing Transmission of HIV/AIDS and Other STIs.
Most people do not find it easy to talk frankly about preventing STIs, but what is the alternative?

Positive Love
A dating site for people with STIs.
www.positivelove.com

Outercourse Forms of sexual expression, such as massage, hugging, caressing, mutual masturbation, and rubbing bodies together, that do not involve the exchange of body fluids.

Summing Up

Although public attention has been riveted on AIDS for a decade, other STIs, such as chlamydia and genital warts, pose wider threats.

Bacteria are one-celled micro-organisms that cause many illnesses.

The symptoms of chlamydial infections resemble those of gonorrhea but tend to be milder.

Gonorrhea symptoms for men include a penile discharge and burning urination. Most women are asymptomatic.

Syphilis undergoes several stages of development. Although it can lie dormant for many years, it may be lethal.

Vaginitis is usually characterized by a foul-smelling discharge, genital irritation, and burning during urination. Most cases involve bacterial vaginosis, candidiasis, or trichomoniasis.

Viruses are particles of DNA that reproduce by invading a body cell and directing the cell's own reproductive machinery to spin off new viral particles.

AIDS is caused by HIV, which attacks the body's immune system. As HIV disables the body's natural defences, the person becomes vulnerable to opportunistic diseases—such as serious infections and cancers—that are normally held in check. HIV is a blood-borne virus that is also found in semen, vaginal secretions, and breast milk. Common avenues of transmission include sexual intercourse, transfusion with contaminated blood, sharing a hypodermic needle with an infected person, childbirth, and breastfeeding. HIV infection is usually diagnosed through blood, saliva, and urine tests that detect HIV antibodies. There is no cure for AIDS, and an effective, safe vaccine has not yet been developed.

Oral herpes is caused by the *Herpes simplex* virus type 1 (HSV-1). Genital herpes is caused by the *Herpes simplex* virus type 2 (HSV-2), which produces painful, shallow sores and blisters on the genitals.

There are several types of hepatitis caused by different hepatitis viruses. Most cases of hepatitis are transmitted sexually or by contact with contaminated blood or fecal matter.

Genital warts are caused by the human papilloma virus (HPV). HPV has been linked to cancers of the genital tract, the anus, and the throat.

Pediculosis ("crabs") is caused by pubic lice. Pubic lice attach themselves to pubic hair and feed on the blood of their hosts, which often causes itching.

Scabies is a parasitic infestation with a tiny mite that causes itching.

All provinces and territories have information lines that offer anonymous information and counselling.

STI rates remain high because of biological, psychological, and social factors.

Test Yourself

Multiple-Choice Questions

1. Many Canadian university students are unaware of the HPV virus, which causes ______________.

a. genital herpes
b. hepatitis B
c. genital warts
d. molluscum contagiosum

2. As many as __________ of men and ______________ of women with chlamydia have no symptoms.

a. 15%; 25%
b. 75%; 50%
c. 35%; 10%
d. 25%; 70%

3. Untreated gonorrhea can lead to ______________ in men.

a. premature ejaculation
b. epididymitis
c. pelvic inflammatory disease
d. cervicitis

4. ______________ and ______________ often occur together.

a. Chlamydia and gonorrhea
b. Herpes and HPV
c. Syphilis and shigellosis
d. Trichomonas and scabies

5. The vaccine Gardasil immunizes against which STI?

a. herpes
b. HPV
c. HIV
d. none of the above

6. About ______________ of women will experience at least one yeast infection during their lifetime.

a. 15%
b. 50%
c. 75%
d. 90%

7. HIV directly attacks the immune system by destroying ______________.

a. pathogenic cells
b. CD4 cells
c. red blood cells
d. platelets

8. All of the following have been shown to transmit HIV infection except

a. artificial insemination with infected semen
b. kissing
c. breastfeeding
d. unprotected sexual intercourse

9. The current standard of treatment for HIV/AIDS, known as ______________________, consists of a mixture of antiretroviral drugs and protease inhibitors.

a. ELISA
b. AIDSBS
c. HAART
d. LSMFT

10. Which of the following is a cure for genital herpes?

a. freezing the herpes lesions with liquid nitrogen
b. applying acyclovir ointment three times a day
c. penicillin or other antibiotics for two weeks
d. there is no cure for genital herpes

11. Which of the following is not considered to be an effective prevention strategy for reducing your risk of STIs?

a. avoiding the use of alcohol or other drugs
b. using birth-control pills effectively
c. avoiding high-risk sexual behaviours
d. using latex condoms for all forms of genital sexual activity

Answers to the Test Yourself questions in each chapter are found on page 509.

Critical Thinking Questions

1. How would you bring up the topic of sexually transmitted infections with a new sexual partner? What might stop you from bringing up the subject?
2. Would you tell a potential sex partner about any STIs that you have, or about any risky sexual behaviour you have engaged in? Why or why not?
3. How would you feel if you found out that your spouse or sexual partner had infected you with an STI? What effect do you think this would have on the relationship?
4. You and some friends are sitting around over a beer or two. One of your friends is certain that he or she could tell what sort of person would have an STI, and would never have sex with "someone like that." How could you respond to this statement?

Visit MyPsychKit at www.mypsychkit.com, where you can do quizzes and link to additional resources on topics discussed in this text.

CHAPTER FIFTEEN

Sexual Variations

Normal versus Deviant Sexual Behaviour

The Paraphilias

Innovative Canadian Research: Female Paraphilics

Fetishism

Transvestism

Exhibitionism

Obscene Telephone Calling and Chat Scatophilia

Applied Knowledge: Responding to Exhibitionists and Obscene Phone Callers

Voyeurism

Sexual Masochism

Innovative Canadian Research: "Normal" Voyeurism

A World of Diversity: It Seems Like Voyeurs Are Everywhere

Sexual Sadism

Innovative Canadian Research: Women's Submissive Desires as Expressed on Weblogs

Frotteurism

Other Paraphilias

Theoretical Perspectives

Biological Perspectives

Psychoanalytic Perspectives

Cognitive-Behavioural Perspectives

Sociological Perspectives

An Integrated Perspective: The "Lovemap"

A World of Diversity: Sexual Addiction and Compulsivity

Treatment of the Paraphilias

Psychotherapy

Cognitive-Behaviour Therapy

Medical Approaches

People often wonder about their own sexuality. A common concern is, "Am I normal?" To answer this question we need to be aware of the criteria for defining normality. In this chapter we analyze the concept of normality and discuss a number of sexual behaviours that are viewed as deviating from the norm. First, let us consider how we define *normality*.

Normal versus Deviant Sexual Behaviour

One common approach to defining normality is based on a statistical norm. From this perspective, rare or unusual sexual behaviours are abnormal or deviant. The statistical approach may seem value-free, because the measuring stick of normality is based on the frequency of behaviour, not on any judgment of its social acceptability. By this standard, engaging in coitus while standing, or more than seven times a week, might be considered deviant. However, the choice of behaviours we subject to statistical comparison is not divorced from our underlying values. *Statistical* infrequency, then, is not a sufficient criterion for classifying behaviour as abnormal or deviant. We must also consider whether the sexual practice deviates from a *social* norm.

What is considered normal in one culture or at a particular time may be considered abnormal in other cultures and at other times. A gay male or lesbian sexual orientation was considered abnormal throughout most of Western history and was labelled a mental disorder by the American Psychiatric Association. But in 1973, the "disorder" of gay male or lesbian sexual orientation was dropped from the association's official diagnostic manual.

In our own culture, sexual practices such as oral sex and masturbation were once considered deviant or abnormal. Today, however, they are practised so widely that few people would label them deviant. Concepts of "normalcy" and "deviance," then, reflect the mores and customs of a particular culture at a given time.

Another way to determine sexual deviance is to classify sexual practices as deviant when they involve the persistent preference for nongenital sexual outlets (Seligman & Hardenburg, 2000). If a man prefers fondling a woman's panties to engaging in sexual relations with her, or prefers to masturbate against her foot rather than engage in coitus, his behaviour is likely to be labelled deviant.

Because of the confusing array of meanings of the terms *deviant* and *abnormal*, we prefer to speak about unusual patterns of sexual arousal or behaviour as "atypical variations" in sexual behaviour rather than as "sexual deviations." Atypical patterns of sexual arousal or behaviour that become problematic in the eyes of the individual or of society are labelled *paraphilias* by the American Psychiatric Association in its catalogue of sexual disorders (DSM-IV-TR, 2000). Clinicians consider paraphilias to be mental disorders. But milder forms of these behaviours may be practised by many people and fall within the normal spectrum of human sexuality. According to Ottawa psychiatrist Paul Fedoroff, a major factor in delineating paraphilic disorders is that they "involve sex without the possibility of a consensual, mutually reciprocal relationship" (Fedoroff, 2003, p. 336).

The Paraphilias

Paraphilias involve sexual arousal in response to unusual stimuli such as children or other nonconsenting persons (including unsuspecting people whom one watches or to whom one exposes one's genitals), nonhuman objects (such as shoes, leather, rubber, or undergarments), or pain or humiliation (Seligman & Hardenburg, 2000). The psychiatric diagnosis of paraphilia requires that the person has acted on the urges in socially unacceptable ways or is distinctly distressed by them.

Paraphilia A diagnostic category used by the American Psychiatric Association to describe atypical patterns of sexual arousal or behaviour that become problematic in the eyes of the individual or society, such as fetishism and exhibitionism. The urges are recurrent and either are acted on or are distressing to the individual.

Innovative Canadian Research

FEMALE PARAPHILICS

Many people believe that women do not engage in paraphilic activities, partly because so little research has been conducted in this area. One of the relatively few studies on female paraphilics was conducted by Paul Fedoroff, an Ottawa psychiatrist and one of Canada's leading experts on paraphilias, along with colleagues Alicia Fishell and Beverly Fedoroff. The study was based on 14 women who were referred to clinics in Canada, the United States, or Great Britain. Each of the women typically had more than one paraphilic disorder, the most common of which were pedophilia, sexual sadism, and exhibitionism. Only 3 of the 14 women reported having experienced past sexual victimization.

In one of the cases, a heterosexual woman was self-referred because of a tendency to exhibit:

> She described a ritual of undressing herself and masturbating with the lights on in front of her apartment window, approximately 5 times a month. While she was aroused by the idea of being seen by male strangers, she denied any wish to engage in sex with anyone who saw her. Unless she was involved in "really bizarre situations," she had primary anorgasmia even when masturbating.
>
> At one point she began driving her truck through unfamiliar neighbourhoods with pet food in an attempt to befriend cats and dogs which she would "abduct." She would coax the cats to lick her genitals by placing honey on her vaginal area. She would perform oral sex on male dogs whom she "abducted" in a similar manner. She also described sexual fantasies about having sex with boys and girls between the ages of 8 and 10. On one occasion she had "punished" an 8-year-old boy she was baby-sitting by squeezing his penis and "physically smacked him around." She was sexually aroused by this activity and would often masturbate while recalling this episode.
>
> Three years prior to assessment, she had become involved in a unique form of prostitution in which she would flag down taxis from her truck and then proceed to talk the taxi driver into paying to have sex with her. She did the same thing with men she met on "phone sex lines." She did this for about a year and then stopped because she said, "It wasn't me." She had been engaged but found she could not have sex with her male partner unless she acted out her paraphilic interests (activities that caused him to leave her). (p. 133)

Fedoroff et al. offer these comments on the case:

> This woman's presentation is typical of many self-referred men who are not facing charges in that there are multiple, highly idiosyncratic and obligatory sex "rituals" described. She was "obsessed" with sex, devoting the majority of her waking days to fulfilling her sexual desires. However, she also described high levels of sex guilt (a finding also characteristic of male sex offenders). Although she found these activities highly sexually arousing, they were at the same time highly aversive to her, particularly "because she was a Christian." This case is also instructive because her partner (in this case, a male) was not supportive of her paraphilic activities. This woman found it impossible to forgo her paraphilic activities, even though she knew it spelled the end of the most important romantic relationship she had ever established. (p. 133)

Source: Adapted from Fedoroff, J. P., Fishell, A., & Fedoroff, B. (1999). A Case Series of Women Evaluated for Paraphilic Disorders. The Canadian Journal of Human Sexuality, *8, 127–140.*

People with paraphilias usually feel that their urges are insistent, demanding, or compulsory (Fedoroff, 2003). They may describe themselves as overcome by these urges now and then. People with paraphilias tend to experience their urges as beyond their control, just as drug addicts and compulsive gamblers see themselves as helpless to avert irresistible urges. For these reasons, theorists have speculated that paraphilias may represent a type of sexual compulsion or an addiction.

Paraphilias vary in severity. In some cases the person can function sexually in the absence of the unusual stimuli and seldom if ever acts on his or her deviant urges. In other cases the person resorts to paraphilic behaviour only in times of stress. In more extreme forms, the person repeatedly engages in paraphilic behaviour and may become preoccupied with thoughts and fantasies about these experiences. In such cases the person may not be able to become sexually aroused without either fantasizing about the paraphilic stimulus or having it present. For some people, paraphilic behaviour is the only means of attaining sexual gratification.

The person with a paraphilia typically replays the paraphilic act in sexual fantasies to stimulate arousal during masturbation or sexual relations. It is as though he or she is mentally replaying a videotape of the paraphilic scene. The scene grows stale after a while and the individual feels the urge to perform another paraphilic act to make a new "video."

Some paraphilias are generally harmless and victimless, such as *fetishism* and cross-dressing to achieve sexual arousal (*transvestic fetishism*). Indeed, because behaviours such as cross-dressing do not harm others, some experts, such as Charles Moser, a physician in San Francisco, and Peggy Kleinplatz, a psychologist in Ottawa, believe that they should not be categorized as sexual disorders (Moser & Kleinplatz, 2002). Michael Seto and Howard Barbaree of the Centre for Addiction and Mental Health in Toronto further argue that sexual preferences for particular types of people or activities are strongly influenced by cultural values (Seto & Barbaree, 2001). Until a few years ago, for example, homosexuality was considered to be a pathology.

In a separate article Moser and Kleinplatz (2005a) argue that the paraphilias section should be removed from the DSM–IV of the American Psychiatric Association. A main concern is that the section is not based on current scientific findings but rather on political values of what is considered acceptable behaviour. Also, Moser and Kleinplatz argue that unusual sexual interests are not a sign of pathology but rather a variation on the continuum of sexual interests. To illustrate the illogical and subjective aspects of DSM–IV diagnostic criteria, they assert that a strict application of those criteria would lead to the nonsensical conclusion that heterosexuality is a mental disorder (Moser & Kleinplatz, 2005b).

Because of these concerns, Charles Moser (2001) has proposed that the concept of Sexual Interest Disorder (SID) should be substituted for paraphilia. Here Moser calls for eliminating the naming of specific interests because he argues that a behaviour by itself is not an indication of pathology. Rather the key issue is whether that behaviour is causing distress or dysfunction for the individual.

Moser also argues that therapists should not always work toward eliminating a particular sexual interest but should offer clients the option of learning how to express the interest in a healthier manner. However, Moser does not propose that all sexual interests should be acceptable.

Some paraphilic behaviours, such as exposing oneself in public or enticing children into sexual relations, do have victims and may cause severe physical or psychological harm. They are also against the law. Sexual sadism, in which sexual arousal is connected to hurting or humiliating another person, can be very harmful when it is forced upon a nonconsenting person. Some brutal rapes involve sexual sadism.

Except for the case of sexual masochism, paraphilias are believed to occur mostly among men (Seligman & Hardenburg, 2000). (See the nearby Innovative Canadian Research feature for a Canadian study on female paraphilics.) Because people are generally unwilling to talk about them, the prevalence of paraphilias in the general population remains unknown. Much of what we have learned about paraphilias derives from the reported experiences of people who have been apprehended for performing illegal acts (such as exposing themselves in public) and the few who have voluntarily sought help. The characteristics of people who have not been identified or studied remain virtually unknown.

In this chapter we discuss all the major types of paraphilia except *pedophilia*. In pedophilia, children become the objects of sexual arousal. Pedophilia often takes the form of sexual coercion of children, as in incest or sexual molestation. It is discussed in Chapter 16, as a form of sexual coercion.

Fetishism

Fetishism A paraphilia in which an inanimate object such as an article of clothing or items made of rubber, leather, or silk elicit sexual arousal.

In **fetishism**, an inanimate object elicits sexual arousal. Articles of clothing (for example, women's panties, bras, lingerie, stockings, gloves, shoes, or boots) and

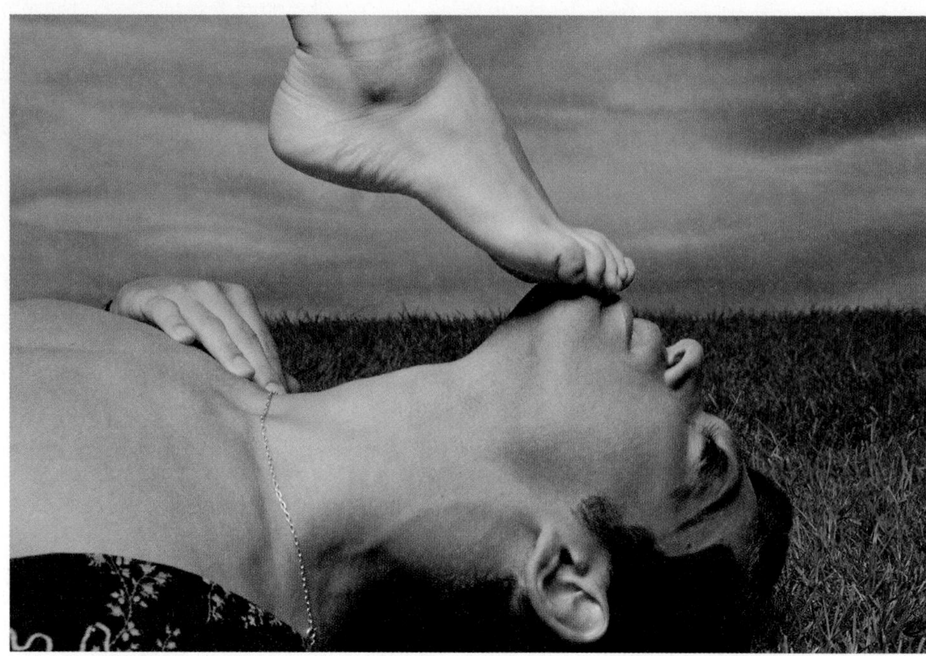

Fetishism.
In fetishism, inanimate objects such as leather shoes or boots, or parts of the body such as feet, elicit sexual arousal.

materials made of rubber, leather, silk, or fur are among the more common fetishistic objects. Leather boots and high-heeled shoes are especially popular.

The fetishist may act on the urges to engage in fetishistic behaviour, such as masturbating by stroking an object or while fantasizing about it, or he may be distressed about such urges or fantasies but not act on them. In a related paraphilia, **partialism**, people are excessively aroused by a particular body part, such as the feet, breasts, or buttocks.

Most fetishes and partialisms are harmless. Fetishistic practices are nearly always private and involve masturbation or are incorporated into coitus with a willing partner. Only rarely have fetishists coerced others into paraphilic activities. Yet some partialists have touched parts of women's bodies in public. And some fetishists have committed burglaries to acquire the fetishistic objects. In Calgary, a man was charged with stealing women's panties during real estate tours of houses that were for sale and then placing obscene phone calls to the occupants of the houses ("Man accused," 2002).

Transvestism

Fetishism appears to include **transvestism**. Although other fetishists become sexually aroused by handling the fetishistic object while they masturbate, transvestites become excited by wearing articles of clothing—the fetishistic objects—of the other gender. A fetishist may find the object or sex involving the object to be erotically stimulating. For the transvestite, the object is sexually alluring only when it is worn. Transvestites are mostly males (Långström & Zucker, 2005). Transvestism has been described among both heterosexual and gay males (Taylor & Rupp, 2004). Many are in committed male–female relationships and otherwise stereotypically masculine in behaviour.

Transvestism differs markedly from transsexualism. It is true that some transvestites and some transsexuals appear to be motived by *autogynephilia*—a condition in which the individual is sexually stimulated by fantasies that their own bodies are

Partialism A paraphilia related to fetishism in which sexual arousal is exaggeratedly associated with a particular body part, such as feet, breasts, or buttocks.

Transvestism A paraphilia in which a person repeatedly cross-dresses to achieve sexual arousal or gratification, or is troubled by persistent, recurring urges to cross-dress.

female (Bailey, 2003b; Lawrence, 2004). However, transvestites are usually sexually gratified by cross-dressing and masturbating or having sex with others while cross-dressing. They may also find it gratifying to masturbate while fantasizing about cross-dressing. However, many transvestites have masculine gender identities and do not seek to change their anatomic sex. Transsexuals usually cross-dress because they are uncomfortable with the attire associated with their anatomic sex and truly wish to be members of the other sex. For this reason, many transsexuals seek sex reassignment.

Transvestism.
Transvestites cross-dress for purposes of obtaining sexual arousal and gratification. Are women who wear blue jeans engaging in transvestic activity? (The answer is no. But, as a critical thinker, explain why.)

Like fetishism in general, the origins of transvestism remain obscure. Evidence of biological hormonal and neurological abnormalities in transvestism is mixed (Bailey, 2003b). Långström and Zucker (2005) surveyed 2450 Swedes and found transvestism in about 2.8% of men and 0.4% of women. A history of transvestism was associated with separation from parents, same-sex sexual experiences, use of pornography, high rates of masturbation, and other paraphilias—namely, sexual masochism, exhibitionism, and voyeurism.

Some men cross-dress for reasons other than sexual arousal and so are not "true transvestites." Some men make a living by impersonating women like Marilyn Monroe and Madonna on stage and are not motivated by sexual arousal. Among some segments of the gay male community, it is fashionable to masquerade as a woman. Gay men do not usually cross-dress to become sexually stimulated, however.

Transvestic behaviours may range from wearing a single female garment when alone to sporting dresses, wigs, makeup, and feminine mannerisms at a transvestite club. Some transvestites become sexually aroused by masquerading as women and attracting the interest of unsuspecting males. They sometimes entice these men or string them along until they find some excuse to back out before their anatomic sex is revealed. The great majority of transvestites do not engage in antisocial or illegal behaviour. Most practise their sexual predilection in private and would be horrified or embarrassed to be discovered by associates while dressed in female attire.

Kathleen Cairns, a Calgary therapist, found that wives of cross-dressers required several sessions with a therapist to deal with the fear, betrayal, and grief they experienced upon learning of their husband's behaviour (Cairns, 1997). She also found that wives were far more concerned than their husbands about their children finding out about the cross-dressing.

Exhibitionism

Exhibitionism ("flashing") entails persistent, powerful urges and sexual fantasies involving exposing one's genitals to unsuspecting strangers for the purpose of achieving sexual arousal or gratification. The urges are either acted on or are disturbing to the individual. Exhibitionists are mostly males.

Exhibitionism A paraphilia characterized by persistent, powerful urges and sexual fantasies that involve exposing one's genitals to unsuspecting strangers for the purpose of achieving sexual arousal or gratification.

What we know of exhibitionists, as with most other people with paraphilias, is almost entirely derived from studies of men who have been apprehended or have been treated by mental health professionals (Langevin, 2006). Such knowledge may

An Exhibitionist.
What are the motives of the exhibitionist? Sexual? Aggressive?

yield a biased picture of exhibitionists. Although about one in three arrests for sexual offences involve exhibitionism, relatively few reported incidents result in apprehension and conviction (Cox, 1988). Studies in England, Guatemala, the United States, and Hong Kong show that fewer than 20% of occurrences are reported to the police (Cox, 1988). The characteristics of most perpetrators may thus differ from those of people who have been available for study.

Exhibitionism usually begins before age 18 (American Psychiatric Association, 2000). The urge to exhibit oneself, if not the actual act, usually begins in early adolescence, generally between the ages of 13 and 16 (Freund et al., 1988). The frequency of exhibitionism declines markedly after the age of 40 (American Psychiatric Association, 2000). The typical exhibitionist does not attempt further sexual contact with the victim. An Ontario study of exhibitionists who were repeat offenders found that 12% were also convicted of other sexual offences and 17% were convicted of violent crimes (Rabinowitz et al., 2002).

The police may sometimes trivialize exhibitionism as a "nuisance crime," but the psychological consequences can be serious for victims, especially young children. Victims may feel violated and may be bothered by recurrent images or nightmares. They may also develop fears of venturing out on their own.

An Ontario study (Firestone et al., 2006) found that men who exhibit may be at high risk for engaging in more serious offences. About a third of the sample went on to commit a sexual or violent offence.

Some evidence suggests that exhibitionists may be attempting to assert their masculinity by evoking a response from their victims. A number of exhibitionists have reported that they hoped the women would enjoy the experience and be impressed with the size of their penis (Langevin et al., 1979).

Other studies show exhibitionists to be shy, dependent, passive, lacking in sexual and social skills, and even inhibited (Dwyer, 1988). Exhibitionists who are socially shy or inadequate may be using exhibitionism as a substitute for the intimate relationships they cannot develop.

The preferred victims are typically girls or young women (Freund & Blanchard, 1986). The typical exhibitionist drives up to, or walks in front of, a stranger and exposes his penis. In one sample of 130 exhibitionists, about 50% reported that they always or nearly always had an erection when they exposed themselves (Langevin et al., 1979). After his victim has registered fear, disgust, confusion, or surprise, an exhibitionist typically covers himself and flees. He usually masturbates, either while exposing himself or shortly afterward while thinking about the act and the victim's response (American Psychiatric Association, 2000). Some exhibitionists ejaculate during the act. Most of the 238 exhibitionists in an Ontario study reported masturbating to orgasm while exposing themselves or afterward while fantasizing about it (Freund et al., 1988).

Exhibitionism by women seems to be increasing. After the Gwen Jacobs case (in which the Ontario Court of Appeal ruled that it was legal for women to go topless; see Chapter 1), some women purposely bared their breasts in an exhibitionistic manner. In Windsor, Ontario, two young women from Michigan approached police officers and asked if it was legal to go topless in Canada. When the officers said it was, the women raised their tops, exposing their breasts (Canadian Press, 1997). It has now become commonplace at certain public events such as rock concerts for some women to expose their breasts. Also, at various university campuses across Canada and the United States, young women have bared their breasts in public for the *Girls Gone Wild* website. The internet has greatly facilitated a new variation of exhibitionism in which ordinary people can post pictures of themselves either masturbating or having sex with a partner. Some Canadian adult websites have pictures of women exhibiting themselves in public places.

A widely publicized incident occurred at a rowdy hockey game between 11-year-olds in a Toronto suburb. One of the hockey moms taunted parents of the opposing team by lifting her blouse above her chest and shaking her bra-covered breasts from side to side (Vincent, 2004). In another incident, risqué photos of former Winnipeg Blue Bombers cheerleaders were posted on the internet. One showed a woman in the cheerleaders' uniform cupping the breasts of another woman (King, 2008). Hollywood celebrities Paris Hilton and Lindsay Lohan have both been photographed getting in and out of limousines in short skirts and no underwear.

Sometimes a couple will engage in public exhibitionism. At a Toronto Blue Jays game, for example, a man and woman had sex by the window of their hotel room, which directly faced the playing field, and thousands of fans got to watch more than the baseball game. And at the Elora Gorge in Ontario, a man in a car motioned for a 14-year-old boy to approach the car, whereupon the boy saw a woman performing oral sex on the driver. The man and woman were fined for committing an indecent act (Tracey, 2000).

Definitions of exhibitionism also bring into focus the boundaries between normal and abnormal behaviour. Are exotic dancers (stripteasers) or nude sunbathers exhibitionists? After all, aren't they also exposing themselves to strangers? But exotic dancers—male or female—remove their clothes to sexually excite or entertain an audience that is paying to watch them. Their motive is (usually) to earn a living. Sunbathers in their "birthday suits" may also seek to sexually arouse others, not themselves. Of course, they may also be seeking an all-over tan or trying to avoid feeling encumbered by clothing. In any case, stripteasers and sunbathers do not expose themselves to unsuspecting others, and hence these behaviours are not regarded as exhibitionistic.

It is also normal to become sexually excited while stripping before one's sex partner. In fact, stripping has become mainstream, as indicated by the thousands of women from across Canada who have taken "Stripping for Your Lover" workshops taught by former stripper Mary Taylor. Such stripping is done to excite a willing partner, not to surprise or shock a stranger.

Obscene Telephone Calling and Chat Scatophilia

Like exhibitionists, obscene phone callers (almost all of whom are male) seek to become sexually aroused by shocking their victims (Briken et al., 2005; Pakhomou, 2006). Although an exhibitionist exposes his genitals to produce the desired response, the obscene phone caller "exposes" himself verbally by uttering obscenities and sexual provocations to a nonconsenting person. The DSM–IV (American Psychiatric Association, 2000) labels this type of paraphilia **telephone scatologia**. People practising "chat scatophilia" are sexually aroused by sending obscene email, instant messages, and chatroom messages (Abal et al., 2003). These behaviours are sometimes considered a form of exhibitionism.

Relatively few obscene callers are women (Price et al., 2002). Women who are charged with such offences are generally motivated by rage for some actual or fantasized rejection rather than the desire for sexual arousal. They use the phone to hurl sexual invectives against men who they feel have wronged them. By contrast, male obscene phone callers are generally motivated by a desire for sexual excitement and usually choose their victims randomly from the phone book or by chance dialing. They typically masturbate during the phone call or shortly afterward. Most

Telephone scatologia A paraphilia characterized by the making of obscene telephone calls.

obscene telephone callers also engage in other paraphilic acts, especially voyeurism and exhibitionism (Price et al., 2001, 2002).

There are many patterns of obscene phone calling. Some callers limit themselves to obscenities. Others make sexual overtures. Some just breathe heavily into the receiver. Others describe their masturbatory activity to their victims. Some profess to have previously met the victim at a social gathering or through a mutual acquaintance. Some even present themselves as "taking a sex survey" and ask a series of personally revealing questions.

The typical obscene phone caller is a socially inadequate heterosexual male who has had difficulty forming intimate relationships with women (Leue et al., 2004). The relative safety and anonymity of the telephone may shield him from the risk of rejection (Leue et al., 2004). A reaction of shock or fright from his victims may fill him with feelings of power and control that are lacking in his life, especially in his relationships with women. The obscenities may vent rage that he holds against women who have rejected him.

Obscene phone calls are illegal, but it has been difficult for authorities to track down perpetrators. Call tracing can help police track obscene or offending phone callers. Call tracing works in different ways in different locales. Caller ID shows the caller's telephone number on a display panel on the receiving party's telephone. In some locales, people can program their telephone service so that a caller who calls from a private number or one without caller ID receives a message stating that the recipient only accepts calls from people who identify their phone numbers or names. These services may deter some obscene callers, but others may use public phones instead of their home phones. Check with your local telephone company if you are interested in these services.

Applied Knowledge

RESPONDING TO EXHIBITIONISTS AND OBSCENE PHONE CALLERS

How to Respond to an Exhibitionist

It is understandable that an unsuspecting woman who is exposed to an exhibitionist may react with shock, surprise, or fear. Unfortunately, her display of shock or fear may reinforce the flasher's tendencies to expose himself. She may fear that the flasher, who has already broken at least one social code, is likely to assault her physically as well. Fortunately, most exhibitionists do not seek actual sexual contact with their victims and run away before they can be apprehended by the police or passersby.

When possible, showing no reaction or simply continuing on one's way may be the best response. If women do desire to respond to the flasher, they might calmly say something like "You really need professional help. You should see a professional to help you with this problem." All should promptly report the incident to police, so that authorities can apprehend the offender.

How to Respond to an Obscene Phone Caller

What should a woman do if she receives an obscene phone call? Advice generally parallels that given to women who are victimized by exhibitionists. Above all, women are advised to remain calm and not to reveal shock or fright, because such reactions tend to reinforce the caller and increase the probability of repeat calls. Women may be best advised to say nothing at all and gently hang up the receiver. A woman might alternatively offer a brief response that alludes to the caller's problems before hanging up. She might say in a calm but strong voice, "It's unfortunate that you have this problem. I think you should seek professional help." If she should receive repeated calls, the woman might request an unlisted number or contact the police about tracing the calls. Many women list themselves only by their initials in the phone directory so as to disguise their gender. But this practice is so widespread that obscene callers may assume that people listed by initials are women living alone.

Voyeurism

Voyeurism? Exhibitionism? Normal Behaviour? How would you describe this scene?

Voyeurism involves strong, repetitive urges to observe unsuspecting strangers who are naked, disrobing, or engaged in sexual relations (American Psychiatric Association, 2000). The voyeur becomes sexually aroused by the act of watching and typically does not seek sexual relations with the observed person. In Toronto, Kurt Freund and colleagues found that 12% of university males and 23% of a sample of community males had masturbated while watching a female who was unaware of their presence (Freund et al., 1997).

The voyeur may masturbate while peeping or afterward while replaying the incident in his imagination or engaging in voyeuristic fantasies. The voyeur may fantasize about making love to the observed person but have no intention of actually doing so.

Are people voyeurs if they become sexually aroused by the sight of their lovers undressing? What about people who enjoy watching pornographic films or stripteasers? No, no, and no. The people being observed are not unsuspecting strangers. The lover knows that his or her partner is watching. Porn actors and strippers know that others will be viewing them. They would not be performing if they did not expect or have an audience.

It is perfectly normal for men and women to be sexually stimulated by the sight of other people who are nude, undressing, or engaged in sexual relations. Voyeurism is characterized by urges to spy on *unsuspecting* strangers.

Research with voyeurs and exhibitionists usually has been conducted with people who either have been charged with a crime or who have seen a therapist. We lack research on general populations. However, in a national survey conducted in Sweden, 11.5% of men and 4% of women reported that they had been sexually aroused by spying on others having sex. In that same study, 4% of men and 2% of women said they had been sexually aroused by exposing their genitals to a stranger (Langstrom & Seto, 2006).

Although most voyeurs are nonviolent, some commit violent crimes such as assault and rape (Langevin, 2003). Voyeurs who break into and enter homes or buildings, or who tap at windows to gain the attention of victims, are among the more dangerous.

Voyeurism A paraphilia characterized by strong, repetitive urges and related sexual fantasies of observing unsuspecting strangers who are naked, disrobing, or engaged in sexual relations.

Sexual Masochism

Although pleasure and pain may seem like polar opposites, some people experience sexual pleasure through having pain or humiliation inflicted on them by their sex partners. People who associate the receipt of pain or humiliation with sexual arousal

Innovative Canadian Research

"NORMAL" VOYEURISM

Waterloo researchers B. J. Rye and Glenn Meaney (2007) conducted a survey of university students to determine if they would watch an attractive person undressing or two attractive people having sex in hypothetical situations. The gender responses were similar with most (84% males, 74% females) stating that they would watch an attractive person undressing if they would not be caught doing so. However, far fewer females (40%) than males (70%) said they would watch a couple having sex if they would not be caught. For both situations, fewer said they would watch if there was a chance of being caught. The finding that fewer students said they would watch a couple having sex suggests this voyeuristic behaviour is considered to be more invasive of people's privacy.

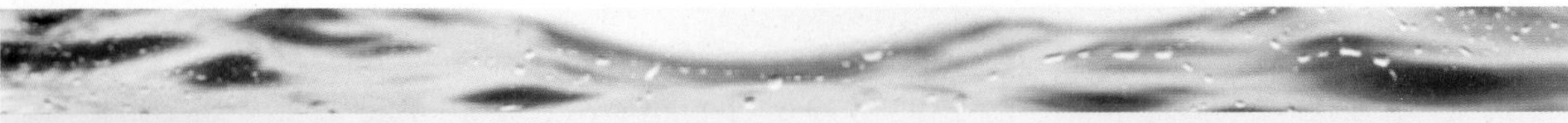

A World of Diversity

IT SEEMS LIKE VOYEURS ARE EVERYWHERE

Traditionally, the voyeur has been categorized as a "peeping Tom" who looks through windows hoping to see a woman undressing. In recent years, voyeurs have been caught in many other kinds of situations. The development of small video cameras and lenses has made voyeurism easier. Consider the following examples:

- In Toronto, a man secretly videotaped women using a washroom in a rooming house.
- In Winnipeg, a restaurant owner installed a camera just above the toilet in the women's washroom.
- In Edmonton, a landlord using a camera hooked up to his computer spied on a female tenant living in the basement apartment.
- In Peterborough, a man hid in the tank of a women's outhouse where he was covered in excrement so that he could watch women urinating and defecating.
- In Toronto, a man attached the lens of a video camera to his shoe and used this to film under women's skirts in shopping malls and other public locations. He posted these video shots for sale on the internet at an "Up-Skirt" website.
- In Toronto, a medical technician used a video camera hidden in a medical laboratory's changeroom to film women undressing.
- In Peterborough, a man used a two-way mirror in a Kentucky Fried Chicken outlet to spy on women who were changing into their work uniforms.
- In Toronto, a man secretly videotaped his sexual behaviour with a teacher's aide and blackmailed her into paying him money so that he would not show the tape to her parents and her employer.
- In Toronto a man sneaked into women's washrooms and peered over the stalls.

In 2005, Parliament passed legislation that makes it a crime to secretly observe or record a person in situations where privacy is expected. This includes situations where someone is nude or engaging in sexual activity. But it also includes situations where a person is fully clothed and someone observes or records them for sexual purposes. Shortly after the legislation was passed, a Toronto man was charged after he was seen at a grocery store crouching down next to young girls and pointing a camera phone under their skirts while their parents were shopping (Powell, 2005).

Because of concerns over the misuse of camera phones many fitness centres and other organizations have banned them, especially in changerooms.

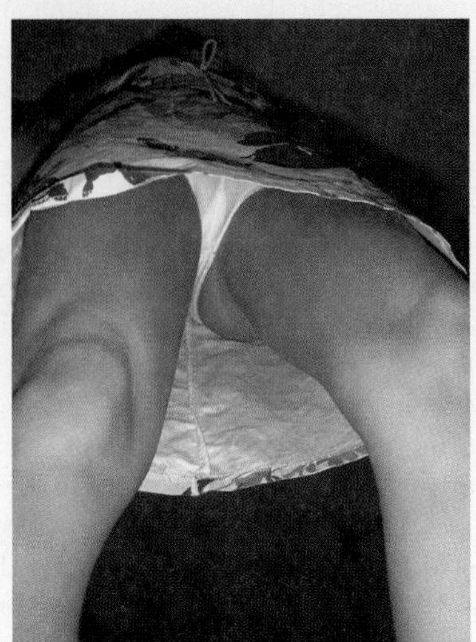

Shooting Private Parts in Public Places. *In places like malls, police are beginning to catch people who are trying to shoot private parts in public places. They aim compact camcorders up women's skirts in crowded stores and shopping malls, parks, and fairs. Sometimes they post the pictures on the internet. Often the pictures wind up for sale on sex sites.*

are called **sexual masochists**. A sexual masochist either acts on or is distressed by persistent urges and sexual fantasies involving the desire to be bound, flogged, humiliated, or made to suffer in some way by a sexual partner so as to achieve sexual excitement. In some cases, the person is incapable of becoming sexually aroused unless pain or humiliation is incorporated into the sexual act.

Sexual masochism is the only paraphilia that is found among women with some frequency (American Psychiatric Association, 2000). Even sexual masochism, however, is much more prevalent among men than women. Male masochists may outnumber females by a margin of 20 to 1 (American Psychiatric Association, 2000).

Sexual masochism A paraphilia characterized by the desire or need for pain or humiliation to enhance sexual arousal so that gratification may be attained.

Bondage Ritual restraint, as by shackles, as practised by many sexual masochists.

The word *masochism* is derived from the name of the Austrian storyteller Leopold von Sacher-Masoch (1835–1895). He wrote tales of men who derived sexual satisfaction from having a female partner inflict pain on them, typically by flagellation (beating or whipping).

Sexual masochists may derive pleasure from various types of punishing experiences, including being restrained (a practice known as **bondage**), blindfolded (sensory bondage), spanked, whipped, or made to perform humiliating acts, such as walking around on all fours and licking the boots or shoes of the sex partner or being subjected to vulgar insults. Some masochists have their partners humiliate them by urinating or defecating on them. Some masochists prefer a particular source of pain. Others seek an assortment. But we should not think that sexual masochists enjoy other types of pain that are not sexually arousing. Sexual masochists are no more likely than anyone else to derive pleasure from the pain they experience when they accidentally stub their toes or touch a hot appliance. Pain has erotic value only within a sexual context. It must be part of an elaborate sexual ritual.

Sexual masochists and **sexual sadists** often form sexual relationships to meet each other's needs. Some sexual masochists enlist the services of prostitutes or obtain the cooperation of their regular sexual partners to enact their masochistic fantasies.

While it may seem contradictory for pain to become connected with sexual pleasure, the association of sexual arousal with mildly painful stimuli is actually quite common. The eroticization of mild forms of pain (love bites, hair pulls, minor scratches) may fall within the normal range of sexual variation. Pain from these sources increases overall bodily arousal, which may enhance sexual excitement. Some of us become sexually excited when our partners "talk dirty" to us or call us vulgar names. When the urge for pain for purposes of sexual arousal becomes so persistent or strong that it overshadows other sources of sexual stimulation, or when the masochistic experience causes physical or psychological harm, many would say that the boundary between normality and abnormality has been breached.

Baumeister (1988a) proposes that independent and responsible selfhood becomes burdensome or stressful at times. Sexual masochism provides a temporary reprieve from the responsibilities of independent selfhood. It is a blunting of one's ordinary level of self-awareness that is achieved by "focusing on immediate sensations (both painful and pleasant) and on being a sexual object" (Baumeister, 1988a, p. 54).

Sexual masochism can range from relatively benign to potentially lethal practices, such as **hypoxyphilia**. Hypoxyphiliacs put plastic bags over their heads, nooses around their necks, or pressure on their chests to deprive themselves of oxygen temporarily and enhance their sexual arousal. They usually fantasize that they are being strangled by a lover. They try to discontinue oxygen deprivation before they lose consciousness, but some miscalculations result in death by suffocation or strangulation.

Sexual sadists People who become sexually aroused by inflicting pain or humiliation on others.

Hypoxyphilia A practice in which a person seeks to enhance sexual arousal, usually during masturbation, by becoming deprived of oxygen.

Sexual sadism A paraphilia characterized by the desire or need to inflict pain or humiliation on others to enhance sexual arousal so that gratification is attained.

Sadomasochism A mutually gratifying sexual interaction between consenting sex partners in which sexual arousal is associated with the infliction and receipt of pain or humiliation. Commonly known as *S&M*.

Sexual Sadism

Sexual sadism is named after the infamous Marquis de Sade (1774–1814), a Frenchman who wrote tales of becoming sexually aroused by inflicting pain or humiliation on others. The virtuous Justine, the heroine of his novel of the same name, endures terrible suffering at the hands of fiendish men.

Sexual sadism is characterized by persistent, powerful urges and sexual fantasies involving the inflicting of pain and suffering on others to achieve sexual excitement or gratification. The urges are acted on or are disturbing enough to cause personal distress. Some sexual sadists cannot become sexually aroused unless they make their sex partners suffer. Others can become sexually excited without such acts.

Some sadists hurt or humiliate willing partners, such as prostitutes or sexual masochists. Others—a small minority—stalk and attack nonconsenting victims.

SADOMASOCHISM **Sadomasochism (S&M)** is *mutually gratifying sexual interactions involving* power exchange between *consenting partners*. A variation is B&D (bondage and discipline) which involves restraining a submissive partner and punishing them either physically or verbally. Today the term *BDSM* is often used instead of *S&M*.

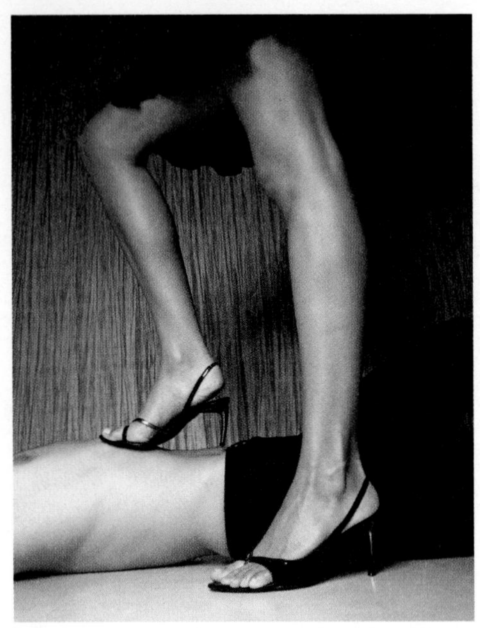

S&M.
An S&M club goer pays money for the services of a dominatrix.

Occasional S&M is quite common among the general population. Couples may incorporate light forms of S&M in their lovemaking now and then, such as mild dominance and submission games or gentle physical restraint. It is also not uncommon for lovers to scratch or bite their partners to heighten their mutual arousal during coitus. They generally do not inflict severe pain or damage, however.

Most S&M encounters are time limited. Often the encounters are built around particular themes involving role play, such as a school teacher and a naughty school boy. Both the dominant person and the submissive agree ahead of time on the rules, and usually they choose a safe word that the submissive will say to stop a particular action that may exceed that person's limits. Once the scene is over, the participants assume their regular relationships (Dancer et al., 2006).

In a small minority of relationships, referred to as *24/7 S&M slavery*, the participants attempt to live full-time in an owner–slave relationship. In one study, the participants were almost evenly divided between female and male, ranging in age from 18 to 72. Of the 66 men, 51 were involved with another man and 15 with a woman. Of the 80 women, 74 were involved with a man and 6 were involved with another woman. According to the study respondents, the majority of these relationships were long lasting and satisfying. It should be noted that the persons adopting the slave role did have the right to exercise their free will if they felt it was in their best interest to do so and thus could leave the relationship at any time (Dancer et al., 2006).

Although some forms of sadomasochism may fall within the boundaries of normal sexual variation, sadomasochism becomes pathological when such fantasies are acted on in ways that become destructive, dangerous, or distressing to oneself or others. How would you categorize the following example?

> A 25-year-old female graduate student described a range of masochistic experiences. She reported feelings of sexual excitement during arguments with her husband when he would scream at her or hit her in a rage. She would sometimes taunt him to make love to her in a brutal fashion, as though she were being raped. She found the brutality and sense of being punished to be sexually stimulating. She had also begun having sex with strange men and enjoyed being physically punished by them during sex more than any other type of sexual stimulus. Being beaten or whipped produced the most intense sexual experiences she had ever had. Although she recognized the dangers posed by her sexual behavior, and felt somewhat ashamed about it, she was not sure that she wanted treatment for "it" because of the pleasure that it provided her (adapted from Spitzer et al., 1989, pp. 87–88).

Some S&M practices can be dangerous. For example, a married couple living near Rockwood, Ontario, played a sex game in their barn whereby they took turns hanging each other with a rope tied to the neck (Dharmajah, 2008). They had engaged in this game numerous times and they videotaped themselves. However, the last time they played this game, the husband lost consciousness and died. The wife was charged with criminal negligence causing death, and sentenced to 12 months of home confinement. Previously, in 1985, the husband had been convicted of manslaughter in the death of a 19-year-old woman whose body was found buried with handcuffs attached to her wrist. The Crown attorney's theory was that the woman died when, during a sex act, the man compressed a nerve in the woman's neck that stopped her heart (Tracey, 2007).

There is a subculture in which sexual sadists and sexual masochists form liaisons to inflict and receive pain and humiliation during sexual activity. It is called the *S&M*

Innovative Canadian Research

WOMEN'S SUBMISSIVE DESIRES AS EXPRESSED ON WEBLOGS

On the internet there are numerous websites dealing with S&M behaviours. Amy Muise (2008), a researcher at the University of Guelph, conducted a study of female weblogs that were focused on sexual desire. In many of these anonymous weblogs, the women wrote about their thoughts, experiences, and feelings regarding submissive sexual desires. Because of the anonymity of the internet, they felt comfortable in revealing personal aspects of their sexual desires that they usually kept hidden. One woman wrote:

> I want to beg to be fucked and flogged. I know I look more innocent than sultry, but my inner slut is inside, just waiting to be set loose. I have kept her hidden all my life, and now that I've opened the door, my slut wants to share everything.

In her analysis of these weblogs, Muise (2008) found that two main themes emerged. First the women described in explicit detail the intense degree of physical arousal, especially in their genitals, they felt in response to their S&M fantasies and experiences. Describing these powerful physical reactions helped to validate their submissive desires.

Second several of the women put their experience in the context of a trusting love relationship they had with their partner. For some women placing their submissive desires within the context of a love relationship helps to legitimize those desires (Muise, 2008).

subculture and is catered to by sex shops that sell S&M paraphernalia and magazines. Paraphernalia includes leather restraints and leather face masks that resemble the ancient masks of executioners. People in the subculture seek one another out through mutual contacts, S&M social organizations, or personal ads in S&M magazines.

Participants in sadomasochism often engage in highly elaborate rituals involving dominance and submission. Rituals are staged as though they were scenes in a play (Gross, 2006). In the "master and slave" game, the sadist leads the masochist around by a leash. The masochist performs degrading or menial acts. In bondage and discipline (B&D), the dominant partner restrains the submissive partner and flagellates (spanks or whips) or sexually stimulates the submissive partner. The erotic appeal of bondage seems to be connected with controlling or being controlled.

Various types of stimulation may be used to administer pain during S&M encounters, but pain is not always used. When it is, it is usually mild or moderate. Psychological pain, or humiliation, is perhaps as common as physical pain. Pain may also be used symbolically, as in the case of a sadist who uses a harmless, soft rubber paddle to spank the masochist. Thus, the erotic appeal of pain for some S&M participants may derive from the ritual of control rather than from the pain itself (Gross, 2006).

Extreme forms of pain, such as torture and severe beatings, are rarely reported by sadomasochists. Masochists may seek pain, but they usually avoid serious injury and dangerous partners (Gross, 2006).

S&M participants may be heterosexual, gay, or bisexual (Gross, 2006). They may assume either the masochistic or the sadistic role, or they may alternate roles depending on the sexual script. People who seek sexual excitement by enacting both sadistic and masochistic roles are known as *sadomasochists*. In heterosexual relationships the partners may reverse traditional gender roles. The man may assume the submissive or masochistic role, and the woman may take the dominant or sadistic role (Gross, 2006).

The causes of sexual masochism and sadism, as of other paraphilias, are unclear. Pain may have direct biological links to pleasure. Natural chemicals called *endorphins*, similar to opiates, are released in the brain in response to pain and produce feelings of euphoria and general well-being. Perhaps, then, pleasure is derived from pain because of the release or augmentation of endorphins.

In society, there is the negative stereotype that people who engage in S&M behaviours are mentally disturbed. However, research does not support this view

Frotteurism.
Frotteurism occurs more often in crowded places such as subways.

(Kleinplatz & Moser, 2005). There is no evidence that people involved in S&M have greater difficulty in establishing intimate relationships than do other people. As well, there is no evidence that engaging in S&M is distressing or dysfunctional. Thus Kleinplatz and Moser conclude that S&M is not pathological.

Frotteurism

Frotteurism (also known as "mashing" or "groping") is rubbing against or touching a nonconsenting person. As with other paraphilias, a diagnosis of frotteurism requires either acting on these urges or being distressed by them. Mashing has been reported exclusively among males (American Psychiatric Association, 2000).

Most mashing takes place in crowded places, such as buses, subway cars, or elevators. The man finds the rubbing or the touching, not the coercive nature of the act, to be sexually stimulating. While rubbing against a woman, he may fantasize a consensual, affectionate sexual relationship with her. Typically, the man incorporates images of his mashing within his masturbation fantasies. Mashing also incorporates a related practice, **toucherism**: the fondling of nonconsenting strangers.

Mashing may be so fleeting and furtive that the woman may not realize what has happened (DSM, 2000). Mashers thus stand little chance of being caught.

Many mashers have difficulty forming relationships with women and are handicapped by fears of rejection. Mashing provides sexual contact in a relatively nonthreatening context.

Other Paraphilias

Let us consider some other, less common, paraphilias.

ZOOPHILIA A person with **zoophilia** experiences repeated, intense urges and related fantasies involving sexual contact with animals. As with other paraphilias, the urges may be acted on or cause personal distress. The term *bestiality* applies to actual sexual contact with an animal.

Although the prevalence of zoophilia in the general population is unknown, Kinsey and his colleagues (1948, 1953) found that about 8% of the men and 3% to 4% of the women interviewed admitted to sexual contacts with animals. Men more often had sexual contact with farm animals, such as calves and sheep. Women more often reported sexual contacts with household pets. Men were more likely to masturbate or copulate with the animals. Women more often reported general body contact. People of both genders reported encouraging the animals to lick their genitals. A few women reported that they had trained a dog to engage in coitus with them. Urban–rural differences also emerged. Rates of bestiality were higher among boys reared on farms. Compared with only a few city boys, 17% of farm boys had reached orgasm at some time through sexual contact with dogs, cows, and goats. These contacts were generally restricted to adolescence, when human outlets were not available. Still, adults sometimes engage in sexual contacts with animals.

In Canada it is a criminal offence to have sex with an animal. In 2003, a 28-year-old Toronto man was charged with cruelty to animals after he was seen having sex with a pregnant Jersey cow. He refused to dismount from the animal even after farm employees repeatedly screamed at him (Godfrey, 2003).

Frotteurism A paraphilia characterized by recurrent, powerful sexual urges and related fantasies that involve rubbing against or touching a nonconsenting person.

Toucherism A practice related to frotteurism and characterized by the persistent urge to fondle nonconsenting strangers.

Zoophilia A paraphilia involving persistent or repeated sexual urges and related fantasies that involve sexual contact with animals.

NECROPHILIA In **necrophilia**, a rare paraphilia, a person desires sex with corpses. Three types of necrophilia have been identified (Holmes & Holmes, 2002). In *regular necrophilia*, the person has sex with a deceased person. In *necrophilic homicide*, the person commits murder to obtain a corpse for sexual purposes. In *necrophilic fantasy*, the person fantasizes about sex with a corpse but does not actually carry out necrophilic acts. Necrophiles often obtain jobs that provide them with access to corpses, such as working in cemeteries, morgues, or funeral homes. The primary motivation for necrophilia appears to be the desire to possess sexually a completely unresisting and nonrejecting partner (Holmes & Holmes, 2002).

OTHER LESS COMMON PARAPHILIAS In **klismaphilia**, sexual arousal is derived from the use of enemas. Klismaphiles generally prefer the receiving role to the giving role. Klismaphiles may have derived sexual pleasure in childhood from the anal stimulation provided by parents giving them enemas.

In **coprophilia**, sexual arousal is connected with feces. The person may desire to be defecated on or to defecate on a sex partner. The association of feces with sexual arousal may also be a throwback to childhood.

In **urophilia**, sexual arousal is associated with urine. As with coprophilia, the person may desire to be urinated on or to urinate on a sexual partner. Also like coprophilia, urophilia may have childhood origins.

Necrophilia A paraphilia characterized by desire for sexual activity with corpses.

Klismaphilia A paraphilia in which sexual arousal is derived from the use of enemas.

Coprophilia A paraphilia in which sexual arousal is attained in connection with feces.

Urophilia A paraphilia in which sexual arousal is associated with urine.

Theoretical Perspectives

The paraphilias are among the most fascinating and perplexing variations in sexual behaviour. Let us consider explanations that have been advanced from the major theoretical perspectives.

Biological Perspectives

Researchers are investigating whether there are biological factors in paraphilic behaviour. The biological perspective looks into factors such as the endocrine system (hormones) and the nervous system in paraphilic behaviour.

Studies appear to confirm that many paraphilics have higher-than-normal sex drives (Haake et al., 2003; Kafka, 2003). A German study, for example, found that people with paraphilias had shorter refractory periods after orgasm by masturbation than most men and experienced a higher frequency of sexual fantasies and urges (Haake et al., 2003). Kafka (2003) refers to this heightened sex drive as *hypersexual desire*—the opposite of hypoactive sexual desire disorder (see Chapter 13).

But these studies address the strength of the sex drive, not the direction it takes. More recent studies have used the electroencephalograph (EEG) to investigate electrical responses in the brain among paraphilics and control subjects (e.g., Kirenskaya-Berus & Tkachenko, 2003). They measured what is termed *evoked electrical potentials* to erotic stimuli in a sample of 62 right-handed men, half of whom were considered to be normal in terms of their sexual fantasies and behaviours (the control subjects), and half of whom had been diagnosed as paraphilic (fetishistic and sadomasochistic) (Waismann et al., 2003). The men were shown three sets of 57 slides each in random order—57 paraphilic slides that portrayed depicting fetishistic and sadomasochistic themes; 57 "normal" slides that depicted nude women, coitus, and oral sex; and 57 neutral slides of landscapes, street scenes, and the like. An electrical response labelled "P600" was determined to be the best indicator of sexual arousal in men. It was found that the main site for evoking the P600 response to "normal" sexual stimuli was on the right side of the brain. The main site for paraphilic stimuli was the left frontal part of the brain. Paraphilic men showed a significantly greater response than the control subjects in the P600 response in the left frontal part of the brain.

Moreover, control subjects were more likely to differentiate between paraphilic and normal stimuli on the right side of the brain.

Another neurological study may offer some insight into masochism. A research team from Massachusetts General Hospital found that the same neural circuits in the brain are often activated either by painful or by pleasurable stimuli (Becerra et al., 2001). The researchers discovered that a painfully hot (115°F) stimulus to the hand activated areas of the brain believed to involve "reward" circuitry. The researchers had set out to find ways to help chronic pain patients and not to investigate sexual masochism, but their findings certainly have implications for masochism.

As time goes on, we may learn more about potential biological foundations of paraphilic behaviour. A better understanding of these atypical patterns of sexual behaviour may lead to the development of more effective treatments.

Psychoanalytic Perspectives

Psychoanalytic theory suggests that paraphilias are psychological defences, usually against unresolved castration anxiety dating to the Oedipus complex (Friedman & Downey, 2001; Horne, 2003). Perhaps the sight of a woman's vagina threatens to arouse castration anxiety in the transvestite, reminding him that women do not have a penis and that he might suffer the same fate. Sequestering his penis beneath women's clothing symbolically asserts that women do have penises, which provides unconscious reassurance against his own fears of castration. By exposing his genitals, perhaps the exhibitionist unconsciously seeks reassurance that his penis is secure. It is as if he were asserting, "Look! I have a penis!" Shock or surprise on the victim's face confirms that his penis exists, temporarily relieving castration anxiety. Perhaps masturbation with an object such as a shoe allows the fetishist to gratify his sexual desires while keeping a safe distance from the dangers that he unconsciously associates with sexual contact with women. Or the fetishistic object itself—the shoe, in this case—may unconsciously symbolize the penis. Are sadists attempting to defend themselves against unconscious feelings of impotence by inflicting pain on others?

One psychoanalyst associates a type of male sexual masochism with a history of suppressed or repressed feelings of sexual guilt and shame (Schrut, 2005). As an adult, the male wants to be punished for feelings of wrongdoing at the same time he experiences sexual arousal. The pain or humiliation makes the experience "okay."

The paraphilias have provided a fertile ground for psychoanalytic theories. However, whatever evidence there is consists of case studies and anecdotes, which are open to interpretation.

Cognitive-Behavioural Perspectives

Cognitive–behavioural theorists generally believe that fetishes and other paraphilias are learned through experience. An object may acquire sexually arousing properties through association with sexual arousal or orgasm. Alfred Kinsey and his colleagues (1953) wrote:

> Even some of the most extremely variant types of human sexual behavior may need no more explanation than is provided by our understanding of the processes of learning and conditioning. Behavior which may appear bizarre, perverse, or unthinkably unacceptable to some persons, and even to most persons, may have significance for other individuals because of the way in which they have been conditioned (pp. 645–646).

For example, a boy who glimpses his mother's stockings hanging on the towel rack while he is masturbating may develop a fetish for stockings. Orgasm in the presence of the object reinforces the erotic connection, especially if it is repeated.

Friedrich and Gerber (1994) studied five adolescent boys who practised hypoxyphilia and found extensive early histories of choking in combination with physical or sexual abuse. The combination seems to have encouraged each of the boys to associate choking with sexual arousal.

Cognitive–behavioural explanations of sexual masochism focus on the pairing of sexual excitement with punishment. For example, a child may be punished when discovered masturbating. Or a boy may reflexively experience an erection if his penis accidentally rubs against the parent's body as he is being spanked. With repeated encounters like these, pain and pleasure may become linked.

Many exhibitionists, voyeurs, frotteurs, and other people with paraphilias have few interpersonal skills relating to women and may avoid "normal" social interactions with them for fear of rejection (Leue et al., 2004). Their furtive, paraphilic behaviours may provide sexual release without the risk of rejection.

Observational learning may also play a role. Parents, for example, may inadvertently model exhibitionistic behaviour to young sons, which can lead the sons to eroticize the act of exposing themselves. Young people may also read books or magazines, or view films or TV programs with paraphilic content. Media may give them the idea of trying paraphilic behaviour, and they may find it exciting, especially if acts such as exhibitionism or voyeurism provide a rush of adrenaline.

Sociological Perspectives

Sociological perspectives focus on the effects of the group and of society on individual and group behaviour. For example, although most people indulge paraphilias privately, sexual masochists and sadists require a partner. Most sadomasochists learn S&M rituals, make sexual contacts, acquire sexual paraphernalia, and confirm their sadomasochistic self-identities within what is termed an *S&M subculture*—a loosely connected network of S&M clubs, specialty shops, organizations, magazines, and so on. But the S&M subculture exists in the context of the larger society, and its rituals mirror widely based social and gender roles.

Martin Weinberg (1987) proposes a sociological model that focuses on the social context of sadomasochism. S&M rituals generally involve some form of dominance and submission. Weinberg (1987) attributes their erotic appeal to the opportunity to reverse the customary power relationships that exist between males and females and between social classes. Within the confines of the carefully scripted S&M encounter, the meek can be powerful and the powerful, meek. People from lower social classes or in menial jobs may be drawn to S&M so they can enact a dominant role. Dominance and submission games allow people to accentuate or reverse the gender stereotypes that identify masculinity with dominance and femininity with submissiveness. Interviews with, and observations of, sadomasochists suggest that most often dominance–submission relationships tend to be consistent with traditional masculine and feminine gender roles in society (Damon, 2002; Santtila et al., 2002). Although there are many exceptions, men more often tend to be dominant and women to be submissive in S&M rituals.

An Integrated Perspective: The "Lovemap"

Paraphilias may have complex biopsychosocial origins (Seligman & Hardenburg, 2000). Might our understanding of them thus be best approached from a theoretical framework that incorporates multiple perspectives? John Money (2003), for example, traces the origins of paraphilias to childhood. He believes that childhood experiences etch a pattern in the brain, called a lovemap. This lovemap determines the

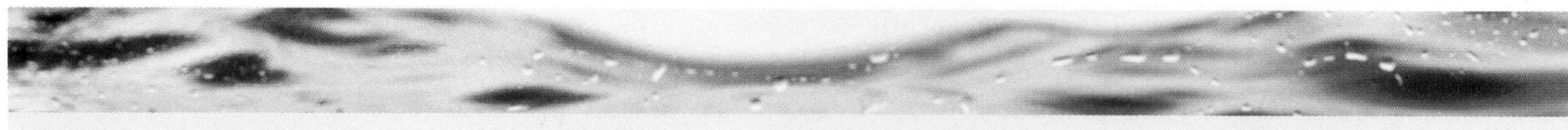

A World of Diversity

SEXUAL ADDICTION AND COMPULSIVITY

In Prince Edward Island, a politician resigned from the Liberal caucus of the legislature after admitting that he had billed more than $1000 in phone-sex charges to his legislature calling card. At a news conference, he said that he was addicted to phoning females on adult phone lines (Canadian Press, 1995a). That is, he had lost control over his sexual behaviour. What is a sexual addiction? What is sexual compulsivity?

Do People Become Addicted to Cybersex?
According to Dr. Mark Schwartz of the Masters and Johnson Institute, "Sex on the net is like heroin," for some people. "It grabs them and takes over their lives." Some people spend hours each day masturbating to pornographic images they find online, or engaging in "mutual" online sex with someone they contact through a chatroom. Is becoming hooked on cybersex a safe kind of "addiction"? What do you think?

What Is a Sexual Addiction?

A person with a sexual addiction

- Uses sexual behaviour as a means of reducing anxiety
- Lacks control over his or her sexual impulses
- Typically experiences minimal satisfaction from sexual contacts
- Feels bad about his or her sexual contacts but engages in the behaviour repeatedly
- Engages in illicit sexual behaviour that endangers his or her own well-being and the well-being of his or her family
- Cannot resist sexual opportunities
- Continues sexual contacts that are nonintimate, dangerous, or undesirable

Characteristics of addiction include *tolerance* and *withdrawal symptoms*. As with other addictions, the sexually addicted person may experience tolerance—that is, may seek increasingly illicit sexual contacts or experiences. When the sexual activity is discontinued, the person may also experience withdrawal symptoms, such as anxiety and preoccupation with the craved activity.

What Is Sexual Compulsivity?

Sexual compulsivity is an obsessive-compulsive disorder. In an obsessive-compulsive disorder, an individual cannot eradicate certain thoughts or ideas from his or her mind and has extreme difficulty controlling his or her behaviour. For example, some people have "checking" compulsions in which they check and recheck whether they have locked every door and window before they can leave home. (And then they may check some more and remain uneasy about the possibility of error.) Sexual compulsivity is manifested by means of sexual activity and may involve a specific paraphilia. Like sexual addiction, a sexual compulsion becomes the centre of the person's life. As such, it may interfere with personal relationships, work, and health. There may also be legal consequences.

Sources: American Psychiatric Association, 2000; ***www.mastersandjohnson.com****, 2000.*

types of stimuli and activities that become sexually arousing to the individual. In the case of paraphilias, lovemaps become distorted by early traumatic experiences such as incest, antisexual upbringing, and abuse or neglect.

Research suggests that voyeurs and exhibitionists were often the victims of childhood sexual abuse (Lee et al., 2002). Not all children exposed to such influences develop paraphilic compulsions, however. For reasons that remain unknown, some children exposed to such influences appear to be more vulnerable to developing distorted lovemaps than others. A genetic predisposition, hormonal factors, brain abnormalities, or a combination of these and other factors may play a role in determining one's vulnerability to vandalized lovemaps.

Treatment of the Paraphilias

The treatment of paraphilias raises a number of issues. First, many people with paraphilias do not want or seek treatment, at least not voluntarily. Ontario criminologist Ron Langevin (2006), for example, followed nearly 800 sex offenders from the 1960s through to the 2000s and found that only about half desired treatment and completed a course of treatment. But many offenders are seen by health care providers only when they come into conflict with the law or at the urging of their family members or partners. They often deny that they are offenders, even after they are apprehended and convicted.

Paraphilic behaviour is a source of pleasure, so many people are not motivated to give it up. The individual typically perceives his problems as stemming from society's intolerance, not from feelings of guilt or shame.

Second, helping professionals may encounter ethical problems when they are asked to contribute to a judicial process by trying to persuade a sex offender that he (virtually all are male) *ought* to change his behaviour. Helping professionals traditionally help clients clarify or meet their own goals; it is not their role to impose societal goals on the individual. Many helping professionals believe that the criminal justice system, not they, ought to enforce social standards.

The third issue is a treatment problem. Therapists realize that they are generally less successful with resistant or recalcitrant clients. Unless the motivation to change is present, therapeutic efforts are often wasted.

The fourth problem is the issue of perceived responsibility. Sex offenders almost invariably claim that they are unable to control their urges and impulses. However, accepting personal responsibility for one's actions is a prelude to change.

Despite these issues, many offenders are referred for treatment by the courts. A few seek therapy themselves because they have come to see how their behaviour harms themselves or others. Let us consider some of the ways in which therapists treat people with these atypical sexual behaviour patterns.

Psychotherapy

Psychoanalysis focuses on resolving the unconscious conflicts that are believed to originate in childhood and to give rise in adulthood to pathological problems such as paraphilias. The aim of therapy is to help bring unconscious conflicts, principally Oedipal conflicts, into conscious awareness so that they can be worked through in light of the individual's adult personality.

Psychoanalytic therapy for the paraphilias has not been subjected to experimental analysis. We thus do not know whether successes are due to the psychoanalytic treatment itself or to other factors, such as spontaneous improvement or a client's willingness to change.

Cognitive-Behaviour Therapy

Whereas traditional psychoanalysis tends to entail a lengthy process of exploration of the childhood origins of problem behaviours, **cognitive-behaviour therapy** is briefer and focuses directly on changing behaviour. Cognitive-behaviour therapy has spawned a number of techniques to help eliminate paraphilic behaviours and strengthen appropriate sexual behaviours. These techniques include systematic desensitization, aversion therapy, social skills training, covert sensitization, and orgasmic reconditioning, to name a few.

Systematic desensitization attempts to break the link between the sexual stimulus (such as a fetishistic stimulus) and the inappropriate response (sexual arousal). The client is first taught to relax selected muscle groups in the body. Muscle relaxation is then paired repeatedly with each of a series of progressively more

Cognitive-behaviour therapy The systematic application of the principles of learning to help people modify problem behaviour.

Systematic desensitization A method for terminating the connection between a stimulus (such as a fetishistic object) and an inappropriate response (such as sexual arousal to the paraphilic stimulus). Muscle relaxation is practised in connection with each stimulus in a series of increasingly arousing stimuli, so that the person learns to remain relaxed (and not sexually aroused) in their presence.

Aversion therapy A method for terminating undesirable sexual behaviour in which the behaviour is repeatedly paired with an aversive stimulus such as electric shock so that a conditioned aversion develops.

Covert sensitization A form of aversion therapy in which thoughts of engaging in undesirable behaviour are paired repeatedly with imagined aversive stimuli.

Pedophiles Persons with pedophilia, a paraphilia involving sexual interest in children.

Social skills training Behaviour therapy methods that rely on a therapist's coaching and practice to build social skills.

Orgasmic reconditioning A method for strengthening the connection between sexual arousal and appropriate sexual stimuli (such as fantasies about an adult of the other gender) by repeatedly pairing the desired stimuli with orgasm.

arousing paraphilic images or fantasies. Relaxation comes to replace sexual arousal in response to each of these stimuli, even the most provocative.

In **aversion therapy**, the undesirable sexual behaviour (for example, masturbation to fetishistic fantasies) is paired repeatedly with an aversive stimulus (such as a harmless but painful electric shock or a nausea-inducing chemical) in the hope that the client will develop a conditioned aversion to the paraphilic behaviour.

Covert sensitization is a variation of aversion therapy in which paraphilic fantasies are paired with an aversive stimulus in imagination. In a broad-scale application, 38 **pedophiles** and 62 exhibitionists, more than half of whom were court-referred, were treated by pairing imagined aversive images or odours with fantasies of the problem behaviour (Maletzky, 1980). Clients were instructed to fantasize pedophiliac or exhibitionistic scenes. Then,

> At a point when sexual pleasure is aroused, aversive images are presented. Examples might include a pedophiliac fellating a child, but discovering a festering sore on the boy's penis, an exhibitionist exposing to a woman but suddenly being discovered by his wife or the police, or a pedophiliac laying a young boy down in a field, only to lie next to him in a pile of dog feces. (Maletzky, 1980, p. 308)

Maletzky used this treatment weekly for six months and then followed it with booster sessions every three months over a three-year period. The procedure resulted in at least a 75% reduction in the deviant activities and fantasies for over 80% of the study participants, at follow-up periods of up to 36 months.

Social skills training focuses on helping the individual improve his ability to relate to the other gender. The therapist might first model a desired behaviour, such as how to ask a woman out on a date or how to handle a rejection. The client might then role-play the behaviour, with the therapist playing the part of the woman. Following the role-play enactment, the therapist would provide feedback and additional guidance and modelling to help the client improve his skills. This process would be repeated until the client mastered the skill.

Is Her Behaviour Appropriate or Inappropriate? *Research indicates that parental nudity that is not sexually suggestive is not harmful to the child.*

Orgasmic reconditioning aims to increase sexual arousal to socially appropriate sexual stimuli by pairing culturally appropriate imagery with orgasmic pleasure. The person is instructed to become sexually aroused by masturbating to paraphilic images or fantasies. But as he approaches the point of orgasm, he switches to appropriate imagery and focuses on it during orgasm. These images and fantasies eventually acquire the capacity to elicit sexual arousal. Orgasmic reconditioning is often combined with other techniques, such as social skills training, so that more desirable social behaviours can be strengthened as well.

Although behaviour therapy techniques tend to have higher reported success rates than most other methods, they too are limited by reliance on uncontrolled case studies. Without appropriate controls, we cannot isolate the effective elements of therapy or determine that the results were not due merely to the passage of time or other factors unrelated to the treatment. It is possible that clients who are highly motivated to change may succeed in doing so with *any* systematic approach.

Medical Approaches

There is no medical "cure" for the paraphilias. Yet some progress has recently been reported in using antidepressants such as Prozac (fluoxetine hydrochloride) in treating exhibitionism, voyeurism, and fetishism (Roesler & Witztum, 2000). Why Prozac? In addition to treating depression, Prozac has been helpful in treating obsessive-compulsive disorder, a type of emotional disorder involving recurrent obsessions (intrusive ideas) and/or compulsions (urges to repeat a certain behaviour or thought). Researchers speculate that paraphilias may be linked to obsessive-compulsive disorder (Kruesi et al., 1992). People with paraphilias often experience intrusive, repetitive thoughts or images of the paraphilic object or stimulus, such as mental images of young children. Many also report feeling compelled to carry out the paraphilic acts repeatedly. Paraphilias may belong to what researchers have dubbed an obsessive-compulsive spectrum of behaviours (Kruesi et al., 1992).

Anti-androgen drug A chemical substance that reduces the sex drive by lowering the level of testosterone in the bloodstream.

People who experience such intense urges that they are at risk of committing sexual offences may be helped by **anti-androgen drugs**, which reduce the level of testosterone in the bloodstream (Roesler & Witztum, 2000). Testosterone is closely linked to sex drive and interest. *Medroxyprogesterone acetate* (MPA) (trade name: Depo-Provera), which is administered in weekly injections, is the anti-androgen that has been used most extensively in the treatment of sex offenders. In men, anti-androgens reduce testosterone to a level that is typical of a prepubertal boy (Bradford, 2001). They consequently reduce sexual desire and the frequency of erections and ejaculations (Bradford, 2001).

Depo-Provera suppresses the sexual appetite in men. It can lower the intensity of sex drive and erotic fantasies and urges so that the man may feel less compelled to act on them (Roesler & Witztum, 2000). The use of anti-androgens is sometimes incorrectly referred to as *chemical castration.* Surgical castration—the surgical removal of the testes—has sometimes been performed on convicted rapists and violent sex offenders (Roesler & Witztum, 2000). Unlike surgical castration, the effects of anti-androgens can be reversed when the treatment is terminated.

Evidence suggests that anti-androgens help some people when they are used in conjunction with psychological treatment (Roesler & Witztum, 2000). However, according to Ottawa psychiatrist Paul Fedoroff (1995), the value of anti-androgens has been limited by high refusal and dropout rates. Questions also remain concerning side effects.

Ottawa psychiatrist John Bradford has conducted extensive research into the use of pharmacological approaches in treating sexual deviation. In one study, Bradford and others (1995) used the SSRI (selective serotonin reuptake inhibitor) sertraline with pedophiles. The drug reduced all the deviant sexual behaviours but did not decrease normal sexual arousal to consenting sex with adults.

Bradford (2000) has suggested a six-level schema for treatment based on the severity of the deviation. The first level involves the use of cognitive–behavioural treatment, which is provided in all treatment programs. The second level involves treating mild paraphilia, beginning with SSRIs such as Prozac, which is used in treating depression. If the SSRIs are not effective within four to six weeks, a small dose of an anti-androgen would be added in level 3. For moderate and some severe cases, anti-androgen or hormonal treatments would be given in level 4. In more severe cases (level 5), these treatments would be given through injections. For the most serious cases, and especially for those determined to be catastrophic (level 6), the therapist would seek to completely reduce androgens and the sex drive through high dosages of anti-androgens or a luteinizing-hormone-releasing hormone (LHRH).

At all levels of treatment, the goal is to suppress deviant fantasies, urges, and behaviours. Treatment at levels 4 and 5 aims for a strong reduction in sex drive, and at level 6 for the elimination or near-elimination of the sex drive (Bradford, 2000). The broader objective of these treatments is to reduce the possibility of recidivism and further victimization.

Although we have amassed a great deal of research on atypical variations in sexual behaviour, our understanding of them and our treatment approaches to them remain largely in their infancy.

Summing Up

Atypical patterns of sexual arousal or behaviour that become problematic in the eyes of the individual or society are labelled *paraphilias.*

The psychiatric diagnosis of paraphilia requires that the person has acted on these persistent urges in socially unacceptable ways or is distinctly distressed by them.

In fetishism, an inanimate object comes to elicit sexual arousal. Transvestites become excited by wearing articles of clothing—the fetishistic objects—of the other gender.

An exhibitionist experiences the compulsion to expose himself to strangers. The obscene phone caller is motivated to become sexually aroused by shocking his victim. Voyeurs become sexually aroused by watching and do not seek sexual relations with the target. Sexual masochists associate the receipt of pain or humiliation with sexual arousal. Sexual sadism is characterized by persistent, powerful urges and sexual fantasies involving the inflicting of pain and suffering on others to achieve sexual excitement or gratification. Most frotteuristic acts—rubbing against nonconsenting persons, also known as mashing—take place in crowded places, such as buses, subway cars, or elevators.

Zoophiles desire to have sexual contact with animals. Necrophiles desire to have sexual contact with dead bodies.

The links between paraphilias and biological factors have yet to be fully explored.

Classical psychoanalytic theory suggests that paraphilias in males are psychological defences against castration anxiety.

Some learning theorists have argued that unusual stimuli may acquire sexually arousing properties through association with sexual arousal or orgasm. According to Weinberg's sociological model, the erotic appeal of S&M rituals may result from the opportunity to reverse the customary power relationships that exist between the genders and social classes in society at large.

Money suggests that childhood experiences etch a pattern in the brain—a lovemap—that determines the types of stimuli and activities that become sexually arousing. In the case of paraphilias, these lovemaps become distorted by early traumatic experiences.

Psychoanalysis aims to bring unconscious Oedipal conflicts that prompt paraphilic behaviour into awareness so that they can be worked through in adulthood.

Cognitive-behaviour therapy attempts to eliminate paraphilic behaviours through techniques such as systematic desensitization, aversion therapy, social skills training, covert sensitization, and orgasmic reconditioning.

SSRIs, which are usually used as antidepressants, tend to curb compulsive behaviour and depress sexual response, and have been used with some paraphilic individuals.

Test Yourself

Multiple-Choice Questions

1. Sexual behaviours may be considered deviant as a result of the imposition of

a. social norms
b. research norms
c. physical needs
d. psychological needs

2. One of the major difficulties in discussing atypical sexual behaviours is

a. finding volunteers for research studies
b. establishing what constitutes "normal" sexual behaviour
c. determining underlying thoughts and emotions
d. helping people who feel guilty or ashamed

3. Except for ____________, paraphilias are found almost exclusively in men.

a. partialism
b. sexual masochism
c. transvestism
d. phone sex

4. A man who is troubled by his desire to dress in women's clothing for the purposes of sexual gratification is labelled a ____________.

a. transsexual
b. partialist
c. frotteur
d. transvestite

5. A finding that is true for all paraphilias is that they

a. pose a physical threat to the victims
b. are evidence that the perpetrator is out of touch with reality
c. are more common among males
d. can be treated by psychoanalytic psychotherapy

6. Hypoxyphilia is an activity related to

a. sexual sadism
b. sexual masochism
c. fetishism
d. zoophilia

7. Stripteasers and sunbathers at nude beaches

a. are not regarded as exhibitionists
b. engage in a form of mild exhibitionism
c. are referred to as "flashers"
d. are referred to as "normal exhibitionists"

8. Telephone scatalogia is considered to be most closely related to

a. coprophilia
b. sexual sadism
c. voyeurism
d. exhibitionism

9. When cognitive-behavioural therapists work with people with paraphilias, they may use all of the following methods *except*

a. covert sensitization
b. orgasmic reconditioning
c. systematic desensitization
d. antidepressant drugs

10. A brain pattern of the ideal lover and ideal erotic activities is known as a ________________.

a. sexual script
b. lovemap
c. gender stereotype
d. fantasy

Answers to the Test Yourself questions in each chapter are found on page 509.

Critical Thinking Questions

1. How do you decide if a sexual behaviour is "normal"? Where do you draw the line for others? For yourself?
2. When is it okay to cross-dress? For a costume party? As part of a role in a play? At a viewing of *The Rocky Horror Picture Show*? In class? As you answered these questions, were you thinking of men or women?
3. Criminal behaviours such as flashing are sometimes referred to as "nuisance" offences, implying that they are basically harmless. Do you agree or disagree? If you have ever experienced one of these offences, do you think your experience affected your answer?
4. Can you think of any explanations for the finding that nearly all people with paraphilias are male?

PEARSON mypsychkit™

Visit MyPsychKit at www.mypsychkit.com, where you can do quizzes and link to additional resources on topics discussed in this text.

CHAPTER SIXTEEN

Sexual Coercion

This chapter is about sexual coercion. As well as actual force or threat, sexual coercion includes *any* sexual activity between an adult and a child. Even when children cooperate, sexual relations with children are considered coercive because children are below the legal age of consent. In this chapter we also look at diverse forms of sexual pressure and sexual harassment.

Sexual assault Nonconsensual bodily contact for a sexual purpose.

Sexual Assault

Until 1983 the word *rape* was used in the Canadian Criminal Code to describe forced sexual intercourse. (The American justice system still uses the word, although the definition varies from state to state.) **Sexual assault** has replaced *rape* as the term used in the Canadian legal system. There are three levels of sexual assault. Level 1 encompasses any nonconsensual bodily contact for a sexual purpose, including touching, kissing, and oral, vaginal, and anal sex. Bodily contact can involve any part of the accused's body or an object. Level 2 is sexual assault with a weapon, in which the weapon is used to threaten or injure the victim. Level 3 is aggravated sexual assault, in which the victim is maimed or disfigured or has her or his life endangered. The central issue in determining whether an assault has occurred is whether consent was freely given. The person has to be capable of giving consent; therefore, a person who is drunk, under the influence of drugs, unconscious, fearful, or underage is unable to give consent.

Underlying changes to the Criminal Code was the perspective that sexual assault is an act of power and dominance rather than of sex. The Canadian law regarding sexual assault is gender neutral, in that it recognizes that sexual assault can be committed by women against men as well as by someone of the same gender. The law also acknowledges that sexual assault can be committed by one's spouse.

It is important to note that consent for one type of sexual behaviour does not mean consent for other behaviours. In Guelph, Ontario, a man received a jail sentence because he engaged in anal sex despite his partner's objections. After having sexual relations together for some months, the man asked the woman about having anal sex; she did not want to try it, however. A week later, during a sexual interaction that had included vaginal intercourse, he penetrated the woman anally despite her resistance. The woman later went to the police, and the man was charged with sexual assault ("Sexual assault plea," 1994). In another case, a Toronto man received a jail sentence after he removed his condom during sexual intercourse. The victim had consented to having intercourse only if the man was wearing a condom, but he continued having sex with her nonetheless (Oakes, 1994). In another example, an orderly visited the maternity ward in a Toronto hospital and told female patients

Canadian Trends

INCIDENCE OF SEXUAL ASSAULT

According to Statistics Canada (2003b), in 2002 there were 27 100 sexual offences reported to the police. Level 1 offences accounted for 88% of these and the more serious assault levels 2 and 3 accounted for 2%, with other sexual offences (mainly against children) accounting for 10%. Once reported, sexual offences are less likely than other violent offences to result in charges. However, once convicted, sexual offenders in adult court are more likely to be imprisoned than other violent offenders (Statistics Canada, 2003b).

The number of reported sexual assaults decreased by 36% from 1993 to 2002 (the decrease occurred every year, except for a 1% increase from 2000 to 2001). Rates of sexual assault vary considerably across the country, with the lowest rate per 100 000 population in Quebec (50) and the highest rates in Canada's North (Yukon 254, Northwest Territories 360, and Nunavut 788). Among cities, the highest rates are in St. John's and Saskatoon. Youth between the ages of 12 and 17 account for 17% of sexual assaults. Among adults, males are the offender in 98% of sexual assaults. The rate of offending is highest among males between the ages of 25 and 44 and lowest for males aged 55 and older (Statistics Canada, 2002g).

People charged with sexual offences are less likely than other violent offenders to be found guilty in adult court. However, sexual offenders found guilty in adult court are more likely than other violent offenders to receive a prison sentence (Statistics Canada, 2002g).

What proportion of women are sexually assaulted? Social surveys on sexual assault experiences produce varying findings, depending on what questions are asked and what groups are sampled:

- In 1993, Statistics Canada surveyed a national sample of 13 300 Canadian women. The survey asked if, since the age of 16, the women had experienced unwanted sexual touching or force or attempted force aimed at engaging them in any sexual activity. Thirty-nine percent of the women reported having experienced one or both of these situations (Roberts, 1994).
- Twelve percent of female students surveyed at an Ontario university reported having been forced to have sex by physical threats, and 8% said they had been forced to have sex because of verbal threats (Rye, 2001).
- In the Ethnocultural Communities Facing AIDS study of Canadian immigrants from diverse regions of the world, 39% of women and 19% of men from English-speaking Caribbean countries reported that they had been coerced or forced to have sex against their will, compared with 8% of women and 1% of men from the Latin American communities (Maticka-Tyndale et al., 1996). (This study is described in more detail in Chapter 1.)

Although people of all ages, races, and social classes are sexually assaulted, children and younger women are more likely to be assaulted. In 2003, in Canada, 61% of victims of sexual offences reported to police were children and youth under the age of 18 (Statistics Canada, 2005g). Among this age group, 80% of sexual assault victims are female. A study of street youth in Toronto found that young women who are homeless are at even greater risk of being sexually assaulted (Gaetz, 2004).

that he was a lactation consultant (there were in fact no male lactation consultants at the hospital). Because he was wearing the appropriate hospital gown, the patients assumed he was there to show them how to breastfeed properly. He was later charged with sexual assault after one of the patients asked a nurse if the lactation consultant would be returning ("House arrest," 2002).

In Canada, people who are infected with HIV can be charged with sexual assault if they do not disclose their HIV status to their partners before engaging in sexual behaviour with them. Across Canada there have been several such convictions (discussed in Chapter 14).

Most sexual assaults go unreported; according to the 1993 Statistics Canada survey, only 6% of women who experienced sexual assault had reported it to the police. The belief that the incident was too minor to report, the expectation that the police would not be able to do anything, and the desire to protect their privacy were the main reasons the women gave for not reporting (Roberts, 1994).

On the other hand, there are also some cases in which an alleged assault did not take place. One of the most publicized examples of this occurred when a councillor in Alberta disappeared for three days and was found in Las Vegas. She initially claimed she had been kidnapped and sexually assaulted. However, she later retracted her story (Canadian Press, 2003a).

A World of Diversity

NOT ALL SEX OFFENDERS ARE MEN

Not too long ago it used to be believed that women did not commit sexual assaults. However, in recent years there have been numerous media stories of sexual assaults committed by women:

- In Hamilton, Ontario, a teenage girl sought revenge against another girl who she said had stolen her boyfriend. She forced the other girl to take off her clothes and left her naked in an underground parking garage ("Girl lied," 2001).
- In St. Catharines, Ontario, a 42-year-old woman pleaded guilty to assault after she undid her son's pants and forcefully grabbed his genitals in front of his friends ("Mother guilty," 1999).
- In Uxbridge, Ontario, two female employees (aged 41 and 29) at a young-offender facility were charged with sexually assaulting male inmates ("Jail workers," 2002).
- In Guelph, Ontario, a 31-year-old woman admitted in court that she had sex with her son's 13-year-old friend (Tracey, 2001).
- In Kitchener, Ontario, a 35-year-old woman pleaded guilty to having sexual intercourse with her two teenage sons on two separate occasions (Wood, 2004).
- In Saskatoon, a 13-year-old girl pleaded guilty to forcing an older teenage girl to work as a street prostitute (Canadian Press, 2001a).
- In Vernon, British Columbia, a 24-year-old woman who pretended she was a man in order to have sex with young women was convicted of sexually assaulting five girls between the ages of 12 and 17 (Canadian Press, 1995b).
- In Kamloops, British Columbia, a 32-year-old mother was convicted of sexual exploitation for having sex with her 16-year-old female foster child. The woman and the teenager began living together as a couple in a love relationship (Bailey, I., 2000).
- In Hamilton, Ontario, a 28-year-old mother was charged with having a sexual relationship with a 14-year-old boy (Legall, 2008).

Sometimes, sexual assault by a woman involves aiding or abetting men who are attacking another woman. In such cases, a woman may be used to lure another woman to a reasonably safe place for the assault, or the woman may hold the other woman down while she is assaulted.

It remains true, however, that the vast majority of sexual assaults are committed by men.

In Toronto, a male elementary school teacher was found to be not guilty after he had been charged with sexually assaulting a 13-year-old student (Small, 2007). The teacher was so traumatized by the allegation that he said he may never teach again. The student admitted that prior to the allegations she had had a crush on the teacher and left a phone message saying she loved him. The student was embarrassed when the man's wife phoned and said the message was inappropriate. After seeing a television show detailing a sexual assault, the student relied on the story line of the program in fabricating sexual assault allegations against the teacher in hopes that the teacher would be transferred to another school (Small, 2007).

It is important to put cases of false reporting in perspective. Such cases are vastly outnumbered by sexual assaults that go unreported.

In Canada there is a rising incidence of drug-facilitated sexual assaults. A study based in British Columbia concluded that in 2002, 27% of sexual assaults involved drugs such as GHB and Rohypnol (McGregor et al., 2004). These drugs are typically mixed in with drinks served to the victim. They are odourless and tasteless and result in loosened inhibitions and amnesia for up to 12 hours. Often the victims have little or no memory of what occurred after ingesting the drug and thus are less likely to report the incident.

In Toronto, a man visiting a couple put a drug into a drink and served it to them. He then sexually assaulted both the man and the woman. In court the two victims reported that for brief moments they observed the accused sexually assaulting one or both of them, but because of the drug's effect, they could not act to stop the assaults. The accused was found guilty of sexual assault and of administering a noxious substance (Small, 2004).

Stranger sexual assault Sexual assault that is committed by an assailant previously unknown to the person who is assaulted.

Acquaintance sexual assault Sexual assault by an acquaintance of the person who is assaulted.

Types of Sexual Assault

One of the central myths in our culture is that most sexual assaults are perpetrated by strangers lurking in dark alleyways or by intruders who climb through open windows in the middle of the night. In fact, most women are assaulted by men they know—and often by men they have come to trust (Roberts, 1994).

STRANGER SEXUAL ASSAULT **Stranger sexual assault** is committed by an assailant (or assailants) not previously known to the person attacked. In 2002, only 20% of reported sexual assaults in Canada were committed by a stranger (Statistics Canada, 2003b). The stranger often selects targets who seem vulnerable—women who live alone, who are older or mentally challenged, who are walking down deserted streets, or who are asleep or intoxicated. After choosing a target, the assailant may search for a safe time and place to commit the crime, such as a deserted, run-down part of town, a darkened street, or a second-floor apartment without window bars or locks.

Sometimes an assailant will use a phony ploy to get a woman to lower her guard. In Toronto a man posed as a photographer for a university and asked women on campus if he could take their picture for a project. The women were assaulted after going to a more secluded area ("Women warned," 2008).

ACQUAINTANCE SEXUAL ASSAULT Canadians are more likely to be assaulted by people they know than by strangers. In Canada in 2002, 51% of victims of sexual offences were sexually assaulted by a friend or acquaintance, while 28% were victimized by a family member (Statistics Canada, 2003b). **Acquaintance sexual assaults** are much less likely than assaults by strangers to be reported to the police (Schafran, 1995), in part because victims may not perceive coercion by acquaintances as an assault.

DATE SEXUAL ASSAULT One of the most common forms of acquaintance sexual assault occurs within the dating context. Date sexual assault is more likely to occur when the couple has too much to drink and then parks in the man's car or goes back to his residence (Cole, 2006). The man tends to perceive his partner's willingness to return home with him as a signal of sexual interest, even if she resists his advances.

Other men assume that women who frequent places like singles bars are expressing tacit agreement to have sex with men who show interest in them. Some assailants believe that a woman who resists advances is just "protesting too much" so that she will not appear "easy." They interpret resistance as coyness, in other words, as a ploy in the cat-and-mouse game that to them typifies the "battle of the sexes." They may believe that when a woman says "No," she means "Maybe," and when she says "Maybe," she means "Yes." They may thus not see themselves as committing sexual assault—but of course they are.

It is important, however, to acknowledge that most people will not force a non-consenting person to have sex. For example, in a study of New Brunswick university students, Byers and Lewis (1988) found that most males accepted a dating partner's refusal to have sex.

The issue of consent lies at the heart of whether a sexual act is an assault. Unlike cases of stranger assault, date sexual assault occurs within a context in which sexual relations could occur voluntarily. Thus, the issue of consent can become murky. The defendant may concede that sexual intercourse took place but claim that it was consensual. Judges and juries face the task of discerning shadings in the meaning of "consent." Lawyers on both sides vie to persuade them to see things their way.

Sexual assault charges in a dating situation often come down to his word against hers. Her word often becomes less persuasive in the eyes of the jury if it was clear that she had consented to mutual activities beforehand, such as sharing dinner, attending the movies together, accompanying him to his home, sharing a drink

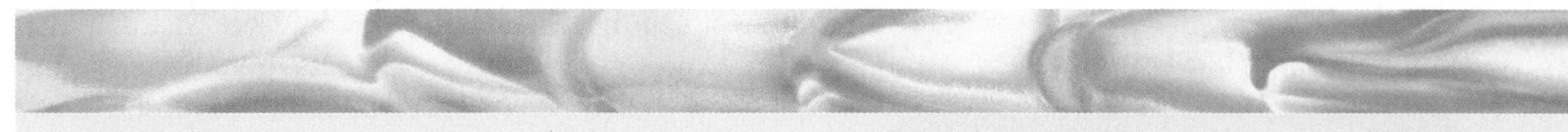

A Closer Look

ANATOMY OF A DATE SEXUAL ASSAULT: ANN AND JIM

Ann

I first met him at a party. He was really good looking and he had a great smile. I wanted to meet him but I wasn't sure how. I didn't want to appear too forward. Then he came over and introduced himself. We talked and found we had a lot in common. I really liked him. When he asked me over to his place for a drink, I thought it would be okay. He was such a good listener, and I wanted him to ask me out again.

When we got to his room, the only place to sit was on the bed. I didn't want him to get the wrong idea, but what else could I do? We talked for awhile and then he made his move. I was so startled. He started by kissing. I really liked him so the kissing was nice. But then he pushed me down on the bed. I tried to get up and I told him to stop. He was so much bigger and stronger. I got scared and I started to cry. I froze and he sexually assaulted me.

It took only a couple of minutes and it was terrible, he was so rough. When it was over he kept asking me what was wrong, like he didn't know. He had just forced himself on me and he thought that was OK. He drove me home and said he wanted to see me again. I'm so afraid to see him. I never thought it would happen to me.

Jim

I first met her at a party. She looked really hot, wearing a sexy dress that showed off her great body. We started talking right away. I knew that she liked me by the way she kept smiling and touching my arm while she was speaking. She seemed pretty relaxed so I asked her back to my place for a drink. . . . When she said yes, I knew that I was going to get lucky!

When we got to my place, we sat on the bed kissing. At first, everything was great. Then, when I started to lay her down on the bed, she started twisting and saying she didn't want to. Most women don't like to appear too easy, so I knew that she was just going through the motions. When she stopped struggling, I knew that she would have to throw in some tears before we did it.

She was still very upset afterward, and I just don't understand it! If she didn't want to have sex, why did she come back to the room with me? You could tell by the way she dressed and acted that she was no virgin, so why she had to put up such a big struggle I don't know.

alone, and perhaps kissing or petting. Let us state in no uncertain terms, however, that it does not matter whether the woman wore a "sexy" outfit, was "on the pill," or shared a passionate kiss or embrace with the man. If the encounter ended with the woman's being forcibly violated, then it is a sexual assault. When a woman says no, a man must take no for an answer.

The problem of date sexual assault has been subjected to closer public scrutiny in recent years. "Take Back the Night" marches have become a common form of student protest on university campuses against the sexual misconduct of men. Many universities have mandated date sexual assault seminars and workshops.

GANGS AND SEXUAL ASSAULT Exercise of power appears to be the major motive behind gang assaults, although some attackers may also be expressing anger against women.

The Koss college survey (Koss et al., 1987) showed that sexual assaults involving a group of assailants tend to be more vicious than individual assaults (Gidycz & Koss, 1990). Relatively few survivors of gang assaults reported the attack to police or sought support from a crisis centre.

SEXUAL ASSAULT AGAINST MALES According to 1997 data from police forces in six provinces, 18% of sexual offence victims are men; however, males comprise 31% of victims under the age of 12 (Statistics Canada, 1997). In a study of university students in New Brunswick, about one-fifth of the men reported that in the previous year they had been coerced into having sex (O'Sullivan et al., 1998).

This finding runs contrary to the stereotype that men are willing to have sex all the time. Many women believe this stereotype, as demonstrated in a study of women living in the Kitchener/Waterloo area of Ontario (Clements-Schreiber & Rempel, 1995). Eighty-five percent of the women believed that it is easy for a woman to sexually arouse

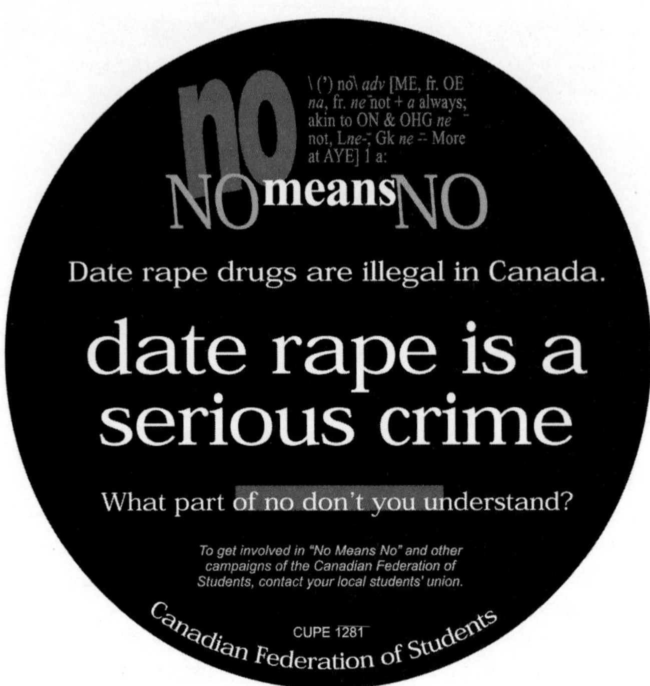

Combating Sexual Assault on Campus.
Many Canadian universities and colleges have instituted awareness programs to combat the problem of date sexual assault and other sexual assaults on campus.

a man if she wants to, and 68% believed that men enjoy getting sexual advances from women even when they don't respond positively. According to the researchers, it is beliefs such as these that might make women think that male refusals should not be taken seriously.

Sarrel and Masters (1982) reported 11 cases of men who were sexually assaulted by women, including one case of a 37-year-old man who was coerced into sexual intercourse by two women who accosted him at gunpoint. In another case, a 27-year-old man fell asleep in his hotel room with a woman he had just met in a bar and then awakened to find that he was bound to his bed, gagged, and blindfolded. He was then forced into sexual intercourse with four different women, who threatened him with castration if he did not perform satisfactorily.

Although not considered sexual assault, some women use sexual enticement as a means of robbing a man. In Guelph, Ontario, after a man went to the apartment of a woman he had met, she began performing oral sex on him and stole money from his wallet in the process (Tracey, 1999). In Toronto, a woman arranged dates with men after putting personal ads in newspapers. She would find a reason to persuade the man to use an automatic teller machine, note his PIN number, and later steal his wallet ("Woman faces," 2000). In Winnipeg, a man met a woman through a chat line and agreed to go to her house for a "sexual fantasy." When he arrived, two men stole his wallet and forced him to give them his PIN number ("Chat-line romance," 2000). In Brampton, Ontario, a 34-year-old man arranged to meet a woman he chatted with online. When he arrived, he was met by two men who robbed him at knifepoint, threatened to shoot him, and held him captive for 14 hours (Appleby, 2005). There may well be many other cases that are not reported because adult males would typically be embarrassed about being in these situations. What is most interesting about these examples of male victimization is that there are no education programs warning adult males about being cautious on the internet.

Despite the examples given, most sexual assaults against men are committed by other men. While they often occur in prison settings, some occur outside prison walls. In recent years the media have been full of stories about men in positions of authority, such as teachers and priests, assaulting boys.

Males can also be assaulted in college sports hazing rituals. A rookie football player withdrew from McGill University after his teammates forced him to go down on all fours and prodded him anally with a broom handle. Other rookies were coerced into simulating oral sex on one another in their boxer shorts (Peritz, 2005).

Male survivors tend to suffer greater physical injury than female survivors (Kaufman et al., 1980). Males are more often attacked by multiple assailants, are held captive longer, and are more often reluctant to report the assault (Gerrol & Resick, 1988; Groth & Burgess, 1980; Myers, 1989). After all, victimization does not fit the male stereotype of capacity for self-defence. Men are expected to be not only strong but also silent. However, male survivors may suffer traumatic effects similar to those suffered by female survivors (Bogin, 2006).

SEXUAL ASSAULT AGAINST GAY AND BISEXUAL MEN There have been few studies of sexual assault on gay and bisexual men. Researchers in Vancouver (Ratner et al., 2003) asked 358 gay and bisexual men aged 19 to 35 if they had ever been forced into unwanted sex. Fourteen percent reported having been coerced or forced into sex before the age of 14. Half of the reported incidents involved forced receptive anal intercourse. Men who had been sexually coerced had lower self-esteem and higher rates of depression. They were more likely to abuse alcohol and to have attempted suicide.

MARITAL SEXUAL ASSAULT Although there are many countries where it is not against the law for a husband to sexually assault his wife, in Canada it is clearly illegal. Motives for marital sexual assault vary. A husband may be unwilling to accept a rebuff because he believes that he is entitled to sexual access to his wife any time he desires it. He may believe it is his wife's duty to satisfy his sexual needs even when she is uninterested. Some men use sex to dominate their wives. Others degrade their wives through sex, especially after arguments. Sexual coercion often occurs within a pattern of violence, battering, and physical intimidation (Johnson, 2003).

The Complexity of Sexual Consent

A central issue in cases of sexual assault is that of sexual consent. As presented in the A Closer Look feature, differing perceptions of sexual consent can be problematic in dating situations.

Melanie Beres (2007), a University of Alberta researcher, conducted a comprehensive review and analysis of the research on sexual consent. She found that sexual consent has been conceptualized and defined in numerous ways. Also, many scholars have discussed sexual consent without defining the term, because it is often assumed that everyone shares the same understanding of the term. Following are some of Beres's key findings from the literature on sexual consent:

- Some researchers argue that a person who says yes to sexual advances is giving consent even under coercion or force. Others disagree and state that consent can be given only if there is no coercion.
- Researchers disagree over whether sexual consent must be given verbally. For example, does sexual consent mean that a person must say yes to a sexual request, or is it sufficient for the person to not stop a partner's physical advances, or does sexual consent involve a combination of both of these acts?
- Some scholars view sexual consent as an agent of moral transformation that turns an illegal and objectionable activity into a potentially pleasurable and morally permissible activity.
- Sexual consent is usually seen as overly simplistic, involving a yes or no response to a sexual request.
- Only a few researchers have studied the ways in which people actually ask for and give consent.
- Research on, and discussion of, sexual consent has mainly taken place in the context of a heterosexual bias. This perspective mistakenly assumes that sexual consent from men is not needed because of the stereotype that men are always willing to have sex.
- Researchers usually assume that women seldom if ever initiate a sexual encounter.
- Sex educators provide female students with strategies for saying no to sex but not for how to say yes.
- Little research has been done on sexual consent involving gay men and lesbians.
- Most of the research on sexual consent is related to violent sexual activity. Research about the more common consensual sexual interactions is limited.

Beres (2007) believes it is essential for future researchers to clearly define sexual consent for the reader. She also stresses the need to develop interactive models using qualitative research methods. This approach will help us to better understand how sexual consent is perceived and how it is actually communicated in sexual relationships. (An example of this research is Beres's study of communicating sexual consent with casual sex partners: see Chapter 7.)

Terry Humphreys (2007) at Trent University has also researched the complexities of the sexual consent process. He is especially critical of educational programs that assume simply saying no means no. Humphreys's own research has indicated that the sexual consent process involves many factors. One of his main findings is that most women and men have nonverbal means of asking for, and giving, sexual consent. Typically people indirectly indicate consent in a number of ways, such as by *not* pulling away from a partner. Most people find making a direct, verbal sexual request very awkward. Also, if a person does say no to a sexual request, most men and women believe that a reason for the refusal should be given. (Humphreys's research is discussed in more detail in Chapter 7.)

Social Attitudes and Myths That Encourage Sexual Assault

Many people believe a number of myths about sexual assault, such as "Women say no when they mean yes," "All women like a man who is pushy and forceful," and "The way women dress, they are just asking to be assaulted." Yet another myth is that deep down, women want to be assaulted (Osman, 2003).

Sexual assault myths create a social climate that legitimizes sexual assault. Though both men and women may subscribe to sexual assault myths, researchers at the University of British Columbia found that male students show greater acceptance of these myths than do female students (Kennedy & Gorzalka, 2002). There are also ethnic differences, with Asian students being more likely to accept these myths. However, the longer the Asian students have been in Canada, the less likely they are to accept these myths. Men also cling more stubbornly to myths about date sexual assault, even after taking date sexual assault education classes designed to challenge these views (Lenihan et al., 1992). Such myths do not occur in a social vacuum. They are related to other social attitudes, including gender-role stereotyping, perception of sex as adversarial, and acceptance of violence in relationships.

Many observers contend that our society encourages sexual assault by socializing males into socially and sexually dominant roles. Males are often conditioned from childhood for aggressive and competitive behaviour.

Research with university students supports the connection between stereotypical masculine identification and tendencies to sexual assault. In New Brunswick, researchers compared students who believed in strictly traditional gender roles with students who held less rigid attitudes. Men who engaged in coercive sex were found to be more likely to hold more traditional views of women's roles and more likely to hold coercion-supportive beliefs (Byers & Eno, 1991). Men with traditional views were more likely to ignore a partner's saying that she does not want to have sex. The "traditionalists" express a greater likelihood of committing sexual assault, are more accepting of violence against women, are more likely to blame sexual assault survivors, and are more aroused by depictions of sexual assault (Raichle & Lambert, 2000).

Young men may come to view dates not as chances to get to know their partners but as opportunities for sexual conquest, in which the object is to overcome their partners' resistance. Sexual behaviour and sports in our culture are linked through common idioms. A young man may be taunted by his friends after a date with a woman with such questions as "Did you score?" or, more bluntly, "Did you get in?"

Some researchers, such as Queen's University psychologist Vernon Quinsey, hypothesize that evolutionary psychology can account for the role of male sexual competitiveness in sexual assault. According to this perspective, since the main constraint on male reproductive success is the limited number of potential mating partners, males

Applied Knowledge

"ROPHIES"—THE DATE RAPE DRUG

Rophies, roofies, R2, roofenol, roachies, la rocha, rope, or whatever you call it is dubbed the "date rape" drug because it has been slipped into the drinks of unsuspecting women, lowers their inhibitions, lessens their ability to resist a sexual assault, and, when mixed with alcohol, often causes blackouts that prevent victims from remembering what happened to them. For this reason, Rohypnol has also been called the "forget pill," "trip-and-fall," and "mind erasers." The drug has no taste or odour, so the victims don't realize what is happening when an assailant slips it into a drink. About 10 minutes after taking it, the woman may feel dizzy and disoriented, simultaneously too hot and too cold, or nauseated. She may have difficulty speaking and moving, and then pass out. She may "black out" for eight to 24 hours, having little or no memory of what happened.

Rohypnol is prescribed as a treatment for insomnia and as a sedative hypnotic in other countries. It is in the same class of drugs as the tranquillizer Valium, but about 10 times stronger.

Rohypnol is often used with other drugs, such as alcohol, to create a dramatic "high." Rohypnol intoxication is generally associated with impaired judgment, memory, and motor skills, and can make a victim unable to resist or recall a sexual attack. Effects begin within 30 minutes, peak within two hours, and can persist for eight hours or more.

Here are some ideas for avoiding problems with Rohypnol:

- Be wary about accepting drinks from anyone you don't know well or long enough to trust.
- Don't put your drink down and leave it unattended, even to go to the bathroom.
- If you think that you have been a victim, notify authorities immediately.

Source: U.S. Department of Health and Human Services. Fact sheets prepared by the National Institute on Drug Abuse (Rohypnol and GHB): ***www.drugabuse.gov/Infofacts/RohypnolGHB.html.***

are obliged to compete with each other for mating opportunities. In order to increase their opportunities, some men will engage in sexual coercion (Quinsey, 2002). For example, Lalumiere and Quinsey (1996) found that men with extensive casual-sex experience have higher rates of sexual coercion than other men.

Characteristics of Sexually Coercive Men

Although sexual aggressiveness may be woven into our social fabric, not all men are equally vulnerable to such cultural influences. Canadian researchers are playing a leading role in determining factors that predict which men are more likely to be sexually coercive.

Some sexually coercive men feel socially inadequate and report that they cannot find willing partners. Some lack social skills and avoid social interactions with women (Overholser & Beck, 1986). Some are basically antisocial and have long histories of violent behaviour (Knight et al., 1991). Several Canadian studies have identified particular characteristics of sexually coercive men. Both sensation seeking and an early history of behavioural problems are strongly related to sexual coercion (Harris et al., 2003; Lalumiere & Quinsey, 1996). Sexually coercive men were found to have high levels of hostility, poor sexual adjustment, and serious problems with alcohol (Firestone et al., 1998). Men with these characteristics tend to act on their impulses regardless of the cost to the person they attack. Some were sexually victimized or physically assaulted as children (Sack & Mason, 1980). As adults, they may be identifying with the aggressor role in interpersonal relationships. Drinking alcohol may also dampen self-restraint and spur sexual aggressiveness. In an Ontario population survey, adults who reported experiencing parental sexual abuse were more than twice as likely to have had parents who had substance abuse problems (Walsh et al., 2003). Additionally, Toronto researchers (Langevin et al., 2006) found that sex offenders tended to come from families having alcohol problems. The researchers speculated that parental alcohol addiction often was a factor in the parents' sons having developmental and learning

Innovative Canadian Research

CHARACTERISTICS OF MALE AND FEMALE VICTIMS OF SEXUAL COERCION

University of Guelph researchers (Hartwick et al., 2007) conducted a study of university students to compare the characteristics of male and female victims of sexual coercion. More women (48%) than men (39%) had experienced sexual coercion, with the main difference being that more women (34%) than men (23%) had experienced coerced kissing and fondling. However, the rates of coerced sexual intercourse were almost the same (females 21%; males 18%). The most common coercive strategies were getting the person intoxicated and inducing guilt. Coerced men were more likely to experience intoxication and coerced women were more likely to experience being made to feel guilty for refusing sex. Strangers tended to use the intoxication coercive strategy, whereas dating partners and friends tended to use the guilt coercive strategy. Both men and women who had a higher number of sex partners were more likely to experience coercive sexual intercourse. A key finding was that both sexes were more likely to have experienced sexual coercion if they believed the stereotype of men's greater sexual accessibility, that is, that men are always wanting sex. The researchers speculated that men who believe this feel guilty that they are not living up to this expectation if they refuse sex, while some women may feel they should give in to a man's greater sexual needs (Hartwick et al., 2007).

problems. In another Ontario study, sexual offenders had significantly greater problems with alcohol abuse than other violent offenders (Looman et al., 2004). The researchers speculated that something about the combination of alcohol abuse and problems with intimacy contributes specifically to sexual offending.

In a sample of men from a Canadian city, beliefs in sexual assault myths and hostility were *not* predictive of male coercive behaviour (Senn et al., 2000). The fact that this is one of the few studies on sexual coercion that has attempted to randomly sample men from the community may account for findings that differ in some ways from those of other studies. The study did find that men who were sexually coercive were more likely to have experienced childhood abuse, had more sexual partners during adolescence, and lacked the ability to express their emotions (Senn et al., 2000). In another study of male sexual aggressors, University of Montreal researchers reported that male adult sexual aggressors were more likely to have experienced childhood sexual abuse, pornography during childhood/adolescence, and deviant sexual fantasies during childhood/adolescence (Beauregard et al., 2004).

For some sexually coercive men, violence and sexual arousal become enmeshed. Thus, they seek to combine sex and violence to enhance their sexual arousal. Some studies find that sexually coercive men are more sexually aroused (as measured by the size of erections) by verbal descriptions, films, or audiotapes that portray themes of sexual assault than are other people (Lalumiere et al., 2003).

Motives in Sexual Assault

Although sexual arousal is an obvious and important element in sexual assault (Barbaree & Marshall, 1991), some researchers argue that anger and power are the basic motivations for sexual assault (Groth & Birnbaum, 1979). Other researchers believe that sexual motivation plays a key role in at least some sexual assaults (Baumeister et al., 2002).

Adjustment of Sexual Assault Survivors

Many people who have survived being sexually assaulted by a stranger fear for their lives during the attack (Polusny & Arbisi, 2006). Regardless of whether weapons or threats are used, the experience of being dominated by an unpredictable and threatening

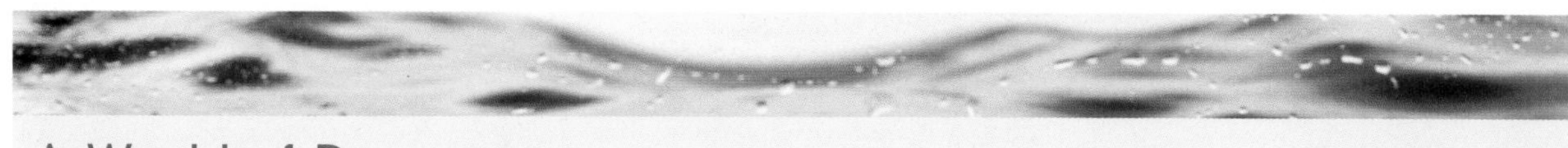

A World of Diversity

THE (HIGHLY CONTROVERSIAL!) EVOLUTIONARY VIEW OF SEXUAL ASSAULT

According to evolutionary psychologists, it might just be true. One argument is that sexual assault is a common—even "normal"—way of mating in many species (Archer & Vaughan, 2001; Lalumière et al., 2005a, 2005b). Evolutionary psychologists tend to agree that sexually aggressive prehistoric males were more likely to transmit their genes to future generations (Malamuth et al., 2005; Thornhill & Palmer, 2000). Modern-day society may value personal qualities (such as intelligence and reliability) and social behaviours (such as maintaining lasting relationships) as being more important than brute strength. Modern society has also outlawed sexual aggression—viewing it as a crime against the woman who is victimized, rather than as a crime against the "property" of some other man. But modern society and the legal system are "new" things on the planet, and the human genetic code has evolved over millions of years. There might thus remain a "natural" tendency for males to be more sexually aggressive than females and to try to take what they want (Lalumière et al., 2005a, 2005b).

According to evolutionary theory, those traits that help an individual reach sexual maturity and reproduce are more likely to be passed on to future generations. Could such a trait in males be sexual aggressiveness? Could sexual aggressiveness be somehow embedded in the human genetic code?

Although the evolutionary perspective may view sexual coerciveness in men as "natural," many or most psychologists agree that sexual assault is inexcusable and criminal, and that males can *choose* not to be aggressive (Koss, 2003). Perhaps men carry genes that now and then give rise to aggressive impulses, some of which involve sex, but men also carry other genes that enable them to picture themselves in the place of the victim and choose *not* to behave aggressively. Empathy—that is, experiencing the feelings of another person—may be more common in women than in men, but it is not absent in men and can be cultivated in men, as has been shown by sexual assault prevention programs (Foubert & Newberry, 2006).

assailant is terrifying. The victim does not know whether she will survive and may feel helpless to do anything about it.

Many survivors are in crisis in the days and weeks after the sexual assault (Campbell, 2006; Macy et al., 2006). They have insomnia and cry frequently. They tend to report eating problems, cystitis, headaches, irritability, mood changes, anxiety and depression, and menstrual irregularity (Kaczmarek et al., 2006). They may become withdrawn, sullen, and mistrustful. Some people tend to believe that women who are sexually assaulted are at least partly to blame for the assault (Boros et al., 2005); therefore, some survivors experience feelings of guilt and shame. Emotional distress tends to peak in severity by about three weeks after the assault and generally remains high, before beginning to abate about a month or two later (Koss et al., 2003). Many survivors encounter more lasting problems. Victims' feelings of being powerless to affect their own fate can endure and change their personality (McEwan et al., 2005). Survivors may also encounter problems at work, such as problems relating to co-workers or bosses, or difficulties in concentrating. Relationships with spouses or partners may also be impaired. Survivors often report a lack of sexual desire, fears of sex, and difficulty becoming sexually aroused (Koss et al., 2003). Sexual assault survivors may also suffer physical injuries and may contract sexually transmitted infections, even AIDS, as a result of a sexual assault.

Most women fail to report sexual assaults to police. Why? Reasons include fears of retaliation, the social stigma attached to the survivors of sexual assault, doubts that others will believe them, feelings that it would be hopeless to try to bring charges against the perpetrator, concerns about negative publicity, and fears about the emotional distress to which they would be subjected if the case were to go to trial (Campbell, 2006; Logan et al., 2006).

Applied Knowledge

IF YOU ARE SEXUALLY ASSAULTED . . .

Elizabeth Powell (1996) offers the following suggestions to those who are sexually assaulted:

1. Don't change anything about your body—don't wash, don't even comb your hair. Leave your clothes as they are. Otherwise you could destroy evidence.
2. Strongly consider reporting the incident to police. You may prevent another woman from being assaulted, and you will be taking charge, starting on the path from victim to survivor.
3. Ask a relative or friend to take you to a hospital if you can't get an ambulance or a police car. If you call the hospital, tell them why you're requesting an ambulance, in case they are able to send someone trained to deal with sexual assault cases.
4. Seek help in an assertive way. Seek medical help. Injuries you are unaware of may be detected. Insist that a written or photographic record be made to document your condition. If you decide to file charges, the prosecutor may need this evidence to obtain a conviction.
5. Question health professionals. Ask about your biological risks. Ask what treatments are available. Ask for whatever will help make you comfortable. Call the shots. Demand confidentiality if that's what you want. Refuse what you don't want.

You may also wish to call a sexual assault hotline or sexual assault crisis centre for advice, if one is available in your area. A sexual assault crisis volunteer may be available to accompany you to the hospital and help see you through the medical evaluation and police investigation if you report the attack.

Post-traumatic stress disorder A type of stress reaction brought on by a traumatic event and characterized by flashbacks of the experience in the form of disturbing dreams or intrusive recollections, a sense of emotional numbing or restricted range of feelings, and heightened body arousal. Abbreviated *PTSD.*

SEXUAL ASSAULT AND PSYCHOLOGICAL DISORDERS Sexual assault survivors are at higher-than-average risk of developing anxiety disorders and depression, and of abusing alcohol and other substances. Researchers at Carleton University found that university women who had experienced sexual coercion in their dating relationships were more likely to have lower levels of self-esteem and sexual self-esteem. They were also more likely to experience depression (Offman & Matheson, 2004). Survivors may experience **post-traumatic stress disorder (PTSD)** (Koss et al., 2003), a disorder brought on by exposure to a traumatic event; for example, it is often seen in soldiers who have been in combat (American Psychiatric Association, 2000). People with PTSD may have flashbacks to the traumatic experience, disturbing dreams, emotional numbing, and nervousness. PTSD may persist for years. The person may also develop fears of situations connected with the traumatic event. For example, a woman who was sexually assaulted in an elevator may develop a fear of riding in elevators. Researchers also report that women who blame themselves for the sexual assault tend to suffer more severe depression and adjustment problems, including sexual problems (Koss et al., 2002).

Treatment of Sexual Assault Survivors

Canadian Association of Sexual Assault Centres
Lists sexual assault crisis centres and transition houses.
www.casac.ca

Treatment of sexual assault survivors typically involves a two-stage process of helping the victim through the crisis after the attack and then helping to foster long-term adjustment. Crisis intervention typically provides survivors with support and information to help them express their feelings and develop strategies for coping with the trauma.

Psychotherapy, involving group or individual approaches, can help the survivor cope with the emotional consequences of sexual assault, avoid self-blame, improve self-esteem, validate the welter of feelings surrounding the experience, and establish or maintain loving relationships. Therapists also recognize the importance of helping the sexual assault survivor mobilize social support. In major cities and many towns, concerned men and women have formed sexual assault crisis centres and hotlines, peer counselling groups, and referral agencies geared to assessing and meeting survivors' needs after the assault. Some counsellors are specially trained to mediate between survivors of sexual assault and their loved ones. These counsellors help people to discuss and work through the often complex emotional legacy of sexual assault. Phone numbers for these services can be obtained from crisis centres, women's shelters, hospital emergency departments, the police department, or the telephone directory.

A national survey of rape crisis and sexual assault centres in Canada found that many were facing a precarious financial situation because of insufficient government funding (Beres et al., in press). Thus these agencies rely heavily on the unpaid services of volunteers in order to provide adequate services to sexual assault and abuse survivors. Most of these agencies are also politically active, raising awareness of issues of violence and inequality experienced by Canadian women (Beres et al., in press).

Preventing Sexual Assault

Eliminating sexual assault altogether would probably require massive changes in cultural attitudes and socialization processes. However, educational intervention on a smaller scale may reduce its incidence. Many colleges and universities offer educational programs about date sexual assault.

Until the basic cultural attitudes that support sexual assault change, however, "sexual assault prevention" means that women must take a number of precautions. Why should women be advised to take measures to avoid sexual assault? Is not the very listing of such measures a subtle way of blaming the woman if she should fall prey to an attacker? No! To provide the information is not to blame the person who is attacked. The offender is *always* responsible for the assault.

Taking Back the Night.
Whose fault is it if a woman is sexually assaulted when she goes out alone at night? Many women—and men who care about women—have marched to demonstrate their disgust with the men who might assault them if they were out walking by themselves and with a society that too often blames the victim for what happens to her.

Applied Knowledge

SEXUAL ASSAULT PREVENTION

Taking certain precautions, such as these recommended by the Boston Women's Health Book Collective (2005), may lower a woman's risk of being assaulted.

- Establish a set of signals with other women in the building or neighbourhood.
- List yourself in the phone directory and on the mailbox by your first initials only.
- Use deadbolt locks.
- Keep doorways and entries well lit.
- Keep your keys handy when approaching the car or the front door.
- Avoid deserted areas.
- Do not allow strange men into your house or apartment without first checking their credentials.
- Check out the back seat of your car before entering.
- Don't give rides to hitchhikers (including women hitchhikers).

Here are some suggestions for avoiding date sexual assault:

- Tell your partner how far you would like to go so that he will know what the limits are. For example, if your partner starts fondling you in ways that make you uncomfortable, you might say, "I'd prefer if you didn't touch me there. I really like you, but I prefer not getting so intimate at this point in our relationship."
- Meet new dates in public places, and avoid driving with a stranger or a group of people you've met. When meeting a new date, drive in your own car and meet your date at a public place. Don't drive with strangers or offer rides to strangers or groups of people.
- State your refusal definitively. Be firm in refusing a sexual overture. Look your partner straight in the eye. The more definite you are, the less likely that your partner will misinterpret your wishes.
- Become aware of your fears. Take notice of any fears of displeasing your partner that might stifle your assertiveness. If your partner is truly respectful of you, you need not fear an angry or demeaning response. But if your partner is not respectful, it is best to become aware of it and end the relationship right there.
- Pay attention to your "vibes." Trust your gut-level feelings. Many victims of acquaintance sexual assault said afterward that they had had a strange feeling about the man but failed to pay attention to it.
- Be especially cautious if you are in a new environment, be it a college or a foreign country. You may be especially vulnerable to exploitation when you are becoming acquainted with a new environment, different people, and different customs.
- If you have broken off a relationship with someone you don't really like or feel good about, don't let him into your place. Many so-called date sexual assaults are committed by ex-lovers and ex-boyfriends.

Confronting an Attacker: Should You Fight, Flee, or Plead?

What if you are accosted by a sexual assailant? Should you try to fight him off, flee, or plead with him to stop? Some women have thwarted attacks by pleading or crying. Screaming may ward off some attacks (Gidycz et al., 2006). Running away sometimes works. No single strategy is likely to be helpful in all sexual assault cases.

Self-defence training may help women become better prepared to fend off an assailant (Gidycz et al., 2006). Yet physical resistance may spur some assailants to become more aggressive. Effective self-defence is built upon the use of multiple strategies, ranging from attempts to avoid potential sexual assault situations (such as by installing a home security system or walking only in well-lit areas), to acquiescence when active resistance would seem too risky, to the use of more active verbal or physical forms of resistance in some low-risk situations (Gidycz et al., 2006).

Coercive Verbal Pressure Tactics

Verbal sexual coercion is persistent verbal pressure or the use of seduction "lines" to manipulate a person into sexual activity. Verbal coercion is difficult to define precisely. People use a wide spectrum of persuasion ranging from coaxing to outright bullying and threats; in the middle of the spectrum is a grey area that might be considered coercive by some but not by others. Verbal coercion is used far more often than physical coercion. In a study involving students from more than 40 universities and community colleges across Canada, DeKeseredy and Kelly (1993) found that since beginning university, 32% of the women had given in to sex play (not involving intercourse) because they were overwhelmed by a man's continual arguments and pressure; 20% said they had given in to sexual intercourse because of this kind of verbal pressure. Among a community sample of men from an Ontario city, 23% reported that they had used arguments and verbal pressure to try to get a woman to engage in sex play, and 9% said they had used this kind of pressure to have sexual intercourse (Senn et al., 2000).

In Toronto, a 59-year-old pastor and spiritual healer threatened a 24-year-old parishioner by telling her that evil spirits would pursue her if she did not have sexual intercourse with him and become pregnant with his child (Small, 2008). The woman gave in to his threats and eventually gave birth to a baby girl. When the woman asked for child support, the pastor threatened to kill her. The pastor was convicted of sexual assault and sentenced to four years in prison. Originally, the woman was introduced to the pastor when, at 17 years of age, she had been brought by her mother to the pastor for spiritual healing. The pastor said that she had been cursed by another woman and instructed her to take spiritual baths during which the pastor had the woman bathe naked while he scrubbed her (Small, 2008).

Researchers in Toronto studied young adults who were involved in street life to find out what strategies were used to coerce a dating partner into having sex (Strike et al., 2001). The sample included heterosexual, gay, lesbian, and bisexual people. Almost all the men and women had experienced being pressured to have sex, and 62% of the men and 42% of the women admitted pressuring a date to have sex. The tactics used to get sex included

- *Using alcohol and drugs to decrease a partner's reluctance to have sex.* Some of those who had been coerced said they used alcohol or drugs to loosen their own inhibitions.
- *Using obligations, expectations, and guilt.* Some coerced their partner by threatening to end the relationship or to get sex elsewhere. Another strategy involved saying how much they were looking forward to having sex. Some would make their partner feel that they were obliged to have sex, and would try to make them feel guilty for not having it. A commonly held belief was that if one's partner paid for date-related expenses such as dinner and drinks, one was obliged to have sex.
- *Exploiting emotional and economic vulnerability.* People with low self-esteem may be told that they are worthless and should consider themselves lucky to be in their current relationship. Some of the men and women admitted that they manipulated a person who had little or no economic resources by providing food, housing, or money in return for sex. A more extreme example of this exploitation occurred when a man provided a woman with shelter and demanded that she provide sex not only to him but to his friends as well.

A number of the participants in the study admitted that they had developed a sophisticated set of strategies to obtain sex, strategies that included knowing when and how to use them. While some would continue to pressure a reluctant partner, others stopped trying to get sex when the partner was adamant in refusing it. Those who had been coerced to have sex often resigned themselves to simply getting it over with so that their partner would stop bothering them (Strike et al., 2001).

With a community-based sample of men living in Windsor, Ontario, Senn and colleagues (2000) found that the most common strategy used to coerce a reluctant partner into having sex involved continual arguments and verbal pressure. The second most common strategy involved providing the woman with alcohol or drugs.

A common sexual stereotype is that women never have to use pressure tactics to engage in sex with a male partner. Researchers at the University of Guelph found that some young women used a diversity of sexual pressure tactics to get a reluctant male partner to engage in sex (Parr-LeFeuve & Desmarais, 2005).

Verbal coercion also occurs in same-sex relationships. In a study of these relationships in Canada and the United States, Melanie Beres (2002) found that 23% of women involved in lesbian relationships have experienced sexual coercion from another woman. The rates for men are somewhat higher, with 35% having experienced sexual coercion from another man.

Sexual Abuse of Children

Many view sexual abuse of children as among the most heinous of crimes. Canadians are shocked and horrified when they find out about children being sexually abused. One of the most publicized cases was the sexual abuse of boys by priests at the Mount Cashel orphanage in Newfoundland. Eleven priests were convicted of those offences and the Newfoundland government paid $11 million to 40 abuse victims. Children who are sexually assaulted often suffer social and emotional problems that impair their development and persist into adulthood, affecting their self-esteem and their ability to form intimate relationships.

In 2003, there were just over 9000 reported sexual assaults against children and youth aged 17 and under (Statistics Canada, 2005g); 80% of the victims were female and two-thirds of these females were between 11 and 17 years old. In a sample of men from an Ontario city, 8% reported having been sexually abused in childhood (Senn et al., 2000).

Sexual abuse of children ranges from exhibitionism, kissing, fondling, and sexual touching to oral sex and anal intercourse and, with girls, vaginal intercourse. Sexual contact between an adult and a child is abusive, even if the child is willing, because children are legally incapable of consenting to sexual activity. (Acts such as touching children's sexual organs while changing or bathing them, sleeping with children, or appearing nude before them are not usually considered sexual contact; they are open to interpretation but are often innocent [Haugaard, 2000].)

Voluntary sexual activity *between children* of similar ages is not sexual abuse. Children often engage in consensual sex play with peers or siblings, as in "playing doctor" or in mutual masturbation. Although such experiences may be recalled in adulthood

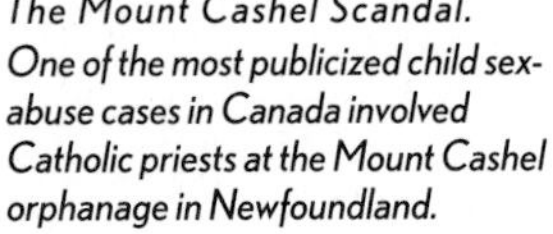

The Mount Cashel Scandal. *One of the most publicized child sex-abuse cases in Canada involved Catholic priests at the Mount Cashel orphanage in Newfoundland.*

with feelings of shame or guilt, they are not typically harmful. When the experience involves coercion, or when one child is significantly older or in a position of power over the younger child, the sexual contact may be considered sexual abuse.

In Canada it is against the law for an adult or teenager to engage in any type of sexual activity, ranging from kissing to intercourse, with a child under the age of 14 (except for sexual activity between a child who is at least 12 years old and someone less than two years older).

In Prince Edward Island, a 19-year-old male with a promising baseball career was sentenced to 45 days in jail after he admitted that he had received oral sex from two girls aged 12 and 13. The man claimed that he believed the girls were older than 14 and that they were the ones who had initiated contact and offered to perform oral sex (Canadian Press, 2003b). This story resulted in media articles suggesting that "rainbow parties" in which young teenage girls take turns performing oral sex on several males are commonplace. However, the extent to which such behaviour actually occurs is unknown. According to the Canada Youth and Aids Survey, 28% of grade 9 girls and 32% of grade 9 boys have experienced oral sex at least once (Boyce et al., 2003).

In 1985, Parliament amended the Criminal Code and made it an offence for a person in a position of trust or authority to have any sexual contact, consensual or not, with a person under 18. Interestingly, there has been more controversy about this law when the accused has been a female, probably because of traditional stereotypes that young males who are involved sexually with an older female are "lucky" rather than being exploited.

In Sechelt, British Columbia, a 29-year-old female high school teacher was convicted of exploiting a minor after she had consensual sexual relations with one of her high school students, who was 17 years old. The male high school student publicly opposed the conviction because he said that he was the one who pursued and seduced the teacher. He claimed that he was not a victim, and even his mother approved of the relationship (Dreidger, 2003). In recent years there have been several cases across Canada of female teachers being charged with having sexual relationships with male students. In another example, a 42-year-old grade 7 teacher in Cornwall, Ontario, was found guilty of sexually assaulting one of her 13-year-old male students. She and the student had kissed and fondled one another in the basement of her home (Seymour, 2008).

Female teachers have also been charged with sexual assault of female students. In Toronto, a female high school teacher was charged in the sexual assault of a 17-year-old girl who was taught by the teacher. The teacher was accused of fondling the girl and exchanging sexually explicit emails with her (Mitchell, 2006).

To provide greater protection to youth aged 14 to 18, in 2002 legislation created a new category of sexual exploitation—adults who, because of their age and/or position of authority, are able to coerce young people into having sex. An addition to the Criminal Code also makes it illegal for adults to use the internet to lure a person whom they believe is under the age of 18 for the purpose of committing sexual assault, or to entice a child believed to be under the age of 14 into sexual relations.

Pamela Rogers Turner.
Pamela Rogers Turner was sentenced to nine months in prison for having sex with one of her 13-year-old students.

The first person charged under this law was a 33-year-old Toronto man who arranged a meeting with an 11-year-old girl he met on the internet. He was also charged with sexual assault after he spent the night with the girl in a hotel room. The man was convicted of internet luring, abduction of a person under age 16, and sexual interference (Levy, 2004). In Barrie, Ontario, a 14-year-old boy was charged with internet luring of two girls who were under the age of 14. He met the girls on an internet chat program and is believed to be the youngest person ever charged with this offence (Love, 2004).

Internet luring crosses national borders. A 32-year-old man from Belgium was arrested at a Montreal hotel where he was charged with sexual offences and internet luring when he was found there with a 13-year-old missing girl. The pair had been chatting online for several months. Interestingly, the police reported that the girl was not happy to see them when they arrived at the hotel to arrest the man (Banerjee, 2008).

Another international example is that of a Kingston man who persuaded more than 100 young girls (ages 9 to 13) from across Canada and the United Kingdom to expose themselves on the internet via a webcam. The man hacked into the email accounts of the girls and obtained their lists of friends. Then he would assume the identity of one of the friends and encourage the girls to take off their clothes in front of the camera. He would then tell them he was not one of their friends and threaten to send their pictures to their friends and parents, and to post them on the web unless they exposed themselves on camera and engaged in sexual acts he told them to do. They were also threatened with sexual assault, bodily harm, and death if they did not obey his commands. The man was charged with internet luring and making and distributing child pornography (Canadian Press, 2006).

To combat internet luring, police have laid traps by posing as children in chatrooms. In 2005, a Toronto detective posed as a 12-year-old girl on the Yahoo chatroom "Teen Oh Canada Chat." A man "entered" the chatroom and engaged in casual conversation with the "girl." After a few months, they arranged to meet to have sex. At this meeting, the police arrested a 36-year-old pastor (Naili & Josey, 2005).

In 2008, the federal Parliament raised the legal age of consent from 14 to 16 to protect adolescents in that age group from adult sexual exploitation. The new law allowed for a "close-in-age" provision of five years, so that it would be legal for a 19-year-old to have sex with a 15-year-old. Gay rights organizations claimed the age of consent law is discriminatory toward gay males, because it is illegal in Canada to engage in anal sex with someone who is under the age of 18.

In Bountiful, British Columbia, a fundamentalist Mormon sect not only flouts Canadian laws with its practice of polygamy but also has forced teenage girls as young as 13 to marry much older men (Braham, 2008). Winston Blackmore, the bishop of the religious group, has admitted to having sex with minors. He argues that freedom of religion in Canada does not permit the justice system to interfere with the church's beliefs. However, in 2009, Blackmore and another sect leader were charged by the British Columbia government with engaging in polygamy. In the United States, Warren Jeffs, the leader of the American version of this Mormon sect, was sentenced to prison after he was found guilty of two counts of assisted rape, because he had forced underage teenage girls to marry men in their fifties (Braham, 2008).

Patterns of Abuse

Children from stable, middle-class families appear to be generally at lower risk of experiencing sexual abuse than children from poorer, less cohesive families (Edwards et al., 2003). In most cases, children who are sexually abused are not accosted by the proverbial stranger lurking in the schoolyard. According to Canadian police reports in 2003, half of all victims under the age of six were sexually assaulted by a family member and only 4% were assaulted by a stranger. Among victims aged 14 to 17, 20% were assaulted by a family member and another 20% were assaulted by a stranger (Statistics Canada, 2005g). In many cases, the molesters are people who are close to them: relatives, step-relatives, family friends, and neighbours (Edwards et al., 2003).

Parents who discover that their child has been abused by a family member are often reluctant to notify authorities. The decision to report the abuse to the police depends largely on the relationship between the abuser and the person who discovers the abuse (Finkelhor, 2005a).

Typically, the child initially trusts the abuser. Physical force is seldom needed to gain compliance, largely because of the child's helplessness, gullibility, and submission to adult authority. Whereas most sexually abused children are abused only once, those who are abused by family members are more likely to suffer repeated acts of abuse (Briere & Runtz, 1987).

Genital fondling is the most common type of abuse (Edwards et al., 2003). In one sample of women who had been molested in childhood, most of the contacts involved genital fondling (38% of cases) or exhibitionism (20% of cases). Intercourse is rare. Repeated abuse by a family member, however, commonly follows a pattern that begins with affectionate fondling during the preschool years, and progresses to oral sex or mutual masturbation during the early school years and then to sexual penetration (vaginal or anal intercourse) during preadolescence or adolescence.

Abused children rarely report the abuse, often because of fear of retaliation from the abuser or because they believe they will be blamed for it. Adults may suspect abuse if a child shows sudden personality changes or develops fears, problems in school, or difficulty eating or sleeping. A pediatrician may discover physical signs of abuse during a medical exam.

TYPES OF ABUSERS The overwhelming majority of people who sexually abuse children (both boys and girls) are males (Turner et al., 2006). Although most child abusers are adults, some are adolescents. Male adolescent sex offenders are more likely than other adolescents to have been molested themselves as boys.

Although the great majority of sexual abusers are male, the number of female sexual abusers may be greater than has been generally believed (Zernike, 2005). Many female sexual abusers may go undetected because society accords women a much freer range of physical contact with children than it does men. A study of a sample of Canadian police officers and psychiatrists found that, among these groups, there was a culture of denial of women as potential sexual aggressors (Denov, 2001).

CHILD SEX TOURISM Some Canadians travel to developing countries to have sex with children, partly because there is less chance of being prosecuted in those countries. In 1997, the Canadian government changed the Criminal Code so that Canadians who sexually abuse children while out of the country could be prosecuted. In 2002, prosecution was made easier by an amendment that no longer required the agreement of the country where the offence occurred. In 2005, the first conviction was obtained under this legislation. A B.C. man was convicted of having sex with children under the age of 14 in Cambodia (Girard, 2005).

In 2008, two Quebec men were charged with the sexual abuse of children in an orphanage in Haiti. Yet, because of lax enforcement, few Canadians who are charged in other countries with child sex abuse are ever prosecuted in Canada (Bains, 2008).

Pedophilia

Pedophilia is a paraphilia in which an adult finds children to be the preferred and sometimes exclusive objects of sexual desire. The prevalence of pedophilia in the general population is unknown. Although pedophiles are sometimes called child

Pedophilia A type of paraphilia that is defined by sexual attraction to an unusual stimulus: children.

molesters, not all child molesters are pedophiles. Pedophilia involves persistent or recurrent sexual attraction to children. Some molesters, however, may seek sexual contacts with children only when they are under unusual stress or lack other sexual outlets. Thus they do not meet the clinical definition of pedophilia.

Pedophiles are almost exclusively male, although some isolated cases of female pedophiles have been reported (Finkelhor, 2005b). Some pedophiles are sexually attracted only to children; others are sexually attracted to adults as well. Some pedophiles limit their sexual interest in children to incestuous relationships with family members; others abuse children to whom they are unrelated. Some pedophiles limit their sexual interest in children to looking at them or undressing them, or fondle them or masturbate in their presence. Some manipulate or coerce children into oral, anal, or vaginal intercourse.

Children tend not to be worldly wise. They can often be taken in by pedophiles who tell them that they want to "show them something," "teach them something," or "do something with them that they will like." Some pedophiles seek to gain the child's affection, and, later, to discourage the child from disclosing the sexual activity by showering the child with attention and gifts. Others threaten the child or the child's family to prevent disclosure.

Although most pedophiles may not wear trench coats and hang around schoolyards, there is research evidence that many of them have personality disorders (Madsen et al., 2006). Research finds them to be emotionally unstable, disagreeable, angry, impulsive, and mistrustful. A study by Toronto researchers found that many offenders had grown up in families with insecure attachment experiences (Stripe et al., 2006).

Some pedophiles who are lacking in social skills may turn to children after failing to establish gratifying relationships with adult women. Many pedophiles distort reality in ways that enable them to pursue sexual activity with children (Marziano et al., 2006).

Pedophiles often

- see children as sexual beings who want to have sex with adults
- believe that sex does not harm children and may be beneficial
- think of themselves as being so important that they are entitled to have sex with whomever they want (Marziano et al., 2006)

Ray Blanchard and colleagues at the Centre for Addiction and Mental Health in Toronto are exploring how disturbances in early neurodevelopment are related to pedophilia. They find that pedophiles are more likely to have experienced serious head injuries before the age of six and that these injuries are associated with lower levels of intelligence and memory loss. Also, pedophilia is somewhat related to being left-handed, which may be attributed to altered fetal development (Blanchard et al., 2007; Cantor et al., 2004, 2005a).

A group of Ontario researchers has also found that men who have older brothers are more prone to sexually coercing both children and adults (Lalumiere et al., 1998). Also, males with older brothers are more likely to choose male victims. In another Ontario study (Cantor et al., 2006), pedophilia was related to having failed one or more years of school and to having been enrolled in special education. In a separate study, Cantor et al. (2005b) found that pedophiles had lower IQ levels.

In a groundbreaking study of brain differences, Cantor et al. (2008) found significant brain differences between pedophiles and other men that may exist at birth. Specifically, by using magnetic resonance imaging, the researchers discovered that the wiring that connects the brain regions responsible for sexual response is thinner in pedophiles. The findings indicate that the part of the brain related to identifying sexual partners does not develop normally in pedophiles.

Toronto researchers (Seto et al., 2006) found in using penile tests of sexual arousal that men charged with child pornography offences were highly likely to be aroused by sexual images of children. In fact, the researchers concluded that child pornography offences are a stronger indicator of pedophilia than are sexual offences against children. One explanation the researchers give is that some men who sexually assault young victims are attracted to those who show some signs of sexual development rather than the fact that the victims are young (Seto et al., 2006).

What is the relationship between committing child pornography offences and other sexual offences? In a sample of adult males convicted of child pornography offences, Michael Seto and Angela Eke (2005) found that 24% had previous sexual offences involving contact. Child pornography offenders who had committed a prior or concurrent contact sexual offence were the most likely to offend again.

So There Really Was a Monster in Her Bedroom. Not all monsters are make-believe. Some, like the perpetrators of incest, are members of the family.

Incest

Incest involves people who are related by blood, or *consanguineous*. The law may also proscribe coitus between, say, a stepfather and stepdaughter. Although a few societies have permitted incestuous pairings among royalty, all known cultures have some sort of incest taboo.

FATHER–DAUGHTER INCEST Father–daughter incest often begins with affectionate cuddling or embraces and then progresses to teasing sexual play, lengthy caresses, hugs, kisses, and genital contact, even penetration. In some cases genital contact occurs more abruptly, usually when the father has been drinking or arguing with his wife. Force is not typically used to gain compliance, but daughters are sometimes physically overcome and injured by their fathers.

BROTHER–SISTER INCEST In sibling incest, the brother usually initiates sexual activity and assumes the dominant role. Some brothers and sisters may view their sexual activity as natural and not know that it is taboo.

Evidence on the effects of incest between brothers and sisters is mixed. In a study of university undergraduates, those who reported childhood incest with siblings did not reveal greater evidence of sexual adjustment problems than other undergraduates (Greenwald & Leitenberg, 1989). Sibling incest is most likely to be harmful when it is recurrent or forced or when parental response is harsh.

MOTHER–SON INCEST Mother–son incest occurs far less frequently than father–daughter incest. However, it may also be that boys who are sexually abused by their mothers are less likely to report it. Nevertheless, these cases do occur.

In an unusual case in Cambridge, Ontario, a mother and son had three children. The son was 16 years old when he fathered the first child with his mother. In an attempt to cover up the incestuous relationship, the son fabricated identity documents. Both mother and son were found guilty of incest (Wood, 2005).

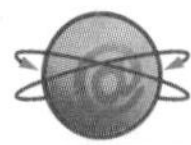

Survivors of Incest Anonymous
SIA World Service Office.
www.siawso.org

FAMILY FACTORS IN INCEST Incest frequently occurs within the context of general family disruption; there may also be spouse abuse, a dysfunctional marriage, or alcoholic or physically abusive parents. Stressful events in the father's life, such as the loss of a job or problems at work, often precede the initiation of incest (Welldon, 2005).

Fathers who abuse older daughters tend to be domineering and authoritarian with their families (Waterman, 1986). Fathers who abuse younger, preschool daughters are more likely to be passive, dependent, and low in self-esteem.

Marriages in incestuous families tend to be characterized by an uneven power relationship between the spouses. The abusive father is usually dominant. Another thread that frequently runs through incestuous families is a troubled sexual relationship between the spouses. The wife often rejects the husband sexually (Waterman, 1986).

Incest Marriage or sexual relations between people who are so closely related (by "blood") that sexual relations are prohibited and punishable by law.

Gebhard and his colleagues (1965) found that many fathers who committed incest with their daughters were religiously devout, fundamentalist, and moralistic. Perhaps such men, when sexually frustrated, are less likely to seek extramarital and extrafamilial sexual outlets or to turn to masturbation as a sexual release. In many cases, the father is under stress but does not find adequate emotional and sexual support from his wife (Gagnon, 1977). He turns to a daughter as a wife surrogate, often when he has been drinking alcohol (Gebhard et al., 1965). The daughter may become, in her father's fantasies, the "woman of the house." This fantasy may become his justification for continuing the incestuous relationship. In some incestuous families, a role reversal occurs. The abused daughter assumes many of the mother's responsibilities for managing the household and caring for the younger children.

Incestuous abuse is often repeated from generation to generation. One study found that in 154 cases of children who were sexually abused within the family, more than a third of the male offenders and about half of the mothers had been either abused themselves or exposed to abuse as children (Faller, 1989).

Australian and Canadian researchers (Greenberg et al., 2005) compared the characteristics of male incest offenders who were biological fathers with those who were stepfathers. Both these groups reported serious problems in their own childhood (sexual and physical abuse, being placed outside of the home). Their current problems involved alcohol abuse and sexual functioning, and deviant sexual arousal. Of all the variables analyzed, biological fathers and stepfathers differed statistically only in their sexual arousal to children. Biological fathers were less aroused by sexual abuse of a child than were stepfathers.

Effects of Sexual Abuse of Children

The effects of sexual abuse are varied, and there is no single identifiable syndrome that emerges from sexual abuse (Saywitz et al., 2000). Children who are sexually abused may suffer from a litany of short- and long-term psychological complaints, including anger, depression, anxiety, eating disorders, inappropriate sexual behaviour, aggressive behaviour, self-destructive behaviour, sexual promiscuity, drug abuse, suicide attempts, post-traumatic stress disorder, low self-esteem, sexual dysfunction, mistrust of others, and feelings of detachment (Edwards et al., 2003). Sexual abuse may also have physical effects such as genital injuries and may cause stress-related problems such as stomachaches and headaches.

Abused children commonly "act out." Younger children have tantrums or display aggressive or antisocial behaviour. Older children turn to substance abuse (Kendler et al., 2000). Some abused children become withdrawn and retreat into fantasy or refuse to leave the house. Regressive behaviours, such as thumb sucking, fear of the dark, and fear of strangers, are also common among sexually abused children. On the heels of the assault and in the ensuing years, many survivors of childhood sexual abuse—like many sexual assault survivors—show signs of post-traumatic stress disorder. They suffer flashbacks, nightmares, numbing of emotions, and feelings of estrangement from others (Herrera & McCloskey, 2003).

The sexual development of abused children may also be adversely affected. For example, the survivor may become prematurely sexually active or promiscuous in adolescence and adulthood (Herrera & McCloskey, 2003). Researchers find that adolescent girls who are sexually abused tend to engage in consensual coitus at earlier ages than nonabused peers (Herrera & McCloskey, 2003).

Late adolescence and early adulthood seem to pose especially difficult periods for survivors of childhood sexual abuse. Studies of women in these age groups reveal more psychological and social problems in abused women (Kendler et al., 2000).

Applied Knowledge

PREVENTING SEXUAL ABUSE OF CHILDREN

Many of us were taught by our parents never to accept a ride or an offer of candy from a stranger. However, many instances of sexual abuse are perpetrated by familiar adults–often a family member or friend (Zielbauer, 2000). Prevention programs help children understand what sexual abuse is and how they can avoid it. In addition to learning to avoid strangers, children need to recognize the differences between acceptable touching, such as an affectionate embrace or pat on the head, and unacceptable or "bad" touching. Even children of elementary school age can learn the distinction between "good touching" and "bad touching." Good school-based programs are generally helpful in preparing children to handle an actual encounter with a potential molester. Children who receive comprehensive training are more likely to use strategies such as running away, yelling, or saying no when they are threatened by an abuser. They are also more likely to report such incidents to adults.

Researchers recognize that children can easily be intimidated or overpowered by adults or older children (Miller, 2005). Children may be unable to say no in a sexually abusive situation, even though they want to and know it is the right thing to do. Although children may not always be able to prevent abuse, they can be encouraged to tell someone about it. Most prevention programs emphasize teaching children messages such as "It's not your fault," "Never keep a bad or scary secret," and "Always tell your parents about this, especially if someone says you shouldn't tell them."

Children also need to be alerted to the types of threats they might receive for disclosing the abuse. They are more likely to resist threats if they are reassured that they will be believed if they disclose the abuse, that their parents will continue to love them, and that they and their families will be protected from the molester.

School-based prevention programs focus on protecting the child. In Canada, teachers and helping professionals are required to report suspected abuse to authorities. Tighter controls and better screening are needed to monitor the hiring of daycare employees. Administrators and teachers in preschool and daycare facilities also need to be educated to recognize the signs of sexual abuse and to report suspected cases. Treatment programs to help people who are sexually attracted to children *before* they commit abusive acts would also be of use.

Treatment of Survivors of Sexual Abuse

Psychotherapy in adulthood often becomes the first opportunity for survivors to confront residual feelings of pain, anger, and misplaced guilt. Group or individual therapy can help improve survivors' self-esteem and their ability to develop intimate relationships. Many therapists recommend a multicomponent treatment approach, which may involve individual therapy for the child, mother, and father; group therapy for the adolescent or even preadolescent survivor; art therapy or play therapy for the younger child (e.g., using drawings or puppets to express feelings); marital counselling for the parents; and family therapy for the entire family.

Treatment of Sexual Assailants and Child Molesters

What does *treatment* mean? When a helping professional treats someone, the goal is usually to help that individual. When we speak of treating a sex offender, the goal is just as likely—or more likely—to be to help society by eliminating the problem behaviour.

A group of Canadian and American researchers has conducted an extensive review of the effectiveness of psychological treatment programs for sex offenders. They found that treatment programs conducted prior to 1980 had little effect. However, current treatments to prevent sex offenders from repeating their offences (see below) have shown some effect in reducing rates of recidivism (Hanson et al., 2002). More recently, Ontario researchers have developed treatment programs that resulted in only 3% of sex offenders reoffending (Marshall et al., 2006).

Ottawa researchers have found that rates of recidivism are lower among incest offenders who have not committed any other type of sexual offence. In an Ontario study, 26% of men who had committed a non-incestuous assault committed another sexual assault after their release from prison (Firestone et al., 1998). However, of a sample of men who had committed incest but no other kind of sexual offence, only a small percentage (6.4%) committed sexual offences 12 years after being released from prison (Firestone et al., 1999).

In a comprehensive analysis of treatment programs for adult sexual offenders, researchers in Ontario arrived at a number of conclusions about the programs' likelihood of success (Rice et al., 2001). Treatments that are insight-oriented and focused on building the offenders' self-esteem have not been successful, nor have programs focused only on punishing the offender. Successful programs, on the other hand, are likely to include the following elements:

- skills-based training that emphasizes problem-solving
- modelling of positive societal behaviours
- nonpunitive orientation
- modifying antecedents to criminal behaviour, such as alcohol abuse
- supervised community living experiences that teach relevant everyday living and working skills (Rice et al., 2001)

As discussed in Chapter 15, another treatment approach is that developed by Ottawa psychiatrist John Bradford (2000). This includes the use of prescription drugs such as Prozac for the more difficult cases.

Marshall et al. (2007) emphasize the importance of having offenders take responsibility for their offences. They also teach offenders more effective coping skills as a way of dealing with their relationship problems. For those offenders who continue to have deviant patterns of sexual arousal, Marshall et al. use reconditioning strategies for enhancing appropriate sexual interests and reducing deviant ones.

Some Canadian communities such as Victoria, Winnipeg, and Kitchener, Ontario, have volunteer groups known as Circles of Support and Accountability (COSA), which have the twin goals of community protection and offender rehabilitation. These trained volunteer groups help integrate sexual offenders into the community and help them avoid reoffending by meeting their intimacy and relationship needs. This process assumes that in order to protect the community, offenders do not need to be isolated from the community (Petrunik, 2003). An evaluation project in Ontario found that involvement in a COSA can reduce further sexual offending by more than 60% (Wilson, 2005).

In the past, some programs have used extreme measures such as surgical castration to lower the offender's sex drive. Surgical castration raises ethical concerns because of its invasive character and irreversibility. Anti-androgen drugs such as Depo-Provera chemically reduce testosterone levels and the level of sex drive, but are reversible (Roesler & Witztum, 2000).

In 2004, the Canadian federal government, in response to pressure from community groups, some provincial governments, and police forces, established a national sex offender registry. Convicted sex offenders must register within 15 days of being released from prison and must reregister annually and within two weeks of moving. Police agencies from across Canada have access to this database, which they believe will help them in investigating cases of sexual assault. However, in 2008 an investigation discovered that many offenders were not registered and the list of offenders was not up to date (Friscolanti, 2008).

Marshall et al. (2006) criticize these approaches, because they believe that public notification is more likely to increase re-offending because of the stress the offender experiences. Thus Marshall et al. suggest public notification should be used only with extremely dangerous cases when alternative containment strategies are not available.

Also, some legal experts have argued that the registry violates the human rights of the offender, who can never have his name removed from the list even after having lived as a model citizen for many years. As well, no other category of offender is required to register with the police after being released from prison (Ward et al., 2007). What is your opinion on this issue?

A World of Diversity

SHAME ON EGYPT'S SEXIST BULLIES

When I was only four years old, and still living in Cairo, a man exposed himself to me as I stood on a balcony at my family's home, and gestured for me to come down.

At 15, I was groped as I was performing the rites of the hajj pilgrimage at Mecca, the holiest site for Muslims. Every part of my body was covered except for my face and hands. I'd never been groped before and burst into tears, but I was too ashamed to explain to my family what had happened.

During my 20s, when I had returned to Cairo and wore the *hijab*, a way of dressing that again covers everything but the face and the hands, I was groped so many times that whenever I passed a group of men, I'd place my bag between me and them. Headphones helped block out the disgusting things men—and even boys barely in their teens—hissed at me.

So it was no surprise to learn that 98 per cent of foreign women visiting Egypt and 83 per cent of native Egyptian women who were recently surveyed said that they, too, had been sexually harassed, and they have recounted a catalogue of horrors similar to mine. What an awful time to be a woman in Egypt.

When the Egyptian Centre for Women's Rights reported that 62 per cent of Egyptian men admitted to harassing women, I could only shudder at what sexist bullies so many of my countrymen are.

Even worse, when I read that the majority of the more than 2000 Egyptian men and women that centre surveyed blamed women for bringing on the harassment because of the way they dressed, I honestly thought my countrymen and women had lost their minds.

In Egypt today, up to 80 per cent of women wear one form of veil or another—be it a head scarf or a full-body veil that covers the face too—so you would think it was obvious that sexual harassment had nothing to do with the way a woman dresses. So what is it that drives such a stubborn wish to fault women?

The answer lies in perhaps the saddest of all the centre's findings. Unlike foreign women, most Egyptian women said women should keep their harassment to themselves because they were ashamed or feared it could ruin their reputation. This shame is fuelled by religious and political messages that bombard Egyptian public life, turning women into sexual objects and giving men free rein to their bodies.

In 2006, it was the well-publicized episode of the mufti of Australia comparing women who didn't wear the *hijab* to uncovered meat left out for wild cats. He was educated at Al-Azhar, the religious institution in Egypt that trains clerics from all over the Sunni Muslim world. He was suspended, but his reprehensible views are very much at work among many other clerics.

There is no law criminalizing sexual harassment in Egypt, and police often refuse to report women's complaints. And when it is the police themselves who are harassing women, then clearly women's safety is far from a priority in Egypt.

The state itself taught Egyptians a most spectacular lesson in institutionalized patriarchy when security forces and government-hired thugs sexually assaulted demonstrators, especially women, during an anti-regime protest in 2005, giving a green light to harassers.

At a demonstration against sexual harassment that I attended in Cairo a year later, there were nearly more riot police than protesters. My sister Nora was 20 at the time, and she, with several of her friends, joined the protest. We swapped our sexual harassment stories like veterans comparing war wounds, and we unravelled a taboo that shelters the real criminals of sexual harassment and has kept us hiding in shame.

And that is why I began here with my own stories—to free myself of the tentacles of that shame.

Source: Eltahawy, M. (2008, August 5). Shame on Egypt's sexist bullies. The Toronto Globe and Mail, *p. A11.*

Sexual harassment Deliberate or repeated unsolicited verbal comments, gestures, or physical contact of a sexual nature that the recipient does not welcome.

Sexual Harassment

For legal purposes, **sexual harassment** in the workplace is usually defined as deliberate or repeated unwanted comments, gestures, or physical contact (Craig, 2005; Finkelman, 2005). It is forbidden by both federal and provincial human rights legislation. Sexual harassment makes the workplace or other setting a hostile place. Examples range from unwelcome sexual jokes and sexual innuendos to outright sexual assault. Sexual harassment may include behaviours such as:

- verbal harassment or abuse
- subtle pressure for sexual activity
- remarks about a person's clothing, body, or sexual activities
- leering at or ogling a person's body
- unwelcome touching, patting, or pinching
- brushing against a person's body
- demands for sexual favours accompanied by implied or overt threats concerning one's job or student status
- physical assault

Evidence shows that people subjected to sexual harassment do suffer from it. In a survey of Canadian women in the workforce, among those who had been sexually harassed, 30% reported that their job was affected and 14% reported personal difficulties resulting from the harassment (Crocker & Kalemba, 1999). Some find harassment on the job so unbearable that they resign.

Sexual harassment may have more to do with the abuse of power than with sexual desire (Goleman, 1991; Tedeschi & Felson, 1994). Relatively few cases of sexual harassment involve outright requests for sexual favours. The harasser is usually in a dominant position and abuses that position by exploiting the victim's vulnerability. Sexual harassment may also occur between doctors and patients and between

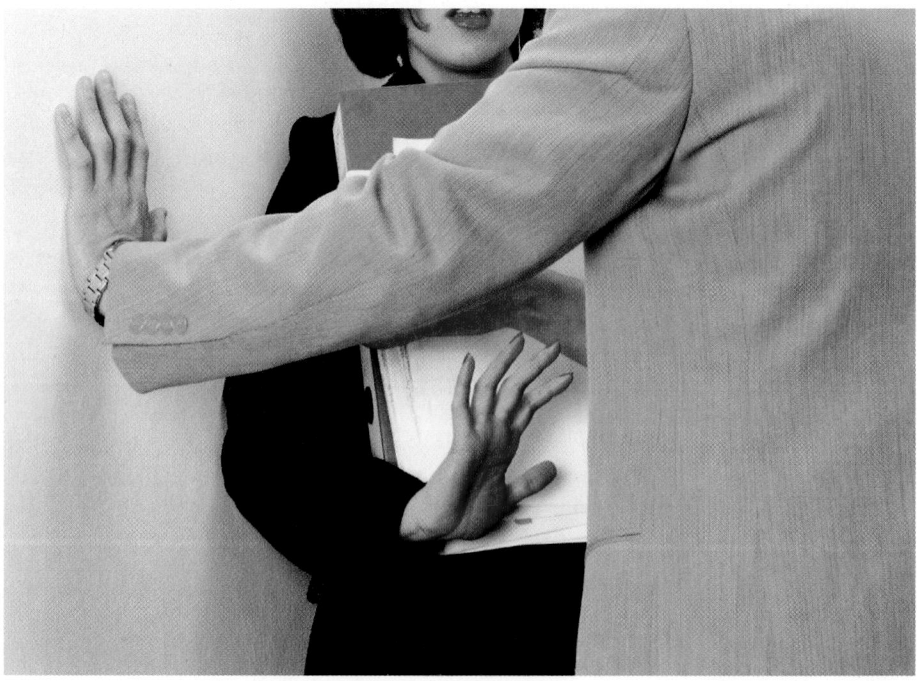

Sexual Harassment.
Many victims of sexual harassment keep such incidents to themselves for fear that they—the victims—will be blamed for the incidents or that their supervisors will fire them for complaining. Perpetrators can claim that they were misunderstood or that the victim is exaggerating.

Innovative Canadian Research

GENDER, ETHNICITY, AND PERCEPTIONS OF SEXUAL HARASSMENT

Often the genders differ in their perceptions of sexual harassment. University of Windsor researchers Pek Ne Knoo and Charlene Senn (2004) asked students to rate the offensiveness of 10 types of email messages. Emails containing sexual content were rated as more offensive by women than by men. In particular, women found a sexual proposition from a stranger extremely offensive; the men found it enjoyable.

Researchers at the University of British Columbia found that male students were more tolerant of behaviours indicative of sexual harassment than were female students (Kennedy & Gorzalka, 2002). As well, Asian students were more tolerant of these behaviours than were non-Asian students. However, the longer the Asian students had been in Canada, the less accepting they were of these behaviours. This trend indicates that over time, Asian Canadians tend to become acculturated to the views of other Canadians regarding sexual harassment (Kennedy & Gorzalka, 2002).

Robin Milhausen (2000) of the University of Guelph surveyed 413 young adults at university and in the community about workplace behaviour and perceptions. The majority of both men and women believed that men have to be more careful than women in the workplace about making sexual jokes, sexual comments, and comments about the physical appearance of a co-worker, and about making any kind of sexual contact with a co-worker. For example, 80% of the men and 68% of the women said that men have to be more careful than women about making sexual comments. Only a minority (15% of men and 29% of women) felt that both genders have to be careful, while hardly any (4% of men and 2% of women) said that women have to be more careful.

therapists and clients. Therapists may use their power and influence to pressure clients into sexual relations. In Canada, professional organizations for teachers, doctors, and therapists have strict ethical guidelines that forbid sexual contact between doctors and patients, therapists and clients, and teachers and students.

Sexual Harassment of Victims From Minority Groups

A Canadian study shed light on different experiences of harassment (Berdahl & Moore, 2006). It compared the experiences of white women, black women, and Filipina women. White women with full rights as citizens felt most free to report the harassment to authorities. Black women and Filipinas felt that the term *sexual harassment* did not fully capture their experience—that their treatment also had to do with the power that white men could exercise over blacks and, especially, live-in Filipina caregivers. It also found that women experienced more sexual harassment than men, and in what the authors call "double jeopardy," minority women encountered more harassment than white women.

Sexual Harassment in the Workplace

Harassers in the workplace can be employers, supervisors, co-workers, or clients of a company. If a worker asks a co-worker for a date and is refused, it is not sexual harassment. If the co-worker persists with unwelcome advances and does not take no for an answer, however, the behaviour crosses the line and becomes harassment.

Perhaps the most severe form of sexual harassment, short of an outright assault, involves an employer or supervisor who demands sexual favours as a condition of employment or advancement. In Canada, Human Rights Commissions have

Canadian Trends

SEXUAL HARASSMENT IN THE WORKPLACE

How common is sexual harassment in the workplace? In a national survey of about 2000 Canadian working women, 56% reported experiencing sexual harassment in the previous year and 77% said that they had experienced sexual harassment in their lifetime (Crocker & Kalemba, 1999). The three most common types of incidents were staring, jokes, and remarks about women or about the respondents themselves. The least common incidents were use of physical force, threats, and bribery.

Another Canadian survey (Compas, 1998) asked respondents how they felt the new rules against sexual harassment had affected gender relations in the workplace. Canadians were clearly divided in their opinions. A third of the respondents believed that the new rules had not changed gender relations; another third believed they had improved relations; and the final third believed that the rules had worsened relations (although they were opposed to sexual harassment, they felt that some rules, for example, those forbidding co-workers from dating each other, had become too strict).

expanded the definition of sexual harassment in the workplace to include any behaviour of a sexual nature that interferes with an individual's work performance or creates a hostile, intimidating, or offensive work environment. Canadian legislation also recognizes sexual harassment as a form of sex discrimination.

Some companies and organizations have gone a step further, banning their employees from having any sexual contact with other employees, even if it is consensual. A Canadian Armed Forces ban on all forms of sexual activity (including flirting and holding hands) at an overseas peacekeeping base led to a 2001 court challenge. The military judge upheld the ban, arguing that sexual activity "could lead to feelings of jealousy, even violence, feelings of favouritism and disrupting the feelings of cohesion and morale" (Weber, 2001, p. A3).

In a widely publicized 2005 case, the City of Toronto suspended a female senior manager and her (married) male second-in-command, who admitted they had had an affair. Concerns were raised that the male assistant's rapid promotion—from temporary employee to a senior position in only 10 months—resulted from favouritism on the part of his boss, who was also his lover.

Despite prohibitions against intimate relationships in the workplace, many people do get involved with a fellow worker. In a recent national survey, about one-third of men and women said they had "slept" with someone they had worked with and more than half said they had a crush on a co-worker (van der Voort, 2008).

Employers can be held responsible not only for their own actions, but also for sexual harassment by their employees when they either knew or *should have known* that harassment was taking place and failed to eliminate it promptly. To protect themselves, many companies and universities have developed programs to educate workers about sexual harassment, established mechanisms for dealing with complaints, and imposed sanctions against harassers.

Relatively few people who encounter sexual harassment in the workplace file formal complaints or seek legal remedies. Among Canadian women, the most common responses to sexual harassment are either to confront the harasser (38%) or to ignore the incident (20%). Relatively few (5%) report it. One percent have quit their jobs because of the harassment. Like people subjected to other forms of sexual coercion, those experiencing sexual harassment often do not report the offence for fear that they will not be believed or will be subjected to retaliation. Some fear they will be branded as "troublemakers" or that they will lose their jobs (Goleman, 1991).

Sexual Harassment on Campus

Kathleen Cairns and Doyle Hatt (1995) of the University of Calgary found that, among graduate students at a large Canadian university, 9% of the women and 2% of the men had experienced sexual harassment. The most common form involved sexist remarks and sexual comments, with very few experiencing sexual coercion. The female students were harassed mainly by male professors and instructors, but also by other students. Male graduate students reported being harassed mainly by female students. Researchers at the Ontario Institute for Studies in Education surveyed psychologists in Ontario about their experiences of sexual harassment while they were in graduate school (Schneider et al., 2002). The reported incidence of harassment was much higher than that found by Cairns and Hatt, most likely because the Ontario researchers measured a wider scope of harassment experiences. Sixty percent of the psychologists reported that by far the most common type of harassment was that of professors telling suggestive jokes or stories. Similar to the Calgary study, very few reported having experienced sexual coercion from their professors.

Harassers are typically (but not always) male. Most students who encounter sexual harassment do not report the incident. If they do, it is usually to a friend and not a person in authority.

Most forms of harassment involve unequal power relationships between the harasser and the person harassed. *Peer harassment* involves people who are equal in power, as in the cases of repeated sexual taunts from fellow employees, students, or colleagues. In some cases, the harasser may even have less formal power than the person harassed. For example, both female and male professors have been sexually harassed by students.

University faculty associations in Canada support policies on sexual harassment. However, faculty associations are also concerned that these policies may in some instances limit academic freedom, and especially the ability to have an open discussion of controversial topics. For example, consider the case of an Ontario university law professor. In teaching his students about the arguments for and against an anti-pornography law, he asked them to adopt a perspective that was contrary to their own. Some of the students, upset at having to argue against their own beliefs, complained to the university's sexual harassment officer. The official warned the instructor that if he repeated the class exercise it could lead to a sexual harassment investigation (Fekete, 1994). What is your opinion of this case? Do you think the professor should not have asked students to take part in this classroom exercise? Or do you think that asking students to adopt a contrary perspective can be an effective way of helping them to better understand points of view that differ from their own and should therefore be considered a legitimate approach to teaching?

Sexual Harassment in the Schools

Playful sexual antics are common during adolescence. However, unwelcome sexual advances and lewd comments go beyond playfulness and have become a concern to many of Canada's teens.

A research team from York University consisting of Loren McMaster, Jennifer Connolly, and Debra Pepler, along with Wendy McCraig of Queen's University, conducted a study of peer-to-peer sexual harassment among 1213 youths from grades 6–8 in a large Canadian city (McMaster et al., 2002). The study defined sexual harassment as unwanted sexual attention, and asked students if they had perpetrated or experienced any of 10 types of sexual harassment. Boys were significantly more likely to report perpetration (36%) than were girls (21%), but both genders were about equally likely to report victimization (boys 42%, girls 38%). For both boys and girls, the three behaviours most commonly experienced were homophobic name

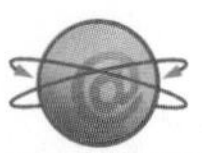

Equality Rules
The Ontario government has established an interactive website for girls aged 8 to 14 on issues of dating violence and sexual harassment. The site teaches girls how to recognize abuse and how to handle negative relationships.

www.EqualityRules.ca

calling; sexual comments, jokes, and looks; and being flashed or mooned. The boys perpetrated more same-sex harassment while the girls perpetrated more cross-sex harassment. The most common form of same-sex harassment among boys was homophobic name calling.

The researchers found that those students who were at a more advanced stage of pubertal development both perpetrated and experienced sexual harassment more than did other students. McMaster et al. (2002) concluded that for some youth, harassment is a phase of development, but for others it is part of a developmental pattern that includes other forms of aggression such as bullying and is a predictor of aggression in future dating relationships.

Higher levels of harassment were found in a study of 565 older adolescents in the provinces of British Columbia and New Brunswick (Dahinten, 2003). The picture that emerges from this poll of teenagers in grades 9–11 indicates that sexual taunts and advances have become part of an unwelcome ritual for many students, especially girls, as they try to make their way through the hallways and stairwells of high schools. Almost all of the students reported experiencing at least one form of sexual harassment during the preceding two months, with about two-thirds of the girls and half of the boys experiencing five or more forms of harassment. The most common forms of harassment for two-thirds of the girls were being the target of sexual comments or whistles, sexual gestures, or stares and derogatory comments about females.

However, most of the behaviours were not labelled as sexual harassment by the students. Of those who had experienced at least one of the 19 items measuring sexual harassment, only 35% of the girls and 14% of the boys replied yes to the general item asking if they had been sexually harassed. This discrepancy in the labelling of behaviours clearly illustrates how the type of measurement one chooses can influence the incidence of harassment that is reported in the research literature. It also raises an important question: Is it legitimate for researchers to categorize behaviours as harassment when the people experiencing them do not consider them harassment? What do you think?

Girls were more likely than boys to report that they were upset when experiencing the sexual harassment behaviours. For boys the most upsetting experiences were "being the target of sexual rumours or graffiti" and "being followed or pestered for a date." Among girls, the most upsetting experiences were "being forced to do something other than kissing or hugging" and "being the target of sexual rumours." Most of the students responded passively to the harassment, and hardly any complained to a teacher or more formally made a complaint through the school system (Dahinten, 2003).

In a more recent survey of Ontario high school students conducted by the Centre for Addiction and Mental Health, a third of the students said at times they had felt unsafe at school. About half of the girls said that at school they were subjected to sexual comments or gestures and a third had been touched in a sexual manner (Rushowy, 2008).

Large-scale studies of youth in both Canada and the U.S. have found that gay males, lesbians, and bisexuals experience more physical and sexual abuse than do heterosexuals (Saewyc et al., 2006). The researchers attribute this to the stigma that is often attached to LGB orientation. However, the researchers also note that most LGB youth are not physically or sexually abused.

Today, there is considerable concern in Canadian high schools about websites that spread sexual rumours about students. The most typical rumours are about boys being gay and girls being promiscuous. These websites can be extremely nasty and hateful, and can demoralize the students who are discussed on them. An even more hurtful form of harassment is posting sexual pictures on a website without the person's consent, as discussed in the nearby A World of Diversity feature.

A World of Diversity

NUDE PHOTOS MAKE WEB CALAMITY FOR GIRL

A 16-year-old Toronto girl is struggling with a cyber nightmare after sexually explicit photos taken by a vengeful ex-boyfriend were posted on the internet. Although child-pornography charges have been laid, police can't get the anonymous webmaster to remove the photos.

The pictures appeared in February, shortly after the girl told police that her former boyfriend had extorted money from her in a matter unrelated to the photos.

He decided to exact his revenge by posting five nude photos of her on the internet. What's more, he constructed the web page to make it seem as though she had placed them there herself.

The accused, who is 16 and can't be identified, wrote a short entry impersonating her.

Detective Constable Chris Purchas of the Toronto Police sex crimes unit said the entry makes the girl appear to be "acting in a promiscuous manner, inviting other people to address her sexually."

It was the teenager's friends who first told her that she had been exposed for all the world to see. It has been two months since she found out. She feels humiliated and has missed several weeks of school, Det. Constable Purchas said.

The photos, which were taken with the girl's consent, are still up on the web, and are starting to appear on other sites.

"What's happening is people are going on the internet and copying them and reposting them on other websites, making other allegations slandering her character and so forth," he said. "These pictures can never be retrieved."

Det. Constable Purchas said that despite their best efforts the police can't even get the original posting down. The website, which is a general-interest, youth-oriented site with thousands of hits each day, is overseen by a U.S.-based company whose main purpose is to block authorities from uncovering the true operators of websites.

"The internet provider is not being very co-operative and they're ignoring our requests to have the pictures removed," he said.

The website has a lot of traffic from Canadian customers, he said, mostly between the ages of 14 and 30, and there is no other pornographic material on the site. It's mainly frequented for discussion boards, he said.

The ex-boyfriend has been charged with possessing and distributing child pornography and with impersonation with intent. Police hope a vigorous prosecution will prevent this type of offence from becoming a new trend.

"That's our fear," Det. Constable Purchas said. "We're trying to send a message in the hope that we won't see more of this."

He said although it's still a relatively rare kind of offence, everyone should be aware that with the advent of the internet racy photos could end up anywhere.

"Be careful what you give to your boyfriends because the potential (for harm) is most certainly there," he said. "Twenty years ago, if a boyfriend had an off-colour picture of a girlfriend and things didn't go well, the most he could do is photocopy it and put it on a bus shed or put it up around the school. Now he has a worldwide forum at his fingertips."

The relationship went sour in October of 2004, about a year after the pair started dating. The girl was 15 when the photos were taken and she knew that her ex-boyfriend still had them when they broke up.

The police say that before they broke up the boy was angry because she had given another male friend an expensive gift. He is alleged to have threatened to hurt her unless she gave him cash. Shortly after he was charged in connection with those allegations, the nude pictures appeared on the web.

Source: Joe Friesen (2005, April 22). Nude Photos Make Web Calamity for Girl. The Globe and Mail. *Reprinted with permission from* The Globe and Mail.

Teachers are also being sexually harassed on websites. A 14-year-old grade 8 student in Toronto was banned from an end-of-the-school-year class trip to Montreal after he made sexual comments about a teacher on Facebook. He said that he thought he saw the female science teacher masturbating at the back of a classroom (Boyle, 2007).

In 2008, the Canadian Teachers' Federation, at its annual meeting in Moncton, New Brunswick, unanimously voted that cyberbullying should be a criminal offence. The teachers said they would lobby members of Parliament to have this offence included in the Criminal Code (Canadian Press, 2008).

Applied Knowledge

HOW TO RESIST SEXUAL HARASSMENT

What would you do if you were sexually harassed by an employer or a professor? How would you handle it? Would you try to ignore it and hope that it would stop? What actions might you take? We offer some suggestions that may be helpful. Recognize, however, that responsibility for sexual harassment always lies squarely with the perpetrator and with the organization that permits sexual harassment to take place, not with the person subjected to the harassment.

1. *Convey a professional attitude.* Harassment may be stopped cold by responding to the harasser with a businesslike, professional attitude.
2. *Discourage harassing behaviour, and encourage appropriate behaviour.* Harassment may also be stopped cold by shaping the harasser's behaviour. Your reactions to the harasser may encourage businesslike behaviour and discourage flirtatious or suggestive behaviour. If a harassing professor suggests that you come back after school to review your term paper so that the two of you will be undisturbed, set limits assertively. Tell the professor that you'd feel more comfortable discussing the paper during regular office hours. Remain task-oriented. Stick to business. The harasser should quickly get the message that you insist on maintaining a strictly professional relationship. If the harasser persists, however, do not blame yourself. You are responsible only for your own actions. When the harasser persists, a more direct response may be appropriate: "Professor Jones, I'd like to keep our relationship on a purely professional basis."
3. *Avoid being alone with the harasser.* If you are being harassed by your professor but need some advice about preparing your term paper, approach him or her after class when other students are milling about, not privately during office hours. Or bring a friend to wait outside the office while you consult the professor.
4. *Maintain a record.* Keep a record of all incidents of harassment to use as documentation in the event that you decide to lodge an official complaint. The record should include the following: (1) where the incident took place; (2) the date and time; (3) what happened, including the exact words that were used, if you can recall them; (4) how you felt; and (5) the names of witnesses.
5. *Talk with the harasser.* It may be uncomfortable to address the issue directly with a harasser, but doing so puts the offender on notice that you are aware of the harassment and want it to stop. It may be helpful to frame your approach in terms of a description of the specific offending actions (e.g., "When we were alone in the office, you repeatedly attempted to touch me or brush up against me"); your feelings about the offending behaviour ("It made me feel like my privacy was being violated"); and what you would like the offender to do ("So I'd like you to agree never to attempt to touch me again, okay?"). Having a talk with the harasser may stop the harassment. If the harasser denies the accusations, it may be necessary to take further action.
6. *Write a letter to the harasser.* Set down on paper a record of the offending behaviour, and put the harasser on notice that the harassment must stop. Your letter might (1) describe what happened ("Several times you have made sexist comments about my body"); (2) describe how you feel ("It made me feel like a sexual object when you talked to me that way"); and (3) describe what you would like the harasser to do ("I want you to stop making sexist comments to me").
7. *Seek support.* Support from people you trust can help you through the often trying process of resisting sexual harassment. Talking with others enables you to express your feelings and receive emotional support, encouragement, and advice. In addition, it may strengthen your case if you have the opportunity to identify and talk with other people who have been harassed by the offender.
8. *File a complaint.* Companies and organizations are required by law to respond reasonably to complaints of sexual harassment. In large organizations, a designated official (a human rights officer) is usually charged with handling such complaints. Set up an appointment with this official to discuss your experiences. The major government agencies that handle charges of sexual harassment are the provincial human rights offices (look in the government section of your phone book for the telephone number of the nearest office).
9. *Seek legal remedies.* Sexual harassment is illegal and actionable. If you are considering legal action, consult a lawyer familiar with this area of law.

In closing, we repeat: The question is not what persons who suffer sexual assault, incest, and sexual harassment will do to redress the harm that has been done to them. The question is what all of us will do to reshape our society so that sex can no longer be used as an instrument of power, coercion, and violence.

Summing Up

The definition of sexual assault involves more than just sexual intercourse.

Types of sexual assaults include stranger sexual assault, acquaintance sexual assault, date sexual assault, and marital sexual assault.

Social attitudes such as gender-role stereotyping, seeing sex as adversarial, and acceptance of violence in interpersonal relationships all help create a climate that encourages sexual assault.

Some sexually coercive men feel socially inadequate, lack social skills, and avoid social interactions with women. Some are basically antisocial and have long histories of violent behaviour.

Sexual assault survivors often experience post-traumatic stress disorder (PTSD).

Treatment of sexual assault survivors typically involves helping them through the crisis period following the attack and then helping to foster long-term adjustment.

Sexual assault prevention involves educating society at large and familiarizing women with a number of precautions that they can take.

Verbal sexual coercion involves the use of verbal pressure or seduction lines to manipulate a person into having sexual relations.

Any form of sexual contact between an adult and a child is abusive, even if force or physical threat is not used, because children are legally incapable of consenting to sexual activity with adults.

In most cases of child sexual abuse, the molesters are close to the children they abuse—relatives, step-relatives, family friends, and neighbours.

Pedophilia is a type of paraphilia in which adults are sexually attracted to children.

Incest is marriage or sexual relations between people who are so closely related that sex is prohibited and punished by virtue of the kinship tie.

Children who are sexually abused often suffer social and emotional problems that impair their development and persist into adulthood, affecting their self-esteem and their formation of intimate relationships.

Psychotherapy may help adult survivors of sexual abuse improve their self-esteem and ability to develop intimate relationships.

The effectiveness of prison-based rehabilitation programs and anti-androgen drugs in curbing repeat offences requires further empirical support.

The definition of sexual harassment in the workplace has been expanded to include any behaviour of a sexual nature that interferes with an individual's work performance or creates a hostile, intimidating, or offensive work environment.

Most incidents of sexual harassment on campus are in the form of sexist comments.

Sexual harassment at school has become an unwelcome ritual that many junior and senior high school students are forced to endure.

Test Yourself

Multiple-Choice Questions

1. Sexual assault involving a weapon would be categorized as __________________ under the Criminal Code of Canada.

a. level 1
b. level 2
c. level 3
d. level 4

2. Sexual assaults are committed most often by

a. strangers
b. family members
c. gangs
d. acquaintances

3. Which of the following is NOT true regarding research on sexual consent?

a. Sexual consent is usually seen as overly simplistic.
b. Many researchers have studied the ways in which people actually ask for, and give, consent.
c. Research and discussion of sexual consent has mainly taken place in the context of a heterosexual bias.
d. Researchers usually assume that women seldom if ever initiate a sexual encounter.

4. Men who believe strongly in stereotypical gender roles are likely to do all of the following except

a. condone violence toward women
b. blame sexual assault survivors for what happened to them
c. ignore a partner's saying that she does not want to have sex
d. play violent video games

5. **All of the following are suggestions about what to do if you are sexually assaulted except**
   a. do not wash, change your clothes, or comb your hair
   b. seek medical help and make sure that any injuries are documented
   c. think about reporting the assault to the police
   d. do not talk to anyone about the assault

6. **Treatment for sexual assault survivors is usually a two-stage process. The first stage involves helping the person through the immediate crisis. The second involves**
   a. remembering exactly what happened on the day of the assault
   b. learning to forgive the offender
   c. fostering long-term adjustment
   d. telling friends and family about the assault

7. **Less forceful forms of resistance, such as pleading or reasoning with the offender,**
   a. are the most effective ways to prevent sexual assault
   b. will reduce the risk of injury
   c. may actually increase the risk of injury
   d. work better for male victims

8. **The most common type of child sexual abuse is ________________.**
   a. genital fondling
   b. vaginal intercourse
   c. oral sex
   d. kissing

9. **The most common type of incest is ________________.**
   a. father-daughter
   b. stepfather-stepdaughter
   c. brother-sister
   d. mother-son

10. **When it comes to assessing behaviours as sexually harassing,**
   a. men perceive more behaviours as offensive than women
   b. men and women have similar perceptions of behaviours
   c. women perceive more behaviours as offensive than men
   d. women perceive all sexual behaviour in the workplace as offensive

Answers to the Test Yourself questions in each chapter are found on page 509.

Critical Thinking Questions

1. Have you ever tried to convince someone to have sexual intercourse with you even after they said no? What eventually happened? How do you feel about it? How would you feel if someone tried this behaviour with your sister?
2. Has anyone ever tried to convince you to have sexual intercourse even when you didn't want to? What happened? How do you feel about it? How do you feel about the other person? About yourself?
3. A woman goes to a bar, has a few too many drinks, dances suggestively with several men, and goes home with one of them. If she later reports that she has been sexually assaulted, do you think she is to blame? If she had been assaulted on the street waiting for a bus at the same time of night, would she be less to blame? Why or why not?
4. Have you ever been sexually harassed by a professor, employer, co-worker, or fellow student? Did you report it? What was the outcome? Are you satisfied with the outcome? If this happened again, what, if anything, would you do differently?

Visit MyPsychKit at www.mypsychkit.com, where you can do quizzes and link to additional resources on topics discussed in this text.

CHAPTER SEVENTEEN

Commercial Sex

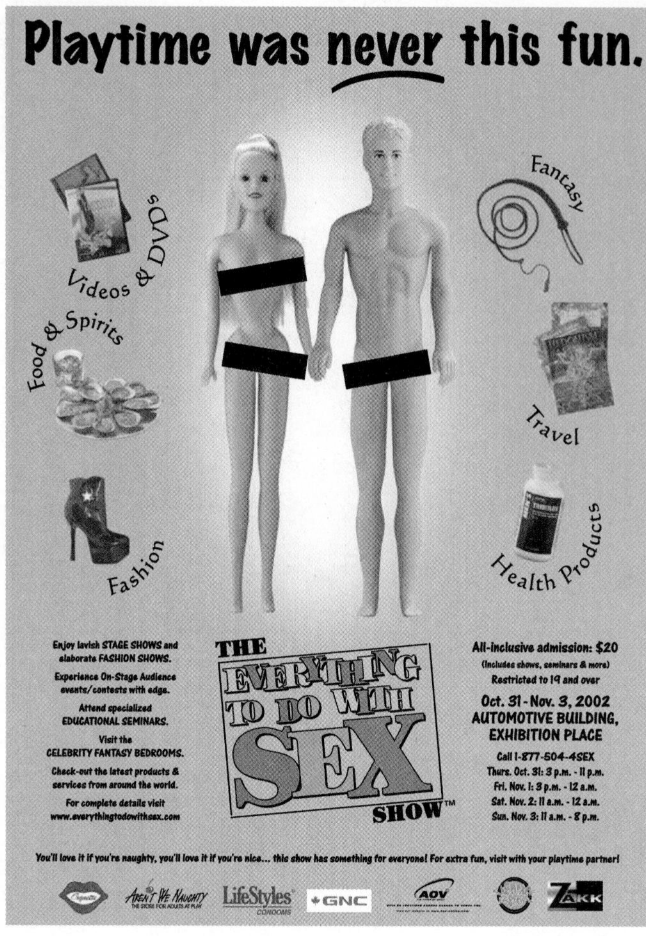

The Everything To Do With Sex Show.
This trade show attracts many thousands of visitors to Toronto. The exhibitors sell all kinds of erotic products, including toys and sex videos. The business of sex is obviously booming in Canada!

A few years ago, England's floppy-haired actor Hugh Grant was caught with a prostitute in a BMW on Hollywood's Sunset Boulevard. Why? His girlfriend was supermodel Elizabeth Hurley, who at the time was promoting the perfume called "Pleasures." Grant exemplified good looks, charm, innocence, and success. Still, he sought the sexual services of a woman for hire.

The World of Commercial Sex: A Disneyland for Adults

Sex as commerce runs the gamut from adult movie theatres and bookshops to strip shows, sex toy shops, escort/outcall services, "massage parlours," "900" telephone services, cybersex (e.g., sex over the internet), and the use of sex appeal in advertisements for a wide range of products. The "world of commercial sex is a kind of X-rated amusement park—Disneyland for Adults" (Edgley, 1989, p. 372). The types of sexual commerce seem unlimited. In Toronto, the annual Everything To Do With Sex Show has hundreds of exhibitors selling all kinds of products and services related to sex. Many thousands of people attend this event.

Prostitution

Prostitution is often called "the world's oldest profession"—for good reason. It can be traced at least to ancient Mesopotamia, where temple prostitution flourished. Prostitution also thrived in medieval Europe and during the sexually repressive Victorian period in the nineteenth century. Then, as now, the major motive for becoming a prostitute was economic. Many poor women were drawn to prostitution as a means of survival. In Victorian England, prostitution was widely regarded as a necessary outlet for men to satisfy their sexual appetites. It was widely held that women would not enjoy sex. Therefore, it was commonly believed that it was better for a man to visit a prostitute than to "soil" his wife with his carnal passions.

Prostitution The sale of sexual activity for money or goods of value, such as drugs.

STRIP CLUBS Stripping is a type of sex work. Women and men who dance in strip clubs typically refer to themselves as "dancers" and most would be extremely offended if anyone called them prostitutes. Many sex workers in strip clubs limit their activity to dancing and doffing their clothes. Others do "lap dances" or "table dances" during which they make contact with customers as they dance. Customers may buy the dance from the club and then also be expected to tip the stripper (Frank, 2002, 2003). Some strip clubs have private shows, "VIP rooms," and the like, where strippers may be alone with their customers. What happens in these private shows may be tightly regulated by the club or may depend on the size of the tip.

Many sex workers engage in that work only on a part-time and/or temporary basis. For example, in her study of female strippers, Jacqueline Lewis of the University

A World of Diversity

"PROSTITUTION" OR "SEX WORK"? WHAT'S IN A NAME?

Many prostitutes have redefined themselves as *sex workers,* and prostitution as *sex work* (Lucas, 2005). The new terms underscore the economic aspects of the work and are less laden with a history of lewdness and depravity. They have also caught on in the research literature. The Commercial Sex Information Service (CSIS) of Vancouver, British Columbia, explains the shift as follows:

> The terms *sex work* and *sex worker* have been coined by sex workers themselves to redefine commercial sex, not as the social or psychological characteristic of a class of women, but as an income-generating activity or form of employment for women and men. As such it can be considered along with other forms of economic activity. An employment or labor perspective is a necessary, if not sufficient, condition for making sex work a part of the mainstream debate on human, women's, and workers' rights at local, national, and international levels.
>
> The lack of international and local protection renders sex workers vulnerable to exploitation in the workplace, and to harassment or violence at the hands of employers, law enforcement officials, clients, and the public. The need for worker protection, including occupational health and safety provisions, is of particular relevance in the current context of HIV/AIDS.

Source: From Redefining Prostitution as Sex Work on the International Agenda *by Jo Bindman, Network of Sex Work Projects, 1997. Reprinted by kind permission Anti-Slavery International 2006.*

of Windsor (1998) distinguished between career and short-term, goal-oriented dancers. The latter group included several university students:

> And I looked at the salaries these people were making and it was, you know, a thousand dollars a night, some nights, and it was really, really substantially helping with their tuition. And these were people working on Master's degrees and Doctorates and all kinds of things and I thought, "Wow, if they can do this, hey, maybe I can." (Lewis, 1998, p. 59)

A recent Canadian trend is for women to take lessons in striptease from professional instructors. Striptease has become so mainstream that many fitness centres

Toronto dance instructor Nicole Arbour teaches striptease workshops at City Dance Corps. She also teaches pole dancing.

are offering classes in erotic dancing. Classes are also offered in pole dancing and belly dancing.

Prostitution and the Law in Canada

Canadian laws governing prostitution are confusing—while prostitution itself is legal, almost all the activities involved with it are illegal. The Criminal Code prohibits a number of activities related to prostitution, including (1) transporting or directing, or offering to transport or direct, another person to a common bawdy house (establishment within which acts of sex for payment occur), (2) keeping, being an inmate of, being found without lawful excuse in, or allowing a place to be used for the purpose of a common bawdy house, and (3) procuring and living off the avails of prostitution. In other words, it is against the law to engage in activities that facilitate prostitution, or to be in a house of prostitution.

Some Canadian cities, such as Edmonton, Vancouver, Calgary, Winnipeg, and Windsor, have attempted to regulate prostitution by licensing escorts and escort agencies. These cities require that owners of escort agencies and the escorts themselves register with the local police and pay a licensing fee. They are also required to keep records of clients' names and addresses. However, obtaining a city licence is no guarantee that these escort services will not face prosecution for engaging in prostitution-related activities.

University of Windsor researchers Eleanor Maticka-Tyndale, Jacqueline Lewis, and Megan Street (2005) have analyzed the process of licensing escorts in Windsor. When escorts and agencies were first given licences, there was a feeling that they would be treated as other legitimate businesses. The city bylaws purposely did not mention the word *sex* in their descriptions of the escort business. However, after obtaining their licences, the escorts felt that the police were treating them as undesirable businesses. They felt victimized when the police used entrapment techniques, such as encouraging the escort to negotiate a fee for sexual service and then charging them for engaging in illegal activities.

In 1983 the Canadian justice minister appointed a special committee (the Fraser Commission) to study pornography and prostitution and to make recommendations to Parliament. Although the committee recommended that prostitution offences be removed from the Criminal Code, the federal government instead brought in more restrictive legislation with the aim of decreasing street prostitution.

In order to make it easier for police forces to prosecute prostitutes as well as their clients, the Criminal Code was changed so that it became illegal to communicate with or stop a person in a public place (including in a motor vehicle) to obtain the sexual services of a prostitute. The new legislation was soon challenged as being inconsistent with the Canadian Charter of Rights and Freedoms. In 1990, the Supreme Court ruled that the freedom of expression as granted by the Charter could be limited because street solicitation caused too great a social nuisance. Nonetheless, while the new legislation did facilitate the prosecution of both prostitutes and clients, it did not in fact decrease street prostitution (Gemme, 1993).

The police and politicians have been particularly concerned about teenage prostitution. Accordingly, Parliament significantly increased penalties for clients who attempt to obtain the sexual services of a person under the age of 18. And in 1999 Alberta passed the Protection of Children Involved in Prostitution Act, which allows police or social workers to apprehend child prostitutes under the age of 18 and keep them in safe houses for up to 72 hours.

Police in Canada often use the strategy of entrapment to obtain convictions against prostitutes and their clients. Plain-clothes male officers pretend they are clients wanting sex—for example, by obtaining topless body rubs at massage studios—in order to determine whether sex is being sold on the premises. Similarly, female police officers will act as "decoys" by standing in a location frequented by street prostitutes. When a man approaches and suggests having sex for money, he is immediately arrested and charged with communicating for the purposes of prostitution.

In 2007 a court judge in Newmarket, Ontario, chastised a police officer who posed as a client at a massage parlour. The officer stripped naked and obtained a body massage from a female attendant, but stopped her when she went to put her hand on his penis to provide a manual release. The judge stated that the actions of the police officer were unnecessary and "outside a protocol of investigative techniques." The judge also dismissed charges against the massage parlour, because he believed that Canadians would not consider masturbation to be sexual (Pron, 2007).

This case illustrates the reality that there are a number of "grey" areas when it comes to the interpretation of laws regarding prostitution. Laws regarding prostitution are continually changing as are the interpretations of the law. As well, across the country, there are wide variations in the degree to which prostitution laws are being enforced by the police.

Police are less likely to entrap those who engage in homosexual prostitution (Gemme, 1993), possibly because male police officers are reluctant to act as decoys for potential male clients. However, the gay and lesbian communities face the possibility of arrest for other kinds of activities. For example, while investigating "Sperm Attack Mondays," where male dancers at a gay strip club would ejaculate on stage, Toronto police laid bawdy-house charges against 11 dancers and 4 customers. Although these were later dropped, the club and its owners were still charged. The police also raided a Toronto gay pornography bar and laid public indecency charges against men who were engaged in consensual sex in cubicles (Woods, 2000).

In recent years politicians and police forces have targeted the customers of prostitutes. For example, in 2005 the provincial government in Manitoba introduced legislation to suspend the driver's licences of men convicted of soliciting a prostitute.

Attempts over the years to legalize prostitution in Canada have all been resisted by government leaders. Because of concern over a high number of deaths among prostitutes in Vancouver and Edmonton, the Canadian Parliament voted in 2003 to establish a Subcommittee on Solicitation Laws. The mandate of this subcommittee was to review and recommend changes to prostitution laws in order to improve the safety of sex workers. The subcommittee heard from academic researchers, legal experts, and sex workers who presented well documented examples of how Canadian laws promote unsafe working conditions for sex workers. These delegations proposed several changes to the Criminal Code that would give sex workers safer work environments. The subcommittee presented its report, entitled "The Challenge of Change: A Study of Canada's Criminal Prostitution Laws," in December 2006. The report acknowledged the analysis of, and recommendations for, greater safety for sex workers as presented to the subcommittee by numerous witnesses. The subcommittee recommended that the federal government should reform current laws so that consensual sexual relations between adults, including sex for money, would not be criminalized. However, it did not offer specific recommendations to promote the safety of sex workers. Instead, the subcommittee focused mainly on the sexual exploitation of children and human trafficking.

The Conservative members of the subcommittee disagreed with the idea that prostitution should be decriminalized. Rather, they viewed prostitution as a degrading activity that no one would willingly consent to be involved in. This view indicates that while the Conservative party remains in power, laws regarding the criminalization of prostitution are likely to stay in place.

Frustrated with inaction on the part of the federal government, in 2007, a small group of lawyers, in collaboration with sex workers, launched constitutional challenges to prostitution laws. In Ontario the legal team led by Osgoode Hall law professor Alan Young worked with the Toronto-based Sex Professionals of Canada and, in British Columbia, the legal team led by Katrina Pacey of the Pivot Legal Society collaborated with the Downtown Eastside Sex Workers United Against Violence Society.

The underlying principle of the constitutional challenge is that Canadian prostitution laws contribute to violence against street sex workers and thus the harm caused by the laws outweighs the benefits to society. Three main provisions of the laws are challenged:

- Communication for the purpose of prostitution is challenged, because it prevents sex workers from screening potentially violent clients.
- The provision against bawdy houses is challenged, because it inhibits sex workers from working in an indoor environment which is safer than working on the streets.
- The provision against living off the avails of prostitution is challenged as being too broad, because it prevents sex workers from hiring security personnel such as escorts who in turn would hire drivers for the prostitutes. However, pimps who exploit sex workers would still be prosecuted.

John Schools

Some Canadian cities have established "john schools" for men who have no previous criminal record but who are charged with communicating for the purposes of prostitution. In return for attending the day-long school, charges against the clients are erased from the official court record. Typically, the men listen to presentations from street prostitutes about the negative effect that prostitution has had on them. They also receive lectures on sexually transmitted infections, and, in some instances, community representatives talk about the impact of street prostitution on their communities. The men are expected to provide a donation to help support the program (Fischer et al., 2002).

Canadian Attitudes Toward Prostitution

The majority of Canadians are in favour of legalizing prostitution. According to the 1998 Compas poll, two-thirds of respondents support legalizing prostitution if it is regulated by health authorities. Church attendance is one of the strongest predictors

Amsterdam's Red-Light District. *Amsterdam's red-light district is one of the city's tourist attractions. Prostitution is legal there and regulated. Condoms are a must. Tourists and locals stroll there by the canals and "window shop." Prim grandmothers sometimes join the audiences at the live sex shows.*

of attitudes toward prostitution, with twice as many of those who attend once a week or more (52%) believing that prostitution should be kept completely against the law, compared with 26% of those who do not attend church once a week or more. Interestingly, people in their twenties or younger are also less accepting of prostitution (Compas, 1998), perhaps because they tend to be more idealistic about relationships. However, most Canadians still personally disapprove of prostitution, with 88% feeling that it is unacceptable to pay for sex (*Maclean's*, 1998).

Streetwalkers Prostitutes who solicit customers on the streets.

Pimps Men who serve as agents for prostitutes and live off their earnings.

Types of Female Prostitutes

Female prostitutes—commonly called hookers, whores, working girls, or escorts—are usually classified according to the settings in which they work. The major types of prostitutes today are streetwalkers; brothel or "house" prostitutes, many of whom work in massage parlours; and "escorts" or call girls (many prostitutes today have their customers "let their fingers do the walking through the Yellow Pages").

STREETWALKERS **Streetwalkers** occupy the bottom rung in the hierarchy of prostitutes. In Canada, about 20% of prostitutes work on the streets (Lowman & Atchison, 2006). They earn the lowest incomes and are usually the least desirable. They also incur the greatest risk of abuse by customers and **pimps**. A study of street prostitutes in western Canada found that many experienced violence not only from clients and pimps but also from other streetwalkers, intimate partners, and police (Nixon et al., 2002).

Between the years 1991 and 2004, 171 female sex workers in Canada were murdered and almost all were streetwalkers. Serial murderers typically target streetwalkers. One of the most publicized was the British Columbia killer Robert Pickton, who in 2007 was sentenced to prison for a mandatory term of at least 25 years for murdering several streetwalkers. In Edmonton, the bodies of 20 sex workers have been found since 1983 and police suspect a serial killer is the culprit. Nevertheless, it should be noted that only a small minority of clients commit violent acts against streetwalkers (Lowman & Atchison, 2006).

Streetwalkers operate in the open. They are thus more likely than other prostitutes to draw attention to themselves and risk arrest (Shaver, 2005). To avoid arrest, streetwalkers may be indirect about their services. They may ask passersby if they are interested in a "good time" or some "fun" rather than offering sex per se.

There is the stereotype of the prostitute as a sexually unresponsive woman who feigns sexual arousal with johns while she keeps one eye glued to the clock. Most street prostitutes in a Philadelphia sample, however, reported that some forms of sex with customers were "very satisfying" (Savitz & Rosen, 1988). More than 60% of the prostitutes reported achieving orgasm with customers at least occasionally. Most prostitutes also reported that they had enjoyable sexual relationships in their private lives and were regularly orgasmic.

In most locales, penalties for prostitution involve small fines or short jail terms. Many police departments, besieged by drug peddling and violent crimes, consider prostitution a "minor" or "nuisance" crime. Many prostitutes find the criminal justice system a revolving door. They pay the fine. They spend a night or two in jail. They return to the streets.

Some streetwalkers support a pimp, especially those who are younger and who have less than high school education (Shaver, 2005). A pimp acts as lover–father–companion–master. He provides streetwalkers with protection, bail, and sometimes room and board, in exchange for a high percentage of their earnings, often more than 90%. Prostitutes are often physically abused by their pimps, who may use threats and beatings as a means of control (Williamson & Cluse-Tolar, 2002).

Streetwalkers who work hotels and conventions generally hold a higher status than those who work the streets or bars. Clients are typically conventioneers or businessmen travelling away from home. Hotel prostitutes must be skilled in conveying

Streetwalkers in Mexico City.

subtle messages to potential clients without attracting the attention of hotel management or security. They usually provide sexual services in the client's hotel room. Some hotel managers will tolerate known prostitutes (usually for a payoff under the table), so long as the women conduct themselves discreetly.

BROTHEL PROSTITUTION Many brothel prostitutes occupy a middle position in the hierarchy of prostitutes, between streetwalkers on one side and call girls on the other. They work in a brothel or—more commonly today—in a massage parlour.

MASSAGE PARLOURS Many massage parlours are legitimate establishments that provide massage—and only massage—to customers. Masseuses and masseurs are licensed by provincial governments, and laws prohibit them from offering sexual services. Many localities require that the masseuse or masseur keep certain parts of her or his body clothed and not touch the client's genitals.

Many massage parlours serve as fronts for prostitution, however. In these establishments, clients typically pay fees for a standard massage and then tip the workers for sexual extras.

To avoid massage parlour regulations, some owners have obtained licences claiming they are holistic health centres or aromatherapy centres. In May 2005 the *Toronto Star* ran front-page exposés of the "holistic health centre" industry, with headlines such as "What can Toronto do about sex dens?" At one of the holistic centres the reporters visited, the manager outlined the additional options available beyond the $40 entrance fee: $20 for a topless massage, $40 for a nude massage, and $60 for a body slide (the nude masseuse slides herself over the naked body of the client). Many places also offer a nude reverse in which clients can massage the naked masseuse (Cribb & Brazao, 2005). The articles created a furor at City Hall, and Toronto City Council instructed its licensing staff and police to clamp down on agencies that were not legitimate health centres.

Massage parlour workers generally offer to perform manual stimulation of the penis ("a local" or a "rub and tug"). Most do not offer oral sex or coitus ("full service"), mistakenly believing this will protect them from prosecution.

ESCORT SERVICES If Hugh Grant had hired an "escort," we would probably never have learned of it. Conventioneers and businessmen are more likely to turn to the listings for "massage" and "escort services" in the telephone directory or under the personal ads in local newspapers than to seek hotel prostitutes. Services that provide "outcall" send masseuses (or masseurs) or escorts to the hotel room.

Escort services are typically (but not always) fronts for prostitution. Escort services are found in every major Canadian city and present themselves as legitimate businesses providing escorts for men. Indeed, one will find female companionship for corporate functions and for unattached men travelling away from home under "escort services." Many escort services provide only prostitution, however, and clients of other escort services sometimes negotiate sexual services after formal escort duties are completed—or in their stead.

Prostitutes who work for escort services often come from middle-class backgrounds and are well educated—the better to hold their own in social conversation. Escort services may establish arrangements with legitimate companies to provide "escorts" for visiting customers or potential clients.

CALL GIRLS **Call girls** occupy the highest rungs on the social ladder of female prostitution. Many of them overlap with escorts. Call girls tend to be the most attractive and well-educated prostitutes and tend to charge more for their services. Many come from middle-class backgrounds. Unlike other types of prostitutes, call girls usually work on their own. Thus they need not split their income with a pimp, escort service, or massage parlour. Consequently, they can afford a luxurious lifestyle when business is good, living in expensive neighbourhoods and wearing stylish clothes, and they can be more selective about the customers they will accept.

Call girls Prostitutes who arrange for their sexual contacts by telephone. *Call* refers both to telephone calls and to being "on call."

Call girls may escort their clients to dinner and social functions, providing not only sex but also charming and gracious conversation (Sanders, 2005). They give clients the feeling that they are important and attractive. They may simulate sexual pleasure and create the illusion that time does not matter. It does, of course. To the call girl, as to other entrepreneurs, time is money.

Call girls may receive clients in their apartments ("incalls") or make "outcalls" to clients' homes and hotels. To protect themselves from police and abusive clients, call girls may insist on seeing a client's business card or learning his home telephone number before personal contact is made. They may investigate whether the customer is in fact the person he purports to be.

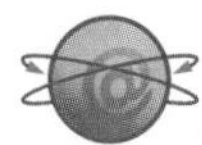

Prostitutes' Education Network
An information service about legislative and cultural issues that affect prostitutes and other sex workers.

www.bayswan.org/penet.html

Support Groups for Sex Workers

Across Canada there are a number of organizations providing support services to sex workers, such as legal aid offered by the Pivot Legal Society in Vancouver. A major Canadian resource is Maggie's & the Prostitutes' Safe Sex Project of Toronto, the first education project in Canada run by sex workers. The project provides information about health promotion, AIDS and STI prevention, Canadian law, and dangerous clients to sex workers. Maggie's has been a model for sex worker peer education projects internationally.

International Human Trafficking

Human trafficking of sex workers is a major global enterprise. Many Asian and Eastern European women are lured to big cities in developing countries or to the West by promises of the good life (Rubenson et al., 2005). Upon arrival, they find themselves enslaved in brothels—working for tips and not allowed to leave.

In Toronto in 2008, six people were arrested for trafficking after police were informed that women from Eastern Europe had been lured to Canada with the promise of modelling jobs. Instead, their passports were taken away from them and they were confined and forced to work in the sex trade (Piercy, 2008).

Characteristics of Female Prostitutes

No single factor explains women's entry into prostitution. Yet poverty and sexual and/or physical abuse figure prominently in the backgrounds of many prostitutes (Carter & Dalla, 2006). They often come from conflict-ridden or single-parent homes in poor urban areas or rural farming communities.

Poverty accounts for the entry of young women into prostitution in many countries. In some Third World nations, such as Thailand, many rural, impoverished parents in effect sell daughters to recruiters who place them in brothels in cities (Kristof, 2006). Many of the women send home whatever money they can and also work hard to try to pay off the procurers and break free of their financial bonds.

In Canada and the United States, many initiates into street prostitution are teenage runaways. While some come from middle-class or affluent homes, others were reared in poverty. Family discord and dysfunction frequently set the stage for their entry into street life and prostitution (Carter & Dalla, 2006). Many teenage runaways perceive life on the street—despite its dangers—to be the only possible escape from family strife and conflict, or from the physical, emotional, or sexual abuse they suffer at home. Teenage runaways with marginal skills and limited means of support may find few alternatives to prostitution. It is not long before the teenage runaway is approached by a pimp or a john. A study of 149 teenage runaways in Toronto found that 67% of the boys and 82% of the girls who had been away from home for more than a year had been offered money to engage in sexual activity with an adult (Hartman et al., 1987).

In a study of street prostitutes in Montreal, Robert Gemme (1998) of the University of Quebec found that 44% had been sexually abused and 33% had been sexually assaulted prior to becoming involved in the sex trade.

Not all sexually abused children become prostitutes, of course. In one sample of predominantly female 16- to 18-year-olds who had been sexually abused, 12% became involved in prostitution (Seng, 1989). A more recent study of female street youth in Montreal found that those who became involved in prostitution were no more likely to have experienced childhood sexual abuse than those who did not become prostitutes (Weber et al., 2004).

Abused children who run away from home are much more likely to become involved in prostitution than those who do not (Seng, 1989). Runaways are also more likely to become drug and alcohol abusers. In the Montreal study (Weber et al., 2004), females who were heavy drug users were more likely to become involved in street prostitution.

Interestingly, in the Montreal study, having a female sex partner was one of the strongest predictors of female street youths becoming prostitutes. This was especially true if the female sex partner was also involved in prostitution (Weber et al., 2004). More research is needed to determine the role that having a female sex partner may play in initiating young street females into prostitution.

It should be noted that the great majority of studies on prostitutes have focused on street prostitutes, and that these findings may not reflect the characteristics of other categories of prostitutes, such as call girls. Frances Shaver (2002) of Concordia University in Montreal has conducted several field studies of prostitutes in Canada, and believes that much of the material on prostitutes overstates the disadvantaged backgrounds of the sex workers. As noted above, for example, some university students may engage in some form of sex work such as stripping because the pay is better than for many other kinds of jobs (Lewis, 1998). Shaver (1996a) argues that researchers who study prostitutes from a deviance perspective typically ignore the fact that some prostitutes voluntarily choose to enter this business and do not feel that they are victims. According to Shaver, they feel they have a lot of control over their work in that "the prostitute sets the price, chooses the client and has the last say as to when, how and even if sex takes place" (p. 219). Shaver believes that many of the problems associated with prostitution would diminish if it were recognized as a legitimate work profession.

Customers of Female Prostitutes

Many prostitutes refer to a customer as a "john." Men who use female prostitutes come from all walks of life and represent all socioeconomic and racial groups. One of the most publicized was Eliot Spitzer, former governor of the state of New York. He was forced to resign as governor when his spending of thousands of dollars on high-priced call girls became public knowledge.

A Vancouver survey of 500 men arrested for soliciting prostitutes found that the johns were in many respects similar to other Canadian men (Kennedy et al., 2003). They ranged in age from 18 to 92, with an average age of 38. More than half were married or in a serious relationship. Their level of income, education, and ethnic background were similar to the Vancouver population. On average the men had

Innovative Canadian Research

MEDIA STEREOTYPES OF SEX WORKERS

University of Victoria researchers Helga Hallgrimsdottir, Rachel Phillips, and Cecilia Benoit (2006) compared media portrayals of sex workers with accounts from sex workers of their personal backgrounds and experiences. The researchers wanted to demonstrate how media portrayals are often inaccurate and present stereotypes that encourage the stigmatization of sex workers. The researchers analyzed articles on sex workers in the Victoria *Times Colonist* newspaper for the years from 1980 to 2004 to illustrate how media portrayals of sex workers have changed over that period.

In general, the newspaper negatively described sex workers as criminals who were morally lost and the source of major social problems, such as drug addiction and violence. They were seen as a bad influence on morality and also as a source of sexually transmitted diseases. Most of the articles focused on streetwalkers, ignoring male sex workers.

There was a change in blame attribution over that time period. Whereas sex workers were seen in the early 1980s as wicked women who should be punished for their sexual transgressions, they were presented in 2004 as victims who had been trapped into sex work by pimps or international sex slave traders and were at the mercy of their clients. In the latter years, the newspaper included more stories about child and adolescent prostitution. For the entire time period of the survey, sex workers were presented as being emotionally damaged.

Hallgrimsdottir et al. (2006) compared a sample of sex workers with these representations. Contrary to media stereotypes of sex workers being portrayed as young girls brought to Canada by international traffickers, the sex workers in the survey had an average age of 32 years and the great majority were born in Canada. One-quarter of the female sex workers were caring for dependent children, a fact not commonly noted in the media. However, many did come from unstable family backgrounds, which does coincide with the media reports.

There were also media distortions regarding why women entered into sex work. The newspaper articles said that sex workers were either forced into sex work or turned to it to finance drug addiction. Hardly any of the sex workers surveyed said they had been forced into the occupation and only a minority said they entered into sex work to pay for their drug addictions. The majority said they voluntarily chose to become sex workers for economic reasons and because they had the opportunity to do so. The newspaper articles definitely did not portray sex work as a career choice for sex workers, although most of the sex workers did see it as an occupation. As with other jobs, there were a diversity of feelings among sex workers regarding their work, yet most of those surveyed felt that the benefits of sex work outweighed the costs.

Research with sex workers in three Maritime cities (Jeffrey & MacDonald, 2006) supports the findings of Hallgrimsdottir et al. (2006). Most of the Maritime sex workers stated they carefully decided which economic choices were available to them and then voluntarily decided that sex work was a better choice than the alternatives, such as living on welfare or working at minimum-wage jobs.

used the services of prostitutes 19 times. Seventy percent reported that no one close to them knew they visited prostitutes. They did not differ from a comparison group of university men in sexual attitudes and sex drive (Kennedy et al., 2003).

Most Canadian studies of clients of prostitutes have used samples from john schools discussed earlier. However, these samples are biased in that they are based on men arrested for soliciting streetwalkers. Vancouver researchers John Lowman and Chris Atchison (2006) obtained a broader range of prostitutes' clients. One-half had a regular sex partner or spouse and two-thirds of these men said they were either satisfied or very happy with their relationship. The most common reason given for their first visit to a sex worker was their availability and visibility. The second reason given was that their decision for doing so was spontaneous.

Most patrons are "occasional johns." Examples include travelling salesmen or military personnel who are stopping over in town without their regular sex partners. Men are more interested than women in sexual novelty or variety (Barash & Lipton, 2001; Schmitt, 2003), and variety may provide a major motive for occasional johns.

"Habitual johns" use prostitutes as their major or exclusive sexual outlet. Some habitual johns have never established an intimate sexual relationship. Some wealthy men who wish to avoid intimate relationships habitually patronize call girls.

Whore–madonna complex A rigid stereotyping of women as either sinners or saints.

"Compulsive johns" feel driven to prostitutes to meet some psychological or sexual need. They may repeatedly resolve to stop using prostitutes but feel unable to control their compulsions. Some compulsive johns engage in acts of fetishism or transvestism with prostitutes but would not inform their wives or girlfriends of their variant interests. Some men who are compulsive users of prostitutes suffer from a **whore–madonna complex**. They see women as either sinners or saints. They can permit themselves to enjoy sex only with prostitutes or would ask only prostitutes to engage in acts such as fellatio. They see marital coitus as a duty or an obligation.

While the risks faced by sex workers have been openly discussed in the research literature and the media, the potential risks faced by customers have been largely ignored, other than the risk of contracting a sexually transmitted infection. In Canada there is a stigma attached to paying for the services of a sex worker. Negative publicity resulting from hiring a sex worker could result in the loss of one's job and/or the breakup of a marriage.

Vancouver researchers John Lowman and Chris Atchison (2006) found that two-thirds of a sample of male clients of sex workers had been victimized on at least one occasion. The most common types of victimization were not receiving services they had paid for and being robbed of possessions or money. Some were assaulted by the sex worker or an accomplice.

There can also be other kinds of financial exploitation. A married stockbroker in British Columbia began an affair with a stripper that lasted for a number of years. When the relationship deteriorated, the stripper threatened to tell the man's wife about the affair unless he gave her money. The stockbroker ended up giving more than $1 million to the stripper (Waldie, 2007).

MOTIVES FOR HIRING PROSTITUTES There appear to be six common motives for using prostitutes:

1. *Sex without negotiation.* The research on sex differences suggests strongly that men have a stronger sex drive than women (Peplau, 2003). Sex work evens things up, making women available at the whim of the man. By turning to prostitutes, men need not spend the time, effort, and money involved in dating and getting to know someone for the sake of sexual activity.
2. *Sex without emotional commitment.* Prostitutes require no emotional commitment from the man other than payment for services rendered. The prostitute will not call him at home or expect to be called in return.
3. *Sex for eroticism and variety.* Many prostitutes offer "something extra" in the way of novel or kinky sex—for example, oral sex, use of costumes (such as leather attire), and S&M rituals (such as bondage and discipline or spanking). Men may desire such activity but be unable to obtain it with their regular partners. They may even be afraid to mention the idea. Prostitutes may also be attractive to men who seek variety or novelty in sex partners.
4. *Prostitution as a social outlet.* In the nineteenth and early twentieth centuries, the brothel served not only as a place to obtain sex but also as a kind of "stopping off" place between home and work. Sex was secondary to the companionship and amiable conversation that men would find in brothels. Similarly, women who attend male strip clubs enjoy "bonding" with their friends at the clubs as well as the stripping itself (Montemurro et al., 2003).
5. *Sex away from home.* The greatest contemporary use of prostitution occurs among men who are away from home, such as businessmen at conventions and sports fans at out-of-town sporting events.
6. *Difficulty attracting a partner.* People who have physical disabilities or disfiguring conditions sometimes seek the services of prostitutes because of difficulty attracting other partners or because of fears of rejection. Some lonely men who lack sex partners may seek prostitutes as substitutes.

Sex workers are also used to promote business transactions. Businesspeople may take clients to a strip club or may hire an escort for a client. In 2008 a U.S. defence contractor was sentenced to prison for bribing a federal congressman. He was convicted of using cash, gifts, and the services of prostitutes to obtain $90 million worth of government contracts. In 2007 German car maker Volkswagen was charged with hiring expensive call girls as a means of servicing and bribing suppliers as well as Volkswagen's own union leaders. Sex can be used as a means of exchange in a diversity of situations. For example, in 2007, a U.S. border guard in Blaine, Washington, was charged with letting a Canadian woman bring drugs into the U.S. in exchange for sex.

Hustlers Men who engage in prostitution with male customers.

Scores Customers of hustlers.

Male Prostitution

Male prostitution includes both male–male and male–female activities. Male prostitutes who service female clients—gigolos—are rare. Gigolos' clients are typically older, wealthy, unattached women. Gigolos may serve as escorts or as surrogate sons for the women, and they may or may not offer sexual services.

An interesting variation of male prostitution involves female tourists from developed countries who travel to developing countries and have sex with local men. Unlike female sex workers, the beach boys who make money from their relations with female tourists do not openly demand a fixed sum of money. Rather, the request for money and other goods is made in a disguised, subtle manner. (See Chapter 12 for a more detailed discussion.)

The overwhelming majority of male prostitutes service gay men. Men who engage in male prostitution are called **hustlers**. Their patrons are typically called **scores**. They typically have less than a grade 11 education and few, if any, marketable skills. The majority come from working-class and lower-class backgrounds. Many male prostitutes, like many female prostitutes, come from families troubled by conflict, alcoholism, and/or physical or sexual abuse (Minichiello et al., 2001).

Hustlers may be gay, bisexual, or heterosexual in orientation. In a large-scale Australian study, half of the male prostitutes surveyed described themselves as gay (Minichiello et al., 2001). About one-third (31%) said they were bisexual, and 5.5% considered themselves "straight."

Frances Shaver (1996a) has compared male and female street prostitutes in Montreal. Half of the women were working for a pimp, but none of the men were. As well, more of the women indicated that sex work was their only source of income. The women serviced twice as many (28.5) clients per week as the men (14.5). However, the men typically spent about twice as long with each client (40 minutes versus 20) and were more likely to include nongenital touching as well as kissing in their services. Finally, the women were much more likely to experience sexual and physical assault as well as robbery. That female prostitutes face greater danger than males do is also reflected in murder statistics. Between the years 1991 and 1995, for example, of the 63 reported murders of sex workers in Canada, 60 were women (Allman, 1999).

Hustlers typically are not attached to a pimp. They generally make contacts with clients in gay bars and social clubs, or by working the streets in areas frequented by gay men. They typically learn to hustle from watching other hustlers ply their trade. Various kinds of male sex workers have been identified (Minichiello et al., 2001):

- *Strippers* dance and strip. Patrons—female and male—may fondle them or sometimes have sex with them.
- *Kept boys* have relationships with older, economically secure men who keep them in an affluent lifestyle. The older male, or "sugar daddy," often assumes a parental role.

- *Call boys*, like call girls, may work on their own or through an agency or escort service.
- *Punks* are prison inmates who are used sexually by other inmates and rewarded with protection or goods such as cigarettes and drugs.
- *Drag prostitutes* are transvestites or presurgical male-to-female transsexuals who impersonate female prostitutes and have sex with men who are frequently unaware of their gender. Some drag prostitutes limit themselves to fellatio on their customers to conceal their gender. Others take the passive role in anal sex (Boles & Elifson, 1994).
- *Brothel prostitutes* are rarer than their female counterparts. Fewer houses of male prostitution exist.
- *Bar hustlers and street hustlers*, like their female counterparts, have the lowest status and ply their trade in gay bars or on streets frequented by gay passersby. Street hustlers are the most common and typically the youngest subtype. They are also the most visible and consequently the ones most likely to draw the attention of the police.

By and large, male prostitution is an adolescent enterprise. The younger the hustler, the higher the fee he can command and the more tricks he can turn. By the time he reaches his mid-twenties, he may be forced to engage in sexual activities he might have rejected when younger or to seek clients in sleazier places.

Why do men purchase the services of male prostitutes? In a British Columbia study, clients of male sex workers generally fell into one of three categories: men who kept their desire to have sex with other men hidden from others; men who wanted to have sex with younger men; and men who could not attract regular male sex partners (Allman, 1999).

STIs and Prostitution

In Montreal, about a third of both male and female prostitutes reported that they had had an STI within the previous two years (Shaver, 1996b). All the women said they always used condoms with clients when engaging in vaginal or anal sex, and 97% always used a condom with oral sex. Among the male prostitutes, 90% reported using a condom with clients during anal sex but only 50% used a condom with oral sex. (Condoms were used far less often with men who were not clients.) A more recent study of Montreal male street youth involved in sex work had similar findings, with many not using condoms, especially when having oral sex (Haley et al., 2004).

In a Vancouver study of female sex workers at massage parlours, 5% reported having had an STI within the previous six months (Johnson et al., 2007). Inconsistent condom use was reported by 9% of the sex workers. A key reason for inconsistent condom use was the financial incentive with some clients who offered more money to have sex without a condom. Also, some sex workers gave in to persistent verbal pressure from a client not to use a condom. Some sex workers of Asian background lacked knowledge about the proper use of condoms.

The sex workers were at greater risk of STI transmission from having sex with people who were not clients, with 63% reporting inconsistent condom use with their lovers. With nonclients, the sex workers believed they were protected, because they felt that their partners were monogamous. Another reason given for non-use of condoms was the feeling that condoms belonged at work and not in a relationship.

A particular risk factor for HIV infection is unprotected anal intercourse. Among female street youth in Montreal, those who engaged in prostitution were twice as likely to have experienced anal intercourse as those who did not engage in prostitution. Many did not consistently use condoms when having anal intercourse (Weber et al., 2002).

A World of Diversity

THE WEST GETS WILDER—A BROTHEL FOR WOMEN

By Mireya Navarro, The New York Times Online

Picture a pleasure oasis in the Nevada desert, a collection of luxurious bungalows featuring bedrooms with fireplaces where sexual fantasies and desires are catered to. Starting at $250 an hour.

But at this house, Heidi's Stud Farm, the prostitutes will be hunky men and the patrons women. Heidi Fleiss, former Hollywood madam, is planning the all-male brothel on 60 acres in Nevada, where prostitution is often legal. "The times have changed so much, with women in control," Ms. Fleiss, 40, said in a telephone interview from Nevada on Thursday. "Women make more money. They are more powerful. And it's a lonely world."

Is that possible? Are American women really ready for what will be among the first brothels of its kind? Will they pay for sex as a no-fuss transaction?

Women have become major consumers of pornographic films and Web sites in recent years, largely because of the privacy afforded by the Internet. But women are also openly displaying interest in all things sexual, from the groups that gather for sex toy parties in private homes to the ritual of celebrating birthdays, bachelorette parties, and even divorces at male strip clubs.

Though some of these sexual outlets are just erotic entertainment, some women seek more.

Nevada already has brothels. Heidi Fleiss plans to add another, although hers would not be of the conventional sort.

"We get offered all the time, 'How much for this guy?'" said Dan Remington, an owner of *Hollywood Men*, a show of male strippers in Hollywood. "We don't do that." On a recent Saturday night more than 100 women screamed, hollered, and gawked at a performance of *Hollywood Men*, as well-toned guys peeled down to their G-strings. The crowd included both young and older women. Would they drive or fly to Heidi's Stud Farm in Crystal, Nevada, near Pahrump, about 88 miles northwest of Las Vegas, to indulge their wild side in a brothel?

"I would do it just for the experience," said Mayra Barreras, 20, a customer service representative for a mortgage company who came to the club with three friends.

"Let's face it," said Bianca Nichole, 19, a college student majoring in computer science, "there's a lot of unhappy women out there. If I were in a bad relationship, and I felt I needed something, I would go too."

Gina Pinon, a college student who was celebrating her birthday at the strip club, said she did not believe she would ever pay for sex "because I could go out and get it for free." Then she added: "But some women would pay for it, women who are in unhappy situations or who are into fantasies. I'd say: 'Go for it. Have your fun.' If men can do it, women can do it too."

Some sex experts and psychologists said a brothel for women is overdue. Many more women would avail themselves of a professional if it were legal, some experts argue, for reasons not unlike those of the men who frequent prostitutes. A regulated business that does criminal and medical screening of its workers would find a market in women, said Patti Britton, the president-elect of the American Association of Sexuality Educators, Counselors and Therapists.

Source: From "The West Gets Wilder—A Brothel for Women" by Mireya Navarro, The New York Times *Online, January 8, 2006.*

Sex with prostitutes is the most important factor in the male–female transmission of HIV in Africa, where the infection is spread predominantly via male–female sexual intercourse. In Canada and the United States, some prostitutes and their clients and other sex partners inject drugs and share contaminated needles. A Canadian study found that sex workers who inject drugs are less likely to use condoms and more likely to be infected with HIV (Allman, 1999). HIV may be spread by unprotected sex from prostitutes to customers and then to the customers' wives or lovers.

SHOULD PROSTITUTION BE LEGALIZED? As a counterpoint to the transmission of HIV and other STIs by many street prostitutes, it can be noted that

Pornography Written, visual, or audiotaped material that is sexually explicit and produced for purposes of eliciting or enhancing sexual arousal. Today, pornography has a negative connotation and is typically associated with SEM that is violent and/or degrading.

Prurient Tending to excite lust; lewd.

in the Netherlands and parts of Nevada, where prostitution is legal and carefully regulated by the state, transmission of STIs is extremely low (Wagenaar, 2006). In Nevada, condoms have been required since 1986, and prostitutes are tested regularly. Not one case of HIV has been reported to have been transmitted in a Nevada brothel (Caporaletti, 2006).

Legalization of prostitution has benefits beyond ensuring regular testing for STIs in licensed brothels. It also turns prostitutes, other brothel employees, and brothel owners into taxpayers, and provides safer venues for prostitution—both for prostitutes and for their customers. Safer settings might help sever some of the links between prostitution and drug abuse. Moreover, brothel owners would be required to obtain proof of age of sex workers.

Opponents of legalization argue on both moral and practical grounds (Grenz, 2006; Munro, 2006). Many traditionalists and feminists alike find it morally reprehensible that civilized societies would legalize practices that degrade women and the value of the family. Moreover, given prostitutes' frequent histories of abuse and sexual exploitation, they wonder whether it can be claimed that prostitutes—even as adults—are ever truly making "free" decisions to enter the world's oldest profession.

Sexually Explicit Material

Sexually explicit material (SEM) is found nearly everywhere. In addition to the adult magazines and the DVD rentals, millions of people use Google or Yahoo to search for pornography on the internet or to rent pornographic films via cable or satellite dish. People are also downloading pornography onto their camera cellphones and video MP3 players.

SEM is typically used to elicit or enhance sexual arousal, often as a masturbation aid (Boies, 2002; Strager, 2003). SEM may also be used by couples to enhance sexual arousal during lovemaking. Some physicians recommend that couples with erectile dysfunction use SEM to help them become aroused. Many couples find that a sexy video, DVD, or cable TV movie enlivens their sexual appetite or suggests novel techniques.

What Is Pornographic?

Webster's Deluxe Unabridged Dictionary defines **pornography** as "writing, pictures, etc., intended to arouse sexual desire." The inclusion of the word *intended* places the determination of what is pornographic in the mind of the person composing the work. Applying this definition makes it all but impossible to determine what is pornographic. If a filmmaker admits that he or she wanted to arouse the audience sexually, we may judge the work to be pornographic even if no naked bodies or explicit sex scenes are shown. On the other hand, explicit representations of people engaged in sexual activity would not be pornographic if the work was intended as an artistic expression rather than created for its **prurient** value. Many works that were once prohibited in Canada because of explicit sexual content, such as the novels *Tropic of Cancer* by Henry Miller and *Lady Chatterley's Lover* by D. H. Lawrence, are now generally considered literary works rather than excursions into pornography.

Art or Obscenity?
Eric Fischl is a mainstream artist, yet some of his subject matter has been labelled obscene by some critics.

Some people oppose pornography on moral grounds. Others oppose pornography because it portrays women in degrading and dehumanizing roles, as sex objects who are subservient to men's wishes, as sexually insatiable nymphomaniacs, or as sexual masochists who enjoy being raped and violated. Moreover, some people hold that depictions of women in sexually subordinate roles may encourage men to treat them as sex objects and increase the potential for rape (Itzin, 2002). In Canada and the United States, efforts to censor pornography were particularly powerful in the 1980s. These censorship efforts continue today, as seen in the nearby A World of Diversity box.

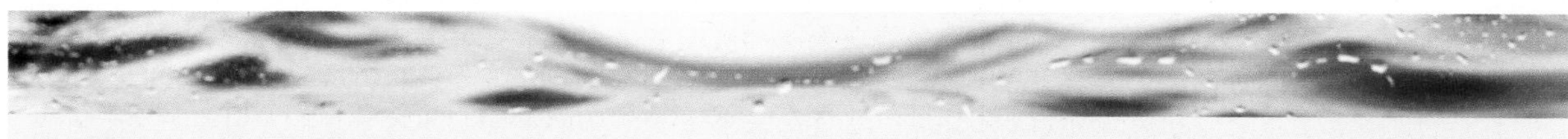

A World of Diversity

SHOULD THIS PHOTO BE CENSORED?

In the spring of 2005 a group of feminists in Guelph, Ontario, were disturbed when *Echo* magazine placed a close-up picture of a woman diving into a pool on the cover of its *Hot Summer Guide* issue. *Echo* is a Guelph publication that advertises local events and happenings.

The woman diving into the pool is Melanie Gillis, the wife of the publisher of the magazine, who took the picture. Gillis is a Guelph photographer who specializes in maternity and family photography. She also does nude photography.

The feminist group upset by the photo removed several copies of the magazine from downtown display boxes and destroyed them. They also removed the cover from several other copies. One of the women left a phone message at the office of *Echo* explaining that the photo objectified women and thereby contributed to misogyny. They found the photo to be "horribly offensive" and "disgusting" (Gillis, 2005).

Following the incident, a number of *Echo* readers wrote letters to the editor deploring the censorship actions. Here are two excerpts from these letters:

> It looks more like you oppressed *Echo*. Not only did you oppress *Echo* but you oppressed everyone in downtown Guelph who relies on the publication for info on coming events and local news.

> Ever heard of having fun! I hate you feminist types who assume that every pretty woman out there who doesn't trash men all the time is dumb, and allowing herself to be objectified. . . . You do not have the right to censor what other people read. . . . People like you are anti-feminist because you remove choice and ridicule women for choosing a path that you would not have taken.

Should This Photo Be Censored?
Some feminists in Guelph destroyed copies of* Echo *magazine for publishing this cover photo. They claimed it objectified women. Do you think they were right to have removed and destroyed copies of the magazine?

What do you think about the reasons given for censoring the photo? Do you feel the actions of the feminist group were justified?

This story of censorship is not an isolated one. Almost every day in Canada people are making decisions about what is or is not appropriate for us to see or read.

Source: Freeman, N. (2005, June 16). Blatant Objectification: Echo's Hot Summer Issue Crossed the Line. Echo, *pp. 10–11; Gillis, M. (2005, June 16). It's My Ass.* Echo, *p. 11.*

Canadian Trends

SEM AND THE LAW IN CANADA

Laws against obscenity provide the legal framework for outlawing the dissemination of pornography. Because the definition of obscenity relies on offending people or running afoul of community standards, that which is deemed obscene may vary from person to person and from culture to culture. The word *obscene* extends beyond sexual matters. One could judge TV violence or beer commercials obscene because they are personally offensive or are offensive to women, even if such depictions do not meet legal criteria for obscenity.

The Supreme Court of Canada has been strongly influenced by the feminist argument that pornography is exploitative of and degrading to women. For example, the Women's Legal Education and Action Fund argues that pornography causes violence against women, a view that was used by the Supreme Court to uphold the right of censorship in the *Regina v. Butler* case. This 1992 case concerned the police raid of a Winnipeg store that sold sexually explicit videos. In his appeal to the Supreme Court, Donald Butler, the owner of the store, argued that according to the Charter of Rights and Freedoms he had a right to freedom of expression.

In upholding the constitutionality of the federal obscenity law, the Supreme Court argued that for a work to be considered "obscene" there must be "undue" exploitation of sex. A "community standard of tolerance" test must be applied in order to determine whether undue exploitation had occurred. The courts must consider whether a community would accept or tolerate others being exposed to these materials, taking into consideration the possibility of harm that may result from such exposure. A key factor is whether the exploitation of sex is seen to be degrading or dehumanizing to society in general and in particular to women.

In the *Butler* case, the Supreme Court devised three categories for obscenity. The first category involves material that mixes sex with violence and/or includes children. The second category includes material that involves sex and degradation and is seen as thus encouraging violence or harm to women. Materials falling into either of these categories are deemed to be obscene. The third category involves SEM that is considered to be nonviolent and not degrading to women and does not involve children. Materials falling into the third category are not categorized as involving the undue exploitation of sex and are therefore considered to be acceptable in Canadian society.

All materials such as books and videos that come into Canada can be confiscated by Canada Customs if they are deemed as violating Canada's obscenity laws. Canada Customs also plays a major role in controlling the availability of SEM in Canada. Prior to December 2000, customs officers could seize materials and prohibit them from arriving at their intended destination without having to offer any justification for their decision. (The onus was on those whose materials were seized to prove in court that they were not obscene.) This happened several times to gay and lesbian bookstores. One of

There is definitely a subjective element in the definition of pornography. An erotic statue that sexually arouses viewers may not be considered pornographic if the sculptor's intent was artistic. A grainy photograph of a naked body that was intended to excite sexually may be pornographic. One alternative definition finds material pornographic when it is judged to be offensive by others. This definition, too, relies on subjective judgment—in this case, that of the person exposed to the material. In other words, one person's pornography is another person's work of art. In Guelph, Ontario, a fountain with a statue of a mother, father, and two children raised objections by some fundamentalist Christian groups who claimed that the statue was pornographic because the people it depicted were naked.

Obscenity That which offends people's feelings or goes beyond prevailing standards of decency or modesty.

Sexually explicit material Written, visual, or audiotaped material that is graphic and produced for purposes of eliciting or enhancing sexual arousal.

Erotica Sexually explicit material that does not involve violence or degradation of women.

Legislative bodies usually write laws about **obscenity** rather than pornography. Even the Supreme Court of Canada has had a difficult time defining obscenity and determining where, if anywhere, laws against obscenity run afoul of the guarantee of the Canadian Charter of Rights and Freedoms.

Let us first define **sexually explicit material** as written, visual, or audiotaped material that is graphic and produced for purposes of eliciting or enhancing sexual arousal. This has been the traditional definition of pornography. In the 1980s feminist groups began to differentiate two types of SEM: pornography and erotica. Pornography was defined as SEM that involved violence and/or degradation of women. **Erotica** was defined as SEM that does not involve violence or degradation of women. Erotica may be as sexually explicit as pornography is.

these stores, Little Sisters in Vancouver, went to court to challenge these censorship practices. As a result, in 2000 the Supreme Court accused Canada Customs of being especially prejudiced toward gay and lesbian erotic materials, and ruled that it must defend its actions in court. The court did, however, accept the right of customs officials to seize gay and lesbian erotic materials deemed to be obscene (MacCharles, 2000).

Civil libertarians were strongly opposed to legal changes resulting from the *Butler* decision, feeling that the new interpretations were too restrictive. They were also concerned about the potential subjectivity involved in trying to determine which materials were degrading. However, in some respects the new interpretation of obscenity allowed for greater permissiveness in legalizing previously banned explicit materials.

The Supreme Court decision had a monumental effect on changing the guidelines used by provincial censorship boards. In Canada, censorship and/or classification of films is the responsibility of the provinces. Until the 1992 *Butler* decision, some provincial censorship boards, particularly in the province of Ontario, banned any scenes of hard-core or penetrative sex. The Ontario censorship board revised its guidelines after 1992, which resulted in the legitimizing of sexually explicit films and videos and an increase in the number of adult video stores. Nevertheless, the board continued to censor more material than did other provinces. For example, in 2001 Ontario banned the film *Fat Girl* because it contains scenes of teenage nudity and sexual activity; the film was shown in British Columbia and Quebec without any cuts having to be made (Pevere, 2001).

Until 2005, all films that were either rented on video or shown in theatres had to be approved by the film review board. According to Robert Warren, chair of the Ontario Film Review Board, more than half the films and videos submitted for review were adult sex movies. In 2000, more than 2000 such films and videos were approved by the board, and 1.25 million copies of sex videos were provided with Ontario Film Review Board stickers indicating that they had been approved. Stores selling obscene films or videos not approved by the film review board could be fined up to $100 000 (Brooks, 2001).

In 2004 an Ontario court judge ruled that the Ontario requirement that all films be approved before they could be shown in the province violated freedom of expression under the Canadian Charter of Rights. Thus the Ontario Film Review Board's power of censorship was ruled as being unconstitutional. The court case resulted from a charge against a gay and lesbian bookstore, the Glad Day Bookshop in Toronto. The store was charged for distributing the sexually explicit video *Descent* without having the video approved by the review board.

In response to the court ruling, the Ontario government declared that the film review board would no longer censor films but would classify them with PG, G, and R ratings. Note that while the provincial government in Ontario no longer censors films, video stores can still be charged by police for selling materials that are defined as obscene under the Criminal Code (Benzie, 2004).

SEM is often classified as either hard-core or soft-core. Hard-core SEM includes graphic and sexually explicit depictions of sex organs and sexual acts. Soft-core material, as represented by R-rated films and *Playboy* photo spreads, features more stylized nude photos and suggested (or simulated) rather than explicit sexual acts.

Child Pornography

People who do not find depictions, however explicit, of consensual sexual activity between adults to be obscene may regard child pornography as obscene. Canada's first Criminal Code law specifically directed toward child pornography was enacted in 1993. It made it illegal to sell child pornography, as well as to possess anything depicting people under the age of 18 as engaging in real or simulated sexual behaviour. It also forbids visual representations that are intended for sexual purposes of the sex organs of people under the age of 18 and written materials and pictures that advocate having sex with an underage person. The law does allow for exemption from prosecution if the material has artistic merit or an educational, scientific, or medical purpose.

One of the most controversial legal decisions regarding pornography occurred in 1999, when a British Columbia Supreme Court judge ruled that the Criminal Code section prohibiting simple possession of child pornographic materials violated a Vancouver man's right to freedom of expression in that his stories about young boys had artistic merit. Many members of Parliament were so incensed by the ruling that they wanted the government to override the Constitution so as to ensure that the child pornography law would be upheld.

In 2001 the Supreme Court of Canada did uphold the law; however, it allowed for minor exceptions. These include private materials, such as drawings or personal journals, that are intended only for the eyes of the person who created them. Another exemption allows for SEM created by children or adolescents, such as a photograph of themselves, which is meant to be kept in strict privacy and only for personal use.

Legislation passed in 2005 narrowed the defence allowed individuals accused of possessing child pornography. The accused must prove that they were using the material for a legitimate purpose related to the administration of justice, science, medicine, education, or art and that this purpose does not pose an undue risk of harm to children.

The definition of child pornography was broadened to include audio formats and written material that describes prohibited sexual activity with children created for a sexual purpose. As well, the maximum penalty for possessing child pornography was increased from 6 to 18 months. The legislation also prohibited advertising child pornography.

To avoid police detection, some people who access child pornography use their laptop computer to tap into someone else's wireless network. In one of the first legal cases involving this situation, Toronto police arrested a man who was in front of a house in his car downloading images of a girl involved in a sex act with an adult. The man was charged with possession of child pornography and theft of communications (Millar, 2003).

The practice of using a laptop to get into someone else's wireless network without their permission is called "war driving." Many people do not turn on the security features for their wireless network, which makes them vulnerable to war drivers who can access the computer and its files and do whatever they want online—including accessing sexually explicit websites (Millar, 2003).

Convicted users of child internet pornography come from all social classes and are of all ages. In one series of raids in January 2008, the Ontario Provincial Police arrested 23 people for possession of child pornography. The offenders were from 16 communities and included a woman and a young offender. The oldest was aged 65. In 2007, a 22-year-old mother living in Kenora, Ontario, was convicted of taking part in sex videos with her two-year-old daughter and of distributing the video on the internet. In Guelph, Ontario, a 16-year-old girl pleaded guilty to possession of child pornography, including images of children as young as six engaged in sexual activity. The girl stated that she is "sexually attracted to young girls" (Tracey, 2008).

Because of societal concerns regarding child pornography, parents may wonder if they are allowed to take any nude photos of their young children. In 2006, a California man who was applying for landed immigrant status in Canada was turned back at the Canadian border because there were pictures of his unclothed toddler son on his cellphone. However, charges of attempting to smuggle child pornography into Canada were later dropped by the police, as it was decided that the photos were not taken for sexual gratification.

Television and SEM

In the 1990s, cable television companies in Canada started offering pay-per-view adult movies, which have become a highly profitable aspect of the cable television business. Canadian satellite companies have also begun to offer adult channels. In the winter of 2001, however, CBC TV presented a documentary about two adult channels that showed sexually explicit scenes involving domination, bondage, and spanking. The negative publicity surrounding the showing of this documentary led the owners of the satellite company to immediately remove the two channels from their offerings.

Employers and SEM

Many Canadian employers have policies that forbid the viewing of SEM in the workplace. Some use filtering software to prevent employees from visiting certain websites and screen email messages for offensive content. Some employees have lost their jobs because they looked at SEM on the internet while at work. In 2003 six employees at the Catholic Children's Aid in Toronto were fired after it was discovered that they had been exchanging SEM in their office emails. Contrary to the stereotype that only males engage in this behaviour, four of the six fired employees were women (Brennan, 2004).

Internet Use of SEM

Canadians are increasingly using the internet to view SEM. Among university students in British Columbia, 42% had viewed sexually explicit materials while online (males 75%, females 27%) and about half had begun viewing them before the age of 17 (Boies, 2002). Those who viewed SEM found it sexually arousing (82%) and learned new sexual techniques from it (63%), while 40% had masturbated while online. Yet 57% were disturbed by what they saw. There were notable gender differences in response, especially with regard to masturbating while online (males 70%, females 22%). Nine percent of both men and women had entered sexually focused chatrooms, and 8% had met sexual partners online. Finding online SEM sexually arousing was one of the best predictors of online SEM experience, especially for masturbating while online (Boies, 2002).

A survey of students at the University of Guelph found higher rates of exposure to online SEM (Byers, 2005). Almost all of the men (95%) and half of the women (53%) had accessed nude pictures, and three-quarters of the men and half of the women had accessed sexually explicit movies while online. The men spent more time per week viewing and sending SEM than did the women (2.8 versus 0.2 hours). Yet, about the same proportion of women (64%) as men (60%) had ever sent sexually explicit emails. Another major gender difference was that 69% of the men but only 18% of the women had saved SEM to their computer (Byers, 2005).

Of the total sample, 92% said they were heterosexual, 5% were bisexual, 2% of the men were gay, and 1% of the women were lesbian. Far more men had accessed lesbian SEM (73%) than gay male SEM (18%). Most of the women had not accessed either of these kinds of SEM. Interestingly, more of the women (27%) had accessed lesbian SEM than gay male material (12%).

Many Canadians are exposed to unsolicited online SEM through email messages and pop-ups. Researchers at Wilfrid Laurier University and the University of Guelph studied student reactions to this type of advertising (Nosko, Wood, & Desmarais, 2007). Males were more likely than females to have positive attitudes about these messages and to follow up by searching online for the explicit websites being promoted. Interestingly, those students who spent more time with computers were more likely to follow through with searches in response to these email messages and pop-ups, as were those who were more curious about online sexual material.

One of the newer forms of cybersex is virtual sex. On the website "Second Life," "residents" or their "avatars" (animated cartoon-like figures) can engage in any activity they want to, including having virtual sex with other residents or avatars (**http://secondlife.com/**).

Gender Differences in Response to SEM

Researchers have found that both men and women are physiologically sexually aroused by SEM. In one study, both men and women were more aroused by depictions of oral sex and intercourse than of petting (Harte et al., 2007). However, the women were more aroused by oral sex stimuli than intercourse. The women's responses varied more than the men's. Both men and women responded physically to sexually explicit stimuli. However, women were more likely to express negative feelings about SEM.

In practice, visual sexually explicit material (sexually explicit pictures or films) is largely a male preserve (Boies, 2002; Goodson et al., 2001). Most erotic visual materials are produced by men for men. Anthony Bogaert (2001) at Brock University found that the most popular type of film preferred by men portrayed women as having insatiable sexual desires. Many women may find SEM a "turn-off" or disgusting, especially when it portrays women in unflattering roles—as "whorish" and subservient to the desires of men.

From the evolutionary perspective, could a basic evolutionary process be at work? Did ancestral men who were more sexually aroused by the sight of a passing female have reproductive advantages over their less arousable peers? Women, by contrast, have fewer mating opportunities and must make the most of any reproductive opportunity by selecting the best possible mate and provider. To be sexually aroused by the sight of male genitalia might encourage random matings, which would undermine women's reproductive success.

Are women really not interested in viewing SEM? A study of women in Sweden found that almost all (85%) had been exposed to SEM (Rogala & Tydén, 2003). Of those who had viewed these materials, 65% believed that their viewing had positive effects, such as making them feel sexy or encouraging them to try new things; 27% reacted negatively (for example, some felt that their partner would want to make them perform sexual behaviours they did not want to be involved in). Also, a large-scale study in Denmark of people aged 18 to 30 found that both men and women generally reported experiencing positive effects from viewing hard-core SEM and few, if any, negative effects were reported. Men tended to report higher levels of positive effect than did women. Those who had higher rates of viewing SEM and who masturbated more perceived more positive effects of SEM (Hald & Malmuth, 2008).

In her book *The Princess at the Window*, Canadian feminist Donna Laframboise (1996) disputes the notion that women are not interested in SEM. She argues that women are simply more likely to prefer written rather than visual pornography. Laframboise uses illustrations from a number of recent erotic romance novels to demonstrate how these novels have become more explicit and daring in recent years. According to Laframboise, "These books are about female desire as a powerful force in its own right, as something that has the ability to overcome fear and shatter social convention" (p. 261).

Although most SEM is produced by men for men, an increasing number of both heterosexual and lesbian women today are producing SEM for women and couples. Across Canada there are numerous sex shops that sell explicit erotic materials for women, such as Toronto's Good For Her and Come As You Are. The Good For Her shop hosts annual Feminist Porn Awards. The awards honour sexually explicit films that showcase women actively and positively engaged in porn roles including director and actor roles. Appearing in sexually explicit films can enhance one's celebrity status, as proven by the careers of Paris Hilton and Pamela Anderson. Porn star Jenna Jameson's book *How to Make Love Like a Porn Star* was on the best-seller lists and she was interviewed on numerous mainstream radio and television shows.

However, there is less acceptance of this kind of sexual freedom for women in many other countries. In Vietnam, popular 19-year-old celebrity Thuy Linh had her television show cancelled after a video of her having sex with her boyfriend appeared on the internet (Stocking, 2007).

More Canadian women are comfortable posing in SEM such as topless or nude photographs. Both the Canadian Women's Nordic Ski Team and the Canadian Women's Rugby Team had some of their members pose in nude or semi-nude calendar

Innovative Canadian Research

WOMEN WHO VISIT SEX SHOPS

An increasing acceptance of SEM among Canadian women is illustrated by the also increasing number of sex shops that are female friendly. Stacey Jacobs (2007), a graduate student at the University of Guelph, conducted a survey of women who visited female-friendly sex shops in Ontario. Most of the women were single and had higher education. Only 15% had children. The women were most likely to visit a sex shop either with a partner or by themselves. The most important reason for making a purchase at the shop was to increase their own sexual pleasure and the second most important reason was to increase their partner's pleasure. The items most commonly purchased in the stores were, in order of frequency: sex toys, lubricants, novelty items, massage oils, lingerie, condoms, sex manuals, BDSM equipment, and SEM. Interestingly, only 19% had purchased sex DVDs or videos in the stores while almost one-half said they purchased these online.

Although most of the women were comfortable in the sex shops, one-third said that they at some time had wanted to ask an employee a question but were too embarrassed or frightened to do so. The women had asked questions mainly about sex toys such as vibrators and lubricants. Two-thirds were more comfortable asking questions when talking to a female rather than to a male employee.

photos to raise funds for their sports team. As well, women of varying ages from across Canada have posed topless in the annual Breast of Canada calendar, a fundraiser for breast cancer prevention.

Also on the rise is boudoir photography, in which women have themselves photographed in sexually provocative poses, for their own enjoyment or as gifts for boyfriends and husbands. Photographer Mark Laurie in Calgary has taken pictures of more than 4000 women over the past 25 years, ranging from seductive poses to completely nude ones (Mark, 2003).

Boudoir Photography.
As shown in this photo by Melanie Gillis, many Canadian women are having seductive pictures of themselves taken by professional photographers as gifts for their boyfriends or husbands.

Innovative Canadian Research

AN EDUCATIONAL PROGRAM TO COUNTERACT THE EFFECTS OF WATCHING INTERNET PORNOGRAPHY

University of Western Ontario researchers Corey Isaacs and William Fisher (2008) developed and tested an educational program to counteract the possible negative effects of watching internet pornography. Male research participants were assigned to one of three conditions. Group 1 viewed violent and degrading pornography accompanied with an educational intervention. Group 2 viewed the same pornography accompanied with a fake intervention that lacked the educational content given to group 1. Group 3 neither viewed pornography nor received an intervention.

The intervention consisted of an interactive computer program designed to sensitize the participants to the negative messages portrayed in violent and degrading pornography. Viewers were presented with examples of pornography having negative messages as well as the reality of the issue of sexual violence. They were encouraged to evaluate the content of sexual media more critically.

The dependent measures were acceptance of rape myths, attraction to sexual aggression, and opinions of SEM. Contrary to the expectations of the researchers, they did not observe any negative effects of viewing pornography for any of the dependent measures. However, the educational intervention did diminish any positive reactions to sexual aggression, and it also encouraged the participants to become more sensitive to, and to reject, violence in pornography.

Many Canadian couples of all sexual orientations use modern technology such as digital cameras to produce homemade SEM for their own private consumption. This involves taking nude photographs and videos of their partner or of both of them having sex together. Some couples post these photos on the internet.

Finally, there are many young women in North America who are voluntarily posing in revealing photos for the websites Girls Gone Wild and Canadian Wild Girls. The photos are typically taken at bars and special events such as spring break in Florida. The women are not paid for this but receive hats or T-shirts. It seems as if posing topless in certain contexts has become more acceptable in Canadian society. The media are definitely supporting this trend, as evidenced by the film *Calendar Girls* in which a group of older women posed nude for a charity fundraising calendar.

Cybersex Addiction

Surveys show that many people, mostly men, now spend dozens of hours each week surfing pornographic and other sex-related websites (Cooper et al., 2000, 2004; Daneback et al., 2006). Those most strongly hooked on online sex may spend hours a day masturbating to pornographic images or—less commonly—having "online sex" with someone contacted via a chatroom or webcam (Daneback et al., 2005, 2006).

Cybersex compulsives are like drug addicts (Cooper et al., 2004; Schneider, 2005). They "use the Internet as an important part of their sexual acting out, much like a drug addict who has a drug of choice. Especially vulnerable are those whose sexuality may have been suppressed and limited all their lives who suddenly find an infinite supply of sexual opportunities" online (Cooper, cited in Brody, 2000). Although some studies find men who become addicted to online sex to have ample sexual opportunities in the real world, other studies find them to be lonelier than men with those opportunities (Yoder et al., 2005).

Online viewing that began as a harmless recreation can become all-consuming and even lead to real sexual encounters with people met online. Cybersex compulsives sometimes ignore their partners and children, and risk their jobs. Schneider

(2005) reports other adverse consequences, including broken relationships. Partners often report feeling betrayed, ignored, and unable to compete with the online fantasies.

A 34-year-old woman married 14 years to a minister told Schneider, "How can I compete with hundreds of anonymous others who are now in our bed, in his head? Our bed is crowded with countless faceless strangers, where once we were intimate" (cited in Brody, 2000).

SEM and Sexual Coercion

Is SEM a harmless diversion or an inducement to commit sexual violence or other antisocial acts? Let us consider sources of evidence in examining this highly charged issue, beginning with the findings of a 1985 Canadian government commission.

THE FRASER COMMISSION REPORT In the 1980s, the Canadian government appointed a special committee to study the issues of prostitution and pornography and to make policy recommendations based on the outcome of its findings. This committee's report became known as the Fraser Commission Report (1985). Despite hearing from numerous individuals and groups that pornography is harmful to society, the Fraser Commission concluded that the available evidence did not support the belief that pornography leads to such antisocial behaviour as violent crime, sexual abuse of children, and the disintegration of communities and society.

SEM AND SEX OFFENDERS Another approach to examining the role of SEM in crimes of sexual violence involves comparing the experiences of sex offenders and nonoffenders with sexually explicit materials. In a review of the research literature, Marshall (1989) found little or no difference in the level of exposure to SEM between incarcerated sex offenders and comparison groups of felons who were incarcerated for nonsexual crimes.

In an Ontario study, 17% of sex offenders reported they used SEM while committing sexual offences. This involved either showing the victims SEM or taking pictures of the victims (Langevin & Curnoe, 2004).

VIOLENT SEM Research suggests that it is the violence in violent SEM—not its sexual explicitness—that hardens men's attitudes toward sexual assault survivors. In a recent Ontario study, Kingston et al. (2008) studied the use of pornography among convicted child sex offenders. Those who viewed deviant, including violent, pornography were more likely to reoffend. Higher frequency of pornography use was more predictive of reoffending among those who were already considered at high risk for reoffending. Kingston et al. speculate that more aggressive men are drawn to images of violent pornography. Pornography reinforces their negative attitudes such as hostility toward women. The researchers note that use of deviant pornography is more predictive of violent sexual reoffending than of sex offending in general.

Research on the effects of SEM should be interpreted with caution, however. We still lack evidence that normal men have been, or would be, spurred to sexually assault women because of exposure to violent SEM or other media depictions of violence.

NONVIOLENT SEM Nonviolent SEM may not contain scenes of sexual violence, but it typically portrays women as sexually promiscuous, insatiable, and subservient. Might such portrayals of women reinforce traditional stereotypes of women as sex objects? Might they lead viewers to condone sexual assault by suggesting that women are essentially promiscuous? Might the depiction of women as readily sexually accessible inspire men to refuse to "take no for an answer" on dates?

Michael Seto, Alexandra Maric, and Howard Barbaree (2001) from the Centre for Addiction and Mental Health in Toronto conducted an extensive review of the research and concluded that there is little empirical support for the idea that SEM causes sexual aggression. Rather, they believe that men who are predisposed to sexual aggression are more likely to choose to view violent SEM and thus are most likely to show the strongest effects. Men who are not predisposed to sexual violence are unlikely to show any effect.

William Fisher, a psychology professor at the University of Western Ontario, has conducted several experimental studies to measure the effects of SEM. In one study, Barak and Fisher (1997) explored the effects of computer-based interactive erotic stimulation on men's attitudes and behaviours toward women. University men who were exposed to computer-based erotic stimuli showed significant increases in sexual arousal but did not show negative changes of attitude or behaviour toward women in comparison with a control condition. Specifically, exposure to interactive erotic stimulation did not result in aggressive behaviour toward women, nor did it affect men's attitudes toward women's rights and roles in society. As well, this exposure did not change men's perceptions of sexual assault myths.

Yet another concern is the possible effect of nonviolent SEM on the viewer's sexual values. Nonviolent SEM typically features impromptu sexual encounters between new acquaintances. Might repeated exposure to such material alter viewers' attitudes toward traditional sexual values? Brown (2003) reports intriguing evidence that repeated exposure to this type of nonviolent SEM loosens traditional sexual and family values. When compared with people who viewed nonsexual films, men and women who were exposed to weekly, hour-long sessions involving scenes of explicit sexual encounters between new acquaintances over a six-week period showed attitudinal changes including greater acceptance of premarital and extramarital sex and of simultaneous sexual relationships with multiple partners.

Prolonged exposure to such SEM may also foster dissatisfaction with the physical appearance and sexual performance of one's intimate partners (Brown, 2003).

Another concern is that SEM does not offer realistic presentations of how most people function sexually. While many people in real life experience sexual problems, the people portrayed in the sexual media never have sexual problems. The actors are always able to have sex any time and any place for hours at a time. Penises are always erect, vaginas are continuously lubricated, and the women have an insatiable desire for sex, as well as orgasms that occur with little effort. Most of the actors do not use condoms and sexually transmitted infections are never discussed.

In sum, research on the effects of nonviolent SEM is so far inconclusive. The effects of nonviolent SEM may be more closely connected with whether women are presented in a dehumanizing manner than with sexual explicitness per se. No research has yet linked sexual explicitness itself with undesirable effects.

A group of researchers from Ireland and universities in western Canada (Morrison et al., 2004) are critical of most previous research for being narrowly focused on using a harm-based approach to studying the effects of SEM. They are also concerned that almost all of the research has surveyed only men and viewed women as victims.

Morrison and colleagues (2004) argue that researchers have generally ignored the fact that an increasing amount of sexually explicit material is being produced by women for women and couples, which indicates that many women are willing consumers of these materials.

To gain a broader perspective, these researchers surveyed 382 females and 202 males attending a university in western Canada. Among both genders, those who had higher sexual self-esteem and lower levels of sexual anxiety had a higher level of exposure to SEM on television or DVDs. Females who had more recent experience with vaginal and anal intercourse were also more likely to have seen SEM. Safer sex practices were not related to the degree of SEM exposure. Based on these findings, the researchers concluded that exposure to SEM is not related to many of the types of harm that are often discussed in the literature.

Summing Up

Commercial sex runs the gamut from "adult" movie theatres and bookshops to strip shows, sex toy shops, brothels, escort services, massage parlours, and "900" telephone services.

One view of prostitution is that it is an immoral activity exploitative of women. The contrasting view is that it is a legitimate occupation that should be legal.

The laws governing prostitution (the exchange of sex for money) in Canada are confusing because while prostitution itself is legal, almost all of the activities that involve prostitution are illegal.

The majority of Canadians support legalizing prostitution, although most disapprove of it personally.

The major types of female prostitutes are streetwalkers, brothel prostitutes (many of whom work in massage parlours), escorts, and call girls. No single factor explains entry into female prostitution.

Those who patronize prostitutes are often referred to as "johns" or "tricks." Most patrons are "occasional johns" with regular sex partners.

Most male prostitutes are "hustlers" who service male clients. Hustlers typically begin selling sex in their teens and may be gay or heterosexual in orientation.

The majority of prostitutes consistently use condoms with clients. Some are pressured by clients and offered more money for not using condoms.

Pornography is "writing, pictures, etc., intended to arouse sexual desire." The judgment of what is pornographic or obscene varies from person to person and from culture to culture.

The feminist movement has had a strong influence on federal laws governing SEM in Canada.

Accessing SEM on the internet is increasingly common.

Although both genders can become physiologically aroused by erotic materials, men are relatively more interested in sexually explicit pictures and films.

Some researchers argue that it is the violence in violent SEM, and not sexual explicitness per se, that promotes violence against women. The effects of nonviolent SEM on normal populations remain unclear.

More recent research is indicating that there are positive benefits of SEM.

Test Yourself

Multiple-Choice Questions

1. Which of the following statements is true?

a. Prostitution is illegal everywhere in Canada.
b. Prostitution is known as the world's newest profession.
c. In Quebec, prostitution is legal in licensed houses.
d. Prostitution itself has never been illegal in Canada.

2. Among prostitutes, ________________ have the lowest status and earn the lowest wages.

a. streetwalkers
b. brothel workers
c. call girls
d. massage parlour workers

3. Among prostitutes, ________________ have the highest status and earn the highest wages.

a. streetwalkers
b. brothel workers
c. call girls
d. massage parlour workers

4. All of the following are important factors in the backgrounds of many young prostitutes except

a. poverty
b. sexual addiction
c. physical abuse
d. sexual abuse

5. Which of the following is not one of the common motives for using prostitutes?

a. sex for eroticism and variety
b. sex without commitment
c. sex away from home
d. sex to test one's sexual orientation

6. Men who engage in prostitution with male customers are commonly known as

a. pimps
b. gigolos
c. hustlers
d. johns

7. **A photograph or video would be considered hard-core SEM if it contained**
   a. hints or suggestions of sexual acts
   b. explicit depictions of sexual acts
   c. stylized nude photos
   d. nonconsensual sexual behaviour

8. **Which of the following statements is true?**
   a. Both men and women experience similar physical responses to sexually explicit materials.
   b. Women are more physically aroused by sexually explicit materials than men.
   c. Men are more physically aroused by sexually explicit materials than women.
   d. Alcohol is a major factor in determining physical responses to sexually explicit materials.

9. **Most of the research on the effects of exposure to sexually explicit materials has focused on**
   a. homosexual sexual behaviour
   b. sex with children
   c. consensual sexual behaviour
   d. sex and violence

10. **In the educational intervention to reduce possible negative effects of pornography, which of the following groups was not included in the study?**
    a. one group viewed violent pornography and received the educational intervention
    b. one group viewed violent pornography and received a fake intervention
    c. one group viewed nonviolent pornography and received the intervention
    d. one group neither viewed pornography nor received an intervention

Answers to the Test Yourself questions in each chapter are found on page 509.

Critical Thinking Questions

1. Should all aspects of prostitution be legal in Canada? Why or why not?
2. Take a look at one of your favourite magazines. Do you see advertisers using sex to sell their products? If these images were shown just as pictures, rather than as ads, would you see them as art or pornography? Explain your answer.
3. Have you ever used sexually explicit material with a sex partner? Do you think this has helped or hurt your relationship?
4. You are having a late-night discussion about sexually explicit material over a few beers with some friends. One of them says that since most sex offenders drank milk as children, we should ban milk along with the sexually explicit material. How would you respond to this comment?

Visit MyPsychKit at www.mypsychkit.com, where you can do quizzes and link to additional resources on topics discussed in this text.

Answer Key

Chapter 1	Chapter 2	Chapter 3	Chapter 4	Chapter 5	Chapter 6
1. b	**1.** a	**1.** c	**1.** c	**1.** c	**1.** a
2. b	**2.** c	**2.** b	**2.** c	**2.** b	**2.** c
3. c	**3.** d	**3.** b	**3.** c	**3.** d	**3.** c
4. d	**4.** a	**4.** c	**4.** b	**4.** a	**4.** b
5. a	**5.** c	**5.** d	**5.** b	**5.** d	**5.** d
6. a	**6.** b	**6.** a	**6.** d	**6.** a	**6.** a
7. d	**7.** b	**7.** c	**7.** c	**7.** b	**7.** b
8. a	**8.** d	**8.** d	**8.** a	**8.** c	**8.** d
9. b	**9.**)	**9.** c	**9.** c	**9.** b	**9.** c
10. a	**10.** c	**10.** a	**10.** d	**10.** b	**10.** a

Chapter 7	Chapter 8	Chapter 9	Chapter 10	Chapter 11	Chapter 12
1. d	**1.** d	**1.** d	**1.** c	**1.** c	**1.** a
2. c	**2.** b	**2.** b	**2.** a	**2.** a	**2.** c
3. d	**3.** b	**3.** b	**3.** c	**3.** b	**3.** d
4. d	**4.** a	**4.** c	**4.** d	**4.** b	**4.** d
5. a	**5.** b	**5.** b	**5.** d	**5.** b	**5.** c
6. c	**6.** c	**6.** c	**6.** d	**6.** a	**6.** b
7. c	**7.** b	**7.** a	**7.** c	**7.** c	**7.** d
8. c	**8.** d	**8.** c	**8.** b	**8.** d	**8.** b
9. d	**9.** b	**9.** b	**9.** d	**9.** d	**9.** b
10. d	**10.** d	**10.** a	**10.** d	**10.** d	**10.** c

Chapter 13	Chapter 14	Chapter 15	Chapter 16	Chapter 17
1. c	**1.** c	**1.** a	**1.** b	**1.** d
2. d	**2.** d	**2.** b	**2.** d	**2.** a
3. c	**3.** b	**3.** b	**3.** b	**3.** c
4. a	**4.** a	**4.** d	**4.** d	**4.** b
5. c	**5.** b	**5.** c	**5.** d	**5.** d
6. b	**6.** b	**6.** b	**6.** c	**6.** c
7. d	**7.** b	**7.** a	**7.** c	**7.** b
8. d	**8.** c	**8.** d	**8.** a	**8.** a
9. a	**9.** d	**9.** d	**9.** a	**9.** d
10. c	**10.** b	**10.** b	**10.** c	**10.** c

References

Abal, Y. N., Maríín, J. A. L., & Sánchez, S. R. (2003). A new paraphilia of the XXI century: Chat-scatophilia. *Archivos Hispano-americanos de Sexologíia, 9*(1), 81–104.

Abbott, E. (1999). *A history of celibacy*. New York: HarperCollins.

Abell, J., Locke, A., Condor, S., Gibson, S., & Stevenson, C. (2006). Trying similarity, doing difference: The role of interviewer self-disclosure in interview talk with young people. *Qualitative Research, 6*(2), 221–244.

Abraham, C. (2006, December 23). Critics troubled by new fertility panel. *The Globe and Mail*, pp. A1, A8.

Adachi, M., et al. (2000). Androgen-insensitivity syndrome as a possible coactivator disease. *The New England Journal of Medicine* online, *343*(12).

Adam, B. (2006a.) New gay relations: Relationship innovation in male relationships? *Sexualities, 9*(1), 5–26.

Adam, B. (2006b). Infectious behaviour: Imputing subjectivity to HIV behaviour. *Social Theory and Health, 4*, 168–179.

Adam, B. (2007). Cultural trends in safe and unsafe sex. Paper presented at the annual meeting of the International Academy of Sex Research, Vancouver, BC.

Adam, B., Husbands, W., Murray, J., & Maxwell, J. (2005). AIDS optimism, condom fatigue, or self-esteem? Explaining unsafe sex among gay and bisexual men. *Journal of Sex Research, 42*(3), 238–248.

Adam, B. D. (2000a). Age preferences among gay and bisexual men. *GLQ, 6*(3), 413–414.

Adam, B. D. (2000b). Love and sex in constructing identity among men who have sex with men. *International Journal of Sexuality and Gender Studies, 5*(5), 325–339.

Adam, B. D., Maticka-Tyndale, E., & Cohen, J. J. (2001). *Living with combination therapies*. A report to the Ontario HIV Treatment Network.

Adams, H. E., Wright, L. W., Jr., & Lohr, B. A. (1996). Is homophobia associated with homosexual arousal? *Journal of Abnormal Psychology, 105*, 440–445.

Adams, N. (2006). Systemic therapy techniques for sexual difficulties. In Hiller, J., et al. (Eds.). *Sex, mind, and emotion: Innovation in psychological theory and practice* (pp. 209–227). London, UK: Karnac Books.

Agrawal, A. (1997). Gendered bodies: The case of the "third gender" in India. *Contributions to Indian Sociology, 31*, 273–297.

Ah Shene, D. (2003). Crystal meth. *Developments, 23*(2). Alberta Alcohol and Drug Abuse Commission. [Online]. Available: http://corp.aadac.com/services/developments_newsletter/dev_news_vol23_issue2.asp

Ahmed, R. A. (1991). Women in Egypt and the Sudan. In L. L. Adler (ed.), *Women in cross-cultural perspective* (pp. 107–134). New York: Praeger.

Alderson, K. (2007). "What's love got to do with it?" Defining and measuring sexual orientation. Paper presented at the Annual Meeting of the Canadian Sex Research Forum, Banff, Alberta.

Alderson, K. G. (2003). The ecological model of gay male identity. *Canadian Journal of Human Sexuality, 12*, 75–85.

Alderson, K. G., & Jevne, R. F. J. (2003). Yin and yang in mortal combat: The psychic conflict beneath the coming out process for gay males. *Guidance and Counselling, 18*, 128–141.

Alexander, J. (2006). An introduction to queer theory. *Sexualities, 9*(1), 115–117.

Al-Krenawi, A., & Graham, J. R. (1999). The story of Bedouin-Arab women in a polygamous marriage. *Women's Studies International Forum, 22*, 497–509.

Allen, P. L. (2000). *The wages of sin: Sex and disease, past and present*. Chicago: University of Chicago Press.

Allman, D. (1999). *M is for mutual: A is for acts*. Ottawa: Health Canada.

Altemeyer, B. (2001). Changes in attitudes toward homosexuals. *Journal of Homo-sexuality, 42*(2), 63–75.

Alterman, E. (1997, November). Sex in the '90s. *Elle*, pp. 128–134.

Althof, S. E. (1994). Paper presented at the annual meeting of the American Urological Association, San Francisco, CA.

Alzate, H., & Hoch, Z. (1986). The "G spot" and "female ejaculation": A current appraisal. *Journal of Sex and Marital Therapy, 12*(3), 211–220.

American Fertility Association. (2006, February). [Online]. **www.theafa.org**

American Psychiatric Association. (2000). *Diagnostic and statistical manual of mental disorders* (Fourth ed). Washington, DC: Author.

Amodio, D. M., & Showers, C. J. (2005). "Similarity breeds liking" revisited: The moderating role of commitment. *Journal of Social and Personal Relationships, 22*(6), 817–836.

Andersen, M. L., Bignotto, M., & Tufik, S. (2003). The effect of apomorphine on genital reflexes in male rats deprived of paradoxical sleep. *Physiology & Behavior, 80*(2–3), 211–215.

Andersen, M. L., & Tufik, S. (2005). Effects of progesterone blockade over cocaine-induced genital reflexes of paradoxical sleep-deprived male rats. *Hormones and Behavior, 47*(4), 477–484.

Anderson, J. L., et al. (1992). Was the Duchess of Windsor right? A cross-cultural review of the socioecology of ideals of female body shape. *Ethology and Sociobiology, 13*, 197–227.

Apperloo, M. J. A., et al. (2003). In the mood for sex: The value of androgens. *Journal of Sex & Marital Therapy, 29*(2), 87–102.

Appleby, T. (2005, March 23). Man's chat room friendship leads to abduction ordeal. *The Globe and Mail*.

Archer, J., & Vaughan, A. E. (2001). Evolutionary theories of rape. *Psychology, Evolution & Gender, 3*(1), 95–101.

Armstrong, K., Eisen, A., & Weber, B. (2000). Assessing the risk of breast cancer. *The New England Journal of Medicine* online, *342*(8).

Armstrong, N. (2003, August 29). Oral sex "no big deal," 13-year-old testifies. *National Post*.

Aronson, K. (2003). Alcohol: A recently identified risk factor for breast cancer. *Canadian Medical Association Journal, 168*(9), 1147–1148.

Associated Press (2008, April 10). Five homosexuals jailed for "debauchery." *Toronto Star*, p. AA2.

Astley, S. J., & Clarren, S. K. (2001). Measuring the facial phenotype of individuals with prenatal alcohol exposure: Correlations with brain dysfunction. *Alcohol & Alcoholism, 36*(2), 147–159.

Auld, A. (2007, September 17). N.S. teen tortured by 3 girls: Police. *Toronto Star*, p. A2.

Auld, R. B., & Brock, G. (2002). Sexuality and erectile dysfunction: Results of a national survey. *Journal of Sexual & Reproductive Medicine, 2*, 50–54.

Bagley, C., & D'Augelli, A. R. (2000). Suicidal behaviour in gay, lesbian, and bisexual youth. *British Medical Journal, 320*, 1617–1618.

Bailey, I. (2000, April 26). They are a couple and proud of it. *National Post*, pp. A1, A2.

Bailey, J. M. (2003a). Personal communication.

Bailey, J. M. (2003b). *The man who would be queen: The science of gender-bending and transsexualism.* Washington, DC: Joseph Henry Press.

Bailey, J. M., Kirk, K. M., Zhu, G., Dunne, M. P., & Martin, N. G. (2000). Do individual differences in sociosexuality represent genetic or environmentally contingent strategies? Evidence from the Australian twin registry. *Journal of Personality & Social Psychology, 78*(3), 537–545.

Bailey, J. M., & Zucker, K. J. (1995). Childhood sex-typed behavior and sexual orientation: A conceptual analysis and quantitative review. *Developmental Psychology, 31*, 43–55.

Bailey, J. M., et al. (1999). A family history study of male sexual orientation using three independent samples. *Behavior Genetics, 29*(2), 79–86.

Bailey, R. C. (2000). A study in rural Uganda of heterosexual transmission of human immunodeficiency virus. *New England Journal of Medicine, 343*(5).

Bailey, S. (2008, January 15). Native population growing. *The Canadian Press.*

Bains, C. (2008, April 2). Canada has global sex abuse problem, expert finds. *Waterloo Region Record*, p. Z5.

Baldwin, J. D., & Baldwin, J. I. (1989). The socialization of homosexuality and heterosexuality in a non-Western society. *Archives of Sexual Behavior, 18*, 13–29.

Bancroft, J. (1984). Hormones and human sexual behavior. *Journal of Sex and Marital Therapy, 10*, 3–21.

Bancroft, J. (Ed.). (2003). *Sexual development in childhood.* Bloomington: Indiana University Press.

Bancroft, J., Carnes, L., Janssen, E., Goodrich, D., & Long, J. S. (2005b). Erectile and ejaculatory problems in gay and heterosexual men. *Archives of Sexual Behavior, 34*(3), 285–297.

Bancroft, J., et al. (2005c). The relevance of the dual control model to male sexual dysfunction: The Kinsey Institute/BASRT collaborative project. *Sexual & Relationship Therapy, 20*, 13–30.

Banerjee, S. (2008, June 17). Belgian faces sex-related charges. *Toronto Star*, p. A14.

Barak, A., & Fisher, W. A. (1997). Effects of interactive computer erotica on men's attitudes and behavior toward women: An experimental study. *Computers in Human Behavior, 13*, 353–369.

Barash, D. P., & Lipton, J. E. (2001). *The myth of monogamy.* New York: Freeman.

Barbach, L. G. (1975). *For yourself: The fulfillment of female sexuality.* New York: Doubleday.

Barbaree, H. E., & Marshall, W. L. (1991). The role of male sexual arousal in rape: Six models. *Journal of Consulting and Clinical Psychology, 59*, 621–630.

Barisic, S. (1998, February 18). Study: Breast milk is still best. The Associated Press online.

Barnard, N. D., Scialli, A. R., Hurlock, D., & Bertron, P. (2000). Diet and sex-hormone binding globulin, dysmenorrhea, and premenstrual symptoms. *Obstetrics & Gynecology, 95*, 245–250.

Barnes, M. L., & Sternberg, R. J. (1997). A hierarchical model of love and its prediction of satisfaction in close relationships. In Sternberg, R. J., & Hojjat, M. (Eds.), *Satisfaction in close relationships* (pp. 79–101). New York: Guilford Press.

Barrett, M. (2006). What everyone should know about human papilomavirus (HPV): Questions and answers. *The Canadian Journal of Human Sexuality, 15*(3–4), 171–174.

Barrett, M., King, A., Levy, J., Maticka-Tyndale, E., & McKay, A. (1997). Canada. In R. Francoeur (ed.) *The Continuum complete international encyclopedia of sexuality* (pp. 221–343). New York: Continuum Publishing Company.

Barrett, M. B. (1990). *Invisible lives: The truth about millions of women-loving women.* New York: Harper & Row (Perennial Library).

Barsky, J. L., Friedman, M. A., & Rosen, R. C. (2006). Sexual dysfunction and chronic illness: The role of flexibility in coping. *Journal of Sex & Marital Therapy, 32*(3), 235–253.

Bartoshuk, L. M., & Beauchamp, G. K. (1994). Chemical senses. *Annual Review of Psychology, 45*, 419–449.

Basow, S. A., & Rubenfeld, K. (2003). "Troubles talk": Effects of gender and gender-typing. *Sex Roles, 48*(3–4), 183–187.

Basson, R. (2000, May). Paper presented at the annual meeting of the American College of Obstetricians and Gynecologists, San Francisco, CA.

Basson, R. (2001). Human sex-response cycles. *Journal of Sex and Marital Therapy, 27*, 33–43.

Basson, R. (2002). A model of women's sexual arousal. *Journal of Sex and Marital Therapy, 28*, 1–10.

Basson, R. (2004). Recent advances in women's sexual function and dysfunction. *Menopause, 11*(6 Pt 2), 714–725.

Basson, R., & Brotto, L. A. (2003). Sexual psychophysiology and effects of sildenafil citrate in oestrogenised women with acquired genital arousal disorder and impaired orgasm: A randomised controlled trial. *BJOG: An International Journal of Obstetrics and Gynaecology, 110*(11), 1014–1024.

Basson, R., McInnes, R., Smith, M. D., Hodgson, G., & Koppiker, N. (2002). Efficacy and safety of sildenafil citrate in women with sexual dysfunction associated with female sexual arousal disorder. *Journal of Women's Health & Gender-Based Medicine, 11*(4), 367–378.

Bauer, G. (2001, November). Boys must be boys. *Canadian Living*, pp. 186–192.

Bauerle, S. Y., Amirkhan J. H., & Hupka, R. B. (2002). An attribution theory analysis of romantic jealousy. *Motivation & Emotion, 26*(4), 297–319.

Baumeister, R. F. (1988a). Gender differences in masochistic scripts. *Journal of Sex Research, 25*, 478–499.

Baumeister, R. F. (2000). Gender differences in erotic plasticity: The female sex drive as socially flexible and responsive. *Psychological Bulletin, 126*, 347–374.

Baumeister, R. F., Catanese, K. R., & Wallace, H. M. (2002). Conquest by force: A narcissistic reactance theory of rape and sexual coercion. *Review of General Psychology, 6*(1), 92–135.

Bawden, J. (2002, January 19). Toppling TV taboos. *Starweek Magazine*, p. 6.

Bean, J. L. (2002). Expressions of female sexuality. *Journal of Sex & Marital Therapy, 28*(Suppl1), 29–38.

Beauregard, E., Lussier, P., & Proulx, J. (2004). An exploration of developmental factors related to deviant sexual preferences among adult rapists. *Sexual Abuse: A Journal of Research and Treatment, 16*(2), 151–161.

Becerra, L., Breiter, H. C., Wise, R., Gonzalez, R. G., & Borsook, D. (2001). Reward circuitry activation by noxious thermal stimuli. *Neuron, 32*(5), 927–946.

Beck, J. G. (1993). Vaginismus. In W. O'Donohue & J. H. Geer (eds.), *Handbook of sexual dysfunctions: Assessment and treatment* (pp. 381–397). Boston: Allyn & Bacon.

Bem, S. L. (1975). Sex role adaptability: One consequence of psychological androgyny. *Journal of Personality and Social Psychology, 31*, 634–643.

Bem, S. L. (1993). *The lenses of gender.* New Haven, CT: Yale University Press.

Bem, S. L., Martyna, W., & Watson, C. (1976). Sex typing and androgyny: Further explorations of the expressive domain. *Journal of Personality and Social Psychology, 34*, 1016–1023.

Bennett, S., & Assefi, N. (2005). School-based pregnancy prevention programs: A systematic review of randomized controlled studies. *Journal of Adolescent Health, 36*, 72–81.

Ben-Ze'ev, A. (2003). Privacy, emotional closeness, and openness in cyberspace. *Computers in Human Behavior, 19*(4), 451–467.

Benzie, R. (2004, December 10). Film board cut out as censor. *The Toronto Star*, p. A4.

Berdahl, J. L., & Moore, C. (2006). Workplace harassment: Double jeopardy for minority women. *Journal of Applied Psychology, 91*(2), 426–436.

Bereket, T., & Adam, B. (2006). The emergence of gay identities in contemporary Turkey. *Sexualities, 9*(2), 131–151.

Beres, M. (2006). Sexual miscommunication? Untangling communication between casual sex partners. Doctorate thesis, University of Alberta.

Beres, M., Crow, B., & Gotell, L. (2008, in press). The perils of institutionalization in neoliberal times: Results of a national survey of Canadian sexual assault and rape crisis centres. *Canadian Journal of Sociology.*

Beres, M. A. (2002). *Sexual consent behaviors in same sex relationships.* Unpublished master's thesis, University of Guelph.

Beres, M. A. (2007). "Spontaneous" sexual consent: An analysis of sexual consent literature. *Feminism & Psychology, 17*(1), 93–108.

Beres, M. A., Herold, E., & Maitland, S. B. (2004). Sexual consent behaviors in same-sex relationships, *Archives of Sexual Behavior, 33,* 475–486.

Berger, L. (2000, June 25). A racial gap in infant deaths, and a search for reasons. *The New York Times,* p. WH13.

Bergeron, S., Binik, Y. M., Khalife, S., Pagidas, K., Glazer, H. I., Meana, M., & Amsel, R. (2001). A randomized comparison of group cognitive-behavioral therapy, surface electromyographic biofeedback, and vestibulectomy in the treatment of dyspareunia resulting from vulvar vestibulitis. *Pain, 91,* 297–306.

Bergeron, S., Khalifé, S., Glazer, H. I., & Binik, Y. M. (2008). Surgical and behavioral treatments for vestibulodynia: Two-and-one-half-year follow-up and predictors and outcome. *Obstetrics & Gynecology, 111*(1), 159-166.

Bergeron, S., & Lord, M. (2003). The integration of pelvi-perineal re-education and cognitive-behavioural therapy in the multidisciplinary treatment of the sexual pain disorders. *Sexual & Relationship Therapy, 18*(2), 135–141.

Berman, L. A. (2000). Paper presented at the annual meeting of the American Urological Association, Atlanta, GA.

Bernstein, I. M., et al. (2005). Maternal smoking and its association with birth weight. *Obstetrics & Gynecology, 106,* 986–991.

Berscheid, E. (2003). On stepping on land mines. In Sternberg, R. J. (Ed.), *Psychologists defying the crowd: Stories of those who battled the establishment and won* (pp. 33–44). Washington, DC: American Psychological Association.

Berscheid, E., & Reis, H. T. (1998). Attraction and close relationships. In D. T. Gilbert, S. T. Fiske, et al. (Eds.), *The handbook of social psychology, Vol. 2* (4th ed.) (pp. 193–281). New York: McGraw-Hill.

Bhugra, D. (2005). Queer theory. *Sexual and Relationship Therapy, 20*(4), 476.

Bhugra, D., Rahman, Q., & Bhintade, R. (2006). Sexual fantasy in gay men in India: A comparison with heterosexual men. *Sexual and Relationship Therapy, 21*(2), 197–207.

Bibby, R. (2006). The boomer factor: What Canada's most famous generation is leaving behind. Bastian Books.

Bibby, R. W. (2001). *Canada's teens: Today, yesterday and tomorrow.* Toronto: Stoddart.

Bielay, B., & Herold, E. S. (1995). Popular magazines as a source of sexuality information for university women. *Journal of Canadian Sexuality, 4,* 247–261.

Binik, Y. M. (2005). Should dyspareunia be retained as a sexual dysfunction in *DSM-V?* A painful classification decision. *Archives of Sexual Behavior, 34*(1), 11–21.

Binik, Y. M., Reissing, E., Pukall, C., Flory, N., Payne, K. A., & Khalife, S. (2002). The female sexual pain disorders: Genital pain or sexual dysfunction? *Archives of Sexual Behavior, 31,* 425–429.

Bixler, R. H. (1989). Diversity: A historical/comparative perspective. *Behavioral and Brain Sciences, 12,* 15–16.

Blais, K., Collin-Vezina, D., Marcellin, K., & Picard, A. (2004). Current reality of homosexual couples: Clinical implications in the context of partnership counseling. *Canadian Psychology, 45*(2), 174–186.

Blanchard, R. (1988). Nonhomosexual gender dysphoria. *Journal of Sex Research, 24,* 188–193.

Blanchard, R. (1989). The concept of autogynephilia and the typology of male gender dysphoria. *Journal of Nervous & Mental Disease, 177*(10), 616–623.

Blanchard, R., & Bogaert, A. F. (2004). Proportion of homosexual men who owe their sexual orientation to fraternal birth order: An estimate based on two national probability samples. *American Journal of Human Biology, 16*(2), 151–157.

Blanchard, R., Cantor, J. M., Bogaert, A. F., Breedlove, S. M., & Ellis, L. (2006). Interaction of fraternal birth order and handedness in the development of male homosexuality. *Hormones and Behavior, 49,* 405–414.

Blanchard, R., Christensen, B. K., Strong, S. M., Cantor, J. M., Kuban, M. E., Klassen, P., Dickey, R., & Blak, T. (2002). Retrospective self-reports of childhood accidents causing unconsciousness in phallometrically diagnosed pedophiles. *Archives of Sexual Behaviour, 31*(6), 511–526.

Blanchard, R., Kolla, N. J., Cantor, J. M., Klassen, P. E., Dickey, R., Kuban, M. E., et al. (2007). IQ, handedness, and pedophilia in adult male patients stratified by referral source. *Sex Abuse, 19,* 285–309.

Blanchard, R., & Lippa, R. A. (2007). Birth order, sibling sex ratio, handedness, and sexual orientation of male and female participants in a BBC internet research project. *Archives of Sexual Behaviour, 36,* 163–176.

Blanchard, R., Steiner, B. W., & Clemmensen, L. H. (1985). Gender dysphoria, gender reorientation, and the clinical management of transsexualism. *Journal of Consulting and Clinical Psychology, 53,* 295–304.

Bloch, M., Rotenberg, N., Koren, D., & Ehud, K. (2006). Risk factors for early postpartum depressive symptoms. *General Hospital Psychiatry, 28*(1), 3–8.

Bockting, W. O., & Fung, L. C. T. (2006). Genital reconstruction and gender identity disorders. In D. B. Sarwer et al. (Eds.), *Psychological aspects of reconstructive and cosmetic plastic surgery: Clinical, empirical, and ethical perspectives* (pp. 207–229). New York: Lippincott Williams & Wilkins.

Bodenmann, G., Ledermann, T., Blattner, D., & Galluzzo, C. (2006). Associations among everyday stress, critical life events, and sexual problems. *Journal of Nervous and Mental Disease, 194*(7), 494–501.

Boesveld, S. (2008, January 2). Facebook mania hits 1 million in Toronto. *Toronto Star,* p. A10.

Bogaert, A. F. (1996). Volunteer bias in human sexuality research: Evidence for both sexuality and personality differences in males. *Archives of Sexual Behavior, 25*(2) 125–140.

Bogaert, A. F. (2001). Personality, individual differences, and preferences for sexual media. *Archives of Sexual Behavior, 30*(1), 29–53.

Bogaert, A. F. (2005a). Age at puberty and father absence in a national probability sample. *Journal of Adolescence, 28*(4), 541–546.

Bogaert, A. F. (2005b). Sibling sex ratio and sexual orientation in men and women: New tests in two national probability samples. *Archives of Sexual Behavior, 34*(1), 111–116.

Bogaert, A. F. (2006a). Toward a conceptual understanding of asexuality. *Review of General Psychology, 10*(3), 241–250.

Bogaert, A. F. (2006b). Biological versus nonbiological older brothers and men's sexual orientation. *Proceedings of the National Academy of Sciences of the United States of America, 103*(28), 10771–10774.

Bogaert, A. F. & Jamieson, L. (2008). Justice beliefs and other predictors of the timing of "coming out" in gay and bisexual men. Paper presented at the Guelph Sexuality Conference, Guelph, ON.

Bogin, G. Y. (2006). Out of the darkness: Male adolescents and the experience of sexual victimization. *School Social Work Journal, 30*(2), 1–21.

Boies, S. C. (2002). University students' uses of and reactions to online sexual information and entertainment: Links to online and offline sexual behavior. *Canadian Journal of Human Sexuality, 11*(2), 77–89.

Boles, J., & Elifson, K. W. (1994). Sexual identity and HIV: The male prostitute. *Journal of Sex Research, 31*, 39–46.

Bolton, J. M., Sareen, J., & Reiss, J. P. (2006). Genital anaesthesia persisting six years after sertraline discontinuation. *Journal of Sex & Marital Therapy, 32*(4), 327–330.

Bonoguore, T. (2007, July 18). Still Single? Time to move west. *Toronto Star.*

Born, L., Soares, C. N., Phillips, S., Jung, M., & Steiner, M. (2006). Women and reproductive-related trauma. In Yehuda, R. (Ed.). (2006). *Psychobiology of posttraumatic stress disorders: A decade of progress* (pp. 491–494). Vol. 1071. New York: Blackwell Publishing.

Boros, S., Mateuca, A., & Matus, M. (2005). The role of social identity in attributions—Evaluating the guilt in rape assault. *Cognitie Creier Comportament, 9*(1), 35–57.

Boston Women's Health Book Collective. (1992). *The new our bodies, ourselves.* New York: Simon & Schuster.

Boston Women's Health Book Collective. (2005). *Our bodies, ourselves: A new edition for a new era.* New York: Touchstone.

Bowlby, J. (1969). *Attachment and loss.* Vol. 1. New York: Basic Books.

Boyce, W., Craig, W., & Elger, F. (2008). *Healthy settings for young people in Canada.* Public Health Agency of Canada.

Boyce, W., Doherty, M., Fortin, C., & Mackinnon. D. (2003). *Canadian youth, sexual health and HIV/AIDS study.* Toronto: Council of Ministers of Education.

Boyce, W., King, M., & Roche, J. (2008). *Healthy settings for young people in Canada.* Ottawa, ON: Public Health Agency of Canada.

Boyle, T. (2007, April 30). Pupils punished over Facebook comments. *Toronto Star*, p. E5.

Bradford, J. M. W. (1998). Treatment of men with paraphilia. *The New England Journal of Medicine, 338*, 464–465.

Bradford, J. M. W. (2000). The treatment of sexual deviation using a pharmacological approach. *Journal of Sex Research, 37*, 248–257.

Bradford, J. M. W. (2001). The neurobiology, neuropharmacology, and pharmacological treatment of the paraphilias and compulsive sexual behaviour. *Canadian Journal of Psychiatry, 46*(1), 26–34.

Bradford, J. M. W., Greenberg, D., Gojer, J., Martindale, J. J., & Goldberg, M. (1995). Sertraline in the treatment of pedophilia: An open label study. *New Research Program Abstract SNR441;* American Psychiatric Association Meeting; (May 24) Miami, Florida.

Bradford, J. M. W., & Pawlak, A. (1993). Double-blind placebo crossover study of cyproterone acetate in the treatment of the paraphilias. *Archives of Sexual Behavior, 22*(5), 383–402.

Braham, D. (2008). *The secret lives of saints: Child brides and lost boys in Canada's polygamous Mormon sect.* Toronto: Random House Canada.

Brean, J. (2008, May 21). Campus abortion debate reaches compromise. *National Post*, p. A6.

Brennan, R. (2004, July 13). Ontario rehires "smut" traders. *The Toronto Star.*

Briere, J., & Runtz, M. (1987). Post sexual abuse trauma: Data and implications for clinical practice. *Journal of Interpersonal Violence, 2*, 367–379.

Briken, P., Hill, A., Nika, E., & Berner, W. (2005). Obscene telephone calls—Relations to paraphilias, paraphilia related disorders and stalking. *Psychiatrische Praxis, 32*(6), 304–307.

Broder, M. S., Kanouse, D. E., Mittman, B. S., & Bernstein, S. J. (2000). The appropriateness of recommendations for hysterectomy. *Obstetrics & Gynecology, 95*, 199–206.

Brody, J. E. (1995a, May 3). Breast scans may indeed help women under 50. *The New York Times*, p. C11.

Brody, J. E. (1995b, August 30). Hormone replacement therapy for men: When does it help? *The New York Times*, p. C8.

Brody, J. E. (1998a, February 18). Studies confirm alcohol's link to breast cancer. *The New York Times* online.

Brody, J. E. (1998b, May 19). Sour note in the Viagra symphony. *The New York Times*, p. F7.

Brody, J. E. (2000, May 16). Cybersex gives birth to a psychological disorder. *The New York Times*, pp. F7, F12.

Bronner, E. (1998, February 1). "Just say maybe. No sexology, please. We're Americans." *The New York Times*, p. WK6.

Brooks, J. (2001, May 31). Film review delay at issue in video store trial. *The Toronto Star.*

Brotman, S., Ryan, B., & Cormier, R. (2003). The health and social service needs of gay and lesbian elders and their families in Canada. *The Gerontologist, 43*(2), 192–202.

Brotto, L., Heiman, J., Goff, B., Greer, B., Lentz, G., Swisher, E., et al. (2008). A psychoeducational intervention for sexual dysfunction in women with gynecologic cancer. *Archives of Sexual Behavior, 37*(2), 317–329.

Brotto, L. A., Basson, R., & Luria, M. (2008). A mindfulness-based group psychoeducational intervention targeting sexual arousal disorder in women. *Journal of Sexual Medicine, 5*(7), 1646–1659.

Brotto, L. A., Chik, H. M., Ryder, A. G., Gorzalka, B. B., & Seal, B. N. (2005). Acculturation and sexual function in Asian women. *Archives of Sexual Behaviour, 34*(6), 613–626.

Brotto, L. A., Chou, A. Y., Singh, T., & Woo, J. S. T. (in press). Reproductive health practices among Indian, Indo-Canadian, Canadian East Asian, and Euro-Canadian women: The role of acculturation. *Journal of Obstetrics and Gynaecology Canada.*

Brotto, L. A., & Gorzalka, B. B. (2002). Genital and subjective sexual arousal in postmenopausal women: Influence of laboratory-induced hyperventilation. *Journal of Sex & Marital Therapy, 28*(Suppl1), 39–53.

Brotto, L. A., & Heiman, J. R. (2007). Mindfulness in sex therapy: Applications for women with sexual difficulties following gynecologic cancer. *Sex and Marital Therapy, 22*(1), 3–11.

Brotto, L. A., Woo, J. S. T., & Ryder, A. G. (2007). Acculturation and sexual function in Canadian East Asian men. *Journal of Sexual Medicine, 4*, 72–82.

Brown, D. (2003). Pornography and erotica. In Bryant, J., Roskos-Ewoldsen, D., & Cantor, J. (Eds.). *Communication and emotion: Essays in honor of Dolf Zillmann* (pp. 221–253). LEA's communication series. Hillsdale, NJ: Lawrence Erlbaum Associates.

Brown, G. R., & Haaser, R. C. (2005). Sexual disorders. In Levenson, J. L. (Ed.), *The American psychiatric publishing textbook of psychosomatic medicine* (pp. 359–386). Washington, DC: American Psychiatric Publishing.

Brown, L. M., McNatt, P. S., & Cooper, G. D. (2003). Ingroup romantic preferences among Jewish and non-Jewish white undergraduates. *International Journal of Intercultural Relations, 27*(3), 335–354.

Brown, N. R., & Sinclair, R. C. (1999). Estimating number of lifetime sexual partners: Men and women do it differently. *Journal of Sex Research, 36*(3), 292–297.

Brown, R., Balousek, S., Mundt, M., & Fleming, M. (2005). Methadone maintenance and male sexual dysfunction. *Journal of Addictive Diseases, 24*(2), 91–106.

Brown, R. A. (1994). Romantic love and the spouse selection criteria of male and female Korean college students. *The Journal of Social Psychology, 134*(2), 183–189.

Brown, T. (2002). A proposed model of bisexual identity development that elaborates on experiential differences of women and men. *Journal of Bisexuality, 2*(4), 67–91.

Brym, R., & Lenton, R. (2001). Love online: A report on digital dating in Canada. [Online].

Available: **www.nelson.com/nelson/harcourt/sociology/newsociety3e/loveonline.pdf**

Bumpass, L. (1995, July 6). Cited in J. Steinhauer. No marriage, no apologies. *The New York Times*, pp. C1, C7.

Buss, D. M. (1994). *The evolution of desire: Strategies of human mating*. New York: Basic Books.

Buss, D. M. (2003). The dangerous passion: Why jealousy is as necessary as love and sex. *Archives of Sexual Behavior, 32*(1), 79–80.

Buss, D. M. (Ed.). (2005). *The handbook of evolutionary psychology*. Hoboken, NJ: John Wiley & Sons.

Butler, J. (1993). *Bodies that matter: On the discursive limits of sex*. New York: Routledge.

Butler, J. (2003). *Kritik der ethischenGewalt.* Adorno lectures. 2002. Frankfurt am Main: Institut fur Sozialforschung an der Johann Wolfgang Goethe-Universitat.

Buunk, B. P., Dijkstra, P., Fetchenhauer, D., & Kenrick, D. T. (2002). Age and gender differences in mate selection criteria for various involvement levels. *Personal Relationships, 9*, 271–278.

Byerly, M. J., et al. (2006). Sexual dysfunction associated with second-generation antipsychotics in outpatients with schizophrenia or schizoaffective disorder: An empirical evaluation of olanzapine, risperidone, and quetiapine. *Schizophrenia Research, 86*(1–3), 244–250.

Byers, E. S., & Demmons, S. (1999). Sexual satisfaction and sexual self-disclosure within dating relationships. *Journal of Sex Research, 36*, 180–189.

Byers, E. S., & Eno, R. (1991). Predicting men's sexual coercion and aggression from attitudes, dating history and sexual response. *Journal of Psychology and Human Sexuality, 4*, 55–69.

Byers, E. S., & Grenier, G. (2003). Premature or rapid ejaculation: Heterosexual couples' perceptions of men's ejaculatory behavior. *Archives of Sexual Behavior, 32*(3), 261–270.

Byers, E. S., & Heinlein, L. (1989). Predicting initiations and refusals of sexual activities in married and cohabiting heterosexual couples. *Journal of Sex Research, 26*, 210–231.

Byers, E. S., & Lewis, K. (1988). Dating couples' disagreements over the desired level of sexual intimacy. *Journal of Sex Research, 24*, 15–29.

Byers, E. S., Sears, H. A., Voyer, S. D., Thurlow, J. L., Cohen, J. N., & Weaver, A. D. (2003). An adolescent perspective on sexual health education at school and at home: I. High school students. *Canadian Journal of Human Sexuality, 12*(1), 1–17.

Byers, L. (2005). *Gendered use of and exposure to SEMI.* Paper presented at the 2005 Canadian Sociology Association Annual Meeting, London, ON.

Byrd, J., Hyde, J. S., DeLamater, J. D., & Plant, E. A. (1998). Sexuality during pregnancy and the year postpartum. *Journal of Family Practice, 47*(4), 305–308.

Caceres, C. F., & van-Griensven, G. J. P. (1994). Male homosexual transmission of HIV-1. *AIDS, 8*(8), 1051–1061.

Cairns, K. V. (1997). Counseling the partners of heterosexual male cross-dressers. *Canadian Journal of Human Sexuality, 6*, 297–306.

Cairns, K. V., & Hatt, D. G. (1995). Discrimination and sexual harassment in a graduate student sample. *Canadian Journal of Human Sexuality, 4*, 169–176.

Calhoun, K. S., & Atkeson, B. M. (1991). *Treatment of rape victims: Facilitating social adjustment.* New York: Pergamon Press.

Callen, J., & Pinelli, J. (2004). Incidence and duration of breastfeeding for term infants in Canada, United States, Europe, and Australia: Literature review. *Birth, 31*(4), 285–292.

Calzavara, L. M., Bullock, S. L., Myers, T., Marshall, V. W., & Cockerill, R. (1999). Sexual partnering and risk of HIV/STD among Aboriginals. *Canadian Journal of Public Health, 90*(3), 186–191.

Calzavara, L., Burchell, A. N., Remis, R. S., et al. (2003). Delayed application of condoms is a risk factor for human immunodeficiency virus infection among homosexual and bisexual men. *American Journal of Epidemiology, 157*(3), 210–217.

Calzavara, L. M., Coates, R., Raboud, J., Farewell, V., Read, S., Shepherd, F., Fanning, M., & MacFadden, D. (1992). Association between alcohol and drug use prior to sex and high risk sexual behavior in the Toronto sexual contact study cohort. *Canadian Journal of Infectious Diseases, 3*, 45A.

Campbell, R. (2006). Rape survivors' experiences with the legal and medical systems: Do rape victim advocates make a difference? *Violence Against Women, 12*(1), 30–45.

Canadian Cancer Society. (2002). **www.cancer.ca**

Canadian Cancer Society. (2008). Canadian cancer statistics 2008. Available: **www.cancer.ca/vgn/images/portal/cit_86751114/10/34/614137951cw_library_**

Canadian Institute for Health Information. (2004). *Giving birth in Canada: A regional profile.*

Canadian Institute for Health Information. (2007). Giving birth in Canada: Regional trends from 2001–2002 to 2005–2006. Available: **http://secure.cihi.ca/cihiweb/en/downloads/Childbirth_AiB_FINAL_E.pdf**

Canadian Press. (1995a, March 24). Sex calls topple MP. *The Guelph Mercury.*

Canadian Press. (1995b, July 2). Woman posed as man for sex. *The Guelph Mercury.*

Canadian Press. (1997, May 2). American girls flash Windsor cops. *The Guelph Mercury.*

Canadian Press. (1999, March 10). Lau and Kinsella settle lawsuit, avoiding trial.

Canadian Press. (2003a, May 21). Alberta alderwoman signs deal on U.S. charges. *The Guelph Mercury*, p. A9.

Canadian Press. (2003b, December 23). Baseball hopeful gets jail for sex crimes against teens. *The Guelph Mercury.*

Canadian Press. (2005a, August 31). Woman granted divorce for husband's affair with man. *The Guelph Mercury.*

Canadian Press. (2005b). Polygamists in BC pose legal quandary. *The Toronto Star.*

Canadian Press. (2006, July 29). Child porn case a wake-up call. *Guelph Mercury*, p. A5.

Canadian Press. (2007, September 10). Importance of marriage strong for individuals. *Toronto Star*, p. A6.

Canadian Press. (2008, July 14). Teachers vote in favour of criminalizing cyberbullying. *TheToronto Star*, p. A5.

Cantor, J. M., Blanchard, R., Christensen, B. K., Dickey, R., Klassen, P. E., Beckstead, A. L., et al. (2004). Intelligence, memory, and handedness in pedophilia. *Neuropsychology, 18*(1), 3–14.

Cantor, J. M., Blanchard, R., Robichaud, L. K., & Christensen, B. K. (2005b). Quantitative reanalysis of aggregate data on IQ in sexual offenders. *Psychological Bulletin, 131*(4), 555–568.

Cantor, J. M., Kabani, N., Christensen, B. K., Zipursky, R. B., Barbaree, H. E., Dickey, R., Klassen, P. E., Mikulis, D. J., Kuban, M. E., Blak, T., Richards, B. A., Hanratty, M. K., & Blanchard, R. (2008). Cerebral white matter deficiencies in pedophilic men. *Journal of Psychiatric Research, 42*, 167–183.

Cantor, J. M., Klassen, P. E., Dickey, R., Christensen, B. K., Kuban, M. E., Blak, T., et al. (2005a). Handedness in pedophilia and hebephillia. *Archives of Sexual Behaviour, 34*(4), 447–459.

Cantor, J. M., Kuban, M. E., Blak, T., Klassen, P. E., Dickey, R., & Blanchard, R. (2006). Grade failure and special education placement in sexual offenders' educational histories. *Archives of Sexual Behaviour, 35*(6), 743–751.

Caporaletti, J. (2006, September 20). Prostitution is a world-wide problem. [Online]. **www.collegiatetimes.com**.

Carey, B. (2005, May 31). Watching new love as it sears the brain. *The New York Times.*

Carmody, J., Reed, G., Kristeller, J., & Merriam, P. (2008). Mindfulness, spirituality, and health-related symptoms. *Journal of Psychosomatic Research, 64*(4), 393–403.

Carrère, S., Buehlman, K. T., Gottman, J. M., Coan, J. A., & Ruckstuhl, L. (2000). Predicting marital stability and divorce in newlywed couples. *Journal of Family Psychology, 14*(1), 42–58.

Carrier, S., Morales, A., & Defoy, I. (2005). Viagra long-term efficacy and quality of life: Results of Canadian long-term study. Paper presented to World Congress of Sexology, Montreal.

Carter, D. J., & Dalla, R. L. (2006). Transactional analysis case report: Street-level prostituted women as mental health care clients. *Sexual Addiction & Compulsivity, 13*(1), 95–119.

Castellsague, X., et al. (2002). Male circumcision, penile human papillomavirus infection, and cervical cancer in female partners. *New England Journal of Medicine, 346*(15), 1105–1112.

Catlin, G. (2002). The health divide: How the sexes differ. *Health Reports, 12*(3), 9–52.

Chat-line romance a trap. (2000, February 4). *The Toronto Star.*

Child, T. J., Henderson, A. M., & Tan, S. L. (2004). The desire for multiple pregnancy in male and female infertility patients. *Human Reproduction, 19*(3), 558–561.

Chiose, S. (2001). *Good girls do: Sex chronicles of a shameless generation.* Toronto: ECW Press.

Chivers, M., & Bailey, J. M. (2005). A sex difference in features that elicit genital response. *Biological Psychology, 70*(2), 115–120.

Chivers, M., Seto, M., & Blanchard, R. (2007). Gender and sexual orientation differences in sexual response to sexual activities versus gender of actors in sexual films. *Journal of Personality and Social Psychology, 93*(6), 1108–1121.

Choi, P. Y. (1992). The psychological benefits of physical exercise: Implications for women and the menstrual cycle. [Special issue: The menstrual cycle]. *Journal of Reproductive and Infant Psychology, 10*, 111–115.

Christin-Maitre, S., Bouchard, P., & Spitz, I. M. (2000). Drug therapy: Medical termination of pregnancy. *The New England Journal of Medicine* online, *342*(13).

Clark, W. (2003). *Pockets of belief: Religious attendance patterns in Canada.* Statistics Canada. *Canadian Social Trends*, Spring. [Catalogue No. 11-008]

Clayton, A., Keller, A., & McGarvey, E. L. (2006). Burden of phase-specific sexual dysfunction with SSRIs. *Journal of Affective Disorders, 91*(1), 27–32.

Cleary, J., Barhman, R., MacCormack, T. & Herold, E. (2002). Discussing sexual health with a partner: A qualitative study with young women. *Canadian Journal of Human Sexuality, 11*(3–4), 117–132.

Clements-Schreiber, M. E., & Rempel, J. K. (1995). Women's acceptance of stereotypes about male sexuality: Correlations with strategies to influence reluctant partners. *Canadian Journal of Human Sexuality, 4*(4), 223–236.

Cnattingius, S. (2004). The epidemiology of smoking during pregnancy: Smoking prevalence, maternal characteristics, and pregnancy outcomes. *Nicotine & Tobacco Research, 6*(Suppl. 2), S125–S140.

Cnattingius, S., Bergstrom, R., Lipworth, L., & Kramer, M. S. (1998). Prepregnancy weight and the risk of adverse pregnancy outcomes. *The New England Journal of Medicine, 338*, 147–152.

Coates, R. A., Calzavara, L. M., Read, S. E., et al. (1988). Risk factors for HIV infection in male sexual contacts of men with AIDS or an AIDS-related condition. *American Journal of Epidemiology, 128*(4), 729–739.

Coates, R. A., Soskolne, C. L., Calzavara, L., et al. (1986). The reliability of sexual histories in AIDS-related research: Evaluation of an interview administered questionnaire. *Canadian Journal of Public Health*, 77, 343–348.

Cochran, W. G., Mosteller, F., & Tukey, J. W. (1953). Statistical problems of the Kinsey Report. *Journal of the American Statistical Association, 48*, 673–716.

Cohen, A. B., & Tannenbaum, I. J. (2001). Lesbian and bisexual women's judgments of the attractiveness of different body types. *Journal of Sex Research, 38*(3), 226–232.

Cohen, J. N., Byers, E. S., Sears, H. A., & Weaver, A. D. (2004). Sexual health education: Attitudes, knowledge, and comfort of teachers in New Brunswick schools. *Canadian Journal of Human Sexuality, 13*(1), 1–15.

Cohen, L. S., et al. (2006). Relapse of major depression during pregnancy in women who maintain or discontinue antidepressant treatment. *Journal of the American Medical Association, 295*(5), 499–507.

Cohen, M. S. (2000). Preventing sexual transmission of HIV—New ideas from sub-Saharan Africa. *The New England Journal of Medicine, 342*(13), 970–973.

Cohen–Bendahan, C. C. C., van de Beek, C., & Berenbaum, S. A. (2005). Prenatal sex hormone effects on child and adult sex-typed behavior: Methods and findings. *Neuroscience & Biobehavioral Reviews, 29*(2), 353–384.

Cohen-Kettenis, P. T., Owen, A., Kaijser, V. G., Bradley, S. J., & Zucker, K. J. (2003). Demographic characteristics, social competence, and behavior problems in children with gender identity disorder: A cross-national, cross-clinic comparative analysis. *Journal of Abnormal Child Psychology, 31*(1), 41–53.

Colapinto, J. (2000). *As nature made him: The boy who was raised as a girl.* New York: HarperCollins.

Colapinto, J. (2004, June 3). Gender gap: What were the real reasons behind David Reimer's suicide? [Online]. **www.slate.com/id/2101678**

Cole, F. S. (2000). Extremely preterm birth—Defining the limits of hope. *The New England Journal of Medicine, 343*(6).

Cole, S. S. (1988). Women's sexuality, and disabilities. *Women and Therapy*, 7, 277–294.

Cole, T. B. (2006). Rape at US colleges often fueled by alcohol. *Journal of the American Medical Association, 296*(5), 504–505.

Collaer, M. L., & Hines, M. (1995). Human behavioral sex differences: A role for gonadal hormones during early development? *Psychological Bulletin, 118*, 55–107.

Compas (1998). [Modern life survey of the Canadian adult population]. Unpublished raw data.

Connell, E. & Hunt, A. (2006). Sexual ideology and sexual physiology in the discourses of sex advice literature. *The Canadian Journal of Human Sexuality, 15*(1), 23–45.

Connolly, J., Craig, W., Goldberg, A., & Pepler, D. (2004). Mixed-gender groups, dating, and romantic relationships in early adolescence. *Journal of Research on Adolescence, 14*(2), 185–207.

Connolly, J., Pepler, D., Craig, W., & Taradash, A. (2000). Dating experiences of bullies in early adolescence. *Child Maltreatment, 5*(4), 299–310.

Cooper, A., Delmonico, D. L., & Burg, R. (2000). Cybersex users, abusers, and compulsives: New findings and implications. *Sexual Addiction & Compulsivity*, 7(1–2), 5–29.

Cooper, A., Delmonico, D. L., Griffin–Shelley, E., & Mathy, R. M. (2004). Online sexual activity: An examination of potentially problematic behaviors. *Sexual Addiction & Compulsivity, 11*(3), 129–143.

Corty, E. W. (2006). Sexual dysfunction. In F. Andrasik (Ed.), *Comprehensive handbook of personality and psychopathology. Vol. 2: Adult psychopathology* (pp. 423–435). Hoboken, NJ: John Wiley & Sons.

Cotten-Huston, A. L., & Waite, B. M. (2000). Anti-homosexual attitudes in college students: Predictors and classroom interventions. *Journal of Homosexuality, 38*(3), 117–133.

Courtois, F. J., Charvier, K. F., Leriche, A., Vézina, J.-G., Côté, M., & Bélanger, M. (2007). Blood pressure changes during sexual stimulation, ejaculation and midodrine treatment in men with spinal cord injury. *British Journal of Urology, 101*, 331–337.

Cove, J., & Petrak, J. (2004). Factors associated with sexual problems in HIV-positive gay men. *International Journal of STD & AIDS, 15*(11), 732–736.

Cox, C. L., Wexler, M. O., Rusbult, C. E., & Gaines, S. O., Jr. (1997). Prescriptive support and commitment processes in close relationships. *Social Psychology Quarterly, 60*(1), 79–90.

Cox, D. J. (1988). Incidence and nature of male genital exposure behavior as reported by college women. *Journal of Sex Research, 24,* 227–234.

Coyle, J. P. (2006). Treating difficult couples: Helping clients with coexisting mental and relationship disorders. *Family Relations: Interdisciplinary Journal of Applied Family Studies, 55*(1), 146–147.

Craig, R. J. (2005). Harassment. In R. J. Craig (Ed.), *Personality-guided forensic psychology. Personality-guided psychology* (pp. 155–167). Washington, DC: American Psychological Association.

Craig, W. M., & Pepler, D. J. (1997). Observations of bullying and victimization in the school yard. *Canadian Journal of Social Psychology, 13,* 41–60.

Crawford, T. (2008, May 27). Giving it another shot. *Toronto Star,* p. L1.

Crews, D. (1994). Animal sexuality. *Scientific American, 270*(1), 108–114.

Cribb, R., & Brazao, D. (2005, May 10). What can Toronto do about sex dens? Holistic centres "a never-ending mess" for city "Holistic" spas upset nearby residents Police not enforcing "moral offences". *Toronto Star,* p. A01.

Crocker, D., & Kalemba, V. (1999). The incidence and impact of women's experiences of sexual harassment in Canadian workplaces. *The Canadian Review of Sociology and Anthropology, 36*(4), 541–558.

Crosby, R. A., Sanders, S. A., Yarber, W. L., Graham, C. A., & Dodge, B. (2002). Condom use errors and problems among college men. *Sexually Transmitted Diseases, 29,* 552–557.

Crossette, B. (1998, March 23). Mutilation seen as risk for the girls of immigrants. *The New York Times,* p. A3.

Crowley, T., Richardson, D., Goldmeier, D., & BASHH Special Interest Group for Sexual Dysfunction. (2006). Recommendations for the management of vaginismus: BASHH Special Interest Group for Sexual Dysfunction. *International Journal of STD & AIDS, 17*(1), 14–18.

Crum, N. F., Furtek, K. J., Olson, P. E., Amling, C. L., & Wallace, M. R. (2005). A review of hypogonadism and erectile dysfunction among HIV-infected men during the pre- and post-HAART eras: Diagnosis, pathogenesis, and management. *AIDS Patient Care and STDs, 19*(10), 869–885.

Csoka, A. B., & Shipko, S. (2006). Persistent sexual side effects after SSRI discontinuation. *Psychotherapy and Psychosomatics, 75*(3), 187–188.

Cummings, A., & Leschied, W. (Eds.) (2002). *Violence in the lives of adolescent girls: Implications for educators and counsellors.* New York: Edwin Mellen Press.

Cunningham, A. L., et al. (2006). Prevalence of infection with herpes simplex virus types 1 and 2 in Australia: A nationwide population based survey. *Sexually Transmitted Infections, 82,* 164–168.

Cunningham, M. R., et al. (1995). "Their ideas of beauty are, on the whole, the same as ours": Consistency and variability in the cross-cultural perception of female physical attractiveness. *Journal of Personality and Social Psychology, 68*(2), 261–279.

Cutler, W. B. (1999). Human sex-attractant hormones: Discovery, research, development, and application in sex therapy. *Psychiatric Annals, 29*(1), 54–59.

Cutler, W. B., Friedmann, E., & McCoy, N. L. (1998). Pheromonal influences on sociosexual behavior in men. *Archives of Sexual Behavior, 27*(1), 1–13.

D'Amico, A. V., et al. (2000). Biochemical outcome following external beam radiation therapy with or without androgen suppression therapy for clinically localized prostate cancer. *Journal of the American Medical Association, 284,* 1280–1283.

Dabbs, J. M., Jr., & Morris, R. (1990). Testosterone, social class, and antisocial behavior in a sample of 4,462 men. *Psychological Science, 1,* 1–3.

Dahinten, V. S. (2003). Peer sexual harassment in adolescence: The function of gender. *The Canadian Journal of Nursing Research, 35*(2), 56–73.

Dalby, P. (2007, September 17). Cancer's on hold so life can go on. *Toronto Star,* p. X7.

Daly, K. J., & Sobol, M. P. (1994). Public and private adoption: A comparison of service and accessibility. *Family Relations, 43,* 86–93.

Damon, W. (2002). Dominance, sexism, and inadequacy: Testing a compensatory conceptualization in a sample of heterosexual men involved in SM. *Journal of Psychology & Human Sexuality, 14*(4), 25–45.

Dancer, P. L., Kleinplatz, P. J., & Moser, C. (2006). 24/7 SM slavery. *Journal of Homosexuality, 50*(2–3), 81–101.

Daneback, K., Cooper, A., & Månsoon, S. (2005). An internet study of cybersex participants. *Archives of Sexual Behavior, 34*(3), 321–328.

Daneback, K., Ross, M. W., & Månsson, S. (2006). Characteristics and behaviors of sexual compulsives who use the internet for sexual purposes. *Sexual Addition & Compulsivity, 13*(1), 53–67.

Danielsson, I., Sjoberg, I., & Ostman, C. (2001). Acupuncture for the treatment of vulvar vestibulitis: A pilot study. *Acta Obstetricia Et Gynecologia Scandinavica, 80*(5), 437.

Darling, C. A., Davidson, J. K., & Jennings, D. A. (1991). The female sexual response revisited: Understanding the multi-orgasmic experience in women. *Archives of Sexual Behavior, 20,* 527–540.

Davidson, J. K. (2004). *Fearless sex: A babe's guide to overcoming your romantic obsessions and getting the sex life you deserve,* 2nd ed. Gloucester, MA: Fair Winds Press.

Davidson, J. K., & Hoffman, L. E. (1986). Sexual fantasies and sexual satisfaction: An empirical analysis of erotic thought. *Journal of Sex Research, 22,* 184–205.

Davidson-Harden, J., Fisher, W. A., & Davidson, P. R. (2000). Attitudes toward people in exclusive dating relationships who initiate condom use. *Canadian Journal of Human Sexuality, 9,* 1–14.

Davies, M. (2004). Correlates of negative attitudes toward gay men: Sexism, male role norms, and male sexuality. *Journal of Sex Research, 41*(3), 259–266.

Davis, D., Shaver, P. R., & Vernon, M. L. (2003). Physical, emotional, and behavioral reactions to breaking up: The roles of gender, age, emotional involvement, and attachment style. *Personality & Social Psychology Bulletin, 29*(7), 871–884.

Davis, K. E., & Frieze, I. H., & Maiuro, R. D. (Eds.). (2002). *Stalking: Perspectives on victims and perpetrators* (pp. 212–236). New York: Springer.

Davis, S. (2000). Testosterone and sexual desire in women. *Journal of Sex Education & Therapy, 25*(1), 25–32.

Dawood, K., Pillard, R. C., Horvath, C., Revelle, W., & Bailey, J. M. (2000). Familial aspects of male homosexuality. *Archives of Sexual Behavior, 29*(2), 155–163.

de Raad, B., & Doddema-Winsemius, M. (1992). Factors in the assortment of human mates: Differential preferences in Germany and the Netherlands. *Personality and Individual Differences, 13,* 103–114.

Decaire, B., & Foster, D. (in press). *Feminist counselling: Theory, issues and practice.* Toronto: Women's Press.

Dekeseredy, W., & Kelly, K. (1993). The incidence and prevalence of woman abuse in Canadian university and college dating relationships. *Canadian Journal of Sociology, 18,* 137–159.

Dekker, J. (1993). Inhibited male orgasm. In W. O'Donohue & J. H. Geer (Eds.), *Handbook of sexual dysfunctions: Assessment and treatment* (pp. 279–301). Boston: Allyn & Bacon.

DeMont, J. (1999, December). Doing it and enjoying it. *Maclean's,* 44–46.

den Tonkelaar, I., & Oddens, B. J. (2000). Determinants of long-term hormone replacement therapy and reasons for early discontinuation. *Obstetrics & Gynecology, 95*(4), 507–512.

Dennerstein, L., Dudley, E. C., Hopper, J. L., Guthrie, J. R., & Burger, H. G. (2000). A prospective population-based study of menopausal symptoms. *Obstetrics & Gynecology, 96*(3), 351–358.

Dennerstein, L., & Goldstein, I. (2005). Postmenopausal female sexual dysfunction: At a crossroads. *Journal of Sexual Medicine, 2*(Suppl. 3), 116–117.

Dennerstein, L., & Hayes, R. D. (2005). Confronting the challenges: Epidemiological study of female sexual dysfunction and the menopause. *Journal of Sexual Medicine, 2*(Suppl. 3), 118–132.

Dennis, W. (1992). *Hot and bothered: Men and women, sex and love in the nineties.* Toronto: Key Porter Books.

Denov, M. S. (2001). A culture of denial: Exploring professional perspectives on female sex offending. *Canadian Journal of Criminology, 43*(3), 303–329.

Derby, C. A. (2000, October 2). Cited in Study finds exercise reduces the risk of impotence. The Associated Press.

Devor, H. (1997). *FTM: Female-to-male transsexuals.* Bloomington, IN: Indiana University Press.

Devor, H. (2002). Who are "we"? Where sexual orientation meets gender identity. *Journal of Gay & Lesbian Psychotherapy, 6*(2), 5–21.

Dharmajah, T. (2008, July 17). No jail after sex-game death. *Guelph Mercury*, p. A1.

Di Giulio, G., & Reissing, E. (2004). *Evaluation of clinical psychologists' provision of sexual health care needs.* Paper presented at Canadian Sex Research Forum Meeting, Fredericton, NB.

Diamond, L. M. (2003a). Was it a phase? Young women's relinquishment of lesbian/bisexual identities over a 5-year period. *Journal of Personality & Social Psychology, 84*(2), 352–364.

Diamond, L. M. (2003b). What does sexual orientation orient? A biobehavioral model distinguishing romantic love and sexual desire. *Psychological Review, 110*(1), 173–192.

Diamond, M. (1996). Prenatal predisposition and the clinical management of some pediatric conditions. *Journal of Sex & Marital Therapy, 22*(3), 139–147.

Dijkstra, P., & Buunk, B. P. (2002). Sex differences in the jealousy-evoking effect of rival characteristics. *European Journal of Social Psychology, 32*(6), 829–852.

Dindia, K., & Timmermann, L. (2003). Accomplishing romantic relationships. In J. O. Greene & B. R. Burleson (Eds.), *Handbook of communication and social interaction skills* (pp. 685–721). Mahwah, NJ: Erlbaum.

Downs, M., & Nazario, B. (2003, February 11). *Aphrodisiacs through the ages.* WebMD Features. [Online].

Dredger, A. (2008). The controversy surrounding *The Man Who Would be Queen: A Case History of the Politics of Science, Identity, and Sex in the Internet Age. Archives of Sexual Behavior, 37*, 366–421.

Dreidger, S. (2003, May 19). The teacher's lesson. *Maclean's.*

Dreidger, S. D. (2002, September 30). What parents don't know (or won't admit). *Maclean's*, 20–26.

Dreyfuss, I. A. (1998. February 8). Exercise may cut breast cancer risk. Associated Press online.

Drigotas, S. M., Rusbult, C. E., & Verette, J. (1999). Level of commitment, mutuality of commitment, and couple well-being. *Personal Relationships, 6*(3), 389–409.

Driver, J., Tabares, A., Shapiro, A., Nahm, E. Y., & Gottman, J. M. (2003). Interactional patterns in marital success and failure: Gottman laboratory studies. In F. Walsh (Ed.). *Normal family processes: Growing diversity and complexity* (3rd ed.) (pp. 493–513). New York: Guilford Press.

Drolet, M. (2002). *The "who, what, when and where" of gender pay differentials.* (Catalogue No. 71-584-MPE). Ottawa, ON: Minister of Industry.

Duenwald, M. (2002, July 16). Hormone therapy: One size, clearly, no longer fits all. *The New York Times.*

Duggavathi, R., Volle, D., Mataki, C., Antal, M., Messaddeq, N., Auwerx, J., Murphy, B., & Schoonjans, K. (2008). Liver receptor homolog 1 is essential for ovulation. *Genes & Development, 22*, 1871–1876.

Dunn, K., Cherkas, L., & Spector, T. (2005). Genetic influences on variation in female orgasmic function. *Biology Letters, 1, 2.*

Dunn, M. E. (1998). Cited in Leary, W. E. (1998, September 29). Older people enjoy sex, survey says. *The New York Times*, p. F8.

Dwyer, M. (1988). Exhibitionism/voyeurism. *Journal of Social Work and Human Sexuality, 7*, 101–112.

Dye, M. L., & Davis, K. E. (2003). Stalking and psychological abuse: Common factors and relationship-specific characteristics. *Violence & Victims, 18*(2), 163–180.

Eagle Canada. (2008, May 9). Gay teens surveyed feel unsafe in school. **www.egale.ca/index.asp?lang=E&menu=1&item=1393**

Eason, E., & Feldman, P. (2000). Much ado about a little cut: Is episiotomy worthwhile? *Obstetrics & Gynecology, 95*(4), 616–618.

Eckler, R. (2000). Why I'll never make it on to *Blind Date. National Post.*

Edgley, C. (1989). Commercial sex: Pornography, prostitution, and advertising. In K. McKinney & S. Sprecher (eds.), *Human sexuality: The societal and interpersonal context* (pp. 370–424). Norwood, NJ: Ablex.

Edgley, K. (2002). Condom use among heterosexual couples. Unpublished doctoral dissertation, University of Ottawa.

Edser, S. J., & Shea, J. D. (2002). An exploratory investigation of bisexual men in monogamous, heterosexual marriages. *Journal of Bisexuality, 2*(4), 5–29.

Edwards, V. J., Holden, G. W., Felitti, V. J., & Anda, R. F. (2003). Relationship between multiple forms of childhood maltreatment and adult mental health in community respondents: Results from the Adverse Childhood Experiences study. *American Journal of Psychiatry, 160*(8), 1453–1460.

Egan, D. (2005, October). Designer vaginas. *Chatelaine*, pp. 161–165.

Elia, J. P., Swanson, C., & Goldberg, A. R. (2003). More queer: Resources on queer theory. *Journal of Homosexuality, 45*(2–4), 391–400.

Ellis, E. M. (2000). *Divorce wars: Interventions with families in conflict.* Washington, DC: American Psychological Association.

Ellis, L., Robb, B., & Burke, D. (2005). Sexual orientation in the United States and Canadian college students. *Archives of Sexual Behavior, 34*(5), 569–581.

Eltahawy, M. (2008, August 5). Shame on Egypt's sexist bullies. *The Toronto Globe and Mail*, p. A11.

Emanuele, E., et al. (2006). Raised plasma nerve growth factor levels associated with early-stage romantic love. *Psychoneuroendocrinology, 31*(3), 288–294.

Emard, J. F., Drouin, G., Thouez, J. P., & Ghadirian, P. (2001). Vasectomy and prostate cancer in Quebec, Canada. *Health & Place, 7*(2), 131–139.

Engler, K., Otis, J., Alary, M., Masse, B., Remis, R. S., Girard, M., et al. (2005). An exploration of sexual behaviour and self-definition in a cohort of men who have sex with men. *The Canadian Journal of Human Sexuality, 14*(3–4), 87–104.

Epstein, R. (2008). The Assisted Human Reproduction Act and LGBTQ communities. A paper submitted by the AHRA/LGBTQ Working Group. Toronto: Sherbourne Health Centre.

Esmail, S., Munro, B., & Gibson, N. (2007). Couple's experience with multiple sclerosis in the context of their sexual relationship. *Sexuality and Disability, 25*(4), 163–177.

Esmail, S., Selman, J., Munro, B., Heather, J., Ponsetti, J., & Knupp, H. (2007). Using theatre to achieve student-centered sexual education. Paper presented at the Annual Conference of the Canadian Sex Research Forum. Banff, AB.

Evans, J. (2001). Men nurses and masculinities: Exploring gendered and sexual relations in nursing. Unpublished doctoral dissertation, Dalhousie University, Halifax.

Everitt, B. J. (1990). Sexual motivation: A neural and behavioural analysis of the mechanisms underlying appetitive and copulatory responses of male rats. *Neuroscience and Biobehavioral Reviews, 14,* 217–232.

Fagot, B. I., Rodgers, C. S., & Leinbach, M. D. (2000). Theories of gender socialization. In T. Eckes & H. M. Trautner (Eds.). *The developmental social psychology of gender* (pp. 65–89). Mahwah, NJ: Lawrence Erlbaum Associates.

Fakhry, C., & Gillison, M. L. (2006). Clinical implications of human papillomavirus in head and neck cancers. *Journal of Clinical Oncology, 24*(17), 2606–2611.

Faller, K. C. (1989). Why sexual abuse? An exploration of the intergenerational hypothesis. *Child Abuse and Neglect, 13,* 543–548.

Fallon, A. E., & Rozin, P. (1985). Sex differences in perceptions of desirable body shape. *Journal of Abnormal Psychology, 94,* 102–105.

Fang, C. (2008). Perceived stress is associated with impaired T-cell response to HPV16 in women with cervical dysplasia. *Annals of Behavioral Medicine*. 10, 1007.

Fausto-Sterling, A. (May/April 1993). The five sexes: Why male and female are not enough. *The Sciences*, 20–25.

Federman, D. D. (1994). Life without estrogen. *The New England Journal of Medicine, 331,* 1088–1089.

Federoff, J. P. (1995). Antiandrogens vs. serotonergic medications in the treatment of sex offenders: A preliminary compliance study. *Canadian Journal of Human Sexuality, 4,* 111–123.

Fedoroff, J. P., Fishell, A., & Fedoroff, B. (1999). A case series of women evaluated for paraphilic disorders. *The Canadian Journal of Human Sexuality, 8,* 127–140.

Fedoroff, P. (2003). The paraphilic world. In S. B. Levine, C. R. Risen, & S. E. Althof (Eds.), *Handbook of clinical sexuality for mental health professionals* (pp. 333–355). New York: Brunner-Routledge.

Feinberg, D. R., et al. (2006). Menstrual cycle, trait estrogen level, and masculinity preferences in the human voice. *Hormones and Behavior, 49*(2), 215–222.

Feingold, A. (1991). Sex differences in the effects of similarity and physical attractiveness on opposite-sex attraction. *Basic and Applied Social Psychology, 12,* 357–367.

Fekete, J. (1994). *Moral panic: Biopolitics rising.* Montreal: Robert Davies Publishing.

Fergus, K. D., Gray, R. E., & Fitch, M. I. (2002). Sexual dysfunction and the preservation of manhood: Experiences of men with prostate cancer. *Journal of Health Psychology*, 7(3), 303–316.

Fergus, S. (2006, May/June). Sexual behaviours of Canadian youth reporting same-sex attraction. CAHR Abstracts 2006. *Canadian Journal of Infectious Diseases and Medical Microbiology*, 17. Supplement A.

Festa, E. D., et al. (2004). Sex differences in cocaine-induced behavioral responses, pharmacokinetics, and monoamine levels. *Neuropharmacology, 46*(5), 672–687.

Fichner-Rathus, L. (2004). *Understanding art.* Belmont, CA: Wadsworth.

Finkelhor, D., Cross, T. P., & Cantor, E. N. (2005a). The justice system for juvenile victims: A comprehensive model of case flow. *Trauma, Violence, & Abuse, 6*(2), 83–102.

Finkelhor, D., Ormrod, R., Turner, H., & Hamby, S. L. (2005b). The victimization of children and youth: A comprehensive, national survey. *Child Maltreatment: Journal of the American Professional Society on the Abuse of Children, 10*(1), 5–25.

Finkelman, J. M. (2005). Sexual harassment: The organizational perspective. In Barnes, A. (Ed.). *The handbook of women, psychology, and the law* (pp. 64–78). New York: John Wiley & Sons.

Finkenauer, C., & Hazam, H. (2000). Disclosure and secrecy in marriage: Do both contribute to marital satisfaction? *Journal of Social & Personal Relationships, 17*(2), 245–263.

Firestone, P., Bradford, J. M., McCoy, M., Greenberg, D. M., Amy, S., & Larose, M. R. (1998). Recidivism in convicted rapists. *Journal of the American Academy of Psychiatry and the Law, 26,* 185–200.

Firestone, P., Bradford, J. M., McCoy, M., Greenberg, D. M., Larose, M. R., & Amy, S. (1999). Prediction of recidivism in incest offenders. *Journal of Interpersonal Violence, 14,* 511–531.

Firestone, P., Kingston, D. A., Wexler, A., & Bradford, J. M. (2006). Long-term follow-up of exhibitionists: Psychological, phallometric, and offense characteristics. *The Journal of the American Academy of Psychiatry and the Law, 34,* 349–359.

Firestone, R. W., Firestone, L. A., & Catlett, J. (2006a). *Sex and love in intimate relationships.* Washington, DC: American Psychological Association.

Firestone, R. W., Firestone, L. A., & Catlett, J. (2006b). Sexual withholding. In R. W. Firestone, L. A. Firestone, & J. Catlett (Eds.), *Sex and love in intimate relationships* (pp. 171–195). Washington, DC: American Psychological Association.

Fischer, B., Wortley, S., Webster, C., & Kirst, M. (2002). The socio-legal dynamics and implications of "diversion": The case study of the Toronto "john school" diversion programme for prostitution offenders. *Criminal Justice,* 2(4), 385–410.

Fischtein, D. S., & Herold, E. S. (2002, June). *Gender differences in sexual attitudes and behaviours among Canadian adults: A national survey.* Poster session presented at the annual meeting of the International Academy of Sex Research, Hamburg, Germany.

Fischtein, D. S., Herold, E. S., & Desmarais, S. (2007). How much does gender explain in sexual attitudes and behaviors? A survey of Canadian adults. *Archives of Sexual Behaviour, 36,* 451–461.

Fisher, B. S., Daigle, L. E., Cullen, F. T., & Turner, M. G. (2003b). Reporting sexual victimization to the police and others: Results from a national-level study of college women. *Criminal Justice & Behavior, 30*(1), 6–38.

Fisher, H. E. (2000). Brains do it: Lust, attraction and attachment. *Cerebrum, 2,* 23–42.

Fisher, J. D., & Fisher, W. A. (1992). Changing AIDS-risk behavior. *Psychological Bulletin, 111,* 455–474.

Fisher, W. (2007). Prevention for positives: Development, implementation and evaluation of a clinician-delivered intervention to promote safer sexual behavior among HIV+ patients in clinical care. Paper presented at the Annual Meeting of the Canadian Sex Research Forum, Banff, Alberta.

Fisher, W., Boroditsky, R., & Morris, B. (2004a). The 2002 Canadian contraception study: Part 1. *Journal of Obstetrics and Gynaecology Canada, 26*(6), 580–590.

Fisher, W., Boroditsky, R., & Morris, B. (2004b). The 2002 Canadian contraception study: Part 2. *Journal of Obstetrics and Gynaecology Canada, 26*(7), 646–656.

Fisher, W., et al. (2005). Association of PDE-5 inhibitor use in men with ED and sexual function of partners. Paper presented at the World Congress of Sexology, Montreal.

Fisher, W. A., & Black, A. (2007). Contraception in Canada: A review of method choices, characteristics, adherence and approaches to counselling. *Canadian Medical Association Journal, 176*(7), 953–961.

Fisher, W. A., Boroditsky, R., & Bridges, M. L. (1999). The 1998 Canadian contraception study. *Canadian Journal of Human Sexuality, 8*(3), 161–220.

Fisher, W. A., Singh, S. S., Shuper, P. A., Carey, M., Otchet, F., MacLean-Brine, D., et al. (2005). Characteristics of women undergoing repeat induced abortion. *Canadian Medical Association Journal, 172*(5), 637–641.

Fishman, J. R., & Mamo, L. (2001). What's in a disorder: A cultural analysis of medical and pharmaceutical constructions of male and female sexual dysfunction. *Women & Therapy, 24*(1–2), 179–193.

Flaxman, S. M., & Sherman, P. W. (2000). Morning sickness: A mechanism for protecting mother and embryo. *The Quarterly Review of Biology, 5*(2), 113–148.

Florence, E., et al. (2004). Prevalence and factors associated with sexual dysfunction among HIV-positive women in Europe. *AIDS Care, 16*(5), 550–557.

Forbes, A., While, A., Mathes, L., & Griffiths, P. (2006). Health problems and health-related quality of life in people with multiple sclerosis. *Clinical Rehabilitation, 20*(1), 67–78.

Ford, C. S., & Beach, F. A. (1951). *Patterns of sexual behavior.* New York: Harper & Row.

Foster, D. (2005a). The formation and continuance of lesbian families in Canada. *Canadian Bulletin of Canadian History, 22*(2), 281–297.

Foster, D. (2005b). Why do children do so well in lesbian households? Research on lesbian parenting. *Canadian Woman Studies, 24*(2/3), 51–56.

Foster, D., & Decaire, B. (in press). Female sexuality: Beyond the organ recital. In L. R. Ross (Ed.), *Feminist counselling: Theory, issues, and practice*. Toronto: Women's Press.

Foubert, J. D., & Newberry, J. T. (2006). Effects of two versions of an empathy-based rape prevention program on fraternity men's survivor empathy, attitudes, and behavioral intent to commit rape or sexual assault. *Journal of College Student Development, 47*(2), 133–148.

Franco, E. L., Schlecht, N. F., & Saslow, D. (2003). The epidemiology of cervical cancer. *Cancer Journal, 9*(5), 348–359.

Frank, K. (2002). *G-strings and sympathy: Strip club regulars and male desire.* Raleigh, NC: Duke University Press.

Frank, K. (2003). Just trying to relax: Masculinity, masculinizing practices, and strip club regulars. *The Journal of Sex Research, 40*(1), 61–75.

Frayser, S. (1985). *Varieties of sexual experience: An anthropological perspective on human sexuality*. New Haven, CT: Human Relations Area Files Press.

Freeman, N. (2005, June 16). Blatant objectification: Echo's Hot Summer Issue crossed the line. *Echo,* pp. 10–11.

Freud, S. (1922/1959). Analysis of a phobia in a 5-year-old boy. In A. & J. Strachey (Ed. & Trans.), *Collected papers,* Vol. 3. New York: Basic Books. (Original work published 1909.)

Freund, K., & Blanchard, R. (1986). The concept of courtship disorder. *Journal of Sex and Marital Therapy, 12,* 79–92.

Freund, K., Seto, M., & Kubian, M. (1997). Frotteurism and the theory of courtship disorder. In D. R. Laws & W. O'Donohue (Eds.), *Sexual deviance: Theory, assessment, and treatment* (pp. 111–130). New York: Guilford.

Freund, K., Watson, R., & Rienzo, D. (1988). The value of self-reports in the study of voyeurism and exhibitionism. *Annals of Sex Research 1,* 243–262.

Friedman, R. C., & Downey, J. I. (1994). Homosexuality. *The New England Journal of Medicine, 331,* 923–930.

Friedman, R. C., & Downey, J. I. (2001). The Oedipus complex and male homosexuality. In P. Hartocollis (Ed), *Mankind's Oedipal destiny: Libidinal and aggressive aspects of sexuality* (pp. 113–138). Madison, CT: International Universities Press.

Friedrich, W. M., Fisher, J., Broughton, D., Houston, M., & Shafran, C. R. (1998). Normative sexual behavior in children: A contemporary sample. *Pediatrics, 101*(4), e9. [Electronic article].

Friedrich, W. N., & Gerber, P. N. (1994). Autoerotic asphyxia: The development of a paraphilia. *Journal of the American Academy of Child and Adolescent Psychiatry, 33*(7), 970–974.

Friesen, J. (2005, April 22). Nude photos make Web calamity for girl. *The Globe and Mail.*

Frisch, R. (1997). Cited in Angier, N. (1997a). Chemical tied to fat control could help trigger puberty. *The New York Times,* p. C3.

Frisch, R. E. (2002). *Female fertility and the body fat connection.* Chicago: University of Chicago Press.

Friscolanti, M. (2008, July 29). Taking the handcuffs off to keep track of sex offender. *Maclean's,* 18–21.

Frohlich, P., & Meston, C. (2002). Sexual functioning and self-reported depressive symptoms among college women. *Journal of Sex Research, 39*(4), 321–325.

Frohlich, P. F., & Meston, C. M. (2005). Tactile sensitivity in women with sexual arousal disorder. *Archives of Sexual Behavior, 34*(2), 207–217.

Fugl–Meyer, K. S., Öberg, K., Lundberg, P. O., Lewin, B., & Fugl–Meyer, A. (2006). On orgasm, sexual techniques, and erotic perceptions in 18- to 74-year-old Swedish women. *Journal of Sexual Medicine, 3*(1), 56–68.

Gaetz, S. (2004). Safe streets for whom? Homeless youth, social exclusion, and criminal victimization. *Canadian Journal of Criminology & Criminal Justice, 46*(4), 423–455.

Gagnon, J. H. (1977). *Human sexualities.* Glenview, IL: Scott, Foresman.

Garcia, L. T. (2006). Perceptions of sexual experience and preferences for dating and marriage. *The Canadian Journal of Human Sexuality, 15*(2), 85–94.

Gavin, N. I., et al. (2005). Perinatal depression: A systematic review of prevalence and incidence. *Obstetrics & Gynecology, 106,* 1071–1083.

Gay, P. (1984). *The bourgeois experience: Victoria to Freud.* New York: Oxford University Press.

Gebhard, P. H. (1976). The institute. In M. S. Weinberg (Ed.), *Sex research: Studies from the Kinsey Institute*. New York: Oxford University Press.

Gebhard, P. H., et al. (1965). *Sex offenders: An analysis of types.* New York: Harper & Row.

Gemme, R. (1993). Prostitution: A legal, criminological and sexological perspective. *The Canadian Journal of Human Sexuality, 4,* 227–238.

Gemme, R. (1998). Legal and sexological aspects of adult street prostitution: A case for sexual pluralism. In J. E. Elias, V. L. Bullough, V. Elias, & G. Brewer (Eds.), *Prostitution: On whores, hustlers and johns* (pp. 474–487). New York: Prometheus Books.

George, W. H., Stoner, S. A., Norris, J., Lopez, P. A., & Lehman, G. L. (2000). Alcohol expectancies and sexuality: A self-fulfilling prophecy analysis of dyadic perceptions and behavior. *Journal of Studies on Alcohol, 61*(1), 168–176.

Gerressu, M., Mercer, C., Graham, C., Wellings, K., & Johnson, M. (2008). Prevalence of masturbation and associated factors in a British National Probability Survey. *Archives of Sexual Behavior, 37,* 266–278.

Gerrol, R., & Resick, P. A. (1988, November). Sex differences in social support and recovery from victimization. Paper presented at the meeting of the Association for Advancement of Behavior Therapy, New York.

Gibbons, L., & Waters, C. (2003). Prostate cancer testing. (Statistics Canada Catalogue 82-003). *Health Reports,* 14, 3.

Gibson, V. (2002). *Cougar: A guide for older women dating younger men.* Toronto: Key Porter.

Gidycz, C. A., & Koss, M. P. (1990). A comparison of group and individual sexual assault victims. *Psychology of Women Quarterly, 14,* 325–342.

Gidycz, C. A., Rich, C. L., Orchowski, L., King, C., & Miller, A. K. (2006). The evaluation of a sexual assault self-defense and risk-reduction program for college women: A prospective study. *Psychology of Women Quarterly, 30*(2), 173–186.

Gilbert, S. (1996, September 25). No long-term link is found between pill and breast cancer. *The New York Times,* p. C9.

Giles, G., Severi, G., English, D., et al. (2003). Sexual factors and prostate cancer. *British Journal of Urology, 92*(3), 211–216.

Gillis, J. S., & Avis, W. E. (1980). The male-taller norm in mate selection. *Personality and Social Psychology Bulletin, 6*, 396–401.

Gillis, M. (2005, June 16). It's my ass. *Echo*, p. 11.

Girard, D. (2005, June 2). First conviction in sex tourism case. *The Toronto Star*.

Girl lied about sex assault: Police. (2001, April 27). *The Toronto Star.*

Glass, S. P., & Wright, T. L. (1992). Justifications of extramarital relationships: The association between attitudes, behaviors, and gender. *Journal of Sex Research, 29*, 361–387.

Gnagy, S., Ming, E. E., Devesa, S. S., Hartge, P., & Whittemore, A. S. (2000). Declining ovarian cancer rates in U.S. women in relation to parity and oral contraceptive use. *Epidemiology, 11*(2), 102–105.

Gobrogge, K., Perkins, P., Baker, J., & Balcer, K. (2007). Homosexual mating preferences from an evolutionary perspective: Sexual selection theory revised. *Archives of Sexual Behavior, 36*, 717–723.

Godfrey, T. (2003, December 19). Drifter arrested after cow assault. *The Toronto Sun*.

Gold, S. R., & Gold, R. G. (1993). Sexual aversions: A hidden disorder. In W. O'Donohue & J. H. Geer (eds.), *Handbook of sexual dysfunctions: Assessment and treatment* (pp. 83–102). Boston: Allyn & Bacon.

Goldstein, I. (1998). Cited in Kolata, G. (1998, April 4). Impotence pill: Would it also help women? *The New York Times*, pp. A1, A6.

Goldstein, I., & Alexander, J. L. (2005). Practical aspects in the management of vaginal atrophy and sexual dysfunction in perimenopausal and postmenopausal women. *Journal of Sexual Medicine*, 2(Suppl. 3), 154–165.

Goldstein, I., Meston, C., Davis, S., & Traish, A. (Eds.). (2006). *Female sexual dysfunction*. New York: Parthenon.

Goleman, D. (1991, October 22). Sexual harassment: It's about power, not lust. *The New York Times*, pp. C1, C12.

Goleman, D. (1995, June 14). Sex fantasy research said to neglect women. *The New York Times*, p. C14.

Goodson, P., McCormick, D., & Evans, A. (2001). Searching for sexually explicit materials on the internet: An exploratory study of college students' behavior and attitudes. *Archives of Sexual Behavior, 30*(2), 101–118.

Gordon, A. E., et al. (2002). Why is smoking a risk factor for sudden infant death syndrome? *Child: Care, Health & Development, 28*(Suppl. 1), 23–25.

Gordon, A. R. (2005). Queer theory, gender theory: An instant primer. *Culture, Health & Sexuality*, 7(6), 642–644.

Goulet, J. (2006). The "berdache"/"two-spirit": A comparison of anthropological and native constructions of gendered identities among the Northern Athapaskans. *Journal of the Royal Anthropological Institute, 683*(19).

Gower, P., & Philp, M. (2002a, November 24). Two dads and a family. *The Toronto Star*, pp. A1, A16–A17.

Gower, P., & Philp, M. (2002b, November 27). The curse of alcohol and pregnancy. *The Toronto Star*, pp. A1, A16–A17.

Grabrick, D. M., et al. (2000). Risk of breast cancer with oral contraceptive use in women with a family history of breast cancer. *Journal of the American Medical Association, 284*(14), 1791–1798.

Grace, A. P., & Wells, K. (2006). The quest for a queer inclusive cultural ethics: Setting directions for teachers' preservice and continuing professional development. *Challenging homophobia and heterosexism*. Willy Periodicals. pp. 51–61

Grace, A. P., & Wells, K. (2007). Gay and bisexual male youth as educator activists and cultural workers: The queer critical praxis of three Canadian high-school students. *International Journal of Inclusive Education, 1*(22), 2–22.

Graham, D. (2008, January 17). New superbug hitting gay men. *Toronto Star* online.

Green, R. (1987). *The "sissy boy syndrome" and the development of homosexuality*. New Haven, CT: Yale University Press.

Greenberg, D. M., Firestone, P., Nunes, K. L., Bradford, J. M., & Curry, S. (2005). Biological fathers and stepfathers who molest their daughters: Psychological, phallometric and criminal features. *Sexual Abuse: A Journal of Research and Treatment, 17*(1), 39–46.

Greenwald, E., & Leitenberg, H. (1989). Long-term effects of sexual experiences with siblings and non-siblings during childhood. *Archives of Sexual Behavior, 18*, 389–399.

Grenier, G. (2007). *The 10 conversations you must have before you get married (And how to have them)*. Toronto: Key Porter.

Grenier, G., & Byers, E. S. (2001). Operationalizing premature or rapid ejaculation. *Journal of Sex Research, 38*, 369–378.

Grenz, S. (2006). Review of *The Politics of Prostitution. Women's Movements, Democratic States and the Globalisation of Sex Commerce and Not for Sale: Feminists Resisting Prostitution and Pornography. Sexualities*, 9(2), 256–259.

Gross, B. (2006). The pleasure of pain. *Forensic Examiner, 15*(1), 57–61.

Gross, J. (2006, April 20). Learning to savor a full life, love life included. *The New York Times*.

Groth, A. N., & Birnbaum, H. J. (1979). *Men who rape: The psychology of the offender.* New York: Plenum Press.

Groth, A. N., & Burgess, A. W. (1980). Male rape: Offenders and victims. *American Journal of Psychiatry, 137*, 806–810.

Gruszecki, L., Forchuk, C., & Fisher, W. A. (2005). Factors associated with common sexual concerns in women: New findings from the Canadian Contraception Study. *The Canadian Journal of Human Sexuality, 14*(1–2), 1–13.

Gupta, M. (1994). Sexuality in the Indian subcontinent. *Sexual and Marital Therapy*, 9(1), 57–69.

Guzick, D. S., & Hoeger, K. (2000). Sex, hormones, and hysterectomies. *The New England Journal of Medicine* online, *343*(10).

Haake, P., et al. (2003). Acute neuro-endocrine response to sexual stimulation in sexual offenders. *Canadian Journal of Psychiatry, 48*(4), 265–271.

Halapy, E. E., Chiarelli, A. M., Klar, N., & Knight, J. (2004). Breast screening outcomes in women with and without a family history of breast and/or ovarian cancer. *Journal of Medical Screening, 11*(1), 32–38.

Hald, G., & Malmuth, N. (2008). Self-perceived effects of pornography consumption. *Archives of Sexual Behavior.* 37, 614–625.

Haley, N., Roy, E., Leclerc, P., Boudreau, J. F., & Boivin, J. F. (2004). HIV risk profile of male street youth involved in survival sex. *Sexually Transmitted Infections, 80*(6) 526–530.

Hallgrimsdottir, H. K., Phillips, R., & Benoit, C. (2006). Fallen women and rescued girls: Social stigma and media narratives of the sex industry in Victoria, B.C., from 1980–2005. *The Canadian Review of Sociology and Anthropology, 43*(3), 265–280.

Halpern, D. F. (2003). Sex differences in cognitive abilities. *Applied Cognitive Psychology, 17*(3), 375–376.

Hamer, D. H., et al. (1993, July 16). A linkage between DNA markers on the X chromosome and male sexual orientation. *Science, 261*, 321–327.

Hamilton, T. (2002, August 14). New breast cancer checks hailed. *The Toronto Star*, pp. A1, A19.

Hampton, M. R., Jeffery, B., McWatters, B., & Smith, P. (2005). Influence of teens' perceptions of parental disapproval and peer behaviour on their initiation of sexual intercourse. *The Canadian Journal of Human Sexuality, 14*(3–4), 105–121.

Hanson, R. K., Gordon, A., Harris, A. J. R., et al. (2002). First report of the collaborative outcome data project on the effectiveness of psychological treatment for sex offenders. *Sexual Abuse, 14*, 155–168.

Hardwick, D., & Patychuck, D. (1999). Geographic mapping demonstrates the association between social inequality, teen births, and STDs among youth. *Canadian Journal of Human Sexuality, 8*, 77–89.

Harris, C. R. (2003). A review of sex differences in sexual jealousy, including self-report data, psychophysiological responses, interpersonal violence, and morbid jealousy. *Personality & Social Psychology Review*, 7(2), 102–128.

Harris, M., & Johnson, O. (2000). *Cultural anthropology*, 5th ed. Boston: Allyn & Bacon.

Hart, J., et al. (1991). Sexual behaviour in pregnancy: A study of 219 women. *Journal of Sex Education and Therapy, 17*, 86–90.

Harte, C. B., Rand, M., Adkins, R., & Meston, C. (2007). Gender-differential subjective sexual arousal patterns to diverse sexual stimuli. Paper presented at the annual meeting of the International Academy of Sex Research, Vancouver, British Columbia.

Hartman, C. R., Burgess, A. W., & McCormack, A. (1987). Pathways and cycles of runaways: A model for understanding repetitive runaway behavior. *Hospital and Community Psychiatry, 38*, 292–299.

Hartwick, C., Desmarais, S., & Hennig, K. (2007). Characteristics of male and female victims of sexual coercion. *The Canadian Journal of Human Sexuality, 16*(1–2), 31–44.

Harvey, C. (2000, September 4). Where to go for help. *The Los Angeles Times* online.

Harvey, S. (1987). Female sexual behavior: Fluctuations during the menstrual cycle. *Journal of Psychosomatic Research, 31*, 101–110.

Hatcher, R. A., et al. (Eds.) (2006). *Contraceptive technologies*,18th rev. ed. New York: Ardent Media.

Hatfield, E. (1988). Passionate and companionate love. In R. J. Sternberg & M. L. Barnes (eds.), *The psychology of love* (pp. 191–217). New Haven, CT: Yale University Press.

Hatfield, E., & Rapson, R. L. (2002). Passionate love and sexual desire: Cultural and historical perspectives. In A. L. Vangelisti, H. T. Reis, et al. (Eds.), *Stability and change in relationships: Advances in personal relationships* (pp. 306–324). New York: Cambridge University Press.

Haubrich, D. J., Myers, T., Calzavara, L., Ryder, K., & Medved, W. (2004). Gay and bisexual men's experiences of bathhouse culture and sex: "Looking for love in all the wrong places." *Culture, Health & Sexuality, 6*(1), 19–29.

Haugaard, J. J. (2000). The challenge of defining child sexual abuse. *American Psychologist, 55*(9), 1036–1039.

Hayes, R., & Dennerstein, L. (2005). The impact of aging on sexual function and sexual dysfunction in women: A review of population-based studies. *Journal of Sexual Medicine, 2*(3), 317–330.

Health After 50. (2002).

Health Canada. (2001). Sexually transmitted diseases data tables. Division of Sexual Health Promotion and STD Prevention and Control, Bureau of HIV/AIDS, STD & TB. Ottawa: Health Canada.

Health Canada. (2007). It's your health: Human papillomavirus (HPV). Available: **www.hc-sc.gc.ca/hl-vs/iyh-vsv/diseases-maladies/hpv-vph-eng.php**

Health24.com. (2006, February 10). *The girl child.* [Online]. **www.health24.com/sex/sexuality_throughout_life**

Heiman, J. R., & LoPiccolo, J. (1987). *Becoming orgasmic*, 2nd ed. Englewood Cliffs, NJ: Prentice-Hall.

Hellstrom, W. J. G., Nehra, A., Shabsigh, R., & Sharlip, I. D. (2006). Premature ejaculation: The most common male sexual dysfunction. *Journal of Sexual Medicine, 3*(Suppl. 1), 1–3.

Hendrick, C., & Hendrick, S. (1986). A theory and method of love. *Journal of Personality and Social Psychology, 50*, 392–402.

Hendrick, C., & Hendrick, S. (2003). Romantic love: Measuring Cupid's arrow. In S. Lopez & C. R. Snyder (Eds.), *Positive psychological assessment: A handbook of models and measures* (pp. 235–249). Washington, DC: American Psychological Association.

Hendrick, C., & Hendrick, S. (Eds.) (2000). *Close relationships: A sourcebook.*Thousand Oaks, CA: Sage.

Hendrick, S. S., & Hendrick, C. (2002). Love. In C. R. Snyder & S. J. Lopez (Eds.). *Handbook of positive psychology* (pp. 472–484). London: Oxford University Press.

Herek, G. M. (1988). Heterosexuals and attitudes toward lesbians and gay men: Correlates and gender differences. *Journal of Sex Research*, 25(4), 451–477.

Herold, E. S. (1984). *Sexual behaviour of Canadian young people*. Markham, ON: Fitzhenry & Whiteside.

Herold, E. S., Corbesi, B., & Collins, J. (1994). Psychosocial aspects of female topless behavior on Australian beaches. *Journal of Sex Research, 31*, 133–142.

Herold, E. S., Garcia, R., & DeMoya, T. (2001). Female tourists and beach boys: Romance or sex tourism? *Annals of Tourism Research, 28*, 978–997.

Herold, E. S., & Goodwin, M. S. (1981). Premarital sexual guilt and contraceptive attitudes and behavior. *Family Relations, 30*, 247–253.

Herold, E. S., & Mewhinney, D. K. (1993). Gender differences in casual sex and AIDS prevention: A survey of dating bars. *The Journal of Sex Research, 30*, 36–42.

Herold, E. S., & Way, L. (1983). Oral-genital sexual behavior in a sample of university females. *The Journal of Sex Research, 19*, 327–338.

Herold, E. S., & Way, L. (1988). Sexual self-disclosure among university women. *Journal of Sex Research, 24*, 1–14.

Herrera, V. M., & McCloskey, L. A. (2003). Sexual abuse, family violence, and female delinquency: Findings from a longitudinal study. *Violence & Victims, 18*(3), 319–334.

Hester, J. D. (2005). Eunuchs and the postgender Jesus: Matthew 19:12 and transgressive sexualities. *Journal for the Study of the New Testament, 28*(1), 13–40.

Hill, R. A., Donovan, S., & Koyama, N. F. (2005). Female sexual advertisement reflects resource availability in twentieth-century UK society. *Human Nature, 16*(3), 266–277.

Hill, T. (2005). Female sexual frustration. Unpublished M.A. thesis, University of Guelph.

Hines, T. M. (2001). The G-spot: A modern gynecological myth. *American Journal of Obstetrics and Gynecology, 185*(2), 359–362.

Hird, M. J. (2004). Naturally queer. *Feminist Theory, 5*(1), 85–89.

Hird, M. J. (2006). Sex diversity and evolutionary psychology. *The Psychologist, 19*(1), 30–32.

Hite, S. (1976). *The Hite report.* New York: Macmillan.

Hogg, R. S., Yip, B., Chan, K. J., Wood, E., Craib, K. J., O'Shaughnessy, M. V., & Montaner, J. S. (2001). Rates of disease progression by baseline CD4 cell count and viral load after initiating triple-drug therapy. *Journal of the American Medical Association, 286*(20), 2568–2577.

Holmes, D., Obyrne, P., & Gastaldo, D. (2007). Setting the space for sex: Architecture, desire and health issues in gay bathhouses. *International Journal of Nursing Studies, 44*, 273–284.

Holmes, D., & Warner, D. (2005). The anatomy of a forbidden desire: Men, penetration and semen exchange. *Nursing Inquiry, 12*(1), 10–20.

Holmes, S. T., & Holmes, R. M. (2002). *Sex crimes*. Thousand Oaks, CA: Sage Publications.

Honeycutt, J. M., & Cantrill, G. (2001). *Cognition, communication, and romantic relationships*. Mahwah, NJ: Erlbaum.

Horne, A. (2003). Oedipal aspirations and phallic fears: On fetishism in childhood and young adulthood. *Journal of Child Psychotherapy, 29*(1), 37–52.

House arrest in "lactation" case. (2002, October 12). *The Toronto Star,* p. A25.

Howard-Hassmann, R. E. (2001). The gay cousin: Learning to accept gay rights. *Journal of Homosexuality, 42*(1), 127–149.

Huber, J. D., & Herold, E. (2006). Sexually overt approaches in singles bars. *Canadian Journal of Human Sexuality, 15*(3–4), 233–146.

Huber, J. D., & Kleinplatz, P. J. (2002). Sexual orientation identification of men who have sex with men in public settings in Canada. *Journal of Homosexuality, 42*(3), 1–20.

Hudson, W. W., & Ricketts, W. A. (1980). Index of homophobia: A strategy for the measurement of homophobia. *Journal of Homosexuality,* 5(4), 357–372.

Hughes, I. A. (2000). A novel explanation for resistance to androgens. *The New England Journal of Medicine* online, *343*(12).

Humphreys, T. (2007a). The complexity of sexual consent negotiations. Paper presented at the Annual Guelph Conference on Human Sexuality, Guelph, Ontario.

Humphreys, T. (2007b). Understanding virginity: First sexual experiences & attachment. Paper presented at the Annual Meeting of the Society for the Scientific Study of Human Sexuality. Indianapolis, IN.

Humphreys, T., DeCicco, T., King, D., & Kartes, K. (2007). Sex dreams & waking sexual activity: Is there a connection? Poster session presented at the Annual Meeting of the Society for the Scientific Study of Sexuality. Indianapolis, IN.

Humphreys, T., & Herold, E. (2003). Should universities and colleges mandate sexual behavior: Student perceptions of Antioch college's consent policy. *Journal of Psychology and Human Sexuality, 15,* 35–52.

Humphreys, T., & Herold, E. (2007). Sexual consent in heterosexual relationships: Development of a new measure. *Sex Roles, 57,* 305–315.

Humphreys, T., & Newby, J. (2007). Initiating new sexual behaviours in heterosexual relationships. *The Canadian Journal of Human Sexuality, 16*(3–4), 77–88.

Humphreys, T. P. (2004). Understanding sexual consent: An empirical investigation of the normative script for young heterosexual adults. In M. Cowling & P. Reynolds (Eds.), *Making sense of sexual consent.* Aldershot, UK: Ashgate.

Humphries, K. H., & Gill, S. (2003). Risks and benefits of hormone replacement therapy: The evidence speaks. *Canadian Medical Association Journal, 168*(8), 1001–1010.

Hunt, A., & Curtis, B. (2006). A genealogy of the genital kiss: Oral sex in the twentieth century. *The Canadian Journal of Human Sexuality, 15*(2), 69–84.

Hurst, L. (2003, August 17). A long trip to the altar. *The Toronto Star.*

Hussain, A. (2002, June 26). It's official: Men really are afraid of commitment. Reuters.

Imperato-McGinley, J., et al. (1974). Steroid 5 reductase deficiency in man: An inherited form of male pseudohermaphroditism. *Science, 186,* 1213–1215.

Ince, J. (2003). *The politics of lust.* Vancouver: Pivotal Press.

Info Reports. (2005). *World health organization updates guidance on how to use contraceptives,* 4.

Isaacs, C. R., & Fisher, W. A. (2008). A computer-based educational intervention to address potential negative effects of internet pornography. *Communication Studies, 59*(1), 1–18.

Isay, R. A. (1990). Psychoanalytic theory and the therapy of gay men. In D. P. McWhirter, S. A. Sanders, & J. M. Reinisch (eds.), *Homosexuality/heterosexuality: Concepts of sexual orientation* (pp. 283–303). New York: Oxford University Press.

Itzin, C. (2002). Pornography and the construction of misogyny. *Journal of Sexual Aggression, 8*(3), 4–42.

Jacobs, S. (2007). The characteristics and perceptions of women who visit adult retail stores. Unpublished master's thesis, University of Guelph.

Jail workers charged. (2002, May 24). *The Toronto Star.*

Jamison, P. L., & Gebhard, P. H. (1988). Penis size increase between flaccid and erect states: An analysis of the Kinsey data. *Journal of Sex Research, 24,* 177–183.

Jansen, E., McBride, K., & Yarber, W. (2008). Factors that influence sexual arousal in men: A focus group study. *Journal of Sex Research, 37,* 252–265.

Janssen, E. (Ed.). (2006). *The psychophysiology of sex.* Bloomington, IN: Indiana University Press.

Janssen, E., & Bancroft, J. (2006). The dual-control model: The role of sexual inhibition & excitation in sexual arousal and behavior. In Janssen, E. (Ed.), *The psychophysiology of sex.* Bloomington, IN: Indiana University Press.

Janssen, E., Prause, N., & Geer, J. (2006). The sexual response. In J. T. Cacioppo, L. G. Tassinary, & G. G. Berntson (Eds.), *Handbook of psychophysiology,* 3rd ed. New York: Cambridge University Press.

Javed, N. (2008, May 24). GTA's secret world of polygamy. *Toronto Star,* p. A10.

Jeffrey, L. A., & MacDonald, G. (2006). "It's the money, honey": The economy of sex work in the Maritimes. *Canadian Review of Sociology & Anthropology, 43*(3), 113–327.

Jenish, D. (1994, January 3). Canada under the covers. *Maclean's,* 20–26.

Johannes, C. B., et al. (2000). Incidence of erectile dysfunction in men 40 to 69 years old: Longitudinal results from the Massachusetts male aging study. *The Journal of Urology, 163,* 460.

Johns, A., & Lush, G. (2004). *Adolescent sexual decision-making in Newfoundland and Labrador.* St. Johns, NF: Planned Parenthood Newfoundland and Labrador.

Johnson, C., Remple, V., & Bungay, V. (2007). Inconsistent condom use by indoor commercial sex workers (CSW) in Vancouver, British Columbia: A quantitative and qualitative study. Paper presented at the CAHR Conference, Toronto, Ontario.

Johnson, H. (2003). The cessation of assaults on wives. *Journal of Comparative Family Studies, 34*(1), 75–91.

Johnstone, S. J., et al. (2001). Obstetric risk factors for postnatal depression in urban and rural community samples. *Australian & New Zealand Journal of Psychiatry, 35*(1), 69–74.

Josey, S. (2002, May 11). Gay prom battle ends with a waltz. *Toronto Star.*

Kaczmarek, P., LeVine, E., & Segal, A. F. (2006). Section 6. Civil and criminal trial matters. In P. Kaczmarek, E. LeVine, & A. F. Segal (Eds.) *Law & mental health professionals: New Mexico* (pp. 269–296). Washington, DC: American Psychological Association.

Kaestle, C. (2007). Sexual behaviors of opposite sex couples through emerging adulthood. *Perspectives on Sexual and Reproductive Health, 39,* 134–140.

Kafka, M. P. (2003). Sex offending and sexual appetite: The clinical and theoretical relevance of hypersexual desire. *International Journal of Offender Therapy & Comparative Criminology, 47*(4), 439–451.

Kaiser Family Foundation, Holt, T., Greene, L., & Davis, J. (2003). *National Survey of Adolescents and Young Adults: Sexual health knowledge, attitudes and experiences.* Menlo Park, CA: Henry J. Kaiser Family Foundation.

Kaler, A. (2005). Peer commentaries on Binik (2005): Classifying pain: What's at stake for women with dyspareunia. *Archives of Sexual Behavior, 34*(1), 34–36.

Kaplan, H. S. (1974). *The new sex therapy: Active treatment of sexual dysfunctions.* New York: Brunner/Mazel.

Kaplan, H. S. (1979). *Disorders of sexual desire.* New York: Simon & Schuster.

Kaplan, H. S. (1987). *Sexual aversion, sexual phobias, and panic disorder.* New York: Brunner/Mazel.

Karakiewicz, P. I., Tanguay, S., Kattan, M. W., Elhilali, M. M., & Aprikian, A. G. (2004). Erectile and urinary dysfunction after radical prostatectomy for prostate cancer in Quebec: A population-based study of 2415 men. *European Urology, 46*(2), 188–194.

Karama, S., Lecours, A., Leroux, J., et al. (2002). Areas of brain activation during viewing of erotic film excerpts. *Human Brain Mapping, 16*, 1–13.

Katz, S., & Marshall, B. (2003). New sex for old: Lifestyle, consumerism, and the ethics of aging well. *Journal of Aging Studies, 17*(1), 3–16.

Kaufman, A., et al. (1980). Male rape victims: Noninstitutionalized assault. *American Journal of Psychiatry, 137*, 221–223.

Kaufman, M., Silverberg, C., & Odette, F. (2007). *The ultimate guide to sex and disability*. San Francisco, CA: Cleis Press.

Kegel, A. H. (1952). Sexual functions of the pubococcygeus muscle. *Western Journal of Surgery, 60*, 521–524.

Kelly, M. P., Strassberg, D. S., & Kircher, J. R. (1990). Attitudinal and experiential correlates of anorgasmia. *Archives of Sexual Behavior, 19*, 165–177.

Kendler, K. S., et al. (2000). Childhood sexual abuse and adult psychiatric and substance use disorders in women: An epidemiological and co-twin control analysis. *Archives of General Psychiatry, 57*(10), 953–959.

Kendler, K. S., Thornton, L. M., Gilman, S. E., & Kessler, R. C. (2000). Sexual orientation in a U.S. national sample of twin and nontwin sibling pairs. *American Journal of Psychiatry, 157*, 1843–1846.

Kennedy, M. A., & Gorzalka, B. B. (2002). Asian and non-Asian attitudes toward rape, sexual harassment, and sexuality. *Sex Roles, 46*(7–8), 227–238.

Kennedy, M. A., Gorzalka, B. B., & Yuille, J. C. (2003). Prostitution myths held by consumers of the sex trade. Paper presented at annual meeting of American Psychological Association, Toronto.

Keung, N. (1999, March 12). Is circumcision really necessary? *The Toronto Star*, pp. F1, F2.

Kim, A. A., Kent, C. K., & Klausner, J. D. (2002). Increased risk of HIV and sexually transmitted disease transmission among gay or bisexual men who use Viagra, San Francisco 2000–2001. *AIDS, 16*(10), 1425–1428.

Kimble, D. P. (1992). *Biological psychology*, 2nd ed. Fort Worth, TX: Harcourt.

Kimlika, T., Cross, H., & Tarnai, J. (1983). A comparison of androgynous, feminine, masculine, and undifferentiated women on self-esteem, body satisfaction, and sexual satisfaction. *Psychology of Women Quarterly, 1*, 291–294.

King, A. J. C., Beazley, R. P., Warren, W. K., Hankins, C. A., Robertson, A. S., & Radford, J. L. (1989). Highlights from the Canada youth and AIDS study. *Journal of School Health, 59*(4), 139–145.

King, T. (2008, July 22). Cheerleaders coach resigns over saucy photos on Net. *Guelph Mercury*, p. A5.

Kingston, D. A., Fedoroff, P., Firestone, P., Curry, S., & Bradford, J. M. (2008). Pornography use and sexual aggression: The impact of frequency and type of pornography use on recidivism among sexual offenders. *Aggressive Behavior, 34*(4), 341–351.

Kinsey, A. C., Pomeroy, W. B., & Martin, C. E. (1948). *Sexual behavior in the human male*. Philadelphia: W. B. Saunders.

Kinsey, A. C., Pomeroy, W. B., Martin, C. E., & Gebhard, P. H. (1953). *Sexual behavior in the human female*. Philadelphia: W. B. Saunders.

Kinsman, G. (1996). *The regulation of desire: Sexuality in Canada*. Montreal: Black Rose Books.

Kippax, S., & Smith, G. (2001). Anal intercourse and power in sex between men. *Sexualities, 4*(4), 413–434.

Kirenskaya-Berus, A. V., & Tkachenko, A. A. (2003). Characteristic features of EEG spectral characteristics in persons with deviant sexual behavior. *Human Physiology, 29*(3), 278–287.

Kirkpatrick, R. C. (2000). The evolution of human homosexual behavior. *Current Anthropology, 41*(3), 385–413.

Kito, M. (2005). Self-disclosure in romantic relationships and friendships among American and Japanese college students. *Journal of Social Psychology, 145*(2), 127–140.

Kjerulff, K. H., et al. (2000). Effectiveness of hysterectomy. *Obstetrics & Gynecology, 95*, 319–326.

Klein, E. A. (2000). *Management of prostate cancer*. Totowa, NJ: Humana Press.

Klein, R., & Knauper, B. (2002). The role of suppression, inquiry, and mental representations of condoms in condom discontinuation. Paper presented at the annual meeting of the Canadian Sex Research Forum, Toronto.

Klein, R., & Knauper, B. (2003). The role of cognitive avoidance of STIs for discussing safer sex practices and for condom use consistency. *Canadian Journal of Human Sexuality, 12*(3–4), 137.

Kleinplatz, P. J. (1997). "Educational" sex videos. What are they teaching? *Canadian Journal of Human Sexuality, 6*, 39–43.

Kleinplatz, P. J. (2003). What's new in sex therapy? From stagnation to fragmentation. *Sexual & Relationship Therapy, 18*(1), 95–106.

Kleinplatz, P. J. (Ed.) (2001). *New directions in sex therapy: Innovations and alternatives*. New York: Brunner-Routledge.

Kleinplatz, P. J., & Krippner, S. (2007). Spirituality and sexuality: Celebrating erotic transcendence and spiritual embodiment. In S. G. Mijares & G. S. Khalsa (Eds.), *The psychospiritual clinician's handbook: Alternative methods for understanding and treating mental disorders* (pp. 301–318). New York: Routledge.

Kleinplatz, P. J., & Menard, A. D. (2007). Building blocks toward optimal sexuality: Constructing a conceptual model. *The Family Journal: Counselling and Therapy for Couples and Families, 15*(1), 72–78.

Kleinplatz, P. J., & Moser, C. (2005). Is SM pathological? *Lesbian & Gay Psychology Review, 6*(3), 255–260.

Kline, D., Gold, F., Canso, D., Winsor, Y., Stevenson, J., Taylor, D., Ogilvie, G., & Rekart, M. (2007). *Feasibility and acceptability of conducting research with male patrons of female sex workers*. Vancouver: BC Centre for Disease Control.

Klohnen, E. C., & Luo, S. (2003). Interpersonal attraction and personality: What is attractive: Self similarity, ideal similarity, complementarity or attachment security? *Journal of Personality and Social Psychology, 85*(4), 709–722.

Klusmann, D. (2002). Sexual motivation and the duration of partnership. *Archives of Sexual Behavior, 31*, 275–287.

Klüver, H., & Bucy, P. C. (1939). Preliminary analysis of functions of the temporal lobes in monkeys. *Archives of Neurology and Psychiatry, 42*, 979.

Knapp, M. L., & Vangelisti, A. L. (2000). *Interpersonal communication and human relationships*,4th ed. Boston: Allyn & Bacon.

Knauper, B., Aydin, C., Atkinson, K., Guberman, C., & Kornik, R. (2002). Paper presented at the annual meeting of the Canadian Sex Research Forum, Toronto.

Knäuper, B., Kornik, R., Atkinson, K., Guberman, C., & Aydin, C. (2005). Motivation influences the underestimation of cumulative risk. *Personality and Social Psychology Bulletin, 31*(11), 1511–1523.

Kniffin, K. M., & Wilson, D. S. (2004). The effect of nonphysical traits on the perception of physical attractiveness: Three naturalistic studies. *Evolution and Human Behavior, 25*(2), 88–101.

Knight, R. A., et al. (1991). *Antisocial personality disorder and Hare assessments of psychopathy among sexual offenders*. Manuscript in preparation.

Knox, D., Schacht, C., & Zusman, M. E. (1999). Love relationships among college students. *College Student Journal, 31*(4), 445–448.

Koch, P. B., Mansfield, P. K., Thurau, D., & Carey, M. (2005). "Feeling frumpy": The relationships between body image and sexual response changes in midlife women. *The Journal of Sex Research, 42*(3), 215–224.

Kohlberg, L. (1966). A cognitive-developmental analysis of children's sex-role concepts and attitudes. In E. E.

Maccoby (Ed.), *The development of sex differences.* Stanford, CA: Stanford University Press.

Kolata, G. (1998, September 9). Researchers report success in method to pick baby's sex. *The New York Times.* [Online].

Komisaruk, B. R., & Whipple, B. (2005). Brain activity imaging during sexual response in women with spinal cord injury. In Hyde, J. S. (Ed.), *Biological substrates of human sexuality* (pp. 109–145). Washington, DC: American Psychological Association.

Koo, M. M., Rohan, T. E., Jain, M., McLaughlin, J. R., & Corey, P. N. (2002). A cohort study of dietary fibre intake and menarche. *Public Health Nutrition, 5*(2), 353–360.

Korobov, N., & Thorne, A. (2006). Intimacy and distancing: Young men's conversations about romantic relationships. *Journal of Adolescent Research, 21*(1), 27–55.

Koss, M. P. (2003). Evolutionary models of why men rape: Acknowledging the complexities. In Travis, C. B. (Ed.), *Evolution, gender, and rape* (pp. 191–205). Cambridge, MA: MIT Press.

Koss, M. P., Bailey, J. A., Yuan, N. P., Herrera, V. M., & Lichter, E. L. (2003). Depression and PTSD in survivors of male violence: Research and training initiatives to facilitate recovery. *Psychology of Women Quarterly, 27*(2), 130–142.

Koss, M. P., Figueredo, A. J., & Prince, R. J. (2002). Cognitive mediation of rape's mental, physical and social health impact: Tests of four models in cross-sectional data. *Journal of Consulting & Clinical Psychology, 70*(4), 926–941.

Koss, M. P., Gidycz, C. A., & Wisniewski, N. (1987). The scope of rape: Incidence and prevalence of sexual aggression and victimization in a national sample of higher education students. *Journal of Consulting and Clinical Psychology, 55*, 162–170.

Kramer, M. S., et al. (2000). The contribution of mild and moderate preterm birth to infant mortality. *Journal of the American Medical Association, 284*, 843–849.

Kresin, D. (1993). Medical aspects of inhibited sexual desire disorder. In W. O'Donohue & J. H. Geer (Eds.), *Handbook of sexual dysfunctions: Assessment and treatment* (pp. 15–52). Boston: Allyn & Bacon.

Kristof, N. D. (2006, January 22). Slavery in our time. *The New York Times*, Section 4, p. 17.

Kruesi, M. J. P., et al. (1992). Paraphilias: A double-blind cross-over comparison of clomipramine versus desipramine. *Archives of Sexual Behavior, 21*, 587–594.

Kuffel, S. W., & Heiman, J. R. (2006). Effects of depressive symptoms and experimentally adopted schemas on sexual arousal and affect in sexually healthy women. *Archives of Sexual Behavior, 35*(2), 163–177.

Kuiper, B., & Cohen-Kettenis, P. (1988). Sex reassignment surgery: A study of 141 Dutch transsexuals. *Archives of Sexual Behavior, 17*, 439–457.

Kukkonen, T. M., Binik, Y. M., Amsel, R., & Carrier, S. (2007). Thermography as a physiological measure of sexual arousal in both men and women. *Journal of Sexual Medicine*, 4, 93–105.

Kurdek, L. A. (2005). What do we know about gay and lesbian couples? *Current Directions in Psychological Science, 14*(5), 251–254.

Kurdek, L. A. (2006). Differences between partners from heterosexual, gay, and lesbian cohabiting couples. *Journal of Marriage and Family, 68*(2), 509–528.

La Rose, L. (2008, February 13). Most believe in love at first sight, survey suggests. *Toronto Star.*

Ladas, A. K., Whipple, B., & Perry, J. D. (1982). *The G spot and other recent discoveries about human sexuality.* New York: Holt, Rinehart & Winston.

Laframboise, D. (1996). *The princess at the window: A new gender morality.* Toronto: Penguin Books.

Lalonde, R. N., Hynie, M., Pannu, M., & Tatla, S. (2004). The role of culture in interpersonal relationships: Do second generation South Asian Canadians want a traditional partner? *Journal of Cross-Cultural Psychology, 35*(5), 503–524.

Lalumière, M. L., Blanchard, R., & Zucker, K. J. (2000). Sexual orientation and handedness in men and women: A meta-analysis. *Psychological Bulletin 126*(4), 575–592.

Lalumière, M. L., Harris, G. T., Quinsey, V. L., & Rice, M. E. (1998). Sexual deviance and number of older brothers among sex offenders. *Sexual Abuse, 10*, 5–15.

Lalumière, M. L., Harris, G. T., Quinsey, V. L., & Rice, M. E. (2005a). Introduction. In M. L. Lalumière, G. T. Harris, V. L. Quinsey, & M. E. Rice (Eds.), *The causes of rape: Understanding individual differences in male propensity for sexual aggression* (pp. 3–6). Washington, DC: American Psychological Association.

Lalumière, M. L., Harris, G. T., Quinsey, V. L., & Rice, M. E. (2005b). Antisociality and mating effort. In M. L. Lalumière, G. T. Harris, V. L. Quinsey, & M. E. Rice (Eds.), *The causes of rape: Understanding individual differences in male propensity for sexual aggression* (pp. 61–103). Washington, DC: American Psychological Association.

Lalumière, M. L., & Quinsey, V. L. (1996). Sexual deviance, antisociality, mating effort, and the use of sexually coercive behaviors. *Personality and Individual Differences, 21*, 33–48.

Lalumière, M. L., & Quinsey, V. L. (1998). Sexual deviance, antisociality, mating effort, and the use of sexually coercive behaviors. *Personality and Individual Differences, 21*, 33–48.

Lalumière, M. L., Quinsey, V. L., Harris, G. T., Rice, M. E., & Trautrimas, C. (2003). Are rapists differently aroused by coercive sex in phallometric assessments? *Annals New York Academy of Sciences, 989*, 211–224.

Lamanna, M. A., & Riedmann, A. (2005). *Marriages and families*, 8th ed. Belmont, CA: Wadsworth.

LaMarre, A. K., Paterson, L. Q., & Gorzalka, B. B. (2003). Breastfeeding and postpartum maternal sexual functioning: A review. *Canadian Journal of Human Sexuality, 12*(3–4), 151–168.

Lamaze, F. (1981). *Painless childbirth.* New York: Simon & Schuster.

Lamba, H., Goldmeier, D., Mackie, N. E., & Scullard, G. (2004). Antiretroviral therapy is associated with sexual dysfunction and with increased serum oestradiol levels in men. *International Journal of STD & AIDS, 15*(4), 234–237.

Lamberti, D. (1997). Cited in Alterman, E. (1997, November). Sex in the '90s. *Elle.*

Landolt, M. A., Bartholomew, K., Saffrey, C., Oram, D., & Perlman, D. (2004). Gender nonconformity, childhood rejection, and adult attachment: A study of gay men. *Archives of Sexual Behavior, 33*(2), 117–128.

Lang, D. (2007). Association between recent gender-based violence and pregnancy, sexually transmitted infections, condom use and negotiation of safe sex practices among HIV+ women. *Journal of Acquired Immune Deficiency Syndrome, 46*, 216–221.

Langevin, R. (2003). A study of the psychosexual characteristics of sex killers: Can we identify them before it is too late? *International Journal of Offender Therapy & Comparative Criminology, 47*(4), 366–382.

Langevin, R. (2006). Acceptance and completion of treatment among sex offenders. *International Journal of Offender Therapy and Comparative Criminology, 50*(4), 402–417.

Langevin, R., & Curnoe, S. (2004). The use of pornography during the commission of sexual offenses. *International Journal of Offender Therapy and Comparative Criminology, 48*(5), 572–586.

Langevin, R., Langevin, M., Curnoe, S., & Bain, J. (2006). Generational substance abuse among male sexual offenders and paraphilics. *Victims & Offenders, 1*(4), 395–409.

Langevin, R., et al. (1979). Experimental studies of the etiology of genital exhibitionism. *Archives of Sexual Behavior, 8*, 307–332.

Langhinrichsen-Rohling, J., Palarea, R. E., Cohen, J., & Rohlin, M. L. (2002).

Breaking up is hard to do: Unwanted pursuit behaviors following the dissolution of a romantic relationship. In K. E. Davis, & I. H. Frieze, et al. (Eds.), *Stalking: Perspectives on victims and perpetrators* (pp. 212–236). New York: Springer.

Langille, D. B. (2002). Factors associated with sexual intercourse before age 15 in Nova Scotia female adolescents. Paper presented at the annual meeting of the Canadian Sex Research Forum, Toronto.

Langille, D. B., Flowerdew, G., & Andreou, P. (2004). Teenage pregnancy in Nova Scotia communities: Associations with contextual factors. *Canadian Journal of Human Sexuality, 13*(2), 83–94.

Langlois, J. H., et al. (2000). Maxims or myths of beauty? A meta-analytic and theoretical review. *Psychological Bulletin, 126*(3), 390–423.

Långström, N., & Seto, M. (2006). Exhibitionistic and voyeuristic behavior in a Swedish national population survey. *Archives of Sexual Behavior, 35,* 427–435.

Långström, N., & Zucker, K. J. (2005). Transvestic fetishism in the general population: Prevalence and correlates. *Journal of Sex & Marital Therapy, 31*(2), 87–95.

Larson, L. E., Goltz, J. W., & Munro, B. E. (2000). *Families in Canada: Social contexts, continuities and changes.* Scarborough, ON: Prentice Hall Allyn and Bacon.

Laumann, E. O., et al. (2006). A cross-national study of subjective sexual well-being among older women and men: Findings from the global study of sexual attitudes and behaviors. *Archives of Sexual Behavior, 35*(2), 145–161.

Laumann, E. O., Gagnon, J. H., Michael, R. T., & Michaels, S. (1994). *The social organization of sexuality: Sexual practices in the United States.* Chicago: University of Chicago Press.

Laumann, E. O., Nicolosi, A., Glasser, D. B., Paik, A., Gingell, C., Moreira, E., et al. (2005). Sexual problems among women and men aged 40–80: Prevalence and correlates identified in the global study of sexual attitudes and behaviors. *International Journal of Impotence Research, 17*(1), 39.

Laumann, E., Paik, A., & Glasser, D. (2006). A cross-national study of subjective sexual well-being among older women and men: Findings from the Global Study of Sexual Attitudes and Behaviors. *Archives of Sexual Behavior, 35,* 145–161.

Laumann, E. O., Paik, A., & Rosen, R. C. (1999). Sexual dysfunction in the United States: Prevalence and predictors. *Journal of the American Medical Association, 281*(6), 537–544.

Lavoisier, P., et al. (1995). Clitoral blood flow increases following vaginal pressure stimulation. *Archives of Sexual Behavior, 24,* 37–45.

Law, J. (2000). The politics of breastfeeding: Assessing risk, dividing labor. *Signs, 25*(2), 407–450.

Lawrence, A. (2007). Cultural differences in individualism predict prevalence of non-homosexual male-to-female transsexualism. Paper presented at the Annual Meeting of the International Academy of Sex Research. Vancouver.

Lawrence, A., Latty, E., Chivers, M., & Bailey, J. M. (2005). Measurement of sexual arousal in postoperative male-to-female transsexuals using vaginal photoplethysmography. *Archives of Sexual Behavior, 34*(2), 135–145.

Lawrence, A. A. (2004). Autogynephilia: A paraphilic model of gender identity disorder. *Journal of Gay & Lesbian Psychotherapy, 8*(1–2), 69–87.

Lawrence, A. A. (2005). Sexuality before and after male-to-female sex reassignment surgery. *Archives of Sexual Behavior, 34*(2), 147–166.

Lawrence, K., & Byers, E. S. (1995). Sexual satisfaction in long-term heterosexual relationships: The interpersonal exchange model of sexual satisfaction. *Personal Relationships, 2,* 267–285.

Leary, W. E. (1990, September 13). New focus on sperm brings fertility successes. *The New York Times,* p. B11.

Lederman, M. M., & Valdez, H. (2000). Immune restoration with antiretroviral therapies: Implications for clinical management. *Journal of the American Medical Association, 284,* 223–228.

Lee, J. K. P., Jackson, H. J., Pattison, P., & Ward, T. (2002). Developmental risk factors for sexual offending. *Child Abuse & Neglect, 26*(1), 73–92.

Legall, P. (2008, September 11). Hamilton mother facing sexual assault charges. *Guelph Mecury,* p. A5.

Legato, M. J. (2000, May 12). Cited in "Study of children born without penises finds nature determines gender." The Associated Press online.

Leiblum, S., & Chivers, M. (2007). Normal and persistent genital arousal in women: New perspectives. *Journal of Sex & Marital Therapy, 33*(4), 357–373.

Leinders-Zufall, T., et al. (2000). Ultrasensitive pheromone detection by mammalian vomeronasal neurons. *Nature, 405,* 792–796.

Leitenberg, H., & Henning, K. (1995). Sexual fantasy. *Psychological Bulletin, 117,* 469–496.

Lenihan, G., Rawlins, M. E., Eberly, C. G., Buckley, B., & Masters, B. (1992). Gender differences in rape supportive attitudes before and after a date rape education intervention. *Journal of College Student Development, 33,* 331–338.

Lepischak, B. (2004). Building community for Toronto's lesbian, gay, bisexual, transsexual and transgender youth. *Journal of Gay & Lesbian Social Services: Issues in Practice, Policy & Research, 16*(3–4), 81–98.

Leue, A., Borchard, B., & Hoyer, J. (2004). Mental disorders in a forensic sample of sexual offenders. *European Psychiatry, 19*(3), 123–130.

Levin, R. J. (2003a). The G-spot: Reality or illusion? *Sexual and Relationship Therapy, 18*(1), 117–119.

Levine, D. (2000). Virtual attraction: What rocks your boat. *CyberPsychology & Behavior 3*(4), 565–573.

Levine, G. I. (1991). Sexually transmitted parasitic diseases. *Primary Care: Clinics in Office Practice, 18,* 101–128.

Levinger, G. (1980). Toward the analysis of close relationships. *Journal of Experimental Social Psychology, 16,* 510–544.

Levy, H. (2004, November 25). Internet luring sentence sparks outrage. *Toronto Star.*

Lewis, J. (1998). Learning to strip: The socialization experiences of exotic dancers. *The Canadian Journal of Human Sexuality, 7,* 51–66.

Lichtenstein, P., et al. (2000). Environmental and heritable factors in the causation of cancer—Analyses of cohorts of twins from Sweden, Denmark, and Finland. *The New England Journal of Medicine, 343*(2), 78–85.

Liptak, A. (2003, January 23). Circumcision opponents use the legal system and legislatures. *The New York Times.* [Online].

Liu, K. E., & Fisher, W. A. (2002). Canadian physician's role in contraception from the 19th century to now. *Journal of Obstetrics and Gynaecology Canada, 24*(3), 239–244.

Logan, T. K., Walker, R., Jordan, C. E., & Leukefeld, C. G. (2006). Justice system options and responses. In T. K. Logan, R. Walker, C. E. Jordan, & C. G. Leukefeld (Eds.), *Women and victimization: Contributing factors, interventions, and implications* (pp. 161–194). Washington, DC: American Psychological Association.

Loiselle, A. (2008, April 5). Man who spread HIV gets 18 years; Judge calls his conduct "dispicable and selfish" but denies bid to have him declared dangerous offender. *Toronto Star,* p. A22.

Looman, J., Abracen, J., DiFazio, R., & Maillet, G. (2004). Alcohol and drug abuse among sexual and nonsexual offenders: Relationship to intimacy deficits and coping strategy. *Sexual Abuse: A Journal of Research and Treatment, 16*(3), 177–189.

Lotery, H. E., McClure, N., & Galask, R. P. (2004). Vulvodynia. *Lancet, 363*(9414), 1058–1060.

Lott, B. (1985). The potential enhancement of social/personality psychology through feminist research and vice versa. *American Psychologist, 40,* 155–164.

Love, N. (2004, March 20). Boy, 14, charged with luring girls over 'Net. *Toronto Star.*

Lowman, J., & Atchison, C. (2006). Men who buy sex: A survey in the greater Vancouver regional district. *The Canadian Review of Sociology and Anthropology, 43*(3), 281–296.

Lowry, R., et al. (1994). Substance use and HIV-related sexual behaviors among U.S. high school students: Are they related? *American Journal of Public Health, 84*(7), 1116–1120.

Lucas, A. M. (2005). The work of sex work: Elite prostitutes' vocational orientations and experiences. *Deviant Behavior, 26*(6), 513–546.

Lue, T. F. (2000). Drug therapy: Erectile dysfunction. *The New England Journal of Medicine, 342*(24).

Lutfey, K., Link, C., Rosen, R., Wiegel, M., & McKinlay, J. (2008). Prevalence and correlates of sexual activity and function in women: Results from the Boston area community health (BACH) survey. *Archives of Sexual Behavior, 37*, 51–66.

Lykins, A. D., Janssen, E., & Graham, C. A. (2006). The relationship between negative mood and sexuality in heterosexual college women and men. *Journal of Sex Research, 43*(2), 136–143.

Maaita, M. J., Bhaumik, J., & Davies, A. E. (2002). Sexual function after using tension-free vaginal tape for the surgical treatment of genuine stress incontinence. *British Journal of Urology International, 90*(6), 540.

MacCharles, T. (2000, December 16). Customs can stop gay erotica: Top court. *The Toronto Star*, p. A13.

MacDonald, T. K., MacDonald, G., Zanna, M. P., & Fong, G. T. (2000). Alcohol, sexual arousal, and intentions to use condoms in young men: Applying alcohol myopia theory to risky sexual behavior. *Health Psychology, 19*, 290–298.

MacIntosh, H., & Reissing, E. D. (in press). Legal same-sex marriage: The impact on the personal, social and relational lives of gay & lesbian couples. *Journal of Marital and Family Therapy.*

Mackie, M. (1991). *Gender relations in Canada: Further explorations.* Markham, ON: Butterworths Canada Ltd.

Maclean's magazine (1998, July 20). Findings from the GoldParlo Poll. *Maclean's*, 10.

MacNeil, S. (2004). It takes two: Modeling the role of sexual self-disclosure in sexual satisfaction. (Doctoral dissertation, **www.il.proquest.com/umi/**). *Dissertation Abstracts International: Section B: The Sciences & Engineering, 65* (1-B), 481. (UMI Dissertation Order Number AAINQ87631; Print).

MacNeil, S., & Byers, E. S. (1997). The relationships between sexual problems, communication and sexual satisfaction. *Canadian Journal of Human Sexuality, 6*(4), 277–283.

MacQueen, K. (2003, May 26). Boy vs. girl. *Maclean's*, 26–32.

MacQueen, K. (2006, November 20). They like us! *Maclean's*, pp. 34–39.

Macy, R. J., Nurius, P. S., & Norris, J. (2006). Responding in their best interests: Contextualizing women's coping with acquaintance sexual aggression. *Violence Against Women, 12*(5), 478–500.

Madsen, L., Parsons, S., & Grubin, D. (2006). The relationship between the five-factor model and DSM personality disorder in a sample of child molesters. *Personality and Individual Differences, 40*(2), 227–236.

Mah, K., & Binik, Y. (2002). Do all orgasms feel alike? Evaluating a two-dimensional model of the orgasm experience across gender and sexual context. *The Journal of Sex Research, 39*, 104–114.

Mah, K., & Binik, Y. (2005). Are orgasms in the mind or the body? Psychosocial versus physiological correlates or orgasmic pleasure and satisfaction. *Journal of Sex & Marital Therapy, 31*(3), 187–200.

Mahoney, D. (1994). *Staying connected: The coming out stories of parents with a lesbian daughter or gay son.* Unpublished master's thesis, University of Guelph.

Maisel, L., & Meggars, H. (2007). Now and then: Females learning and practicing masturbation. Poster session presented at the Annual Meeting of the Society for the Scientific Study of Sexuality, Indianapolis, IN.

Major, B., Cozzarelli, C., Cooper, M. L., Zubek, J., Richards, C., et al. (2000). Psychological responses of women after first-trimester abortion. *Archives of General Psychiatry, 57*, 777–784.

Major, C. J., Read, S. E., Coates, R. A., et al. (1991). Comparison of saliva and blood for human immunodeficiency virus prevalence testing. *Journal of Infectious Diseases, 163*(4), 699–702.

Malamuth, N. M., Huppin, M., & Paul, B. (2005). Sexual coercion. In D. M. Buss (Ed.), *The handbook of evolutionary psychology* (pp. 394–418). Hoboken, NJ: John Wiley & Sons.

Maletzky, B. M. (1980). Self-referred vs. court-referred sexually deviant patients: Success with assisted covert sensitization. *Behavior Therapy, 11*, 306–314.

Malinowski, B. (1929). *The sexual life of savages in north-western Melanesia.* New York: Eugenics.

Man accused of stealing panties agrees to counselling. (2002, April 28). *National Post*, p. A6.

Mantovani, F. (2001). Cyber-attraction: The emergence of computer-mediated communication in the development of interpersonal relationships. In L. Anolli, R. Cieri, & G. Riva (eds.), *Say not to say: New perspectives on miscommunication* (pp. 236–252). Amsterdam, Holland: IOS Press.

Maranda, M. J., Han, C., & Rainone, G. A. (2004). Crack cocaine and sex. *Journal of Psychoactive Drugs, 36*(3), 315–322.

Marazziti, D. (2005). The neurobiology of love. *Current Psychiatry Reviews, 1*(3), 331–335.

Marchbanks, P. A., et al. (2000). Cigarette smoking and epithelial ovarian cancer by histological type. *Obstetrics & Gynecology, 95*, 255–260.

Marchione, M. (2008, February 13). Prostate cancer treatment can wait. *Associated Press.*

Marcus, D. K., & Miller, R. S. (2003). Sex differences in judgments of physical attractiveness: A social relations analysis. *Personality & Social Psychology Bulletin, 29*(3), 325–335.

Mark, M. (2003, October 1). Consenting adults: A look behind closed doors in Calgary. *The Calgary Sun.*

Marrazzo, J. M. (2005). Sexual practices, risk perception and knowledge of sexually transmitted disease risk among lesbian and bisexual women. *Perspectives on Sexual and Reproductive Health, 37*, 6–12.

Marshall, W. L. (1989). Pornography and sex offenders. In D. Zillmann & J. Bryant (Eds.), *Pornography: Research advances and policy considerations* (pp. 185–214). Hillsdale, NJ: Lawrence Erlbaum Associates.

Marshall, W. L., Marshall, L. E., & Serran, G. A. (2007). Strategies in the treatment of paraphilias: A critical review. *Annual Review of Sex Research, 17*, 162–182.

Marshall, W. L., Marshall, L. E., Serran, G. A., & Fernandez, Y. M. (2006). *Treating sexual offenders: An integrated approach.* New York: Routledge.

Marsiglio, W. (1993). Adolescent males' orientation toward paternity and contraception. *Family Planning Perspectives, 25*, 22–31.

Marsman, J. C., & Herold, E. S. (1986). Attitudes toward sex education and values in sex education. *Family Relations, 35*, 357–361.

Martino, S. C., et al. (2006). Exposure to degrading versus nondegrading music lyrics and sexual behavior among youth. *Pediatrics, 118*, e420–e441.

Martins, Y., Preti, G., Crabtree, C. R., Runyan, T., Vainius, A. A., & Wysocki, C. J. (2005). Preference for human body odors is influenced by gender and sexual orientation. *Psychological Science, 16*(9), 694.

Martz, J. M., et al. (1998). Positive illusion in close relationships. *Personal Relationships, 5*(2), 159–181.

Marziano, V., Ward, T., Beech, A. R., & Pattison, P. (2006). Identification of five fundamental implicit theories underlying cognitive distortions in child abusers: A preliminary study. *Psychology, Crime & Law, 12*(1), 97–105.

Masheb, R. M., Lozano–Blanco, C., Kohorn, E. I., Minkin, M. J., & Kerns, R. D. (2004). Assessing sexual function and dyspareunia with the female sexual function index (FSFI) in women with vulvodynia. *Journal of Sex & Marital Therapy, 30*(5), 315–324.

Masters, W. H., & Johnson, V. E. (1966). *Human sexual response.* Boston: Little, Brown.

Masters, W. H., & Johnson, V. E. (1970). *Human sexual inadequacy.* Boston: Little, Brown.

Masters, W. H., & Johnson, V. E. (1979). *Homosexuality in perspective.* Boston: Little, Brown.

Maticka-Tyndale, E. (1997). Reducing the incidence of sexually transmitted disease through behavioral and social change. *Canadian Journal of Human Sexuality, 6*(2), 89–104.

Maticka-Tyndale, E. (2001). Sexual health and Canadian youth: How do we measure up? *Canadian Journal of Human Sexuality, 10*, 1–17.

Maticka-Tyndale, E., Gallant, M., Brouillard-Coyle, C., Holland, D., Metcalfe, K., Wildish, J., et al. (2005). The sexual scripts of Kenyan young people and HIV prevention. *Culture, Health & Sexuality,* 7(1), 27–41.

Maticka-Tyndale, E., Godin, G., LeMay, G., Adrien, A., Manson-Singer, S., Willms, D., et al. (1996). Canadian ethnocultural communities facing AIDS: Overview and summary of survey results from phase III. *Canadian Journal of Public Health, 87*(supp. 1), S38–S43.

Maticka-Tyndale, E., & Herold, E. S. (1997). The scripting of sexual behaviour: Canadian university students on spring break in Florida. *The Canadian Journal of Human Sexuality, 6*, 317–328.

Maticka-Tyndale, E., Herold, E. S., & Mewhinney, D. K. (1998). Casual sex on spring break: Intentions and behaviors of Canadian students. *Journal of Sex Research, 35*, 254–264.

Maticka-Tyndale, E., Lewis, J., & Street, M. (2005). Making a place for escort work: A case study. *The Journal of Sex Research, 42*(1), 46–53.

Maticka-Tyndale, E., McKay, A., & Barrett, M. (2001). *Teenage sexual and reproductive behavior in developed countries: Country report for Canada.* New York: Alan Guttmacher Institute.

Maticka-Tyndale, E., Shirpak, K. R., & Chinichian, M. (2007). Providing for the sexual health needs of Canadian immigrants. *Canadian Journal of Public Health, 98*(3), 183–186.

Maticka-Tyndale, E., & Smylie, L. (in press). Sexual rights: Striking a balance. *International Journal of Sexual Health.*

Maticka-Tyndale, E., Wildish, J., & Gichuru, M. (2007). Quasi-experimental evaluation of a national primary school HIV intervention in Kenya. *Evaluation and Program Planning, 30*, 172–186.

Maticka-Tyndale, M., & Brooke, C. (2005). Sexuality in Canada: Research. Paper presented at the XVII World Congress of Sexology, Montreal.

Matthews, A. K., Hughes, T. L., & Tartaro, J. (2006). Sexual behavior and sexual dysfunction in a community sample of lesbian and heterosexual women. In A. M. Omoto & H. S. Kurtzman (Eds.), *Sexual orientation and mental health: Examining identity and development in lesbian, gay, and bisexual people, Contemporary perspectives on lesbian, gay, and bisexual psychology* (pp. 185–205). Washington, DC: American Psychological Association.

Maybach, K. L., & Gold, S. R. (1994). Hyperfemininity and attraction to macho and non-macho men. *Journal of Sex Research, 31*(2), 91–98.

Mayo Clinic. (2006, October 10). Vulvodynia. [Online]. **www.mayoclinic.com/health/vulvodynia/DS00159**

Mazur, T. *The infant's developing sexuality.* Accessed February 10, 2006. [Online]. **www2.hu-berlin.de/sexology/gesund/archiv/sen/ch07.htm#b11-children%20and%20sex**.

McArthur, M. J. (1990). Reality therapy with rape victims. *Archives of Psychiatric Nursing, 4*, 360–365.

McCabe, K. A. (2000). Child pornography and the internet. *Social Science Computer Review, 18*(1), 73–76.

McCabe, M. P. (2004). Exacerbation of symptoms among people with multiple sclerosis: Impact on sexuality and relationships over time. *Archives of Sexual Behavior, 33*(6), 593–601.

McCabe, M. P. (2005). The role of performance anxiety in the development and maintenance of sexual dysfunction in men and women. *International Journal of Stress Management, 12*(4), 379–388.

McCabe, S. E., et al. (2005). Selection and socialization effects of fraternities and sororities on US college student substance use: A multi-cohort national longitudinal study. *Addiction, 100*(4), 512–524.

McCarthy, B. W., Bodnar, L. E., & Handal, M. (2004). Integrating sex therapy and couple therapy. In Harvey, J. H., Wenzel, A., & Sprecher, S. (Eds.). *The handbook of sexuality in close relationships* (pp. 573–593). Philadelphia, PA: Lawrence Erlbaum Associates.

McCarthy, B. W., & Fucito, L. M. (2005). Integrating medication, realistic expectations, and therapeutic interventions in the treatment of male sexual dysfunction. *Journal of Sex & Marital Therapy, 31*(4), 319–328.

McCarthy, B. W., Ginsberg, R. L., & Fucito, L. M. (2006). Resilient sexual desire in heterosexual couples. *Family Journal: Counseling and Therapy for Couples and Families, 14*(1), 59–64.

McCoy, N. L., & Pitino, L. (2002). Pheromonal influences on sociosexual behavior in young women. *Physiology & Behavior, 75*(3), 367–375.

McCreary Centre Society. (2007). Not yet equal: The health of lesbian, gay, & bisexual youth in BC. Vancouver: Author.

McDonough, Y. Z. (1998, January 24). What Barbie really taught me. *The New York Times Magazine*, 70.

McElduff, A., & Beange, H. (2003). Men's health and well-being: Testosterone deficiency. *Journal of Intellectual & Developmental Disability, 28*(2), 211–213.

McEwan, S. L., de Man, A. F., & Simpson-Housley, P. (2005). Acquaintance rape, ego-identity achievement, and locus of control. *Social Behavior and Personality,* 33(6), 587–592.

McGregor, M. J., Ericksen, J., Ronald, L. A., Janssen, P. A., Van Vliet, A., & Schulzer, M. (2004). Rising incidence of hospital-reported drug-facilitated sexual assault in a large urban community in Canada. *Canadian Journal of Public Health, 95*(6), 441–445.

McKay, A. (1998). *Sexual ideology and schooling.* London, ON: The Althouse Press.

McKay, A. (2005). Sexuality and substance use: The impact of tobacco, alcohol, and selected recreational drugs on sexual function. *Canadian Journal of Human Sexuality, 14*(1–2), 47–56.

McKay, A. (2006a). Chlamydia screening programs: A review of the literature. Part 2: Testing procedures and educational interventions for primary care physicians. *The Canadian Journal of Human Sexuality, 15*(1), 13–22.

McKay, A. (2006b). Chlamydia screening programs: A review of the literature. Part 1: Issues in the promotion of chlamydia testing of youth by primary care physicians. *The Canadian Journal of Human Sexuality, 15*(1), 1–11.

McKay, A. (2007). The effectiveness of latex condoms for prevention of STI/HIV. *The Canadian Journal of Human Sexuality, 16*(1-2), 57–61.

McKay, A., & Barrett, B. (2008). Rising reported rates of chlamydia among young women in Canada: What do they tell us about trends in the actual prevalence of the infection? *The Canadian Journal of Human Sexuality,* 17(1), 61–69.

McMaster, L. E., Connolly, J., Pepler, D., & Craig, W. M. (2002). Peer to peer sexual harassment in early adolescence: A developmental perspective. *Development and Psycho-pathology, 14,* 91–105.

Mead, M. (1935). *Sex and temperament in three primitive societies.* New York: Dell.

Meaney, G., & Rye, B. (2007). Sex, sexuality and leisure. In R. McCarville & K. MacKay (Eds.), *Leisure for Canadians.* State College, PA: Venture Publishing.

Meaney, G., & Rye, B. J. (2008). Portrayals of homosexuality in introductory human sexuality textbooks. Paper presented at the Guelph Sexuality Conference, Guelph, ON.

Meininger, E., Saewyc, E. M., Clark, T., Skay, C., Poon, C., Robinson, E., Pettingell, S., & Homma, Y. (2007). Enacted stigma and HIV risk behaviors in sexual minority youth of European heritage across three countries. *Journal of Adolescent Health, 40(2),* S27.

Meininger, E., Saewyc, E. M., Skay, C., Clark, T., Poon, C., Robinson, E., Pettingell, S., & Homma, Y. (2007). Enacted sigma and HIV risk behaviors in sexual minority youth of European heritage across three countries. [abstract]. *Journal of Adolescent Health, 40,* S27.

Menard, A. D., & Kleinplatz, P. K. (2008). 21 moves guaranteed to make his thighs go up in flames: Depictions of "great sex" in popular magazines. *Sexuality & Culture, 12*(1), 1–20.

Menon, V. (2002, May 14). Window undressing. *The Toronto Star,* p. B1.

Mercury Staff. (2007, December 21). Dance floor incident leads to assault charges. *Guelph Mercury.*

Merrill, R. M., & Brawley, O. W. (2000). Prostate cancer incidence and mortality rates among White and Black men. *Epidemiology* online, *11*(2).

Mertz, G. J., et al. (1992). Risk factors for the sexual transmission of genital herpes. *Annals of Internal Medicine, 116,* 197–202.

Meston, C. M., & Frohlich, P. F. (2000). The neurobiology of sexual function. *Archives of General Psychiatry,* 57(11), 1012–1030.

Meston, C. M., & Gorzalka, B. B. (1992). Psychoactive drugs and human sexual behavior: The role of serotonergic activity. *Journal of Psychoactive Drugs, 24,* 1–40.

Meston, C. M., & Gorzalka, B. B (1995). The effects of sympathetic activation on physiological and subjective sexual arousal in women. *Behavior Research and Therapy, 33,* 651–664.

Meston, C. M., Heiman, J. R., Trapnell, P., & Paulhus, D. (1998). Socially desirable responding and sexuality self-reports. *The Journal of Sex Research, 35,* 148–157.

Meston, C. M., Trapnell, P. D., & Gorzalka, B. B. (1996). Ethnic and gender differences in sexuality: Variations in sexual behavior between Asian and non-Asian university students. *Archives of Sexual Behavior, 25,* 33–72.

Mewhinney, D. K., Herold, E. S., & Maticka-Tyndale, E. (1995). Sexual scripts and risk-taking of Canadian university students on spring break in Daytona Beach, Florida. *Canadian Journal of Human Sexuality, 4,* 273–288.

Meyer-Bahlburg, H., Dolezal, C., & Schober, J. (2007). Self-ratings of genital anatomy and sexual function by women using the Sagasf-F. Paper presented at the annual conference of the International Academy of Sex Research, Vancouver, BC.

Michael, R. T., Gagnon, J. H., Laumann, E. O., & Kolata, G. (1994). *Sex in America: A definitive survey.* Boston: Little, Brown.

Michel, A., & Pédinielli, J.-L. (2005). Vers une conceptualisation du transsexualisme. *Annales Médico-Psychologiques, 163*(5), 379–386.

Migliardi, P. (2007). *Unheard voices of ethno-racial minority youth.* Winnipeg: Sexuality Education Resource Centre.

Mikach, S. M., & Bailey, J. M. (1999). What distinguishes women with unusually high numbers of sex partners? *Evolution & Human Behavior, 20*(3), 141–150.

Milhausen, R. (2004). Factors that inhibit and enhance sexual arousal in college men and women. Unpublished doctoral dissertation, Indiana University, Indianapolis, Indiana.

Milhausen, R. R. (2000). Double standard or reverse double standard: A comparative analysis of male and female perspectives. Unpublished master's thesis, University of Guelph.

Milhausen, R. R., & Herold, E. S. (1999). Does the sexual double standard still exist? Perceptions of university women. *Journal of Sex Research, 36*(4), 361–368.

Milhausen, R. R., & Herold, E. S. (2001). Reconceptualizing the sexual double standard. *Journal of Psychology and Human Sexuality, 13,* 63–83.

Milhausen, R. R., Leblanc, L., Todd, L., Rotman, J., Andrecheck, K., Lee, A., Spring, L., Morrow, E., & the Undergraduate Research Group in Sexuality. (2007). The role of social desirability and gender in romantic partner choice: Evidence from a lie detector study. Paper presented at the Annual Meeting of the Society for the Scientific Study of Sexuality's Annual Meeting, Indianapolis, Indiana.

Millar, C. (2003, November 22). Web porn accessed from car. *The Toronto Star.*

Miller, R. (2005). Overcoming violence against women and girls: The international campaign to eradicate a worldwide problem. *Culture, Health & Sexuality,* 7(5), 519–521.

Miller, S. A., & Byers, E. S. (2004). Actual and desired duration of foreplay and intercourse: Discordance and misperceptions within heterosexual couples. *Journal of Sex Research, 41*(3), 301–309.

Miller, S. A., & Byers, S. E. (2005). The training of clinical psychologists in Canada: How prepared are students to deal with clients' sexual problems? Paper presented at the World Congress of Sexology, Montreal.

Miller, W., & Maclean, H. (2005). Breastfeeding practices. Ottawa: Statistics Canada [Catalogue 82-003 Health Reports, Vol. 16, 2, March 2005.]

Minai, N. (1981). *Women in Islam: Tradition and transition in the Middle East.* London: John Murray.

Minichiello, V., et al. (2001). Male sex workers in three Australian cities: Socio-demographic and sex work characteristics. *Journal of Homosexuality, 42*(1), 29–51.

Minister of Health (2002, May 9). *House of Commons of Canada Bill C-56: An act respecting assisted human reproduction.* House of Commons of Canada, [49-50-51], 1st session, 37th Parliament.

Missailidis, K., & Gebre-Medhin, M. (2000). Female genital mutilation in eastern Ethiopia. *The Lancet, 356,* 137–138.

Mitchell, B. (2006, October 16). Sex assault charge for Peel teacher. *Toronto Star,* p. C4.

Modell, J. G., May, R. S., & Katholi, C. R. (2000). Effect of bupropion-SR on orgasmic dysfunction in nondepressed subjects: A pilot study. *Journal of Sex & Marital Therapy, 26*(3), 231–240.

Mohan, R., & Bhugra, D. (2005). Literature update: A critical review. *Sexual and Relationship Therapy, 20*(1), 115–122.

Molloy, G. L., & Herold, E. S. (1985). Sexual counseling for the physically disabled: A comparison of health care professionals' attitudes and practices. *Canadian Family Physician, 31,* 2277–2285.

Money, J. (1994). The concept of gender identity disorder in childhood and adolescence after 39 years. *Journal of Sex and Marital Therapy, 20*(3), 163–177.

Money, J. (2003). History, causality, and sexology. *Journal of Sex Research, 40*(3), 237–239.

Money, J., Lehne, G., & Pierre-Jerome, F. (1984). Micropenis: Adult follow-up and comparison of size against new norms. *Journal of Sex and Marital Therapy, 10,* 105–116.

Monsebraaten, L. (2006, April 15). Dark side of girl power. *Toronto Star,* p. A1.

Montemurro, B., Bloom, C., & Madell, K. (2003). Ladies night out: A typology of women patrons of a male strip club. *Deviant Behavior, 24*(4), 333–352.

Moore, D. R., & Heiman, J. R. (2006). Women's sexuality in context: Relationship factors and female sexual functioning. In

I. Goldstein, C. Meston, S. Davis, & A. Traish (Eds.), *Female sexual dysfunction.* New York: Parthenon.

Morley, J. E., & Perry, H. M., III. (2003). Androgens and women at the menopause and beyond. *Journals of Gerontology: Series A: Biological Sciences & Medical Sciences, 58A*(5), 409–416.

Morris, L. B. (2000, June 25). For the partum blues, a question of whether to medicate. *The New York Times.* [Online].

Morrison, E. S., et al. (1980). *Growing up sexual.* New York: Van Nostrand Reinhold.

Morrison, G. G., Harriman, R., Morrison, M. A., Bearden, A., & Ellis, S. (2004). Correlates of exposure to sexually explicit material among Canadian post-secondary students. *The Canadian Journal of Human Sexuality, 13*(3–4), 143–157.

Morrison, M. A., & Morrison, T. G. (2002). Modern homonegativity: Development and validation of a scale measuring modern prejudice toward gay men and lesbian women. *Journal of Homosexuality, 43*(2), 15–37.

Morry, M. M., & Gaines, S. O. (2005). Relationship satisfaction as a predictor of similarity ratings: A test of the attraction–similarity hypothesis. *Journal of Social and Personal Relationships, 22*(4), 561–584.

Mortola, J. F. (1998). Premenstrual syndrome—Pathophysiologic considerations. *The New England Journal of Medicine, 338*, 256–257.

Moser, C. (2001). Paraphilia: A critique of a confused concept. In P. Kleinplatz (Ed.), *New directions in sex therapy: Innovations and alternatives* (pp. 91–108). New York: Brunner-Routledge.

Moser, C., & Kleinplatz, P. J. (2002, Spring). Transvestic fetishism: Psychopathology or iatrogenic artifact? *New Jersey Psychologist*, pp. 16–17.

Moser, C., & Kleinplatz, P. J. (2005a). DSM-IV-TR and the paraphilias: An argument for removal. *Journal of Psychology & Human Sexuality, 17*(3–4), 91–109.

Moser, C., & Kleinplatz, P. J. (2005b). Does heterosexuality belong in the DSM? *Lesbian & Gay Psychology Review, 6*(3), 261–267

Mosher, W. D., Chandra, A., & Jones, J. (2005). *Sexual behavior and selected health measures: Men and women 15–44 years of age, United States, 2002. Advance data from vital and health statistics.* Centers for Disease Control and Prevention. National Center for Health Statistics, No. 362.

Mother guilty of assault. (1999, February 18). *National Post.*

Muehlenhard, C. L. (2000). Categories and sexuality. *The Journal of Sex Research, 37*(2), 101–107.

Muise, A. (2006). A discourse analytic study of the discursive management of female sexual desire in online weblogs. Poster session presented at the Annual Guelph Sexuality Conference, Guelph, Ontario.

Muise, A. (2008, September). The discursive management of female sexual desire in online weblogs. Paper presented at the 32nd Annual Meeting of the Canadian Sex Research Forum, Ottawa, Ontario.

Muise, A., Christofides, E., & Desmarais, S. (2008). Who are you "poking"?: Students' experience of jealousy on Facebook. Poster session presented at the Annual Guelph Conference on Human Sexuality, Guelph, Ontario.

Mulick, P. S., & Wright, L. W., Jr. (2002). Examining the existence of biphobia in the heterosexual and homosexual populations. *Journal of Bisexuality, 2*(4), 45–64.

Munro, V. E. (2006). Stopping traffic? A comparative study of responses to the trafficking in women for prostitution. *British Journal of Criminology, 46*(2), 318–333.

Murray, J., & Adam, B. (2001). Aging, sexuality and HIV issues among older gay men. *The Canadian Journal of Human Sexuality, 10*, 75–90.

Murray, J. B. (1995). Evidence for acupuncture's analgesic effectiveness and proposals for the physiological mechanisms involved. *Journal of Psychology: Interdisciplinary and Applied, 129*(4), 443–461.

Murray, S. O., & Roscoe, W. (1997). *Islamic homosexualities: Culture, history, and literature.* New York: New York University Press.

Mustanski, B., Chivers, M., & Bailey, M. (2003). A critical review of recent biological research on human sexual orientation. *Annual Review of Sex Research, 13*, 89–140.

Mustanski, B. S., Dupree, M. G., Nievergelt, C. M., Bocklandt, S., Schork, N. J., & Hamer, D. H. (2005). A genomewide scan of male sexual orientation. *Human Genetics, 116*, 272–278.

Myers, M. F. (1989). Men sexually assaulted as adults and sexually abused as boys. *Archives of Sexual Behavior, 18*, 203–215.

Myers, T., Aguinaldo, J. P., Dakers, D., et al. (2004). How drug using men who have sex with men account for substance use during sexual behaviours: Questioning assumptions of HIV prevention and research. *Addiction Research and Theory, 12*(3), 213–229.

Myers, T., & Allman, D. 2004. *Ontario Men's Survey.* Ottawa: Canadian Public Health Association.

Myers, T., Allman, D., Calzavara, L., et al. (2004). *Ontario men's survey.* Toronto: University of Toronto, HIV Social, Behavioural and Epidemiological Studies Unit.

Myers, T., Allman, D., Calzavara, L., Maxwell, J., Remis, R., Swantee, C., & Travers, R. (2004a). Ontario men's survey. Library and Archives Canada Cataloguing in Publication. Available: **cbr.cbrc.net/files/1126039797/Ontario%20Mens%20Survey%20Final%20Report.pdf**

Myers, T., Bullock, S. L., Calzavara, L. M., Cockerill, R., & Marshall, V. W. (1997). Differences in sexual risk-taking behaviour with state of inebriation in an Aboriginal population in Ontario, Canada. *Journal of Studies in Alcohol, 58*, 312–322.

Myers, T., Calzavara, L. M., Cockerill, R., Marshall, V. W., & Bullock, S. L. (1993). *The Ontario First Nations AIDS and healthy lifestyle survey.* Ottawa, ON: Canadian Public Health Association.

Myers, T., Godin, G., Calzavara, L., Lambert, J., & Locker, D. (1993). *The Canadian survey of gay and bisexual men and HIV infection: Men's survey.* Ottawa, ON: Canadian AIDS Society.

Myers, T., Godin, G., Lambert, J., Calzavara, L., & Locker, D. (1996). Sexual risk and HIV-testing behaviour by gay and bisexual men in Canada. *AIDS Care, 8*(3), 297–309.

Myers, T., Orr, K. W., Locker, D., & Jackson, E. A. (1993). Factors affecting gay and bisexual men's decisions and intentions to seek HIV testing. *American Journal of Public Health, 83*, 701–704.

Nadler, R. D. (1990). Homosexual behavior in nonhuman primates. In D. P. McWhirter, S. A. Sanders, & J. M. Reinisch (Eds.), *Homosexuality/heterosexuality: Concepts of sexual orientation* (pp. 138–170). New York: Oxford University Press.

Naili, H., & Josey, S. (2005, August 11). Pastor faces sex charges. *The Toronto Star.*

Narchi, H. (2003). Infantile masturbation mimicking paroxysmal disorders. *Journal of Pediatric Neurology, 1*(1), 43–45.

National Cancer Institute. (2000). Available: **www.nci.nih.gov**

National Center for Biotechnology Information (NCBI). (2000, March 30). National Institutes of Health. Available: **www.ncbi.nlm.nih.gov/disease/SRY.htm**

Netting, N. S., & Burnett, M. L. (2004). Twenty years of student sexual behavior: Subcultural adaptations to a changing health environment. *Adolescence, 39*(153), 19–38.

Nichols, M. (1999, February 22). Men's sexual health. *Maclean's*, 30–31.

Nickel, J. C., Elhilali, M., Vallancien, G., & ALF-ONE Study Group. (2005). Benign prostatic hyperplasia (BPH) and prostatitis: Prevalence of painful ejaculation in men with clinical BPH. *BJU International, 95*(4), 571–574.

Nicolosi, A., Laumann, E., Glasser, D., Moreira, E., & Paik, A. (2004). Sexual behavior and sexual dysfunctions after age 40: The global study of sexual attitudes and behaviors. *Urology, 64*, 991–997.

Nieder, T., & Sieffge-Krenke, I. (2001). Coping with stress in different phases of romantic development. *Journal of Adolescence, 24*(3), 297–311.

Nina's Unstoppable! desire to be herself. (2007, June 14). *Toronto Star*, p. 5.

Nixon, K., Tutty, L., Downe, P., Gorkoff, K., & Ursel, J. (2002). The everyday occurrence: Violence in the lives of girls exploited through prostitution. *Violence Against Women. Special Violence Against Women and Girls in Prostitution, 8*(9), 1016–1043.

Nobre, P. J., & Pinto-Gouveia, J. (2006). Dysfunctional sexual beliefs as vulnerability factors for sexual dysfunction. *Journal of Sex Research, 43*(1), 68–75.

Norton, A. (2000, September 1). *Exercise helps men avoid impotence.* Reuters News Agency. [Online].

Nosek, M. A., et al. (2004). The meaning of health for women with physical disabilities: A qualitative analysis. *Family & Community Health,* 27(1), 6–21.

Nosko, A., Wood, E., & Desmarais, S. (2007). Unsolicited online sexual material: What affects our attitudes and likelihood to search for more? *The Canadian Journal of Human Sexuality, 16*(1–2), 1–10.

Nour, N. W. (2000). Cited in Dreifus, C. (2000, July 11). A conversation with Dr. Nawal M. Nour: A life devoted to stopping the suffering of mutilation. *The New York Times* online.

Nurnberg, G., Hensley, P., & Heiman, J. (2008). Sildenafil treatment of women with antidepressant-associated sexual dysfunction: A randomized controlled trial. *Journal of the American Medical Association, 300*(4), 395–404.

O'Doherty, J., et al. (2003). Beauty in a smile: The role of medial orbitofrontal cortex in facial attractiveness. *Neuropsychologia, 41*(2), 147–155.

O'Keeffe, M. J., et al. (2003). Learning, cognitive, and attentional problems in adolescents born small for gestational age. *Pediatrics, 112*(2), 301–307.

O'Sullivan, L. F. (2003). The development of romantic relationships in adolescence. *Archives of Sexual Behavior, 32*(3), 292–294.

O'Sullivan, L. F., & Byers, E. S. (1992). College students' incorporation of initiator and restrictor roles in sexual dating interactions. *Journal of Sex Research, 29*, 435–446.

O'Sullivan, L. F., Byers, E. S., & Finkelman, L. (1998). A comparison of male and female college students' experiences of sexual coercion. *Psychology of Women Quarterly, 22*, 177–195.

Oakes, G. (1994, February 4). Lover who removed his condom jailed 45 days for sexual assault. *The Toronto Star.*

Oates, M., & Offman, A. (2007). Global self-esteem and sexual self-esteem as predictors of sexual communication in intimate relationships. *The Canadian Journal of Human Sexuality, 16*, 89–100.

Ochs, E. P., & Binik, Y. M. (1999). The use of couple data to determine reliability of self-reported sexual behavior. *Journal of Sex Research, 36*(4), 1–11.

Ochs, E. P., & Binik, Y. M. (2000). A sex-expert system on the internet: Fact or fantasy. *Cyber Psychology & Behavior, 3*, 617–629.

Offman, A., & Matheson, K. (2005). Sexual compatibility and sexual function in intimate relationships. *The Canadian Journal of Human Sexuality, 14*(1–2), 31–39.

Ogden, G., et al. (2007). Spiritual dimensions of sexual health: Broadening clinical perspectives of women's desire. In A. F. Owens & M. S. Tepper (Eds.), *Sexual health, 4* (pp. 131–152). Westport, CT: Praeger.

Ogilvie, M. (2008, June 19). New egg-freezing technique gives women more options. *Toronto Star*, p. A20.

Olfson, M., Uttaro, T., Carson, W. H., & Tafesse, E. (2005). Male sexual dysfunction and quality of life in schizophrenia. *Journal of Clinical Psychiatry, 66*(3), 331–338.

Open Society Institute. (2007). Women, harm reduction, and HIV. New York: Author.

Ortega, V., Ojeda, P., Sutil, F., & Sierra, J. C. (2005). Culpabilidad sexual en adolescentes: Estudio de algunos factores relacionados. *Anales de Psicología, 21*(2), 268–275.

Osman, S. L. (2003). Predicting men's rape perceptions based on the belief that "No" really means "Yes." *Journal of Applied Social Psychology, 33*(4), 683–692.

Overholser, J. C., & Beck, S. (1986). Multimethod assessment of rapists, child molesters, and three control groups on behavioral and psychological measures. *Journal of Consulting and Clinical Psychology, 54*, 682–687.

Pakhomou, S. M. (2006). Methodological aspects of telephone scatologia: A case study. *International Journal of Law and Psychiatry, 29*(3), 178–185.

Palace, E. M. (1995). Modification of dysfunctional patterns of sexual arousal through autonomic arousal and false physiological feedback. *Journal of Consulting and Clinical Psychology, 63*, 604–615.

Panel rejects "self-love" at least in the morning. (2007, August 31). *Toronto Star*, p. E7.

Parr-LeFeuve, R., & Desmarais, S. (2005). Do young women use sexual pressure to initiate sex? Unpublished paper. University of Guelph, Dept. of Psychology.

Parrott, D., Zeichner, A., & Hoover, R. (2006). Sexual prejudice and anger network activation: Mediating role of negative affect. *Aggressive Behavior, 32*(1), 7–16.

Pasupathy, D., & Smith, G. C. (2005). The analysis of factors predicting antepartum stillbirth. *Minerva Ginecology, 57*(4), 397–410.

Patha, P., et al. (2006). Discordance between sexual behavior and self-reported sexual identity: A population-based survey of New York City men. *Annals of Internal Medicine, 145*, 416–425.

Patriquin, M. (2007, October 22). Canada: A nation of bigots? *Maclean's*, 17–22.

Pawlowski, B., & Koziel, S. (2002). The impact of traits offered in personal advertisements on response rates. *Evolution & Human Behavior, 23*(2), 139–149.

Payne, K. A., Binik, Y. M., Pukall, C. F., Thaler, L., Amsel, R., & Khalifé, S. (2007). Effects of sexual arousal on genital and non-genital sensation: A comparison of women with vulvar vestibulitis syndrome and healthy controls. *Archives of Sexual Behaviour, 36*, 289–300.

Payne, K. A., Thaler, K., Kukkonen, T. M., Carrier, S., & Binik, Y. M. (2007). Sensation and sexual arousal in circumcised and uncircumcised men. *Journal of Sexual Medicine, 4*(3), 667–674.

Pearson, H. (2008, July 17). Making babies: The next 30 years. *Nature, 454*(7202), 260–262.

Pek, N. K., & Senn, C. Y. (2004). Not wanted in the inbox! Evaluations of unsolicited and harassing e-mail. *Psychology of Women Quarterly, 28*, 204–214.

Pelletier, L. A., & Herold, E. S. (1988). The relationship of age, sex guilt and sexual experience with female sexual fantasies. *Journal of Sex Research, 24*, 250–256.

Peplau, L. A. (2003). Human sexuality: How do men and women differ? *Current Directions in Psychological Science, 12*(2), 37–40.

Perel, E. (2006). *Mating in captivity.* New York: HarperCollins Publishers.

Peris, A. (2006, February 8). *Fertilitext: At the pharmacy: OTC.* [Online]. **www.fertilitext.org/p3_pharmacy/OTCproducts.html**

Peritz, I. (2005, September 23). Student leaves McGill over sports hazing ritual. *The Globe and Mail.*

Perrett, D. I. (1994). *Nature.* Cited in Brody, J. E. (1994, March 21). Notions of beauty transcend culture, new study suggests. *The New York Times*, p. A14.

Perry, A. (2003, February 21). Women seek more from the modern workplace. *The Toronto Star.*

Perry, D. G., & Bussey, K. (1979). The social learning theory of sex differences: Imitation is alive and well. *Journal of*

Personality and Social Psychology, 37, 1699–1712.

Perry, J. D., & Whipple, B. (1981). Pelvic muscle strength of female ejaculation: Evidence in support of a new theory of orgasm. *Journal of Sex Research, 17*, 22–39.

Perry, P. J., et al. (2001). Bioavailable testosterone as a correlate of cognition, psychological status, quality of life, and sexual function in aging males: Implications for testosterone replacement therapy. *Annals of Clinical Psychiatry, 13*(2), 75–80.

Petrunik, M. (2003). The hare and the tortoise: Dangerousness and sex offender policy in the United States and Canada. *Canadian Journal of Criminology & Criminal Justice, 45*(1), 43–72.

Pevere, G. (2001, November 24). See no evil. *The Toronto Star*, p. J1.

Pfaus, J. G., Kippin, T. E., & Coria-Avila, G. (2003).What can animal models tell us about human sexual response? *Annual Review of Sex Research*, 14, 1–63.

PHERO. (1999, November 26). The teen prenatal study of the Sudbury, Manitoulin and Algoma Districts. *Communique: Public Health Research, Education and Development Program*, 236–243.

Piercy, J. (2008, January 12). Six charged in human trafficking ring. *Toronto Star*.

Pike, L. B. (2005, July 1). *Sexuality and your child.* MU Extension, University of Missouri–Columbia.

Pillard, R. C., & Weinrich, J. D. (1986). Evidence of familial nature of male homosexuality. *Archives of Sexual Behavior, 43*, 808–812.

Pinkerton, S. D., Bogart, L. M., Cecil, H., & Abramson, P. R. (2002). Factors associated with masturbation in collegiate sample. *Journal of Psychology & Human Sexuality, 14*(2–3), 103–121.

Planned Parenthood Federation of Canada. (1999). A history of birth control in Canada. [Brochure].

Plant, E. A., Hyde, J. S., Keltner, D., & Devine, P. G. (2000). The gender stereotyping of emotions. *Psychology of Women Quarterly, 24*(1), 81–92.

Plaut, S. M. (2006). Consent to sexual relations. *Archives of Sexual Behavior, 35*(1), 101–103.

Plomin, R., & Asbury, K. (2005). Nature and nurture: Genetic and environmental influences on behavior. *Annals of the Amercian Academy of Political and Social Science, 600*, 86–98.

Pollack, H. A. (2001). Sudden infant death syndrome, maternal smoking during pregnancy, and the cost-effectiveness of smoking cessation intervention. *American Journal of Public Health, 91*(3), 432–436.

Pollard, J. (2006). Ontario women and breast health. *Institute for Social Resarch Newsletter*, 21(1). Toronto: York University.

Polusny, M. A., & Arbisi, P. A. (2006). Assessment of psychological distress and disability after sexual assault in adults. In G. Young, et al. (Eds.), *Psychological knowledge in court: PTSD, pain, and TBI* (pp. 97–125). Berlin, Germany: Springer Science + Business Media.

Potosky, A. L., et al. (2000). Health outcomes after prostatectomy or radiotherapy for prostate cancer: Results from the Prostate Cancer Outcomes Study. *Journal of the National Cancer Institute, 92*, 1582–1592.

Pound, N., Javed, M., Ruberto, C., Shaikh, M., & Del Vaille, A. P. (2002). Duration of sexual arousal predicts semen parameters for masturbatory ejaculates. *Physiology & Behavior, 76*(4), 685–689.

Powell, B. (2005, September 21). The down side of camera cellphones. *The Toronto Star*, p. A4.

Powell, B., & Chung, E. (2005, May 18). HIV case adds charges; Five women say they weren't told of illness; Accused's wife dies of AIDS-related sickness. *Toronto Star*, p. B05.

Powell, E. (1996). *Sex on your terms.* Boston: Allyn & Bacon.

Powell, J., & Wojnarowska, F. (1999). Acupunture for vulvodynia. *Journal of the Royal Society of Medicine, 92*, 579–581.

PPFC. (2002). Emergency contraception: Get the facts! [Online]. Available: **www.ppfc.ca/faqs/access.htm**

Prashad, S. (2004, February 14). When cupid's arrow strikes at the office. *Toronto Star*, p. D14.

Prentice, T. (2005). Alarming rates of HIV/AIDS for Canada's Aboriginal women. *The Canadian Women's Health Network Magazine, 8*, 1–4.

Preti, G., et al. (1986). Human axillary secretions influence women's menstrual cycles: The role of donor extract of females. *Hormones and Behavior, 20*, 474–482.

Preti, G., Wysocki, C. J., Barnhart, K. T., Sondheimer, S. J., & Leyden, J. J. (2003). Male axillary extracts contain pheromones that affect pulsatile secretion of luteinizing hormone and mood in women recipients. *Biology of Reproduction, 68*(6), 2107–2113.

Price, M., Gutheil, T. G., Commons, M. L., Kafka, M. P., & Dodd-Kimmey, S. (2001). Telephone scatologia: Comorbidity and theories of etiology. *Psychiatric Annals, 31*(4), 226–232.

Price, M., Kafka, M. P., Commons, M. L., Gutheil, T. G., & Simpson, W. (2002). Telephone scatologia: Comorbidity with other paraphilias and paraphilia-related disorders. *International Journal of Law & Psychiatry, 25*(1), 37–49.

Pron, N. (2007, September 11). Parlour's "manual release" ruled legal; Charges thrown out in masturbation case. *Toronto Star*, p. A2.

Provost, M. P., Kormos, C., Kosakoski, G., & Quinsey, V. L. (2006). Sociosexuality in women and preference for facial masculinization and somatotype in men. *Archives of Sexual Behaviour, 35*(3), 305–312.

Provost, M. P., Quinsey, V. L., & Troje, N. F. (in press). Differences in gait across the menstrual cycle and their attractiveness to men. *Archives of Sexual Behaviour.*

Public Health & Epidemiology Report Ontario. (2002, March/April). The Ontario Ministry of Health and Long-Term Care: AIDS and Sexual Health infoline 2000 Annual Report. *Public Health Branch, 13*(3), 39–41.

Public Health Agency of Canada. (2003). Ovarian cancer in Canada. Available: **www.phac-aspc.gc.ca/publicat/updates/ovar-99_e.html**

Public Health Agency of Canada. (2005a). *HIV and AIDS in Canada. Surveillance report to December 31, 2004.*

Public Health Agency of Canada. (2005b). Self-learning module, STD. Yeast vaginosis. Available: **www.phac-aspc.gc.ca/slm-maa/slides/other/pages/15.html**

Public Health Agency of Canada. (2006). Supplement 2004 Canadian sexually transmitted infections surveillance report. *Canada Communicable Disease Report, 33S1.* Available: **www.phac-aspc.gc.ca/publicat/ccdr-rmtc/07pdf/33s1_e.pdf**

Public Health Agency of Canada. (2007a). Breast cancer. Available: **www.phac-aspc.gc.ca/ccdpc-cpcmc/topics/cancer_breast_e.html**

Public Health Agency of Canada. (2007b). Prostate cancer. Available: **www.phac-aspc.gc.ca/ccdpc-cpcmc/topics/cancer_prost_e.html**

Public Health Agency of Canada. (2007c). Surveillance and Epidemiology Section, Community Acquired Infections Division, Centre for Communicable Diseases and Infection Control.

Public Health Agency of Canada. (2007d). HIV and AIDS in Canada. Available: **www.phac-aspc.gc.ca/aids-sida/publication/survreport/pdf/tables0607.pdf**

Public Health Agency of Canada. (2008). Hepatitis B fact sheet. Available: **www.phac-aspc.gc.ca/hcai-iamss/bbp-pts/hepatitis/hep_b_e.html**

Puente, S., & Cohen, D. (2003). Jealousy and the meaning (or nonmeaning) of violence. *Personality & Social Psychology Bulletin, 29*(4), 449–460.

Pukall, C., Young, R., Roberts, M., Sutton, K., & Smith K. (2007). The vulvalgesiometer as a device to measure genital pressure-pain threshold. *Physiological Measurement, 28*, 1–8.

Pukall, C. F., Payne, K. A., Binik, Y. M., & Khalife, S. (2003). Pain measurement in vulvodynia. *Journal of Sex & Marital Therapy, 29*(s), 111–120.

Pukall, C. F., Payne, K. A., Kao, A., Khalifé, S., & Binik, Y. M. (2005). Dyspareunia. In R. Balon, & R. T. Segraves (Eds.), *Handbook of sexual dysfunction* (pp. 249–272). New York: Taylor and Francis.

Punyanunt-Carter, N. M. (2006). An analysis of college students' self-disclosure behaviors on the internet. *College Student Journal, 40*(2), 329–331.

Quinsey, V. L. (2002). Evolutionary theory and animal behavior. *Legal and Criminological Psychology, 7,* 1–13.

Rabinowitz, S. R., Firestone, P., Bradford, J. M., & Greenberg, D. M. (2002). Prediction of recidivism in exhibitionists: Psychological, phallometric, and offense factors. *Sexual Abuse: Journal of Research & Treatment, 14*(4), 329–347.

Radlove, S. (1983). Sexual response and gender roles. In E. R. Allgeier & N. B. McCormick (Eds.), *Changing boundaries: Gender roles and sexual behavior.* Palo Alto, CA: Mayfield.

Raichle, K., & Lambert, A. J. (2000). The role of political ideology in mediating judgments of blame in rape victims and their assailants: A test of the just world, personal responsibility, and legitimization hypotheses. *Personality & Social Psychology Bulletin, 26*(7), 853–863.

Rakic, Z., Starcevic, V., Starcevic, V. P., & Marinkovic, J. (1997). Testosterone treatment in men with erectile disorder and low levels of total testosterone in serum. *Archives of Sexual Behavior, 26*(5), 495–504.

Rako, S. (2003). *No more periods? The risks of menstrual suppression and other cutting-edge issues about hormones and women's health.* New York: Crown.

Ralph, D., & McNicholas, T. (2000). UK management guidelines for erectile dysfunction. *British Medical Journal, 321,* 499–503.

Randall, H., & Byers, S. (2003). What is sex? Students' definitions of having sex, sexual partner, and unfaithful sexual behaviour. *The Canadian Journal of Human Sexuality, 12,* 87–96.

Rao, V. (2008, May 3). Let my avatar buy your avatar coffee. *Toronto Star,* p. L15.

Rathus, S. A. (2003). *Voyages: Childhood and adolescence.* Belmont, CA: Wadsworth.

Rathus, S. A. (2006). *Childhood and adolescence: Voyages in development,* 2nd ed. Belmont, CA: Thomson Learning/ Wadsworth.

Ratner, P. A., Johnson, J. L., Shoveller, J. A., Chan, K., Martindale, S. L., Schilder, A. J., et al. (2003). Non-consensual sex experienced by men who have sex with men: Prevalence and association with mental health. *Patient Education and Counseling, 49*(1), 67–74.

Rattner, M., Choudhri, Y., Murphy, P., Goneau-Lessard, K., & Burke, N. (2007). Survey says! Results from the HIV/AIDS Attitudinal Tracking Survey 2006. Paper presented at the annual conference of the Canadian Association of HIV Research, Toronto, Ontario.

Rawson, R. A., Washton, A., Domier, C. P., & Reiber, C. (2002). Drugs and sexual effects: Role of drug type and gender. *Journal of Substance Abuse Treatment, 22*(2), 103–108.

Reinisch, J. M. (1990). *The Kinsey Institute new report on sex: What you must know to be sexually literate.* New York: St. Martin's Press.

Reissing, E. D., Laliberte, G. M., & Davis, H. J. (2005). Young women's sexual adjustment: The role of sexual self-scheme, sexual self-efficacy, sexual aversion and body attitudes. *The Canadian Journal of Human Sexuality, 14*(3–4), 77–85.

Reissing, E. K., Binik, Y. M., Khalife, S., Cohen, D., & Amsel, R. (2004). Vaginal spasm, pain, and behavior: An empirical investigation of the diagnosis of vaginismus. *Archives of Sexual Behavior, 33*(1), 5–17.

Rempel, J. K., & Baumgartner, B. (2003). The relationship between attitudes towards menstruation and sexual attitudes, desires, and behavior in women. *Archives of Sexual Behavior, 32*(2), 155–163.

Rempel, L. A. (2004). Factors influencing the breastfeeding decisions of long-term breastfeeders. *Journal of Human Lactation: Official Journal of International Lactation Consultant Association, 20*(3), 306–318.

Renaud, C. A., & Byers, E. S. (1999). Exploring the frequency, diversity and content of university students' positive and negative sexual cognitions. *Canadian Journal of Human Sexuality, 8,* 17–30.

Renaud, P., Rouleau, J. L., Granger, L., Barsetti, I., & Bouchard, S. (2002). Measuring sexual preferences in virtual reality: A pilot study. *Cyberpsychology and Behavior, 5*(1), 1–9.

Reuters. (2006, March 17). When it comes to sex and romance. *National Post,* p. A6.

Reynolds, S. J., et al. (2004). Male circumcision and risk of HIV-1 and other sexually transmitted infections in India. *The Lancet, 363*(9414), 1039.

Ribner, D. S., & Kleinplatz, P. J. (2007). The hole in the sheet and other myths about sexuality and Judaism. *Sexual and Relationship Therapy, 22*(4), 445–456.

Ricci, E., Parazzini, F., & Pardi, G. (2000). Caesarean section and antiretroviral treatment. *The Lancet, 355*(9202), 496–502.

Richters, J. (2007). Researching sex between women. Paper presented at the Proceedings of the World Association of Sexual Health XVIII Congress, Sydney, Australia.

Richters, J., deVisser, R., Rissel, C., & Smith, A. (2006). Sexual practices at last sexual encounter and occurrence of orgasm in a national survey. *The Journal of Sex Research, 43*(3), 217–226.

Richters, J., Hendry, O. L., & Kippax, S. (2003). When safe sex isn't safe. *Culture, Health & Sexuality, 5*(1), 37–52.

Richters, J., Smith, A., de Visser, R., Grulich, A., & Rissle, C. (2006). Circumcision in Australia: Prevalence and effects on sexual health. *International Journal of STD, 17,* 547–554.

Rickwood, A. M. K., Kenny, S. E., & Donnell, S. C. (2000). Towards evidence based circumcision of English boys: Survey of trends in practice. *British Medical Journal, 321,* 792–793.

Riedmann, A., Lamanna, M., & Nelson, A. (2003). *Marriages and families,* 1st Canadian ed. Toronto: Thomson Canada.

Rieger, G., Chivers, M., & Bailey, J. (2005). Sexual arousal patterns of bisexual men. *Psychological Science, 16*(8), 579–584.

Riggio, R. E., & Woll, S. B. (1984). The role of nonverbal cues and physical attractiveness in the selection of dating partners. *Journal of Social and Personal Relationships, 1,* 347–357.

Rimm, E. (May 2000). *Lifestyle may play role in potential for impotence.* Presented at the annual meeting of the American Urological Association, Atlanta, GA.

Roberts, J. M. (2000). Recent advances: Obstetrics. *British Medical Journal, 321*(7252), 33–35.

Roberts, J. V. (1994). Criminal justice processing of sexual assault cases. *Juristat Service Bulletin.* Canadian Centre for Justice Statistics, *14,* 1–19.

Roberts, S. (2005, November 4). Woman faces new fraud charges. *Toronto Star.*

Robinson, J. D., & Parks, C. W. (2003). Lesbian and bisexual women's sexual fantasies, psychological adjustment, and close relationship functioning. *Journal of Psychology & Human Sexuality, 15*(4), 185–203.

Rodriguez, I., Greer, C. A., Mok, M. Y., & Mombaerts, P. (2000). A putative pheromone receptor gene expressed in human olfactory mucosa. *Nature Genetics, 26*(1), 18–19.

Roesler, A., & Witztum, E. (2000). Pharmacotherapy of paraphilias in the next millennium. *Behavioral Sciences & the Law, 18*(1), 43–56.

Rogala, C., & Tydén, T. (2003). Does pornography influence young women's sexual behavior? *Women's Health Issues,* 13(1), 39–43.

Roscoe, W. (2000). *Changing ones: Third and fourth genders in native North America.* New York: Palgrave Macmillan.

Rose, P. G. (1996). Endometrial carcinoma. *The New England Journal of Medicine, 335,* 640–649.

Rosen, N. O., Knäuper, B., Mozessohn, L., & Ho, M. R. (2005). Factors affecting knowledge of sexually transmitted infection transmissibility in healthcare providers: Results from a national survey. *Sexually Transmitted Diseases, 32*(10), 619–624.

Ross, L. E. (2005). Perinatal mental health in lesbian mothers: A review of potential risk and protective factors. *Women & Health, 41*(3).

Rotermann, M. (2005). Sex, condoms, and STDs among young people. *Health Reports, 16*(3). Statistics Canada: Analytical Studies and Reports. Available: **www.statcan.ca/english/ads/82-003-XPE/pdf/16-3-04.pdf**

Roughgarden, J. (2004). *Evolution's rainbow: Diversity, gender, and sexuality in nature and people.* Berkeley: University of California Press.

Royce, R. A., Seña, A., Cates, W., Jr., & Cohen, M. S. (1997). Sexual transmission of HIV. *The New England Journal of Medicine, 336,* 1072–1078.

Rubenson, B., Hanh, L. T., Höjer, B., & Johansson, E. (2005). Young sex-workers in Ho Chi Minh City telling their life stories. *Childhood: A Global Journal of Child Research, 12*(3), 391–411.

Rusbult, C. E., Martz, J. M., & Agnew, C. R. (1998). The Investment Model Scale: Measuring commitment level, satisfaction level, quality of alternatives, and investment size. *Personal Relationships, 5*(4), 357–391.

Rusbult, C. E., & Van Lange, P. A. M. (2003). Interdependence, interaction and relationships. *Annual Review of Psychology, 54,* 351–375.

Rushowy, K. (2008, February 22). Safe Schools Action Team to advise education ministry. *Toronto Star.*

Rye, B. J. (2001, June). Sex differences in sexual attitudes and sexual behaviours of a sample of university students. Poster session presented at the annual Guelph Sexuality Conference, Guelph, ON.

Rye, B. J., Elmslie, P., & Chalmers, A. (2007). Meeting a transsexual person: Experiences within a classroom setting. *Canadian Online Journal of Queer Studies in Education, 3*(1), **https://jps.library.utoronto.ca/index.php/jqstudies/article/viewFile/3269/1444**

Rye, B. J., & Meaney, G. (2007). Voyeurism: It is good as long as we do not get caught. *International Journal of Sexual Health, 19*(1), 47–56.

Rye, B. J., & Meaney, G. (2008). Self-defence, sexism, and etiological beliefs: Predictors of attitudes toward gay and lesbian adoption.

Rye, B. J., Meaney, G., & Redden, E. (2008). Three measures of homonegativity. Paper presented at the Annual Guelph Conference, Guelph, Ontario.

Rye, B. J., Yessis, J., Brunk, T., McKay, A., Morris, S., & Meaney, G. (2008). Outcome evaluation of Girl Time: Grade 7/8 Healthy Sexuality Program. *The Canadian Journal of Human Sexuality, 17*(1–2), 15–36.

Sack, W. H., & Mason, R. (1980). Child abuse and conviction of sexual crimes: A preliminary finding. *Law and Human Behavior, 4,* 211–215.

Sadalla, E. K., Kenrick, D. T., & Vershure, B. (1987). Dominance and heterosexual attraction. *Journal of Personality and Social Psychology, 52,* 730–738.

Saewyc, E. M., Poon, C., Wang, N., Homma, Y., Smith, A., & The McCreary Centre Society. (2007). *Not yet equal: The health of lesbian, gay, & bisexual youth in BC.* Vancouver, BC: The McCreary Centre Society.

Saewyc, E. M., Skay, C. L., Pettingell, S. L., Reis, E. A., Bearinger, L., Resnick, M., et al. (2006a). Hazards of stigma: The sexual and physical abuse of gay, lesbian, and bisexual adolescents in the United States and Canada. *Child Welfare, 85*(2), 195–213.

Saewyc, E. M., Skay, C., Richens, K., Reis, E., Poon, C., & Murphy, A. (2006). Sexual orientation, sexual abuse, and HIV-risk behaviors among adolescents in the Pacific Northwest. *American Journal of Public Health, 96*(6), 1104–1110.

Sagan, C., & Dryan, A. (1990, April 22). The question of abortion: A search for answers. *Parade Magazine,* 4–8.

Sagarin, B. J., Becker, D. V., Guadagno, R. E., Nicastle, D., & Millevoi, A. (2003). Sex differences (and similarities) in jealousy. The moderating influence of infidelity experience and sexual orientation of the infidelity. *Evolution & Human Behavior, 24*(1), 17–23.

Sand, M., Fisher, W., Rosen, R., Heiman., J., & Eardley, I. (2008). Erectile dysfunction and constructs of masculinity and quality of life in the multinational men's attitudes to life events and sexuality (MALES) study. *Journal of Sexual Medicine, 5*(3), 583–594.

Sanders, T. (2005). "It's just acting": Sex workers' strategies for capitalizing on sexuality. *Gender, Work & Organization, 12*(4), 319–342.

Sangrador, J. L., & Yela, C. (2000). "What is beautiful is loved": Physical attractiveness in love relationships in a representative sample. *Social Behavior & Personality, 28*(3), 207–218.

Santtila, P., Sandnabba, N. K., Alison, L., & Nordling, N. (2002). Investigating the underlying structure in sadomasochistically oriented behavior. *Archives of Sexual Behavior, 31*(2), 185–196.

Sarrel, P., & Masters, W. (1982). Sexual molestation of men by women. *Archives of Sexual Behavior, 11,* 117–131.

Savage, L. (2008, August 4). Stifling free speech globally. *Maclean's,* 26–29.

Savic, I., & Lindstrom, P. (2008). PET and MRI show differences in cerebral asymmetry and functional connectivity between homo- and heterosexual subjects. *Proceedings of the National Academy of Sciences, 105*(27), 9403–9408.

Savin-Williams, R. C. (2001). Suicide attempts among sexual minority youths: Population and measurement issues. *Journal of Consulting and Clinical Psychology, 69*(6): 983–991.

Savin-Williams, R. C. (2005). *The new gay teenager.* Cambridge, MA: Harvard University Press.

Savin-Williams, R. C. (2006). Who's gay? Does it matter? *Current Directions in Psychological Science, 15*(1), 40–44.

Savin-Williams, R. C., & Diamond, L. M. (2000). Sexual identity trajectories among sexual-minority youths: Gender comparisons. *Archives of Sexual Behavior, 29*(6), 607–627.

Savitz, L., & Rosen, L. (1988). The sexuality of prostitutes: Sexual enjoyment reported by "streetwalkers." *Journal of Sex Research, 24,* 200–208.

Saywitz, K. J., Mannarino, A. P., Berliner, L., & Cohen, J. A. (2000). Treatment for sexually abused children and adolescents. *American Psychologist, 55*(9), 1040–1049.

Schafran, L. H. (1995, August 26). Rape is still underreported. *The New York Times,* p. A19.

Schlichter, A. (2004). *Contesting "straights," "lesbians," "queer heterosexuals," and the critique of heteronormativity.* Binghamton, NY: The Haworth Press.

Schmidt, S. (2002, April 13). Ridicule replaces violence. *National Post,* p. A5.

Schmitt, D., Shackelford, T., Duntley, J., et al. (2002). Is there an early-30s peak in female sexual desire? Cross-sectional evidence from the United States and Canada. *The Canadian Journal of Human Sexuality, 11,* 1–18.

Schmitt, D. P. (2003). Universal sex differences in the desire for sexual variety: Tests from 52 nations, 6 continents, and 13 islands. *Journal of Personality and Social Psychology, 85*(1), 85–104.

Schneider, J. P. (2005). Addiction is addiction is addiction. *Sexual Addiction & Compulsivity, 12*(2/3), 75–77.

Schneider, M., Baker, S., & Stermac, L. (2002). Sexual harassment experiences of psychologists and psychological associates during their graduate school training. *The Canadian Journal of Human Sexuality, 11,* 159–170.

Schover, L. R., Fouladi, R. T., Warneke, C. L., Neese, L., Klein, E. A., Zippe, C., et al. (2004). Seeking help for erectile dysfunction after treatment for prostate cancer. *Archives of Sexual Behavior, 33*(5), 443–454.

Schrader, A. M., & Wells, K. (2007). *Challenging silence, challenging censorship: Inclusive resources, strategies and policy directives for addressing bisexual, gay, lesbian, trans-identified, and two-spirited realities in school and public libraries.* Ottawa: Canadian Teachers' Federation

Schroeder-Printzen, I., et al. (2000). Surgical therapy in infertile men with ejaculatory duct obstruction: Technique and outcome of a standardized surgical approach. *Human Reproduction, 15*, 1364–1368.

Schrut, A. (2005). A psychodynamic (nonoedipal) and brain function hypothesis regarding a type of male sexual masochism. *Journal of the American Academy of Psychoanalysis and Dynamic Psychiatry, 33*(2), 333–349.

Schultz, W. W., et al. (2005). Women's sexual pain and its management. *Journal of Sexual Medicine, 2*(3), 301–316.

Scott, J., & Humphreys, T. P. (2007, June). Parents as a source of sexual education for their physically disabled children. Poster presentation at the annual Guelph Sexuality Conference, Guelph, Ontario.

Secker-Walker, R. H., & Vacek, P. M. (2003). Relationships between cigarette smoking during pregnancy, gestational age, maternal weight gain, and infant birthweight. *Addictive Behaviors, 28*(1), 55–66.

Seidman, S. M. (2003). The aging male: Androgens, erectile dysfunction, and depression. *Journal of Clinical Psychiatry, 64*(Suppl. 10), 31–37.

Seligman, L., & Hardenburg, S. A. (2000). Assessment and treatment of paraphilias. *Journal of Counseling & Development, 78*(1), 107–113.

Semans, J. (1956). Premature ejaculation: A new approach. *Southern Medical Journal, 49*, 353–358.

Seng, M. J. (1989). Child sexual abuse and adolescent prostitution: A comparative analysis. *Adolescence, 24*, 665–675.

Senn, C. Y., & Desmarais, S. (2001). Are our recruitment practices for sex studies working across gender? The effect of topic and gender of recruiter on participation rates of university men and women. *Journal of Sex Research, 38*(2), 111–117.

Senn, C. Y., & Desmarais, S. (2006). A new wrinkle on an old concern: Are the new ethics review requirements for explicit warnings in consent forms affecting the results of sexuality research? *The Canadian Journal of Human Sexuality, 15*(3–4), 123–132.

Senn, C. Y., Desmarais, S., Verberg, N., & Wood, E. (2000). Predicting coercive sexual behavior across the lifespan in a random sample of Canadian men. *Journal of Social & Personal Relationships, 17*, 93–115.

Servais, L. (2006). Sexual health care in persons with intellectual disabilities. *Mental Retardation and Developmental Disabilities Research Reviews, 12*(1), 48–56.

Seto, M. C., & Barbaree, H. E. (2001). Paraphilias. In V. B. Van Hasseit & M. Hersen (Eds.), *Aggression & violence: An introductory text* (pp. 198–213). New York: Allyn & Bacon.

Seto, M. C., Cantor, J. M., & Blanchard, R. (2006). Child pornography offenses are a valid diagnostic indicator of pedophilia. *Journal of Abnormal Psychology, 115*(3), 610–615.

Seto, M. C., & Eke, A. W. (2005). The criminal histories and later offending of child pornography offenders. *Sexual Abuse: A Journal of Research and Treatment, 17*(2), 201–210.

Seto, M. C., Maric, A., & Barbaree, H. E. (2000). The role of pornography in the etiology of sexual aggression. *Aggression and Violent Behavior, 6*, 35–53.

Seto, M. C., Maric, A., & Barbaree, H. E. (2001). The role of pornography in the etiology of sexual aggression. *Aggression and Violent Behavior, 6*, 35–53.

Sexual assault plea shortens sentence. (1994, June 1). *The Guelph Mercury.*

Seymour, A. (2008, August 29). Teacher found guilty of sexual assault low risk to re-offend, psychiatrist says. *The Ottawa Citizen.*

Shackelford, T. K., Buss, D. M., & Bennett, K. (2002). Forgiveness or breakup: Sex differences in responses to a partner's infidelity. *Cognition & Emotion, 16*(2), 299–307.

Shaver, F. M. (1996a). Prostitution: On the dark side of the service industry. In T. Fleming (Ed.), *Post critical criminology* (pp. 42–45). Scarborough, ON: Prentice Hall.

Shaver, F. M. (1996b). The regulation of prostitution: Setting the morality trap. In B. Schissel & L. Mahood, *Social control in Canada* (pp. 204–226). Toronto: Oxford University Press.

Shaver, F. M. (2002, November). Prostitution portraits: A cautionary tale. Paper presented at the Annual Meeting of the Society for the Scientific Study of Sexuality, Montreal.

Shaver, F. M. (2005). Sex work research: Methodological and ethical challenges. *Journal of Interpersonal Violence, 20*(3), 296–319.

Shaver, P., Hazan, C., & Bradshaw, D. (1988). Love as attachment. In R. J. Sternberg & M. L. Barnes (Eds.), *The psychology of love* (pp. 68–99). New Haven, CT: Yale University Press.

Shaw, J. (2007). Look in the phonebook under "A": Women's experiences in attempting to access abortion services in Canadian hospitals. Paper presented at the Guelph Sexuality Conference, Guelph, Ontario.

Sheehy, G. (1998). *Understanding men's passages.* New York: Random House.

Shercliffe, R. J., Hamton, M., McKay-McNabb, K., Jeffery, B., Beattie, P., & McWatters, B. (2007). Cognitive and demographic factors that predict self-efficacy to use condoms in vulnerable and marginalized aboriginal youth. *The Canadian Journal of Human Sexuality, 16*(1–2), 45–56.

Sherwin, B. B., Gelfand, M. M., & Brender, W. (1985). Androgen enhances sexual motivation in females: A prospective, crossover study of sex steroid administration in the surgical menopause. *Psychosomatic Medicine, 47*, 339–351.

Shevell, T., et al. (2005). Assisted reproductive technology and pregnancy outcome. *Obstetrics & Gynecology, 106*, 1039–1045.

Shibley-Hyde, J., & Durik, A. M. (2000). Gender differences in erotic plasticity—Evolutionary or sociocultural forces? Comment on Baumeister (2000). *Psychological Bulletin, 126*, 375–379.

Shields, S. A., Wong, T., Mann, J., et al. (2004). Prevalence and correlates of chlamydia infection in Canadian street youth. *Journal of Adolescent Health, 34*(5), 384–390.

Shorter, E. (2005). *Written in the flesh: A history of desire.* Toronto: University of Toronto Press.

Shoveller, J. A., Johnson, J. L., Langille, D. B., & Mitchell, T. (2004). Socio-cultural influences on young people's sexual development. *Social Science & Medicine, 59*(3), 473–487.

Silverthorne, Z. A., & Quinsey, V. L. (2000). Sexual partner age preferences of homosexual and heterosexual men and women. *Archives of Sexual Behavior, 29*, 67–76.

Simonsen, G., Blazina, C., & Watkins, C. E., Jr. (2000). Gender role conflict and psychological well-being among gay men. *Journal of Counseling Psychology, 47*(1), 85–89.

Singer, J., & Singer, I. (1972). Types of female orgasm. *Journal of Sex Research, 8*, 255–267.

Singh, D., Vidaurri, M., Zambarano, R. J., & Dabbs, J. M., Jr. (1999). Lesbian erotic role identification: Behavioral, morphological, and hormonal correlates. *Journal of Personality and Social Psychology, 76*(6), 1035–1049.

Sipski, M. L., Alexander, C. J., & Rosen, R. (2001). Sexual arousal and orgasm in women. *Annals of Neurology, 49*(1), 35–44.

Small, P. (2004, June 30). Used drug for sex assault. *The Toronto Star*.

Small, P. (2007, December 28). Teacher scarred by charges. *Toronto Star*, p. A10.

Small, P. (2008, March 27). Pastor gets four years for sex assault on woman. *The Toronto Star*.

Smith, A., Saewyc, E., Albert, M., MacKay, L., Northcott, M., and The McCreary Centre Society. (2007). *Against the odds: A profile of marginalized and street-involved youth in BC*. Vancouver, BC: The McCreary Centre Society.

Smith, K. B., Pukall, C. F., Tripp, D. A., & Nickel, J. C. (2007). Sexual and relationship functioning in men with chronic prostatitis/ chronic pelvic pain syndrome and their partners. *Archives of Sexual Behaviour, 36*, 301–311.

Smith, T. W. (1992). Discrepancies between men and women in reporting number of sexual partners: A summary from four countries. *Social Biology, 26*, 203–211.

Smith, Y. L. S., Van Goozen, S. H. M., Kuiper, A. J., & Cohen-Kettenis, P. T. (2005). Sex reassignment: Outcomes and predictors of treatment for adolescent and adult transsexuals. *Psychological Medicine, 35*(1), 89–99.

Smylie, L., Medaglia, S., & Maticka-Tyndale, E. (2006). The effect of social capital and socio-demographics on adolescent risk and sexual health behaviours. *The Canadian Journal of Human Sexuality, 15*(2), 95–112.

Society of Obstetricians and Gynaecologists of Canada. (2008, June 25). Media advisories: Rising C-section rates add risks during childbirth and place excess strain on the healthcare system, warn Canadian obstetricians. Available: **www.sogc.org/media/advisories-20080625_e.asp**

Sodroski, J., et al. (1998). *Nature*. Cited in Scientists uncover "key" to AIDS virus. (1998, June 18). The Associated Press CNN.

Sommerfeld, J. (2000, April 18). Lifting the curse: Should monthly periods be optional? MSNBC online.

Soon, J. A., Levine, M., Osmond, B. L., Ensom, M. H. H., & Fielding, D. W. (2005). Effects of making emergency contraception available without a physician's prescription: A population-based study. *Canadian Medical Association Journal*, 7, 172.

Spark, R. F. (1991). *Male sexual health: A couple's guide*. Mount Vernon, NY: Consumer Reports Books.

Spencer, N. (2006). Explaining the social gradient in smoking in pregnancy: Early life course accumulation and cross-sectional clustering of social risk exposures in the 1958 British national cohort. *Social Science & Medicine, 62*(5), 1250–1259.

Spitzer, R. L., et al. (1989). *DSM-III-R casebook*. Washington, DC: American Psychiatric Press.

Sprecher, S., Sullivan, Q., & Hatfield, E. (1994). Mate selection preferences: Gender differences examined in a national sample. *Journal of Personality and Social Psychology, 66*(6), 1074–1080.

Squier, S. & Littlefield, M. M. (2004). Feminist theory and/of science: Feminist Theory special issue. *Feminist Theory, 5*(2), 123–126.

Stanford, J. L., et al. (2000). Urinary and sexual function after radical prostatectomy for clinically localized prostate cancer: The Prostate Cancer Outcomes Study. *Journal of the American Medical Association, 283*, 354–360.

Statistics Canada. (1997). Sex offenders. *Juristat.* [Catalogue #8S-002XIE].

Statistics Canada. (2002a). 2001 Census: A profile of the Canadian population: Where we live. [Catalogue #96F0030XIE01001 2001].

Statistics Canada. (2002b). 2001 Census: Families and household profile: Canada. [online] Available: **www12.statcan.ca/english/census01/products/analytic/companion/fam/canada.cfm**

Statistics Canada. (2002c). *The Daily—Changing conjugal life in Canada.* [online] Available: **www.statcan.ca/Daily/English/020711/d020711a.htm**

Statistics Canada. (2002d). General social survey—Cycle 15: Changing conjugal life in Canada. [Catalogue No. 89-576-XIE].

Statistics Canada (2002e). Crime statistics in Canada, 2001. *Juristat, 22*(b). [Catalogue. No. 85-002XIE].

Statistics Canada. (2003a). University enrolment by age groups. *The Daily*, April 17.

Statistics Canada (2003b). Sexual offences. *The Daily*, July 25. [online]. Available: **www.statcan.ca/daily/English/050420/d050420a.htm**

Statistics Canada. (2004a). *The Daily*, June 15. Canadian Community Health Survey. [online]. Available: **www.statcan.ca/Daily/English/040615/d040615b.htm**

Statistics Canada. (2004b). *Spotlight: Mixed unions*. [online]. Available: **www.statcan.ca/english/freepub/11-002-XIE/2004/06/17404/17404_04p.htm**

Statistics Canada. (2005a). *Study: Is post-secondary access more equitable in Canada or the United States?* [online]. Available: **www.statcan.ca/Daily/english/050315/d050315c.htm**

Statistics Canada. (2005b). Early sexual intercourse, condom use and sexually transmitted diseases. [online] Available: **www.statcan.ca/Daily/English/050503/d050503a.htm**

Statistics Canada. (2005c). *The Daily, June* 7, Study: *Mature singles who don't expect to marry*. [online]. Available: **www.statcan.ca/Daily/English/050607/d050607a.htm**

Statistics Canada. (2005d). Children and youth as victims of violent crime. *The Daily*, April 20. [online]. Available: **www.statcan.ca/daily/English/050420/d050420a.htm**

Statistics Canada. (2006a). Births 2004. *The Daily*, July 31. [online] Available: **www.statcan.ca/Daily/English/060731/d060731b.htm**

Statistics Canada. (2006b). Cervical cancer screening. (Catalogue No 89-503-XIE). Available: **www.statcan.ca/english/freepub/89-503-XIE/0010589-503-XIE.pdf**

Statistics Canada. (2006c). *Women in the workplace*. (Catalogue. NO. 89F0133XIE) [online]. Available: **www.statcan.ca/english/freepub/89F0133XIE/89F0133XIE2003000.pdf**

Statistics Canada. (2006d). *The Daily—Deaths*. [online]. Available: **www.statcan.ca/Daily/English/061220/d061220b.htm**

Statistics Canada. (2007a). *The Daily—2006 Census: Immigration, citizenship, language, mobility and migration*. [online] Available: **www.statcan.ca/Daily/English/071204/d071204a.htm**

Statistics Canada. (2007b). *The Daily—Births*. [online]. Available: **www.statcan.ca/Daily/English/070921/d070921b.htm**

Statistics Canada. (2007c). Births and birth rate by province and territory. (Catalogue No. 91-213-X.). [online]. Available: **www40.statcan.ca/l01/cst01/demo04b.htm**

Statistics Canada. (2007d). Maternal employment, breastfeeding and health. Available: **www.statcan.ca/Daily/English/070619/d070619d.htm**

Statistics Canada. (2007e). Marriages, 2003. *The Daily*, January 17. (84F0212XWE). [online]. Available: **www.statcan.ca/Daily/English/070117/d070117a.htm**

Statistics Canada. (2007f). 2006 Census information on same-sex, common-law and married couples. [online]. Available: **www12.statcan.ca/english/census06/reference/same_sex_common_law.cfm**

Statistics Canada. (2007g). Population: Age and sex. *Canadian Social Trends*. Catalogue No. 11-008.

Statistics Canada. (2008a, April). 2006 Census: Ethnic origin and visible minorities. [Catalogue No. 97-562-XCB2006004].

Statistics Canada. (2008b). Canadian Internet Use Survey 2007. *The Daily*, June 12. [online]. Available: **www.statcan.ca/Daily/English/080612/d080612b.htm**

Statistics Canada. (2008c). Study: Life after teenage motherhood. *The Daily*, May 23. [online]. Available: **www.statcan.ca/Daily/English/080523/d080523c.htm**

Statistics Canada. (2008d). Teen sexual behaviour and condom use 1996/1997 to 2005. *The Daily*, August 20. [online]. Available: **www.statisticscanada.com/Daily/English/080820/d080820c.htm**

Statistics Canada. (2008e). Trends in teen sexual behaviour and condom use. *Health Reports, 19*(3). (82-003-XWE).

Statistics Canada. (2008f). *The Daily—Deaths, 2005.* [84F0211XWE]. [online]. Available: **www.statcan.ca/Daily/English/080114/d080114b.htm**

Stearns, V., Beebe, K. L., Iyengar, M., & Dube, E. (2003). Paroxetine controlled release in the treatment of menopausal hot flashes. *Journal of the American Medical Association, 289*, 2827–2834.

Stein, Z., & Susser, M. (2000). The risks of having children in later life. *British Medical Journal, 320*(7251), 1681–1682.

Steinberg, D. (2004, September 8). Lap victory. *San Francisco Weekly.*

Sternberg, R. J. (1986). A triangular theory of love. *Psychological Review, 93*, 119–135.

Sternberg, R. J. (1988). *The triangle of love: Intimacy, passion, commitment.* New York: Basic Books.

Sternberg, R. J. (2004). A triangular theory of love. In Reis, H. T., & Rusbult, C. E. (Eds.). *Close relationships: Key readings* (pp. 213–227). London: Taylor & Francis.

Stockett, M. K. (2005). On the importance of difference: Re-envisioning sex and gender in ancient Mesoamerica. *World Archaeology, 37*(4), 566–578.

Stocking, B. (2007, October 26). Hanoi Hilton: Paris-like sex tape a shocker. *Toronto Star*, p. A2.

Stolberg, S. G. (1998a, January 18). Quandary on donor eggs: What to tell the children. *The New York Times*, pp. 1, 20.

Storms, M. D. (1980). Theories of sexual orientation. *Journal of Personality and Social Psychology, 38*, 783–792.

Strager, S. (2003). What men watch when they watch pornography. *Sexuality & Culture: An Interdisciplinary Quarterly*, 7(1), 50–61.

Strassberg, D. S., & Holty, S. (2003). An experimental study of women's internet personal ads. *Archives of Sexual Behavior, 32*(3), 253–260.

Strike, C., Myers, T., Calzavara, L., & Haubrich, D. (2001). Sexual coercion among young street involved adults: Perpetrators and victims' perspectives. *Violence and Victims, 16*, 537–551.

Stripe, T., Abracen, J., Stermac, L., & Wilson, R. (2006). Sexual offenders' state-of-mind regarding childhood attachment: A controlled investigation. *Sexual Abuse: A Journal of Research and Treatment, 18*, 289–302.

Subramanian, S. (2007, July 2). Wombs for Rent. *Maclean's*, 40–47.

Sulak, P. J., et al., (2000). Hormone withdrawal symptoms in oral contraceptive users. *Obstetrics & Gynecology, 95*, 261–266.

Sullivan, N. (2003). *A critical introduction to queer theory.* Edinburgh, Scotland: Edinburgh University Press.

Suschinsky, K., Lalumiere, M., & Chivers, M. (2007). Sex differences in patterns of sexual arousal: Measurement artifacts or true phenomena. Paper presented at the Annual Meeting of the Canadian Sex Research Forum, Banff, Alberta.

Szabo, R., & Short, R. V. (2000). How does male circumcision protect against HIV infection? *British Medical Journal, 320*, 1592–1594.

Tan, R. S. (2002). Managing the andropause in aging men. *Clinical Geriatrics.* [Online]. **www.mmhc.com/cg/articles/CG9907/Tan.html**

Tannahill, R. (1980). *Sex in history.* Briarcliff Manor, NY: Stein and Day.

Tarone, R. E., Cho, K. C., & Brawley, O. W. (2000). Implications of stage-specific survival rates in assessing recent declines in prostate cancer mortality rates. *Epidemiology, 11*(2), 167–170.

Taylor, M. J., Rudkin, L., & Hawton, K. (2005). Strategies for managing antidepressant-induced sexual dysfunction: Systematic review of randomised controlled trials. *Journal of Affective Disorders, 88*(3), 241–254.

Taylor, V., & Rupp, L. J. (2004). Chicks with dicks, men in dresses: What it means to be a drag queen. *Journal of Homosexuality, 46*(3–4), 113–133.

Tedeschi, J. T., & Felson, R. B. (1994). *Violence, aggression, and coercive actions.* Washington, DC: American Psychological Association.

Tessler Lindau, S., Schumm, L., Laumann, E., & Levinson, W. (2007). A study of sexuality and health among older adults in the United States. *New England Journal of Medicine, 357*(8), 51–67.

Thompson, D. S. (Ed.) (1993). *Every woman's health: The complete guide to body and mind.* New York: Simon & Schuster.

Thompson, I. M., et al. (2005). Erectile dysfunction and subsequent cardiovascular disease. *Journal of the American Medical Association, 294*(23), 2996–3002.

Thompson, J. K., & Tantleff, S. (1992). Female and male ratings of upper torso: Actual, ideal, and stereotypical conceptions. *Journal of Social Behavior and Personality*, 7, 345–354.

Thornhill, R., & Palmer, C. (2000). *A natural history of rape: Biological bases of sexual coercion.* Cambridge, MA: MIT Press.

Tiefer, L. (2001). A new view of women's sexual problems: Why new? Why now? *The Journal of Sex Research, 38*, 89–96.

Tiefer, L. (2006). Sex therapy as a humanistic enterprise. *Sexual and Relationship Therapy, 21*(3), 359–375.

Totman, R. (2004). *The third sex: Kathoey: Thailand's ladyboys.* London: Souvenir Press.

Townsend, J. M. (1995). Sex without emotional involvement: An evolutionary interpretation of sex differences. *Archives of Sexual Behavior, 24*, 173–206.

Tracey, S. (1999, March 25). Woman gets bail on theft charge. *The Guelph Mercury.*

Tracey, S. (2000, February 29). Couple fined for exposing teen to sex episode in Gorge. *The Guelph Mercury*, p. A8.

Tracey, S. (2001, January 26). Woman admits to sex with boy. *The Guelph Mercury.*

Tracey, S. (2007, September 12). Man died during sex act. *Guelph Mercury*, p. A1.

Tracey, S. (2008, June 17). Teen girl pleads guilty to child porn charges. *Toronto Star*, p. A1.

Trotter, E. C., & Alderson, K. G. (2007). University students' definitions of having sex, sexual partner, and virginity loss: The influence of participant gender, sexual experience, and contextual factors. *The Canadian Journal of Human Sexuality, 16*(1–2), 11–29.

Trulsson, O., & Rådestad, I. (2004). The silent child—Mothers' experiences before, during, and after stillbirth. *Birth: Issues in Perinatal Care, 31*(3), 189–195.

Tsui, L., & Nicoladis, E. (2004). Losing it: Similarities and differences in first intercourse experiences of men and women. *Canadian Journal of Human Sexuality, 13*(2), 95–106.

Tuiten, A., et al. (2000). Time course of effects of testosterone administration on sexual arousal in women. *Archives of General Psychiatry, 57*, 149–153.

Tunariu, A. D., & Reavey, R. (2003). Men in love: Living with sexual boredom. *Sexual and Relationship Therapy, 13*(1), 63–94.

Turner, H. A., Finkelhor, D., & Ormrod, R. (2006). The effect of lifetime victimization on the mental health of children and adolescents. *Social Science & Medicine, 62*(1), 13–27.

Twist, M. (2005). Relationship therapy with same-sex couples. *Journal of Marital & Family Therapy, 31*(4), 413.

Tyler, T. (2004, September 14). Spouse ruling allows first gay divorce. *The Toronto Star.*

Udry, J. R. (2001). Feminist critics uncover determinism, positivism, and antiquated theory. *American Sociological Review, 66*(4), 611–618.

Understanding prostate problems. (2007, May 2). **www.prostatecare.com/up_understanding.html**

United Nations Special Session on AIDS. (2001, June 25–27). *Preventing HIV/AIDS among young people.* New York: United Nations.

Vaculík, M., & Hudecek, T. (2005). Development of close relationships in the internet environment. *Ceskoslovenská Psychologie, 49*(2), 157–174.

Valentich, M., & Gripton, J. (1992). Gender-sensitive practice in sexual problems. *Canadian Journal of Human Sexuality, 1*, 11–18.

Valocchi, S. (2005). Not yet queer enough: The lessons of queer theory for the sociology of gender and sexuality. *Gender & Society, 19*(6), 750–770.

van Anders, S. M., Chernick, A. B., Chernick, B. A., Hampson, E., & Fisher, W. A. (2005). Preliminary clinical experience with androgen administration for pre- and postmenopausal women with hypoactive sexual desire. *Journal of Sex & Marital Therapy, 31*, 1–13.

van Anders, S. M., & Hampson, E. (2005). Testing the prenatal androgen hypothesis: Measuring digit ratios, sexual orientation, and spatial abilities in adults. *Hormones and Behavior, 47*, 92–98.

Van Brunschot, E. G. (2003). Community policing and "john schools." *The Canadian Review of Sociology and Anthropology, 40*(2), 215–232.

Van der Voort, J. (2008, February 12). Annual survey shows we bring love, sex and lies to work each day. *Toronto Star*.

Van Til, L., MacQuarrie, C., & Herbert, R. (2003). Understanding the barriers to cervical cancer screening among older women. *Qualitative Health Research, 13*(8), 1116–1131.

VanderLaan, D. P., & Vasey, P. L. (2008). Mate retention behavior of men and women in heterosexual and homosexual relationships. *Archives of Sexual Behavior, 37*, 572–585.

Vasey, P. L. (2002). Sexual partner preference in female Japanese macaques. *Archives of Sexual Behavior, 31*(1), 51–62.

Vasey, P. L., & Bartlett, N. H. (2007). What can the Samoan "faf'afafine" teach us about the Western concept of gender identity disorder in childhood. *Perspectives in Biology and Medicine, 50*(4), 481–490.

Vasey, P. L., Foroud, A., Duckworth, N., & Kovacovsky, S. D. (2006). Male-female and female-female mounting in Japanese macaques: A comparative study of posture and movement. *Archives of Sexual Behavior, 35*(2), 117–129.

Verma, S. (2005, March 23). "Party-goer" accused in HIV assault of CFB Borden soldier; More could be infected. *Toronto Star*, p. A01.

Vervoort, D. (1999). Gay fathers coming out to their children: Reaching for integrity. Unpublished master's thesis, University of Guelph.

Villar, F., Villamizar, D. J., & López-Chivrall, S. (2005). Components of loving experience in old age: Older people and long-term relationships. *Revista Espanola de Geriatria y Gerontologia, 40*(3), 166–177.

Vincent, D. (2004, December 10). GTHL bans flashing mother. *The Toronto Star*.

Vo, C. (2001). Vietnamese immigrant gay men: Cultural and personal influences on sexual health. Unpublished master's thesis, University of Guelph.

Voeller, B. (1991). AIDS and heterosexual anal intercourse. *Archives of Sexual Behavior, 20*, 233–276.

Wagenaar, H. (2006). Democracy and prostitution: Deliberating the legalization of brothels in the Netherlands. *Administration & Society, 38*(2), 98–235.

Waismann, R., Fenwick, P. B. C., Wilson, G. D., Hewett, T. D., & Lumsden, J. (2003). EEG responses to visual erotic stimuli in men with normal and paraphilic interests. *Archives of Sexual Behavior, 32*(2), 135–144.

Wald, A., et al. (1995). Virologic characteristics of subclinical and symptomatic genital herpes infections. *The New England Journal of Medicine, 333*, 770–775.

Waldie, P. (2007, October 19). The fund manager, the stripper and the missing millions. *The Globe and Mail*.

Waldinger, M. D., Zwinderman, A. H., & Olivier, B. (2001). Antidepressants and ejaculation: A double-blind, randomized, placebo-controlled, fixed-dose study with paroxetine, sertraline and nefazodone. *Journal of Clinical Psychopharmacology, 21*(3), 293–297.

Walfish, S., & Mayerson, M. (1980). Sex role identity and attitudes toward sexuality. *Archives of Sexual Behavior, 9*, 199–204.

Wallerstein, J. S., & Blakeslee, S. (1989). *Second chances: Women and children a decade after divorce*. New York: Ticknor & Fields.

Walsh, C., MacMillan, H. L., & Jamieson, E. (2003). The relationship between parental substance abuse and child maltreatment: Findings from the Ontario health supplement. *Child Abuse & Neglect, 27*(12), 1409–1425.

Ward, T., Gannon, T. A., & Birgden, A. (2007). Human rights and the treatment of sex offenders. *Sexual Abuse, 19*, 195–216.

Waterman, J. (1986). Overview of treatment issues. In K. McFarlane et al. (Eds.), *Sexual abuse of young children: Evaluation and treatment* (pp. 197–203). New York: Guilford.

Weaver, A. D., Byers, E. S., Sears, H. A., Cohen, J. N., & Randall, H. E. S. (2002). Sexual health education at school and at home: Attitudes and experiences of New Brunswick parents. *Canadian Journal of Human Sexuality, 11*(1), 19–31.

Weaver, S. J., & Herold, E. S (2000). Casual sex and women: Measurement and motivations issues. *Journal of Psychology and Human Sexuality, 12*, 23–41.

Weber, A. E., Boivin, J. F., Blais, L., Haley, N., & Roy, E. (2002). HIV risk profile and prostitution among female street youths. *Journal of Urban Health, 79*(4), 525–535.

Weber, A. E., Boivin, J. F., Blais, L., Haley, N., & Roy, E. (2004). Predictors of initiation into prostitution among female street youths. *Journal of Urban Health—Bulletin of New York Academy of Medicine, 81*(4), 584–595.

Weber, B. (2001, January 10). No sex please, we're in the army. *The Toronto Star*, p. A3.

Weinberg, T. S. (1987). Sadomasochism in the United States: A review of recent sociological literature. *Journal of Sex Research, 23*, 50–69.

Weinrich, J. D., & Klein, F. (2002). Bi-gay, bi-straight, and bi-bi: Three bisexual subgroups identified using cluster analysis of the Klein Sexual Orientation Grid. *Journal of Bisexuality, 2*(4), 109–139.

Welldon, E. V. (2005). Incest: A therapeutic challenge. In Ambrosio, G. (Ed.), *On incest: Psychoanalytic perspectives* (pp. 81–100). London: Karnac Books.

Wells, K. (2006). *Gay-straight student alliance handbook*. Ottawa: Canadian Teachers' Federation.

Wells, K. (2008). Generation queer: Sexual minority youth and Canadian schools. *Education Canada, 48*(1), 18–23.

Wentland, J. (2006). Sexual pleasure orientation in heterosexual women. Unpublished master's thesis, University of Guelph.

Wheeler, B. (2006, December 23). Top 10 of 2006 Nelly Furtado. *The Globe and Mail*, p. R2.

Whipple, B., & Komisaruk, B. R. (1988). Analgesia produced in women by genital self-stimulation. *Journal of Sex Research, 24*, 130–140.

White, N. (2008, June 17). If those sheets could talk . . . well, now they can tell all. *Toronto Star*.

Whitten, P. (2001). *Anthropology: Contemporary perspectives*, 8th ed. Boston: Allyn & Bacon.

Wiebe, R., Sent, L., Fong, S., & Chan, J. (2002). Barriers to use of oral contraceptives in ethnic Chinese women presenting for abortion. *Contraception, 65*(2), 159–163.

Wieselquist, J., Rusbult, C. E., Foster, C. A., & Agnew, C. R. (1999). Commitment, pro-relationship behavior, and trust in close relationships. *Journal of Personality & Social Psychology, 77*(5), 942–966.

Wilcox, A. J., Dunson, D., & Baird, D. D. (2000). The timing of the "fertile window" in the menstrual cycle: Day-specific estimates from a prospective study. *British Medical Journal, 321*, 1259–1262.

Williams, C., Newman, P., Massaquoi, N., Brown, M., and Logie, C. (2007). Sisters, mothers, daughters and aunties: Structural barriers and opportunities for HIV prevention among Black women. Paper presented at the annual conference of the Canadian Association of HIV Research, Toronto, Ontario.

Williams, M. (1999, June 15). Study: Patch could restore sex drive. The Associated Press.

Williams, M. E. (Ed.). (2001). *Abortion: Opposing viewpoints.* Farmington Hills, MI: Greenhaven Press.

Williams, V. S. L., et al. (2006). Estimating the prevalence and impact of antidepressant-induced sexual dysfunction in 2 European countries: A cross-sectional patient survey. *Journal of Clinical Psychiatry, 67*(2), 204–210.

Williamson, C., & Cluse-Tolar, T. (2002). Pimp-controlled prostitution: Still an integral part of street life. *Violence Against Women, 8*(9), 1074–1092.

Wilson, J. M. B., Tripp, D. A., & Boland, F. J. (2005). The relative contributions of waist-to-hip ratio and body mass index to judgments of attractiveness. *Sexualities, Evolution & Gender,* 7(3), 245–267.

Wilson, R. J. (2005). Circles of support and accountability: 10 years and counting. Paper presented at World Congress of Sexology, Montreal.

Wilson, W., et al. (2000). Brain morphological changes and early marijuana use: A magnetic resonance and positron emission tomography study. *Journal of Addictive Diseases, 19*(1), 1–22.

Winer, R., Hughes, J., Feng, Q., O'Reilly, S., Kiviat, N., Holmes, K., & Koutsky, L. (2006). Condom use and the risk of genital human papillomavirus infection in young women. *New England Journal of Medicine, 354,* 2645–2654.

Wingood, G. M., & DiClemente, R. J. (Eds.). (2002). *Handbook of women's sexual and reproductive health.* New York: Kluwer Academic/Plenum Publishers.

Winter, S. (2003). Research and discussion paper: Language and identity in transgender: Gender wars and the case of the Thai kathoey. Paper presented at the Hawaii conference on Social Sciences, Waikiki, HI.

Woman faces 37 charges. (2000, February 25). *The Toronto Star.*

Women warned about potential sex offender. (2008, August 3). *Toronto Star,* p. A3.

Wong-Reiger, D., LaBrie, M., Guyon, G., & Smith, L. (1996). *Evaluation of physician-based condom and pill education project.* International Conference on AIDS, Vancouver.

Woo, J. S. T., & Brotto, L. A. (in press). Age of first sexual intercourse and acculturation: Effects on adult sexual responding. *Journal of Sexual Medicine.*

Wood, D. (2002, April 3). Man admits passing HIV to four women. *The Toronto Star,* p. A4.

Wood, D. (2004, October 3). Mother confesses to sex with sons. *The Toronto Star.*

Wood, D. (2005, August 18). Cambridge mother and son guilty of incest. *The Record.*

Wood, E., Nosko, A., Desmarais, S., Ross, C., & Irvine, C. (2006). Online and traditional paper-and-pencil survey administration: Examining experimenter presence, sensitive material and long surveys. *The Canadian Journal of Human Sexuality, 15*(3–4), 147–155.

Wood, J. T. (2005). *Gendered lives: Communication, gender, and culture,* 6th ed. Belmont, CA: Wadsworth.

Wood, N. S., et al. (2000). Neurologic and developmental disability after extremely preterm birth. *The New England Journal of Medicine* online, *343*(6).

Woods, A. (2000, October 7). Lesbian bathhouse organizers charged. *The Toronto Star,* p. B1.

Woods, A. (2008, August 26). Tories act to avoid abortion debate. *Toronto Star,* p. A15.

Workers cry foul over sex policy. (1996, December 19). *The Guelph Mercury,* p. A7.

World Congress of Sexology, Sydney, Australia.

World Health Organization. (2008) Epidemiological fact sheets.

Wyatt, T. (2003). *Pheromones and animal behaviour: Communication by smell and taste.* Cambridge, UK: Cambridge University Press.

Yela, C. (2006). The evaluation of love: Simplified version of the scales for Yela's tetrangular model based on Sternberg's model. *European Journal of Psychological Assessment, 22*(1), 21–27.

Yoder, V. C., Virden, T. B., III, & Amin, K. (2005). Internet pornography and loneliness: An association? *Sexual Addiction & Compulsivity, 12*(1), 19–44.

Youthography Ping Survey. (February 2004). Canadian Youth (13–29). 1358 respondents.

Zaviacic, M., & Whipple, B. (1993). Update on the female prostate and the phenomenon of female ejaculation. *Journal of Sex Research, 30,* 148–151.

Zaviacic, M., et al. (1988a). Concentrations of fructose in female ejaculate and urine: A comparative biochemical study. *Journal of Sex Research, 24,* 319–325.

Zaviacic, M., et al. (1988b). Female urethral expulsions evoked by local digital stimulation of the G-spot: Differences in the response patterns. *Journal of Sex Research, 24,* 311–318.

Zernike, K. (2005, December 11). The siren song of sex with boys. *The New York Times.* [Online].

Zheng, S.L., Sun, J., Wiklund, F., Smith, S., Stattin, P., Li, G., Adami, H.-O., Hsu, F.-C., Zhu, Y., Balter, K., Kader, A. K., Turner, A., Liu, W., Bleecker, E., Meyers, D., Duggan, D., Carpten, J., Chang, B.-L., Isaacs, W., Xu, J., & Gronberg, H. (2008). Cumulative association of five genetic variants with prostate cancer. *New England Journal of Medicine, 358,* 910–919.

Zielbauer, P. (2000, May 22). Sex offender listings on Web set off debate. *The New York Times* online.

Zucker, K. J. (2002). Intersexuality and gender identity differentiation. *Journal of Pediatric and Adolescent Gynecology, 15*(3), 3–13.

Zucker, K. J. (2005a). Gender identity disorder in children and adolescents. *Annual Review of Clinical Psychology, 1*(1), 467–492.

Zucker, K. J. (2005b). Gender identity disorder in girls. In D. J. Bell, S. L. Foster, & E. J. Mash (Eds.). *Handbook of behavioral and emotional problems in girls. Issues in clinical child psychology* (pp. 285–319). Kluwer Academic/Plenum Publishers.

Zucker, K. J., Beaulieu, N., Bradley, S. J., Grimshaw, G. M., & Wilcox, A. (2001). Handedness in boys with gender identity disorder. *Journal of Child Psychology and Psychiatry, 42*(6), 767–776.

Zucker, K. J., Bradley, S. J., & Sanikhani, M. (1997). Sex differences in referral rates of children with gender identity disorder: Some hypotheses. *Journal of Abnormal Child Psychology, 25*(3), 217–227.

Zusman, M. E., & Knox, D. (1998). Relationship problems of casual and involved university students. *College Student Journal, 32*(4), 606–609.

Name Index

G

H

I

J

K

L

M

Subject Index

J

K

L

Q

R

T

U

V

W

Y

Z

Photo Credits

Chapter 1: p. 1, © Simon Marcus/CORBIS; p. 12, © DPA/The Image Works; p. 16, © PhotoAlto/Alamy; p. 18, © Scala/Art Resource; p. 20, Erotic scene (gouache on paper), Indian School, (18th century)/Archives Charmet, Private Collection/ The Bridgeman Art Library; p. 23, © Stockbyte/Getty Images; p. 26 (top) Courtesy www.fcn.ca; p. 26 (bottom), Photo by Lawrance Bailey © Ministry of Cultural Development; p. 27, © LWADann Tardif/CORBIS. **Chapter 2:** p. 35, © Robert Brenner/PhotoEdit; page 39, © PhotoAlto/Alamy; p. 40, © Rachel Epstein/PhotoEdit; p. 41, © Bettmann/CORBIS; p. 42, Courtesy of The Canadian Journal of Human Sexuality; p. 46, © Rebecca Henry,Mirabel Studios, 2006, Courtesy of Kate Frank; p. 47 (both), Courtesy of Farrall Instruments. **Chapter 3:** p. 55, Jupiter Images Unlimited; p. 59 (left and centre), © Susan Lerner/Joel Gordon Photography; p. 59 (right), © Tee A. Corinne papers, University of Oregon Libraries; p. 61, © Catherine Leroy/SIPA Press; p. 64, © Susan Lerner/Joel Gordon Photography; p. 66, Photo taken by Donna Harris; p. 72, www.melaniegillis.com; p. 73 (left), © Susan Lerner/Joel Gordon Photography; p. 73 (centre and right), © 2007 Custom Medical Stock Photo, All rights reserved; p. 81, © Barr Laboratories/Getty Images; p. 84 (left and right), © Joel Gordon; p. 84 (centre), © 2007 Custom Medical Stock Photo, All rights reserved; p. 86, © Professor Pietro M.Motta/Photo Researchers, Inc. **Chapter 4:** p. 101, © bilderlounge/Alamy; p. 102, Steve Russell/Toronto Star; p. 103, © LWA/CORBIS; p. 104, © ThinkStock LLC/Index Stock Imagery; p. 105, © ThinkStock/SuperStock; p. 108, © Everynight Images/Alamy; p. 112, © Cheryl Maeder/CORBIS. **Chapter 5:** p. 131, © Steve Raymer/CORBIS; p. 136 (left and right), From John Money, *Sex Errors of the Body and Related Syndromes: A Guide for Counseling Children, Adolescents, and Their Families, Second Edition*, 1994, p. 37 (left) and 46 (right); Reprinted courtesy of The John Money Collections at The Kinsey Institute for Research in Sex, Gender, and Reproduction, Inc.; p. 139 (both), © Bettmann/CORBIS; p. 140, Photo: Pete Soos; p. 141, © Simon Rawles/Alamy; p. 142, © Reuters/CORBIS; p. 143 (both), www.melaniegillis.com; p. 144, © BSIP Agency/Index Stock Imagery; p. 149, © Tony Freeman/PhotoEdit; p. 152, © Jack Hollingsworth/CORBIS; p. 156, © Radius Images/Alamy. **Chapter 6:** p. 160: © Yellow Dog Productions/Getty Images; p. 162, © Brooke Fasani/CORBIS; p. 165 (both), © SPL/Photo Researchers, Inc.; p. 166 (left), © Laura Cavanaugh/UPI/Landov; p. 166 (left centre), © Adam van Bunnens/Alamy; p. 166 (right centre), © Thinkstock/Alamy; p. 166 (right), © Digital Vision Ltd./SuperStock; p. 168 (left), © Caterina Bernardi/Getty Images; p. 168 (right), © Michael Newman/PhotoEdit; p. 170, © David Young-Wolff/PhotoEdit; p. 171, © Dana Edmunds/Getty Images. **Chapter 7:** p. 179, © Slater King/zefa/CORBIS; p. 183, © Tom Grill/CORBIS; p. 184, © Digital Vision/Getty Images; p. 185: Courtesy of Discovery Health Channel; p. 189, © Eddie Arrossi/Alamy; p. 191, © Joson/zefa/CORBIS; p. 192, © Corinne Malet/PhotoAlto/Getty Images; p. 194, © Brown W. Cannon III/Getty Images. **Chapter 8:** p. 200, © Jason Horowitz/zefa/CORBIS; p. 210 (top) © R. Jerome Ferraro/Getty Images; p. 210 (bottom), © Ryan McVay/Getty Images; p. 211, www.melaniegillis.com; p. 222, © Michael N. Paras. **Chapter 9:** p. 226, © Girl Ray/Getty Images; p. 227, © Focus Features/The Kobal Collection; p. 228, Tony Fong; p. 234, Front cover from THE NEW GAY TEENAGER by Ritch C. Savin-Williams, reprinted by permission of the publisher, Harvard University Press, Cambridge, Mass.: Copyright © 2005 by the President and Fellows of Harvard College; p. 239, CP PHOTO/Tom Hanson; p. 247, © Michael Newman/PhotoEdit. **Chapter 10:** p. 255, © Mango Productions/CORBIS; p. 256, © Francis Leroy/ Photo Researchers, Inc.; p. 258, © David Young-Wolff/PhotoEdit; p. 265, © M. Kulyk/Photo Researchers, Inc.; p. 267, Patti Gower/Atkinson Foundation; p. 271 (top left), © Claude Edelmann/Photo Researchers, Inc.; p. 271 (top right and bottom), © Petit Format/Photo Researchers, Inc.; p. 274, © plainpicture GmbH & Co. KG/Alamy; p. 276, © SIU/Photo Researchers, Inc.; p. 278, © Susan Leavines/Photo Researchers, Inc.; p. 279 (left), © 2007 D. G. Arnold/Custom Medical Stock Photo, All rights reserved; p. 279 (right), © Sean Sprague/The Image Works; p. 282, © Mary Kate Denny/PhotoEdit. **Chapter 11:** p. 285, Neil Setchfield © Rough Guides/Dorling Kindersley; p. 286, History of Contraception CD-ROM, Janssen-Ortho Inc.; p. 292, © UPI/Landov; p. 295 (top), © ThinkStock LLC/Index Stock Imagery; p. 303, © Joel Gordon; p. 306 (top), CP Photo/John Lehmann; p. 306 (bottom), © Greg Smith/CORBIS. **Chapter 12:** p. 312: © age fotostock/ SuperStock; p. 314, © Ericka McConnell/Getty Images; p. 315, Michael Newman/PhotoEdit; p. 316, © Robert Brenner/ PhotoEdit; p. 320, Courtesy of Sue Johanson; p. 323, © Frank Siteman/PhotoEdit; p. 325, © Little Blue Wolf Productions/CORBIS; p. 333, Tony Bock/Toronto Star; p. 334, © Frank Herholdt/Getty Images; p. 337, Taxi/Ron Chapple; p. 340, Aaron Vincent Elkaim/Toronto Star; p. 342, CP Photo/Toronto Sun/Veronica Henri; p. 348, www.ashleymadison .com; p. 349, © Bob Daemmrich/The Image Works; p. 350, Tanis Toohey/Toronto Star; p. 351, © Laurence Monneret/ Getty Images. **Chapter 13:** p. 357, © Noel Hendrickson/Getty Images; p. 360, © Michael Newman/PhotoEdit; p. 370, © BananaStock/Jupiter Images; p. 373, Courtesy Sinclair Institute; p. 374, © Bob Daemmrich/Stock Boston; p. 378, © 2007 G. Thomas Bishop/Custom Medical Stock Photo, All rights reserved; p.379, © Phanie/Photo Researchers, Inc.; p. 380, Courtesy of NuGyn Inc. **Chapter 14:** p. 390, © Reed Kaestner/CORBIS; p. 391, Courtesy of ISIS, Inc., Oakland, CA; p. 393, © David Young-Wolff/PhotoEdit; p. 395, © and courtesy of Dr. Nicholas J. Fiumara; p. 396, © 2007 Custom Medical Stock Photo, All rights reserved; p. 398, © 2007 NMSB/Custom Medical Stock Photo, All rights reserved; p. 401, © Bill Longcore/ Photo Researchers, Inc.; p. 402, © C. Lyttle/zefa/CORBIS; p. 403, © AP Images/Haraz N. Ghanbari; p. 404, Courtesy of

AIDS Committee of Toronto; p. 405, © Dr. John Wilson/Photo Researchers, Inc.; p. 407, © Biophoto Associates/Photo Researchers, Inc.; p. 408, © E. Gray/SPL/Photo Researchers, Inc.; p. 419, © Richard Lord/PhotoEdit. **Chapter 15:** p. 422, © Walter Lockwood/CORBIS; p. 426, © Templer/zefa/CORBIS; p. 427, © Luis Enrique Ascui/Reuters/Landov; p. 428, © Jutta Klee/CORBIS; p. 431, © Walter Lockwood/CORBIS; p. 432, Courtesy of Upskirtsniper.com; p. 434, © Claire Artman/zefa/CORBIS; p. 436, © Digital Vision/Getty Images; p. 440, © Bill Aron/PhotoEdit; p. 442, © Bob Daemmrich/The Image Works. **Chapter 16:** p. 446, © image100/CORIBS; p. 452, OPSEU No Means No coaster provided courtesy of Canadian Federation of Students; p. 459, © Sean Cayton/The Image Works; p. 462, CP Photo/Andrew Vaughn; p. 463, © AP Images/Mark Humphrey; p. 467, Courtesy of Laporte County Child Abuse Prevention Council; p. 472, © image100/CORIBS. **Chapter 17:** p. 481, © Randy Faris/CORBIS; p. 482, Advertisement provided by Freeland Marketing Inc., producers of the Everything to do with Sex Show™; p. 483, Keith Beaty/Toronto Star; p. 486, © Floris Leeuwenberg/The Cover Story/CORBIS; p. 488, © AP Images/Marco Ugarte; p. 495, © John Van Hasselt/CORBIS; p. 496, *Bad Boy*, 1981, oil on canvas, 66 x 96 inches 1981, © Eric Fischl; p. 497, Photo: Sean Rosen; p. 503, Photo: www.melaniegillis.com.

- reasons why someone may be at greater risk of sexual violence
  - drinking, young, college.
  - bar/party, stranger.
  - forcable rape more tramatiz then incapicated rape

- effects of sexual violence on a person
  - long term - depression, anxiety, ptsD.
  - short term.
  - coping strategies.